Index of Applications

MAT 210/211

Brief Calculus and Mathematics for Business Analysis

Stefan Waner | Steven Costenoble

CENGAGE
Learning™

Australia • Brazil • Japan • Korea • Mexico • Singapore • Spain • United Kingdom • United States

CENGAGE
Learning™

MAT 210/211: Brief Calculus and Mathematics for Business Analysis

Finite Math and Applied Calculus, 5th Edition
Stefan Waner I Steven Costenoble

© 2011, 2007 Cengage Learning. All rights reserved.

Executive Editors:
 Maureen Staudt
 Michael Stranz

Senior Project Development Manager:
 Linda deStefano

Marketing Specialist:
 Courtney Sheldon

Senior Production/Manufacturing Manager:
 Donna M. Brown

PreMedia Manager:
 Joel Brennecke

Sr. Rights Acquisition Account Manager:
 Todd Osborne

Cover Image:
 Getty Images*

*Unless otherwise noted, all cover images used by Custom Solutions, a part of Cengage Learning, have been supplied courtesy of Getty Images with the exception of the Earthview cover image, which has been supplied by the National Aeronautics and Space Administration (NASA).

For product information and technology assistance, contact us at
Cengage Learning Customer & Sales Support, 1-800-354-9706
For permission to use material from this text or product,
submit all requests online at cengage.com/permissions
Further permissions questions can be emailed to
permissionrequest@cengage.com

This book contains select works from existing Cengage Learning resources and was produced by Cengage Learning Custom Solutions for collegiate use. As such, those adopting and/or contributing to this work are responsible for editorial content accuracy, continuity and completeness.

Compilation © 2010 Cengage Learning

ISBN-13: 978-1-111-72002-5

ISBN-10: 1-111-72002-9

Cengage Learning
5191 Natorp Boulevard
Mason, Ohio 45040
USA

Cengage Learning is a leading provider of customized learning solutions with office locations around the globe, including Singapore, the United Kingdom, Australia, Mexico, Brazil, and Japan. Locate your local office at:
international.cengage.com/region.

Cengage Learning products are represented in Canada by Nelson Education, Ltd.
For your lifelong learning solutions, visit **www.cengage.com /custom.**
Visit our corporate website at **www.cengage.com.**

Printed in the United States of America

Table of Contents

(*Note – this is a "custom" textbook that has been designed specifically for this course in a joint effort between your instructor and the publisher. Please note that some chapters have been removed intentionally and some pages may be black & white as dictated by the changes.)

Determinants and Cramer's Rule

Calculus Applied to Probability and Statistics

Extreme Values

PREFACE

Finite Mathematics and Applied Calculus, Fifth Edition, is intended as a one- or two-term course for students majoring in business, the social sciences, or the liberal arts. Like earlier editions, the Fifth Edition of *Finite Mathematics and Applied Calculus* is designed to address the challenge of generating enthusiasm and mathematical sophistication in an audience that is too often under-prepared for and uninspired by traditional mathematics courses. We meet this challenge by focusing on real-life applications that students can relate to, by presenting mathematical concepts intuitively and thoroughly, and by employing a writing style that is informal, engaging, and occasionally humorous.

In renewing our commitment to these goals, we have further improved the text by revising the Table of Contents—combining some sections and rearranging others—to promote better flow and organization, enhancing the technology notes to include step-by-step instructions at point of use, and adding notes to the student to provide further clarification and explanation where necessary. Please see the "New to This Edition" section that follows for additional information about these changes.

The Fifth Edition continues to implement support for a wide range of instructional paradigms: from settings using little or no technology to courses taught in computerized classrooms, and from classes in which a single form of technology is used exclusively to those incorporating several technologies. We feature three forms of technology in this text—TI-83/84 Plus graphing calculators, Excel spreadsheets, and powerful online utilities created specifically for this book—in a way that allows them to be integrated or omitted. In particular, our comprehensive support for Excel, both in the text and online, is highly relevant for students who are studying business and economics, where skill with spreadsheets may be vital to their future careers.

Our Approach to Pedagogy

Real World Orientation We are particularly proud of the diversity, breadth, and abundance of examples and exercises included in this edition. A large number are based on real, referenced data from business, economics, the life sciences, and the social sciences. Examples and exercises based on dated information have generally been replaced by more current versions; applications based on unique or historically interesting data have been kept.

Adapting real data for pedagogical use can be tricky; available data can be numerically complex, intimidating for students, or incomplete. We have modified and streamlined many of the real world applications, rendering them as tractable as any "made-up" application. At the same time, we have been careful to strike a pedagogically sound balance between applications based on real data and more traditional "generic" applications. Thus, the density and selection of real data-based applications have been tailored to the pedagogical goals and appropriate difficulty level for each section.

Readability We would like students to read this book. We would also like students to *enjoy* reading this book. Thus, we have written the book in a conversational and student-oriented style, and have made frequent use of question-and-answer dialogues to encourage the development of the student's mathematical curiosity and intuition. We hope that this text will give the student insight into how a mathematician develops and thinks about mathematical ideas and their applications.

Rigor We feel that mathematical rigor can work easily in conjunction with the kind of applied focus and conceptual approach that are earmarks of this book. We have, especially in the Fifth Edition, worked hard to ensure that we are always mathematically honest without being unnecessarily formal. Sometimes we do this through the question-and-answer dialogues and sometimes through the "Before we go on . . ." discussions that follow examples, but always in a manner designed to provoke the interest of the student.

Five Elements of Mathematical Pedagogy to Address Different Learning Styles

The "Rule of Four" is a common theme in many texts. Implementing this approach, we discuss many of the central concepts **numerically**, **graphically** and **algebraically**, and clearly delineate these distinctions. The fourth element, **verbal communication** of mathematical concepts, is emphasized through our discussions on translating English sentences into mathematical statements, and our Communication and Reasoning exercises at the end of each section. A fifth element, **interactivity**, is integrated through expanded use of question-and-answer dialogues, but is seen most dramatically within the student Web site. Using this resource, students can use interactive tutorials specific to concepts and examples covered in sections and online utilities that automate a variety of tasks, from graphing to regression and matrix algebra. Added recently to the site are more challenging "game" tutorials, with randomized questions, scoring systems, and even "health points."

Exercise Sets The substantial collection of exercises provides a wealth of material that can be used to challenge students at almost every level of preparation, and includes everything from straightforward drill exercises to interesting and rather challenging applications. The exercise sets have been carefully graded to increase in complexity from basic exercises and exercises that are similar to examples in the text to more interesting and advanced ones, marked in this edition as "more advanced" for easy reference. There are also several much more difficult exercises, designated as "challenging." The advanced and challenging exercises encourage students to think beyond the straightforward situations and calculations in the earlier exercises. We have also included, in virtually every section, interesting applications based on real data, Communication and Reasoning exercises that help students articulate mathematical concepts, and exercises ideal for the use of technology.

Many of the scenarios used in application examples and exercises are revisited several times throughout the book. Thus, students will find themselves using a variety of techniques, from graphing through the use of derivatives and elasticity, to analyze the same application. Reusing scenarios and important functions provides unifying threads and shows students the complex texture of real-life problems.

New to This Edition

Content

- Chapter 1 (page 39): Chapter 1 now includes a new section, *Functions and Models*, in which we bring together a variety of applied topics such as revenue, profit, demand, supply, and change over time that occur throughout the book. We have also streamlined the rest of the chapter; functions are now introduced in a single section rather than two, and linear functions and models are similarly discussed in a single section.

- Chapter 7 (page 445): The chapter on probability has been extensively and philosophically revised; "theoretical probability" in 4e is replaced by *probability models*, more accurately reflecting what computations based on equally likely outcomes do. The second section now deals exclusively with relative frequency, while the third section focuses on abstract probability distributions and, by way of application, probability models based on equally likely outcomes.

- **Chapter 8 (page 547):** Our discussion of Bernoulli trials now includes the observation (reiterated throughout the chapter) that these are not just special types of experiments, but apply to repetitions of any experiment.

- **Chapter 11 (page 781):** Derivatives of sums and constant multiples are now moved to the beginning of Chapter 4 on techniques of differentiation (where they properly belong).

- **Chapter 12 (page 865):** Second and higher order derivatives are now discussed in their own section with a great deal of added material on concavity and acceleration.

- **Chapter 15 (page 1079):** We have changed the exposition of constrained maxima and minima to give more emphasis to Lagrange multipliers over substitution methods. Functions of several variables are now discussed in a single section rather than two.

- We now include the discussion of derivatives and integrals of functions involving absolute values in simple closed form, thus expanding the variety of functions available for modeling.

- We have expanded the list of additional optional sections, available to include in custom-published versions of the text, and now offer sections on: Taylor polynomials, the chain rule for multivariate calculus, calculus applied to probability, the extreme value theorem and optimization with boundary constraints for functions of several variables, and determinants and Cramer's rule.

Current Topics in the Applications

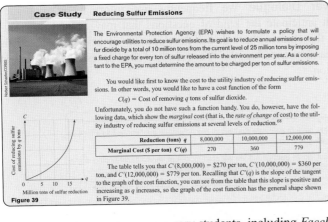

Case Study **Reducing Sulfur Emissions**

The Environmental Protection Agency (EPA) wishes to formulate a policy that will encourage utilities to reduce sulfur emissions. Its goal is to reduce annual emissions of sulfur dioxide by a total of 10 million tons from the current level of 25 million tons by imposing a fixed charge for every ton of sulfur released into the environment per year. As a consultant to the EPA, you must determine the amount to be charged per ton of sulfur emissions.

You would like first to know the cost to the utility industry of reducing sulfur emissions. In other words, you would like to have a cost function of the form

$C(q)$ = Cost of removing q tons of sulfur dioxide.

Unfortunately, you do not have such a function handy. You do, however, have the following data, which show the *marginal* cost (that is, the *rate of change* of cost) to the utility industry of reducing sulfur emissions at several levels of reduction.[68]

Reduction (tons) q	8,000,000	10,000,000	12,000,000
Marginal Cost ($ per ton) $C'(q)$	270	360	779

The table tells you that $C'(8,000,000) = \$270$ per ton, $C'(10,000,000) = \$360$ per ton, and $C'(12,000,000) = \$779$ per ton. Recalling that $C'(q)$ is the slope of the tangent to the graph of the cost function, you can see from the table that this slope is positive and increasing as q increases, so the graph of the cost function has the general shape shown in Figure 39.

Figure 39

- **Case Studies** Each chapter ends with a section entitled "Case Study," an extended application that uses and illustrates the central ideas of the chapter, focusing on the development of mathematical models appropriate to the topics. The Case Studies have been extensively revised, and in many cases completely replaced by new ones that reflect topics of current interest, such as subprime mortgages, hybrid car production, and the diet problem (in linear programming).

- We have added numerous real data exercises and examples based on topics that are either of intense current interest or of general interest to contemporary students, including *Facebook, XBoxes, iPhones, eBay,* real estate foreclosures and home construction, subprime mortgages, stock market gyrations, travel to Cancun, and the oil industry in the United States and Mexico. (Also see the Index of Companies, in the inside back cover, of the corporations we reference in the applications.)

76. 🖩 ▽ *Information Highway* The amount of information transmitted each month in the early years of the Internet (1988 to 1994) can be modeled by the equation

$$q(t) = \frac{2e^{0.69t}}{3 + 1.5e^{-0.4t}} \qquad (0 \le t \le 6)$$

where q is the amount of information transmitted each month in billions of data packets and t is the number of years since the start of 1988.[33]

a. Use technology to estimate $q'(2)$.
b. Assume that it costs \$5 to transmit a million packets of data. What is the marginal cost $C'(q)$?
c. How fast was the cost increasing at the start of 1990?

Money Stock Exercises 77–80 are based on the following demand function for money (taken from a question on the GRE Economics Test):

$$M_d = 2 \times y^{0.6} \times r^{-0.3} \times p$$

where

M_d = *demand for nominal money balances (money stock)*
y = *real income*
r = *an index of interest rates*
p = *an index of prices*

These exercises also use the idea of *percentage rate of growth*:

Percentage Rate of Growth of $M = \dfrac{\text{Rate of Growth of } M}{M}$

$$= \frac{dM/dt}{M}$$

77. ◆ (from the GRE Economics Test) If the interest rate and price level are to remain constant while real income grows at

87. ▽ Formulate a simple procedure for deciding whether to apply first the chain rule, the product rule, or the quotient rule when finding the derivative of a function.

88. ▽ Give an example of a function f with the property that calculating $f'(x)$ requires use of the following rules in the given order: (1) the chain rule, (2) the quotient rule, and (3) the chain rule.

89. ◆ Give an example of a function f with the property that calculating $f'(x)$ requires use of the chain rule five times in succession.

90. ◆ What can you say about composites of linear functions?

Exercises

- Exercises that are not based entirely on examples in the text are designated as "more advanced" (and indicated by an icon in the exercise set) as a guide for students and instructors.

- We have expanded the exercise sets themselves and carefully reorganized them to gradually increase in level and to include more basic skills exercises that carefully follow the examples.

- Many more of the exercises now have "hints" that either refer to an example in the text where a similar problem is solved, or offer some advice to the student.

- We have added numerous new "communication and reasoning" exercises—many dealing with common student errors and misconceptions—and further expanded the chapter review exercise sections.

Pedagogy

- **Supplementary Notes** We have added new Notes to the student, located in the side column of the text. These Notes include a wide variety of additional information for the student—further explanation or clarification of a concept, reminders of previously learned material or references for further study, and additional tips for using technology.

- **Technology Notes** have been enhanced to include step-by-step instructions and keystrokes at point of use, to enable better integration of graphing calculators and spreadsheets. As always, these notes can be omitted without loss of continuity.

✱ **NOTE** See the discussion at the end of the first example below.

using Technology

Web Site
www.FiniteandCalc.org
Everything for Finite Math
→ Math Tools for Chapter 2
→ Pivot and Gauss-Jordan Tool

Once you have set up the system of equations, you can obtain the solution in a single step using the Pivot and Gauss-Jordan Tool at the Web site:

Enter the augmented matrix of the system as shown, and press "Reduce Completely." You can then use the reduced matrix to write down the unique solution or general solution as discussed in Section 2.2.

Hallmark Features

- **Question-and-Answer Dialogue** We frequently use informal question-and-answer dialogues that anticipate the kind of questions that may occur to the student and also guide the student through the development of new concepts. This feature has been streamlined, as has the "Frequently Asked Questions" feature at the end of each section.

Ⓠ : *Do we always have to calculate the limit of the difference quotient to find a formula for the derivative function?*

Ⓐ : As it turns out, no. In Section 4.1 we will start to look at shortcuts for finding derivatives that allow us to bypass the definition of the derivative in many cases.

- **Before we go on . . . feature** Most examples are followed by supplementary discussions, which may include a check on the answer, a discussion of the feasibility and significance of a solution, or an in-depth look at what the solution means.

- **Quick Examples** Most definition boxes include quick, straightforward examples that a student can use to solidify each new concept.

> **Linear Equation**
>
> A linear equation in the n variables $x_1, x_2, \ldots, x_n$ has the form
>
> $$a_1x_1 + \cdots + a_nx_n = b. \qquad (a_1, a_2, \ldots, a_n, b \text{ constants})$$
>
> The numbers $a_1, a_2, \ldots, a_n$ are called the **coefficients**, and the number b is called the **constant term**, or **right-hand side**.
>
> **Quick Examples**
>
> **1.** $3x - 5y = 0$ ⠀⠀⠀⠀ Linear equation in x and y
> Coefficients: 3, −5 Constant term: 0
>
> **2.** $x + 2y - z = 6$ ⠀⠀⠀⠀ Linear equation in x, y, z
> Coefficients: 1, 2, −1 Constant term: 6
>
> **3.** $30x_1 + 18x_2 + x_3 + x_4 = 19$ ⠀⠀⠀⠀ Linear equation in x_1, x_2, x_3, x_4
> Coefficients: 30, 18, 1, 1 Constant term: 19

- **Communication and Reasoning Exercises for Writing and Discussion** These are exercises designed to broaden the student's grasp of the mathematical concepts and develop modeling skills. They include exercises in which the student is asked to provide his or her own examples to illustrate a point or design an application with a given solution. They also include fill-in-the-blank type exercises and exercises that invite discussion and debate. These exercises often have no single correct answer.

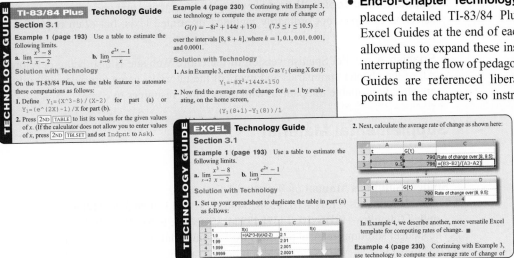

- **End-of-Chapter Technology Guides** We have placed detailed TI-83/84 Plus and Microsoft® Excel Guides at the end of each chapter. This has allowed us to expand these instructions while not interrupting the flow of pedagogy in the text. These Guides are referenced liberally at appropriate points in the chapter, so instructors and students can easily use this material or not, as they prefer. Groups of exercises for which the use of technology is suggested or required appear throughout the exercise sets.

The Web Site

The authors' Web site, accessible through www.FiniteandCalc.com, has been evolving for several years, with growing recognition. Students, raised in an environment in which computers suffuse both work and play, can use their Web browsers to engage with the material in an active way. The following features of the authors' Web site are fully integrated with the text and can be used as a personalized study resource:

- **Interactive Tutorials** Highly interactive tutorials, with guided exercises that parallel the text and a great deal of help and feedback to assist the student.

- **Game Versions of Tutorials** More challenging tutorials with randomized questions that work as games (complete with "health" scores, "health vials," and an assessment of one's performance at the end of the game) are offered alongside the traditional tutorials. These game tutorials, which mirror the traditional "more gentle" tutorials, do not give the student the answers, but instead offer hints in exchange for health points, so that just staying alive (not running out of health) can be quite challenging. Because the questions are randomized and scores are automatically calculated, these tutorials can be used for in-class quizzes, as the authors themselves have done.

- **Detailed Chapter Summaries** Comprehensive summaries with interactive elements review all the basic definitions and problem solving techniques discussed in each chapter. These are a terrific pre-test study tool for students.

- **Downloadable Excel Tutorials** Detailed Excel tutorials are available for almost every section of the book. These interactive tutorials expand on the examples given in the text.

- **Online Utilities** Our collection of easy-to-use online utilities, written in JavaScript, allows students to solve many of the technology-based application exercises directly on the Web page. The utilities available include a function grapher and evaluator that also does derivatives, regression tools, and a numerical integration tool. These utilities require nothing more than a standard Web browser.

- **Chapter True-False Quizzes** Short quizzes based on the key concepts in each chapter assist the student in further mastery of the material.

- **Supplemental Topics** We include complete interactive text and exercise sets for a selection of topics not ordinarily included in printed texts, but often requested by instructors.

- **Spanish** A parallel Spanish version of the entire Web site is also being developed. All of the chapter summaries and many of the tutorials, game tutorials, and utilities are already available in Spanish, with many more resources to come.

Supplemental Material

For Students

Student Solutions Manual *by Waner and Costenoble*
Finite Mathematics—ISBN-10: **0538734485**, ISBN-13: **9780538734486**
Applied Calculus—ISBN-10: **1439049904**, ISBN-13: **9781439049907**
The student solutions manual provides worked-out solutions to the odd-numbered exercises in the text as well as complete solutions to all the chapter review tests.

NetTutor™
Cengage Learning is pleased to provide students with online tutoring and chatting capabilities through NetTutor. NetTutor utilizes a WorldWideWhiteboard application, a Web-based application that allows students and tutors to interact with one another through text and images, and also offers audio and video over Internet Protocol or VOIP, where voice is transmitted through the Internet. The WorldWide Whiteboard software offers the ability to easily create custom groups, which contain course-specific functions, symbol palettes and buttons.

For Instructors

Instructor's Solution Manual *by Waner and Costenoble*
Finite Mathematics—ISBN-10: **0538734469**, ISBN-13: **9780538734462**
Applied Calculus—ISBN-10: **1439049831**, ISBN-13: **9781439049839**
The instructor's solutions manual provides worked-out solutions to all of the exercises in the text.

PowerLecture CD with ExamView
Finite Mathematics—ISBN-10: **0538734477**, ISBN-13: **9780538734479**
Applied Calculus—ISBN-10: **1439049890**, ISBN-13: **9781439049891**
This comprehensive CD-ROM contains the Instructor's Solutions Manual, PowerPoint lecture notes, and ExamView computerized testing to create, deliver, and customize tests. The PowerLecture CD also includes a multimedia library containing all of the art from the book in MS PowerPoint as well as individual JPEG files.

Test Bank
The test bank—available on the PowerLecture CD—contains numerous multiple choice and free response questions for those instructors who prefer a more traditional method of test preparation.

Enhanced WebAssign

Instant feedback and ease of use are just two reasons why WebAssign is the most widely used homework system in higher education. WebAssign allows you to assign, collect, grade, and record homework assignments via the Web. Now this proven homework system has been enhanced to include links to textbook sections, video examples, and problem-specific tutorials. Enhanced WebAssign is more than a homework system—it is a complete learning system for math students.

Acknowledgments

This project would not have been possible without the contributions and suggestions of numerous colleagues, students, and friends. We are particularly grateful to our colleagues at Hofstra and elsewhere who used and gave us useful feedback on previous editions. We are also grateful to everyone at Cengage Learning for their encouragement and guidance throughout the project. Specifically, we would like to thank Carolyn Crockett and Liz Covello for their unflagging enthusiasm and Jeannine Lawless for whipping the book into shape.

We would also like to thank Jerrold Grossman for his meticulous critique of the manuscript, Lynn Lustberg and the production team for their patience in dealing with our often shifting demands, and the numerous reviewers and accuracy checkers who provided many helpful suggestions that have shaped the development of this book.

Doug Burkholder, *Lenoir-Rhyne University*
Leslie Cohn, *The Citadel*
Melanie Fulton, *High Point University*
Jerrold W. Grossman, *Oakland University*
Celeste Hernandez, *Richland College*
Dean Leoni, *Edmonds Community College*
Michael J. Kallaher, *Washington State University*
Karla Karstans, *University of Vermont*
Vincent Koehler, *University of Vermont*
Karl Kruppstadt, *University of Minnesota, Duluth*
Robert H. Lewis, *Fordham University*
David Miller, *William Paterson University*
Phillip Miller, *Indiana University Southeast*
Jack Y. Narayan, *SUNY Oswego*
Sergei Ovchinnikov, *San Francisco State University*
Lauri Papay, *Santa Clara University*
Jean Nicholas Pestieau, *Suffolk County Community College*

Leela Rakesh, *Central Michigan University*
Nelson de la Rosa, *Miami Dade College, Kendall*
Arthur Rosenthal, *Salem State College*
Carol H. Serotta, *Cabrini College*
Mary Ann Teel, *University of North Texas*
Tzvetalin S. Vassilev, *North Carolina Central University*
Marie A. Vitulli, *University of Oregon*
Richard West, *Francis Marion University*
Donna Wilson, *University of Texas at El Paso*

Stefan Waner
Steven R. Costenoble

2

Systems of Linear Equations and Matrices

Case Study Hybrid Cars—Optimizing the Degree of Hybridization

You are involved in new model development at one of the "big three" automobile companies. The company is planning to introduce two new plug-in hybrid electric vehicles: the subcompact "Green Town Hopper" and the midsize "Electra Supreme," and your department must decide on the degree of hybridization (DOH) for each of these models that will result in the largest reduction in gasoline consumption. The data you have available show the gasoline saving for only three values of the DOH. **How do you estimate the optimal value?**

Lee Waters/TRANSTOCK

123

Introduction

In Chapter 1 we studied single functions and equations. In this chapter we seek solutions to **systems** of two or more equations. For example, suppose we need to *find two numbers whose sum is* 3 *and whose difference is* 1. In other words, we need to find two numbers x and y such that $x + y = 3$ and $x - y = 1$. The only solution turns out to be $x = 2$ and $y = 1$, a solution you might easily guess. But, how do we know that this is the only solution, and how do we find solutions systematically? When we restrict ourselves to systems of *linear* equations, there is a very elegant method for determining the number of solutions and finding them all. Moreover, as we will see, many real-world applications give rise to just such systems of linear equations.

We begin in Section 2.1 with systems of two linear equations in two unknowns and some of their applications. In Section 2.2 we study a powerful matrix method, called *row reduction*, for solving systems of linear equations in any number of unknowns. In Section 2.3 we look at more applications.

Computers have been used for many years to solve the large systems of equations that arise in the real world. You probably already have access to devices that will do the row operations used in row reduction. Many graphing calculators can do them, as can spreadsheets and various special-purpose applications, including utilities available at the Web site. Using such a device or program makes the calculations quicker and helps avoid arithmetic mistakes. Then there are programs (and calculators) into which you simply feed the system of equations and out pop the solutions. We can think of what we do in this chapter as looking inside the "black box" of such a program. More important, we talk about how, starting from a real-world problem, to get the system of equations to solve in the first place. No computer will do this conversion for us yet.

2.1 Systems of Two Equations in Two Unknowns

Suppose you have $3 in your pocket to spend on snacks and a drink. If x represents the amount you'll spend on snacks and y represents the amount you'll spend on a drink, you can say that $x + y = 3$. On the other hand, if for some reason you want to spend $1 more on snacks than on your drink, you can also say that $x - y = 1$. These are simple examples of **linear equations in two unknowns**.

Linear Equations in Two Unknowns

A **linear equation in two unknowns** is an equation that can be written in the form

$$ax + by = c$$

with a, b, and c being real numbers. The number a is called the **coefficient of x** and b is called the **coefficient of y**. A **solution** of an equation consists of a pair of numbers: a value for x and a value for y that satisfy the equation.

Quick Example

In the linear equation $3x - y = 15$, the coefficients are $a = 3$ and $b = -1$. The point $(x, y) = (5, 0)$ is a solution, because $3(5) - (0) = 15$.

In fact, a single linear equation such as $3x - y = 15$ has infinitely many solutions: We could solve for $y = 3x - 15$ and then, for every value of x we choose, we can get the corresponding value of y, giving a solution (x, y). As we saw in Chapter 1, these solutions are the points on a straight line, the *graph* of the equation.

In this section we are concerned with pairs (x, y) that are solutions of *two* linear equations at the same time. For example, $(2, 1)$ is a solution of both of the equations $x + y = 3$ and $x - y = 1$, because substituting $x = 2$ and $y = 1$ into these equations gives $2 + 1 = 3$ (true) and $2 - 1 = 1$ (also true), respectively. So, in the simple example we began with, you could spend $2 on snacks and $1 on a drink.

In the following set of examples, you will see how to graphically and algebraically solve a system of two linear equations in two unknowns. Then we'll return to some more interesting applications.

EXAMPLE 1   Two Ways of Solving a System: Graphically and Algebraically

Find all solutions (x, y) of the following system of two equations:

$$x + y = 3$$
$$x - y = 1.$$

Solution   We will see how to find the solution(s) in two ways: graphically and algebraically. Remember that a solution is a pair (x, y) that simultaneously satisfies *both* equations.

Method 1: Graphical   We already know that the solutions of a single linear equation are the points on its graph, which is a straight line. For a point to represent a solution of two linear equations, it must lie simultaneously on both of the corresponding lines. In other words, it must be a point where the two lines cross, or intersect. A look at Figure 1 should convince us that the lines cross only at the point $(2, 1)$, so this is the only possible solution.

Method 2: Algebraic   In the algebraic approach, we try to combine the equations in such a way as to eliminate one variable. In this case, notice that if we add the left-hand sides of the equations, the terms with y are eliminated. So, we add the first equation to the second (that is, add the left-hand sides and add the right-hand sides*):

$$x + y = 3$$
$$\underline{x - y = 1}$$
$$2x + 0 = 4$$
$$2x \quad = 4$$
$$x \quad = 2.$$

Now that we know that x has to be 2, we can substitute back into either equation to find y. Choosing the first equation (it doesn't matter which we choose), we have

$$2 + y = 3$$
$$y = 3 - 2$$
$$= 1.$$

We have found that the only possible solution is $x = 2$ and $y = 1$, or

$$(x, y) = (2, 1).$$

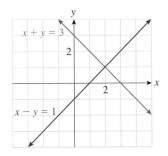

Figure 1

* **NOTE** We can add these equations because when we add equal amounts to both sides of an equation, the results are equal. That is, if $A = B$ and $C = D$, then $A + C = B + D$.

 using Technology

See the Technology Guides at the end of the chapter for detailed instructions on how to do the calculations and the graph in part (a) of Example 1 using a

TI-83/84 Plus or Excel. Here is an outline:

TI-83/84 Plus

Y= screen: Y₁=-X+3

Y₂=X-1

Graph: WINDOW ; Xmin = -4,

Xmax = 4; ZOOM 0

Trace to estimate the point of intersection.

[More details on page 175.]

Excel

Headings x, $y1$, and $y2$ in cells A1–C1 x-values -4, 4 in A2, A3

Formulas =-A2+3 and =A2-1 in B1 and C1 and copy down to B2–C2

Graph the data in columns A–C with a line-segment scatter plot.

To see a closer view, change the values in A2–A3.

[More details on page 177.]

Web Site

www.FiniteandCalc.org

Student Home

→ Online Utilities

→ Function Evaluator and Grapher

Enter -x+3 for y_1 and x-1 for y_2.

Set Xmin = -4, Xmax = 4 and press "Plot Graphs."

Place the cursor on the intersection to estimate its coordinates (shown under the graph).

➡ **Before we go on...** In our discussion of the break-even point in Section 1.4, we found the intersection of two straight lines by setting equal two linear functions of x (cost and revenue). We could find the solution in Example 1 here in a similar way: First we solve our two equations for y to obtain

$$y = -x + 3$$
$$y = x - 1$$

and then we equate the right-hand sides and solve to find $x = 2$. The value for y is then found by substituting $x = 2$ in either equation.

Q : *So why don't we solve all systems of equations this way?*

A : The elimination method extends more easily to systems with more equations and unknowns. It is the basis for the matrix method of solving systems—a method we discuss in Section 2.2. So, we shall use it exclusively for the rest of this section. ∎

Example 2 illustrates the drawbacks of the graphical method.

EXAMPLE 2 Solving a System: Algebraically vs. Graphically

Solve the system

$$3x + 5y = 0$$
$$2x + 7y = 1.$$

Solution

Method 1: Graphical First, solve for y, obtaining $y = -\dfrac{3}{5}x$ and $y = -\dfrac{2}{7}x + \dfrac{1}{7}$. Graphing these equations, we get Figure 2.

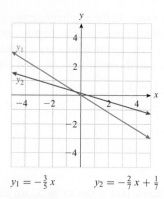

$$y_1 = -\tfrac{3}{5}x \qquad y_2 = -\tfrac{2}{7}x + \tfrac{1}{7}$$

Figure 2

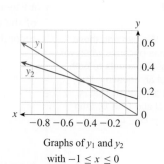

Graphs of y_1 and y_2 with $-1 \le x \le 0$

Figure 3

The lines appear to intersect slightly above and to the left of the origin. Redrawing with a finer scale (or zooming in using graphing technology), we can get the graph in Figure 3.

If we look carefully at Figure 3, we see that the graphs intersect near $(-0.45, 0.27)$. Is the point of intersection *exactly* $(-0.45, 0.27)$? (Substitute these values into the equations to find out.) In fact, it is impossible to find the exact solution of this system graphically, but we now have a ballpark answer that we can use to help check the following algebraic solution.

Method 2: Algebraic We first see that adding the equations is not going to eliminate either x or y. Notice, however, that if we multiply (both sides of) the first equation by 2 and the second by -3, the coefficients of x will become 6 and -6. *Then* if we add them, x will be eliminated. So we proceed as follows:

$$2(3x + 5y) = 2(0)$$
$$-3(2x + 7y) = -3(1)$$

gives

$$6x + 10y = 0$$
$$-6x - 21y = -3.$$

Adding these equations, we get

$$-11y = -3$$

so that

$$y = \frac{3}{11} = 0.\overline{27}.$$

Substituting $y = \dfrac{3}{11}$ in the first equation gives

$$3x + 5\left(\frac{3}{11}\right) = 0$$
$$3x = -\frac{15}{11}$$
$$x = -\frac{5}{11} = -0.\overline{45}.$$

The solution is $(x, y) = \left(-\frac{5}{11}, \frac{3}{11}\right) = (-0.\overline{45}, 0.\overline{27})$.

Notice that the algebraic method gives us the exact solution that we could not find with the graphical method. Still, we can check that the graph and our algebraic solution agree to the accuracy with which we can read the graph. To be absolutely sure that our answer is correct, we should check it:

$$3\left(-\frac{5}{11}\right) + 5\left(\frac{3}{11}\right) = -\frac{15}{11} + \frac{15}{11} = 0 \quad ✔$$

$$2\left(-\frac{5}{11}\right) + 7\left(\frac{3}{11}\right) = -\frac{10}{11} + \frac{21}{11} = 1. \quad ✔$$

Get in the habit of checking your answers.

➡ **Before we go on...**

Q: *In solving the system in Example 2 algebraically, we multiplied (both sides of) the equations by numbers. How does that affect their graphs?*

A: Multiplying both sides of an equation by a nonzero number has no effect on its solutions, so the graph (which represents the set of all solutions) is unchanged. ∎

Before doing some more examples, let's summarize what we've said about solving systems of equations.

Graphical Method for Solving a System of Two Equations in Two Unknowns

Graph both equations on the same graph. (For example, solve each for y to find the slope and y-intercept.) A point of intersection gives the solution to the system. To find the point, you may need to adjust the range of x-values you use. To find the point accurately you may need to use a smaller range (or zoom in if using technology).

Algebraic Method for Solving a System of Two Equations in Two Unknowns

Multiply each equation by a nonzero number so that the coefficients of x are the same in absolute value but opposite in sign. Add the two equations to eliminate x; this gives an equation in y that we can solve to find its value. Substitute this value of y into one of the original equations to find the value of x. (Note that we could eliminate y first instead of x if it's more convenient.)

Sometimes, something appears to go wrong with these methods. The following examples show what can happen.

EXAMPLE 3 Inconsistent System

Solve the system

$$x - 3y = 5$$
$$-2x + 6y = 8.$$

Solution To eliminate x, we multiply the first equation by 2 and then add:

$$2x - 6y = 10$$
$$-2x + 6y = 8.$$

Adding gives

$$0 = 18.$$

But this is absurd! This calculation shows that if we had two numbers x and y that satisfied both equations, it would be true that $0 = 18$. As 0 is *not* equal to 18, there can be no such numbers x and y. In other words, *the system has no solutions*, and is called an **inconsistent system**.

In slope-intercept form these lines are $y = \frac{1}{3}x - \frac{5}{3}$ and $y = \frac{1}{3}x + \frac{4}{3}$. Notice that they have the same slope but different y-intercepts. This means that they are parallel, but different lines. Plotting them confirms this fact (Figure 4).

Because they are parallel, they do not intersect. A solution must be a point of intersection, so we again conclude that there is no solution.

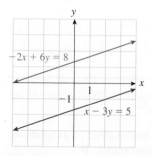

Figure 4

EXAMPLE 4 Redundant System

Solve the system

$$x + y = 2$$
$$2x + 2y = 4.$$

Solution Multiplying the first equation by -2 gives

$$-2x - 2y = -4$$
$$2x + 2y = 4.$$

Adding gives the not-very-enlightening result

$$0 = 0.$$

Now what has happened? Looking back at the original system, we note that the second equation is really the first equation in disguise. (It is the first equation multiplied by 2.) Put another way, if we solve both equations for y, we find that, in slope-intercept form, both equations become the same:

$$y = -x + 2.$$

The second equation gives us the same information as the first, so we say that this is a **redundant**, or **dependent system**. In other words, we really have only one equation in two unknowns. From Chapter 1, we know that a single linear equation in two unknowns has infinitely many solutions, one for each value of x. (Recall that to get the corresponding solution for y, we solve the equation for y and substitute the x-value.) The entire set of solutions can be summarized as follows:

$$x \text{ is arbitrary}$$
$$y = 2 - x. \qquad \text{Solve the first equation for } y.$$

This set of solutions is called the **general solution** because it includes all possible solutions. When we write the general solution this way, we say that we have a **parameterized solution** and that x is the **parameter**.

We can also write the general solution as

$$(x, 2 - x) \quad x \text{ arbitrary}.$$

Different choices of the parameter x lead to different **particular solutions**. For instance, choosing $x = 3$ gives the particular solution

$$(x, y) = (3, -1).$$

Because there are infinitely many values of x from which to choose, there are infinitely many solutions.

What does this system of equations look like graphically? The two equations are really the same, so their graphs are identical, each being the line with x-intercept 2 and y-intercept 2. The "two" lines intersect at every point, so there is a solution for each point on the common line. In other words, we have a "whole line of solutions" (Figure 5).

We could also have solved the first equation for x instead and used y as a parameter, obtaining another form of the general solution:

$$(2 - y, y) \quad y \text{ arbitrary}. \qquad \text{Alternate form of the general solution}$$

The line of solutions ($y = 2 - x$) and some particular solutions

Figure 5

We summarize the three possible outcomes we have encountered.

> ## Possible Outcomes for a System of Two Linear Equations in Two Unknowns
>
> 1. **A single (or *unique*) solution** This happens when the lines corresponding to the two equations are distinct and not parallel so that they intersect at a single point. (See Example 1.)
> 2. **No solution** This happens when the two lines are parallel. We say that the system is **inconsistent**. (See Example 3.)
> 3. **An infinite number of solutions** This occurs when the two equations represent the same straight line, and we say that such a system is **redundant**, or **dependent.** In this case, we can represent the solutions by choosing one variable arbitrarily and solving for the other. (See Example 4.)
>
> In cases 1 and 3, we say that the system of equations is **consistent** because it has at least one solution.

You should think about straight lines and convince yourself that these are the only three possibilities.

APPLICATIONS

EXAMPLE 5 Blending

Acme Baby Foods mixes two strengths of apple juice. One quart of Beginner's juice is made from 30 fluid ounces of water and 2 fluid ounces of apple juice concentrate. One quart of Advanced juice is made from 20 fluid ounces of water and 12 fluid ounces of concentrate. Every day Acme has available 30,000 fluid ounces of water and 3,600 fluid ounces of concentrate. If the company wants to use all the water and concentrate, how many quarts of each type of juice should it mix?

Solution In all applications we follow the same general strategy.

1. ***Identify and label the unknowns.*** What are we asked to find? To answer this question, it is common to respond by saying, "The unknowns are Beginner's juice and Advanced juice." Quite frankly, this is a baffling statement. Just what is unknown about juice? We need to be more precise:

   The unknowns are (1) *the **number of quarts** of Beginner's juice and* (2) *the **number of quarts** of Advanced juice made each day.*

   So, we label the unknowns as follows: Let

   x = number of quarts of Beginner's juice made each day

   y = number of quarts of Advanced juice made each day.

2. ***Use the information given to set up equations in the unknowns.*** This step is trickier, and the strategy varies from problem to problem. Here, the amount of juice the company can make is constrained by the fact that they have limited amounts of water and concentrate. This example shows a kind of application we will often see, and it is helpful in these problems to use a table to record the amounts of the resources used.

using Technology to Check Your Answer

Once you have set up the system of equations correctly, you can check your answer by using the Pivot and Gauss-Jordan tool on the Web site.

Web Site
www.FiniteandCalc.org
Everything for Finite Math
→ Math Tools for Chapter 2
→ Pivot and Gauss-Jordan Tool

To check Example 5, enter the coefficients of x and y and the right-hand sides of the two equations as shown (no commas in numbers!).

x1	x2	x3
30	20	30000
2	12	3600

Then click "Reduce Completely." The answer will appear in the last column. (In the next section we will see how this works.)

	Beginner's (x)	Advanced (y)	Available
Water (fl oz)	30	20	30,000
Concentrate (fl oz)	2	12	3,600

We can now set up an equation for each of the items listed in the left column of the table.

Water: We read across the first row. If Acme mixes x quarts of Beginner's juice, each quart using 30 fluid ounces of water, and y quarts of Advanced juice, each using 20 fluid ounces of water, it will use a total of $30x + 20y$ fluid ounces of water. But we are told that the total has to be 30,000 fluid ounces. Thus, $30x + 20y = 30,000$. This is our first equation.

Concentrate: We read across the second row. If Acme mixes x quarts of Beginner's juice, each using 2 fluid ounces of concentrate, and y quarts of Advanced juice, each using 12 fluid ounces of concentrate, it will use a total of $2x + 12y$ fluid ounces of concentrate. But we are told that the total has to be 3,600 fluid ounces. Thus, $2x + 12y = 3,600$.

Now we have two equations:

$$30x + 20y = 30,000$$
$$2x + 12y = 3,600.$$

To make the numbers easier to work with, let's divide (both sides of) the first equation by 10 and the second by 2:

$$3x + 2y = 3,000$$
$$x + 6y = 1,800.$$

We can now eliminate x by multiplying the second equation by -3 and adding:

$$\begin{aligned} 3x + 2y &= 3,000 \\ -3x - 18y &= -5,400 \\ \hline -16y &= -2,400. \end{aligned}$$

So, $y = 2,400/16 = 150$. Substituting this into the equation $x + 6y = 1,800$ gives $x + 900 = 1,800$, and so $x = 900$. The solution is $(x, y) = (900, 150)$. In other words, the company should mix 900 quarts of Beginner's juice and 150 quarts of Advanced juice.

EXAMPLE 6 Blending

A medieval alchemist's love potion calls for a number of eyes of newt and toes of frog, the total being 20, but with twice as many newt eyes as frog toes. How many of each is required?

Solution As in the preceding example, the first step is to identify and label the unknowns. Let

$$x = \text{number of newt eyes}$$
$$y = \text{number of frog toes.}$$

As for the second step—setting up the equations—a table is less appropriate here than in the preceding example. Instead, we translate each phrase of the problem into an equation. The first sentence tells us that the total number of eyes and toes is 20. Thus,

$$x + y = 20.$$

The end of the first sentence gives us more information, but the phrase "twice as many newt eyes as frog toes" is a little tricky: does it mean that $2x = y$ or that $x = 2y$? We can decide which by rewording the statement using the phrases "the *number of* newt eyes," which is x, and "the *number of* frog toes," which is y. Rephrased, the statement reads:

*The **number of** newt eyes is twice the **number of** frog toes.*

(Notice how the word "twice" is forced into a different place.) With this rephrasing, we can translate directly into algebra:

$$x = 2y.$$

In standard form ($ax + by = c$), this equation reads

$$x - 2y = 0.$$

Thus, we have the two equations:

$$x + y = 20$$
$$x - 2y = 0.$$

To eliminate x, we multiply the second equation by -1 and then add:

$$x + y = 20$$
$$-x + 2y = 0.$$

We'll leave it to you to finish solving the system and find that $x = 13\frac{1}{3}$ and $y = 6\frac{2}{3}$.

So, the recipe calls for exactly $13\frac{1}{3}$ eyes of newt and $6\frac{2}{3}$ toes of frog. The alchemist needs a very sharp scalpel and a very accurate balance (not to mention a very strong stomach).

We saw in Chapter 1 that the *equilibrium price* of an item (the price at which supply equals demand) and the *break-even point* (the number of items that must be sold to break even) can both be described as the intersection points of two lines. In terms of the language of this chapter, what we were really doing was solving a system of two linear equations in two unknowns, as illustrated in the following problem.

EXAMPLE 7 Equilibrium Price

The demand for refrigerators in West Podunk is given by

$$q = -\frac{p}{10} + 100,$$

where q is the number of refrigerators that the citizens will buy each year if the refrigerators are priced at p dollars each. The supply is

$$q = \frac{p}{20} + 25,$$

where now q is the number of refrigerators the manufacturers will be willing to ship into town each year if they are priced at p dollars each. Find the equilibrium price and the number of refrigerators that will be sold at that price.

Solution Figure 6 shows the demand and supply curves. The equilibrium price occurs at the point where these two lines cross, which is where demand equals supply.

Figure 6

The graph suggests that the equilibrium price is $500, and zooming in confirms this.

To solve this system algebraically, first write both equations in standard form:

$$\frac{p}{10} + q = 100$$

$$-\frac{p}{20} + q = 25.$$

We can clear fractions and also prepare to eliminate p if we multiply the first equation by 10 and the second by 20:

$$p + 10q = 1,000$$

$$-p + 20q = 500,$$

and so:

$$30q = 1,500$$

$$q = 50.$$

Substituting this value of q into either equation gives us $p = 500$. Thus, the equilibrium price is $500, and 50 refrigerators will be sold at this price.

We could also have solved this system of equations by setting the two expressions for q (the supply and the demand) equal to each other:

$$-p/10 + 100 = p/20 + 25$$

and then solving for p. (See the **Before we go on** discussion at the end of Example 1.)

FAQs

Setting Up the Equations

Q: *Looking through these examples, I notice that in some, we can tabulate the information given and read off the equations (as in Example 5), whereas in others (like Example 6), we have to reword each sentence to turn it into an equation. How do I know what approach to use?*

A: There is no hard-and-fast rule, and indeed some applications might call for a bit of each approach. However, it is generally not hard to see when it would be useful to tabulate values: Lists of the numbers of ingredients or components generally lend themselves to tabulation, whereas phrases like "twice as many of these as those" generally require direct translation into equations (after rewording if necessary).

2.1 EXERCISES

▼ more advanced   ◆ challenging
Ⓣ indicates exercises that should be solved using technology

In Exercises 1–14, find all solutions of the given system of equations and check your answer graphically. HINT [See Examples 1–4.]

1. $x - y = 0$
   $x + y = 4$

2. $x - y = 0$
   $x + y = -6$

3. $x + y = 4$
   $x - y = 2$

4. $2x + y = 2$
   $-2x + y = 2$

5. $3x - 2y = 6$
   $2x - 3y = -6$

6. $2x + 3y = 5$
   $3x + 2y = 5$

7. $0.5x + 0.1y = 0.7$
   $0.2x - 0.2y = 0.6$

8. $-0.3x + 0.5y = 0.1$
   $0.1x - 0.1y = 0.4$

9. $\dfrac{x}{3} - \dfrac{y}{2} = 1$
   $\dfrac{x}{4} + y = -2$

10. $-\dfrac{2x}{3} + \dfrac{y}{2} = -\dfrac{1}{6}$
   $\dfrac{x}{4} - y = -\dfrac{3}{4}$

11. $2x + 3y = 1$
   $-x - \dfrac{3y}{2} = -\dfrac{1}{2}$

12. $2x - 3y = 1$
   $6x - 9y = 3$

13. $2x + 3y = 2$
   $-x - \dfrac{3y}{2} = -\dfrac{1}{2}$

14. $2x - 3y = 2$
   $6x - 9y = 3$

Ⓣ *In Exercises 15–24, use technology to obtain approximate solutions graphically. All solutions should be accurate to one decimal place. (Zoom in for improved accuracy.)*

15. $2x + 8y = 10$
   $x + y = 5$

16. $2x - y = 3$
   $x + 3y = 5$

17. $3.1x - 4.5y = 6$
   $4.5x + 1.1y = 0$

18. $0.2x + 4.5y = 1$
   $1.5x + 1.1y = 2$

19. $10.2x + 14y = 213$
   $4.5x + 1.1y = 448$

20. $100x + 4.5y = 540$
   $1.05x + 1.1y = 0$

21. ▼ Find the intersection of the line through $(0, 1)$ and $(4.2, 2)$ and the line through $(2.1, 3)$ and $(5.2, 0)$.

22. ▼ Find the intersection of the line through $(2.1, 3)$ and $(4, 2)$ and the line through $(3.2, 2)$ and $(5.1, 3)$.

23. ▼ Find the intersection of the line through $(0, 0)$ and $(5.5, 3)$ and the line through $(5, 0)$ and $(0, 6)$.

24. ▼ Find the intersection of the line through $(4.3, 0)$ and $(0, 5)$ and the line through $(2.1, 2.2)$ and $(5.2, 1)$.

APPLICATIONS

25. *Resource Allocation* You manage an ice cream factory that makes two flavors: Creamy Vanilla and Continental Mocha. Into each quart of Creamy Vanilla go 2 eggs and 3 cups of cream. Into each quart of Continental Mocha go 1 egg and 3 cups of cream. You have in stock 500 eggs and 900 cups of cream. How many quarts of each flavor should you make in order to use up all the eggs and cream? HINT [See Example 5.]

26. *Class Scheduling* Enormous State University's math department offers two courses: Finite Math and Applied Calculus. Each section of Finite Math has 60 students, and each section of Applied Calculus has 50. The department will offer a total of 110 sections in a semester, and 6,000 students would like to take a math course. How many sections of each course should the department offer in order to fill all sections and accommodate all of the students? HINT [See Example 5.]

27. *Nutrition* Gerber Mixed Cereal for Baby contains, in each serving, 60 calories and 11 grams of carbohydrates.[1] Gerber Mango Tropical Fruit Dessert contains, in each serving, 80 calories and 21 grams of carbohydrates.[2] If you want to provide your child with 200 calories and 43 grams of carbohydrates, how many servings of each should you use?

28. *Nutrition* Anthony Altino is mixing food for his young daughter and would like the meal to supply 1 gram of protein and 5 milligrams of iron. He is mixing together cereal, with 0.5 grams of protein and 1 milligram of iron per ounce, and fruit, with 0.2 grams of protein and 2 milligrams of iron per ounce. What mixture will provide the desired nutrition?

29. *Nutrition* One serving of Campbell's Pork & Beans contains 5 grams of protein and 21 grams of carbohydrates.[3] A typical slice of white bread provides 2 grams of protein and 11 grams of carbohydrates per slice. The U.S. RDA (Recommended Daily Allowance) is 60 grams of protein each day.

   a. I am planning a meal of "beans on toast" and wish to have it supply one-half of the RDA for protein and 139 grams of carbohydrates. How should I prepare my meal?

   b. Is it possible to have my meal supply the same amount of protein as in part (a) but only 100 g of carbohydrates?

30. *Nutrition* One serving of Campbell's Pork & Beans contains 5 grams of protein and 21 grams of carbohydrates.[4] A typical slice of "lite" rye bread contains 4 grams of protein and 12 grams of carbohydrates.

   a. I am planning a meal of "beans on toast" and wish to have it supply one third of the U.S. RDA for protein (see the preceding exercise), and 80 grams of carbohydrates. How should I prepare my meal?

   b. Is it possible to have my meal supply the same amount of protein as in part (a) but only 60 grams of carbohydrates?

---

[1] Source: Nutrition information printed on the box.
[2] Source: Nutrition information printed on the jar.
[3] According to the label information on a 16 oz. can.
[4] Ibid.

Protein Supplements *Exercises 31–34 are based on the following data on three popular protein supplements. (Figures shown correspond to a single serving.)*[5]

	Protein (g)	Carbohydrates (g)	Sodium (mg)	Cost ($)
Designer Whey® (Next)	18	2	80	0.50
Muscle Milk® (Cytosport)	32	16	240	1.60
Pure Whey Protein Stack® (Champion)	24	3	100	0.60

31. You are thinking of combining Designer Whey and Muscle Milk to obtain a 7-day supply that provides exactly 280 grams of protein and 56 grams of carbohydrates. How many servings of each supplement should you combine in order to meet your requirements? What will it cost?

32. You are thinking of combining Muscle Milk and Pure Whey Protein Stack to obtain a supply that provides exactly 640 grams of protein and 3,200 mg of sodium. How many servings of each supplement should you combine in order to meet your requirements? What will it cost?

33. ▼ You have a mixture of Designer Whey and Pure Whey Protein Stack that costs a total of $14 and supplies exactly 540 g of protein. How many grams of carbohydrates does it supply?

34. ▼ You have a mixture of Designer Whey and Muscle Milk that costs a total of $14 and supplies exactly 104 g of carbohydrates. How many grams of protein does it supply?

35. Investments: Tech Stocks In November 2008, **Apple** (AAPL) stock dropped from $105 to $95 per share, and **Microsoft** (MSFT) dropped from $21 to $20 per share.[6] If you invested a total of $3,570 in these stocks at the end of October and sold them for $3,250 at the end of November, how many shares of each stock did you buy?

36. Investments: Energy Stocks In November 2008, **British Petroleum** (BP) stock dropped from $50 to $48 per share, and **Exxon Mobil** (XOM) started and ended the month at $75 per share.[7] If you invested a total of $5,750 in these stocks at the end of October and sold them for $5,670 at the end of November, how many shares of each stock did you buy?

37. ▼ **Investments: Bank Stocks** In November 2008, **Bank of America** (BAC) cost $16 per share and yielded 3% per year in dividends, while **JPMorgan Chase** (JPM) cost $30 per share and

yielded 5% per year in dividends.[8] If you invested a total of $15,200 in these stocks and earned $696 in dividends in a year, how many shares of each stock did you purchase? (Assume the dividend rate was unchanged for the year.)

38. ▼ **Investments: Utility Stocks** In October 2008, **Consolidated Edison** (ED) cost $40 per share and yielded 6% per year in dividends, while **Southern Union Company** (SUG) cost $12 per share and yielded 4.5% per year in dividends.[9] If you invested a total of $27,600 in these stocks and earned $1,602 in dividends in a year, how many shares of each stock did you purchase? (Assume the dividend rate was unchanged for the year.)

39. Voting An appropriations bill passes the U.S. House of Representatives with 49 more members voting in favor than against. If all 435 members of the House vote for or against the bill, how many voted in favor and how many voted against?

40. Voting The U.S. Senate has 100 members. For a bill to pass with a supermajority, at least twice as many senators must vote in favor of the bill as vote against it. If all 100 senators vote in favor of or against a bill, how many must vote in favor for it to pass with a supermajority?

41. Intramural Sports The best sports dorm on campus, Lombardi House, has won a total of 12 games this semester. Some of these games were soccer games, and the others were football games. According to the rules of the university, each win in a soccer game earns the winning house 2 points, whereas each win in a football game earns them 4 points. If the total number of points Lombardi House earned was 38, how many of each type of game did they win?

42. Law Enormous State University's campus publication, *The Campus Inquirer*, ran a total of 10 exposés five years ago, dealing with alleged recruiting violations by the football team and with theft by the student treasurer of the film society. Each exposé dealing with recruiting violations resulted in a $4 million libel suit, and the treasurer of the film society sued the paper for $3 million as a result of each exposé concerning his alleged theft. Unfortunately for *The Campus Inquirer*, all the lawsuits were successful, and the paper wound up being ordered to pay $37 million in damages. (It closed down shortly thereafter.) How many of each type of exposé did the paper run?

43. Purchasing *(from the GMAT)* Elena purchased brand X pens for $4.00 apiece and brand Y pens for $2.80 apiece. If Elena purchased a total of 12 of these pens for $42.00, how many brand X pens did she purchase?

44. Purchasing *(based on a question from the GMAT)* Earl is ordering supplies. Yellow paper costs $5.00 per ream while white paper costs $6.50 per ream. He would like to order 100 reams total, and has a budget of $560. How many reams of each color should he order?

45. Equilibrium Price The demand and supply functions for pet chias are, respectively, $q = -60p + 150$ and $q = 80p - 60$,

---

[5] Source: Nutritional information supplied by the manufacturers (www.netrition.com). Cost per serving is approximate and varies.

[6] Share prices are approximate at or close to the dates cited. Source: www.finance.google.com.

[7] Ibid.

[8] Ibid.

[9] Ibid.

where p is the price in dollars. At what price should the chias be marked so that there is neither a surplus nor a shortage of chias? HINT [See Example 7.]

46. Equilibrium Price The demand and supply functions for your college newspaper are, respectively, $q = -10{,}000p + 2{,}000$ and $q = 4{,}000p + 600$, where p is the price in dollars. At what price should the newspapers be sold so that there is neither a surplus nor a shortage of papers? HINT [See Example 7.]

47. Supply and Demand *(from the GRE Economics Test)* The demand curve for widgets is given by $D = 85 - 5P$, and the supply curve is given by $S = 25 + 5P$, where P is the price of widgets. When the widget market is in equilibrium, what is the quantity of widgets bought and sold?

48. Supply and Demand *(from the GRE Economics Test)* In the market for soybeans, the demand and supply functions are $Q_D = 100 - 10P$ and $Q_S = 20 + 5P$, where Q_D is quantity demanded, Q_S is quantity supplied, and P is price in dollars. If the government sets a price floor of $7, what will be the resulting surplus or shortage?

49. Equilibrium Price In June 2001, the retail price of a 25-kg bag of cornmeal was $8 in Zambia; by December, the price had risen to $11. The result was that one retailer reported a drop in sales from 15 bags/day to 3 bags/day.[10] Assume that the retailer is prepared to sell 3 bags/day at $8 and 15 bags/day at $11. Find linear demand and supply equations and then compute the retailer's equilibrium price.

50. Equilibrium Price At the start of December 2001, the retail price of a 25 kg bag of cornmeal was $10 in Zambia, while by the end of the month, the price had fallen to $6.[11] The result was that one retailer reported an increase in sales from 3 bags/day to 5 bags/day. Assume that the retailer is prepared to sell 18 bags/day at $8 and 12 bags/day at $6. Obtain linear demand and supply equations, and hence compute the retailer's equilibrium price.

51. Pollution Joe Slo, a college sophomore, neglected to wash his dirty laundry for 6 weeks. By the end of that time, his roommate had had enough and tossed Joe's dirty socks and T-shirts into the trash, counting a total of 44 items. (A pair of dirty socks counts as one item.) The roommate noticed that there were three times as many pairs of dirty socks as T-shirts. How many of each item did he throw out?

52. Diet The local sushi bar serves 1-ounce pieces of raw salmon (consisting of 50% protein) and $1\frac{1}{4}$-ounce pieces of raw tuna (40% protein). A customer's total intake of protein amounts to $1\frac{1}{2}$ ounces after consuming a total of three pieces. How many of each did the customer consume? (Fractions of pieces are permitted.)

53. ▼ Management *(from the GMAT)* A manager has $6,000 budgeted for raises for four full-time and two part-time employees. Each of the full-time employees receives the same raise, which is twice the raise that each of the part-time employees receives. What is the amount of the raise that each full-time employee receives?

54. ▼ Publishing *(from the GMAT)* There were 36,000 hardback copies of a certain novel sold before the paperback version was issued. From the time the first paperback copy was sold until the last copy of the novel was sold, nine times as many paperback copies as hardback copies were sold. If a total of 441,000 copies of the novel were sold in all, how many paperback copies were sold?

COMMUNICATION AND REASONING EXERCISES

55. A system of three equations in two unknowns corresponds to three lines in the plane. Describe how these lines might be positioned if the system has a unique solution.

56. A system of three equations in two unknowns corresponds to three lines in the plane. Describe several ways that these lines might be positioned if the system has no solutions.

57. Both the supply and demand equations for a certain product have negative slope. Can there be an equilibrium price? Explain.

58. You are solving a system of equations with x representing the number of rocks and y representing the number of pebbles. The solution is $(200, -10)$. What do you conclude?

59. ▼ Referring to Exercise 25, suppose that the solution of the corresponding system of equations was 198.7 gallons of vanilla and 100.89 gallons of mocha. If your factory can produce only whole numbers of gallons, would you recommend rounding the answers to the nearest whole number? Explain.

60. ▼ Referring to Exercise 25 but using different data, suppose that the general solution of the corresponding system of equations was $(200 - y, y)$, where $x =$ number of gallons of vanilla, and $y =$ number of gallons of mocha. Your factory can produce only whole numbers of gallons. There are infinitely many ways of making the ice cream, mixes, right? Explain.

61. ▼ Select one: Multiplying both sides of a linear equation by a nonzero constant results in a linear equation whose graph is

(A) parallel to   (B) the same as
(C) not always parallel to   (D) not the same as

the graph of the original equation.

62. ▼ Select one: If the addition or subtraction of two linear equations results in the equation $3 = 3$, then the graphs of those equations are

(A) equal   (B) parallel
(C) perpendicular   (D) none of the above

---

[10] The prices quoted are approximate. (Actual prices varied from retailer to retailer.) Source: *New York Times*, December 24, 2001, p. A4.
[11] Ibid.

63. ▼ Select one: If the addition or subtraction of two linear equations results in the equation $0 = 3$, then the graphs of those equations are

(A) equal   (B) parallel
(C) perpendicular (D) not parallel

64. ▼ Select one: If adding two linear equations gives $x = 3$, and subtracting them gives $y = 3$, then the graphs of those equations are

(A) equal   (B) parallel
(C) perpendicular (D) not parallel

65. ▼ Invent an interesting application that leads to a system of two equations in two unknowns with a unique solution.

66. ▼ Invent an interesting application that leads to a system of two equations in two unknowns with no solution.

67. ◆ How likely do you think it is that a "random" system of two equations in two unknowns has a unique solution? Give some justification for your answer.

68. ◆ How likely do you think it is that a "random" system of three equations in two unknowns has a unique solution? Give some justification for your answer.

2.2 Using Matrices to Solve Systems of Equations

In this section we describe a systematic method for solving systems of equations that makes solving large systems of equations in any number of unknowns straightforward. Although this method may seem a little cumbersome at first, it will prove *immensely* useful in this and the next several chapters. First, some terminology:

Linear Equation

A linear equation in the n variables $x_1, x_2, \ldots, x_n$ has the form

$$a_1 x_1 + \cdots + a_n x_n = b. \qquad (a_1, a_2, \ldots, a_n, b \text{ constants})$$

The numbers $a_1, a_2, \ldots, a_n$ are called the **coefficients**, and the number b is called the **constant term**, or **right-hand side**.

Quick Examples

1. $3x - 5y = 0$

   Linear equation in x and y
   Coefficients: 3, −5 Constant term: 0

2. $x + 2y - z = 6$

   Linear equation in x, y, z
   Coefficients: 1, 2, −1 Constant term: 6

3. $30x_1 + 18x_2 + x_3 + x_4 = 19$

   Linear equation in x_1, x_2, x_3, x_4
   Coefficients: 30, 18, 1, 1 Constant term: 19

Note When the number of variables is small, we will almost always use $x, y, z, \ldots$ (as in Quick Examples 1 and 2) rather than $x_1, x_2, x_3, \ldots$ as the names of the variables. ■

Notice that a linear equation in any number of unknowns (for example, $2x - y = 3$) is entirely determined by its coefficients and its constant term. In other words, if we were simply given the row of numbers

$$[2 \quad -1 \quad 3]$$

we could easily reconstruct the original linear equation by multiplying the first number by x, the second by y, and inserting a plus sign and an equals sign, as follows:

$$2 \cdot x + (-1) \cdot y = 3$$

or $\quad 2x - y = 3.$

Similarly, the equation

$$-4x + 2y = 0$$

is represented by the row

$$[-4 \quad 2 \quad 0],$$

and the equation

$$-3y = \frac{1}{4}$$

is represented by

$$\begin{bmatrix} 0 & -3 & \frac{1}{4} \end{bmatrix}.$$

As the last example shows, the first number is always the coefficient of x and the second is the coefficient of y. If an x or a y is missing, we write a zero for its coefficient. We shall call such a row the **coefficient row** of an equation.

If we have a system of equations, for example the system

$$\begin{aligned} 2x - y &= 3 \\ -x + 2y &= -4, \end{aligned}$$

we can put the coefficient rows together like this:

$$\begin{bmatrix} 2 & -1 & 3 \\ -1 & 2 & -4 \end{bmatrix}.$$

We call this the **augmented matrix** of the system of equations. The term *augmented* means that we have included the right-hand sides 3 and -4. We will often drop the word *augmented* and simply refer to the matrix of the system. A **matrix** (plural: **matrices**) is nothing more than a rectangular array of numbers as above.

Matrix, Augmented Matrix

A **matrix** is a rectangular array of numbers. The **augmented matrix** of a system of linear equations is the matrix whose rows are the coefficient rows of the equations.

Quick Example

The augmented matrix of the system

$$\begin{aligned} x + y &= 3 \\ x - y &= 1 \end{aligned}$$

is

$$\begin{bmatrix} 1 & 1 & 3 \\ 1 & -1 & 1 \end{bmatrix}.$$

We'll be studying matrices in their own right more carefully in Chapter 3.

Q: *What good are coefficient rows and matrices?*

A: Think about what we do when we multiply both sides of an equation by a number. For example, consider multiplying both sides of the equation $2x - y = 3$ by -2 to get $-4x + 2y = -6$. All we are really doing is multiplying the coefficients and the right-hand side by -2. This corresponds to *multiplying the row* $[2 \ -1 \ 3]$ *by* -2, that is, multiplying every number in the row by -2. We shall see that any manipulation we want to do with equations can be done instead with rows, and this fact leads to a method of solving equations that is systematic and generalizes easily to larger systems.

Here is the same operation both in the language of equations and the language of rows. (We refer to the equation here as *Equation* 1, or simply E_1 for short, and to the row as *Row* 1, or R_1.)

	Equation	*Row*
	E_1: $2x - \ y = 3$	$[\ 2 \quad -1 \quad 3] \quad R_1$
Multiply by -2 :	$(-2)E_1$: $-4x + 2y = -6$	$[-4 \quad 2 \ -6] \quad (-2)R_1$

Multiplying both sides of an equation by the number a corresponds to multiplying the coefficient row by a.

Now look at what we do when we add two equations:

	Equation	*Row*
	E_1: $2x - \ y = 3$	$[\ 2 \ -1 \quad 3] \quad R_1$
	E_2: $-x + 2y = -4$	$[-1 \quad 2 \ -4] \quad R_2$
Add:	$E_1 + E_2$: $x + \ y = -1$	$[\ 1 \quad 1 \ -1] \quad R_1 + R_2$

All we are really doing is *adding the corresponding entries in the rows*, or *adding the rows*. In other words,

Adding two equations corresponds to adding their coefficient rows.

In short, the manipulations of equations that we saw in the preceding section can be done more easily with rows in a matrix because we don't have to carry x, y, and other unnecessary notation along with us; x and y can always be inserted at the end if desired.

The manipulations we are talking about are known as **row operations**. In particular, we use three **elementary row operations**.

✳ NOTE We are using the term *elementary row operations* a little more freely than most books. Some mathematicians insist that $a = 1$ in an operation of Type 2, but the less restrictive version is very useful.

† NOTE Multiplying an equation or row by zero gives us the not very surprising result $0 = 0$. In fact, we lose any information that the equation provided, which usually means that the resulting system has more solutions than the original system.

Elementary Row Operations*

Type 1: Replacing R_i by $a R_i$ (where $a \neq 0$)†
In words: multiplying or dividing a row by a nonzero number.

Type 2: Replacing R_i by $a R_i \pm b R_j$ (where $a \neq 0$)
Multiplying a row by a nonzero number and adding or subtracting a multiple of another row.

using Technology

See the Technology Guides at
the end of the chapter to see
how to do row operations using
a TI-83/84 Plus or Excel.

Web Site
www.FiniteandCalc.org

  Everything for Finite Math

    → Math Tools for Chapter 2

    → Pivot and Gauss-Jordan
      Tool

Enter the matrix in columns
$x1, x2, x3, \ldots$. To do a row
operation, type the instruction(s)
next to the row(s) you are
changing as shown, and click
"Do Row Ops" once.

Type 3: Switching the order of the rows
This corresponds to switching the order in which we write the equations; occasionally this will be convenient.

For Types 1 and 2, we write the instruction for the row operation *next to the row we wish to replace*. (See the quick examples below.)

Quick Examples

Type 1: $\begin{bmatrix} 1 & 3 & -4 \\ 0 & 4 & 2 \end{bmatrix} 3R_2 \rightarrow \begin{bmatrix} 1 & 3 & -4 \\ 0 & 12 & 6 \end{bmatrix}$ Replace R_2 by $3R_2$.

Type 2: $\begin{bmatrix} 1 & 3 & -4 \\ 0 & 4 & 2 \end{bmatrix} 4R_1 - 3R_2 \rightarrow \begin{bmatrix} 4 & 0 & -22 \\ 0 & 4 & 2 \end{bmatrix}$ Replace R_1 by $4R_1 - 3R_2$.

Type 3: $\begin{bmatrix} 1 & 3 & -4 \\ 0 & 4 & 2 \\ 1 & 2 & 3 \end{bmatrix} R_1 \leftrightarrow R_2 \rightarrow \begin{bmatrix} 0 & 4 & 2 \\ 1 & 3 & -4 \\ 1 & 2 & 3 \end{bmatrix}$ Switch R_1 and R_2.

One very important fact about the elementary row operations is that they do not change the solutions of the corresponding system of equations. In other words, the new system of equations that we get by applying any one of these operations will have exactly the same solutions as the original system: It is easy to see that numbers that make the original equations true will also make the new equations true, because each of the elementary row operations corresponds to a valid operation on the original equations. That any solution of the new system is a solution of the old system follows from the fact that these row operations are *reversible*: The effects of a row operation can be reversed by applying another row operation, called its **inverse**. Here are some examples of this reversibility. (Try them out in the above Quick Examples.)

Operation	Inverse Operation
Replace R_2 by $3R_2$.	Replace R_2 by $\frac{1}{3}R_2$.
Replace R_1 by $4R_1 - 3R_2$.	Replace R_1 by $\frac{1}{4}R_1 + \frac{3}{4}R_2$.
Switch R_1 and R_2.	Switch R_1 and R_2.

Our objective, then, is to use row operations to change the system we are given into one with exactly the same set of solutions, in which it is easy to see what the solutions are.

Solving Systems of Equations by Using Row Operations

Now we put rows to work for us in solving systems of equations. Let's start with a complicated looking system of equations:

$$-\frac{2x}{3} + \frac{y}{2} = -3$$
$$\frac{x}{4} - y = \frac{11}{4}.$$

We begin by writing the matrix of the system:

$$\begin{bmatrix} -\frac{2}{3} & \frac{1}{2} & -3 \\ \frac{1}{4} & -1 & \frac{11}{4} \end{bmatrix}.$$

Now what do we do with this matrix?

Step 1 *Clear the fractions and/or decimals (if any) using operations of Type* **1.** To clear the fractions, we multiply the first row by 6 and the second row by 4. We record the operations by writing the symbolic form of an operation next to the row it will change, as follows.

$$\begin{bmatrix} -\frac{2}{3} & \frac{1}{2} & -3 \\ \frac{1}{4} & -1 & \frac{11}{4} \end{bmatrix} \begin{matrix} 6R_1 \\ 4R_2 \end{matrix}$$

By this we mean that we will replace the first row by $6R_1$ and the second by $4R_2$. Doing these operations gives

$$\begin{bmatrix} -4 & 3 & -18 \\ 1 & -4 & 11 \end{bmatrix}.$$

Step 2 *Designate the first nonzero entry in the first row as the* **pivot.** In this case we designate the entry -4 in the first row as the "pivot" by putting a box around it:

$$\begin{bmatrix} \boxed{-4} & 3 & -18 \\ 1 & -4 & 11 \end{bmatrix}. \quad \leftarrow \text{Pivot row}$$

$\uparrow$
Pivot column

Q : *What is a "pivot"?*

A : A **pivot** is an entry in a matrix that is used to "clear a column." (See Step 3.) In this procedure, we will always select the first nonzero entry of a row as our pivot. In Chapter 4, when we study the simplex method, we will select our pivots differently.

Step 3 *Use the pivot to clear its column using operations of Type* **2.** By **clearing a column**, we mean changing the matrix so that the pivot is the only nonzero number in its column. The procedure of clearing a column using a designated pivot is also called **pivoting.**

$$\begin{bmatrix} \boxed{-4} & 3 & -18 \\ 0 & \# & \# \end{bmatrix} \leftarrow \text{Desired row 2 (the "\#"s stand for as yet unknown numbers)}$$

$\uparrow$
Cleared pivot column

We want to replace R_2 by a row of the form $aR_2 \pm bR_1$ to get a zero in column 1. Moreover—and this will be important when we discuss the simplex method in Chapter 4— *we are going to choose positive values for both a and b.** We need to choose a and b so that we get the desired cancellation. We can do this quite mechanically as follows:

* NOTE Thus, the only place a negative sign may appear is between aR_2 and bR_1 as indicated in the formula $aR_2 \pm bR_1$.

a. Write the name of the row you need to change on the left and that of the pivot row on the right.

$$R_2 \qquad R_1$$

$\uparrow$　　　$\uparrow$

Row to change　Pivot row

b. Focus on the pivot column, $\begin{bmatrix} -4 \\ 1 \end{bmatrix}$. Multiply each row by the *absolute value* of the entry currently in the other. (We are not permitting a or b to be negative.)

$$4R_2 \qquad\qquad 1R_1$$
$$\uparrow \qquad\qquad\quad \uparrow$$
From Row 1   From Row 2

The effect is to make the two entries in the pivot column numerically the same. Sometimes, you can accomplish this by using smaller values of a and b.

c. If the entries in the pivot column have opposite signs, insert a plus (+). If they have the same sign, insert a minus (−). Here, we get the instruction

$$4R_2 + 1R_1.$$

d. Write the operation next to the row you want to change, and then replace that row using the operation:

$$\begin{bmatrix} \boxed{-4} & 3 & -18 \\ 1 & -4 & 11 \end{bmatrix} \begin{matrix} \\ 4R_2 + 1R_1 \end{matrix} \rightarrow \begin{bmatrix} -4 & 3 & -18 \\ 0 & -13 & 26 \end{bmatrix}.$$

We have cleared the pivot column and completed Step 3.

＊ NOTE We are deviating somewhat from the traditional procedure here. It is traditionally recommended first to divide the pivot row by the pivot, turning the pivot into a 1. This allows one to use $a = 1$, but usually results in fractions. The procedure we use here is easier for hand calculations and, we feel, mathematically more elegant, because it eliminates the need to introduce fractions. See the end of this section for an example done using the traditional procedure.

Note In general, the row operation you use should always have the following form＊:

$$aR_c \qquad\qquad \pm \qquad\qquad bR_p$$
$$\uparrow \qquad\qquad\qquad\qquad\quad \uparrow$$
Row to change   Pivot row

with a and b both positive.

The next step is one that can be performed at any time. ■

Simplification Step (Optional) *If, at any stage of the process, all the numbers in a row are multiples of an integer, divide by that integer*—a Type 1 operation.

This is an optional but extremely helpful step: It makes the numbers smaller and easier to work with. In our case, the entries in R_2 are divisible by 13, so we divide that row by 13. (Alternatively, we could divide by −13. Try it.)

$$\begin{bmatrix} -4 & 3 & -18 \\ 0 & -13 & 26 \end{bmatrix} \begin{matrix} \\ \frac{1}{13}R_2 \end{matrix} \rightarrow \begin{bmatrix} -4 & 3 & -18 \\ 0 & -1 & 2 \end{bmatrix}$$

Step 4 *Select the first nonzero number in the second row as the pivot, and clear its column.* Here we have combined two steps in one: selecting the new pivot and clearing the column (pivoting). The pivot is shown below, as well as the desired result when the column has been cleared:

$$\begin{bmatrix} -4 & 3 & -18 \\ 0 & \boxed{-1} & 2 \end{bmatrix} \rightarrow \begin{bmatrix} \# & 0 & \# \\ 0 & -1 & 2 \end{bmatrix}. \quad \leftarrow \text{desired row}$$
$$\uparrow \qquad\qquad\qquad\qquad \uparrow$$
Pivot column   Cleared pivot column

We now wish to get a 0 in place of the 3 in the pivot column. Let's run once again through the mechanical steps to get the row operation that accomplishes this.

a. Write the name of the row you need to change on the left and that of the pivot row on the right:

$$\boldsymbol{R_1} \qquad\qquad\qquad \boldsymbol{R_2}$$
$$\uparrow \qquad\qquad\qquad\quad \uparrow$$
Row to change   Pivot row

b. Focus on the pivot column, $\begin{bmatrix} 3 \\ -1 \end{bmatrix}$. Multiply each row by the absolute value of the entry currently in the other:

$$\underset{\underset{\text{From Row 2}}{\uparrow}}{\mathbf{1}R_1} \qquad \underset{\underset{\text{From Row 1}}{\uparrow}}{\mathbf{3}R_2}$$

c. If the entries in the pivot column have opposite signs, insert a plus $(+)$. If they have the same sign, insert a minus $(-)$. Here, we get the instruction

$$1R_1 + 3R_2.$$

d. Write the operation next to the row you want to change and then replace that row using the operation.

$$\begin{bmatrix} -4 & 3 & -18 \\ 0 & \boxed{-1} & 2 \end{bmatrix} \begin{array}{c} R_1 + 3R_2 \\ \\ \end{array} \rightarrow \begin{bmatrix} -4 & 0 & -12 \\ 0 & -1 & 2 \end{bmatrix}$$

Now we are essentially done, except for one last step.

Final Step *Using operations of Type* **1,** *turn each pivot (the first nonzero entry in each row) into a* **1.** We can accomplish this by dividing the first row by -4 and multiplying the second row by -1:

$$\begin{bmatrix} -4 & 0 & -12 \\ 0 & -1 & 2 \end{bmatrix} \begin{array}{c} -\frac{1}{4}R_1 \\ -R_2 \end{array} \rightarrow \begin{bmatrix} 1 & 0 & 3 \\ 0 & 1 & -2 \end{bmatrix}.$$

The matrix now has the following nice form:

$$\begin{bmatrix} \boxed{1} & 0 & \# \\ 0 & \boxed{1} & \# \end{bmatrix}.$$

(This is the form we will always obtain with two equations in two unknowns when there is a unique solution.) This form is nice because, when we translate back into equations, we get

$$1x + 0y = 3$$
$$0x + 1y = -2.$$

In other words,

$$x = 3 \quad \text{and} \quad y = -2$$

and so we have found the solution, which we can also write as $(x, y) = (3, -2)$.

The procedure we've just demonstrated is called **Gauss-Jordan*** **reduction** or **row reduction**. It may seem too complicated a way to solve a system of two equations in two unknowns, and it is. However, for systems with more equations and more unknowns, it is very efficient.

In Example 1 below we use row reduction to solve a system of linear equations in *three* unknowns: x, y, and z. Just as for a system in two unknowns, a **solution** of a system in any number of unknowns consists of values for each of the variables that, when substituted, satisfy all of the equations in the system. Again, just as for a system in two unknowns, any system of linear equations in any number of unknowns has either no solution, exactly one solution, or infinitely many solutions. There are no other possibilities.

✳ **NOTE** Carl Friedrich Gauss (1777–1855) was one of the great mathematicians, making fundamental contributions to number theory, analysis, probability, and statistics, as well as many fields of science. He developed a method of solving systems of linear equations by row reduction, which was then refined by Wilhelm Jordan (1842–1899) into the form we are showing you here.

Solving a system in three unknowns graphically would require the graphing of planes (flat surfaces) in three dimensions. (The graph of a linear equation in three unknowns is a flat surface.) The use of row reduction makes three-dimensional graphing unnecessary.

EXAMPLE 1 Solving a System by Gauss-Jordan Reduction

Solve the system

$$x - \ y + 5z = -6$$
$$3x + 3y - \ z = 10$$
$$x + 3y + 2z = 5.$$

Solution The augmented matrix for this system is

$$\begin{bmatrix} 1 & -1 & 5 & -6 \\ 3 & 3 & -1 & 10 \\ 1 & 3 & 2 & 5 \end{bmatrix}.$$

Note that the columns correspond to x, y, z, and the right-hand side, respectively. We begin by selecting the pivot in the first row and clearing its column. Remember that clearing the column means that we turn *all* other numbers in the column into zeros. Thus, to clear the column of the first pivot, we need to change two rows, setting up the row operations in exactly the same way as above.

$$\begin{bmatrix} \boxed{1} & -1 & 5 & -6 \\ 3 & 3 & -1 & 10 \\ 1 & 3 & 2 & 5 \end{bmatrix} \begin{matrix} \\ R_2 - 3R_1 \rightarrow \\ R_3 - R_1 \end{matrix} \begin{bmatrix} 1 & -1 & 5 & -6 \\ 0 & 6 & -16 & 28 \\ 0 & 4 & -3 & 11 \end{bmatrix}$$

Notice that both row operations have the required form

$$a R_c \pm b R_1$$

↑   ↑

Row to change   Pivot row

with a and b both positive.

Now we use the optional simplification step to simplify R_2:

$$\begin{bmatrix} 1 & -1 & 5 & -6 \\ 0 & 6 & -16 & 28 \\ 0 & 4 & -3 & 11 \end{bmatrix} \tfrac{1}{2}R_2 \rightarrow \begin{bmatrix} 1 & -1 & 5 & -6 \\ 0 & 3 & -8 & 14 \\ 0 & 4 & -3 & 11 \end{bmatrix}.$$

Next, we select the pivot in the second row and clear its column:

$$\begin{bmatrix} 1 & -1 & 5 & -6 \\ 0 & \boxed{3} & -8 & 14 \\ 0 & 4 & -3 & 11 \end{bmatrix} \begin{matrix} 3R_1 + R_2 \\ \\ 3R_3 - 4R_2 \end{matrix} \rightarrow \begin{bmatrix} 3 & 0 & 7 & -4 \\ 0 & 3 & -8 & 14 \\ 0 & 0 & 23 & -23 \end{bmatrix}.$$

R_1 and R_3 are to be changed.
R_2 is the pivot row.

We simplify R_3.

$$\begin{bmatrix} 3 & 0 & 7 & -4 \\ 0 & 3 & -8 & 14 \\ 0 & 0 & 23 & -23 \end{bmatrix} \tfrac{1}{23}R_3 \rightarrow \begin{bmatrix} 3 & 0 & 7 & -4 \\ 0 & 3 & -8 & 14 \\ 0 & 0 & 1 & -1 \end{bmatrix}$$

using Technology

See the Technology Guides at the end of the chapter to see how to use a TI-83/84 Plus or Excel to solve this system of equations.

Web Site

www.FiniteandCalc.org

Everything for Finite Math

→ Math Tools for Chapter 2

→ Pivot and Gauss-Jordan Tool

Enter the augmented matrix in columns $x1$, $x2$, $x3$, ... At each step, type in the row operations exactly as written above next to the rows to which they apply. For example, for the first step type: R2-3R1 next to Row 2, and R3-R1 next to Row 3. Click "Do Row Ops" once, and then "Clear Row Ops" to prepare for the next step. For the last step, type (1/3)R1 next to Row 1, and (1/3)R2 next to Row 2. Click "Do Row Ops" once. The utility also does other things, such as automatic pivoting and complete reduction in one step. Use these features to check your work.

Now we select the pivot in the third row and clear its column:

$$\begin{bmatrix} 3 & 0 & 7 & -4 \\ 0 & 3 & -8 & 14 \\ 0 & 0 & \boxed{1} & -1 \end{bmatrix} \begin{matrix} R_1 - 7R_3 \\ R_2 + 8R_3 \end{matrix} \rightarrow \begin{bmatrix} 3 & 0 & 0 & 3 \\ 0 & 3 & 0 & 6 \\ 0 & 0 & 1 & -1 \end{bmatrix}.$$

R_1 and R_2 are to be changed.
R_3 is the pivot row.

Finally, we turn all the pivots into 1s:

$$\begin{bmatrix} 3 & 0 & 0 & 3 \\ 0 & 3 & 0 & 6 \\ 0 & 0 & 1 & -1 \end{bmatrix} \begin{matrix} \frac{1}{3}R_1 \\ \frac{1}{3}R_2 \end{matrix} \rightarrow \begin{bmatrix} 1 & 0 & 0 & 1 \\ 0 & 1 & 0 & 2 \\ 0 & 0 & 1 & -1 \end{bmatrix}.$$

The matrix is now reduced to a simple form, so we translate back into equations to obtain the solution:

$$x = 1, \ y = 2, \ z = -1, \text{ or } (x, y, z) = (1, 2, -1).$$

Notice the form of the very last matrix in the example:

$$\begin{bmatrix} 1 & 0 & 0 & \# \\ 0 & 1 & 0 & \# \\ 0 & 0 & 1 & \# \end{bmatrix}.$$

The 1s are on the **(main) diagonal** of the matrix; the goal in Gauss-Jordan reduction is to reduce our matrix to this form. If we can do so, then we can easily read off the solution, as we saw in Example 1. However, as we will see in several examples in this section, it is not always possible to achieve this ideal state. After Example 6, we will give a form that is always possible to achieve.

EXAMPLE 2 Solving a System by Gauss-Jordan Reduction

Solve the system:

$$2x + y + 3z = 1$$
$$4x + 2y + 4z = 4$$
$$x + 2y + z = 4.$$

Solution

$$\begin{bmatrix} \boxed{2} & 1 & 3 & 1 \\ 4 & 2 & 4 & 4 \\ 1 & 2 & 1 & 4 \end{bmatrix} \begin{matrix} \\ R_2 - 2R_1 \\ 2R_3 - R_1 \end{matrix} \rightarrow \begin{bmatrix} 2 & 1 & 3 & 1 \\ 0 & 0 & -2 & 2 \\ 0 & 3 & -1 & 7 \end{bmatrix}$$

Now we have a slight problem: The number in the position where we would like to have a pivot—the second column of the second row—is a zero and thus cannot be a pivot. There are two ways out of this problem. One is to move on to the third column and pivot on the -2. Another is to switch the order of the second and third rows so that we can use the 3 as a pivot. We will do the latter.

$$
\begin{bmatrix} 2 & 1 & 3 & 1 \\ 0 & 0 & -2 & 2 \\ 0 & 3 & -1 & 7 \end{bmatrix} \begin{matrix} \\ \\ R_2 \leftrightarrow R_3 \end{matrix} \rightarrow \begin{bmatrix} 2 & 1 & 3 & 1 \\ 0 & \boxed{3} & -1 & 7 \\ 0 & 0 & -2 & 2 \end{bmatrix} \begin{matrix} 3R_1 - R_2 \\ \\ \\ \end{matrix}
$$

$$
\rightarrow \begin{bmatrix} 6 & 0 & 10 & -4 \\ 0 & 3 & -1 & 7 \\ 0 & 0 & -2 & 2 \end{bmatrix} \begin{matrix} \\ \\ -\frac{1}{2}R_3 \end{matrix} \rightarrow \begin{bmatrix} 6 & 0 & 10 & -4 \\ 0 & 3 & -1 & 7 \\ 0 & 0 & \boxed{1} & -1 \end{bmatrix} \begin{matrix} R_1 - 10R_3 \\ R_2 + R_3 \\ \\ \end{matrix}
$$

$$
\rightarrow \begin{bmatrix} 6 & 0 & 0 & 6 \\ 0 & 3 & 0 & 6 \\ 0 & 0 & 1 & -1 \end{bmatrix} \begin{matrix} \frac{1}{6}R_1 \\ \frac{1}{3}R_2 \\ \\ \end{matrix} \rightarrow \begin{bmatrix} 1 & 0 & 0 & 1 \\ 0 & 1 & 0 & 2 \\ 0 & 0 & 1 & -1 \end{bmatrix}
$$

Thus, the solution is $(x, y, z) = (1, 2, -1)$, as you can check in the original system.

EXAMPLE 3   Inconsistent System

Solve the system:

$$
\begin{aligned}
x + y + z &= 1 \\
2x - y + z &= 0 \\
4x + y + 3z &= 3.
\end{aligned}
$$

Solution

$$
\begin{bmatrix} \boxed{1} & 1 & 1 & 1 \\ 2 & -1 & 1 & 0 \\ 4 & 1 & 3 & 3 \end{bmatrix} \begin{matrix} \\ R_2 - 2R_1 \\ R_3 - 4R_1 \end{matrix} \rightarrow \begin{bmatrix} 1 & 1 & 1 & 1 \\ 0 & \boxed{-3} & -1 & -2 \\ 0 & -3 & -1 & -1 \end{bmatrix} \begin{matrix} 3R_1 + R_2 \\ \\ R_3 - R_2 \end{matrix}
$$

$$
\rightarrow \begin{bmatrix} 3 & 0 & 2 & 1 \\ 0 & -3 & -1 & -2 \\ 0 & 0 & 0 & 1 \end{bmatrix}
$$

Stop. That last row translates into $0 = 1$, which is nonsense, and so, as in Example 3 in Section 2.1, we can say that this system has no solution. We also say, as we did for systems with only two unknowns, that a system with no solution is **inconsistent**. A system with at least one solution is **consistent**.

➡ **Before we go on...**

Q : *How, exactly, does the nonsensical equation $0 = 1$ tell us that there is no solution of the system in Example 3?*

A : Here is an argument similar to that in Example 3 in Section 2.1: If there *were* three numbers x, y, and z satisfying the original system of equations, then manipulating the equations according to the instructions in the row operations above leads us to conclude that $0 = 1$. Because 0 is *not* equal to 1, there can be no such numbers x, y, and z. ∎

EXAMPLE 4   Infinitely Many Solutions

Solve the system:

$$
\begin{aligned}
x + y + z &= 1 \\
\frac{1}{4}x - \frac{1}{2}y + \frac{3}{4}z &= 0 \\
x + 7y - 3z &= 3.
\end{aligned}
$$

Solution

$$\begin{bmatrix} 1 & 1 & 1 & 1 \\ \frac{1}{4} & -\frac{1}{2} & \frac{3}{4} & 0 \\ 1 & 7 & -3 & 3 \end{bmatrix} \begin{array}{l} \\ 4R_2 \end{array} \rightarrow \begin{bmatrix} \boxed{1} & 1 & 1 & 1 \\ 1 & -2 & 3 & 0 \\ 1 & 7 & -3 & 3 \end{bmatrix} \begin{array}{l} \\ R_2 - R_1 \\ R_3 - R_1 \end{array}$$

$$\rightarrow \begin{bmatrix} 1 & 1 & 1 & 1 \\ 0 & -3 & 2 & -1 \\ 0 & 6 & -4 & 2 \end{bmatrix} \begin{array}{l} \\ \\ \frac{1}{2}R_3 \end{array} \rightarrow \begin{bmatrix} 1 & 1 & 1 & 1 \\ 0 & \boxed{-3} & 2 & -1 \\ 0 & 3 & -2 & 1 \end{bmatrix} \begin{array}{l} 3R_1 + R_2 \\ \\ R_3 + R_2 \end{array}$$

$$\rightarrow \begin{bmatrix} 3 & 0 & 5 & 2 \\ 0 & -3 & 2 & -1 \\ 0 & 0 & 0 & 0 \end{bmatrix}$$

There are no nonzero entries in the third row, so there can be no pivot in the third row. We skip to the final step and turn the pivots we did find into 1s.

$$\begin{bmatrix} 3 & 0 & 5 & 2 \\ 0 & -3 & 2 & -1 \\ 0 & 0 & 0 & 0 \end{bmatrix} \begin{array}{l} \frac{1}{3}R_1 \\ -\frac{1}{3}R_2 \end{array} \rightarrow \begin{bmatrix} 1 & 0 & \frac{5}{3} & \frac{2}{3} \\ 0 & 1 & -\frac{2}{3} & \frac{1}{3} \\ 0 & 0 & 0 & 0 \end{bmatrix}$$

Now we translate back into equations and obtain:

$$x \quad + \tfrac{5}{3}z = \tfrac{2}{3}$$
$$y - \tfrac{2}{3}z = \tfrac{1}{3}$$
$$0 = 0.$$

But how does this help us find a solution? The last equation doesn't tell us anything useful, so we ignore it. The thing to notice about the other equations is that we can easily solve the first equation for x and the second for y, obtaining

$$x = \tfrac{2}{3} - \tfrac{5}{3}z$$
$$y = \tfrac{1}{3} + \tfrac{2}{3}z.$$

This is the solution! We can choose z to be any number and get corresponding values for x and y from the formulas above. This gives us infinitely many different solutions. Thus, the general solution (see Example 4 in Section 2.1) is

$$x = \tfrac{2}{3} - \tfrac{5}{3}z$$
$$y = \tfrac{1}{3} + \tfrac{2}{3}z \qquad\qquad \text{General solution}$$
$$z \text{ is arbitrary.}$$

We can also write the general solution as

$$\left(\tfrac{2}{3} - \tfrac{5}{3}z, \tfrac{1}{3} + \tfrac{2}{3}z, z\right) \ z \text{ arbitrary.} \qquad \text{General solution}$$

This general solution has z as the parameter. Specific choices of values for the parameter z give particular solutions. For example, the choice $z = 6$ gives the particular solution

$$x = \tfrac{2}{3} - \tfrac{5}{3}(6) = -\tfrac{28}{3}$$
$$y = \tfrac{1}{3} + \tfrac{2}{3}(6) = \tfrac{13}{3} \qquad\qquad \text{Particular solution}$$
$$z = 6,$$

while the choice $z = 0$ gives the particular solution $(x, \ y, \ z) = \left(\tfrac{2}{3}, \tfrac{1}{3}, 0\right)$.

Note that, unlike the system given in preceding example, the system given in this example does have solutions, and is thus *consistent*.

✱ NOTE In fact, you can check that the third equation, E_3, is equal to $3E_1 - 8E_2$. Thus, the third equation could have been left out because it conveys no more information than the first two. The process of row reduction always eliminates such a redundancy by creating a row of zeros.

➡ **Before we go on...** Why were there infinitely many solutions to Example 4? The third equation was really a combination of the first and second equations to begin with, so we effectively had only two equations in three unknowns.✱ Choosing a specific value for z (say, $z = 6$) has the effect of supplying the "missing" equation.

Q: *How do we know when there are infinitely many solutions?*

A: When there are solutions (we have a consistent system, unlike the one in Example 3), and when the matrix we arrive at by row reduction has fewer pivots than there are un-knowns. In Example 4 we had three unknowns but only two pivots.

Q: *How do we know which variables to use as parameters in a parameterized solution?*

A: The variables to use as parameters are those in the columns without pivots. In Example 4 there were pivots in the x and y columns, but no pivot in the z column, and it was z that we used as a parameter. ∎

EXAMPLE 5   Four Unknowns

Solve the system:

$$
\begin{aligned}
x + 3y + 2z - w &= 6 \\
2x + 6y + 6z + 3w &= 16 \\
x + 3y - 2z - 11w &= -2 \\
2x + 6y + 8z + 8w &= 20.
\end{aligned}
$$

Solution

$$
\begin{bmatrix}
\boxed{1} & 3 & 2 & -1 & 6 \\
2 & 6 & 6 & 3 & 16 \\
1 & 3 & -2 & -11 & -2 \\
2 & 6 & 8 & 8 & 20
\end{bmatrix}
\begin{matrix}
\\
R_2 - 2R_1 \\
R_3 - R_1 \\
R_4 - 2R_1
\end{matrix}
\rightarrow
\begin{bmatrix}
1 & 3 & 2 & -1 & 6 \\
0 & 0 & 2 & 5 & 4 \\
0 & 0 & -4 & -10 & -8 \\
0 & 0 & 4 & 10 & 8
\end{bmatrix}
$$

There is no pivot available in the second column, so we move on to the third column.

$$
\begin{bmatrix}
1 & 3 & 2 & -1 & 6 \\
0 & 0 & \boxed{2} & 5 & 4 \\
0 & 0 & -4 & -10 & -8 \\
0 & 0 & 4 & 10 & 8
\end{bmatrix}
\begin{matrix}
R_1 - R_2 \\
\\
R_3 + 2R_2 \\
R_4 - 2R_2
\end{matrix}
\rightarrow
\begin{bmatrix}
1 & 3 & 0 & -6 & 2 \\
0 & 0 & 2 & 5 & 4 \\
0 & 0 & 0 & 0 & 0 \\
0 & 0 & 0 & 0 & 0
\end{bmatrix}
\begin{matrix}
\\
\frac{1}{2}R_2 \\
\\
\\
\end{matrix}
$$

$$
\rightarrow
\begin{bmatrix}
1 & 3 & 0 & -6 & 2 \\
0 & 0 & 1 & \frac{5}{2} & 2 \\
0 & 0 & 0 & 0 & 0 \\
0 & 0 & 0 & 0 & 0
\end{bmatrix}
$$

Translating back into equations, we get:

$$
\begin{aligned}
x + 3y - 6w &= 2 \\
z + \tfrac{5}{2}w &= 2.
\end{aligned}
$$

(We have not written down the equations corresponding to the last two rows, each of which is $0 = 0$.) There are no pivots in the y or w columns, so we use these two variables as parameters. We bring them over to the right-hand sides of the equations above and write the general solution as

$$x = 2 - 3y + 6w$$
$$y \text{ is arbitrary}$$
$$z = 2 - \tfrac{5}{2}w$$
$$w \text{ is arbitrary}$$

or

$$(x, y, z, w) = (2 - 3y + 6w, y, 2 - 5w/2, w) \ y, w \text{ arbitrary.}$$

➡ **Before we go on...** In Examples 4 and 5, you might have noticed an interesting phenomenon: If at any time in the process, two rows are equal or one is a multiple of the other, then one of those rows (eventually) becomes all zero. ∎

Up to this point, we have always been given as many equations as there are unknowns. However, we shall see in the next section that some applications lead to systems where the number of equations is not the same as the number of unknowns. As the following example illustrates, such systems can be handled the same way as any other.

EXAMPLE 6 Number of Equations ≠ Number of Unknowns

Solve the system:

$$x + \quad y = 1$$
$$13x - 26y = -11$$
$$26x - 13y = 2.$$

Solution We proceed exactly as before and ignore the fact that there is one more equation than unknown.

$$\begin{bmatrix} \boxed{1} & 1 & 1 \\ 13 & -26 & -11 \\ 26 & -13 & 2 \end{bmatrix} \begin{matrix} \\ R_2 - 13R_1 \\ R_3 - 26R_1 \end{matrix} \rightarrow \begin{bmatrix} 1 & 1 & 1 \\ 0 & -39 & -24 \\ 0 & -39 & -24 \end{bmatrix} \begin{matrix} \\ \tfrac{1}{3}R_2 \\ \tfrac{1}{3}R_3 \end{matrix}$$

$$\rightarrow \begin{bmatrix} 1 & 1 & 1 \\ 0 & \boxed{-13} & -8 \\ 0 & -13 & -8 \end{bmatrix} \begin{matrix} 13R_1 + R_2 \\ \\ R_3 - R_2 \end{matrix} \rightarrow \begin{bmatrix} 13 & 0 & 5 \\ 0 & -13 & -8 \\ 0 & 0 & 0 \end{bmatrix} \begin{matrix} \tfrac{1}{13}R_1 \\ -\tfrac{1}{13}R_2 \\ \\ \end{matrix}$$

$$\rightarrow \begin{bmatrix} 1 & 0 & \tfrac{5}{13} \\ 0 & 1 & \tfrac{8}{13} \\ 0 & 0 & 0 \end{bmatrix}$$

Thus, the solution is $(x, y) = \left(\tfrac{5}{13}, \tfrac{8}{13}\right)$.

If, instead of a row of zeros, we had obtained, say, [0 0 6] in the last row, we would immediately have concluded that the system was inconsistent.

The fact that we wound up with a row of zeros indicates that one of the equations was actually a combination of the other two; you can check that the third equation can be obtained by multiplying the first equation by 13 and adding the result to the second. Because the third equation therefore tells us nothing that we don't already know from the first two, we call the system of equations **redundant**, or **dependent**. (Compare Example 4 in Section 2.1.)

➡ **Before we go on...** If you now take another look at Example 5, you will find that we could have started with the following smaller system of two equations in four unknowns

$$x + 3y + 2z - \quad w = 6$$
$$2x + 6y + 6z + 3w = 16$$

and obtained the same general solution as we did with the larger system. Verify this by solving the smaller system.   ■

The preceding examples illustrated that we cannot always reduce a matrix to the form shown before Example 2, with pivots going all the way down the diagonal. What we *can* always do is reduce a matrix to the following form:

Reduced Row Echelon Form

A matrix is said to be in **reduced row echelon form** or to be **row-reduced** if it satisfies the following properties.

P1. The first nonzero entry in each row (called the **leading entry** of that row) is a 1.

P2. The columns of the leading entries are **clear** (i.e., they contain zeros in all positions other than that of the leading entry).

P3. The leading entry in each row is to the right of the leading entry in the row above, and any rows of zeros are at the bottom.

Quick Examples

$$\begin{bmatrix} 1 & 0 & 0 & 2 \\ 0 & 1 & 0 & 4 \\ 0 & 0 & 1 & -3 \end{bmatrix}, \begin{bmatrix} 0 & 1 & -3 \\ 0 & 0 & 0 \end{bmatrix}, \text{ and } \begin{bmatrix} 1 & 0 & 0 & -2 \\ 0 & 0 & 1 & 4 \\ 0 & 0 & 0 & 0 \end{bmatrix} \text{ are row-reduced.}$$

$$\begin{bmatrix} 1 & 1 & 0 & 2 \\ 0 & 1 & 0 & 4 \\ 0 & 0 & 1 & -3 \end{bmatrix}, \begin{bmatrix} 0 & 1 & -3 \\ 0 & 0 & 1 \end{bmatrix}, \text{ and } \begin{bmatrix} 0 & 0 & 1 & 4 \\ 1 & 0 & 0 & -2 \\ 0 & 0 & 0 & 0 \end{bmatrix} \text{ are not row-reduced.}$$

You should check in the examples we did that the final matrices were all in reduced row echelon form.

It is an interesting and useful fact, though not easy to prove, that any two people who start with the same matrix and row-reduce it will reach exactly the same row-reduced matrix, even if they use different row operations.

The Traditional Gauss-Jordan Method

In the version of the Gauss-Jordan method we have presented, we eliminated fractions and decimals in the first step and then worked with integer matrices, partly to make hand computation easier and partly for mathematical elegance. However, complicated fractions and decimals present no difficulty when we use technology. The following example illustrates the more traditional approach to Gauss-Jordan reduction used in many of the computer programs that solve the huge systems of equations that arise in practice.*

✱ NOTE Actually, for reasons of efficiency and accuracy, the methods used in commercial programs are close to, but not exactly, the method presented here. To learn more, consult a text on numerical methods.

EXAMPLE 7 Solving a System with the Traditional Gauss-Jordan Method

Solve the following system using the traditional Gauss-Jordan method:

$$2x + y + 3z = 5$$
$$3x + 2y + 4z = 7$$
$$2x + y + 5z = 10.$$

Solution We make two changes in our method. First, there is no need to get rid of decimals (because computers and calculators can handle decimals as easily as they can integers). Second, after selecting a pivot, *divide the pivot row by the pivot value, turning the pivot into a* 1. It is easier to determine the row operations that will clear the pivot column if the pivot is a 1.

If we use technology to solve this system of equations, the sequence of matrices might look like this:

$$\begin{bmatrix} \boxed{2} & 1 & 3 & 5 \\ 3 & 2 & 4 & 7 \\ 2 & 1 & 5 & 10 \end{bmatrix} \begin{matrix} \frac{1}{2}R_1 \\ \\ \\ \end{matrix} \rightarrow \begin{bmatrix} \boxed{1} & 0.5 & 1.5 & 2.5 \\ 3 & 2 & 4 & 7 \\ 2 & 1 & 5 & 10 \end{bmatrix} \begin{matrix} \\ R_2 - 3R_1 \\ R_3 - 2R_1 \end{matrix}$$

$$\rightarrow \begin{bmatrix} 1 & 0.5 & 1.5 & 2.5 \\ 0 & \boxed{0.5} & -0.5 & -0.5 \\ 0 & 0 & 2 & 5 \end{bmatrix} \begin{matrix} \\ 2R_2 \\ \\ \end{matrix} \rightarrow \begin{bmatrix} 1 & 0.5 & 1.5 & 2.5 \\ 0 & \boxed{1} & -1 & -1 \\ 0 & 0 & 2 & 5 \end{bmatrix} \begin{matrix} R_1 - 0.5R_2 \\ \\ \\ \end{matrix}$$

$$\rightarrow \begin{bmatrix} 1 & 0 & 2 & 3 \\ 0 & 1 & -1 & -1 \\ 0 & 0 & \boxed{2} & 5 \end{bmatrix} \begin{matrix} \\ \\ \frac{1}{2}R_3 \end{matrix} \rightarrow \begin{bmatrix} 1 & 0 & 2 & 3 \\ 0 & 1 & -1 & -1 \\ 0 & 0 & \boxed{1} & 2.5 \end{bmatrix} \begin{matrix} R_1 - 2R_3 \\ R_2 + R_3 \\ \\ \end{matrix}$$

$$\rightarrow \begin{bmatrix} 1 & 0 & 0 & -2 \\ 0 & 1 & 0 & 1.5 \\ 0 & 0 & 1 & 2.5 \end{bmatrix}.$$

The solution is $(x, y, z) = (-2, 1.5, 2.5)$.

using Technology

Web Site
www.FiniteandCalc.org
Follow
→ Everything for Finite Math
→ Math Tools for Chapter 2
to find the following resources:
- An online Web page that pivots and does row operations automatically
- A TI-83/84 Plus program that pivots and does other row operations
- An Excel worksheet that pivots and does row operations automatically

---

Q: *The solution to Example 7 looked quite easy. Why didn't we use the traditional method from the start?*

A: It looked easy because we deliberately chose an example with simple numbers. In all but the most contrived examples, the decimals or fractions involved get very complicated very quickly.

FAQs

Getting Unstuck, Going Round in Circles, and Knowing When to Stop

Q: *Help! I have been doing row operations on this matrix for half an hour. I have filled two pages, and I am getting nowhere. What do I do?*

A: Here is a way of keeping track of where you are *at any stage of the process* and also deciding what to do next.

Starting at the top row of your current matrix:

1. Scan along the row until you get to the leading entry: the first nonzero entry. If there is none–that is, the row is all zero–go to the next row.
2. Having located the leading entry, scan up and down its *column*. If its column is not clear (that is, it contains other nonzero entries), use your leading entry as a pivot to clear its column as in the examples in this section.
3. Now go to the next row and start again at Step 1.

When you have scanned all the rows and find that all the columns of the leading entries are clear, it means you are done (except possibly for reordering the rows so that the leading entries go from left to right as you read down the matrix, and zero rows are at the bottom).

Q: *No good. I have been following these instructions, but every time I try to clear a column, I unclear a column I had already cleared. What is going on?*

A: Are you using *leading entries* as pivots? Also, are you *using the pivot* to clear its column? That is, are your row operations all of the following form?

$$aR_c \pm bR_p$$

$$\uparrow \qquad \uparrow$$

Row to change   Pivot row

The instruction next to the row you are changing should involve only that row and the pivot row, even though you might be tempted to use some other row instead.

Q: *Must I continue until I get a matrix that has 1s down the leading diagonal and 0s above and below?*

A: Not necessarily. You are completely done when your matrix is row-reduced: Each leading entry is a 1, the column of each leading entry is clear, and the leading entries go from left to right. You are done *pivoting* when the column of each leading entry is clear. After that, all that remains is to turn each pivot into a 1 (the "Final Step") and, if necessary, rearrange the rows.

2.2 EXERCISES

▼ more advanced   ◆ challenging

T indicates exercises that should be solved using technology

In Exercises 1–42, use Gauss-Jordan row reduction to solve the given systems of equation. We suggest doing some by hand, and others using technology. HINT [See Examples 1–6.]

1. $x + y = 4$
$x - y = 2$

2. $2x + y = 2$
$-2x + y = 2$

3. $3x - 2y = 6$
$2x - 3y = -6$

4. $2x + 3y = 5$
$3x + 2y = 5$

5. $2x + 3y = 1$
$-x - \dfrac{3y}{2} = -\dfrac{1}{2}$

6. $2x - 3y = 1$
$6x - 9y = 3$

7. $2x + 3y = 2$
$-x - \dfrac{3y}{2} = -\dfrac{1}{2}$

8. $2x - 3y = 2$
$6x - 9y = 3$

9. $x + y = 1$
$3x - y = 0$
$x - 3y = -2$

10. $x + y = 1$
$3x - 2y = -1$
$5x - y = \dfrac{1}{5}$

11.
$$x + y = 0$$
$$3x - y = 1$$
$$x - y = -1$$

12.
$$x + 2y = 1$$
$$3x - 2y = -2$$
$$5x - y = \frac{1}{5}$$

13.
$$0.5x + 0.1y = 1.7$$
$$0.1x - 0.1y = 0.3$$
$$x + y = \frac{11}{3}$$

14.
$$-0.3x + 0.5y = 0.1$$
$$x - y = 4$$
$$\frac{x}{17} + \frac{y}{17} = 1$$

15.
$$-x + 2y - z = 0$$
$$-x - y + 2z = 0$$
$$2x - z = 4$$

16.
$$x + 2y = 4$$
$$y - z = 0$$
$$x + 3y - 2z = 5$$

17.
$$x + y + 6z = -1$$
$$\frac{1}{3}x - \frac{1}{3}y + \frac{2}{3}z = 1$$
$$\frac{1}{2}x + z = 0$$

18.
$$x - \frac{1}{2}y = 0$$
$$\frac{1}{3}x + \frac{1}{3}y + \frac{1}{3}z = 2$$
$$\frac{1}{2}x - \frac{1}{2}z = -1$$

19.
$$-\frac{1}{2}x + y - \frac{1}{2}z = 0$$
$$-\frac{1}{2}x - \frac{1}{2}y + z = 0$$
$$x - \frac{1}{2}y - \frac{1}{2}z = 0$$

20.
$$x - \frac{1}{2}y = 0$$
$$\frac{1}{2}x - \frac{1}{2}z = -1$$
$$3x - y - z = -2$$

21.
$$x + y + 2z = -1$$
$$2x + 2y + 2z = 2$$
$$\frac{3}{5}x + \frac{3}{5}y + \frac{3}{5}z = \frac{2}{5}$$

22.
$$x + y - z = -2$$
$$x - y - 7z = 0$$
$$\frac{2}{7}x - \frac{8}{7}z = 14$$

23.
$$-0.5x + 0.5y + 0.5z = 1.5$$
$$4.2x + 2.1y + 2.1z = 0$$
$$0.2x + 0.2z = 0$$

24.
$$0.25x - 0.5y = 0$$
$$0.2x + 0.2y - 0.2z = -0.6$$
$$0.5x - 1.5y + z = 0.5$$

25.
$$2x - y + z = 4$$
$$3x - y + z = 5$$

26.
$$3x - y - z = 0$$
$$x + y + z = 4$$

27.
$$0.75x - 0.75y - z = 4$$
$$x - y + 4z = 0$$

28.
$$2x - y + z = 4$$
$$-x + 0.5y - 0.5z = 1.5$$

29. ▼ $3x + y - z = 12$
   (Yes: One equation in three unknowns!)

30. ▼ $x + y - 3z = 21$

31. ▼
$$x + y + 2z = -1$$
$$2x + 2y + 2z = 2$$
$$0.75x + 0.75y + z = 0.25$$
$$-x - 2z = 21$$

32. ▼
$$x + y - z = -2$$
$$x - y - 7z = 0$$
$$0.75x - 0.5y + 0.25z = 14$$
$$x + y + z = 4$$

33. ▼
$$x + y + 5z = 1$$
$$y + 2z + w = 1$$
$$x + 3y + 7z + 2w = 2$$
$$x + y + 5z + w = 1$$

34. ▼
$$x + y + 4w = 1$$
$$2x - 2y - 3z + 2w = -1$$
$$4y + 6z + w = 4$$
$$2x + 4y + 9z = 6$$

35. ▼
$$x + y + 5z = 1$$
$$y + 2z + w = 1$$
$$x + y + 5z + w = 1$$
$$x + 2y + 7z + 2w = 2$$

36. ▼
$$x + y + 4w = 1$$
$$2x - 2y - 3z + 2w = -1$$
$$4y + 6z + w = 4$$
$$3x + 3y + 3z + 7w = 4$$

37. ▼
$$x - 2y + z - 4w = 1$$
$$x + 3y + 7z + 2w = 2$$
$$2x + y + 8z - 2w = 3$$

38. ▼
$$x - 3y - 2z - w = 1$$
$$x + 3y + z + 2w = 2$$
$$2x - z + w = 3$$

39. ▼
$$x + y + z + u + v = 15$$
$$y - z + u - v = -2$$
$$z + u + v = 12$$
$$u - v = -1$$
$$v = 5$$

40. ▼
$$x - y + z - u + v = 1$$
$$y + z + u + v = 2$$
$$z - u + v = 1$$
$$u + v = 1$$
$$v = 1$$

41. ▼
$$x - y + z - u + v = 0$$
$$y - z + u - v = -2$$
$$x - 2v = -2$$
$$2x - y + z - u - 3v = -2$$
$$4x - y + z - u - 7v = -6$$

42. ▼
$$x + y + z + u + v = 15$$
$$y + z + u + v = 3$$
$$x + 2y + 2z + 2u + 2v = 18$$
$$x - y - z - u - v = 9$$
$$x - 2y - 2z - 2u - 2v = 6$$

T *In Exercises 43–46, use technology to solve the systems of equations. Express all solutions as fractions.*

43.
$$\begin{aligned} x + 2y - z + w &= 30 \\ 2x \quad\ \ - z + 2w &= 30 \\ x + 3y + 3z - 4w &= 2 \\ 2x - 9y \quad\ \ + w &= 4 \end{aligned}$$

44.
$$\begin{aligned} 4x - 2y + z + w &= 20 \\ 3y + 3z - 4w &= 2 \\ 2x + 4y \quad\ \ - w &= 4 \\ x + 3y + 3z \quad\ \ &= 2 \end{aligned}$$

45.
$$\begin{aligned} x + 2y + 3z + 4w + 5t &= 6 \\ 2x + 3y + 4z + 5w + t &= 5 \\ 3x + 4y + 5z + w + 2t &= 4 \\ 4x + 5y + z + 2w + 3t &= 3 \\ 5x + y + 2z + 3w + 4t &= 2 \end{aligned}$$

46.
$$\begin{aligned} x - 2y + 3z - 4w \quad &= 0 \\ -2x + 3y - 4z + t &= 0 \\ 3x - 4y \quad\ \ + w - 2t &= 0 \\ -4x \quad\ \ + z - 2w + 3t &= 0 \\ y - 2z + 3w - 4t &= 1 \end{aligned}$$

T *In Exercises 47–50, use technology to solve the systems of equations. Express all solutions as decimals, rounded to one decimal place.*

47. $1.6x + 2.4y - 3.2z = 4.4$
$5.1x - 6.3y + 0.6z = -3.2$
$4.2x + 3.5y + 4.9z = 10.1$

48. $2.1x + 0.7y - 1.4z = -2.3$
$3.5x - 4.2y - 4.9z = 3.3$
$1.1x + 2.2y - 3.3z = -10.2$

49. $-0.2x + 0.3y + 0.4z - t = 4.5$
$2.2x + 1.1y - 4.7z + 2t = 8.3$
$9.2y \quad\ \ - 1.3t = 0$
$3.4x \quad\ \ + 0.5z - 3.4t = 0.1$

50. $1.2x - 0.3y + 0.4z - 2t = 4.5$
$1.9x \quad\ \ - 0.5z - 3.4t = 0.2$
$12.1y \quad\ \ - 1.3t = 0$
$3x + 2y - 1.1z \quad\ \ = 9$

COMMUNICATION AND REASONING EXERCISES

51. What is meant by a pivot? What does pivoting do?

52. Give instructions to check whether or not a matrix is row-reduced.

53. You are row-reducing a matrix and have chosen a -6 as a pivot in Row 4. Directly above the pivot, in Row 1, is a 15. What row operation can you use to clear the 15?

54. You are row-reducing a matrix and have chosen a -4 as a pivot in Row 2. Directly below the pivot, in Row 4, is a -6. What row operation can you use to clear the -6?

55. In the matrix of a system of linear equations, suppose that two of the rows are equal. What can you say about the row-reduced form of the matrix?

56. In the matrix of a system of linear equations, suppose that one of the rows is a multiple of another. What can you say about the row-reduced form of the matrix?

57. ▼ Your friend Frans tells you that the system of linear equations you are solving cannot have a unique solution because the reduced matrix has a row of zeros. Comment on his claim.

58. ▼ Your other friend Hans tells you that because he is solving a consistent system of five linear equations in six unknowns, he will get infinitely many solutions. Comment on his claim.

59. ▼ If the reduced matrix of a consistent system of linear equations has five rows, three of which are zero, and five columns, how many parameters does the general solution contain?

60. ▼ If the reduced matrix of a consistent system of linear equations has five rows, two of which are zero, and seven columns, how many parameters does the general solution contain?

61. ▼ Suppose a system of equations has a unique solution. What must be true of the number of pivots in the reduced matrix of the system? Why?

62. ▼ Suppose a system has infinitely many solutions. What must be true of the number of pivots in the reduced matrix of the system? Why?

63. ▼ Give an example of a system of three linear equations with the general solution $x = 1$, $y = 1 + z$, z arbitrary. (Check your system by solving it.)

64. ▼ Give an example of a system of three linear equations with the general solution $x = y - 1$, y arbitrary, $z = y$. (Check your system by solving it.)

2.3 Applications of Systems of Linear Equations

In the examples and the exercises of this section, we consider scenarios that lead to systems of linear equations in three or more unknowns. Some of these applications will strike you as a little idealized or even contrived compared with the kinds of problems you might encounter in the real world.* One reason is that we will not have tools to handle more realistic versions of these applications until we have studied linear programming in Chapter 4.

* NOTE See the discussion at the end of the first example below.

In each example that follows, we set up the problem as a linear system and then give the solution; the emphasis in this section is on modeling a scenario by a system of linear equations and then interpreting the solution that results, rather than the mechanics needed to obtain the solution. For practice, you should do the row reduction necessary to get the solution.

istockphoto.com

EXAMPLE 1 Resource Allocation

The Arctic Juice Company makes three juice blends: PineOrange, using 2 quarts of pineapple juice and 2 quarts of orange juice per gallon; PineKiwi, using 3 quarts of pineapple juice and 1 quart of kiwi juice per gallon; and OrangeKiwi, using 3 quarts of orange juice and 1 quart of kiwi juice per gallon. Each day the company has 800 quarts of pineapple juice, 650 quarts of orange juice, and 350 quarts of kiwi juice available. How many gallons of each blend should it make each day if it wants to use up all of the supplies?

Solution We take the same steps to understand the problem that we took in Section 2.1. The first step is to identify and label the unknowns. Looking at the question asked in the last sentence, we see that we should label the unknowns like this:

$x =$ number of gallons of PineOrange made each day

$y =$ number of gallons of PineKiwi made each day

$z =$ number of gallons of OrangeKiwi made each day.

Next, we can organize the information we are given in a table:

	PineOrange (x)	*PineKiwi (y)*	*OrangeKiwi (z)*	*Total Available*
Pineapple Juice (qt)	2	3	0	800
Orange Juice (qt)	2	0	3	650
Kiwi Juice (qt)	0	1	1	350

Notice how we have arranged the table; we have placed headings corresponding to the unknowns along the top, rather than down the side, and we have added a heading for the available totals. This gives us a table that is essentially the matrix of the system of linear equations we are looking for. (However, read the caution in the **Before we go on** section.)

using Technology

Web Site

www.FiniteandCalc.org

  Everything for Finite Math

   → Math Tools for Chapter 2

   → Pivot and Gauss-Jordan
     Tool

Once you have set up the
system of equations, you can
obtain the solution in a single
step using the Pivot and
Gauss-Jordan Tool at the
Web site:

Enter the augmented matrix of
the system as shown, and
press "Reduce Completely."
You can then use the reduced
matrix to write down the unique
solution or general solution as
discussed in Section 2.2.

x1	x2	x3	x4
2	3	0	800
2	0	3	650
0	1	1	350

1	0	0	100
0	1	0	200
0	0	1	150

Now we read across each row of the table. The fact that we want to use exactly the amount of each juice that is available leads to the following three equations:

$$2x + 3y = 800$$
$$2x + 3z = 650$$
$$ y + z = 350.$$

The solution of this system is $(x, y, z) = (100, 200, 150)$, so Arctic Juice should make 100 gallons of PineOrange, 200 gallons of PineKiwi, and 150 gallons of OrangeKiwi each day.

➡ **Before we go on...**

Caution

We do not recommend relying on the coincidence that the table we created to organize the information in Example 1 happened to be the matrix of the system; it is too easy to set up the table "sideways" and get the wrong matrix. You should always write down the system of equations *and be sure you understand each equation.* For example, the equation $2x + 3y = 800$ in Example 1 indicates that the number of quarts of pineapple juice that will be used $(2x + 3y)$ is equal to the amount available (800 quarts). By thinking of the reason for each equation, you can check that you have the correct system. If you have the wrong system of equations to begin with, solving it won't help you.

Q : *Just how realistic is the scenario in Example 1?*

A : This is a very unrealistic scenario, for several reasons:

1. Isn't it odd that we happened to end up with exactly the same number of equations as unknowns? Real scenarios are rarely so considerate. If there had been four equations, there would in all likelihood have been no solution at all. However, we need to understand these idealized problems before we can tackle the real world.

2. Even if a real-world scenario does give the same number of equations as unknowns, there is still no guarantee that there will be a unique solution consisting of positive values. What, for instance, would we have done in this example if x had turned out to be negative?

3. The requirement that we use exactly all the ingredients would be an unreasonable constraint in real life. When we discuss linear programming, we will be able to substitute the more reasonable constraint that you use no more than is available, and we will add the more reasonable objective that you maximize profit. ■

EXAMPLE 2 **Aircraft Purchases:** **Airbus and Boeing**

A new airline has recently purchased a fleet of Airbus A330-300s, Boeing 767-200ERs, and Boeing Dreamliner 787-9s to meet an estimated demand for 4,800 seats. The A330-300s seat 320 passengers and cost $200 million each, the 767-200ERs each seat 250 passengers and cost $125 million each, while the Dreamliner 787-9s seat 275 passengers and cost $200 million each.* The total cost of the fleet, which had twice as many Dreamliners as 767s, was $3,100 million. How many of each type of aircraft did the company purchase?

---

*The prices are approximate 2008 prices. Prices and seating capacities found at the companies' Web sites and in Wikipedia.

Solution We label the unknowns as follows:

$$x = \text{number of Airbus A330-300s}$$
$$y = \text{number of Boeing 767-200ERs}$$
$$z = \text{number of Boeing Dreamliner 787-9s.}$$

We must now set up the equations. We can organize some (but not all) of the given information in a table:

	A330-300	*767-200ER*	*787-9 Dreamliner*	*Total*
Capacity	320	250	275	4,800
Cost ($ million)	200	125	200	3,100

Reading across, we get the equations expressing the facts that the airline needed to seat 4,800 passengers and that it spent $3,100 million:

$$320x + 250y + 275z = 4{,}800$$
$$200x + 125y + 200z = 3{,}100.$$

There is an additional piece of information we have not yet used: the airline bought twice as many Dreamliners as 767s. As we said in Section 2.1, it is easiest to translate a statement like this into an equation if we first reword it using the phrase "the number of." Thus, we say: "The number of Dreamliners ordered was twice the number of 767s ordered," or

$$z = 2y$$
$$2y - z = 0.$$

We now have a system of three equations in three unknowns:

$$320x + 250y + 275z = 4{,}800$$
$$200x + 125y + 200z = 3{,}100$$
$$2y - \quad z = 0.$$

Solving the system, we get the solution $(x, y, z) = (5, 4, 8)$. Thus, the airline ordered five A330-300s, four 767-200ERs, and eight Dreamliner 787-9s.

EXAMPLE 3 Traffic Flow

Traffic through downtown Urbanville flows through the one-way system shown in Figure 7.

Traffic counting devices installed in the road (shown as boxes) count 200 cars entering town from the west each hour, 150 leaving town on the north each hour, and 50 leaving town on the south each hour.

a. From this information, is it possible to determine how many cars drive along Allen, Baker, and Coal streets every hour?

b. What is the maximum possible traffic flow along Baker Street?

c. What is the minimum possible traffic along Allen Street?

d. What is the maximum possible traffic flow along Coal Street?

Figure 7

Solution

a. Our unknowns are:

x = number of cars per hour on Allen Street

y = number of cars per hour on Baker Street

z = number of cars per hour on Coal Street.

Assuming that, at each intersection, cars do not fall into a pit or materialize out of thin air, the number of cars entering each intersection has to equal the number exiting. For example, at the intersection of Allen and Baker Streets there are 200 cars entering and $x + y$ cars exiting:

$$\text{Traffic in} = \text{Traffic out}$$
$$200 = x + y.$$

At the intersection of Allen and Coal Streets, we get:

$$\text{Traffic in} = \text{Traffic out}$$
$$x = z + 150,$$

and at the intersection of Baker and Coal Streets, we get:

$$\text{Traffic in} = \text{Traffic out}$$
$$y + z = 50.$$

We now have the following system of equations:

$$\begin{aligned} x + y \quad\;\; &= 200 \\ x \quad\;\; - z &= 150 \\ y + z &= 50. \end{aligned}$$

If we solve this system using the methods of the preceding section, we find that it has infinitely many solutions. The general solution is:

$$x = z + 150$$
$$y = -z + 50$$
$$z \text{ is arbitrary.}$$

Because we do not have a unique solution, it is *not* possible to determine how many cars drive along Allen, Baker and Coal Streets every hour.

b. The traffic flow along Baker Street is measured by y. From the general solution,

$$y = -z + 50$$

where z is arbitrary. How arbitrary is z? It makes no sense for any of the variables x, y, or z to be negative in this scenario, so $z \geq 0$. Therefore, the largest possible value y can have is

$$y = -0 + 50 = 50 \text{ cars per hour.}$$

c. The traffic flow along Allen Street is measured by x. From the general solution,

$$x = z + 150$$

where $z \geq 0$, as we saw in part (b). Therefore, the smallest possible value x can have is

$$x = 0 + 150 = 150 \text{ cars per hour.}$$

d. The traffic flow along Coal Street is measured by z. Referring to the general solution, we see that z shows up in the expressions for both x and y:

$$x = z + 150$$
$$y = -z + 50.$$

In the first of these equations, there is nothing preventing z from being as big as we like; the larger we make z, the larger x becomes. However, the second equation places a limit on how large z can be: If $z > 50$, then y is negative, which is impossible. Therefore, the largest value z can take is 50 cars per hour.

From the discussion above, we see that z is not completely arbitrary: We must have $z \geq 0$ and $z \leq 50$. Thus, z has to satisfy $0 \leq z \leq 50$ for us to get a realistic answer.

➡ **Before we go on...** Here are some questions to think about in Example 3: If you wanted to nail down x, y, and z to see where the cars are really going, how would you do it with only one more traffic counter? Would it make sense for z to be fractional? What if you interpreted x, y, and z as *average* numbers of cars per hour over a long period of time?

Traffic flow is only one kind of flow in which we might be interested. Water and electricity flows are others. In each case, to analyze the flow, we use the fact that the amount entering an intersection must equal the amount leaving it. ■

EXAMPLE 4 Transportation

A car rental company has four locations in the city: Southwest, Northeast, Southeast, and Northwest. The Northwest location has 20 more cars than it needs, and the Northeast location has 15 more cars than it needs. The Southwest location needs 10 more cars than it has, and the Southeast location needs 25 more cars than it has. It costs $10 (in salary and gas) to have an employee drive a car from Northwest to Southwest. It costs $20 to drive a car from Northwest to Southeast. It costs $5 to drive a car from Northeast to Southwest, and it costs $10 to drive a car from Northeast to Southeast. If the company will spend a total of $475 rearranging its cars, how many cars will it drive from each of Northwest and Northeast to each of Southwest and Southeast?

Solution

Figure 8 shows a diagram of this situation. Each arrow represents a route along which the rental company can drive cars. At each location is written the number of extra cars the location has or the number it needs. Along each route is written the cost of driving a car along that route.

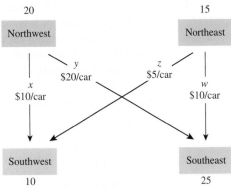

Figure 8

The unknowns are the number of cars the company will drive along each route, so we have the following four unknowns, as indicated in the figure:

x = number of cars driven from Northwest to Southwest
y = number of cars driven from Northwest to Southeast
z = number of cars driven from Northeast to Southwest
w = number of cars driven from Northeast to Southeast.

Consider the Northwest location. It has 20 more cars than it needs, so the total number of cars being driven out of Northwest should be 20. This gives us the equation

$$x + y = 20.$$

Similarly, the total number of cars being driven out of Northeast should be 15, so

$$z + w = 15.$$

Considering the number of cars needed at the Southwest and Southeast locations, we get the following two equations as well:

$$x + z = 10$$
$$y + w = 25.$$

There is one more equation that we should write down, the equation that says that the company will spend $475:

$$10x + 20y + 5z + 10w = 475.$$

Thus, we have the following system of five equations in four unknowns:

$$
\begin{aligned}
x + \;\; y \qquad\qquad\qquad &= 20 \\
z + \;\; w &= 15 \\
x \qquad + \; z \qquad\quad &= 10 \\
y \qquad + \;\; w &= 25 \\
10x + 20y + 5z + 10w &= 475
\end{aligned}
$$

Solving this system, we find that $(x, y, z, w) = (5, 15, 5, 10)$. In words, the company will drive 5 cars from Northwest to Southwest, 15 from Northwest to Southeast, 5 from Northeast to Southwest, and 10 from Northeast to Southeast.

➡ **Before we go on...** A very reasonable question to ask in Example 4 is, Can the company rearrange its cars for less than $475? Even better, what is the least possible cost? In general, a question asking for the optimal cost may require the techniques of linear programming, which we will discuss in Chapter 4. However, in this case we can approach the problem directly. If we remove the equation that says that the total cost is $475 and solve the system consisting of the other four equations, we find that there are infinitely many solutions and that the general solution may be written as

$$
\begin{aligned}
x &= w - 5 \\
y &= 25 - w \\
z &= 15 - w \\
w & \text{ is arbitrary.}
\end{aligned}
$$

This allows us to write the total cost as a function of w:

$$10x + 20y + 5z + 10w = 10(w - 5) + 20(25 - w) + 5(15 - w) + 10w$$
$$= 525 - 5w.$$

So, the larger we make w, the smaller the total cost will be. The largest we can make w is 15 (why?), and if we do so we get $(x, y, z, w) = (10, 10, 0, 15)$ and a total cost of $450. ∎

2.3 EXERCISES

▼ more advanced   ◆ challenging
Ⓣ indicates exercises that should be solved using technology

APPLICATIONS

1. *Resource Allocation* You manage an ice cream factory that makes three flavors: Creamy Vanilla, Continental Mocha, and Succulent Strawberry. Into each batch of Creamy Vanilla go 2 eggs, 1 cup of milk, and 2 cups of cream. Into each batch of Continental Mocha go 1 egg, 1 cup of milk, and 2 cups of cream, while into each batch of Succulent Strawberry go 1 egg, 2 cups of milk, and 1 cup of cream. You have in stock 350 eggs, 350 cups of milk, and 400 cups of cream. How many batches of each flavor should you make in order to use up all of your ingredients? HINT [See Example 1.]

2. *Resource Allocation* You own a hamburger franchise and are planning to shut down operations for the day, but you are left with 13 bread rolls, 19 defrosted beef patties, and 15 opened cheese slices. Rather than throw them out, you decide to use them to make burgers that you will sell at a discount. Plain burgers each require 1 beef patty and 1 bread roll, double cheeseburgers each require 2 beef patties, 1 bread roll, and 2 slices of cheese, while regular cheeseburgers each require 1 beef patty, 1 bread roll, and 1 slice of cheese. How many of each should you make? HINT [See Example 1.]

3. *Resource Allocation* Urban Community College is planning to offer courses in Finite Math, Applied Calculus, and Computer Methods. Each section of Finite Math has 40 students and earns the college $40,000 in revenue. Each section of Applied Calculus has 40 students and earns the college $60,000, while each section of Computer Methods has 10 students and earns the college $20,000. Assuming the college wishes to offer a total of six sections, to accommodate 210 students, and to bring in $260,000 in revenues, how many sections of each course should it offer? HINT [See Example 2.]

4. *Resource Allocation* The Enormous State University History Department offers three courses, Ancient, Medieval, and Modern History, and the chairperson is trying to decide how many sections of each to offer this semester. The department is allowed to offer 45 sections total, there are 5,000 students who would like to take a course, and there are 60 professors to teach them. Sections of Ancient History have 100 students each, sections of Medieval History hold 50 students each, and sections of Modern History have 200 students each. Modern History sections are taught by a team of 2 professors, while Ancient and Medieval History need only 1 professor per section. How many sections of each course should the chair schedule in order to offer all the sections that they are allowed to, accommodate all of the students, and give one teaching assignment to each professor? HINT [See Example 2.]

5. *Music CD Sales* In 2007, total revenues from sales of recorded rock, religious, and classical music amounted to $4 billion. Religious music brought in twice as much as classical music, and rock music brought in $3 billion more than religious music.[12] How much revenue was earned in each of the three categories of recorded music?

6. *Music CD Sales* In 2007, combined revenues from sales of country music and children's music amounted to $1.5 billion. Country music brought in 12 times as much revenue as soundtracks, and children's music three times as much as soundtracks.[13] How much revenue was earned in each of the three categories of recorded music?

7. *Purchasing Aircraft* In Example 2 we saw that Airbus A330-300s seat 320 passengers and cost $200 million each, Boeing 767-200ERs seat 250 passengers and cost $125 million each, while Boeing Dreamliner 787-9s seat 275 passengers and cost $200 million each. You are the purchasing manager of an airline company and have a spending goal of $2,900 million for the purchase of new aircraft to seat a total of 4,480 passengers. Your company has a policy of supporting U.S. industries, and you have been instructed to buy twice as many Dreamliners as Airbus A330-300s. Given the selection of three aircraft, how many of each should you order?

---

[12] Revenues are based on total manufacturers' shipments at suggested retail prices, and are rounded to the nearest $0.1 billion. Source: Recording Industry Association of America (www.riaa.com).
[13] Ibid.

8. *Purchasing Aircraft* Refer to Exercise 7. René DuFleur has just been appointed the new CEO of your airline, and you have received instructions that the company policy is now to purchase 25% more Airbus A330-300s than Boeing 767-200ERs (that is, 1.25 times as many Airbus A330-300s as 767-200ERs). Further, the desired seating capacity has been revised downward to 2,600 passengers, and the cost target to $1,500 million. Given the selection of three aircraft, how many of each should you order?

9. *Supply* A bagel store orders cream cheese from three suppliers, Cheesy Cream Corp. (CCC), Super Smooth & Sons (SSS), and Bagel's Best Friend Co. (BBF). One month, the total order of cheese came to 100 tons (they do a booming trade). The costs were $80, $50, and $65 per ton from the three suppliers respectively, with total cost amounting to $5,990. Given that the store ordered the same amount from CCC and BBF, how many tons of cream cheese were ordered from each supplier?

10. *Supply* Refer to Exercise 9. The bagel store's outlay for cream cheese the following month was $2,310, when it purchased a total of 36 tons. Two more tons of cream cheese came from Bagel's Best Friend Co. than from Super Smooth & Sons. How many tons of cream cheese came from each supplier?

11. *Pest Control* Aragorn the Great has boasted to his hordes of followers that many a notorious villain has fallen to his awesome sword: His total of 560 victims consists of evil sorcerers, trolls, and orcs. These he has slain with a total of 620 mighty thrusts of his sword; evil sorcerers and trolls each requiring two thrusts (to the chest) and orcs each requiring one thrust (to the neck). When asked about the number of trolls he has slain, he replies, "I, the mighty Aragorn, despise trolls five times as much as I despise evil sorcerers. Accordingly, five times as many trolls as evil sorcerers have fallen to my sword!" How many of each type of villain has he slain?

12. *Manufacturing Perfume* The Fancy French Perfume Company recently had its secret formula divulged. It turned out that it was using, as the three ingredients, rose oil, oil of fermented prunes, and alcohol. Moreover, each 22-ounce econo-size bottle contained 4 more ounces of alcohol than oil of fermented prunes, while the amount of alcohol was equal to the combined volume of the other two ingredients. How much of each ingredient did it use in an econo-size bottle?[14]

13. ▼ *Donations* The Enormous State University Good Works Society recently raised funds for three worthwhile causes: the Math Professors' Benevolent Fund (MPBF), the Society of Computer Nerds (SCN), and the NY Jets. Because the society's members are closet jocks, the society donated twice as much to the NY Jets as to the MPBF, and equal amounts to the first two funds (it is unable to distinguish between mathematicians and nerds). Further, for every $1 it gave to the MPBF, it decided to keep $1 for itself; for every $1 it gave to the SCN, it kept $2, and for every $1 to the Jets, it also kept $2. The

treasurer of the Society, Johnny Treasure, was required to itemize all donations for the Dean of Students, but discovered to his consternation that he had lost the receipts! The only information available to him was that the society's bank account had swelled by $4,200. How much did the society donate to each cause?

14. ▼ *Tenure* Professor Walt is up for tenure, and wishes to submit a portfolio of written student evaluations as evidence of his good teaching. He begins by grouping all the evaluations into four categories: good reviews, bad reviews (a typical one being "GET RID OF WALT! THE MAN CAN'T TEACH!"), mediocre reviews (such as "I suppose he's OK, given the general quality of teaching at this college"), and reviews left blank. When he tallies up the piles, Walt gets a little worried: There are 280 more bad reviews than good ones and only half as many blank reviews as bad ones. The good reviews and blank reviews together total 170. On an impulse, he decides to even up the piles a little by removing 280 of the bad reviews, and this leaves him with a total of 400 reviews of all types. How many of each category of reviews were there originally?

T ***Airline Costs*** *Exercises 15 and 16 are based on the following chart, which shows the amount spent by five U.S. airlines to fly one available seat one mile in the third quarter of 2008.*[15] *Set up each system and then solve using technology. (See the technology note in the margin on page 156.)*

Airline	United	American	Continental	Delta	Southwest
Cost	14.8¢	13.9¢	13.2¢	13.8¢	10.7¢

15. ▼ Suppose that, on a 3,000-mile New York–Los Angeles flight, **United**, **American**, and **Southwest** flew a total of 210 empty seats, costing them a total of $86,010. If **United** had three times as many empty seats as **American**, how many empty seats did each of these three airlines carry on its flight?

16. ▼ Suppose that, on a 2,000-mile Miami-Memphis flight, **Continental**, **Delta**, and **Southwest** flew a total of 200 empty seats, costing them a total of $51,500. If **Delta** had twice as many empty seats as **Southwest**, how many empty seats did each of these three airlines carry on its flight?

Investing Bond Funds *Exercises 17 and 18 are based on the following data on three bond funds at* **Fidelity**.[16]

	2008 Loss
FCTFX (Fidelity California Muni)	6%
FSAZX (Fidelity Arizona Muni)	5%
FUSFX (Fidelity Ultra-Short)	7%

---

[14] Most perfumes consist of 10% to 20% perfume oils dissolved in alcohol. This may or may not be reflected in this company's formula!

[15] Costs are rounded to the nearest 0.1¢. Source: Company financial statements, obtained from their respective Web sites. The cost per available seat-mile is a commonly used operating statistic in the airline industry.

[16] Losses are approximate, and for the year ending November 30, 2008. Source: www.fidelity.com.

17. You invested a total of $9,000 in the three funds at the end of 2007, including an equal amount in FSAZX and FUSFX. Your 2008 loss for the year from the first two funds amounted to $400. How much did you invest in each of the three funds?

18. You invested a total of $6,000 in the three funds at the end of 2007, including an equal amount in FCTFX and FSAZX. Your total losses for 2008 amounted to $360. How much did you invest in each of the three funds?

Investing in Stocks Exercises 19 and 20 are based on the following data on **General Electric, Wal-Mart,** *and* **Exxon Mobil** *stocks.*[17]

	Price	Dividend Yield
GE (General Electric)	$16	7%
WMT (Wal-Mart)	$56	2%
XOM (Exxon Mobil)	$80	2%

19. ▼ You invested a total of $8,400 in shares of the three stocks at the given prices, and expected to earn $248 in annual dividends. If you purchased a total of 200 shares, how many shares of each stock did you purchase?

20. ▼ You invested a total of $11,200 in shares of the three stocks at the given prices, and expected to earn $304 in annual dividends. If you purchased a total of 250 shares, how many shares of each stock did you purchase?

21. ▒ *Internet Audience* At the end of 2003, the four companies with the largest number of home Internet users in the United States were **Microsoft, Time Warner, Yahoo,** and **Google,** with a combined audience of 284 million users.[18] Taking x to be the Microsoft audience in millions, y the Time Warner audience in millions, z the Yahoo audience in millions, and u the Google audience in millions, it was observed that

$$z - u = 3(x - y) + 6$$
$$x + y = 50 + z + u$$

and $x - y + z - u = 42.$

How large was the audience of each of the four companies in November 2003?

22. ▒ *Internet Audience* At the end of 2003, the four organizations ranking 5 through 8 in home Internet users in the United States were **eBay,** the U.S. government, **Amazon,** and **Lycos,** with a combined audience of 112 million users.[19] Taking x to be the eBay audience in millions, y the U.S. Government

audience in millions, z the Amazon audience in millions, and u the Lycos audience in millions, it was observed that

$$y - z = z - u$$
$$x - y = 3(y - u) + 5$$

and $x - y + z - u = 12.$

How large was the audience of each of the four companies in November 2003?

23. ▼ *Market Share: Homeowners Insurance* The three market leaders in homeowners insurance in Missouri are **State Farm, American Family Insurance Group,** and **Allstate.** Based on data from 2007, two relationships between the Missouri homeowners insurance percentage market shares are found to be

$$x = 1 + y + z$$
$$z = 16 - 0.2w,$$

where x, y, z, and w are, respectively, the percentages of the market held by **State Farm, American Family, Allstate,** and other companies.[20] Given that the four groups account for the entire market, obtain a third equation relating x, y, z, and w, and solve the associated system of three linear equations to show how the market shares of **State Farm, American Family,** and **Allstate** depend on the share held by other companies. Which of the three companies' market share is most impacted by the share held by other companies?

24. ▼ *Market Share: Auto Insurance* Repeat the preceding exercise using the following relationships among the auto insurance percentage market shares:

$$x = -40 + 5y + z$$
$$z = 3 - 2y + w.$$

25. *Inventory Control* Big Red Bookstore wants to ship books from its warehouses in Brooklyn and Queens to its stores, one on Long Island and one in Manhattan. Its warehouse in Brooklyn has 1,000 books and its warehouse in Queens has 2,000. Each store orders 1,500 books. It costs $1 to ship each book from Brooklyn to Manhattan and $2 to ship each book from Queens to Manhattan. It costs $5 to ship each book from Brooklyn to Long Island and $4 to ship each book from Queens to Long Island.

a. If Big Red has a transportation budget of $9,000 and is willing to spend all of it, how many books should Big Red ship from each warehouse to each store in order to fill all the orders?

b. Is there a way of doing this for less money? HINT [See Example 4.]

26. *Inventory Control* The Tubular Ride Boogie Board Company has manufacturing plants in Tucson, AZ and Toronto, Ontario. You have been given the job of coordinating distribution of the latest model, the Gladiator, to outlets in Honolulu and Venice Beach. The Tucson plant, when operating at full

---

[17] Stocks were trading at or near the given prices in November 2008. Dividends are rounded, based on values on November 30, 2008. Source: www.finance.google.com.

[18] Source: Nielsen/NetRatings January 1, 2004 (www.nielsen-netratings.com/).

[19] Ibid.

[20] Source: Missouri Dept. of Insurance (www.insurance.mo.gov).

capacity, can manufacture 620 Gladiator boards per week, while the Toronto plant, beset by labor disputes, can produce only 410 boards per week. The outlet in Honolulu orders 500 Gladiator boards per week, while Venice Beach orders 530 boards per week. Transportation costs are as follows:

Tucson to Honolulu: $10 per board; Tucson to Venice Beach: $5 per board.

Toronto to Honolulu: $20 per board; Toronto to Venice Beach: $10 per board.

a. Assuming that you wish to fill all orders and assure full capacity production at both plants, is it possible to meet a total transportation budget of $10,200? If so, how many Gladiator boards are shipped from each manufacturing plant to each distribution outlet?

b. Is there a way of doing this for less money? HINT [See Example 4.]

27. ▼ *Tourism in the '90s* In the 1990s, significant numbers of tourists traveled from North America and Europe to Australia and South Africa. In 1998, a total of 1,390,000 of these tourists visited Australia, while 1,140,000 of them visited South Africa. Further, 630,000 of them came from North America and 1,900,000 of them came from Europe.[21] (Assume no single tourist visited both destinations or traveled from both North America and Europe.)

a. The given information is not sufficient to determine the number of tourists from each region to each destination. Why?

b. If you were given the additional information that a total of 2,530,000 tourists traveled from these two regions to these two destinations, would you now be able to determine the number of tourists from each region to each destination? If so, what are these numbers?

c. If you were given the additional information that the same number of people from Europe visited South Africa as visited Australia, would you now be able to determine the number of tourists from each region to each destination? If so, what are these numbers?

28. ▼ *Tourism in the '90s* In the 1990s, significant numbers of tourists traveled from North America and Asia to Australia and South Africa. In 1998, a total of 2,230,000 of these tourists visited Australia, while 390,000 of them visited South Africa. Also, 630,000 of these tourists came from North America, and a total of 2,620,000 tourists traveled from these two regions to these two destinations.[22] (Assume no single tourist visited both destinations or traveled from both North America and Asia.)

a. The given information is not sufficient to determine the number of tourists from each region to each destination. Why?

b. If you were given the additional information that a total of 1,990,000 tourists came from Asia, would you now be

able to determine the number of tourists from each region to each destination? If so, what are these numbers?

c. If you were given the additional information that 200,000 tourists visited South Africa from Asia, would you now be able to determine the number of tourists from each region to each destination? If so, what are these numbers?

29. ▼ *Alcohol* The following table shows some data from a 2000 study on substance use among 10th graders in the United States and Europe.[23]

	Used Alcohol	*Alcohol-Free*	*Totals*
U.S.	x	y	14,000
Europe	z	w	95,000
Totals	63,550	45,450	

a. The table leads to a linear system of four equations in four unknowns. What is the system? Does it have a unique solution? What does this indicate about the given and the missing data?

b. ⬛ Given that the number of U.S. 10th graders who were alcohol-free was 50% more than the number who had used alcohol, find the missing data.

30. ▼ *Tobacco* The following table shows some data from the same study cited in Exercise 29.[24]

	Smoked Cigarettes	*Cigarette-Free*	*Totals*
U.S.	x	y	14,000
Europe	z	w	95,000
Totals		70,210	109,000

a. The table leads to a linear system of four equations in four unknowns. What is the system? Does it have a unique solution? What does this indicate about the missing data?

b. ⬛ Given that 31,510 more European 10th graders smoked cigarettes than U.S. 10th graders, find the missing data.

31. *Traffic Flow* One-way traffic through Enormous State University is shown in the figure, where the numbers indicate daily counts of vehicles.

[21] Figures are rounded to the nearest 10,000. Sources: South African Dept. of Environmental Affairs and Tourism; Australia Tourist Commission/*The New York Times*, January 15, 2000, p. C1.
[22] Ibid.

[23] "Used Alcohol" indicates consumption of alcohol at least once in the past 30 days. Source: Council of Europe/University of Michigan. "Monitoring the Future"/*New York Times*, February 21, 2001, p. A10.
[24] "Smoked Cigarettes" indicates that at least one cigarette was smoked in the past 30 days. Source: Ibid.

a. Is it possible to determine the daily flow of traffic along each of the three streets from the information given? If your answer is *yes*, what is the traffic flow along each street? If your answer is *no*, what additional information would suffice?

b. Is a flow of 60 vehicles per day along Southwest Lane consistent with the information given?

c. What is the minimum traffic flow possible along Northwest Lane consistent with the information given? HINT [See Example 3.]

32. *Traffic Flow* The traffic through downtown East Podunk flows through the one-way system shown below.

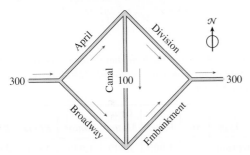

Traffic counters find that 300 vehicles enter town from the west each hour, and 300 leave town toward the east each hour. Also, 100 cars drive down Canal Street each hour.

a. Write down the general solution of the associated system of linear equations. Is it possible to determine the number of vehicles on each street per hour?

b. On which street could you put another traffic counter in order to determine the flow completely?

c. What is the minimum traffic flow along April Street consistent with the information given? HINT [See Example 3.]

33. *Traffic Flow* The traffic through downtown Johannesburg follows the one-way system shown below, with traffic movement recorded at incoming and outgoing streets (in cars per minute) as shown.

a. Set up and solve a system of equations to solve for the traffic flow along the middle sections of the four streets.

b. Is there sufficient information to calculate the traffic along the middle section of Jeppe Street? If so, what is it; if not, why not?

c. Given that 400 cars per minute flow down the middle section of Bree Street, how many cars per minute flow down the middle section of Simmons?

d. What is the minimum traffic flow along the middle section of Harrison Street?

e. Is there an upper limit to the possible traffic down Simmons Street consistent with the information given? Explain.

34. *Traffic Flow* Town of Hempstead officials were planning to make Hempstead Turnpike and the surrounding streets into one-way streets to prepare for the opening of Hofstra USA. In an experiment, they restricted traffic flow along the streets near Hofstra as shown in the diagram. The numbers show traffic flow per minute and the arrows indicate the direction of traffic.

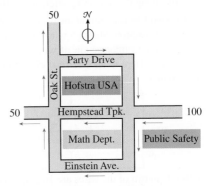

a. Set up and solve the associated traffic flow problem with the following unknowns:
x = traffic per minute along the middle stretch of Oak St.,
y = traffic per minute along the middle stretch of Hempstead Tpk.,
z = traffic per minute along Einstein Ave., and
u = traffic per minute along Party Drive.

b. If 20 cars per minute drive along Party Drive, what is the traffic like along the middle stretch of Oak Street?

c. If 20 vehicles per minute drive along Einstein Ave., and 90 vehicles per minute drive down the middle stretch of Hempstead Tpk., how many cars per minute drive along the middle stretch of Oak Street?

d. If Einstein Avenue is deserted, what is the minimum traffic along the middle stretch of Hempstead Tpk.?

35. ▼ ***Traffic Management*** The Outer Village Town Council has decided to convert its (rather quiet) main street, Broadway, to a one-way street, but is not sure of the direction of most of the traffic. The accompanying diagram illustrates the downtown area of Outer Village, as well as the *net* traffic flow along the intersecting streets (in vehicles per day). (There are no one-way streets; a net traffic flow in a certain direction is defined as the traffic flow in that direction minus the flow in the opposite direction.)

a. Is the given information sufficient to determine the net traffic flow along the three portions of Broadway shown? If your answer is *yes*, give the traffic flow along each stretch. If your answer is *no*, what additional information would suffice? *Hint* [For the direction of net traffic flow, choose either east or west. If a corresponding value is negative, it indicates net flow in the opposite direction.]

b. Assuming that there is little traffic (less than 160 vehicles per day) east of Fleet Street, in what direction is the net flow of traffic along the remaining stretches of Broadway?

36. ▼ *Electric Current* Electric current measures (in **amperes** or **amps**) the flow of electrons through wires. Like traffic flow, the current entering an intersection of wires must equal the current leaving it.[25] Here is an electrical circuit known as a **Wheatstone bridge.**

a. If the currents in two of the wires are 10 amps and 5 amps as shown, determine the currents in the unlabeled wires in terms of suitable parameters.

b. In which wire should you measure the current in order to know all of the currents exactly?

37. ▼ *Econometrics* (*from the GRE Economics Test*) This and the next exercise are based on the following simplified model of the determination of the money stock.

$$M = C + D$$
$$C = 0.2D$$
$$R = 0.1D$$
$$H = R + C$$

where

M = money stock
C = currency in circulation
R = bank reserves
D = deposits of the public
H = high-powered money

If the money stock were $120 billion, what would bank reserves have to be?

38. ▼ *Econometrics* (*from the GRE Economics Test*) With the model in the previous exercise, if H were equal to $42 billion, what would M equal?

CAT Scans *CAT (Computerized Axial Tomographic) scans are used to map the exact location of interior features of the human body. CAT scan technology is based on the following principles: (1) different components of the human body (water, gray matter, bone, etc.) absorb X-rays to different extents; and (2) to measure the X-ray absorption by a specific region of, say, the brain, it suffices to pass a*

number of line-shaped pencil beams of X-rays through the brain at different angles and measure the total absorption for each beam, which is the sum of the absorptions of the regions through which it passes. The accompanying diagram illustrates a simple example. (The number in each region shows its absorption, and the number on each X-ray beam shows the total absorption for that beam.)[26]

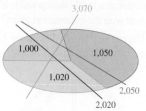

In Exercises 39–44, use the table and the given X-ray absorption diagrams to identify the composition of each of the regions marked by a letter.

Type	Air	Water	Gray Matter	Tumor	Blood	Bone
Absorption	0	1,000	1,020	1,030	1,050	2,000

39. ▼

40. ▼

41. ▼

42. ▼

[25] This is known as **Kirchhoff's Current Law,** named after Gustav Robert Kirchhoff (1824–1887). Kirchhoff made important contributions to the fields of geometric optics, electromagnetic radiation and electrical network theory.

[26] Based on a COMAP article *Geometry, New Tools for New Technologies,* by J. Malkevitch, Video Applications Library, COMAP, 1992. The absorptions are actually calibrated on a logarithmic scale. In real applications, the size of the regions is very small, and very large numbers of beams must be used.

43. ▼ Identify the composition of site *x*.

(The horizontal and slanted beams each pass through five regions.)

44. ▼ Identify the composition of site *x*.

(The horizontal and slanted beams each pass through five regions.)

45. ◆ *Voting* In the 75th Congress (1937–1939) the U.S. House of Representatives had 333 Democrats, 89 Republicans, and 13 members of other parties. Suppose that a bill passed the House with 31 more votes in favor than against, with 10 times as many Democrats voting for the bill as Republicans, and with 36 more non-Democrats voting against the bill than for it. If every member voted either for the bill or against it, how many Democrats, how many Republicans, and how many members of other parties voted in favor of the bill?

46. ◆ *Voting* In the 75th Congress (1937–1939) there were in the Senate 75 Democrats, 17 Republicans, and 4 members of other parties. Suppose that a bill passed the Senate with 16 more votes in favor than against, with three times as many Democrats voting in favor as non-Democrats voting in favor, and 32 more Democrats voting in favor than Republicans voting in favor. If every member voted either for the bill or against it, how many Democrats, how many Republicans, and how many members of other parties voted in favor of the bill?

47. ◆ *Investments* Things have not been going too well here at Accurate Accounting, Inc. since we hired Todd Smiley. He has a tendency to lose important documents, especially around April, when tax returns of our business clients are due. Today Smiley accidentally shredded Colossal Conglomerate Corp.'s investment records. We must therefore reconstruct them based on the information he can gather. Todd recalls that the company earned an $8 million return on investments totaling $65 million last year. After a few frantic telephone calls to sources in Colossal, he learned that Colossal had made investments in four companies last year: X, Y, Z, and W. (For reasons of confidentiality, we are withholding their names.) Investments in company X earned 15% last year, investments in Y depreciated by 20% last year, investments in Z neither appreciated nor depreciated last year, while investments in W earned 20% last year. Smiley was also told that Colossal invested twice as much in company X as in company Z, and three times as much in company W as in company Z. Does Smiley have sufficient information to piece together Colossal's investment portfolio before its tax return is due next week? If so, what does the investment portfolio look like?

48. ◆ *Investments* Things are going from bad to worse here at Accurate Accounting, Inc.! Colossal Conglomerate Corp.'s tax return is due tomorrow and the accountant Todd Smiley seems to have no idea how Colossal earned a return of $8 million on a $65 million investment last year. It appears that, although the returns from companies X, Y, Z, and W were as listed in Exercise 47, the rest of the information there was wrong. What Smiley is now being told is that Colossal only invested in companies X, Y, and Z and that the investment in X amounted to $30 million. His sources in Colossal still maintain that twice as much was invested in company X as in company Z. What should Smiley do?

COMMUNICATION AND REASONING EXERCISES

49. Are Exercises 1 and 2 realistic in their expectation of using up all the ingredients? What does your answer have to do with the solution(s) of the associated system of equations?

50. Suppose that you obtained a solution for Exercise 3 or 4 consisting of positive values that were not all whole numbers. What would such a solution signify about the situation in the exercise? Should you round these values to the nearest whole numbers?

In Exercises 51–56, x, y and z represent the weights of the three ingredients X, Y, and Z in a gasoline blend. Say which of the following is represented by a linear equation in x, y, and z, and give a form of the equation when it is:

51. The blend consists of 100 pounds of ingredient *X*.

52. The blend is free of ingredient *X*.

53. The blend contains 30% ingredient *Y* by weight.

54. The weight of ingredient *X* is the product of the weights of ingredients *Y* and *Z*.

55. ▼ There is at least 30% ingredient *Y* by weight.

56. ▼ There is twice as much ingredient *X* by weight as *Y* and *Z* combined.

57. ▼ Make up an entertaining word problem leading to the following system of equations.

$$10x + 20y + 10z = 100$$
$$5x + 15y \qquad = 50$$
$$x + \ y + \ z = 10$$

58. ▼ Make up an entertaining word problem leading to the following system of equations.

$$10x + 20y \qquad\qquad = 300$$
$$10z + 20w = 400$$
$$20x \qquad + 10z \qquad = 400$$
$$10y \qquad + 20w = 300$$

KEY CONCEPTS

Web Site www.FiniteandCalc.org
Go to the student Web site at
www.FiniteandCalc.org to find a
comprehensive and interactive
Web-based summary of Chapter 2.

2.1 Systems of Two Equations in Two Unknowns

Linear equation in two unknowns *p. 124*
Coefficient *p. 124*
Solution of an equation in two unknowns *p. 124*
Graphical method for solving a system of two linear equations *p. 128*

Algebraic method for solving a system of two linear equations *p. 128*
Possible outcomes for a system of two linear equations *p. 130*
Redundant or dependent system *p. 130*
Consistent system *p. 130*

2.2 Using Matrices to Solve Systems of Equations

Linear equation (in any number of unknowns) *p. 137*
Matrix *p. 138*

Augmented matrix of a system of linear equations *p. 138*
Elementary row operations *p. 139*
Pivot *p. 141*
Clearing a column; pivoting *p. 141*
Gauss-Jordan or row reduction *p. 143*
Reduced row echelon form *p. 150*

2.3 Applications of Systems of Linear Equations

Resource allocation *p. 155*
(Traffic) flow *p. 157*
Transportation *p. 159*

REVIEW EXERCISES

In each of Exercises 1–6, graph the equations and determine how many solutions the system has, if any.

1. $x + 2y = 4$
$2x - y = 1$

2. $0.2x - 0.1y = 0.3$
$0.2x + 0.2y = 0.4$

3. $\frac{1}{2}x - \frac{3}{4}y = 0$
$6x - 9y = 0$

4. $2x + 3y = 2$
$-x - 3y/2 = 1/2$

5. $x + y = 1$
$2x + y = 0.3$
$3x + 2y = \frac{13}{10}$

6. $3x + 0.5y = 0.1$
$6x + y = 0.2$
$\frac{3x}{10} - 0.05y = 0.01$

Solve each of the systems of linear equations in Exercises 7–18.

7. $x + 2y = 4$
$2x - y = 1$

8. $0.2x - 0.1y = 0.3$
$0.2x + 0.2y = 0.4$

9. $\frac{1}{2}x - \frac{3}{4}y = 0$
$6x - 9y = 0$

10. $2x + 3y = 2$
$-x - 3y/2 = 1/2$

11. $x + y = 1$
$2x + y = 0.3$
$3x + 2y = \frac{13}{10}$

12. $3x + 0.5y = 0.1$
$6x + y = 0.2$
$\frac{3x}{10} - 0.05y = 0.01$

13. $x + 2y = -3$
$x - z = 0$
$x + 3y - 2z = -2$

14. $x - y + z = 2$
$7x + y - z = 6$
$x - \frac{1}{2}y + \frac{1}{3}z = 1$
$x + y + z = 6$

15. $x - \frac{1}{2}y + z = 0$
$\frac{1}{2}x - \frac{1}{2}z = -1$
$\frac{3}{2}x - \frac{1}{2}y + \frac{1}{2}z = -1$

16. $x + y - 2z = -1$
$-2x - 2y + 4z = 2$
$0.75x + 0.75y - 1.5z = -0.75$

17. $x = \frac{1}{2}y$
$\frac{1}{2}x = -\frac{1}{2}z + 2$
$z = -3x + y$

18. $x - y + z = 1$
$y - z + w = 1$
$x + z - w = 1$
$2x + z = 3$

Exercises 19–22 are based on the following equation relating the Fahrenheit and Celsius (or centigrade) temperature scales:

$$5F - 9C = 160,$$

where F is the Fahrenheit temperature of an object and C is its Celsius temperature.

19. What temperature should an object be if its Fahrenheit and Celsius temperatures are the same?

20. What temperature should an object be if its Celsius temperature is half its Fahrenheit temperature?

21. Is it possible for the Fahrenheit temperature of an object to be 1.8 times its Celsius temperature? Explain.

22. Is it possible for the Fahrenheit temperature of an object to be 30° more than 1.8 times its Celsius temperature? Explain.

In Exercises 23–28, let x, y, z, and w represent the population in millions of four cities A, B, C, and D. Express the given statement as an equation in x, y, z, and w. If the equation is linear, say so and express it in the standard form $ax + by + cz + dw = k$.

23. The total population of the four cities is 10 million people.

24. City A has three times as many people as cities B and C combined.

25. City D is actually a ghost town; there are no people living in it.

26. The population of City A is the sum of the squares of the populations of the other three cities.

27. City C has 30% more people than City B.

28. City C has 30% fewer people than City B.

APPLICATIONS

Purchasing In Exercises 29–32, you are the buyer for OHaganBooks.com and are considering increasing stocks of romance and horror novels at the new OHaganBooks.com warehouse in Texas. You have offers from two publishers: Duffin House and Higgins Press. Duffin offers a package of 5 horror novels and 5 romance novels for $50, and Higgins offers a package of 5 horror and 11 romance novels for $150.

29. How many packages should you purchase from each publisher to get exactly 4,500 horror novels and 6,600 romance novels?

30. You want to spend a total of $50,000 on books and have promised to buy twice as many packages from Duffin as from Higgins. How many packages should you purchase from each publisher?

31. Your accountant tells you that you can now afford to spend a total of $90,000 on romance and horror books. She also reminds you that you had signed an agreement to spend twice as much money for books from Duffin as from Higgins. How many packages should you purchase from each publisher?

32. Your accountant tells you that you can now afford to spend a total of $60,000 on romance and horror books. She also reminds you that you had signed an agreement to spend the same amount of money at both publishers. How many packages should you purchase from each publisher?

33. *Equilibrium* The demand per year for "Finite Math the O'Hagan Way" is given by $q = -1,000p + 140,000$, where p is the price per book in dollars. The supply is given by $q = 2,000p + 20,000$. Find the price at which supply and demand balance.

34. *Equilibrium* OHaganbooks.com CEO John O'Hagan announces to a stunned audience at the annual board meeting that he is considering expanding into the jumbo jet airline manufacturing business. The demand per year for jumbo jets is given by $q = -2p + 18$ where p is the price per jet in millions of dollars. The supply is given by $q = 3p + 3$. Find the price the envisioned O'Hagan jumbo jet division should charge to balance supply and demand.

35. *Feeding Schedules* Billy-Sean O'Hagan is John O'Hagan's son and a freshman in college. Billy's 36-gallon tropical fish tank contains three types of carnivorous creatures: baby sharks, piranhas and squids, and he feeds them three types of delicacies: goldfish, angelfish and butterfly fish. Each baby shark can consume 1 goldfish, 2 angelfish, and 2 butterfly fish per day; each piranha can consume 1 goldfish and 3 butterfly fish per day (the piranhas are rather large as a result of their diet) while each squid can consume 1 goldfish and 1 angelfish per day. After a trip to the local pet store, he was able to feed his creatures to capacity, and noticed that 21 goldfish, 21 angelfish and 35 butterfly fish were eaten. How many of each type of creature does he have?

36. *Resource Allocation* Duffin House is planning its annual Song Festival, when it will serve three kinds of delicacies: granola treats, nutty granola treats, and nuttiest granola treats. The following table shows the ingredients required (in ounces) for a single serving of each delicacy, as well as the total amount of each ingredient available.

	Granola	Nutty Granola	Nuttiest Granola	Total Available
Toasted Oats	1	1	5	1,500
Almonds	4	8	8	10,000
Raisins	2	4	8	4,000

The Song Festival planners at Duffin House would like to use up all the ingredients. Is this possible? If so, how many servings of each kind of delicacy can they make?

37. *Web Site Traffic* OHaganBooks.com has two principal competitors: JungleBooks.com and FarmerBooks.com. Combined Web site traffic at the three sites is estimated at 10,000 hits per day. Only 10% of the hits at OHaganBooks.com result in orders, whereas JungleBooks.com and FarmerBooks.com report that 20% of the hits at their sites result in book orders. Together, the three sites process 1,500 book orders per day. FarmerBooks.com appears to be the most successful of the three, and gets as many book orders as the other two combined. What is the traffic (in hits per day) at each of the sites?

38. *Sales* As the buyer at OHaganBooks.com you are planning to increase stocks of books about music, and have been monitoring worldwide sales. Last year, worldwide sales of books about rock, rap, and classical music amounted to $5.8 billion. Books on rock music brought in twice as much revenue as books on rap music and they brought in 900% the revenue of books on classical music. How much revenue was earned in each of the three categories of books?

39. *Investing in Stocks* Billy-Sean O'Hagan is the treasurer at his college fraternity, which recently earned $12,400 in its annual carwash fundraiser. Billy-Sean decided to invest all the proceeds in the purchase of three computer stocks: HAL, POM, and WELL.

	Price per Share	Dividend Yield
HAL	$100	0.5%
POM	$20	1.50%
WELL	$25	0%

If the investment was expected to earn $56 in annual dividends, and he purchased a total of 200 shares, how many shares of each stock did he purchase?

40. IPOs Duffin House, Higgins Press, and Sickle Publications all went public on the same day recently. John O'Hagan had the opportunity to participate in all three initial public offerings (partly because he and Marjory Duffin are good friends). He made a considerable profit when he sold all of the stock two days later on the open market. The following table shows the purchase price and percentage yield on the investment in each company.

	Purchase Price per Share	Yield
Duffin House (DHS)	$8	20%
Higgins Press (HPR)	$10	15%
Sickle Publications (SPUB)	$15	15%

He invested $20,000 in a total of 2,000 shares, and made a $3,400 profit from the transactions. How many shares in each company did he purchase?

41. Degree Requirements During his lunch break, John O'Hagan decides to devote some time to assisting his son Billy-Sean, who is having a terrible time coming up with a college course schedule. One reason for this is the very complicated Bulletin of Suburban State University. It reads as follows:

> All candidates for the degree of Bachelor of Science at SSU must take a total of 124 credits from the Sciences, Fine Arts, Liberal Arts, and Mathematics,[27] including an equal number of Science and Fine Arts credits, and twice as many Mathematics credits as Science credits and Fine Arts credits combined, but with Liberal Arts credits exceeding Mathematics credits by exactly one third of the number of Fine Arts credits.

What are all the possible degree programs for Billy-Sean?

42. Degree Requirements Having finally decided on his degree program, Billy-Sean learns that Suburban State University Senate (under pressure from the English Department) has revised the Bulletin to include a "Verbal Expression" component in place of the Fine Arts requirement in all programs (including the sciences):

> All candidates for the degree of Bachelor of Science at SSU must take a total of 120 credits from the Liberal Arts, Sciences, Verbal Expression, and Mathematics, including an equal number of Science and Liberal Arts credits, and twice as many Verbal Expression credits as Science credits and Liberal Arts credits combined, but with Liberal Arts credits exceeding Mathematics credits by one quarter of the number of Verbal Expression Credits.

What are now the possible degree programs for Billy-Sean?

---

[27] Strictly speaking, mathematics is not a science; it is the Queen of the Sciences, although we like to think of it as the Mother of all Sciences.

43. Network Traffic All book orders received at the Order Department at OHaganBooks.com are transmitted through a small computer network to the Shipping Department. The following diagram shows the network (which uses two intermediate computers as routers), together with some of the average daily traffic measured in book orders.

OD = Order department
SD = Shipping department

a. Set up a system of linear equations in which the unknowns give the average traffic along the paths labeled x, y, z, w, and find the general solution.
b. What is the minimum volume of traffic along y?
c. What is the maximum volume of traffic along w?
d. If there is no traffic along z, find the volume of traffic along all the paths.
e. If there is the same volume of traffic along y and z, what is the volume of traffic along w?

44. Business Retreats Marjory Duffin is planning a joint business retreat for Duffin House and OHaganBooks.com at Laguna Surf City, but is concerned about traffic conditions (she feels that too many cars tend to spoil the ambiance of a seaside retreat). She managed to obtain the following map from the Laguna Surf City Engineering Department (all the streets are one-way as indicated). The counters show traffic every five minutes.

a. Set up and solve the associated system of linear equations. *Be sure to give the general solution.* (Take x = traffic along North Beach Way, y = traffic along South Beach Way, z = traffic along Beach View St., u = traffic along Lagoon Drive and v = traffic along Dock Road.)

b. Assuming that all roads are one-way in the directions shown, what, if any, is the maximum possible traffic along Lagoon Drive?

c. The Laguna Surf City Traffic Department is considering opening up Beach View Street to two-way traffic, but an environmentalist group is concerned that this will result in increased traffic on Lagoon Drive. What, if any, is the maximum possible traffic along Lagoon Drive assuming that Beach View Street is two-way and the traffic counter readings are as shown?

45. *Shipping* On the same day that the sales department at Duffin House received an order for 600 packages from the OHaganBooks.com Texas headquarters, it received an additional order for 200 packages from FantasyBooks.com, based in California. Duffin House has warehouses in New York and Illinois. The Illinois warehouse is closing down, and must clear all 300 packages it has in stock. Shipping costs per package of books are as follows:

New York to Texas: $20 New York to California: $50
Illinois to Texas: $30 Illinois to California: $40

Is it possible to fill both orders and clear the Illinois warehouse at a cost of $22,000? If so, how many packages should be sent from each warehouse to each online bookstore?

46. *Transportation Scheduling* Duffin Press is about to start a promotional blitz for its new book, *Physics for the Liberal Arts*. The company has 20 salespeople stationed in Chicago and 10 in Denver, and would like to fly 15 to sales fairs at each of Los Angeles and New York. A round-trip plane flight from Chicago to LA costs $200; from Chicago to NY costs $150; from Denver to LA costs $400; and from Denver to NY costs $200. For tax reasons, Duffin Press needs to budget exactly $6,500 for the total cost of the plane flights. How many salespeople should the company fly from each of Chicago and Denver to each of LA and NY?

Case Study   Hybrid Cars—Optimizing the Degree of Hybridization

You are involved in new model development at one of the "big three" automobile companies. The company is planning to introduce two new plug-in hybrid electric vehicles: the subcompact "Green Town Hopper" and the midsize "Electra Supreme," and your department must decide on the degree of hybridization (DOH) for each of these models that will result in the largest reduction in gasoline consumption. (The DOH of a vehicle is defined as the ratio of electric motor power to the total power, and typically ranges from 10% to 50%. For example, a model with a 20% DOH has an electric motor that delivers 20% of the total power of the vehicle.)

The tables below show the benefit for each of the two models, measured as the estimated reduction in annual gasoline consumption, as well as an estimate of retail cost increment, for various DOH percentages[28]: (The retail cost increment estimate is given by the formula $5,000 + 50(DOH - 10)$ for the Green Town Hopper and $7,000 + 50(DOH - 10)$ for the Electra Supreme.)

Green Town Hopper

DOH (%)	10	20	50
Reduction in Annual Consumption (gals)	180	230	200
Retail Cost Increment ($)	5,000	5,500	7,000

Electra Supreme

DOH (%)	10	20	50
Reduction in Annual Consumption (gals)	220	270	260
Retail Cost Increment ($)	7,000	7,500	9,000

---

[28] The figures are approximate and based on data for two actual vehicles as presented in a 2006 paper entitled *Cost-Benefit Analysis of Plug-In Hybrid Electric Vehicle Technology* by A. Simpson. Source: National Renewable Energy Laboratory, U.S. Department of Energy (www.nrel.gov).

Green Town Hopper

Electra Supreme

Figure 9

Green Town Hopper

Electra Supreme

Figure 10

Notice that increasing the DOH toward 50% results in a decreased benefit. This is due in part to the need to increase the weight of the batteries while keeping the vehicle performance at a desirable level, thus necessitating a more powerful gasoline engine. The *optimum* DOH is the percentage that gives the largest reduction in gasoline consumption, and this is what you need to determine. Since the optimum DOH may not be 20%, you would like to create a mathematical model to compute the reduction R in gas consumption as a function of the DOH x. Your first inclination is to try linear equations—that is, an equation of the form

$$R = ax + b \quad (a \text{ and } b \text{ constants}),$$

but you quickly discover that the data simply won't fit, no matter what the choice of the constants. The reason for this can be seen graphically by plotting R versus x (Figure 9). In neither case do the three points lie on a straight line. In fact, the data are not even *close* to being linear. Thus, you will need curves to model these data. After giving the matter further thought, you remember something your mathematics instructor once said: The simplest curve passing through any three points not all on the same line is a parabola. Since you are looking for a simple model of the data, you decide to try a parabola. A general parabola has the equation

$$R = ax^2 + bx + c$$

where a, b, and c are constants. The problem now is: What are a, b, and c? You decide to try substituting the values of R and x for the Green Town Hopper into the general equation, and you get the following:

$$x = 10, R = 180 \quad \text{gives} \quad 180 = 100a + 10b + c$$
$$x = 20, R = 230 \quad \text{gives} \quad 230 = 400a + 20b + c$$
$$x = 50, R = 200 \quad \text{gives} \quad 200 = 2{,}500a + 50b + c.$$

Now you notice that you have three linear equations in three unknowns! You solve the system:

$$a = -0.15, b = 9.5, c = 100.$$

Thus your reduction equation for the Green Town Hopper becomes

$$R = -0.15x^2 + 9.5x + 100.$$

For the Electra Supreme, we get

$$x = 10, R = 220: \quad 220 = 100a + 10b + c$$
$$x = 20, R = 270: \quad 270 = 400a + 20b + c$$
$$x = 50, R = 260: \quad 260 = 2{,}500a + 50b + c.$$

$$a = -0.1\bar{3}, b = 9, c = 143.\bar{3}$$

and so

$$R = -0.1\bar{3}x^2 + 9x + 143.\bar{3}.$$

Figure 10 shows the parabolas superimposed on the data points. You can now estimate a value for the optimal DOH as the value of x that gives the largest benefit R. Recalling that the x-coordinate of the vertex of the parabola $y = ax^2 + bx + c$ is $x = -\frac{b}{2a}$, you obtain the following estimates:

$$\text{Green Town Hopper: Optimal DOH} = -\frac{9.5}{2(-0.15)} \approx 31.67\%$$

$$\text{Electra Supreme: Optimal DOH} = -\frac{9}{2(-0.1\overline{3})} \approx 33.75\%.$$

You can now use the formulas given earlier to estimate the resulting reductions in gasoline consumption and increases in cost:

Green Town Hopper:

$$\text{Reduction in gasoline consumption} = R \approx -0.15(31.67)^2 + 9.5(31.67) + 100$$
$$\approx 250.4 \text{ gals/year}$$

$$\text{Retail Cost Increment} \approx 5,000 + 50(31.67 - 10) \approx \$6,080$$

Electra Supreme:

$$\text{Reduction in gasoline consumption} = R = -0.1\overline{3}(33.75)^2 + 9(33.75) + 143.\overline{3}$$
$$\approx 295.2 \text{ gals/year}$$

$$\text{Retail Cost Increment} \approx 7,000 + 50(33.75 - 10) \approx \$8,190.$$

You thus submit the following estimates: The optimal degree of hybridization for the Green Town Hopper is about 31.67% and will result in a reduction in gasoline consumption of 250.4 gals/year and a retail cost increment of around $6,080. The optimal degree of hybridization for the Electra Supreme is about 33.75% and will result in a reduction in gasoline consumption of 295.2 gals/year and a retail cost increment of around $8,190.

EXERCISES

1. Repeat the computations above for the "Earth Suburban."

Earth Suburban

DOH (%)	10	20	50
Reduction in Annual Consumption (gals)	240	330	300
Retail Cost Increment ($)	9,000	9,500	11,000

$$\text{Retail cost increment} = 9,000 + 50(DOH - 10)$$

2. ▮ Repeat the analysis for the Green Town Hopper, but this time take x to be the cost increment, in thousands of dollars. (The curve of benefit versus cost is referred to as a *cost-benefit curve*.) What value of DOH corresponds to the optimal cost? What do you notice? Comment on the answer.

3. ▮ Repeat the analysis for the Electra Supreme, but this time use the optimal values, DOH = 33.8, Reduction = 295.2 gals/year in place of the 20% data. What do you notice?

4. Find the equation of the parabola that passes through the points $(1, 2)$, $(2, 9)$, and $(3, 19)$.

5. Is there a parabola that passes through the points $(1, 2)$, $(2, 9)$, and $(3, 16)$?

6. Is there a parabola that passes though the points $(1, 2)$, $(2, 9)$, $(3, 19)$, and $(-1, 2)$?

7. ▮ You submit your recommendations to your manager, and she tells you, "Thank you very much, but we have additional data for the Green Town Hopper: A 30% DOH results in a saving of 255 gals/year. Please resubmit your recommendations taking this into account by tomorrow." HINT [You now have four data points on each graph, so try a general cubic instead: $R = ax^3 + bx^2 + cx + d$. Use a graph to estimate the optimal DOH.]

TI-83/84 Plus   Technology Guide

Section 2.1

Example 1 (page 125)   Find all solutions (x, y) of the following system of two equations:

$$x + y = 3$$
$$x - y = 1.$$

Solution with Technology

You can use a graphing calculator to draw the graphs of the two equations on the same set of axes and to check the solution. First, solve the equations for y, obtaining $y = -x + 3$ and $y = x - 1$. On the TI-83/84 Plus:

1. Set

$$Y_1 = -X + 3$$
$$Y_2 = X - 1$$

2. Decide on the range of x-values you want to use. As in Figure 1, let us choose the range $[-4, 4]$.[29]

3. In the WINDOW menu set Xmin $= -4$ and Xmax $= 4$.

4. Press ZOOM and select Zoomfit to set the y range.

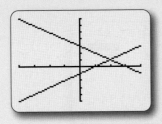

You can now zoom in for a more accurate view by choosing a smaller x-range that includes the point of intersection, like $[1.5, 2.5]$, and using Zoomfit again. You can also use the trace feature to see the coordinates of points near the point of intersection.

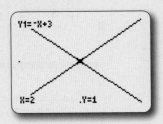

---

[29] How did we come up with this interval? Trial and error. You might need to try several intervals before finding one that gives a graph showing the point of intersection clearly.

To check that $(2, 1)$ is the correct solution, use the table feature to compare the two values of y corresponding to $x = 2$:

1. Press 2ND TABLE.

2. Set X $= 2$, and compare the corresponding values of Y_1 and Y_2; they should each be 1.

Q: *Is it always possible to find the* exact *answer using a TI-83/84 Plus this way?*

A: No. Consider the system:

$$2x + 3y = 1$$
$$-3x + 2y = 1.$$

Its solution is $(x, y) = \left(-\frac{1}{13}, \frac{5}{13}\right)$. (Check it!) If we write this solution in decimal form, we get repeating decimals: $(-0.0769230769230 \ldots, 0.384615384615 \ldots)$. Because the graphing calculator gives the coordinates of points only to several decimal places, it can show only an approximate answer.

Q: *How accurate is the answer shown using the trace feature?*

A: That depends. We can increase the accuracy up to a point by zooming in on the point of intersection of the two graphs. But there is a limit to this: Most graphing calculators are capable of giving an answer correct to about 13 decimal places. This means, for instance, that, in the eyes of the TI-83/84 Plus, 2.000 000 000 000 1 is exactly the same as 2 (subtracting them yields 0). It follows that if you attempt to use a window so narrow that you need approximately 13 significant digits to distinguish the left and right edges, you will run into accuracy problems.

Section 2.2

Row Operations with a TI-83/84 Plus   Start by entering the matrix into [A] using MATRX EDIT. You can then do row operations on [A] using the following instructions (*row, *row+, and rowSwap are found in the MATRX MATH menu).

TECHNOLOGY GUIDE

Row Operation	*TI-83/84 Plus Instruction* (Matrix name is [A])
$R_i \to kR_i$	`*row(k,[A],i)→[A]`
Example: $R_2 \to 3R_2$	`*row(3,[A],2)→[A]`
$R_i \to R_i + kR_j$	`*row+(k,[A],j,i)→[A]`
Examples: $R_1 \to R_1 - 3R_2$	`*row+(-3,[A],2,1)→[A]`
$R_1 \to 4R_1 - 3R_2$	`*row(4,[A],1)→[A]` `*row+(-3,[A],2,1)→[A]`
Swap R_i and R_j	`rowSwap([A],i,j)→[A]`
Example: Swap R_1 and R_2	`rowSwap([A],1,2)→[A]`

Example 1 (page 144)   Solve the system

$$x - y + 5z = -6$$
$$3x + 3y - z = 10$$
$$x + 3y + 2z = 5.$$

Solution with Technology

1. Begin by entering the matrix into `[A]` using `MATRX` `EDIT`. Only three columns can be seen at a time; you can see the rest of the matrix by scrolling left or right.

```
MATRIX[A] 3 ×4
[ A      -1    5       -
[ 3       3   -1       -
[ 1       3    2       -


1,1=1
```

```
MATRIX[A] 3 ×4
  -1     5    -6 ]
   3    -1    10 ]
   3     2     5 ]


1,4=-6
```

2. Now perform the operations given in Example 1:

```
*row+(-3,[A],1,2
)→[A]
 [[1  -1  5   -6]
  [0  6  -16  28]
  [1  3   2    5 ]]
■
```

```
*row+(-1,[A],1,3
)→[A]
 [[1  -1  5   -6]
  [0  6  -16  28]
  [0  4   -3  11]]
■
```

```
*row(1/2,[A],2)→
[A]
 [[1  -1  5   -6]
  [0  3   -8  14]
  [0  4   -3  11]]
■
```

```
*row(3,[A],1)→[A
]
 [[3  -3  15  -18]
  [0  3   -8  14 ]
  [0  4   -3  11 ]]
■
```

```
*row+(1,[A],2,1)
→[A]
 [[3  0  7   -4]
  [0  3  -8  14]
  [0  4  -3  11]]
■
```

```
*row(3,[A],3)→[A
]
 [[3  0   7   -4]
  [0  3   -8  14]
  [0  12  -9  33]]
■
```

```
*row+(-4,[A],2,3
)→[A]
   [[3  0  7   -4 ]
    [0  3  -8  14 ]
    [0  0  23  -23]]
■
```

```
*row(1/23,[A],3)
→[A]
   [[3  0  7  -4]
    [0  3  -8 14]
    [0  0  1  -1]]
■
```

```
*row+(-7,[A],3,1
)→[A]
   [[3  0  0  3 ]
    [0  3  -8 14]
    [0  0  1  -1]]
■
```

```
*row+(8,[A],3,2)
→[A]
   [[3  0  0  3 ]
    [0  3  0  6 ]
    [0  0  1  -1]]
■
```

```
*row(1/3,[A],1)→
[A]
   [[1  0  0  1 ]
    [0  3  0  6 ]
    [0  0  1  -1]]
■
```

```
*row(1/3,[A],2)→
[A]
   [[1  0  0  1 ]
    [0  1  0  2 ]
    [0  0  1  -1]]
■
```

As in Example 1, we can now read the solution from the right hand column: $x = 1$, $y = 2$, $z = -1$.

Note The TI-83/84 Plus has a function, `rref`, that gives the reduced row echelon form of a matrix in one step. (See the text for the definition of reduced row echelon form.) Internally it uses a variation of Gauss-Jordan reduction to do this. ■

EXCEL Technology Guide

Section 2.1

Example 1 (page 125) Find all solutions (x, y) of the following system of two equations:

$$x + y = 3$$
$$x - y = 1.$$

Solution with Technology

You can use Excel to draw the graphs of the two equations on the same set of axes, and to check the solution.

1. Solve the equations for y, obtaining $y = -x + 3$ and $y = x - 1$.

2. To graph these lines, you *could* use the Excel graphing template for smooth curves developed in Chapter 1. However, there is no need to plot a large number of points when graphing a straight line; two points suffice. The following worksheet shows all you really need for a plot of the two lines in question:

	A	B	C
1	x	y1	y2
2	-4	=-A2+3	=A2-1
3	4		

The two values of x give the x-coordinates of the two points we will use as endpoints of the lines. (We have—somewhat arbitrarily—chosen the range $[-4, 4]$ for x.) The formula for the first line, $y = -x + 3$, is in cell B2, and the formula for the second line, $y = x - 1$, is in C2.

3. Copy these two cells as shown to yield the following result:

	A	B	C
1	x	y1	y2
2	-4	7	-5
3	4	-1	3

4. For the graph, select all nine cells and create a scatter graph with line segments joining the data points. Instruct Excel to insert a chart and select the "XY (Scatter)" option. In the same dialogue box, select the option that shows points connected by lines. Click "Next" to bring up a new dialogue box called "Data Type," where you should make sure that the "Series in Columns" option is selected, telling the program that the x- and y-coordinates are arranged vertically, down columns. Your graph should appear as shown in Figure 11.

TECHNOLOGY GUIDE

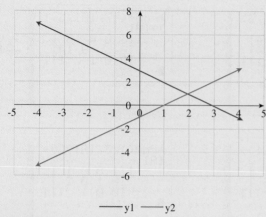

—— y1 —— y2

Figure 11

To zoom in:

1. First decide on a new x-range, say, [1, 3].

2. Change the value in cell A2 to 1 and the value in cell A3 to 3, and Excel will automatically update the y-values and the graph.*

To check that (2, 1) is the correct solution:

1. Enter the value 2 in cell A4 in your spreadsheet.

2. Copy the formulas in B3 and C3 down to row 4 to obtain the corresponding values of y.

	A	B	C
1	x	y1	y2
2	-4	7	-5
3	4	-1	3
4	2	1	1

Because the values of y agree, we have verified that (2, 1) is a solution of both equations.

Q: *Is it always possible to find the exact answer using Excel this way?*

A: No. Consider the system:

$$2x + 3y = 1$$
$$-3x + 2y = 1.$$

Its solution is $(x, y) = \left(-\frac{1}{13}, \frac{5}{13}\right)$. (Check it!) If we write this solution in decimal form, we get repeating decimals: $(-0.0769230769230\ldots, 0.384615384615\ldots)$. Because Excel rounds all numbers to 15 significant digits (so that, in the eyes of Excel, 2.000 000 000 000 001 is exactly the same as 2), it can show only an approximate answer.

Section 2.2

Row Operations with Excel   To Excel, a row is a block of data, or an **array,** and Excel has built-in the capability to handle arrays in much the same way as it handles single cells. Consider the following example:

$$\begin{bmatrix} 1 & 3 & -4 \\ 0 & 4 & 2 \end{bmatrix} 3R_2 \rightarrow \begin{bmatrix} 1 & 3 & -4 \\ 0 & 12 & 6 \end{bmatrix}. \qquad \text{Replace } R_2 \text{ by } 3R_2.$$

1. Enter the original matrix in a convenient location, say the cells A1 through C2.

2. To get the first row of the new matrix, which is simply a copy of the first row of the old matrix, decide where you want to place the new matrix, and highlight *the whole row of the new matrix,* say A4:C4.

＊ NOTE Excel sets the y-range of the graph automatically, and the range it chooses may not always be satisfactory. It may sometimes be necessary to "narrow down" the x- or y-range by double-clicking on the axis in question and specifying a new range.

3. Enter the formula $=$A1:C1 (the easiest way to do this is to type "$=$" and then use the mouse to select cells A1 through C1, i.e., the first row of the old matrix).

	A	B	C	D
1	1	3	-4	
2	0	4	2	3R2
3				
4	=A1:C1			

Enter formula for new first row.

	A	B	C	D
1	1	3	-4	
2	0	4	2	3R2
3				
4	1	3	-4	

Press Control-Shift-Enter.

4. Press **Control-Shift-Enter** (instead of "Enter" alone) and the whole row will be copied.[30] Pressing Control-Shift-Enter tells Excel that your formula is an *array formula,* one that returns an array rather than a single number. Once entered, Excel will show an array formula enclosed in "curly braces." (Note that you must also use Control-Shift-Enter to delete any array you create: Select the block you wish to delete and press Delete followed by Control-Shift-Enter.)

5. Similarly, to get the second row, select cells A5 through C5, where the new second row will go, enter the formula $=$3*A2:C2, and press Control-Shift-Enter. (Again, the easiest way to enter the formula is to type "$=$3*" and then select the cells A2 through C2 using the mouse.)

	A	B	C	D
1	1	3	-4	
2	0	4	2	3R2
3				
4	1	3	-4	
5	=3*A2:C2			

Enter formula for new second row.

	A	B	C	D
1	1	3	-4	
2	0	4	2	3R2
3				
4	1	3	-4	
5	0	12	6	

Press Control-Shift-Enter.

We can perform the following operation in a similar way:

$$\begin{bmatrix} 1 & 3 & -4 \\ 0 & 4 & 2 \end{bmatrix} \begin{array}{c} 4R_1 - 3R_2 \\ \rightarrow \end{array} \begin{bmatrix} 4 & 0 & -22 \\ 0 & 4 & 2 \end{bmatrix}.$$

Replace R_1 by $4R_1 - 3R_2$.

	A	B	C	D
1	1	3	-4	4R1-3R2
2	0	4	2	
3				
4	=4*A1:C1-3*A2:C2			

	A	B	C	D
1	1	3	-4	4R1-3R2
2	0	4	2	
3				
4	4	0	-22	

(To easily enter the formula for $4R_1 - 3R_2 4R_1 - 3R_2$, type "$=$4*," select the first row A1:C1 using the mouse, type "$-$3*," and then select the second row A2:C2 using the mouse.)

Example 1 (page 144)   Solve the system:

$$x - y + 5z = -6$$
$$3x + 3y - z = 10$$
$$x + 3y + 2z = 5.$$

---

[30] Note that on a Macintosh, Command-Enter and Command-Shift-Enter have the same effect as Control-Shift-Enter.

Solution with Technology

Here is the complete row reduction as it would appear in Excel.

	A	B	C	D	E
1	1	-1	5	-6	
2	3	3	-1	10	R2 - 3R1
3	1	3	2	5	R3 - R1
4					
5	=A1:D1				
6	=A2:D2-3*A1:D1				
7	=A3:D3-A1:D1				

	A	B	C	D	E
1	1	-1	5	-6	
2	3	3	-1	10	R2 - 3R1
3	1	3	2	5	R3 - R1
4					
5	1	-1	5	-6	
6	0	6	-16	28	(1/2)R2
7	0	4	-3	11	
8					
9	=A5:D5				
10	=(1/2)*A6:D6				
11	=A7:D7				

	A	B	C	D	E
8					
9	1	-1	5	-6	3R1 + R2
10	0	3	-8	14	
11	0	4	-3	11	3R3 - 4R2
12					
13	=3*A9:D9+A10:D10				
14	=A10*D10				
15	=3*A11:D11-4*A10:D10				

	A	B	C	D	E
12					
13	3	0	7	-4	
14	0	3	-8	14	
15	0	0	23	-23	(1/23)R3
16					
17	=A13:D13				
18	=A14:D14				
19	=(1/23)*A15:D15				

	A	B	C	D	E
16					
17	3	0	7	-4	R1 - 7R3
18	0	3	-8	14	R2 + 8R3
19	0	0	1	-1	
20					
21	=A17:D17-7*A19:D19				
22	=A18:D18+8*A19:D19				
23	=A19:D19				

	A	B	C	D	E
20					
21	3	0	0	3	(1/3)R1
22	0	3	0	6	(1/3)R2
23	0	0	1	-1	
24					
25	=(1/3)*A21:D21				
26	=(1/3)*A22:D22				
27	=A23:D23				

	A	B	C	D
24				
25	1	0	0	1
26	0	1	0	2
27	0	0	1	-1

As in Example 1, we can now read the solution from the right hand column: $x = 1$, $y = 2$, $z = -1$. What do you notice if you change the entries in cells D1, D2, and D3?

3

Matrix Algebra and Applications

Case Study Predicting Market Share

You are the sales director at Selular, a cell-phone provider, and things are not looking good for your company: The recently launched iClone competitor is beginning to chip away at Selular's market share. Particularly disturbing are rumors of fierce brand loyalty by iClone customers, with several bloggers suggesting that iClone retains close to 100% of their customers. Worse, you will shortly be presenting a sales report to the board of directors, and the CEO has "suggested" that your report include 2-, 5-, and 10-year projections of Selular's market share given the recent impact on the market by iClone, and also a "worst-case" scenario projecting what would happen if iClone customers are so loyal that none of them ever switch services. You have results from two market surveys, taken one quarter apart, of the major cell-phone providers, which shows the current market shares and the percentages of subscribers who switched from one service to another during the quarter. **How should you respond?**

Web Site

www.FiniteandCalc.org

At the Web site you will find:

- Section by section tutorials
- A detailed chapter summary
- A true/false quiz
- Additional review exercises
- A matrix algebra tool
- A game theory utility
- The following optional extra sections:

  Determinants

  Using Determinants to Solve Systems: Cramer's Rule

Eyecandy Images Inc./Alamy

Introduction

We used matrices in Chapter 2 simply to organize our work. It is time we examined them as interesting objects in their own right. There is much that we can do with matrices besides row operations: We can add, subtract, multiply, and even, in a sense, "divide" matrices. We use these operations to study game theory and input-output models in this chapter, and Markov chains in a later chapter.

Many calculators, electronic spreadsheets, and other computer programs can do these matrix operations, which is a big help in doing calculations. However, we need to know how these operations are defined to see why they are useful and to understand which to use in any particular application.

3.1 Matrix Addition and Scalar Multiplication

Let's start by formally defining what a matrix is and introducing some basic terms.

Matrix, Dimension, and Entries

An **m x n matrix** A is a rectangular array of real numbers with m rows and n columns. We refer to m and n as the **dimensions** of the matrix. The numbers that appear in the matrix are called its **entries**. We customarily use capital letters $A, B, C, \ldots$ for the names of matrices.

Quick Examples

1. $A = \begin{bmatrix} 2 & 0 & 1 \\ 33 & -22 & 0 \end{bmatrix}$ is a 2×3 matrix because it has two rows and three columns.

2. $B = \begin{bmatrix} 2 & 3 \\ 10 & 44 \\ -1 & 3 \\ 8 & 3 \end{bmatrix}$ is a 4×2 matrix because it has four rows and two columns.

The entries of A are 2, 0, 1, 33, −22, and 0. The entries of B are the numbers 2, 3, 10, 44, −1, 3, 8, and 3.

Hint: Remember that the number of rows is given first and the number of columns second. An easy way to remember this is to think of the acronym "RC" for "Row then Column."

Referring to the Entries of a Matrix

There is a systematic way of referring to particular entries in a matrix. If i and j are numbers, then the entry in the ith row and jth column of the matrix A is called the **ijth entry** of A. We usually write this entry as a_{ij} or A_{ij}. (If the matrix was called B, we would write its ijth entry as b_{ij} or B_{ij}.) Notice that this follows the "RC" convention: The row number is specified first and the column number second.

Quick Example

With $A = \begin{bmatrix} 2 & 0 & 1 \\ 33 & -22 & 0 \end{bmatrix}$,

$a_{13} = 1$ First row, third column

$a_{21} = 33$.   Second row, first column

According to the labeling convention, the entries of the matrix A above are

$$A = \begin{bmatrix} a_{11} & a_{12} & a_{13} \\ a_{21} & a_{22} & a_{23} \end{bmatrix}.$$

In general, the $m \times n$ matrix A has its entries labeled as follows:

$$A = \begin{bmatrix} a_{11} & a_{12} & a_{13} & \cdots & a_{1n} \\ a_{21} & a_{22} & a_{23} & \cdots & a_{2n} \\ \vdots & \vdots & \vdots & \ddots & \vdots \\ a_{m1} & a_{m2} & a_{m3} & \cdots & a_{mn} \end{bmatrix}.$$

We say that two matrices A and B are **equal** if they have the same dimensions and the corresponding entries are equal. Note that a 3×4 matrix can never equal a 3×5 matrix because they do not have the same dimensions.

EXAMPLE 1 Matrix Equality

Let $A = \begin{bmatrix} 7 & 9 & x \\ 0 & -1 & y+1 \end{bmatrix}$ and $B = \begin{bmatrix} 7 & 9 & 0 \\ 0 & -1 & 11 \end{bmatrix}$. Find the values of x and y such that $A = B$.

Solution For the two matrices to be equal, we must have corresponding entries equal, so

$x \quad\; = 0$ $a_{13} = b_{13}$

$y + 1 = 11 \quad$ or $\quad y = 10$. $a_{23} = b_{23}$

➡ **Before we go on...** Note in Example 1 that the matrix equation

$$\begin{bmatrix} 7 & 9 & x \\ 0 & -1 & y+1 \end{bmatrix} = \begin{bmatrix} 7 & 9 & 0 \\ 0 & -1 & 11 \end{bmatrix}$$

is really six equations in one: $7 = 7$, $9 = 9$, $x = 0$, $0 = 0$, $-1 = -1$, and $y + 1 = 11$. We used only the two that were interesting. ■

Row Matrix, Column Matrix, and Square Matrix

A matrix with a single row is called a **row matrix**, or **row vector**. A matrix with a single column is called a **column matrix** or **column vector**. A matrix with the same number of rows as columns is called a **square matrix**.

Quick Examples

The 1×5 matrix $C = [\begin{matrix} 3 & -4 & 0 & 1 & -11 \end{matrix}]$ is a row matrix.

The 4×1 matrix $D = \begin{bmatrix} 2 \\ 10 \\ -1 \\ 8 \end{bmatrix}$ is a column matrix.

The 3×3 matrix $E = \begin{bmatrix} 1 & -2 & 0 \\ 0 & 1 & 4 \\ -4 & 32 & 1 \end{bmatrix}$ is a square matrix.

Matrix Addition and Subtraction

The first matrix operations we discuss are matrix addition and subtraction. The rules for these operations are simple.

Matrix Addition and Subtraction

Two matrices can be added (or subtracted) if and only if they have the same dimensions. To add (or subtract) two matrices of the same dimensions, we add (or subtract) the corresponding entries. More formally, if A and B are $m \times n$ matrices, then $A + B$ and $A - B$ are the $m \times n$ matrices whose entries are given by:

$$(A + B)_{ij} = A_{ij} + B_{ij} \qquad ij\text{th entry of the sum} = \text{sum of the } ij\text{th entries}$$
$$(A - B)_{ij} = A_{ij} - B_{ij}. \qquad ij\text{th entry of the difference} = \text{difference of the } ij\text{th entries}$$

Visualizing Matrix Addition

$$\begin{bmatrix} 2 & -3 \\ 1 & 0 \end{bmatrix} + \begin{bmatrix} 1 & 1 \\ -2 & 1 \end{bmatrix} = \begin{bmatrix} 3 & -2 \\ -1 & 1 \end{bmatrix}$$

Quick Examples

1. $\begin{bmatrix} 2 & -3 \\ 1 & 0 \\ -1 & 3 \end{bmatrix} + \begin{bmatrix} 9 & -5 \\ 0 & 13 \\ -1 & 3 \end{bmatrix} = \begin{bmatrix} 11 & -8 \\ 1 & 13 \\ -2 & 6 \end{bmatrix}$ Corresponding entries added

2. $\begin{bmatrix} 2 & -3 \\ 1 & 0 \\ -1 & 3 \end{bmatrix} - \begin{bmatrix} 9 & -5 \\ 0 & 13 \\ -1 & 3 \end{bmatrix} = \begin{bmatrix} -7 & 2 \\ 1 & -13 \\ 0 & 0 \end{bmatrix}$ Corresponding entries subtracted

using Technology

Technology can be used to enter, add, and subtract matrices. Here is an outline (see the Technology Guides at the end of the chapter for additional details on using a TI-83/84 Plus or Excel):

TI-83/84 Plus

Entering a matrix: `MATRX`; EDIT Select a name, `ENTER`; type in the entries.
Adding two matrices:
Home Screen: `[A]+[B]`
(Use `MATRX`; NAMES to enter them on the home screen.)
[More details on page 254.]

Excel

Entering a matrix: Type entries in a convenient block of cells.
Adding two matrices: Highlight block where you want the answer to appear.
Type "="; highlight first matrix; type "+"; highlight second matrix; press Control+Shift+ Enter.
[More details on page 257.]

Web Site
www.FiniteandCalc.org

Student Home

→ Online Utilities

→ Matrix Algebra Tool

Enter matrices as shown (use a single letter for the name).

```
      Enter your matrices here.
J = [20, 15
10, 12
8, 4]

F = [23, 12,
8, 12
4, 5]
```

To compute their difference, type `F-J` in the formula box and click "Compute." (You can enter multiple formulas separated by commas in the formula box. For instance, `F+J`, `F-J` will compute both the sum and the difference. *Note:* The utility is case sensitive, so be consistent.)

EXAMPLE 2 Sales

The A-Plus auto parts store chain has two outlets, one in Vancouver and one in Quebec. Among other things, it sells wiper blades, windshield cleaning fluid, and floor mats. The monthly sales of these items at the two stores for two months are given in the following tables:

January Sales

	Vancouver	Quebec
Wiper Blades	20	15
Cleaning Fluid (bottles)	10	12
Floor Mats	8	4

February Sales

	Vancouver	Quebec
Wiper Blades	23	12
Cleaning Fluid (bottles)	8	12
Floor Mats	4	5

Use matrix arithmetic to calculate the change in sales of each product in each store from January to February.

Solution The tables suggest two matrices:

$$J = \begin{bmatrix} 20 & 15 \\ 10 & 12 \\ 8 & 4 \end{bmatrix} \quad \text{and} \quad F = \begin{bmatrix} 23 & 12 \\ 8 & 12 \\ 4 & 5 \end{bmatrix}$$

To compute the change in sales of each product for both stores, we want to subtract corresponding entries in these two matrices. In other words, we want to compute the difference of the two matrices:

$$F - J = \begin{bmatrix} 23 & 12 \\ 8 & 12 \\ 4 & 5 \end{bmatrix} - \begin{bmatrix} 20 & 15 \\ 10 & 12 \\ 8 & 4 \end{bmatrix} = \begin{bmatrix} 3 & -3 \\ -2 & 0 \\ -4 & 1 \end{bmatrix}$$

Thus, the change in sales of each product is the following:

	Vancouver	Quebec
Wiper Blades	3	−3
Cleaning Fluid (bottles)	−2	0
Floor Mats	−4	1

Scalar Multiplication

A matrix A can be added to itself because the expression $A + A$ is the sum of two matrices that have the same dimensions. When we compute $A + A$, we end up doubling every entry in A. So we can think of the expression $2A$ as telling us to *multiply every element in A by 2*.

In general, to multiply a matrix by a number, multiply every entry in the matrix by that number. For example,

$$6 \begin{bmatrix} \frac{5}{2} & -3 \\ 1 & 0 \\ -1 & \frac{5}{6} \end{bmatrix} = \begin{bmatrix} 15 & -18 \\ 6 & 0 \\ -6 & 5 \end{bmatrix}.$$

It is traditional when talking about matrices to call individual numbers **scalars**. For this reason, we call the operation of multiplying a matrix by a number **scalar multiplication**.

 using Technology

Technology can be used to compute scalar multiples:

TI-83/84 Plus
Enter the matrix [A] using
MATRX ; EDIT
Home Screen: 0.65[A]

Excel
Enter the matrix *A* in a convenient block of cells.
Highlight block where you want the answer to appear.
Type =0.65*;
highlight matrix *A*;
press Control+Shift+Enter.

Web Site
www.FiniteandCalc.org
  Student Home
    → Online Utilities
    → Matrix Algebra Tool
Enter the matrix *A* as shown.

```
Enter your matrices here.
A = [140, 105
30, 36
96, 48]
```

Type 0.65*A in the formula box and click "Compute."

EXAMPLE 3 Sales

The revenue generated by sales in the Vancouver and Quebec branches of the A-Plus auto parts store (see Example 2) was as follows:

January Sales in Canadian Dollars

	Vancouver	Quebec
Wiper Blades	140.00	105.00
Cleaning Fluid	30.00	36.00
Floor Mats	96.00	48.00

If the Canadian dollar was worth $0.65 U.S. at the time, compute the revenue in U.S. dollars.

Solution We need to multiply each revenue figure by 0.65. Let *A* be the matrix of revenue figures in Canadian dollars:

$$A = \begin{bmatrix} 140.00 & 105.00 \\ 30.00 & 36.00 \\ 96.00 & 48.00 \end{bmatrix}.$$

The revenue figures in U.S. dollars are then given by the scalar multiple

$$0.65A = 0.65 \begin{bmatrix} 140.00 & 105.00 \\ 30.00 & 36.00 \\ 96.00 & 48.00 \end{bmatrix} = \begin{bmatrix} 91.00 & 68.25 \\ 19.50 & 23.40 \\ 62.40 & 31.20 \end{bmatrix}.$$

In other words, in U.S. dollars, $91 worth of wiper blades was sold in Vancouver, $68.25 worth of wiper blades was sold in Quebec, and so on.

Formally, scalar multiplication is defined as follows:

Scalar Multiplication

If *A* is an $m \times n$ matrix and *c* is a real number, then *cA* is the $m \times n$ matrix obtained by multiplying all the entries of *A* by *c*. (We usually use lowercase letters $c, d, e, \ldots$ to denote scalars.) Thus, the ijth entry of *cA* is given by

$$(cA)_{ij} = c(A_{ij}).$$

In words, this rule is: To get the ijth entry of *cA*, multiply the ijth entry of *A* by *c*.

EXAMPLE 4 Combining Operations

Let $A = \begin{bmatrix} 2 & -1 & 0 \\ 3 & 5 & -3 \end{bmatrix}$, $B = \begin{bmatrix} 1 & 3 & -1 \\ 5 & -6 & 0 \end{bmatrix}$, and $C = \begin{bmatrix} x & y & w \\ z & t+1 & 3 \end{bmatrix}$.

Evaluate the following: $4A$, xB, and $A + 3C$.

Solution First, we find $4A$ by multiplying each entry of A by 4:

$$4A = 4 \begin{bmatrix} 2 & -1 & 0 \\ 3 & 5 & -3 \end{bmatrix} = \begin{bmatrix} 8 & -4 & 0 \\ 12 & 20 & -12 \end{bmatrix}.$$

Similarly, we find xB by multiplying each entry of B by x:

$$xB = x \begin{bmatrix} 1 & 3 & -1 \\ 5 & -6 & 0 \end{bmatrix} = \begin{bmatrix} x & 3x & -x \\ 5x & -6x & 0 \end{bmatrix}.$$

We get $A + 3C$ in two steps as follows:

$$A + 3C = \begin{bmatrix} 2 & -1 & 0 \\ 3 & 5 & -3 \end{bmatrix} + 3 \begin{bmatrix} x & y & w \\ z & t+1 & 3 \end{bmatrix}$$

$$= \begin{bmatrix} 2 & -1 & 0 \\ 3 & 5 & -3 \end{bmatrix} + \begin{bmatrix} 3x & 3y & 3w \\ 3z & 3t+3 & 9 \end{bmatrix}$$

$$= \begin{bmatrix} 2+3x & -1+3y & 3w \\ 3+3z & 3t+8 & 6 \end{bmatrix}.$$

Addition and scalar multiplication of matrices have nice properties, reminiscent of the properties of addition and multiplication of real numbers. Before we state them, we need to introduce some more notation.

If A is any matrix, then $-A$ is the matrix $(-1)A$. In other words, $-A$ is A multiplied by the scalar -1. This amounts to changing the signs of all the entries in A. For example,

$$-\begin{bmatrix} 4 & -2 & 0 \\ 6 & 10 & -6 \end{bmatrix} = \begin{bmatrix} -4 & 2 & 0 \\ -6 & -10 & 6 \end{bmatrix}.$$

For any two matrices A and B, $A - B$ is the same as $A + (-B)$. (Why?)

Also, a **zero matrix** is a matrix all of whose entries are zero. Thus, for example, the 2×3 zero matrix is

$$O = \begin{bmatrix} 0 & 0 & 0 \\ 0 & 0 & 0 \end{bmatrix}.$$

Now we state the most important properties of the operations that we have been talking about:

Properties of Matrix Addition and Scalar Multiplication

If A, B, and C are any $m \times n$ matrices and if O is the zero $m \times n$ matrix, then the following hold:

$A + (B + C) = (A + B) + C$	*Associative law*
$A + B = B + A$	*Commutative law*
$A + O = O + A = A$	*Additive identity law*
$A + (-A) = O = (-A) + A$	*Additive inverse law*
$c(A + B) = cA + cB$	*Distributive law*
$(c + d)A = cA + dA$	*Distributive law*
$1A = A$	*Scalar unit*
$0A = O$	*Scalar zero*

These properties would be obvious if we were talking about addition and multiplication of *numbers*, but here we are talking about addition and multiplication of *matrices*. We are using "+" to mean something new: matrix addition. There is no reason why matrix addition has to obey *all* the properties of addition of numbers. It happens that it does obey many of them, which is why it is convenient to call it *addition* in the first place. This means that we can manipulate equations involving matrices in much the same way that we manipulate equations involving numbers. One word of caution: We haven't yet discussed how to multiply matrices, and it probably isn't what you think. It will turn out that multiplication of matrices does *not* obey all the same properties as multiplication of numbers.

Transposition

We mention one more operation on matrices:

Transposition

If A is an $m \times n$ matrix, then its **transpose** is the $n \times m$ matrix obtained by writing its rows as columns, so that the ith row of the original matrix becomes the ith column of the transpose. We denote the transpose of the matrix A by A^T.

Visualizing Transposition

Quick Examples

1. Let $A = \begin{bmatrix} 2 & 0 & 1 & 0 \\ 33 & -22 & 0 & 5 \\ 1 & -1 & 2 & -2 \end{bmatrix}$. Then $A^T = \begin{bmatrix} 2 & 33 & 1 \\ 0 & -22 & -1 \\ 1 & 0 & 2 \\ 0 & 5 & -2 \end{bmatrix}$.

          3 × 4 matrix   4 × 3 matrix

2. $\begin{bmatrix} -1 & 1 & 2 \end{bmatrix}^T = \begin{bmatrix} -1 \\ 1 \\ 2 \end{bmatrix}$.

   1 × 3 matrix   3 × 1 matrix

Properties of Transposition

If A and B are $m \times n$ matrices, then the following hold:

$$(A + B)^T = A^T + B^T$$
$$(cA)^T = c(A^T)$$
$$(A^T)^T = A.$$

---

using Technology

Technology can be used to compute transposes like Quick Example 2 on the right:

TI-83/84 Plus
Enter the matrix [A] using
MATRX ; EDIT
Home Screen: [A]^T.
(The symbol ^{T} is found in
MATRX ; MATH.)

Excel
Enter the matrix A in a convenient 3 × 4 block of cells (e.g., A1–D3).
Highlight a 4 × 3 block for the answer (e.g., A5–C8).
Type =TRANSPOSE(A1:D3)
Press Control+Shift+Enter.

Web Site
www.FiniteandCalc.org
  Student Home
   → Online Utilities
   → Matrix Algebra Tool
Enter the matrix A as shown.

```
Enter your matrices here.
A = [2, 0, 1, 0
33, -22, 0, 5
1, -1, 2, -2]
```

Type A^T in the formula box and click "Compute."

To see why the laws of transposition are true, let us consider the first one: $(A + B)^T = A^T + B^T$. The left-hand side is the transpose of $A + B$, and so is obtained by first adding A and B, and then writing the rows as columns. This is the same as first writing the rows of A and B individually as columns before adding, which gives the right-hand side. Similar arguments can be used to establish the other laws of transposition.

3.1 EXERCISES

▼ more advanced   ◆ challenging
▣ indicates exercises that should be solved using technology

In each of Exercises 1–10, find the dimensions of the given matrix and identify the given entry.

1. $A = [1 \quad 5 \quad 0 \quad \frac{1}{4}]; a_{13}$

2. $B = [44 \quad 55]; b_{12}$

3. $C = \begin{bmatrix} \frac{5}{2} \\ 1 \\ -2 \\ 8 \end{bmatrix}; C_{11}$

4. $D = \begin{bmatrix} 15 & -18 \\ 6 & 0 \\ -6 & 5 \\ 48 & 18 \end{bmatrix}; d_{31}$

5. $E = \begin{bmatrix} e_{11} & e_{12} & e_{13} & \cdots & e_{1q} \\ e_{21} & e_{22} & e_{23} & \cdots & e_{2q} \\ \vdots & \vdots & \vdots & \ddots & \vdots \\ e_{p1} & e_{p2} & e_{p3} & \cdots & e_{pq} \end{bmatrix}; E_{22}$

6. $A = \begin{bmatrix} 2 & -1 & 0 \\ 3 & 5 & -3 \end{bmatrix}; A_{21}$

7. $B = \begin{bmatrix} 1 & 3 \\ 5 & -6 \end{bmatrix}; b_{12}$

8. $C = \begin{bmatrix} x & y & w & e \\ z & t+1 & 3 & 0 \end{bmatrix}; C_{23}$

9. $D = [d_1 \quad d_2 \quad \cdots \quad d_n]; D_{1r}$ (any r)

10. $E = [d \quad d \quad d \quad d]; E_{1r}$ (any r)

11. Solve for $x, y, z,$ and w. HINT [See Example 1.]
$$\begin{bmatrix} x+y & x+z \\ y+z & w \end{bmatrix} = \begin{bmatrix} 3 & 4 \\ 5 & 4 \end{bmatrix}$$

12. Solve for $x, y, z,$ and w. HINT [See Example 1.]
$$\begin{bmatrix} x-y & x-z \\ y-w & w \end{bmatrix} = \begin{bmatrix} 0 & 0 \\ 0 & 6 \end{bmatrix}$$

In Exercises 13–20, evaluate the given expression. Take
$$A = \begin{bmatrix} 0 & -1 \\ 1 & 0 \\ -1 & 2 \end{bmatrix}, B = \begin{bmatrix} 0.25 & -1 \\ 0 & 0.5 \\ -1 & 3 \end{bmatrix}, and$$
$$C = \begin{bmatrix} 1 & -1 \\ 1 & 1 \\ -1 & -1 \end{bmatrix}.$$

HINT [See Quick Examples pages 184 and 188, and Example 4.]

13. $A + B$

14. $A - C$

15. $A + B - C$

16. $12B$

17. $2A - C$

18. $2A + 0.5C$

19. $2A^T$

20. $A^T + 3C^T$

In Exercises 21–28, evaluate the given expression. Take
$$A = \begin{bmatrix} 1 & -1 & 0 \\ 0 & 2 & -1 \end{bmatrix}, B = \begin{bmatrix} 3 & 0 & -1 \\ 5 & -1 & 1 \end{bmatrix}, and$$
$$C = \begin{bmatrix} x & 1 & w \\ z & r & 4 \end{bmatrix}.$$

HINT [See Quick Examples pages 184 and 188, and Example 4.]

21. $A + B$

22. $B - C$

23. $A - B + C$

24. $\frac{1}{2}B$

25. $2A - B$

26. $2A - 4C$

27. $3B^T$

28. $2A^T - C^T$

▣ *Use technology in Exercises 29–36.*
$$Let \; A = \begin{bmatrix} 1.5 & -2.35 & 5.6 \\ 44.2 & 0 & 12.2 \end{bmatrix}, B = \begin{bmatrix} 1.4 & 7.8 \\ 5.4 & 0 \\ 5.6 & 6.6 \end{bmatrix},$$
$$C = \begin{bmatrix} 10 & 20 & 30 \\ -10 & -20 & -30 \end{bmatrix}.$$

29. $A - C$

30. $C - A$

31. $1.1B$

32. $-0.2B$

33. $A^T + 4.2B$

34. $(A + 2.3C)^T$

35. $(2.1A - 2.3C)^T$

36. $(A - C)^T - B$

APPLICATIONS

37. *Sales:* **Apple** The following table shows the number of Mac computers, iPods, and iPhones sold, in millions of units, in the fourth quarter (Q4) of 2006, and the changes over the previous year in each of 2007 Q4 and 2008 Q4.[1]

	Macs	**iPods**	**iPhones***
Q4 2006	1.6	8.8	0
Change in 2007	0.6	1.5	1.1
Change in 2008	0.4	0.9	5.8

*The iPhone was released in June 2007.

Use matrix algebra to find the sales of Macs, iPods, and iPhones in Q4 2007 and Q4 2008. HINT [See Example 2.]

---

[1] Apple's fourth quarter ends on Sept. 27. Source for data: Apple company reports (www.apple.com/investor/).

38. *Construction Spending* The following table shows annualized spending, in billions of dollars, on residential, office, and educational construction in the United States in August 2008, as well as the month-over-month changes for September and October.[2]

	Residential	Office	Educational
August	361	74	106
Change in September	−1	1	0
Change in October	−13	2	1

Use matrix algebra to find the spending on each type of construction in September and October. HINT [See Example 2.]

39. *Inventory* The Left Coast Bookstore chain has two stores, one in San Francisco and one in Los Angeles. It stocks three kinds of book: hardcover, softcover, and plastic (for infants). At the beginning of January, the central computer showed the following books in stock:

	Hard	Soft	Plastic
San Francisco	1,000	2,000	5,000
Los Angeles	1,000	5,000	2,000

Suppose its sales in January were as follows: 700 hardcover books, 1,300 softcover books, and 2,000 plastic books sold in San Francisco, and 400 hardcover, 300 softcover, and 500 plastic books sold in Los Angeles. Write these sales figures in the form of a matrix, and then show how matrix algebra can be used to compute the inventory remaining in each store at the end of January.

40. *Inventory* The Left Coast Bookstore chain discussed in Exercise 39 actually maintained the same sales figures for the first 6 months of the year. Each month, the chain restocked the stores from its warehouse by shipping 600 hardcover, 1,500 softcover, and 1,500 plastic books to San Francisco and 500 hardcover, 500 softcover, and 500 plastic books to Los Angeles.

a. Use matrix operations to determine the total sales over the 6 months, broken down by store and type of book.

b. Use matrix operations to determine the inventory in each store at the end of June.

41. *Profit* Annual revenues and production costs at Luddington's Wellington Boots & Co. are shown in the following spreadsheet.

	A	B	C	D
1	Revenue			
2		2004	2005	2006
3	Full Boots	$10,000	$9,000	$11,000
4	Half Boots	$8,000	$7,200	$8,800
5	Sandals	$4,000	$5,000	$6,000
6				
7	Production Costs			
8		2004	2005	2006
9	Full Boots	$2,000	$1,800	$2,200
10	Half Boots	$2,400	$1,440	$1,760
11	Sandals	$1,200	$1,500	$2,000

Use matrix algebra to compute the profits from each sector each year.

42. *Revenue* The following spreadsheet gives annual production costs and profits at Gauss-Jordan Sneakers, Inc.

	A	B	C	D
1	Production Costs			
2		2004	2005	2006
3	Gauss Grip	$1,800	$2,200	$2,400
4	Air Gauss	$1,400	$1,700	$1,200
5	Gauss Gel	$1,500	$2,000	$1,300
6				
7	Profit			
8		2004	2005	2006
9	Gauss Grip	$10,000	$14,000	$16,000
10	Air Gauss	$8,000	$12,000	$14,000
11	Gauss Gel	$9,000	$14,000	$12,000

Use matrix algebra to compute the revenues from each sector each year.

43. *Population Movement* In 1980 the U.S. population, broken down by regions, was 49.1 million in the Northeast, 58.9 million in the Midwest, 75.4 million in the South, and 43.2 million in the West.[3] In 1990 the population was 50.8 million in the Northeast, 59.7 million in the Midwest, 85.4 million in the South, and 52.8 million in the West. Set up the population figures for each year as a row vector, and then show how to use matrix operations to find the net increase or decrease of population in each region from 1980 to 1990.

44. *Population Movement* In 1990 the U.S. population, broken down by regions, was 50.8 million in the Northeast, 59.7 million in the Midwest, 85.4 million in the South, and 52.8 million in the West.[4] Between 1990 and 2000, the population in the Northeast grew by 2.8 million, the population in the Midwest grew by 4.7 million, the population in the South grew by 14.8 million, and the population in the West grew by 10.4 million. Set up the population figures for 1990 and the growth figures for the decade as row vectors. Assuming that the population will grow by the same numbers from 2000 to 2010 as they did from 1990 to 2000, show how to use matrix operations to find the population in each region in 2010.

Foreclosures *Exercises 45–48 are based on the following table, which shows the numbers of foreclosures in three states during the last four months of 2008.*[5]

	Aug.	Sept.	Oct.	Nov.	Dec.
California	7,100	3,300	5,700	5,000	4,300
Florida	3,500	900	2,400	2,800	2,300
Texas	1,900	1,000	1,900	2,100	2,100

45. Use matrix algebra to determine the total number of foreclosures in each of the given months.

---

[2] Source for data: Census Bureau (www.census.gov).

[3] Source: U.S. Census Bureau, Statistical Abstract of the United States: 2001 (www.census.gov).

[4] Ibid.

[5] Data are rounded to the nearest 100. Source for data: www.currentforeclosures.com/Stats/.

46. Use matrix algebra to determine the total number of fore-closures in each of the given states during the last four months of 2008.

47. Use matrix algebra to determine in which month the difference between the number of foreclosures in California and in Florida was greatest.

48. ▼ Use matrix algebra to determine in which region the difference between the foreclosures in August and December was greatest.

49. ▼ *Inventory* Microbucks Computer Company makes two computers, the Pomegranate II and the Pomegranate Classic, at two different factories. The Pom II requires 2 processor chips, 16 memory chips, and 20 vacuum tubes, while the Pom Classic requires 1 processor chip, 4 memory chips, and 40 vacuum tubes. Microbucks has in stock at the beginning of the year 500 processor chips, 5,000 memory chips, and 10,000 vacuum tubes at the Pom II factory, and 200 processor chips, 2,000 memory chips, and 20,000 vacuum tubes at the Pom Classic factory. It manufactures 50 Pom II's and 50 Pom Classics each month.

  a. Find the company's inventory of parts after two months, using matrix operations.

  b. When (if ever) will the company run out of one of the parts?

50. ▼ *Inventory* Microbucks Computer Company, besides having the stock mentioned in Exercise 49, gets shipments of parts every month in the amounts of 100 processor chips, 1,000 memory chips, and 3,000 vacuum tubes at the Pom II factory, and 50 processor chips, 1,000 memory chips, and 2,000 vacuum tubes at the Pom Classic factory.

  a. What will the company's inventory of parts be after six months?

  b. When (if ever) will the company run out of one of the parts?

51. ▼ *Tourism in the '90s* The following table gives the number of people (in thousands) who visited Australia and South Africa in 1998[6]:

	To	Australia	South Africa
From	**North America**	440	190
	Europe	950	950
	Asia	1,790	200

You predict that in 2008, 20,000 fewer people from North America will visit Australia and 40,000 more will visit South Africa, 50,000 more people from Europe will visit each of Australia and South Africa, and 100,000 more people from Asia will visit South Africa, but there will be no change in the number visiting Australia.

  a. Use matrix algebra to predict the number of visitors from the three regions to Australia and South Africa in 2008.

***

[6] Figures are rounded to the nearest 10,000. Sources: South African Dept. of Environmental Affairs and Tourism; Australia Tourist Commission/ *The New York Times*, January 15, 2000, p. C1.

  b. Take A to be the 3×2 matrix whose entries are the 1998 tourism figures and take B to be the 3×2 matrix whose entries are the 2008 tourism figures. Give a formula (in terms of A and B) that predicts the average of the numbers of visitors from the three regions to Australia and South Africa in 1998 and 2008. Compute its value.

52. ▼ *Tourism in the '90s* Referring to the 1998 tourism figures given in the preceding exercise, assume that the following (fictitious) figures represent the corresponding numbers from 1988.

	To	Australia	South Africa
From	**North America**	500	100
	Europe	900	800
	Asia	1,400	50

Take A to be the 3×2 matrix whose entries are the 1998 tourism figures and take B to be the 3×2 matrix whose entries are the 1988 tourism figures.

  a. Compute the matrix $A - B$. What does this matrix represent?

  b. Assuming that the changes in tourism over 1988–1998 are repeated in 1998–2008, give a formula (in terms of A and B) that predicts the number of visitors from the three regions to Australia and South Africa in 2008.

COMMUNICATION AND REASONING EXERCISES

53. Is it possible for a 2×3 matrix to equal a 3×2 matrix? Explain.

54. If A and B are 2×3 matrices and $A = B$, what can you say about $A - B$? Explain.

55. What does it mean when we say that $(A + B)_{ij} = A_{ij} + B_{ij}$?

56. What does it mean when we say that $(cA)_{ij} = c(A_{ij})$?

57. What would a 5×5 matrix A look like if $A_{ii} = 0$ for every i?

58. What would a matrix A look like if $A_{ij} = 0$ whenever $i \neq j$?

59. ▼ Give a formula for the ijth entry of the transpose of a matrix A.

60. ▼ A matrix is **symmetric** if it is equal to its transpose. Give an example of **a.** a nonzero 2×2 symmetric matrix and **b.** a nonzero 3×3 symmetric matrix.

61. ▼ A matrix is **skew-symmetric** or **antisymmetric** if it is equal to the negative of its transpose. Give an example of **a.** a nonzero 2×2 skew-symmetric matrix and **b.** a nonzero 3×3 skew-symmetric matrix.

62. ▼ Referring to Exercises 60 and 61, what can be said about a matrix that is both symmetric and skew-symmetric?

63. ▼ Why is matrix addition associative?

64. Describe a scenario (possibly based on one of the preceding examples or exercises) in which you might wish to compute $A - 2B$ for certain matrices A and B.

65. Describe a scenario (possibly based on one of the preceding examples or exercises) in which you might wish to compute $A + B - C$ for certain matrices A, B, and C.

3.2 **Matrix Multiplication**

Suppose we buy two CDs at \$3 each and four Zip disks at \$5 each. We calculate our total cost by computing the products' price × quantity and adding:

$$\text{Cost} = 3 \times 2 + 5 \times 4 = \$26.$$

Let us instead put the prices in a row vector

$$P = [3 \quad 5] \qquad \text{The price matrix}$$

and the quantities purchased in a column vector,

$$Q = \begin{bmatrix} 2 \\ 4 \end{bmatrix}. \qquad \text{The quantity matrix}$$

Q : *Why a row and a column?*

A : It's rather a long story, but mathematicians found that it works best this way . . .

Because P represents the prices of the items we are purchasing and Q represents the quantities, it would be useful if the product PQ represented the total cost, a *single number* (which we can think of as a 1×1 matrix). For this to work, PQ should be calculated the same way we calculated the total cost:

$$PQ = [3 \quad 5] \begin{bmatrix} 2 \\ 4 \end{bmatrix} = [3 \times 2 + 5 \times 4] = [26].$$

Notice that we obtain the answer by multiplying each entry in P (going from left to right) by the corresponding entry in Q (going from top to bottom) and then adding the results.

The Product *Row* × *Column*

The **product** AB of a row matrix A and a column matrix B is a 1×1 matrix. The length of the row in A must match the length of the column in B for the product to be defined. To find the product, multiply each entry in A (going from left to right) by the corresponding entry in B (going from top to bottom) and then add the results.

Visualizing

$$
\begin{bmatrix} 2 \\ 10 \\ -1 \end{bmatrix}
$$

$[2 \quad 4 \quad 1]$

2×2	$= 4$	Product of first entries $= 4$
4×10	$= 40$	Product of second entries $= 40$
$1 \times (-1) = -1$		Product of third entries $= -1$
43		Sum of products $= 43$

Quick Examples

1. $[2 \quad 1] \begin{bmatrix} -3 \\ 1 \end{bmatrix} = [2 \times (-3) + 1 \times 1] = [-6 + 1] = [-5]$

2. $[2 \quad 4 \quad 1] \begin{bmatrix} 2 \\ 10 \\ -1 \end{bmatrix} = [2 \times 2 + 4 \times 10 + 1 \times (-1)] = [4 + 40 + (-1)]$

    $= [43]$

Notes

1. In the discussion so far, *the row is on the left and the column is on the right* (RC again). (Later we will consider products where the column matrix is on the left and the row matrix is on the right.)

2. The row size has to match the column size. This means that, if we have a 1×3 row on the left, then the column on the right must be 3×1 in order for the product to make sense. For example, the product

$$[a \quad b \quad c]\begin{bmatrix} x \\ y \end{bmatrix}$$

is not defined. ■

EXAMPLE 1 Revenue

The A-Plus auto parts store mentioned in examples in the previous section had the following sales in its Vancouver store:

	Vancouver
Wiper Blades	20
Cleaning Fluid (bottles)	10
Floor Mats	8

The store sells wiper blades for $7.00 each, cleaning fluid for $3.00 per bottle, and floor mats for $12.00 each. Use matrix multiplication to find the total revenue generated by sales of these items.

Solution We need to multiply each sales figure by the corresponding price and then add the resulting revenue figures. We represent the sales by a column vector, as suggested by the table.

$$Q = \begin{bmatrix} 20 \\ 10 \\ 8 \end{bmatrix}$$

We put the selling prices in a row vector.

$$P = [7.00 \quad 3.00 \quad 12.00]$$

We can now compute the total revenue as the product

$$R = PQ = [7.00 \quad 3.00 \quad 12.00]\begin{bmatrix} 20 \\ 10 \\ 8 \end{bmatrix}$$

$$= [140.00 + 30.00 + 96.00] = [266.00].$$

So, the sale of these items generated a total revenue of $266.00.

Note We could also have written the quantity sold as a row vector (which would be Q^T) and the prices as a column vector (which would be P^T) and then multiplied them in the opposite order ($Q^T P^T$). Try this. ■

EXAMPLE 2 Relationship with Linear Equations

a. Represent the matrix equation

$$[2 \quad -4 \quad 1] \begin{bmatrix} x \\ y \\ z \end{bmatrix} = [5]$$

as an ordinary equation.

b. Represent the linear equation $3x + y - z + 2w = 8$ as a matrix equation.

Solution

a. If we perform the multiplication on the left, we get the 1×1 matrix $[2x - 4y + z]$. Thus the equation may be rewritten as

$$[2x - 4y + z] = [5].$$

Saying that these two 1×1 matrices are equal means that their entries are equal, so we get the equation

$$2x - 4y + z = 5.$$

b. This is the reverse of part (a):

$$[3 \quad 1 \quad -1 \quad 2] \begin{bmatrix} x \\ y \\ z \\ w \end{bmatrix} = [8].$$

➡ **Before we go on...** The row matrix $[3 \quad 1 \quad -1 \quad 2]$ in Example 2 is the row of **coefficients** of the original equation. (See Section 2.1.) ∎

Now to the general case of matrix multiplication:

The Product of Two Matrices: General Case

In general for matrices A and B, we can take the product AB only if the number of columns of A equals the number of rows of B (so that we can multiply the rows of A by the columns of B as above). The product AB is then obtained by taking its ijth entry to be:

$$ij\text{th entry of } AB = \text{Row } i \text{ of } A \times \text{Column } j \text{ of } B. \qquad \text{As defined above}$$

Quick Examples

(R stands for row; C stands for column.)

$$1. \ R_1 \to [2 \quad 0 \quad -1 \quad 3] \begin{matrix} C_1 & C_2 & C_3 \\ \downarrow & \downarrow & \downarrow \end{matrix} \begin{bmatrix} 1 & 1 & -8 \\ 1 & -6 & 0 \\ 0 & 5 & 2 \\ -3 & 8 & 1 \end{bmatrix} = [R_1 \times C_1 \quad R_1 \times C_2 \quad R_1 \times C_3]$$

$$= [-7 \quad 21 \quad -15]$$

$$2. \ \begin{matrix} R_1 \to \\ R_2 \to \end{matrix} \begin{bmatrix} 1 & -1 \\ 0 & 2 \end{bmatrix} \begin{matrix} C_1 & C_2 \\ \downarrow & \downarrow \end{matrix} \begin{bmatrix} 3 & 0 \\ 5 & -1 \end{bmatrix} = \begin{bmatrix} R_1 \times C_1 & R_1 \times C_2 \\ R_2 \times C_1 & R_2 \times C_2 \end{bmatrix} = \begin{bmatrix} -2 & 1 \\ 10 & -2 \end{bmatrix}$$

In matrix multiplication we always take

Rows on the left × Columns on the right.

Look at the dimensions in the two Quick Examples on the previous page.

Match
↓ ↓
$(1 \times 4)(4 \times 3) \to 1 \times 3$

Match
↓ ↓
$(2 \times 2)(2 \times 2) \to 2 \times 2$

The fact that the number of columns in the left-hand matrix equals the number of rows in the right-hand matrix amounts to saying that the middle two numbers must match as above. If we "cancel" the middle matching numbers, we are left with the dimensions of the product.

Before continuing with examples, we state the rule for matrix multiplication formally.

Multiplication of Matrices: Formal Definition

If A is an $m \times n$ matrix and B is an $n \times k$ matrix, then the product AB is the $m \times k$ matrix whose ijth entry is the product

Row i of A × Column j of B
↓   ↓

$$(AB)_{ij} = [a_{i1} \quad a_{i2} \quad a_{i3} \ldots a_{in}] \begin{bmatrix} b_{1j} \\ b_{2j} \\ b_{3j} \\ \vdots \\ b_{nj} \end{bmatrix} = a_{i1}b_{1j} + a_{i2}b_{2j} + a_{i3}b_{3j} + \cdots + a_{in}b_{nj}.$$

EXAMPLE 3 **Matrix Product**

Calculate:

a. $\begin{bmatrix} 2 & 0 & -1 & 3 \\ 1 & -1 & 2 & -2 \end{bmatrix} \begin{bmatrix} 1 & 1 & -8 \\ 1 & 0 & 0 \\ 0 & 5 & 2 \\ -2 & 8 & -1 \end{bmatrix}$ **b.** $\begin{bmatrix} -3 \\ 1 \end{bmatrix} [2 \quad 1]$

Solution

a. Before we start the calculation, we check that the dimensions of the matrices match up.

Match

2×4 4×3

$\begin{bmatrix} 2 & 0 & -1 & 3 \\ 1 & -1 & 2 & -2 \end{bmatrix} \begin{bmatrix} 1 & 1 & -8 \\ 1 & 0 & 0 \\ 0 & 5 & 2 \\ -2 & 8 & -1 \end{bmatrix}$

using Technology

Technology can be used to multiply the matrices in Example 3. Here is an outline for part (a) (see the Technology Guides at the end of the chapter for additional details on using a TI-83/84 Plus or Excel):

TI-83/84 Plus

Enter the matrices A and B using MATRX ; EDIT
Home Screen: [A]*[B]
[More details on page 254.]

Excel

Enter the matrices in convenient blocks of cells (e.g., A1–D2 and F1–H4). Highlight a 2 × 3 block for the answer.
Type =MMULT(A1:D2, F1:H4)
Press Control+Shift+Enter.
[More details on page 259.]

Web Site

www.FiniteandCalc.org

Student Home

→ Online Utilities

→ Matrix Algebra Tool

Enter matrices as shown:

```
Enter your matrices here.
A = [2, 0, -1, 3
1, -1, 2, -2]

B = [1, 1, -8
1, 0, 0
0, 5, 2
-2, 8, -1]
```

Type A*B in the formula box and click "Compute." If you try to multiply two matrices whose product is not defined, you will get an error alert box telling you that.

The product of the two matrices is defined, and the product will be a 2×3 matrix (we remove the matching 4s: $(2 \times 4)(4 \times 3) \to 2 \times 3$). To calculate the product, we follow the previous prescription:

$$
\begin{array}{c}

\begin{array}{ccc} C_1 & C_2 & C_3 \\ \downarrow & \downarrow & \downarrow \end{array}
\end{array}
$$

$$
\begin{matrix} R_1 \to \\ R_2 \to \end{matrix}
\begin{bmatrix} 2 & 0 & -1 & 3 \\ 1 & -1 & 2 & -2 \end{bmatrix}
\begin{bmatrix} 1 & 1 & -8 \\ 1 & 0 & 0 \\ 0 & 5 & 2 \\ -2 & 8 & -1 \end{bmatrix}
=
\begin{bmatrix} R_1 \times C_1 & R_1 \times C_2 & R_1 \times C_3 \\ R_2 \times C_1 & R_2 \times C_2 & R_2 \times C_3 \end{bmatrix}
$$

$$
= \begin{bmatrix} -4 & 21 & -21 \\ 4 & -5 & -2 \end{bmatrix}.
$$

b. The dimensions of the two matrices given are 2×1 and 1×2. Because the 1s match, the product is defined, and the result will be a 2×2 matrix.

$$
\begin{array}{c}
 \begin{array}{cc} C_1 & C_2 \\ \downarrow & \downarrow \end{array}
\end{array}
$$

$$
\begin{matrix} R_1 \to \\ R_2 \to \end{matrix}
\begin{bmatrix} -3 \\ 1 \end{bmatrix}
\begin{bmatrix} 2 & 1 \end{bmatrix}
=
\begin{bmatrix} R_1 \times C_1 & R_1 \times C_2 \\ R_2 \times C_1 & R_2 \times C_2 \end{bmatrix}
=
\begin{bmatrix} -6 & -3 \\ 2 & 1 \end{bmatrix}
$$

Note In part (a) we *cannot* multiply the matrices in the opposite order—the dimensions do not match. We say simply that the product in the opposite order is **not defined**. In part (b) we *can* multiply the matrices in the opposite order, but we would get a 1×1 matrix if we did so. Thus, order is important when multiplying matrices. In general, if AB is defined, then BA need not even be defined. If BA is also defined, it may not have the same dimensions as AB. And even if AB and BA have the same dimensions, they may have different entries. (See the next example.) ∎

EXAMPLE 4   AB versus BA

Let $A = \begin{bmatrix} 1 & -1 \\ 0 & 2 \end{bmatrix}$ and $B = \begin{bmatrix} 3 & 0 \\ 5 & -1 \end{bmatrix}$. Find AB and BA.

Solution Note first that A and B are both 2×2 matrices, so the products AB and BA are both defined and are both 2×2 matrices—unlike the case in Example 3(b). We first calculate AB:

$$
AB = \begin{bmatrix} 1 & -1 \\ 0 & 2 \end{bmatrix} \begin{bmatrix} 3 & 0 \\ 5 & -1 \end{bmatrix} = \begin{bmatrix} -2 & 1 \\ 10 & -2 \end{bmatrix}
$$

Now let's calculate BA.

$$
BA = \begin{bmatrix} 3 & 0 \\ 5 & -1 \end{bmatrix} \begin{bmatrix} 1 & -1 \\ 0 & 2 \end{bmatrix} = \begin{bmatrix} 3 & -3 \\ 5 & -7 \end{bmatrix}
$$

Notice that BA has no resemblance to AB! Thus, we have discovered that, even for square matrices:

Matrix multiplication is not commutative.

In other words, $AB \neq BA$ in general, even when AB and BA both exist and have the same dimensions. (There are instances when $AB = BA$ for particular matrices A and B, but this is an exception, not the rule.)

EXAMPLE 5 Revenue

January sales at the A-Plus auto parts stores in Vancouver and Quebec are given in the following table.

	Vancouver	Quebec
Wiper Blades	20	15
Cleaning Fluid (bottles)	10	12
Floor Mats	8	4

The usual selling prices for these items are $7.00 each for wiper blades, $3.00 per bottle for cleaning fluid, and $12.00 each for floor mats. The discount prices for A-Plus Club members are $6.00 each for wiper blades, $2.00 per bottle for cleaning fluid, and $10.00 each for floor mats. Use matrix multiplication to compute the total revenue at each store, assuming first that all items were sold at the usual prices, and then that they were all sold at the discount prices.

Solution We can do all of the requested calculations at once with a single matrix multiplication. Consider the following two labeled matrices.

$$Q = \begin{array}{c} \\ \text{Wb} \\ \text{Cf} \\ \text{Fm} \end{array} \begin{array}{cc} \text{V} & \text{Q} \\ \begin{bmatrix} 20 & 15 \\ 10 & 12 \\ 8 & 4 \end{bmatrix} \end{array}$$

$$P = \begin{array}{c} \\ \text{Usual} \\ \text{Discount} \end{array} \begin{array}{ccc} \text{Wb} & \text{Cf} & \text{Fm} \\ \begin{bmatrix} 7.00 & 3.00 & 12.00 \\ 6.00 & 2.00 & 10.00 \end{bmatrix} \end{array}$$

The first matrix records the quantities sold, while the second records the sales prices under the two assumptions. To compute the revenue at both stores under the two different assumptions, we calculate $R = PQ$.

$$R = PQ = \begin{bmatrix} 7.00 & 3.00 & 12.00 \\ 6.00 & 2.00 & 10.00 \end{bmatrix} \begin{bmatrix} 20 & 15 \\ 10 & 12 \\ 8 & 4 \end{bmatrix}$$

$$= \begin{bmatrix} 266.00 & 189.00 \\ 220.00 & 154.00 \end{bmatrix}$$

We can label this matrix as follows.

$$R = \begin{array}{c} \\ \text{Usual} \\ \text{Discount} \end{array} \begin{array}{cc} \text{V} & \text{Q} \\ \begin{bmatrix} 266.00 & 189.00 \\ 220.00 & 154.00 \end{bmatrix} \end{array}$$

In other words, if the items were sold at the usual price, then Vancouver had a revenue of $266 while Quebec had a revenue of $189, and so on.

➡ **Before we go on...** In Example 5 we were able to calculate PQ because the dimensions matched correctly: $(2 \times 3)(3 \times 2) \rightarrow 2 \times 2$. We could also have multiplied them in the opposite order and gotten a 3×3 matrix. Would the product QP be meaningful?

In an application like this, not only do the dimensions have to match, but also the *labels* have to match for the result to be meaningful. The labels on the three columns of P are the parts that were sold, and these are also the labels on the three rows of Q. Therefore, we can "cancel labels" at the same time that we cancel the dimensions in the product. However, the labels on the two columns of Q do not match the labels on the two rows of P, and there is no useful interpretation of the product QP in this situation. ■

There are very special square matrices of every size: 1×1, 2×2, 3×3, and so on, called the **identity** matrices.

Identity Matrix

The $n \times n$ identity matrix I is the matrix with 1s down the **main diagonal** (the diagonal starting at the top left) and 0s everywhere else. In symbols,

$$I_{ii} = 1, \quad \text{and}$$
$$I_{ij} = 0 \quad \text{if } i \neq j.$$

Quick Examples

1. 1×1 identity matrix $\qquad I = [1]$

2. 2×2 identity matrix $\qquad I = \begin{bmatrix} 1 & 0 \\ 0 & 1 \end{bmatrix}$

3. 3×3 identity matrix $\qquad I = \begin{bmatrix} 1 & 0 & 0 \\ 0 & 1 & 0 \\ 0 & 0 & 1 \end{bmatrix}$

4. 4×4 identity matrix $\qquad I = \begin{bmatrix} 1 & 0 & 0 & 0 \\ 0 & 1 & 0 & 0 \\ 0 & 0 & 1 & 0 \\ 0 & 0 & 0 & 1 \end{bmatrix}$

Note Identity matrices are always square matrices, meaning that they have the same number of rows as columns. There is no such thing, for example, as the "2×4 identity matrix."

The next example shows why I is interesting. ■

EXAMPLE 6 Identity Matrix

Evaluate the products AI and IA, where $A = \begin{bmatrix} a & b & c \\ d & e & f \\ g & h & i \end{bmatrix}$ and I is the 3×3 identity matrix.

Solution

First notice that A is arbitrary; it could be any 3×3 matrix.

$$AI = \begin{bmatrix} a & b & c \\ d & e & f \\ g & h & i \end{bmatrix} \begin{bmatrix} 1 & 0 & 0 \\ 0 & 1 & 0 \\ 0 & 0 & 1 \end{bmatrix} = \begin{bmatrix} a & b & c \\ d & e & f \\ g & h & i \end{bmatrix}$$

using Technology

Technology can be used to obtain an identity matrix as in Example 6. Here is an outline (see the Technology Guides at the end of the chapter for additional details on using a TI-83/84 Plus or Excel):

TI-83/84 Plus

3×3 identity matrix:
`identity(3)`
Obtained from $\boxed{\text{MATRX}}$; MATH
[More details on page 255.]

Excel

Click on a cell for the top left corner (e.g., B1).
Type `=IF(ROW(B1)-ROW($B$1)=COLUMN(B1)-COLUMN($B$1),1,0)`
Copy across and down.
[More details on page 259.]

Web Site
www.FiniteandCalc.org
  Student Home
    → Online Utilities
    → Matrix Algebra Tool

Just use `I` in the formula box to refer to the identity matrix of any dimension. The program will choose the correct dimension in the context of the formula. For example, if A is a 3 × 3 matrix, then the expression `I-A` uses the 3 × 3 identity matrix for `I`.

and

$$IA = \begin{bmatrix} 1 & 0 & 0 \\ 0 & 1 & 0 \\ 0 & 0 & 1 \end{bmatrix} \begin{bmatrix} a & b & c \\ d & e & f \\ g & h & i \end{bmatrix} = \begin{bmatrix} a & b & c \\ d & e & f \\ g & h & i \end{bmatrix}.$$

In both cases, the answer is the matrix A we started with. In symbols,

$$AI = A$$

and

$$IA = A$$

no matter which 3 × 3 matrix A you start with. Now this should remind you of a familiar fact from arithmetic:

$$a \cdot 1 = a$$

and

$$1 \cdot a = a.$$

That is why we call the matrix I the 3 × 3 *identity* matrix, because it appears to play the same role for 3 × 3 matrices that the identity 1 does for numbers.

➡ **Before we go on...** Try a similar calculation using 2 × 2 matrices: Let $A = \begin{bmatrix} a & b \\ c & d \end{bmatrix}$, let I be the 2 × 2 identity matrix, and check that $AI = IA = A$. In fact, the equation

$$AI = IA = A$$

works for square matrices of every dimension. It is also interesting to notice that $AI = A$ if I is the 2 × 2 identity matrix and A is any 3 × 2 matrix (try one). In fact, if I is any identity matrix, then $AI = A$ whenever the product is defined, and $IA = A$ whenever this product is defined. ■

We can now add to the list of properties we gave for matrix arithmetic at the end of Section 3.1 by writing down properties of matrix multiplication. In stating these properties, we shall assume that all matrix products we write are defined—that is, that the matrices have correctly matching dimensions. The first eight properties are the ones we've already seen; the rest are new.

Properties of Matrix Addition and Multiplication

If A, B and C are matrices, if O is a zero matrix, and if I is an identity matrix, then the following hold:

$A + (B + C) = (A + B) + C$	*Additive associative law*
$A + B = B + A$	*Additive commutative law*
$A + O = O + A = A$	*Additive identity law*
$A + (-A) = O = (-A) + A$	*Additive inverse law*
$c(A + B) = cA + cB$	*Distributive law*
$(c + d)A = cA + dA$	*Distributive law*

$$1A = A \qquad \text{\textit{Scalar unit}}$$
$$0A = O \qquad \text{\textit{Scalar zero}}$$
$$A(BC) = (AB)C \qquad \text{\textit{Multiplicative associative law}}$$
$$c(AB) = (cA)B \qquad \text{\textit{Multiplicative associative law}}$$
$$c(dA) = (cd)A \qquad \text{\textit{Multiplicative associative law}}$$
$$AI = IA = A \qquad \text{\textit{Multiplicative identity law}}$$
$$A(B + C) = AB + AC \qquad \text{\textit{Distributive law}}$$
$$(A + B)C = AC + BC \qquad \text{\textit{Distributive law}}$$
$$OA = AO = O \qquad \text{\textit{Multiplication by zero matrix}}$$

Note that we have not included a multiplicative commutative law for matrices, because the equation $AB = BA$ does not hold in general. In other words, matrix multiplication is *not* exactly like multiplication of numbers. (You have to be a little careful because it is easy to apply the commutative law without realizing it.)

We should also say a bit more about transposition. Transposition and multiplication have an interesting relationship. We write down the properties of transposition again, adding one new one.

Properties of Transposition

$$(A + B)^T = A^T + B^T$$
$$(cA)^T = c(A^T)$$
$$(AB)^T = B^T A^T$$

Notice the change in order in the last one. The order is crucial.

Quick Examples

1. $\left(\begin{bmatrix} 1 & -1 \\ 0 & 2 \end{bmatrix} \begin{bmatrix} 3 & 0 \\ 5 & -1 \end{bmatrix} \right)^T = \begin{bmatrix} -2 & 1 \\ 10 & -2 \end{bmatrix}^T = \begin{bmatrix} -2 & 10 \\ 1 & -2 \end{bmatrix}$ $\qquad (AB)^T$

2. $\begin{bmatrix} 3 & 0 \\ 5 & -1 \end{bmatrix}^T \begin{bmatrix} 1 & -1 \\ 0 & 2 \end{bmatrix}^T = \begin{bmatrix} 3 & 5 \\ 0 & -1 \end{bmatrix} \begin{bmatrix} 1 & 0 \\ -1 & 2 \end{bmatrix} = \begin{bmatrix} -2 & 10 \\ 1 & -2 \end{bmatrix}$ $\qquad B^T A^T$

3. $\begin{bmatrix} 1 & -1 \\ 0 & 2 \end{bmatrix}^T \begin{bmatrix} 3 & 0 \\ 5 & -1 \end{bmatrix}^T = \begin{bmatrix} 1 & 0 \\ -1 & 2 \end{bmatrix} \begin{bmatrix} 3 & 5 \\ 0 & -1 \end{bmatrix} = \begin{bmatrix} 3 & 5 \\ -3 & -7 \end{bmatrix}$ $\qquad A^T B^T$

These properties give you a glimpse of the field of mathematics known as **abstract algebra**. Algebraists study operations like these that resemble the operations on numbers but differ in some way, such as the lack of commutativity for multiplication seen here.

We end this section with more on the relationship between linear equations and matrix equations, which is one of the important applications of matrix multiplication.

EXAMPLE 7 Matrix Form of a System of Linear Equations

a. If

$$A = \begin{bmatrix} 1 & -2 & 3 \\ 2 & 0 & -1 \\ -3 & 1 & 1 \end{bmatrix}, \quad X = \begin{bmatrix} x \\ y \\ z \end{bmatrix}, \quad \text{and } B = \begin{bmatrix} 3 \\ -1 \\ 0 \end{bmatrix}$$

rewrite the matrix equation $AX = B$ as a system of linear equations.

b. Express the following system of equations as a matrix equation of the form $AX = B$:

$$2x + y = 3$$
$$4x - y = -1.$$

Solution

a. The matrix equation $AX = B$ is

$$\begin{bmatrix} 1 & -2 & 3 \\ 2 & 0 & -1 \\ -3 & 1 & 1 \end{bmatrix} \begin{bmatrix} x \\ y \\ z \end{bmatrix} = \begin{bmatrix} 3 \\ -1 \\ 0 \end{bmatrix}.$$

As in Example 2(a), we first evaluate the left-hand side and then set it equal to the right-hand side.

$$\begin{bmatrix} 1 & -2 & 3 \\ 2 & 0 & -1 \\ -3 & 1 & 1 \end{bmatrix} \begin{bmatrix} x \\ y \\ z \end{bmatrix} = \begin{bmatrix} x - 2y + 3z \\ 2x - z \\ -3x + y + z \end{bmatrix}$$

$$\begin{bmatrix} x - 2y + 3z \\ 2x - z \\ -3x + y + z \end{bmatrix} = \begin{bmatrix} 3 \\ -1 \\ 0 \end{bmatrix}$$

Because these two matrices are equal, their corresponding entries must be equal.

$$x - 2y + 3z = 3$$
$$2x \quad\quad - z = -1$$
$$-3x + y + z = 0$$

In other words, the matrix equation $AX = B$ is equivalent to this system of linear equations. Notice that the coefficients of the left-hand sides of these equations are the entries of the matrix A. We call A the **coefficient matrix** of the system of equations. The entries of X are the unknowns and the entries of B are the right-hand sides 3, −1, and 0.

b. As we saw in part (a), the coefficient matrix A has entries equal to the coefficients of the left-hand sides of the equations. Thus,

$$A = \begin{bmatrix} 2 & 1 \\ 4 & -1 \end{bmatrix}.$$

X is the column matrix consisting of the unknowns, while B is the column matrix consisting of the right-hand sides of the equations, so

$$X = \begin{bmatrix} x \\ y \end{bmatrix} \quad \text{and} \quad B = \begin{bmatrix} 3 \\ -1 \end{bmatrix}.$$

The system of equations can be rewritten as the matrix equation $AX = B$ with this A, X, and B.

This translation of systems of linear equations into matrix equations is really the first step in the method of solving linear equations discussed in Chapter 2. There we worked with the **augmented matrix** of the system, which is simply A with B adjoined as an extra column.

Q: *When we write a system of equations as $AX = B$, couldn't we solve for the unknown X by dividing both sides by A?*

A: If we interpret division as multiplication by the inverse (for example, $2 \div 3 = 2 \times 3^{-1}$), we shall see in the next section that certain systems of the form $AX = B$ can be solved in this way, by multiplying both sides by A^{-1}. We first need to discuss what we mean by A^{-1} and how to calculate it. ■

3.2 EXERCISES

▼ more advanced   ◆ challenging
T indicates exercises that should be solved using technology

In Exercises 1–28, compute the products. Some of these may be undefined. Exercises marked **T** *should be done using technology. The others should be done two ways: by hand and by using technology where possible.* HINT [See Example 3.]

1. $\begin{bmatrix} 1 & 3 & -1 \end{bmatrix} \begin{bmatrix} 9 \\ 1 \\ -1 \end{bmatrix}$

2. $\begin{bmatrix} 4 & 0 & -1 \end{bmatrix} \begin{bmatrix} -4 \\ 1 \\ 8 \end{bmatrix}$

3. $\begin{bmatrix} -1 & \frac{1}{2} \end{bmatrix} \begin{bmatrix} -\frac{1}{3} \\ 1 \end{bmatrix}$

4. $\begin{bmatrix} -1 & 1 \end{bmatrix} \begin{bmatrix} \frac{3}{4} \\ \frac{1}{4} \end{bmatrix}$

5. $\begin{bmatrix} 0 & -2 & 1 \end{bmatrix} \begin{bmatrix} x \\ y \\ z \end{bmatrix}$

6. $\begin{bmatrix} 4 & -1 & 1 \end{bmatrix} \begin{bmatrix} -x \\ x \\ y \end{bmatrix}$

7. $\begin{bmatrix} 1 & 3 & 2 \end{bmatrix} \begin{bmatrix} 1 \\ -1 \end{bmatrix}$

8. $\begin{bmatrix} 3 & 2 \end{bmatrix} \begin{bmatrix} 1 & -2 \end{bmatrix}$

9. $\begin{bmatrix} -1 & 1 \end{bmatrix} \begin{bmatrix} -3 & 1 & 4 & 3 \\ 0 & 1 & -2 & 1 \end{bmatrix}$

10. $\begin{bmatrix} 2 & -1 \end{bmatrix} \begin{bmatrix} -3 & 1 & 4 & 3 \\ 4 & 0 & 1 & 3 \end{bmatrix}$

11. $\begin{bmatrix} 1 & -1 & 2 & 3 \end{bmatrix} \begin{bmatrix} -1 & 2 & 0 \\ 2 & -1 & 0 \\ 0 & 5 & 2 \\ -1 & 8 & 1 \end{bmatrix}$

12. $\begin{bmatrix} 0 & 1 & -1 & 2 \end{bmatrix} \begin{bmatrix} 1 & -2 & 1 \\ 0 & 1 & 3 \\ 6 & 0 & 2 \\ -1 & -2 & 11 \end{bmatrix}$

13. $\begin{bmatrix} 1 & 0 & -1 \\ 1 & 1 & 2 \end{bmatrix} \begin{bmatrix} 0 & 1 & -1 \\ 1 & 0 & 1 \\ 4 & 8 & 0 \end{bmatrix}$

14. $\begin{bmatrix} 0 & 1 & -1 \\ 3 & 1 & -1 \end{bmatrix} \begin{bmatrix} 1 & 1 \\ 4 & 2 \\ 0 & 1 \end{bmatrix}$

15. $\begin{bmatrix} 1 & 0 \\ 1 & -1 \end{bmatrix} \begin{bmatrix} 0 & 1 \\ 0 & 1 \end{bmatrix}$

16. $\begin{bmatrix} 1 & -1 \\ 1 & -1 \end{bmatrix} \begin{bmatrix} 3 & -3 \\ 5 & -7 \end{bmatrix}$

17. $\begin{bmatrix} 0 & 1 \\ 0 & 1 \end{bmatrix} \begin{bmatrix} 1 & 0 \\ 1 & -1 \end{bmatrix}$

18. $\begin{bmatrix} 3 & -3 \\ 5 & -7 \end{bmatrix} \begin{bmatrix} 1 & -1 \\ 1 & -1 \end{bmatrix}$

19. $\begin{bmatrix} 1 & -1 \\ 1 & -1 \end{bmatrix} \begin{bmatrix} 2 & 3 \\ 2 & 3 \end{bmatrix}$

20. $\begin{bmatrix} 0 & 1 \\ 1 & 0 \end{bmatrix} \begin{bmatrix} 3 & -3 \\ 2 & -1 \end{bmatrix}$

21. $\begin{bmatrix} 1 & -1 \\ -1 & 1 \end{bmatrix} \begin{bmatrix} 2 & 3 \\ 2 & 3 \\ 1 & 1 \end{bmatrix}$

22. $\begin{bmatrix} 0 & 1 & -1 \\ 0 & -1 & 1 \end{bmatrix} \begin{bmatrix} 3 & -3 \\ 2 & -1 \end{bmatrix}$

23. $\begin{bmatrix} 1 & 0 & -1 \\ 2 & -2 & 1 \\ 0 & 0 & 1 \end{bmatrix} \begin{bmatrix} 1 & -1 & 4 \\ 1 & 1 & 0 \\ 0 & 4 & 1 \end{bmatrix}$

24. $\begin{bmatrix} 1 & 2 & 0 \\ 4 & -1 & 1 \\ 1 & 0 & 1 \end{bmatrix} \begin{bmatrix} 1 & 2 & -4 \\ 4 & 1 & 0 \\ 0 & -2 & 1 \end{bmatrix}$

25. $\begin{bmatrix} 1 & 0 & 1 & 0 \\ -1 & 1 & 0 & 1 \\ -2 & 0 & 1 & 4 \\ 0 & -1 & 0 & 1 \end{bmatrix} \begin{bmatrix} 1 \\ -3 \\ 2 \\ 0 \end{bmatrix}$

26. $\begin{bmatrix} 1 & 1 & -7 & 0 \\ -1 & 0 & 2 & 4 \\ -1 & 0 & -2 & 1 \\ 1 & -1 & 1 & 1 \end{bmatrix} \begin{bmatrix} 1 \\ -3 \\ 2 \\ 1 \end{bmatrix}$

27. **T** $\begin{bmatrix} 1.1 & 2.3 & 3.4 & -1.2 \\ 3.4 & 4.4 & 2.3 & 1.1 \\ 2.3 & 0 & -2.2 & 1.1 \\ 1.2 & 1.3 & 1.1 & 1.1 \end{bmatrix} \begin{bmatrix} -2.1 & 0 & -3.3 \\ -3.4 & -4.8 & -4.2 \\ 3.4 & 5.6 & 1 \\ 1 & 2.2 & 9.8 \end{bmatrix}$

28. **T** $\begin{bmatrix} 1.2 & 2.3 & 3.4 & 4.5 \\ 3.3 & 4.4 & 5.5 & 6.6 \\ 2.3 & -4.3 & -2.2 & 1.1 \\ 2.2 & -1.2 & -1 & 1.1 \end{bmatrix} \begin{bmatrix} 9.8 & 1 & -1.1 \\ 8.8 & 2 & -2.2 \\ 7.7 & 3 & -3.3 \\ 6.6 & 4 & -4.4 \end{bmatrix}$

29. Find[7] $A^2 = A \cdot A$, $A^3 = A \cdot A \cdot A$, A^4, and A^{100}, given that

$$A = \begin{bmatrix} 0 & 1 & 1 & 1 \\ 0 & 0 & 1 & 1 \\ 0 & 0 & 0 & 1 \\ 0 & 0 & 0 & 0 \end{bmatrix}.$$

30. Repeat the preceding exercise with $A = \begin{bmatrix} 0 & 2 & 0 & -1 \\ 0 & 0 & 2 & 0 \\ 0 & 0 & 0 & 2 \\ 0 & 0 & 0 & 0 \end{bmatrix}.$

Exercises 31–38 should be done two ways: (a) by hand; (b) using technology where possible.

Let

$$A = \begin{bmatrix} 0 & -1 & 0 & 1 \\ 10 & 0 & 1 & 0 \end{bmatrix}, \quad B = \begin{bmatrix} 0 & -1 \\ 1 & 1 \\ -1 & 3 \\ 5 & 0 \end{bmatrix}, \quad C = \begin{bmatrix} 1 & -1 \\ 1 & 1 \\ 1 & 1 \\ 1 & 1 \end{bmatrix}.$$

Evaluate:

31. AB **32.** AC **33.** $A(B - C)$ **34.** $(B - C)A$

Let

$$A = \begin{bmatrix} 1 & -1 \\ 0 & 2 \\ 0 & -2 \end{bmatrix}, \quad B = \begin{bmatrix} 3 & 0 & -1 \\ 5 & -1 & 1 \end{bmatrix}, \quad C = \begin{bmatrix} x & 1 & w \\ z & r & 4 \end{bmatrix}.$$

Evaluate:

35. AB **36.** AC **37.** $A(B + C)$ **38.** $(B + C)A$

In Exercises 39–44, calculate (a) $P^2 = P \cdot P$ (b) $P^4 = P^2 \cdot P^2$ and (c) P^8. (Round all entries to four decimal places.) (d) Without computing it explicitly, find P^{1000}.

39. ▼ $P = \begin{bmatrix} 0.2 & 0.8 \\ 0.2 & 0.8 \end{bmatrix}$ **40.** ▼ $P = \begin{bmatrix} 0.1 & 0.9 \\ 0.1 & 0.9 \end{bmatrix}$

41. ▼ $P = \begin{bmatrix} 0.1 & 0.9 \\ 0 & 1 \end{bmatrix}$ **42.** ▼ $P = \begin{bmatrix} 1 & 0 \\ 0.8 & 0.2 \end{bmatrix}$

43. ▼ $P = \begin{bmatrix} 0.25 & 0.25 & 0.50 \\ 0.25 & 0.25 & 0.50 \\ 0.25 & 0.25 & 0.50 \end{bmatrix}$

44. ▼ $P = \begin{bmatrix} 0.3 & 0.3 & 0.4 \\ 0.3 & 0.3 & 0.4 \\ 0.3 & 0.3 & 0.4 \end{bmatrix}$

In Exercises 45–48, translate the given matrix equations into systems of linear equations. HINT [See Example 7.]

45. $\begin{bmatrix} 2 & -1 & 4 \\ -4 & \frac{3}{4} & \frac{1}{3} \\ -3 & 0 & 0 \end{bmatrix} \begin{bmatrix} x \\ y \\ z \end{bmatrix} = \begin{bmatrix} 3 \\ -1 \\ 0 \end{bmatrix}$

46. $\begin{bmatrix} 1 & -1 & 4 \\ -\frac{1}{3} & -3 & \frac{1}{3} \\ 3 & 0 & 1 \end{bmatrix} \begin{bmatrix} x \\ y \\ z \end{bmatrix} = \begin{bmatrix} -3 \\ -1 \\ 2 \end{bmatrix}$

47. $\begin{bmatrix} 1 & -1 & 0 & 1 \\ 1 & 1 & 2 & 4 \end{bmatrix} \begin{bmatrix} x \\ y \\ z \\ w \end{bmatrix} = \begin{bmatrix} -1 \\ 2 \end{bmatrix}$

48. $\begin{bmatrix} 0 & 1 & 6 & 1 \\ 1 & -5 & 0 & 0 \end{bmatrix} \begin{bmatrix} x \\ y \\ z \\ w \end{bmatrix} = \begin{bmatrix} -2 \\ 9 \end{bmatrix}$

In Exercises 49–52, translate the given systems of equations into matrix form. HINT [See Example 7.]

49. $x - y = 4$
$\quad 2x - y = 0$

50. $2x + y = 7$
$\quad -x \quad\ \ = 9$

51. $x + y - z = 8$
$\quad 2x + y + z = 4$
$\quad \dfrac{3x}{4} \quad + \dfrac{z}{2} = 1$

52. $x + y + 2z = -2$
$\quad 4x + 2y - z = -8$
$\quad \dfrac{x}{2} - \dfrac{y}{3} \quad = 1$

APPLICATIONS

53. *Revenue* Your T-shirt operation is doing a booming trade. Last week you sold 50 tie-dye shirts for $15 each, 40 Suburban State University Crew shirts for $10 each, and 30 Lacrosse T-shirts for $12 each. Use matrix operations to calculate your total revenue for the week. HINT [See Example 1.]

54. *Revenue* Karen Sandberg, your competitor in Suburban State U's T-shirt market, has apparently been undercutting your prices and outperforming you in sales. Last week she sold 100 tie dye shirts for $10 each, 50 (low quality) Crew shirts at $5 apiece, and 70 Lacrosse T-shirts for $8 each. Use matrix operations to calculate her total revenue for the week. HINT [See Example 1.]

55. *Revenue* Recall the Left Coast Bookstore chain from the preceding section. In January, it sold 700 hardcover books, 1,300 softcover books, and 2,000 plastic books in San Francisco; it sold 400 hardcover, 300 softcover, and 500 plastic books in Los Angeles. Now, hardcover books sell for $30 each, softcover books sell for $10 each, and plastic books sell for $15 each. Write a column matrix with the price data and show how matrix multiplication (using the sales and price data matrices) may be used to compute the total revenue at the two stores. HINT [See Example 5.]

56. *Profit* Refer back to Exercise 55, and now suppose that each hardcover book costs the stores $10, each softcover book costs $5, and each plastic book costs $10. Use matrix operations to compute the total *profit* at each store in January. HINT [See Example 5.]

57. *Real Estate* The following table shows the cost in dollars to rent one square foot of office real estate for one year at the end

---

[7] $A \cdot A \cdot A$ is $A(A \cdot A)$, or the equivalent $(A \cdot A)A$ by the associative law. Similarly, $A \cdot A \cdot A \cdot A = A(A \cdot A \cdot A) = (A \cdot A \cdot A)A = (A \cdot A)(A \cdot A)$; it doesn't matter where we place parentheses.

of 2008[8] together with the number of square feet your development company intends to purchase in each city.

	Tokyo (inner central)	Dubai	Manhattan (midtown)
Cost per sq. ft.	180	160	100
Number of sq. ft.	200	800	1,000

Use matrix multiplication to estimate the annual cost of the office space.

58. *Real Estate* Repeat Exercise 57 using the following table for London, Moscow, and Hong Kong:

	London (West End)	Moscow	Hong Kong (central CBD)
Cost per sq. ft.	250	230	230
Number of sq. ft.	500	100	600

⬛ ***Income*** *Exercises 59–62 are based on the following Excel sheet, which shows the projected 2020 and 2030 U.S. male and female population in various age groups, as well as per capita incomes.*[9]

	A	B	C	D	E	F
1			2020 Population		2030 population	
2	Age	Mean Income ($1000)	Female (Millions)	Male (Millions)	Female (Millions)	Male (Millions)
3	15 to 24	14	23	24	25	26
4	25 to 44	42	43	43	45	46
5	45 to 64	48	43	41	42	41
6	65 to 84	29	31	20	40	31

59. Use matrix algebra to estimate the total income for females in 2020. (Round the answer to two significant digits.)

60. Use matrix algebra to estimate the total income for males in 2030.

61. Give a single matrix formula that expresses the difference in total income between males and females in 2020, and compute its value, rounded to two significant digits.

62. Give a single matrix formula that expresses the total income in 2030, and compute its value, rounded to two significant digits.

63. *Cheese Production* The total amount of cheese, in billions of pounds, produced in the 13 western and 12 north central U.S. states in 1999 and 2000 was as follows.[10]

	1999	2000
Western States	2.7	3.0
North Central States	3.9	4.0

Thinking of this table as a (labeled) 2×2 matrix P, compute the matrix product $[-1 \quad 1]P$. What does this product represent?

64. *Milk Production* The total amount of milk, in billions of pounds, produced in the 13 western and 12 north central U.S. states in 1999 and 2000 was as follows.[11]

	1999	2000
Western States	56	60
North Central States	57	59

Thinking of this table as a (labeled) 2×2 matrix P, compute the matrix product $P \begin{bmatrix} -1 \\ 1 \end{bmatrix}$. What does this product represent?

Foreclosures *Exercises 65–70 are based on the following chart, which shows the numbers of foreclosures in three states during the last three months of 2008.*[12]

	Oct.	Nov.	Dec.
California	5,700	5,000	4,300
Florida	2,400	2,800	2,300
Texas	1,900	2,100	2,100

65. ▼ Each month, your law firm handles 10% of all foreclosures in California, 5% of all foreclosures in Florida, and 20% of all foreclosures in Texas. Use matrix multiplication to compute the total number of foreclosures handled by your firm in each of the months shown.

66. ▼ Your law firm handled 10% of all foreclosures in each state in October, 30% of all foreclosures in November, and 20% of all foreclosures in December 2008. Use matrix multiplication to compute the total number of foreclosures handled by your firm in each of the states shown.

67. ▼ Let A be the 3×3 matrix whose entries are the figures in the table, and let $B = [1 \quad 1 \quad 0]$. What does the matrix BA represent?

68. ▼ Let A be the 3×3 matrix whose entries are the figures in the table, and let $B = [1 \quad 1 \quad 0]^T$. What does the matrix AB represent?

69. ▼ Write a matrix product whose computation gives the total number by which the combined foreclosures for all three months in California and Texas exceeded the foreclosures in Florida. Calculate the product.

---

[8] Figures are rounded. Source: CB Richard Ellis Group Inc/*New York Observer*, November 2008 (www.observer.com).

[9] The population figures are Census Bureau estimates, and the income figures are 2007 mean per capita incomes. All figures are approximate. Source: U.S. Census Bureau (www.census.gov).

[10] Figures are approximate. Source: Department of Agriculture/*New York Times*, June 28, 2001, p. C1.

[11] Ibid.

[12] Data are rounded to the nearest 100. Source for data: www.currentforeclosures.com/Stats/.

70. ▼ Write a matrix product whose computation gives the total number by which combined foreclosures in October exceeded foreclosures in December. Calculate the product.

71. ▼ *Costs* Microbucks Computer Co. makes two computers, the Pomegranate II and the Pomegranate Classic. The Pom II requires 2 processor chips, 16 memory chips, and 20 vacuum tubes, while the Pom Classic requires 1 processor chip, 4 memory chips, and 40 vacuum tubes. There are two companies that can supply these parts: Motorel can supply them at $100 per processor chip, $50 per memory chip, and $10 per vacuum tube, while Intola can supply them at $150 per processor chip, $40 per memory chip, and $15 per vacuum tube. Write down all of this data in two matrices, one showing the parts required for each model computer, and the other showing the prices for each part from each supplier. Then show how matrix multiplication allows you to compute the total cost for parts for each model when parts are bought from either supplier.

72. ▼ *Profits* Refer back to Exercise 71. It actually costs Motorel only $25 to make each processor chip, $10 for each memory chip, and $5 for each vacuum tube. It costs Intola $50 per processor chip, $10 per memory chip, and $7 per vacuum tube. Use matrix operations to find the total profit Motorel and Intola would make on each model.

73. ▼ *Tourism in the '90s* The following table gives the number of people (in thousands) who visited Australia and South Africa in 1998.[13]

		To **Australia**	**South Africa**
From	**North America**	440	190
	Europe	950	950
	Asia	1,790	200

You estimate that 5% of all visitors to Australia and 4% of all visitors to South Africa decide to settle there permanently. Take A to be the 3×2 matrix whose entries are the 1998 tourism figures in the above table and take

$$B = \begin{bmatrix} 0.05 \\ 0.04 \end{bmatrix} \quad \text{and} \quad C = \begin{bmatrix} 0.05 & 0 \\ 0 & 0.04 \end{bmatrix}.$$

Compute the products AB and AC. What do the entries in these matrices represent?

74. ▼ *Tourism in the '90s* Referring to the tourism figures in the preceding exercise, you estimate that from 1998 to 2008, tourism from North America to each of Australia and South Africa will have increased by 20%, tourism from Europe by 30%, and tourism from Asia by 10%. Take A to

be the 3×2 matrix whose entries are the 1998 tourism figures and take

$$B = \begin{bmatrix} 1.2 & 1.3 & 1.1 \end{bmatrix} \quad \text{and} \quad C = \begin{bmatrix} 1.2 & 0 & 0 \\ 0 & 1.3 & 0 \\ 0 & 0 & 1.1 \end{bmatrix}.$$

Compute the products BA and CA. What do the entries in these matrices represent?

75. ◆ 🖳 *Population Movement* In 2006, the population of the United States, broken down by regions, was 55.1 million in the Northeast, 66.2 million in the Midwest, 110.0 million in the South, and 70.0 million in the West.[14] The matrix P below shows the population movement during the period 2006–2007. (Thus, 98.92% of the population in the Northeast stayed there, while 0.17% of the population in the Northeast moved to the Midwest, and so on.)

	To NE	To MW	To S	To W
From NE	0.9892	0.0017	0.0073	0.0018
From MW	0.0010	0.9920	0.0048	0.0022
From S	0.0018	0.0024	0.9934	0.0024
From W	0.0008	0.0033	0.0045	0.9914

$$P =$$

Set up the 2006 population figures as a row vector. Then use matrix multiplication to compute the population in each region in 2007. (Round all answers to the nearest 0.1 million.)

76. ◆ 🖳 *Population Movement* Assume that the percentages given in the preceding exercise also describe the population movements from 2007 to 2008. Use two matrix multiplications to predict from the data in the preceding exercise the population in each region in 2008.

COMMUNICATION AND REASONING EXERCISES

77. Give an example of two matrices A and B such that AB is defined but BA is not defined.

78. Give an example of two matrices A and B of different dimensions such that both AB and BA are defined.

79. Compare addition and multiplication of 1×1 matrices to the arithmetic of numbers.

80. In comparing the algebra of 1×1 matrices, as discussed so far, to the algebra of real numbers (see Exercise 79), what important difference do you find?

81. Comment on the following claim: Every matrix equation represents a system of equations.

---

[13] Figures are rounded to the nearest 10,000. Sources: South African Dept. of Environmental Affairs and Tourism; Australia Tourist Commission/*The New York Times*, January 15, 2000, p. C1.

[14] Note that this exercise ignores migration into or out of the country. The internal migration figures and 2007 population figures are accurate.
Source: U.S. Census Bureau, Current Population Survey, 2007 Annual Social and Economic Supplement, Internet release date September 2008 (www.census.gov).

82. When is it true that both AB and BA are defined, even though neither A nor B is a square matrix?

83. ▼ Find a scenario in which it would be useful to "multiply" two row vectors according to the rule

$$[a \quad b \quad c][d \quad e \quad f] = [ad \quad be \quad cf].$$

84. ▼ Make up an application whose solution reads as follows.

$$\text{"Total revenue} = [10 \quad 100 \quad 30] \begin{bmatrix} 10 & 0 & 3 \\ 1 & 2 & 0 \\ 0 & 1 & 40 \end{bmatrix} \text{"}$$

85. ▼ What happens in Excel if, instead of using the function MMULT, you use "ordinary multiplication" as shown here?

▲	A	B	C	D	E	F	G
1	2	0	7		1	1	-8
2	1	-1	0		1	0	0
3	-2	1	1		0	5	2
4							
5	=A1:C3*E1:G3						
6							
7							

86. ▼ Define the *naïve product* $A \square B$ of two $m \times n$ matrices A and B by

$$(A \square B)_{ij} = A_{ij} B_{ij}.$$

(This is how someone who has never seen matrix multiplication before might think to multiply matrices.) Referring to Example 1 in this section, compute and comment on the meaning of $P \square (Q^T.)$

3.3 Matrix Inversion

Now that we've discussed matrix addition, subtraction, and multiplication, you may well be wondering about matrix *division*. In the realm of real numbers, division can be thought of as a form of multiplication: Dividing 3 by 7 is the same as multiplying 3 by $1/7$, the inverse of 7. In symbols, $3 \div 7 = 3 \times (1/7)$, or 3×7^{-1}. In order to imitate division of real numbers in the realm of matrices, we need to discuss the multiplicative **inverse**, A^{-1}, of a matrix A.

Note Because multiplication of real numbers is commutative, we can write, for example, $\frac{3}{7}$ as either 3×7^{-1} or $7^{-1} \times 3$. In the realm of matrices, multiplication is not commutative, so from now on we shall *never* talk about "division" of matrices (by "$\frac{B}{A}$" should we mean $A^{-1}B$ or BA^{-1}?). ■

Before we try to find the inverse of a matrix, we must first know exactly what we *mean* by the inverse. Recall that the inverse of a number a is the number, often written a^{-1}, with the property that $a^{-1} \cdot a = a \cdot a^{-1} = 1$. For example, the inverse of 76 is the number $76^{-1} = 1/76$, because $(1/76) \cdot 76 = 76 \cdot (1/76) = 1$. This is the number calculated by the x^{-1} button found on most calculators. Not all numbers have an inverse. For example—and this is the only example—the number 0 has no inverse, because you cannot get 1 by multiplying 0 by anything.

The inverse of a matrix is defined similarly. To make life easier, we shall restrict attention to **square** matrices, matrices that have the same number of rows as columns.*

* **NOTE** Nonsquare matrices *cannot* have inverses in the sense that we are talking about here. This is not a trivial fact to prove.

Inverse of a Matrix

The **inverse** of an $n \times n$ matrix A is that $n \times n$ matrix A^{-1} which, when multiplied by A on either side, yields the $n \times n$ identity matrix I. Thus,

$$AA^{-1} = A^{-1}A = I.$$

If A has an inverse, it is said to be **invertible**. Otherwise, it is said to be **singular**.

> **Quick Examples**
>
> **1.** The inverse of the 1×1 matrix $[3]$ is $[1/3]$, because $[3][1/3] = [1] = [1/3][3]$.
> **2.** The inverse of the $n \times n$ identity matrix I is I itself, because $I \times I = I$. Thus, $I^{-1} = I$.
> **3.** The inverse of the 2×2 matrix $A = \begin{bmatrix} 1 & -1 \\ -1 & -1 \end{bmatrix}$ is $A^{-1} = \begin{bmatrix} \frac{1}{2} & -\frac{1}{2} \\ -\frac{1}{2} & -\frac{1}{2} \end{bmatrix}$,
>
> because $\begin{bmatrix} 1 & -1 \\ -1 & -1 \end{bmatrix} \begin{bmatrix} \frac{1}{2} & -\frac{1}{2} \\ -\frac{1}{2} & -\frac{1}{2} \end{bmatrix} = \begin{bmatrix} 1 & 0 \\ 0 & 1 \end{bmatrix}$ $AA^{-1} = I$
>
> and $\begin{bmatrix} \frac{1}{2} & -\frac{1}{2} \\ -\frac{1}{2} & -\frac{1}{2} \end{bmatrix} \begin{bmatrix} 1 & -1 \\ -1 & -1 \end{bmatrix} = \begin{bmatrix} 1 & 0 \\ 0 & 1 \end{bmatrix}$. $A^{-1}A = I$

Notes

1. It is possible to show that if A and B are square matrices with $AB = I$, then it must also be true that $BA = I$. In other words, once we have checked that $AB = I$, we know that B is the inverse of A. The second check, that $BA = I$, is unnecessary.

2. If B is the inverse of A, then we can also say that A is the inverse of B (why?). Thus, we sometimes refer to such a pair of matrices as an **inverse pair** of matrices. ■

EXAMPLE 1 Singular Matrix

Can $A = \begin{bmatrix} 1 & 1 \\ 0 & 0 \end{bmatrix}$ have an inverse?

Solution No. To see why not, notice that both entries in the second row of AB will be 0, no matter what B is. So AB cannot equal I, no matter what B is. Hence, A is singular.

➡ **Before we go on...** If you think about it, you can write down many similar examples of singular matrices. There is only one number with no multiplicative inverse (0), but there are many matrices having no inverses. ■

Finding the Inverse of a Square Matrix

Q: *In the box, it was stated that the inverse of* $\begin{bmatrix} 1 & -1 \\ -1 & -1 \end{bmatrix}$ *is* $\begin{bmatrix} \frac{1}{2} & -\frac{1}{2} \\ -\frac{1}{2} & -\frac{1}{2} \end{bmatrix}$. *How was that obtained?*

A: We can think of the problem of finding A^{-1} as a problem of finding four unknowns, the four unknown entries of A^{-1}:

$$A^{-1} = \begin{bmatrix} x & y \\ z & w \end{bmatrix}$$

These unknowns must satisfy the equation $AA^{-1} = I$, or

$$\begin{bmatrix} 1 & -1 \\ -1 & -1 \end{bmatrix} \begin{bmatrix} x & y \\ z & w \end{bmatrix} = \begin{bmatrix} 1 & 0 \\ 0 & 1 \end{bmatrix}.$$

If we were to try to find the first column of A^{-1}, consisting of x and z, we would have to solve

$$\begin{bmatrix} 1 & -1 \\ -1 & -1 \end{bmatrix} \begin{bmatrix} x \\ z \end{bmatrix} = \begin{bmatrix} 1 \\ 0 \end{bmatrix}$$

or
$$x - z = 1$$
$$-x - z = 0.$$

To solve this system by Gauss-Jordan reduction, we would row-reduce the augmented matrix, which is A with the column $\begin{bmatrix} 1 \\ 0 \end{bmatrix}$ adjoined.

$$\begin{bmatrix} 1 & -1 & | & 1 \\ -1 & -1 & | & 0 \end{bmatrix} \rightarrow \begin{bmatrix} 1 & 0 & | & x \\ 0 & 1 & | & z \end{bmatrix}$$

To find the second column of A^{-1} we would similarly row-reduce the augmented matrix obtained by tacking on to A the second column of the identity matrix.

$$\begin{bmatrix} 1 & -1 & | & 0 \\ -1 & -1 & | & 1 \end{bmatrix} \rightarrow \begin{bmatrix} 1 & 0 & | & y \\ 0 & 1 & | & w \end{bmatrix}$$

The row operations used in doing these two reductions would be exactly the same. We could do both reductions simultaneously by "doubly augmenting" A, putting both columns of the identity matrix to the right of A.

$$\begin{bmatrix} 1 & -1 & | & 1 & 0 \\ -1 & -1 & | & 0 & 1 \end{bmatrix} \rightarrow \begin{bmatrix} 1 & 0 & | & x & y \\ 0 & 1 & | & z & w \end{bmatrix}$$

We carry out this reduction in the following example. ∎

EXAMPLE 2 Computing Matrix Inverse

Find the inverse of each matrix.

a. $P = \begin{bmatrix} 1 & -1 \\ -1 & -1 \end{bmatrix}$ **b.** $Q = \begin{bmatrix} 1 & 0 & 1 \\ 2 & -2 & -1 \\ 3 & 0 & 0 \end{bmatrix}$

Solution

a. As described above, we put the matrix P on the left and the identity matrix I on the right to get a 2×4 matrix.

$$\begin{bmatrix} 1 & -1 & | & 1 & 0 \\ -1 & -1 & | & 0 & 1 \end{bmatrix}$$
$$\;\;\;\;\;\; P \qquad\qquad I$$

We now row reduce the whole matrix:

$$\begin{bmatrix} 1 & -1 & 1 & 0 \\ -1 & -1 & 0 & 1 \end{bmatrix} \begin{matrix} \\ R_2 + R_1 \end{matrix} \rightarrow \begin{bmatrix} 1 & -1 & 1 & 0 \\ 0 & -2 & 1 & 1 \end{bmatrix} \begin{matrix} 2R_1 - R_2 \\ \end{matrix}$$

$$\rightarrow \begin{bmatrix} 2 & 0 & 1 & -1 \\ 0 & -2 & 1 & 1 \end{bmatrix} \begin{matrix} \frac{1}{2}R_1 \\ -\frac{1}{2}R_2 \end{matrix} \rightarrow \begin{bmatrix} 1 & 0 & | & \frac{1}{2} & -\frac{1}{2} \\ 0 & 1 & | & -\frac{1}{2} & -\frac{1}{2} \end{bmatrix}.$$
$$\qquad\qquad\qquad\qquad\qquad\qquad\qquad\qquad I \qquad\quad P^{-1}$$

We have now solved the systems of linear equations that define the entries of P^{-1}. Thus,

$$P^{-1} = \begin{bmatrix} \frac{1}{2} & -\frac{1}{2} \\ -\frac{1}{2} & -\frac{1}{2} \end{bmatrix}.$$

using Technology

Here is an outline on the use of technology to invert the matrix in Example 2(b) (see the Technology Guides at the end of the chapter for additional details on using a TI-83/84 Plus or Excel):

TI-83/84 Plus

Enter the matrix [A] using MATRX ; EDIT

Home Screen: [A] x^{-1}
ENTER

[More details on page 255.]

Excel

Enter the matrix in a convenient block of cells (e.g., A1–C3). Highlight a 3 × 3 block for the answer.

Type =MINVERSE(A1:C3)
Press Control+Shift+Enter.
[More details on page 259.]

Web Site
www.FiniteandCalc.org
   Student Home
      → Online Utilities
         → Matrix Algebra Tool
Enter Q as shown:

```
   Enter your matrices here.
Q = [1, 0, 1
2, -2,-1
3, 0, 0]
```

Type Q^-1 or Q^(-1) in the formula box and click "Compute."

b. The procedure to find the inverse of a 3×3 matrix (or larger) is just the same as for a 2×2 matrix. We place Q on the left and the identity matrix (now 3×3) on the right, and reduce.

$$
\begin{array}{c} Q \qquad\qquad I \\ \left[\begin{array}{ccc|ccc} 1 & 0 & 1 & 1 & 0 & 0 \\ 2 & -2 & -1 & 0 & 1 & 0 \\ 3 & 0 & 0 & 0 & 0 & 1 \end{array}\right] \begin{array}{l} \\ R_2 - 2R_1 \\ R_3 - 3R_1 \end{array} \rightarrow \left[\begin{array}{ccc|ccc} 1 & 0 & 1 & 1 & 0 & 0 \\ 0 & -2 & -3 & -2 & 1 & 0 \\ 0 & 0 & -3 & -3 & 0 & 1 \end{array}\right] \begin{array}{l} 3R_1 + R_3 \\ R_2 - R_3 \\ \\ \end{array} \rightarrow \end{array}
$$

$$
\left[\begin{array}{ccc|ccc} 3 & 0 & 0 & 0 & 0 & 1 \\ 0 & -2 & 0 & 1 & 1 & -1 \\ 0 & 0 & -3 & -3 & 0 & 1 \end{array}\right] \begin{array}{l} \frac{1}{3}R_1 \\ -\frac{1}{2}R_2 \\ -\frac{1}{3}R_3 \end{array} \rightarrow \left[\begin{array}{ccc|ccc} 1 & 0 & 0 & 0 & 0 & \frac{1}{3} \\ 0 & 1 & 0 & -\frac{1}{2} & -\frac{1}{2} & \frac{1}{2} \\ 0 & 0 & 1 & 1 & 0 & -\frac{1}{3} \end{array}\right] .
$$

$$ \qquad\qquad\qquad\qquad\qquad\qquad\qquad\qquad I \qquad\qquad Q^{-1} $$

Thus,

$$
Q^{-1} = \begin{bmatrix} 0 & 0 & \frac{1}{3} \\ -\frac{1}{2} & -\frac{1}{2} & \frac{1}{2} \\ 1 & 0 & -\frac{1}{3} \end{bmatrix}.
$$

We have already checked that P^{-1} is the inverse of P. You should also check that Q^{-1} is the inverse of Q.

The method we used in Example 2 can be summarized as follows:

Inverting an *n* × *n* Matrix

In order to determine whether an $n \times n$ matrix A is invertible or not, and to find A^{-1} if it does exist, follow this procedure:

1. Write down the $n \times 2n$ matrix $[A \,|\, I]$ (this is A with the $n \times n$ identity matrix set next to it).
2. Row-reduce $[A \,|\, I]$.
3. If the reduced form is $[I \,|\, B]$ (i.e., has the identity matrix in the left part), then A is invertible and $B = A^{-1}$. If you cannot obtain I in the left part, then A is singular. (See Example 3.)

Although there is a general formula for the inverse of a matrix, it is not a simple one. In fact, using the formula for anything larger than a 3×3 matrix is so inefficient that the row-reduction procedure is the method of choice even for computers. However, the general formula is very simple for the special case of 2×2 matrices:

Formula for the Inverse of a 2 × 2 Matrix

The inverse of a 2×2 matrix is

$$
\begin{bmatrix} a & b \\ c & d \end{bmatrix}^{-1} = \frac{1}{ad - bc} \begin{bmatrix} d & -b \\ -c & a \end{bmatrix}, \qquad \text{provided } ad - bc \neq 0.
$$

If the quantity $ad - bc$ is zero, then the matrix is singular (noninvertible). The quantity $ad - bc$ is called the **determinant** of the matrix $\begin{bmatrix} a & b \\ c & d \end{bmatrix}$.

Quick Examples

1. $\begin{bmatrix} 1 & 2 \\ 3 & 4 \end{bmatrix}^{-1} = \dfrac{1}{(1)(4) - (2)(3)} \begin{bmatrix} 4 & -2 \\ -3 & 1 \end{bmatrix} = -\dfrac{1}{2} \begin{bmatrix} 4 & -2 \\ -3 & 1 \end{bmatrix}$

$= \begin{bmatrix} -2 & 1 \\ \frac{3}{2} & -\frac{1}{2} \end{bmatrix}$

2. $\begin{bmatrix} 1 & -1 \\ 2 & -2 \end{bmatrix}$ has determinant $ad - bc = (1)(-2) - (-1)(2) = 0$ and so is singular.

The formula for the inverse of a 2×2 matrix can be obtained using the technique of row reduction. (See the Communication and Reasoning Exercises at the end of the section.)

As we have mentioned earlier, not every square matrix has an inverse, as we see in the next example.

EXAMPLE 3 Singular 3 × 3 Matrix

Find the inverse of the matrix $S = \begin{bmatrix} 1 & 1 & 2 \\ -2 & 0 & 4 \\ 3 & 1 & -2 \end{bmatrix}$, if it exists.

Solution We proceed as before.

$$
\begin{matrix} S \end{matrix} \qquad \begin{matrix} I \end{matrix}
$$

$$
\begin{bmatrix} 1 & 1 & 2 & | & 1 & 0 & 0 \\ -2 & 0 & 4 & | & 0 & 1 & 0 \\ 3 & 1 & -2 & | & 0 & 0 & 1 \end{bmatrix} \begin{matrix} \\ R_2 + 2R_1 \\ R_3 - 3R_1 \end{matrix} \rightarrow \begin{bmatrix} 1 & 1 & 2 & | & 1 & 0 & 0 \\ 0 & 2 & 8 & | & 2 & 1 & 0 \\ 0 & -2 & -8 & | & -3 & 0 & 1 \end{bmatrix} \begin{matrix} 2R_1 - R_2 \\ \\ R_3 + R_2 \end{matrix}
$$

$$
\rightarrow \begin{bmatrix} 2 & 0 & -4 & | & 0 & -1 & 0 \\ 0 & 2 & 8 & | & 2 & 1 & 0 \\ 0 & 0 & 0 & | & -1 & 1 & 1 \end{bmatrix}
$$

We stopped here, even though the reduction is incomplete, because there is *no hope* of getting the identity on the left-hand side. Completing the row reduction will not change the three zeros in the bottom row. So what is wrong? Nothing. As in Example 1, we have here a singular matrix. Any square matrix that, after row reduction, winds up with a row of zeros is singular. (See Exercise 77.)

➡ **Before we go on...** In practice, deciding whether a given matrix is invertible or singular is easy: Simply try to find its inverse. If the process works, then the matrix is invertible, and we get its inverse. If the process fails, then the matrix is singular. If you try to invert a singular matrix using a spreadsheet, calculator, or computer program, you should get an error. Sometimes, instead of an error, you will get a spurious answer due to round-off errors in the device. ■

Using the Inverse to Solve a System of *n* Linear Equations in *n* Unknowns

Having used systems of equations and row reduction to find matrix inverses, we will now use matrix inverses to solve systems of equations. Recall that, at the end of the previous section, we saw that a system of linear equations could be written in the form

$$AX = B$$

where A is the coefficient matrix, X is the column matrix of unknowns, and B is the column matrix of right-hand sides. Now suppose that there are as many unknowns as equations, so that A is a square matrix, and suppose that A is invertible. The object is to solve for the matrix X of unknowns, so we multiply both sides of the equation by the inverse A^{-1} of A, getting

$$A^{-1}AX = A^{-1}B.$$

Notice that we put A^{-1} on the left on both sides of the equation. Order matters when multiplying matrices, so we have to be careful to do the same thing to both sides of the equation. But now $A^{-1}A = I$, so we can rewrite the last equation as

$$IX = A^{-1}B.$$

Also, $IX = X$ (I being the identity matrix), so we really have

$$X = A^{-1}B$$

and we have solved for X!

Moreover, we have shown that, if A is invertible and $AX = B$, then the only *possible* solution is $X = A^{-1}B$. We should check that $A^{-1}B$ is actually a solution by substituting back into the original equation.

$$AX = A(A^{-1}B) = (AA^{-1})B = IB = B.$$

Thus, $X = A^{-1}B$ is a solution and is the only solution. Therefore, if A is invertible, $AX = B$ has exactly one solution.

On the other hand, if $AX = B$ has no solutions or has infinitely many solutions, we can conclude that A is not invertible (why?). To summarize:

Solving the Matrix Equation AX = B

If A is an invertible matrix, then the matrix equation $AX = B$ has the unique solution

$$X = A^{-1}B.$$

Quick Example

The system of linear equations

$$\begin{aligned}
2x \quad\;\;\; + z &= 9 \\
2x + y - z &= 6 \\
3x + y - z &= 9
\end{aligned}$$

can be written as $AX = B$, where

$$A = \begin{bmatrix} 2 & 0 & 1 \\ 2 & 1 & -1 \\ 3 & 1 & -1 \end{bmatrix}, X = \begin{bmatrix} x \\ y \\ z \end{bmatrix} \quad \text{and} \quad B = \begin{bmatrix} 9 \\ 6 \\ 9 \end{bmatrix}.$$

The matrix A is invertible with inverse

$$A^{-1} = \begin{bmatrix} 0 & -1 & 1 \\ 1 & 5 & -4 \\ 1 & 2 & -2 \end{bmatrix}. \quad \text{You should check this.}$$

Thus,

$$X = A^{-1}B = \begin{bmatrix} 0 & -1 & 1 \\ 1 & 5 & -4 \\ 1 & 2 & -2 \end{bmatrix} \begin{bmatrix} 9 \\ 6 \\ 9 \end{bmatrix} = \begin{bmatrix} 3 \\ 3 \\ 3 \end{bmatrix}$$

so that $(x, y, z) = (3, 3, 3)$ is the (unique) solution to the system.

using Technology

Here is an outline on the use of technology to do the calculations in Example 4 (see the Technology Guides at the end of the chapter for additional details on using a TI-83/84 Plus or Excel):

TI-83/84 Plus

Enter the four matrices [A], [B], [C], [D] using MATRX; EDIT

Home Screen: [A]$^{-1}$* [B], [A]$^{-1}$* [C], [A]$^{-1}$* [D]

[More details on page 255.]

Excel

Enter the matrices A and B in convenient blocks of cells (e.g., A1–C3, E1–E3). Highlight a 3 × 1 block for the answer.

Type =MMULT(MINVERSE (A1:C3),E1:E3)

Press Control+Shift+Enter.

[More details on page 260.]

Web Site

www.FiniteandCalc.org

Student Home

→ Online Utilities

→ Matrix Algebra Tool

Enter A^-1*B, A^-1*C, and A^-1*D to compute these products after entering the matrices A, B, C, and D as usual. (See page 196.)

EXAMPLE 4 Solving Systems of Equations Using an Inverse

Solve the following three systems of equations.

a. $\begin{aligned} 2x \quad\;\; + z &= 1 \\ 2x + y - z &= 1 \\ 3x + y - z &= 1 \end{aligned}$ **b.** $\begin{aligned} 2x \quad\;\; + z &= 0 \\ 2x + y - z &= 1 \\ 3x + y - z &= 2 \end{aligned}$ **c.** $\begin{aligned} 2x \quad\;\; + z &= 0 \\ 2x + y - z &= 0 \\ 3x + y - z &= 0 \end{aligned}$

Solution We *could* go ahead and row-reduce all three augmented matrices as we did in Chapter 2, but this would require a lot of work. Notice that the coefficients are the same in all three systems. In other words, we can write the three systems in matrix form as

a. $AX = B$ **b.** $AX = C$ **c.** $AX = D$

where the matrix A is the same in all three cases:

$$A = \begin{bmatrix} 2 & 0 & 1 \\ 2 & 1 & -1 \\ 3 & 1 & -1 \end{bmatrix}.$$

Now the solutions to these systems are

a. $X = A^{-1}B$ **b.** $X = A^{-1}C$ **c.** $X = A^{-1}D$

so the main work is the calculation of the single matrix A^{-1}, which we have already noted (Quick Example above) is

$$A^{-1} = \begin{bmatrix} 0 & -1 & 1 \\ 1 & 5 & -4 \\ 1 & 2 & -2 \end{bmatrix}.$$

Thus, the three solutions are:

a. $X = A^{-1}B = \begin{bmatrix} 0 & -1 & 1 \\ 1 & 5 & -4 \\ 1 & 2 & -2 \end{bmatrix} \begin{bmatrix} 1 \\ 1 \\ 1 \end{bmatrix} = \begin{bmatrix} 0 \\ 2 \\ 1 \end{bmatrix}$

b. $X = A^{-1}C = \begin{bmatrix} 0 & -1 & 1 \\ 1 & 5 & -4 \\ 1 & 2 & -2 \end{bmatrix} \begin{bmatrix} 0 \\ 1 \\ 2 \end{bmatrix} = \begin{bmatrix} 1 \\ -3 \\ -2 \end{bmatrix}$

c. $X = A^{-1}D = \begin{bmatrix} 0 & -1 & 1 \\ 1 & 5 & -4 \\ 1 & 2 & -2 \end{bmatrix} \begin{bmatrix} 0 \\ 0 \\ 0 \end{bmatrix} = \begin{bmatrix} 0 \\ 0 \\ 0 \end{bmatrix}$

➡ **Before we go on...** We have been speaking of *the* inverse of a matrix A. Is there only one? It is not hard to prove that a matrix A cannot have more than one inverse: If B and C were both inverses of A, then

$$\begin{aligned} B &= BI & \text{Property of the identity} \\ &= B(AC) & \text{Because } C \text{ is an inverse of } A \\ &= (BA)C & \text{Associative law} \\ &= IC & \text{Because } B \text{ is an inverse of } A \\ &= C. & \text{Property of the identity} \end{aligned}$$

In other words, if B and C were both inverses of A, then B and C would have to be equal. ∎

FAQs

Which Method to Use in Solving a System

Q:*Now we have two methods to solve a system of linear equations $AX = B$: (1) Compute $X = A^{-1}B$, or (2) row-reduce the augmented matrix. Which is the better method?*

A: Each method has its advantages and disadvantages. Method (1), as we have seen, is very efficient when you must solve several systems of equations with the same coefficients, but it works only when the coefficient matrix is *square* (meaning that you have the same number of equations as unknowns) *and invertible* (meaning that there is a unique solution). The row-reduction method will work for all systems. Moreover, for all but the smallest systems, the most efficient way to find A^{-1} is to use row reduction. Thus, in practice, the two methods are essentially the same when both apply.

3.3 EXERCISES

▼ more advanced   ◆ challenging
[T] indicates exercises that should be solved using technology

In Exercises 1–6, determine whether or not the given pairs of matrices are inverse pairs. HINT [See Quick Examples page 207.]

1. $A = \begin{bmatrix} 0 & 1 \\ 1 & 0 \end{bmatrix}$, $B = \begin{bmatrix} 0 & 1 \\ 1 & 0 \end{bmatrix}$

2. $A = \begin{bmatrix} 2 & 0 \\ 0 & 3 \end{bmatrix}$, $B = \begin{bmatrix} \frac{1}{2} & 0 \\ 0 & \frac{1}{2} \end{bmatrix}$

3. $A = \begin{bmatrix} 2 & 1 & 1 \\ 0 & 1 & 1 \\ 0 & 0 & 1 \end{bmatrix}$, $B = \begin{bmatrix} \frac{1}{2} & -\frac{1}{2} & 0 \\ 0 & 1 & -1 \\ 0 & 0 & 1 \end{bmatrix}$

4. $A = \begin{bmatrix} 1 & 1 & 1 \\ 0 & 1 & 1 \\ 0 & 0 & 1 \end{bmatrix}$, $B = \begin{bmatrix} 1 & -1 & 0 \\ 0 & 1 & -1 \\ 0 & 0 & 1 \end{bmatrix}$

5. $A = \begin{bmatrix} a & 0 & 0 \\ 0 & b & 0 \\ 0 & 0 & 0 \end{bmatrix}$, $B = \begin{bmatrix} a^{-1} & 0 & 0 \\ 0 & b^{-1} & 0 \\ 0 & 0 & 0 \end{bmatrix}$ $(a, b \neq 0)$

6. $A = \begin{bmatrix} a & 0 & 0 \\ 0 & b & 0 \\ 0 & 0 & c \end{bmatrix}$, $B = \begin{bmatrix} a^{-1} & 0 & 0 \\ 0 & b^{-1} & 0 \\ 0 & 0 & c^{-1} \end{bmatrix}$ $(a, b, c \neq 0)$

In Exercises 7–26, use row reduction to find the inverses of the given matrices if they exist, and check your answers by multiplication. HINT [See Example 2.]

7. $\begin{bmatrix} 1 & 1 \\ 2 & 1 \end{bmatrix}$ **8.** $\begin{bmatrix} 0 & 1 \\ 1 & 1 \end{bmatrix}$ **9.** $\begin{bmatrix} 0 & 1 \\ 1 & 0 \end{bmatrix}$ **10.** $\begin{bmatrix} 4 & 0 \\ 0 & 2 \end{bmatrix}$

11. $\begin{bmatrix} 2 & 1 \\ 1 & 1 \end{bmatrix}$ **12.** $\begin{bmatrix} 3 & 0 \\ 0 & \frac{1}{2} \end{bmatrix}$ **13.** $\begin{bmatrix} 2 & 1 \\ 4 & 2 \end{bmatrix}$ **14.** $\begin{bmatrix} 1 & 1 \\ 6 & 6 \end{bmatrix}$

15. $\begin{bmatrix} 1 & 1 & 1 \\ 0 & 1 & 1 \\ 0 & 0 & 1 \end{bmatrix}$ **16.** $\begin{bmatrix} 1 & 2 & 3 \\ 0 & 1 & 2 \\ 0 & 0 & 1 \end{bmatrix}$ **17.** $\begin{bmatrix} 1 & 1 & 1 \\ 1 & 0 & 2 \\ 1 & -1 & 1 \end{bmatrix}$

18. $\begin{bmatrix} 1 & 2 & 3 \\ 0 & 2 & 3 \\ 1 & 0 & 1 \end{bmatrix}$ **19.** $\begin{bmatrix} 1 & 1 & 1 \\ 1 & -1 & 0 \\ 1 & 2 & 3 \end{bmatrix}$ **20.** $\begin{bmatrix} 1 & -1 & 3 \\ 0 & 1 & 3 \\ 1 & 1 & 1 \end{bmatrix}$

21. $\begin{bmatrix} 1 & 1 & 1 \\ 1 & 0 & 1 \\ 1 & -1 & 1 \end{bmatrix}$ **22.** $\begin{bmatrix} 1 & 1 & 1 \\ 0 & 1 & 1 \\ 1 & 0 & 0 \end{bmatrix}$

23. $\begin{bmatrix} 1 & 0 & 1 & 0 \\ -1 & 1 & 0 & 1 \\ -1 & 0 & 0 & 1 \\ 0 & -1 & 0 & 1 \end{bmatrix}$ **24.** $\begin{bmatrix} 0 & 1 & 1 & 0 \\ -1 & 1 & 1 & 1 \\ -1 & 1 & 0 & 1 \\ 0 & -1 & 0 & 1 \end{bmatrix}$

25. $\begin{bmatrix} 1 & 2 & 3 & 4 \\ 0 & 1 & 2 & 3 \\ 0 & 0 & 1 & 2 \\ 0 & 0 & 0 & 1 \end{bmatrix}$ **26.** $\begin{bmatrix} 0 & 0 & 0 & 1 \\ 0 & 0 & 1 & 0 \\ 0 & 1 & 0 & 0 \\ 1 & 0 & 0 & 0 \end{bmatrix}$

In Exercises 27–34, compute the determinant of the given matrix. If the determinant is nonzero, use the formula for inverting a 2×2 matrix to calculate the inverse of the given matrix. HINT [See Quick Examples page 209.]

27. $\begin{bmatrix} 1 & 1 \\ 1 & -1 \end{bmatrix}$ **28.** $\begin{bmatrix} 4 & 1 \\ 0 & 2 \end{bmatrix}$ **29.** $\begin{bmatrix} 1 & 2 \\ 3 & 4 \end{bmatrix}$

30. $\begin{bmatrix} 1 & 0 \\ 0 & 1 \end{bmatrix}$ **31.** $\begin{bmatrix} \frac{1}{6} & -\frac{1}{6} \\ 0 & \frac{1}{6} \end{bmatrix}$ **32.** $\begin{bmatrix} 2 & 1 \\ 4 & 2 \end{bmatrix}$

33. $\begin{bmatrix} 1 & 0 \\ \frac{3}{4} & 0 \end{bmatrix}$ **34.** $\begin{bmatrix} 1 & 1 \\ 1 & 1 \end{bmatrix}$

⬛ *In Exercises 35–42, use technology to find the inverse of the given matrix (when it exists). Round all entries in your answer to two decimal places. [Caution: Because of rounding errors, technology sometimes produces an "inverse" of a singular matrix. These often can be recognized by their huge entries.]*

35. $\begin{bmatrix} 1.1 & 1.2 \\ 1.3 & -1 \end{bmatrix}$

36. $\begin{bmatrix} 0.1 & -3.2 \\ 0.1 & -1.5 \end{bmatrix}$

37. $\begin{bmatrix} 3.56 & 1.23 \\ -1.01 & 0 \end{bmatrix}$

38. $\begin{bmatrix} 9.09 & -5.01 \\ 1.01 & 2.20 \end{bmatrix}$

39. $\begin{bmatrix} 1.1 & 3.1 & 2.4 \\ 1.7 & 2.4 & 2.3 \\ 0.6 & -0.7 & -0.1 \end{bmatrix}$

40. $\begin{bmatrix} 2.1 & 2.4 & 3.5 \\ 6.1 & -0.1 & 2.3 \\ -0.3 & -1.2 & 0.1 \end{bmatrix}$

41. $\begin{bmatrix} 0.01 & 0.32 & 0 & 0.04 \\ -0.01 & 0 & 0 & 0.34 \\ 0 & 0.32 & -0.23 & 0.23 \\ 0 & 0.41 & 0 & 0.01 \end{bmatrix}$

42. $\begin{bmatrix} 0.01 & 0.32 & 0 & 0.04 \\ -0.01 & 0 & 0 & 0.34 \\ 0 & 0.32 & -0.23 & 0.23 \\ 0.01 & 0.96 & -0.23 & 0.65 \end{bmatrix}$

In Exercises 43–48, use matrix inversion to solve the given systems of linear equations. (You previously solved all of these systems using row reduction in Chapter 2.) HINT *[see Quick Example page 211.]*

43. $x + y = 4$
$x - y = 1$

44. $2x + y = 2$
$2x - 3y = 2$

45. $\dfrac{x}{3} + \dfrac{y}{2} = 0$
$\dfrac{x}{2} + y = -1$

46. $\dfrac{2x}{3} - \dfrac{y}{2} = \dfrac{1}{6}$
$\dfrac{x}{2} - \dfrac{y}{2} = -1$

47. $-x + 2y - z = 0$
$-x - y + 2z = 0$
$2x \quad - z = 6$

48. $x + 2y \quad = 4$
$y - z = 0$
$x + 3y - 2z = 5$

In Exercises 49 and 50, use matrix inversion to solve each collection of systems of linear equations. HINT *[See Example 4.]*

49. a. $-x - 4y + 2z = 4$
$x + 2y - z = 3$
$x + y - z = 8$

b. $-x - 4y + 2z = 0$
$x + 2y - z = 3$
$x + y - z = 2$

c. $-x - 4y + 2z = 0$
$x + 2y - z = 0$
$x + y - z = 0$

50. a. $-x - 4y + 2z = 8$
$x \quad - z = 3$
$x + y - z = 8$

b. $-x - 4y + 2z = 8$
$x \quad - z = 3$
$x + y - z = 2$

c. $-x - 4y + 2z = 0$
$x \quad - z = 0$
$x + y - z = 0$

APPLICATIONS

Some of the following exercises are similar or identical to exercises and examples in Chapter 2. Use matrix inverses to find the solutions. We suggest you invert some of the matrices by hand, and others using technology.

51. *Nutrition* A four-ounce serving of Campbell's® Pork & Beans contains 5 grams of protein and 21 grams of carbohydrates.[15] A typical slice of "lite" rye bread contains 4 grams of protein and 12 grams of carbohydrates.

   a. I am planning a meal of "beans-on-toast" and I want it to supply 20 grams of protein and 80 grams of carbohydrates. How should I prepare my meal?

   b. If I require A grams of protein and B grams of carbohydrates, give a formula that tells me how many slices of bread and how many servings of Pork & Beans to use.

52. *Nutrition* According to the nutritional information on a package of Honey Nut Cheerios® brand cereal, each 1-ounce serving of Cheerios contains 3 grams protein and 24 grams carbohydrates.[16] Each half-cup serving of enriched skim milk contains 4 grams protein and 6 grams carbohydrates.

   a. I am planning a meal of cereal and milk and I want it to supply 26 grams of protein, and 78 grams of carbohydrates. How should I prepare my meal?

   b. If I require A grams of protein and B grams of carbohydrates, give a formula that tells me how many servings of milk and Cheerios to use.

53. *Resource Allocation* You manage an ice cream factory that makes three flavors: Creamy Vanilla, Continental Mocha, and Succulent Strawberry. Into each batch of Creamy Vanilla go two eggs, one cup of milk, and two cups of cream. Into each batch of Continental Mocha go one egg, one cup of milk, and two cups of cream. Into each batch of Succulent Strawberry go one egg, two cups of milk, and one cup of cream. Your stocks of eggs, milk, and cream vary from day to day. How many batches of each flavor should you make in order to use up all of your ingredients if you have the following amounts in stock?

   a. 350 eggs, 350 cups of milk, and 400 cups of cream

   b. 400 eggs, 500 cups of milk, and 400 cups of cream

   c. A eggs, B cups of milk, and C cups of cream

54. *Resource Allocation* The Arctic Juice Company makes three juice blends: PineOrange, using 2 quarts of pineapple juice and 2 quarts of orange juice per gallon; PineKiwi, using 3 quarts of pineapple juice and 1 quart of kiwi juice per gallon; and OrangeKiwi, using 3 quarts of orange juice and 1 quart of kiwi juice per gallon. The amount of each kind of juice the company has on hand varies from day to day. How many

---

[15]According to the label information on a 16-oz. can.

[16]Actually, it is 23 grams carbohydrates. We made it 24 grams to simplify the calculation.

gallons of each blend can it make on a day with the following stocks?

a. 800 quarts of pineapple juice, 650 quarts of orange juice, 350 quarts of kiwi juice.

b. 650 quarts of pineapple juice, 800 quarts of orange juice, 350 quarts of kiwi juice.

c. A quarts of pineapple juice, B quarts of orange juice, C quarts of kiwi juice.

Investing: Bond Funds Exercises 55 and 56 are based on the following data on three bond funds at **Fidelity**.[17]

	2008 Loss
FCTFX (Fidelity California Muni)	6%
FSAZX (Fidelity Arizona Muni)	5%
FUSFX (Fidelity Ultra-short)	7%

55. You invested a total of $9,000 in the three funds at the end of 2007, including an equal amount in FSAZX and FUSFX. Your 2008 loss for the year from the first two funds amounted to $400. How much did you invest in each of the three funds?

56. You invested a total of $6,000 in the three funds at the end of 2007, including an equal amount in FCTFX and FSAZX. Your total losses for 2008 amounted to $360. How much did you invest in each of the three funds?

Investing: Stocks Exercises 57 and 58 are based on the following data on **General Electric**, **Wal-Mart**, *and* **Exxon Mobil** *stocks.*[18]

	Price	**Dividend Yield**
GE (General Electric)	$16	7%
WMT (Wal-Mart)	$56	2%
XOM (Exxon Mobil)	$80	2%

57. ▼ You invested a total of $8,400 in shares of the three stocks at the given prices and expected to earn $248 in annual dividends. If you purchased a total of 200 shares, how many shares of each stock did you purchase?

58. ▼ You invested a total of $11,200 in shares of the three stocks at the given prices and expected to earn $304 in annual dividends. If you purchased a total of 250 shares, how many shares of each stock did you purchase?

59. ◆ ▣ *Population Movement* In 2006, the population of the United States, broken down by regions, was 55.1 million in the Northeast, 66.2 million in the Midwest, 110.0 million in the South, and 70.0 million in the West.[19] The matrix P below shows the population movement during the period 2006–2007. (Thus, 98.92% of the population in the Northeast stayed there, while 0.17% of the population in the Northeast moved to the Midwest, and so on.)

$$P = \begin{array}{c} \text{From NE} \\ \text{From MW} \\ \text{From S} \\ \text{From W} \end{array} \begin{array}{cccc} \overset{\text{To}}{\underset{\text{NE}}{}} & \overset{\text{To}}{\underset{\text{MW}}{}} & \overset{\text{To}}{\underset{\text{S}}{}} & \overset{\text{To}}{\underset{\text{W}}{}} \\ \begin{bmatrix} 0.9892 & 0.0017 & 0.0073 & 0.0018 \\ 0.0010 & 0.9920 & 0.0048 & 0.0022 \\ 0.0018 & 0.0024 & 0.9934 & 0.0024 \\ 0.0008 & 0.0033 & 0.0045 & 0.9914 \end{bmatrix} \end{array}$$

Set up the 2006 population figures as a row vector. Assuming that these percentages also describe the population movements from 2005 to 2006, show how matrix inversion and multiplication allow you to compute the population in each region in 2005. (Round all answers to the nearest 0.1 million.)

60. ◆ ▣ *Population Movement* Assume that the percentages given in the preceding exercise also describe the population movements from 2004 to 2005. Show how matrix inversion and multiplication allow you to compute the population in each region in 2004. (Round all answers to the nearest 0.1 million.)

61. ◆ ▣ *Rotations* If a point (x, y) in the plane is rotated counterclockwise through an angle of 45°, its new coordinates (x', y') are given by

$$\begin{bmatrix} x' \\ y' \end{bmatrix} = R \begin{bmatrix} x \\ y \end{bmatrix}$$

where R is the 2×2 matrix $\begin{bmatrix} a & -a \\ a & a \end{bmatrix}$ and $a = \sqrt{1/2} \approx 0.7071$.

a. If the point $(2, 3)$ is rotated counterclockwise through an angle of 45°, what are its (approximate) new coordinates?

b. Multiplication by what matrix would result in a counterclockwise rotation of 90°? 135°? (Express the matrices in terms of R. Hint: Think of a rotation through 90° as two successive rotations through 45°.)

c. Multiplication by what matrix would result in a *clockwise* rotation of 45°?

---

62. ♦ ⊞ *Rotations* If a point (x, y) in the plane is rotated counterclockwise through an angle of 60°, its new coordinates are given by

$$\begin{bmatrix} x' \\ y' \end{bmatrix} = S \begin{bmatrix} x \\ y \end{bmatrix}$$

where S is the 2×2 matrix $\begin{bmatrix} a & -b \\ b & a \end{bmatrix}$ and $a = 1/2$ and $b = \sqrt{3/4} \approx 0.8660$.

  a. If the point $(2, 3)$ is rotated counterclockwise through an angle of 60°, what are its (approximate) new coordinates?
  b. Referring to Exercise 61, multiplication by what matrix would result in a counterclockwise rotation of 105°? (Express the matrices in terms of S and the matrix R from Exercise 61.) [Hint: Think of a rotation through 105° as a rotation through 60° followed by one through 45°.]
  c. Multiplication by what matrix would result in a *clockwise* rotation of 60°?

⊞ *Encryption* *Matrices are commonly used to encrypt data. Here is a simple form such an encryption can take. First, we represent each letter in the alphabet by a number. For example, if we take* <space> $= 0$, $A = 1$, $B = 2$, *and so on,* *"ABORT MISSION" becomes*

[1   2   15   18   20   0   13   9   19   19   9   15   14]

To encrypt this coded phrase, we use an invertible matrix of any size with integer entries. For instance, let us take A to be the 2×2 matrix $\begin{bmatrix} 1 & 2 \\ 3 & 4 \end{bmatrix}$. *We can first arrange the coded sequence of numbers in the form of a matrix with two rows (using zero in the last place if we have an odd number of characters) and then multiply on the left by A.*

Encrypted Matrix $= \begin{bmatrix} 1 & 2 \\ 3 & 4 \end{bmatrix} \begin{bmatrix} 1 & 15 & 20 & 13 & 19 & 9 & 14 \\ 2 & 18 & 0 & 9 & 19 & 15 & 0 \end{bmatrix}$

$= \begin{bmatrix} 5 & 51 & 20 & 31 & 57 & 39 & 14 \\ 11 & 117 & 60 & 75 & 133 & 87 & 42 \end{bmatrix}$

which we can also write as

[5   11   51   117   20   60   31   75   57   133   39   87   14   42].

To decipher the encoded message, multiply the encrypted matrix by A^{-1}.

63. ▼ Use the matrix A to encode the phrase "GO TO PLAN B."
64. ▼ Use the matrix A to encode the phrase "ABANDON SHIP."
65. ▼ Decode the following message, which was encrypted using the matrix A.

[33   69   54   126   11   27   20   60   29   59   65   149   41   87]

66. ▼ Decode the following message, which was encrypted using the matrix A.

[59   141   43   101   7   21   29   59   65   149   41   87]

COMMUNICATION AND REASONING EXERCISES

67. Multiple Choice: If A and B are square matrices with $AB = I$ and $BA = I$, then
  (A) B is the inverse of A.
  (B) A and B must be equal.
  (C) A and B must both be singular.
  (D) At least one of A and B is singular.

68. Multiple Choice: If A is a square matrix with $A^3 = I$, then
  (A) A must be the identity matrix.
  (B) A is invertible.
  (C) A is singular.
  (D) A is both invertible and singular.

69. What can you say about the inverse of a 2×2 matrix of the form $\begin{bmatrix} a & b \\ a & b \end{bmatrix}$?

70. If you think of numbers as 1×1 matrices, which numbers are invertible 1×1 matrices?

71. ▼ Use matrix multiplication to check that the inverse of a general 2×2 matrix is given by

$$\begin{bmatrix} a & b \\ c & d \end{bmatrix}^{-1} = \frac{1}{ad - bc} \begin{bmatrix} d & -b \\ -c & a \end{bmatrix} \text{ (provided } ad - bc \neq 0\text{).}$$

72. ♦ Derive the formula in Exercise 71 using row reduction. (Assume that $ad - bc \neq 0$.)

73. ▼ A **diagonal** matrix D has the following form.

$$D = \begin{bmatrix} d_1 & 0 & 0 & \dots & 0 \\ 0 & d_2 & 0 & \dots & 0 \\ 0 & 0 & d_3 & \dots & 0 \\ \vdots & \vdots & \vdots & \ddots & \vdots \\ 0 & 0 & 0 & \dots & d_n \end{bmatrix}$$

When is D singular? Why?

74. ▼ If a square matrix A row-reduces to the identity matrix, must it be invertible? If so, say why, and if not, give an example of such a (singular) matrix.

75. ▼ If A and B are invertible, check that $B^{-1}A^{-1}$ is the inverse of AB.

76. ▼ Solve the matrix equation $A(B + CX) = D$ for X. (You may assume that all the matrices are square and invertible.)

77. ♦ In Example 3 we said that, if a square matrix A row-reduces to a matrix with a row of zeros it is singular. Why?

78. ♦ Your friend has two square matrices A and B, neither of them the zero matrix, with the property that AB is the zero matrix. You immediately tell him that neither A nor B can possibly be invertible. How can you be so sure?

3.4 Game Theory

It frequently happens that you are faced with making a decision or choosing a best strategy from several possible choices. For instance, you might need to decide whether to invest in stocks or bonds, whether to cut prices of the product you sell, or what offensive play to use in a football game. In these examples, the result depends on something you cannot control. In the first case, your success depends on the future behavior of the economy. In the second case, it depends in part on whether your competitors also cut prices, and in the third case, it depends on the defensive strategy chosen by the opposing team.

We can model situations like these using **game theory**. We represent the various options and payoffs in a matrix and can then calculate the best single strategy or combination of strategies using matrix algebra and other techniques.

Game theory is very new compared with most of the mathematics you learn. It was invented in the 1920s by the noted mathematicians Emile Borel (1871–1956) and John von Neumann (1903–1957). Game theory's connection with linear programming was discovered even more recently, in 1947, by von Neumann, and further advances were made by the mathematician John Nash[20] (1928–), for which he received the 1994 Nobel Prize for Economics.

The Payoff Matrix and Expected Value of a Game

We have probably all played the simple game "Rock, Paper, Scissors" at some time in our lives. It goes as follows: There are two players—let us call them A and B—and at each turn, both players produce, by a gesture of the hand, either paper, a pair of scissors, or a rock. Rock beats scissors (since a rock can crush scissors), but is beaten by paper (since a rock can be covered by paper), while scissors beat paper (since scissors can cut paper). The round is a draw if both A and B show the same item. We could turn this into a betting game if, at each turn, we require the loser to pay the winner 1¢. For instance, if A shows a rock and B shows paper, then A pays B 1¢.

Rock, Paper, Scissors is an example of a **two-person zero-sum game**. It is called a zero-sum game because each player's loss is equal to the other player's gain.* We can represent this game by a matrix, called the **payoff matrix**.

✳ NOTE An example of a *nonzero-sum game* would be one in which the government taxed the earnings of the winner. In that case the winner's gain would be less than the loser's loss.

$$\begin{array}{c} & \mathbf{B} \\ & \begin{array}{ccc} p & s & r \end{array} \\ \mathbf{A} \begin{array}{c} p \\ s \\ r \end{array} & \left[\begin{array}{ccc} 0 & -1 & 1 \\ 1 & 0 & -1 \\ -1 & 1 & 0 \end{array}\right] \end{array}$$

or just

$$P = \left[\begin{array}{ccc} 0 & -1 & 1 \\ 1 & 0 & -1 \\ -1 & 1 & 0 \end{array}\right]$$

if we choose to omit the labels. In the payoff matrix, Player A's options, or **moves**, are listed on the left, while Player B's options are listed on top. We think of A as playing the

---

[20] Nash's turbulent life is the subject of the biography *A Beautiful Mind* by Sylvia Nasar (Simon & Schuster, 1998). The 2001 Academy Award-winning movie of the same title is a somewhat fictionalized account.

rows and B as playing the columns. Positive numbers indicate a win for the row player, while negative numbers indicate a loss for the row player. Thus, for example, the p, s entry represents the outcome if A plays p (paper) and B plays s (scissors). In this event, B wins, and the −1 entry there indicates that A loses 1¢. (If that entry were −2 instead, it would have meant that A loses 2¢.)

Two-Person Zero-Sum Game

A **two-person zero-sum game** is one in which one player's loss equals the other's gain. We assume that the outcome is determined by each player's choice from among a fixed, finite set of moves. If Player A has m moves to choose from and Player B has n, we can represent the game using the **payoff matrix**, the $m \times n$ matrix showing the result of each possible pair of choices of moves.

In each round of the game, the way a player chooses a move is called a **strategy**. A player using a **pure strategy** makes the same move each round of the game. For example, if a player in the above game chooses to play scissors at each turn, then that player is using the pure strategy s. A player using a **mixed strategy** chooses each move a certain percentage of the time in a random fashion; for instance, Player A might choose to play p 50% of the time, and each of s and r 25% of the time.

Our ultimate goal is to be able to determine which strategy is best for each player to use. To do that, we need to know how to evaluate strategies. The fundamental calculation we need is that of the **expected value** of a pair of strategies. Let's look at a simple example.

EXAMPLE 1 Expected Value

Consider the following game:

$$\mathbf{A} \begin{array}{c} \\ p \\ q \end{array} \overset{\displaystyle \overset{\mathbf{B}}{a \qquad b}}{\begin{bmatrix} 3 & -1 \\ -2 & 3 \end{bmatrix}}.$$

Player A decides to pick moves at random, choosing to play p 75% of the time and q 25% of the time. Player B also picks moves at random, choosing a 20% of the time and b 80% of the time. On average, how much does A expect to win or lose?

Solution Suppose they play the game 100 times. Each time they play there are four possible outcomes:

Case 1: A plays p, B plays a.
Because A plays p only 75% of the time and B plays a only 20% of the time, we expect this case to occur $0.75 \times 0.20 = 0.15$, or 15% of the time, or 15 times out of 100. Each time this happens, A gains 3 points, so we get a contribution of $15 \times 3 = 45$ points to A's total winnings.

Case 2: A plays p, B plays b.
Because A plays p only 75% of the time and B plays b only 80% of the time, we expect this case to occur $0.75 \times 0.80 = 0.60$, or 60 times out of 100. Each time this happens, A loses 1 point, so we get a contribution of: $60 \times -1 = -60$ to A's total winnings.

Case 3: A plays q, B plays a.
This case occurs $0.25 \times 0.20 = 0.05$, or 5 out of 100 times, with a loss of 2 points to A each time, giving a contribution of $5 \times -2 = -10$ to A's total winnings.

Case 4: A plays q, B plays b.
This case occurs $0.25 \times 0.80 = 0.20$, or 20 out of 100 times, with a gain of 3 points to A each time, giving a contribution of $20 \times 3 = 60$ to A's total winnings.

Summing to get A's total winnings and then dividing by the number of times the game is played gives the average value of

$$(45 - 60 - 10 + 60)/100 = 0.35$$

so that A can expect to win an average of 0.35 points per play of the game. We call 0.35 the **expected value** of the game when A and B use these particular strategies.

This calculation was somewhat tedious and it would only get worse if A and B had many moves to choose from. There is a far more convenient way of doing exactly the same calculation, using matrix multiplication: We start by representing the player's strategies as matrices. For reasons to become clear in a moment, we record A's strategy as a row matrix:

$$R = [0.75 \quad 0.25].$$

We record B's strategy as a column matrix:

$$C = \begin{bmatrix} 0.20 \\ 0.80 \end{bmatrix}.$$

(We will sometimes write column vectors using transpose notation, writing, for example, $[0.20 \quad 0.80]^T$ for the column above, to save space.) Now: *the expected value is the matrix product RPC where P is the payoff matrix!*

using Technology

The use of technology becomes indispensable when we need to do several calculations or when the matrices involved are big. See the technology note accompanying Example 3 in Section 3.2 on page 195 for instructions on multiplying matrices using a TI-83/84 Plus or Excel. Online, use the Matrix Algebra Tool.

$$\text{Expected value} = RPC = [0.75 \quad 0.25] \begin{bmatrix} 3 & -1 \\ -2 & 3 \end{bmatrix} \begin{bmatrix} 0.20 \\ 0.80 \end{bmatrix}$$

$$= [1.75 \quad 0] \begin{bmatrix} 0.20 \\ 0.80 \end{bmatrix} = [0.35].$$

Why does this work? Write out the arithmetic involved in the matrix product *RPC* to see what we calculated:

$$[0.75 \times 3 + 0.25 \times (-2)] \times 0.20 + [0.75 \times (-1) + 0.25 \times 3] \times 0.80$$

$$= 0.75 \times 3 \times 0.20 + 0.25 \times (-2) \times 0.20 + 0.75 \times (-1) \times 0.80 + 0.25 \times 3 \times 0.80$$
$$= \quad \text{Case 1} \quad + \quad \text{Case 3} \quad + \quad \text{Case 2} \quad + \quad \text{Case 4.}$$

So, the matrix product does all at once the various cases we considered above.

To summarize what we just saw:

The Expected Value of a Game for Mixed Strategies *R* and *C*

The **expected value of a game for given mixed strategies** is the average payoff that occurs if the game is played a large number of times with the row and column players using the given strategies.

To compute the expected value of a game:

1. Write the row player's mixed strategy as a row matrix R.

2. Write the column player's mixed strategy as a column matrix C.

3. Calculate the product RPC, where P is the payoff matrix. This product is a 1×1 matrix whose entry is the expected value e.

Quick Example

Consider "Rock, Paper, Scissors."

$$
\begin{array}{c}
 \\
\mathbf{A}\begin{array}{c} p \\ s \\ r \end{array}
\end{array}
\begin{array}{c}
\mathbf{B} \\
\begin{array}{ccc} p & s & r \end{array} \\
\left[\begin{array}{ccc} 0 & -1 & 1 \\ 1 & 0 & -1 \\ -1 & 1 & 0 \end{array}\right]
\end{array}
$$

Suppose that the row player plays *paper* half the time and each of the other two strategies a quarter of the time, and the column player always plays *scissors*. We write

$$
R = \begin{bmatrix} \dfrac{1}{2} & \dfrac{1}{4} & \dfrac{1}{4} \end{bmatrix}, \quad C = \begin{bmatrix} 0 \\ 1 \\ 0 \end{bmatrix}
$$

so,

$$
e = RPC = \begin{bmatrix} \dfrac{1}{2} & \dfrac{1}{4} & \dfrac{1}{4} \end{bmatrix} \begin{bmatrix} 0 & -1 & 1 \\ 1 & 0 & -1 \\ -1 & 1 & 0 \end{bmatrix} \begin{bmatrix} 0 \\ 1 \\ 0 \end{bmatrix}
$$

$$
= \begin{bmatrix} \dfrac{1}{2} & \dfrac{1}{4} & \dfrac{1}{4} \end{bmatrix} \begin{bmatrix} -1 \\ 0 \\ 1 \end{bmatrix} = -\dfrac{1}{4}.
$$

Thus, player A loses an average of once every four plays.

Solving a Game

Now that we know how to evaluate particular strategies, we want to find the *best* strategy. The next example takes us another step toward that goal.

EXAMPLE 2 Television Ratings Wars

Commercial TV station RTV and cultural station CTV are competing for viewers in the Tuesday prime-time 9–10 PM time slot. RTV is trying to decide whether to show a sitcom, a docudrama, a reality show, or a movie, while CTV is thinking about either a nature documentary, a symphony concert, a ballet, or an opera. A television rating company estimates the payoffs for the various alternatives as follows. (Each point indicates a shift of 1,000 viewers from one channel to the other; thus, for instance, −2 indicates a shift of 2,000 viewers from RTV to CTV.)

		CTV			
		Nature Doc.	**Symphony**	**Ballet**	**Opera**
	Sitcom	2	1	−2	2
RTV	**Docudrama**	−1	1	−1	2
	Reality Show	−2	0	0	1
	Movie	3	1	−1	1

a. If RTV notices that CTV is showing nature documentaries half the time and symphonies the other half, what would RTV's best strategy be, and how many viewers would it gain if it followed this strategy?

b. If, on the other hand, CTV notices that RTV is showing docudramas half the time and reality shows the other half, what would CTV's best strategy be, and how many viewers would it gain or lose if it followed this strategy?

Solution

a. We are given the matrix of the game, P, in the table above, and we are given CTV's strategy $C = [0.50 \ \ 0.50 \ \ 0 \ \ 0]^T$. We are not given RTV's strategy R. To say that RTV is looking for its best strategy is to say that it wants the expected value $e = RPC$ to be as large as possible. So, we take $R = [x \ \ y \ \ z \ \ t]$ and look for values for x, y, z, and t that make RPC as large as possible. First, we calculate e in terms of these unknowns:

$$e = RPC = [x \ \ y \ \ z \ \ t] \begin{bmatrix} 2 & 1 & -2 & 2 \\ -1 & 1 & -1 & 2 \\ -2 & 0 & 0 & 1 \\ 3 & 1 & -1 & 1 \end{bmatrix} \begin{bmatrix} 0.50 \\ 0.50 \\ 0 \\ 0 \end{bmatrix}$$

$$= [x \ \ y \ \ z \ \ t] \begin{bmatrix} 1.5 \\ 0 \\ -1 \\ 2 \end{bmatrix} = 1.5x - z + 2t.$$

Now, the unknowns x, y, z, and t must be nonnegative and add up to 1 (why?). Because t has the largest coefficient, 2, we'll get the best result by making it as large as possible, namely, $t = 1$, leaving $x = y = z = 0$. Thus, RTV's best strategy is $R = [0 \ \ 0 \ \ 0 \ \ 1]$. In other words, RTV should use the pure strategy of showing a movie every Tuesday evening. If it does so, the expected value will be

$$e = 1.5(0) - 0 + 2(1) = 2$$

so RTV can expect to gain 2,000 viewers.

b. Here, we are given $R = [0 \ \ 0.50 \ \ 0.50 \ \ 0]$ and are not given CTV's strategy C, so this time we take $C = [x \ \ y \ \ z \ \ t]^T$ and calculate e:

$$e = RPC = [0 \ \ 0.50 \ \ 0.50 \ \ 0] \begin{bmatrix} 2 & 1 & -2 & 2 \\ -1 & 1 & -1 & 2 \\ -2 & 0 & 0 & 1 \\ 3 & 1 & -1 & 1 \end{bmatrix} \begin{bmatrix} x \\ y \\ z \\ t \end{bmatrix}$$

$$= [-1.5 \ \ 0.5 \ \ -0.5 \ \ 1.5] \begin{bmatrix} x \\ y \\ z \\ t \end{bmatrix} = -1.5x + 0.5y - 0.5z + 1.5t.$$

Now, CTV wants e to be as *small* as possible (why?). Because x has the largest negative coefficient, CTV would like it to be as large as possible: $x = 1$, so the rest of the unknowns must be zero. Thus, CTV's best strategy is $C = [1 \ \ 0 \ \ 0 \ \ 0]^T$, that is, show a nature documentary every night. If it does so, the expected value will be

$$e = -1.5(1) + 0.5(0) - 0.5(0) + 1.5(0) = -1.5$$

so CTV can expect to gain 1,500 viewers.

This example illustrates the fact that, no matter what mixed strategy one player selects, the other player can choose an appropriate *pure* counterstrategy in order to maximize its gain. How does this affect what decisions you should make as one of the players? If you were on the board of directors of RTV, you might reason as follows: Since for every mixed strategy you try, CTV can find a best counterstrategy (as in part (b)) it is in your company's best interest to select a mixed strategy that *minimizes* the effect of CTV's best counterstrategy. This is called the **minimax criterion**.

Minimax Criterion

A player using the **minimax criterion** chooses a strategy that, among all possible strategies, minimizes the effect of the other player's best counterstrategy. That is, an optimal (best) strategy according to the minimax criterion is one that minimizes the maximum damage the opponent can cause.

This criterion assumes that your opponent is determined to win. More precisely, it assumes the following.

Fundamental Principle of Game Theory

Each player tries to use its best possible strategy, and assumes that the other player is doing the same.

This principle is not always followed by every player. For example, one of the players may be nature and may choose its move at random, with no particular purpose in mind. In such a case, criteria other than the minimax criterion may be more appropriate. For example, there is the "maximax" criterion, which maximizes the maximum possible payoff (also known as the "reckless" strategy), or the criterion that seeks to minimize "regret" (the difference between the payoff you get and the payoff you *would have gotten* if you had known beforehand what was going to happen).[21] But, we shall assume here the fundamental principle and try to find optimal strategies under the minimax criterion.

Finding the optimal strategy is called **solving the game**. In general, solving a game can be done using linear programming, as we shall see in the next chapter. However, we can solve 2×2 games "by hand" as we shall see in the next example. First, we notice that some large games can be reduced to smaller games.

Consider the game in the preceding example, which had the following matrix:

$$P = \begin{bmatrix} 2 & 1 & -2 & 2 \\ -1 & 1 & -1 & 2 \\ -2 & 0 & 0 & 1 \\ 3 & 1 & -1 & 1 \end{bmatrix}.$$

Compare the second and third columns through the eyes of the column player, CTV. Every payoff in the third column is as good as or better, from CTV's point of view, than the corresponding entry in the second column. Thus, no matter what RTV does, CTV will do better showing a ballet (third column) than a symphony (second column). We say that the third column **dominates** the second column. As far as CTV is concerned, we might as well forget about symphonies entirely, so we remove the second column. Similarly, the third column dominates the fourth, so we can remove the fourth column, too. This gives us a smaller game to work with:

$$P = \begin{bmatrix} 2 & -2 \\ -1 & -1 \\ -2 & 0 \\ 3 & -1 \end{bmatrix}$$

Now compare the first and last rows. Every payoff in the last row is larger than the corresponding payoff in the first row, so the last row is always better to RTV. Again, we say that the last row dominates the first row, and we can discard the first row. Similarly, the last row dominates the second row, so we discard the second row as well. This reduces us to the following game:

$$P = \begin{bmatrix} -2 & 0 \\ 3 & -1 \end{bmatrix}$$

In this matrix, neither row dominates the other and neither column dominates the other. So, this is as far as we can go with this line of argument. We call this **reduction by dominance**.

Reduction by Dominance

One *row* **dominates** another if every entry in the former is greater than or equal to the corresponding entry in the latter. Put another way, one row dominates another if it is always at least as good for the row player.

One *column* dominates another if every entry in the former is less than or equal to the corresponding entry in the latter. Put another way, one column dominates another if it is always at least as good for the column player.

Procedure for Reducing by Dominance:

1. Check whether there is any row in the (remaining) matrix that is dominated by another row. Remove all dominated rows.

2. Check whether there is any column in the (remaining) matrix that is dominated by another column. Remove all dominated columns.

3. Repeat steps 1 and 2 until there are no dominated rows or columns.

Let us now go back to the "television ratings wars" example and see how we can solve a game using the minimax criterion once we are down to a 2 × 2 payoff matrix.

EXAMPLE 3 Solving a 2 × 2 Game

Continuing the preceding example:

a. Find the optimal strategy for RTV.

b. Find the optimal strategy for CTV.

c. Find the expected value of the game if RTV and CTV use their optimal strategies.

Solution As in the text, we begin by reducing the game by dominance, which brings us down to the following 2×2 game:

		CTV	
		Nature Doc.	Ballet
RTV	Reality Show	−2	0
	Movie	3	−1

a. Now let's find RTV's optimal strategy. Because we don't yet know what it is, we write down a general strategy:

$$R = [x \quad y].$$

Because $x + y = 1$, we can replace y by $1 - x$:

$$R = [x \quad 1 - x].$$

We know that CTV's best counterstrategy to R will be a pure strategy (see the discussion after Example 2), so let's compute the expected value of the game for each of CTV's possible pure strategies:

$$e = [x \quad 1 - x] \begin{bmatrix} -2 & 0 \\ 3 & -1 \end{bmatrix} \begin{bmatrix} 1 \\ 0 \end{bmatrix}$$

$$= (-2)x + 3(1 - x) = -5x + 3$$

$$f = [x \quad 1 - x] \begin{bmatrix} -2 & 0 \\ 3 & -1 \end{bmatrix} \begin{bmatrix} 0 \\ 1 \end{bmatrix}$$

$$= 0x - (1 - x) = x - 1.$$

Figure 1

Because both e and f depend on x, we can graph them as in Figure 1.

If, for instance, RTV happened to choose $x = 0.5$, then the expected values for CTV's two pure strategies are $e = -5(1/2) + 3 = 1/2$ and $f = 1/2 - 1 = -1/2$. The worst outcome for RTV is the lower of the two, f, and this will be true wherever the graph of f is below the graph of e. On the other hand, if RTV chose $x = 1$, the graph of e would be lower and the worst possible expected value would be $e = -5(1) + 3 = -2$. Since RTV can choose x to be any value between 0 and 1, the worst possible outcomes are those shown by the red portion of the graph in Figure 2.

Figure 2

Because RTV is trying to make the worst possible outcome as large as possible (that is, to minimize damages), it is seeking the point on the red portion of the graph that is highest. This is the intersection point of the two lines. To calculate its coordinates, it's easiest to equate the two functions of x:

$$-5x + 3 = x - 1,$$

$$-6x = -4,$$

or

$$x = \frac{2}{3}.$$

The e (or f) coordinate is then obtained by substituting $x = 2/3$ into the expression for e (or f) giving:

$$e = -5\left(\frac{2}{3}\right) + 3$$

$$= -\frac{1}{3}.$$

We conclude that RTV's best strategy is to take $x = 2/3$, giving an expected value of $-1/3$. In other words, RTV's optimal mixed strategy is:

$$R = \begin{bmatrix} \dfrac{2}{3} & \dfrac{1}{3} \end{bmatrix}.$$

Going back to the original game, RTV should show reality shows $2/3$ of the time and movies $1/3$ of the time. It should not bother showing any sitcoms or docudramas. It expects to lose, on average, 333 viewers to CTV, but all of its other options are worse.

b. To find CTV's optimal strategy, we must reverse roles and start by writing its unknown strategy as follows.

$$C = \begin{bmatrix} x \\ 1 - x \end{bmatrix}.$$

We calculate the expected values for the two pure row strategies:

$$e = \begin{bmatrix} 1 & 0 \end{bmatrix} \begin{bmatrix} -2 & 0 \\ 3 & -1 \end{bmatrix} \begin{bmatrix} x \\ 1 - x \end{bmatrix}$$

$$= -2x$$

and

$$f = \begin{bmatrix} 0 & 1 \end{bmatrix} \begin{bmatrix} -2 & 0 \\ 3 & -1 \end{bmatrix} \begin{bmatrix} x \\ 1 - x \end{bmatrix}$$

$$= 3x - (1 - x)$$

$$= 4x - 1.$$

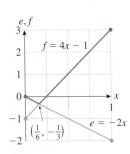

Figure 3

As with the row player, we know that the column player's best strategy will correspond to the intersection of the graphs of e and f (Figure 3). (Why is the upper edge red, rather than the lower edge?) The graphs intersect when

$$-2x = 4x - 1$$

or

$$x = \frac{1}{6}.$$

The corresponding value of e (or f) is

$$e = -2\left(\frac{1}{6}\right) = -\frac{1}{3}.$$

Thus, CTV's optimal mixed strategy is $\begin{bmatrix} \frac{1}{6} & \frac{5}{6} \end{bmatrix}^T$ and the expected value is $-1/3$. So, CTV should show nature documentaries $1/6$ of the time and ballets $5/6$ of the time. It should not bother to show symphonies or operas. It expects to gain, on average, 333 viewers from RTV.

c. We can now calculate the expected value of the game as usual, using the optimal strategies we found in parts (a) and (b).

$$e = RPC$$

$$= \begin{bmatrix} \dfrac{2}{3} & \dfrac{1}{3} \end{bmatrix} \begin{bmatrix} -2 & 0 \\ 3 & -1 \end{bmatrix} \begin{bmatrix} \dfrac{1}{6} \\ \dfrac{5}{6} \end{bmatrix}$$

$$= -\frac{1}{3}$$

➡ **Before we go on...** In Example 3, it is no accident that the expected value with the optimal strategies equals the expected values we found in (a) and (b). If we call the expected value with the optimal strategies the **expected value of the game**, the row player's optimal strategy guarantees an average payoff no smaller than the expected value, while the column player's optimal strategy guarantees an average payoff no larger. Together they force the average value to be the expected value of the game. ■

Expected Value of a Game

The **expected value of a game** is its expected value when the row and column players use their optimal (minimax) strategies. By using its optimal strategy, the row player guarantees an expected value no lower than the expected value of the game, no matter what the column player does. Similarly, by using its optimal strategy, the column player guarantees an expected value no higher than the expected value of the game, no matter what the row player does.

Q: *What about games that don't reduce to* 2×2 *matrices? Are these solved in a similar way?*

A: The method illustrated in the previous example cannot easily be generalized to solve bigger games (i.e., games that cannot be reduced to 2×2 matrices); solving even a 2×3 game using this approach would require us to consider graphs in three dimensions. To be able to solve games of arbitrary size, we need to wait until the next chapter (Section 4.5) where we describe a method for solving a game, using the simplex method, that works for all payoff matrices.

Strictly Determined Games

The following example illustrates an interesting special case.

EXAMPLE 4 Strictly Determined Game

Solve the following game:

$$
\mathbf{A} \begin{array}{c} \\ s \\ t \\ u \end{array}
\begin{array}{c}
\mathbf{B} \\
\begin{array}{ccc} p & q & r \end{array} \\
\left[\begin{array}{ccc} -4 & -3 & 3 \\ 2 & -1 & -2 \\ 1 & 0 & 2 \end{array} \right].
\end{array}
$$

Solution If we look carefully at this matrix, we see that no row dominates another and no column dominates another, so we can't reduce it. Nor do we know how to solve a 3×3 game, so it looks as if we're stuck. However, there is a way to understand this particular game. With the minimax criterion in mind, let's begin by considering the worst possible outcomes for the row player for each possible move. We do this by circling the smallest payoff in each row, the **row minima**:

$$
\mathbf{A} \begin{array}{c} \\ s \\ t \\ u \end{array}
\begin{array}{c}
\mathbf{B} \\
\begin{array}{ccc} p & q & r \end{array} \\
\left[\begin{array}{ccc} \boxed{-4} & -3 & 3 \\ 2 & -1 & \boxed{-2} \\ 1 & \boxed{0} & 2 \end{array} \right]
\end{array}
\begin{array}{l}
\text{Row minima} \\
-4 \\
-2 \\
0 \leftarrow \text{largest}
\end{array}
$$

So, for example, if A plays move s, the worst possible outcome is to lose 4. Player A takes the least risk by using move u, which has the largest row minimum.

We do the same thing for the column player, remembering that smaller payoffs are better for B and larger payoffs worse. We draw a box around the largest payoff in each column, the **column maxima:**

$$\begin{array}{cc} & \mathbf{B} \\ & \begin{array}{ccc} p & q & r \end{array} \\ \mathbf{A} \begin{array}{c} s \\ t \\ u \end{array} & \left[\begin{array}{ccc} -4 & -3 & \boxed{3} \\ \boxed{2} & -1 & -2 \\ 1 & \boxed{0} & 2 \end{array} \right] \end{array}$$

Column maxima   2   0   3
                      ↑
                  smallest

Player B takes the least risk by using move q, which has the smallest column maximum.

Now put the circles and boxes together:

$$\begin{array}{cc} & \mathbf{B} \\ & \begin{array}{ccc} p & q & r \end{array} \\ \mathbf{A} \begin{array}{c} s \\ t \\ u \end{array} & \left[\begin{array}{ccc} \boxed{-4} & -3 & \boxed{3} \\ \boxed{2} & -1 & \boxed{-2} \\ 1 & \boxed{0} & 2 \end{array} \right] \end{array}$$

Notice that the uq entry is both circled and boxed: it is both a row minimum and a column maximum. We call such an entry a **saddle point.**

Now we claim that the optimal strategy for A is to always play u while the optimal strategy for B is to always play q. By playing u, A guarantees that the payoff will be 0 or higher, no matter what B does, so the expected value of the game has to be at least 0. On the other hand, by playing q, B guarantees that the payoff will be 0 or less, so the expected value of the game has to be no more than 0. That means that the expected value of the game must be 0, and A and B have no strategies that could do any better for them than the pure strategies u and q.

➡ **Before we go on...** You should consider what happens in an example like the television rating wars game of Example 3. In that game, the largest row minimum is -1 while the smallest column maximum is 0; there is no saddle point. The row player can force a payoff of at least -1 by playing a pure strategy (always showing movies, for example), but can do better, forcing an average payoff of $-1/3$, by playing a mixed strategy. Similarly, the column player can force the payoff to be 0 or less with a pure strategy, but can do better, forcing an average payoff of $-1/3$, with a mixed strategy. Only when there is a saddle point will pure strategies be optimal. ■

Strictly Determined Game

A **saddle point** is a payoff that is simultaneously a row minimum and a column maximum (both boxed and circled in our approach). If a game has a saddle point, the corresponding row and column strategies are the optimal ones, and we say that the game is **strictly determined.**

using Technology

FAQs

Solving a Game

Q : *We've seen several ways of trying to solve a game. What should I do and in what order?*

A : Here are the steps you should take when trying to solve a game:

1. Reduce by dominance. This should always be your first step.
2. If you were able to reduce to a 1 × 1 game, you're done. The optimal strategies are the corresponding pure strategies, as they dominate all the others.
3. Look for a saddle point in the reduced game. If it has one, the game is strictly determined, and the corresponding pure strategies are optimal.
4. If your reduced game is 2 × 2 and has no saddle point, use the method of Example 3 to find the optimal mixed strategies.
5. If your reduced game is larger than 2 × 2 and has no saddle point, you have to use linear programming to solve it, but that will have to wait until the following chapter.

3.4 EXERCISES

▼ more advanced   ◆ challenging

T indicates exercises that should be solved using technology

In Exercises 1–4, calculate the expected value of the game with payoff matrix

$$P = \begin{bmatrix} 2 & 0 & -1 & 2 \\ -1 & 0 & 0 & -2 \\ -2 & 0 & 0 & 1 \\ 3 & 1 & -1 & 1 \end{bmatrix}$$

using the mixed strategies supplied. HINT [See Example 1.]

1. $R = \begin{bmatrix} 0 & 1 & 0 & 0 \end{bmatrix}$, $C = \begin{bmatrix} 1 & 0 & 0 & 0 \end{bmatrix}^T$

2. $R = \begin{bmatrix} 0 & 0 & 0 & 1 \end{bmatrix}$, $C = \begin{bmatrix} 0 & 1 & 0 & 0 \end{bmatrix}^T$

3. $R = \begin{bmatrix} 0.5 & 0.5 & 0 & 0 \end{bmatrix}$, $C = \begin{bmatrix} 0 & 0 & 0.5 & 0.5 \end{bmatrix}^T$

4. $R = \begin{bmatrix} 0 & 0.5 & 0 & 0.5 \end{bmatrix}$, $C = \begin{bmatrix} 0.5 & 0.5 & 0 & 0 \end{bmatrix}^T$

In Exercises 5–8, either a mixed column or row strategy is given. In each case, use

$$P = \begin{bmatrix} 0 & -1 & 5 \\ 2 & -2 & 4 \\ 0 & 3 & 0 \\ 1 & 0 & -5 \end{bmatrix}$$

and find the optimal pure strategy (or strategies) the other player should use. Express the answer as a row or column matrix. Also determine the resulting expected value of the game. HINT [See Example 2.]

5. $C = \begin{bmatrix} 0.25 & 0.75 & 0 \end{bmatrix}^T$

6. $C = \begin{bmatrix} \frac{1}{3} & \frac{1}{3} & \frac{1}{3} \end{bmatrix}^T$

7. $R = \begin{bmatrix} \frac{1}{2} & 0 & \frac{1}{4} & \frac{1}{4} \end{bmatrix}$

8. $R = \begin{bmatrix} 0.8 & 0.2 & 0 & 0 \end{bmatrix}$

Reduce the payoff matrices in Exercises 9–14 by dominance.

9.

$$\begin{array}{c} \\ A \begin{array}{c} a \\ b \end{array} \end{array} \begin{array}{ccc} p & q & r \\ \begin{bmatrix} 1 & 1 & 10 \\ 2 & 3 & -4 \end{bmatrix} \end{array}$$
   B

10.

$$\begin{array}{c} \\ A \begin{array}{c} a \\ b \end{array} \end{array} \begin{array}{ccc} p & q & r \\ \begin{bmatrix} 2 & 0 & 10 \\ 15 & -4 & -5 \end{bmatrix} \end{array}$$
   B

11.

$$A \begin{array}{c} 1 \\ 2 \\ 3 \end{array} \begin{array}{ccc} a & b & c \\ \begin{bmatrix} 2 & -4 & -9 \\ -1 & -2 & -3 \\ 5 & 0 & -1 \end{bmatrix} \end{array}$$
   B

12.

$$A \begin{array}{c} 1 \\ 2 \\ 3 \end{array} \begin{array}{ccc} a & b & c \\ \begin{bmatrix} 0 & -1 & -5 \\ -3 & -10 & 10 \\ 2 & 3 & -4 \end{bmatrix} \end{array}$$
   B

13.

$$A \begin{array}{c} p \\ q \\ r \\ s \end{array} \begin{array}{ccc} a & b & c \\ \begin{bmatrix} 1 & -1 & -5 \\ 4 & 0 & 2 \\ 3 & -3 & 10 \\ 3 & -5 & -4 \end{bmatrix} \end{array}$$
   B

14.

$$A \begin{array}{c} p \\ q \\ r \\ s \end{array} \begin{array}{ccc} a & b & c \\ \begin{bmatrix} 2 & -4 & 9 \\ 1 & 1 & 0 \\ -1 & -2 & -3 \\ 1 & 1 & -1 \end{bmatrix} \end{array}$$
   B

In Exercises 15–20, decide whether the game is strictly determined. If it is, give the players' optimal pure strategies and the value of the game. HINT [See Example 4.]

15.

$$\begin{array}{c} \\ A \begin{array}{c} a \\ b \end{array} \end{array} \begin{array}{cc} p & q \\ \begin{bmatrix} 1 & 1 \\ 2 & -4 \end{bmatrix} \end{array}$$
   B

16.

$$\begin{array}{c} \\ A \begin{array}{c} a \\ b \end{array} \end{array} \begin{array}{cc} p & q \\ \begin{bmatrix} -1 & 2 \\ 10 & -1 \end{bmatrix} \end{array}$$
   B

17.

$$\begin{array}{c} \\ A \begin{array}{c} a \\ b \end{array} \end{array} \begin{array}{ccc} p & q & r \\ \begin{bmatrix} 2 & 0 & -2 \\ -1 & 3 & 0 \end{bmatrix} \end{array}$$
   B

18.

$$\begin{array}{c} \\ A \begin{array}{c} a \\ b \end{array} \end{array} \begin{array}{ccc} p & q & r \\ \begin{bmatrix} -2 & 1 & -3 \\ -2 & 3 & -2 \end{bmatrix} \end{array}$$
   B

19.

$$
A \begin{array}{c} \\ P \\ Q \\ R \\ S \end{array}
\begin{array}{ccc} a & b & c \end{array}
\left[\begin{array}{ccc}
1 & -1 & -5 \\
4 & -4 & 2 \\
3 & -3 & -10 \\
5 & -5 & -4
\end{array} \right]
$$

with **B** as column heading.

20.

$$
A \begin{array}{c} \\ P \\ Q \\ R \\ S \end{array}
\begin{array}{ccc} a & b & c \end{array}
\left[\begin{array}{ccc}
-2 & -4 & 9 \\
1 & 1 & 0 \\
-1 & -2 & -3 \\
1 & 1 & -1
\end{array} \right]
$$

with **B** as column heading.

In Exercises 21–24, find: (a) the optimal mixed row strategy; (b) the optimal mixed column strategy, and (c) the expected value of the game in the event that each player uses his or her optimal mixed strategy. HINT [See Example 3.]

21. $P = \begin{bmatrix} -1 & 2 \\ 0 & -1 \end{bmatrix}$

22. $P = \begin{bmatrix} -1 & 0 \\ 1 & -1 \end{bmatrix}$

23. $P = \begin{bmatrix} -1 & -2 \\ -2 & 1 \end{bmatrix}$

24. $P = \begin{bmatrix} -2 & -1 \\ -1 & -3 \end{bmatrix}$

APPLICATIONS

Set up the payoff matrix in each of Exercises 25–32.

25. Games to Pass the Time You and your friend have come up with the following simple game to pass the time: at each round, you simultaneously call "heads" or "tails." If you have both called the same thing, your friend wins one point; if your calls differ, you win one point.

26. Games to Pass the Time Bored with the game in Exercise 25, you decide to use the following variation instead: If you both call "heads" your friend wins two points; if you both call "tails" your friend wins 1 point; if your calls differ, then you win two points if you called "heads," and one point if you called "tails."

27. War Games You are deciding whether to invade France, Sweden, or Norway, and your opponent is simultaneously deciding which of these three countries to defend. If you invade a country that your opponent is defending, you will be defeated (payoff: -1), but if you invade a country your opponent is not defending, you will be successful (payoff: $+1$).

28. War Games You must decide whether to attack your opponent by sea or air, and your opponent must simultaneously decide whether to mount an all-out air defense, an all-out coastal defense (against an attack from the sea) or a combined air and coastal defense. If there is no defense for your mode of attack, you win 100 points. If your attack is met by a shared air and coastal defense, you win 50 points. If your attack is met by an all-out defense, you lose 200 points.

29. ▼ Marketing Your fast-food outlet, Burger Queen, has obtained a license to open branches in three closely situated South African cities: Brakpan, Nigel, and Springs. Your market surveys show that Brakpan and Nigel each provide a potential market of 2,000 burgers a day, while Springs provides a potential market of 1,000 burgers per day. Your company can finance an outlet in only one of those cities. Your main competitor, Burger Princess, has also obtained licenses for these cities, and is similarly planning to open only one outlet. If you both happen to locate at the same city, you will share the total business from all three cities equally, but if you locate in different cities, you will each get all the business in the cities in which you have located, plus half the business in the third city. The payoff is the number of burgers you will sell per day minus the number of burgers your competitor will sell per day.

30. ▼ Marketing Repeat Exercise 29, given that the potential sales markets in the three cities are: Brakpan, 2,500 per day; Nigel, 1,500 per day; Springs, 1,200 per day.

31. ▼ Betting When you bet on a racehorse with odds of m–n, you stand to win m dollars for every bet of n dollars if your horse wins; for instance, if the horse you bet is running at 5–2 and wins, you will win \$5 for every \$2 you bet. (Thus a \$2 bet will return \$7.). Here are some actual odds from a 1992 race at Belmont Park, NY.[22] The favorite at 5–2 was Pleasant Tap. The second choice was Thunder Rumble at 7–2, while the third choice was Strike the Gold at 4–1. Assume you are making a \$10 bet on one of these horses. The payoffs are your winnings. (If your horse does not win, you lose your entire bet. Of course, it is possible for none of your horses to win.)

32. ▼ Betting Referring to Exercise 31, suppose that just before the race, there has been frantic betting on Thunder Rumble, with the result that the odds have dropped to 2–5. The odds on the other two horses remain unchanged.

33. Retail Discount Wars Just one week after your Abercrom B men's fashion outlet has opened at a new location opposite **Burger King** in the mall, your rival, Abercrom A, opens up directly across from you, You have been informed that Abercrom A is about to launch either a 30% off everything sale or a 50% off everything sale. You, on the other hand, have decided to either *increase* prices (to make your store seem more exclusive) or do absolutely nothing. You construct the following payoff matrix, where the payoffs represent the number of customers your outlet can expect to gain from Abercrom A:

		Abercrom A	
		30% Off	50% Off
Abercrom B	Do Nothing	-60	-40
	Increase Prices	30	-50

There is a 20% chance that Abercrom A will opt for the "30% off" sale and an 80% chance that they will opt for the "50% Off" sale. Your sense from upper management at Abercrom B is that there is a 50% chance you will be given the go-ahead to raise prices. What is the expected resulting effect on your customer base?

---

[22]Source: *The New York Times*, September 18, 1992, p. B14.

34. *More Retail Discount Wars* Your Abercrom B men's fashion outlet has a 30% chance of launching an expensive new line of used auto-mechanic dungarees (complete with grease stains) and a 70% chance of staying instead with its traditional torn military-style dungarees. Your rival across from you in the mall, Abercrom A, appears to be deciding between a line of torn gym shirts and a more daring line of "empty shirts" (that is, empty shirt boxes). Your corporate spies reveal that there is a 20% chance that Abercrom A will opt for the empty shirt option. The following payoff matrix gives the number of customers your outlet can expect to gain from Abercrom A in each situation:

Abercrom A

$$\text{Abercrom B} \quad \begin{matrix} \text{Mechanics} \\ \text{Military} \end{matrix} \quad \overset{\text{Torn Shirts \quad Empty Shirts}}{\begin{bmatrix} 10 & -40 \\ -30 & 50 \end{bmatrix}}$$

What is the expected resulting effect on your customer base?

35. *Factory Location*[23] A manufacturer of electrical machinery is located in a cramped, though low-rent, factory close to the center of a large city. The firm needs to expand, and it could do so in one of three ways: (1) remain where it is and install new equipment, (2) move to a suburban site in the same city, or (3) relocate in a different part of the country where labor is cheaper. Its decision will be influenced by the fact that one of the following will happen: (I) the government may introduce a program of equipment grants, (II) a new suburban highway may be built, or (III) the government may institute a policy of financial help to companies who move into regions of high unemployment. The value to the company of each combination is given in the following payoff matrix.

Government's Options

Manufacturer's Options		I	II	III
	1	200	150	140
	2	130	220	130
	3	110	110	220

If the manufacturer judges that there is a 20% probability that the government will go with option I, a 50% probability that they will go with option II, and a 30% probability that they will go with option III, what is the manufacturer's best option?

36. *Crop Choice*[24] A farmer has a choice of growing wheat, barley, or rice. Her success will depend on the weather, which could be dry, average, or wet. Her payoff matrix is as follows.

[23]Adapted from an example in *Location in Space: Theoretical Perspectives in Economic Geography* by P. Dicken and P.E. Lloyd (Harper & Row, 1990).
[24]Ibid.

Weather

Crop Choices		Dry	Average	Wet
	Wheat	20	20	10
	Barley	10	15	20
	Rice	10	20	20

If the probability that the weather will be dry is 10%, the probability that it will be average is 60%, and the probability that it will be wet is 30%, what is the farmer's best choice of crop?

37. *Study Techniques* Your mathematics test is tomorrow, and will cover the following topics: game theory, linear programming, and matrix algebra. You have decided to do an "all-nighter" and must determine how to allocate your eight hours of study time among the three topics. If you were to spend the entire eight hours on any one of these topics (thus using a pure strategy) you feel confident that you would earn a 90% score on that portion of the test, but would not do so well on the other topics. You have come up with the following table, where the entries are your expected scores. (The fact that linear programming and matrix algebra are used in game theory is reflected in these numbers).

Test

Your Strategies	Game Theory	Linear Programming	Matrix Algebra
Game Theory	90	70	70
Linear Programming	40	90	40
Matrix Algebra	60	40	90

You have been told that the test will be weighted as follows: game theory: 25%; linear programming: 50%; matrix algebra: 25%.

a. If you spend 25% of the night on game theory, 50% on linear programming, and 25% on matrix algebra, what score do you expect to get on the test?

b. Is it possible to improve on this by altering your study schedule? If so, what is the highest score you can expect on the test?

c. If your study schedule is according to part (a) and your teacher decides to forget her promises about how the test will be weighted and instead base it all on a single topic, which topic would be worst for you, and what score could you expect on the test?

38. *Study Techniques* Your friend Joe has been spending all of his time in fraternity activities, and thus knows absolutely nothing about any of the three topics on tomorrow's math test. (See Exercise 37.) Because you are recognized as an expert on the use of game theory to solve study problems, he has turned to you for advice as to how to spend his "all-nighter." As the following table shows, his situation is not so rosy. (Since he knows no linear programming or matrix algebra, the table shows, for instance, that studying game theory all night will not be much use in preparing him for this topic.)

Test

Joe's Strategies	Game Theory	Linear Programming	Matrix Algebra
Game Theory	30	0	20
Linear Programming	0	70	0
Matrix Algebra	0	0	70

Assuming that the test will be weighted as described in Exercise 37, what are the answers to parts (a), (b), and (c) as they apply to Joe?

39. ▼ *Staff Cutbacks* Frank Tempest manages a large snowplow service in Manhattan, Kansas, and is alarmed by the recent weather trends; there have been no significant snowfalls since 1993. He is therefore contemplating laying off some of his workers, but is unsure about whether to lay off 5, 10, or 15 of his 50 workers. Being very methodical, he estimates his annual net profits based on four possible annual snowfall figures: 0 inches, 20 inches, 40 inches and 60 inches. (He takes into account the fact that, if he is running a small operation in the face of a large annual snowfall, he will lose business to his competitors because he will be unable to discount on volume.)

	0 Inches	20 Inches	40 Inches	60 Inches
5 Laid Off	−$500,000	−$200,000	$10,000	$200,000
10 Laid Off	−$200,000	$0	$0	$0
15 Laid Off	−$100,000	$10,000	−$200,000	−$300,000

a. During the past 10 years, the region has had 0 inches twice, 20 inches twice, 40 inches three times, and 60 inches three times. Based on this information, how many workers should Tempest lay off, and how much would it cost him?

b. There is a 50% chance that Tempest will lay off 5 workers and a 50% chance that he will lay off 15 workers. What is the worst thing Nature can do to him in terms of snowfall? How much would it cost him?

c. The Gods of Chaos (who control the weather) know that Tempest is planning to use the strategy in part (a), and are determined to hurt Tempest as much as possible. Tempest, being somewhat paranoid, suspects it too. What should he do?

40. ▼ *Textbook Writing* You are writing a college-level textbook on finite mathematics, and are trying to come up with the best combination of word problems. Over the years, you have accumulated a collection of amusing problems, serious applications, long complicated problems, and "generic" problems.[25]

Before your book is published, it must be scrutinized by several reviewers who, it seems, are never satisfied with the mix you use. You estimate that there are three kinds of reviewers: the "no-nonsense" types who prefer applications and generic problems, the "dead serious" types, who feel that a college-level text should be contain little or no humor and lots of long complicated problems, and the "laid-back" types, who believe that learning best takes place in a light-hearted atmosphere bordering on anarchy. You have drawn up the following chart, where the payoffs represent the reactions of reviewers on a scale of −10 (ballistic) to +10 (ecstatic):

Reviewers

		No-Nonsense	Dead Serious	Laid-Back
You	**Amusing**	−5	−10	10
	Serious	5	3	0
	Long	−5	5	3
	Generic	5	3	−10

a. Your first draft of the book contained no generic problems, and equal numbers of the other categories. If half the reviewers of your book were "dead serious" and the rest were equally divided between the "no-nonsense" and "laid-back" types, what score would you expect?

b. In your second draft of the book, you tried to balance the content by including some generic problems and eliminating several amusing ones, and wound up with a mix of which one eighth were amusing, one quarter were serious, three eighths were long, and a quarter were generic. What kind of reviewer would be *least* impressed by this mix?

c. What kind of reviewer would be *most* impressed by the mix in your second draft?

41. *Price Wars* Computer Electronics, Inc. (CE) and the Gigantic Computer Store (GCS) are planning to discount the price they charge for the HAL Laptop Computer, of which they are the only distributors. Because Computer Electronics provides a free warranty service, they can generally afford to charge more. A market survey provides the following data on the gains to CE's market share that will result from different pricing decisions:

GCS

		$900	$1,000	$1,200
	$1,000	15%	60%	80%
CE	**$1,200**	15%	60%	60%
	$1,300	10%	20%	40%

a. Use reduction by dominance to determine how much each company should charge. What is the effect on CE's market share?

b. CE is aware that GCS is planning to use reduction by dominance to determine its pricing policy, and wants its market share to be as large as possible. What effect, if any, would the information about GCS have on CE's best strategy?

---

[25] Of the following type: "An oil company has three refineries: A, B, and C, each of which uses three processes: P_1, P_2, and P_3. Process P_1 uses 100 units of chemical C_1 and costs $100 per day. . . ."

42. *More Price Wars* (Refer to Exercise 41.) A new market survey results in the following revised data:

GCS

	$900	$1,000	$1,200
$1,000	20%	60%	60%
CE **$1,200**	15%	60%	60%
$1,300	10%	20%	40%

a. Use reduction by dominance to determine how much each company should charge. What is the effect on CE's market share?

b. In general, why do price wars tend to force prices down?

43. *Wrestling Tournaments* City Community College (CCC) plans to host Midtown Military Academy (MMA) for a wrestling tournament. Each school has three wrestlers in the 190 lb. weight class: CCC has Pablo, Sal, and Edison, while MMA has Carlos, Marcus, and Noto. Pablo can beat Carlos and Marcus, Marcus can beat Edison and Sal, Noto can beat Edison, while the other combinations will result in an even match. Set up a payoff matrix, and use reduction by dominance to decide which wrestler each team should choose as their champion. Does one school have an advantage over the other?

44. *Wrestling Tournaments* (Refer to Exercise 43.) One day before the wrestling tournament discussed in Exercise 43, Pablo sustains a hamstring injury, and is replaced by Hans, who (unfortunately for CCC) can be beaten by both Carlos and Marcus. Set up the payoff matrix, and use reduction by dominance to decide which wrestler each team should choose as their champion. Does one school have an advantage over the other?

45. *The Battle of Rabaul-Lae*[26] In the Second World War, during the struggle for New Guinea, intelligence reports revealed that the Japanese were planning to move a troop and supply convoy from the port of Rabaul at the Eastern tip of New Britain to Lae, which lies just west of New Britain on New Guinea. It could either travel via a northern route which was plagued by poor visibility, or by a southern route, where the visibility was clear. General Kenney, who was the commander of the Allied Air Forces in the area, had the choice of concentrating reconnaissance aircraft on one route or the other, and bombing the Japanese convoy once it was sighted. Kenney's staff drafted the following outcomes for his choices, where the payoffs are estimated days of bombing time:

**Japanese
Commander's Strategies**

		Northern Route	Southern Route
Kenney's Strategies	**Northern Route**	2	2
	Southern Route	1	3

What would you have recommended to General Kenney? What would you have recommended to the Japanese Commander?[27] How much bombing time results if these recommendations are followed?

46. *The Battle of Rabaul-Lae* Referring to Exercise 45, suppose that General Kenney had a third alternative: Splitting his reconnaissance aircraft between the two routes, and resulting in the following estimates:

**Japanese
Commander's Strategies**

		Northern Route	Southern Route
Kenney's Strategies	**Northern Route**	2	2
	Split Reconnaissance	1.5	2.5
	Southern Route	1	3

What would you have recommended to General Kenney? What would you have recommended to the Japanese Commander? How much bombing time results if these recommendations are followed?

47. ▼ *The Prisoner's Dilemma* Slim Lefty and Joe Rap have been arrested for grand theft auto, having been caught red-handed driving away in a stolen 2010 Porsche. Although the police have more than enough evidence to convict them both, they feel that a confession would simplify the work of the prosecution. They decide to interrogate the prisoners separately. Slim and Joe are both told of the following plea-bargaining arrangement: If both confess, they will each receive a 2-year sentence; if neither confesses, they will both receive five-year sentences, and if only one confesses (and thus squeals on the other), he will receive a suspended sentence, while the other will receive a 10-year sentence. What should Slim do?

48. ▼ *More Prisoners' Dilemmas* Jane Good and Prudence Brown have been arrested for robbery, but the police lack sufficient evidence for a conviction, and so decide to interrogate them separately in the hope of extracting a confession. Both Jane and Prudence are told the following: If they both confess, they will each receive a five-year sentence; if neither confesses, they will be released; if one confesses, she will receive a suspended sentence, while the other will receive a ten-year sentence. What should Jane do?

49. ▼ *Campaign Strategies*[28] Florida and Ohio are "swing states" that have a large bounty of electoral votes and are therefore highly valued by presidential campaign strategists. Suppose it is now the weekend before Election Day 2008, and each candidate (McCain and Obama) can visit only one more state. Further, to win the election, McCain needs to win both of these states. Currently McCain has a 40% chance of

---

[26]As discussed in *Games and Decisions* by R.D. Luce and H. Raiffa Section 11.3 (New York: Wiley, 1957). This is based on an article in the *Journal of the Operations Research Society of America* **2** (1954) 365–385.

[27]The correct answers to parts (a) and (b) correspond to the actual decisions both commanders made.

[28]Based on *Game Theory for Swingers: What states should the candidates visit before Election Day?* by Jordan Ellenberg. Source: www.slate.com.

winning Ohio and a 60% chance of winning Florida. Therefore, he has a $0.40 \times 0.60 = 0.24$, or 24% chance of winning the election. Assume that each candidate can increase his probability of winning a state by 10% if he, and not his opponent, visits that state. If both candidates visit the same state, there is no effect.

a. Set up a payoff matrix with McCain as the row player and Obama as the column player, where the payoff for a specific set of circumstances is the probability (expressed as a percentage) that McCain will win both states.

b. Where should each candidate visit under the circumstances?

50. ▼ *Campaign Strategies* Repeat Exercise 49, this time assuming that McCain has an 80% chance of winning Ohio and a 90% chance of winning Florida.

51. *Advertising* The Softex Shampoo Company is considering how to split its advertising budget between ads on two radio stations: WISH and WASH. Its main competitor, Splish Shampoo, Inc. has found out about this, and is considering countering Softex's ads with its own, on the same radio stations. (Proposed jingle: *Softex, Shmoftex; Splash with Splish*) Softex has calculated that, were it to devote its entire advertising budget to ads on WISH, it would increase revenues in the coming month by $100,000 in the event that Splish was running all its ads on the less popular WASH, but would lose $20,000 in revenues if Splish ran its ads on WISH. If, on the other hand, it devoted its entire budget to WASH ads, it would neither increase nor decrease revenues in the event that Splish was running all its ads on the more popular WISH, and would in fact lose $20,000 in revenues if Splish ran its ads on WASH. What should Softex do, and what effect will this have on revenues?

52. *Labor Negotiations* The management team of the Abstract Concrete Company is negotiating a three-year contract with the labor unions at one of its plants, and is trying to decide on its offer for a salary increase. If it offers a 5% increase and the unions accept the offer, Abstract Concrete will gain $20 million in projected profits in the coming year, but if labor rejects the offer, the management team predicts that it will be forced to increase the offer to the union demand of 15%, thus halving the projected profits. If Abstract Concrete offers a 15% increase, the company will earn $10 million in profits over the coming year if the unions accept. If the unions reject, they will probably go out on strike (because management has set 15% as its upper limit) and management has decided that it can then in fact gain $12 million in profits by selling out the

defunct plant in retaliation. What intermediate percentage should the company offer, and what profit should it project?

COMMUNICATION AND REASONING EXERCISES

53. Why is a saddle point called a "saddle point"?

54. Can the payoff in a saddle point ever be larger than all other payoffs in a game? Explain.

55. ◆One day, while browsing through an old *Statistical Abstract of the United States,* you came across the following data which show the number of females employed (in thousands) in various categories according to their educational attainment.[29]

	Managerial/ Professional	Technical/Sales/ Administrative	Service	Precision Production	Operators/ Fabricators
Less Than 4 Years High School	260	1,080	2,020	260	1,400
4 Years of High School Only	2,430	9,510	3,600	570	2,130
1 to 3 Years of College	2,690	5,080	1,080	160	350
At Least 4 Years of College	7,210	2,760	380	70	110

Because you had been studying game theory that day, the first thing you did was to search for a saddle point. Having found one, you conclude that, as a female, your best strategy in the job market is to forget about a college career. Find the flaw in this reasoning.

56. ◆Exercises 37 and 38 seem to suggest that studying a single topic prior to an exam is better than studying all the topics in that exam. Comment on this discrepancy between the game theory result and common sense.

57. ◆Explain what is wrong with a decision to play the mixed strategy [0.5 0.5] by alternating the two strategies: play the first strategy on the odd-numbered moves and the second strategy on the even-numbered moves. Illustrate your argument by devising a game in which your best strategy is [0.5 0.5].

58. ◆Describe a situation in which a both a mixed strategy and a pure strategy are equally effective.

---

[29]Source: *Statistical Abstract of the United States 1991* (111th Ed.) U.S. Department of Commerce, Economics and Statistics Administration, and Bureau of the Census.

3.5 Input-Output Models

In this section we look at an application of matrix algebra developed by Wassily Leontief (1906–1999) in the middle of the twentieth century. In 1973, he won the Nobel Prize in Economics for this work. The application involves analyzing national and regional economies by looking at how various parts of the economy interrelate. We'll work out some of the details by looking at a simple scenario.

First, we can think of the economy of a country or a region as being composed of various **sectors**, or groups of one or more industries. Typical sectors are the manufacturing sector, the utilities sector, and the agricultural sector. To introduce the basic concepts, we shall consider two specific sectors: the coal-mining sector (Sector 1) and the electric utilities sector (Sector 2). Both produce a commodity: the coal-mining sector produces coal, and the electric utilities sector produces electricity. We measure these products by their dollar value. By **one unit** of a product, we mean $1 worth of that product.

Here is the scenario.

1. To produce one unit ($1 worth) of coal, assume that the coal-mining sector uses 50¢ worth of coal (to power mining machinery, say) and 10¢ worth of electricity.

2. To produce one unit ($1 worth) of electricity, assume that the electric utilities sector uses 25¢ worth of coal and 25¢ worth of electricity.

These are *internal* usage figures. In addition to this, assume that there is an *external* demand (from the rest of the economy) of 7,000 units ($7,000 worth) of coal and 14,000 units ($14,000 worth) of electricity over a specific time period (one year, say). Our basic question is: How much should each of the two sectors supply in order to meet both internal and external demand?

The key to answering this question is to set up equations of the form:

Total supply = Total demand.

The unknowns, the values we are seeking, are

x_1 = the total supply (in units) from Sector 1 (coal) and
x_2 = the total supply (in units) from Sector 2 (electricity).

Our equations then take the following form:

Total supply from Sector 1 = Total demand for Sector 1 products

$$x_1 = 0.50x_1 \quad + \quad 0.25x_2 \quad + \quad 7,000$$

Coal required by Sector 1   Coal required by Sector 2   External demand for coal

Total supply from Sector 2 = Total demand for Sector 2 products

$$x_2 = 0.10x_1 \quad + \quad 0.25x_2 \quad + \quad 14,000.$$

Electricity required by Sector 1   Electricity required by Sector 2   External demand for electricity

This is a system of two linear equations in two unknowns:

$$x_1 = 0.50x_1 + 0.25x_2 + 7,000$$
$$x_2 = 0.10x_1 + 0.25x_2 + 14,000.$$

We can rewrite this system of equations in matrix form as follows:

$$\underbrace{\begin{bmatrix} x_1 \\ x_2 \end{bmatrix}}_{\text{Production}} = \underbrace{\begin{bmatrix} 0.50 & 0.25 \\ 0.10 & 0.25 \end{bmatrix} \begin{bmatrix} x_1 \\ x_2 \end{bmatrix}}_{\text{Internal demand}} + \underbrace{\begin{bmatrix} 7,000 \\ 14,000 \end{bmatrix}}_{\text{External demand}}.$$

In symbols,

$$X = AX + D.$$

Here,

$$X = \begin{bmatrix} x_1 \\ x_2 \end{bmatrix}$$

is called the **production vector.** Its entries are the amounts produced by the two sectors. The matrix

$$D = \begin{bmatrix} 7,000 \\ 14,000 \end{bmatrix}$$

is called the **external demand** vector, and

$$A = \begin{bmatrix} 0.50 & 0.25 \\ 0.10 & 0.25 \end{bmatrix}$$

is called the **technology matrix.** The entries of the technology matrix have the following meanings:

$a_{11} = $ units of Sector 1 needed to produce one unit of Sector 1

$a_{12} = $ units of Sector 1 needed to produce one unit of Sector 2

$a_{21} = $ units of Sector 2 needed to produce one unit of Sector 1

$a_{22} = $ units of Sector 2 needed to produce one unit of Sector 2.

You can remember this order by the slogan "In the side, out the top."

Now that we have the matrix equation

$$X = AX + D$$

we can solve it as follows. First, subtract AX from both sides:

$$X - AX = D.$$

Because $X = IX$, where I is the 2×2 identity matrix, we can rewrite this as

$$IX - AX = D.$$

Now factor out X:

$$(I - A)X = D.$$

If we multiply both sides by the inverse of $(I - A)$, we get the solution

$$X = (I - A)^{-1}D.$$

Input-Output Model

In an input-output model, an economy (or part of one) is divided into n **sectors.** We then record the $n \times n$ **technology matrix** A, whose ijth entry is the number of units from Sector i used in producing one unit from Sector j ("in the side, out the top"). To meet an **external demand** of D, the economy must produce X, where X is the **production vector.** These are related by the equations

$$X = AX + D$$

or

$$X = (I - A)^{-1}D. \qquad \text{Provided } (I - A) \text{ is invertible}$$

> ### Quick Example
>
> In the previous scenario, $A = \begin{bmatrix} 0.50 & 0.25 \\ 0.10 & 0.25 \end{bmatrix}$, $X = \begin{bmatrix} x_1 \\ x_2 \end{bmatrix}$, and $D = \begin{bmatrix} 7,000 \\ 14,000 \end{bmatrix}$.
>
> The solution is
> $$X = (I - A)^{-1} D$$
>
> $$\begin{bmatrix} x_1 \\ x_2 \end{bmatrix} = \left(\begin{bmatrix} 1 & 0 \\ 0 & 1 \end{bmatrix} - \begin{bmatrix} 0.50 & 0.25 \\ 0.10 & 0.25 \end{bmatrix} \right)^{-1} \begin{bmatrix} 7,000 \\ 14,000 \end{bmatrix} \qquad \text{Calculate } I - A$$
>
> $$= \begin{bmatrix} 0.50 & -0.25 \\ -0.10 & 0.75 \end{bmatrix}^{-1} \begin{bmatrix} 7,000 \\ 14,000 \end{bmatrix} \qquad \text{Calculate } (I - A)^{-1}$$
>
> $$= \begin{bmatrix} \frac{15}{7} & \frac{5}{7} \\ \frac{2}{7} & \frac{10}{7} \end{bmatrix} \begin{bmatrix} 7,000 \\ 14,000 \end{bmatrix}$$
>
> $$= \begin{bmatrix} 25,000 \\ 22,000 \end{bmatrix}.$$
>
> In other words, to meet the demand, the economy must produce $25,000 worth of coal and $22,000 worth of electricity.

The next example uses actual data from the U.S. economy (we have rounded the figures to make the computations less complicated). It is rare to find input-output data already packaged for you as a technology matrix. Instead, the data commonly found in statistical sources come in the form of "input-output tables," from which we will have to construct the technology matrix.

EXAMPLE 1 Petroleum and Natural Gas

BananaStock/Jupiter Images

Consider two sectors of the U.S. economy: crude petroleum and natural gas (*crude*) and petroleum refining and related industries (*refining*). According to government figures,* in 1998 the crude sector used $27,000 million worth of its own products and $750 million worth of the products of the refining sector to produce $87,000 million worth of goods (crude oil and natural gas). The refining sector in the same year used $59,000 million worth of the products of the crude sector and $15,000 million worth of its own products to produce $140,000 million worth of goods (refined oil and the like). What was the technology matrix for these two sectors? What was left over from each of these sectors for use by other parts of the economy or for export?

Solution First, for convenience, we record the given data in the form of a table, called the **input-output table**. (All figures are in millions of dollars.)

	To	Crude	Refining
From	**Crude**	27,000	59,000
	Refining	750	15,000
	Total Output	87,000	140,000

---

* The data have been rounded to two significant digits. Source: *Survey of Current Business*, December, 2001, U.S. Department of Commerce. The *Survey of Current Business* and the input-output tables themselves are available at the Web site of the Department of Commerce's Bureau of Economic Analysis (www.bea.gov).

The entries in the top portion are arranged in the same way as those of the technology matrix: The ijth entry represents the number of units of Sector i that went to Sector j. Thus, for instance, the 59,000 million entry in the 1, 2 position represents the number of units of Sector 1, crude, that were used by Sector 2, refining. ("In the side, out the top".)

We now construct the technology matrix. The technology matrix has entries $a_{ij} =$ units of Sector i used to produce *one* unit of Sector j. Thus,

$a_{11} =$ units of crude to produce one unit of crude. We are told that 27,000 million units of crude were used to produce 87,000 million units of crude. Thus, to produce *one* unit of crude, $27{,}000/87{,}000 \approx 0.31$ units of crude were used, and so $a_{11} \approx 0.31$. (We have rounded this value to two significant digits; further digits are not reliable due to rounding of the original data.)

$a_{12} =$ units of crude to produce one unit of refined:
$$a_{12} = 59{,}000/140{,}000 \approx 0.42$$

$a_{21} =$ units of refined to produce one unit of crude:
$$a_{21} = 750/87{,}000 \approx 0.0086$$

$a_{22} =$ units of refined to produce one unit of refined:
$$a_{22} = 15{,}000/140{,}000 \approx 0.11.$$

This gives the technology matrix

$$A = \begin{bmatrix} 0.31 & 0.42 \\ 0.0086 & 0.11 \end{bmatrix}.$$ Technology Matrix

In short *we obtained the technology matrix from the input-output table by dividing the Sector 1 column by the Sector 1 total, and the Sector 2 column by the Sector 2 total.*

Now we also know the total output from each sector, so *we have already been given the production vector:*

$$X = \begin{bmatrix} 87{,}000 \\ 140{,}000 \end{bmatrix}.$$ Production Vector

What we are asked for is the external demand vector D, the amount available for the outside economy. To find D, we use the equation

$$X = AX + D$$ Relationship of X, A, and D

where, this time, we are given A and X, and must solve for D. Solving for D gives

$$D = X - AX$$

$$= \begin{bmatrix} 87{,}000 \\ 140{,}000 \end{bmatrix} - \begin{bmatrix} 0.31 & 0.42 \\ 0.0086 & 0.11 \end{bmatrix} \begin{bmatrix} 87{,}000 \\ 140{,}000 \end{bmatrix}$$

$$\approx \begin{bmatrix} 87{,}000 \\ 140{,}000 \end{bmatrix} - \begin{bmatrix} 86{,}000 \\ 16{,}000 \end{bmatrix} = \begin{bmatrix} 1{,}000 \\ 124{,}000 \end{bmatrix}.$$ We rounded to two digits.[†]

The first number, $1,000 million, is the amount produced by the crude sector that is available to be used by other parts of the economy or to be exported. (In fact, because something has to happen to all that crude petroleum and natural gas, this is the amount actually used or exported, where use can include stockpiling.) The second number, $124,000 million, represents the amount produced by the refining sector that is available to be used by other parts of the economy or to be exported.

[†] Why?

using Technology
See the Technology Guides at
the end of the chapter to see
how to compute the technology matrix and the external
demand vector in Example 1
using a TI-83/84 Plus or Excel.

Note that we could have calculated D more simply from the input-output table. The internal use of units from the crude sector was the sum of the outputs from that sector:

$$27{,}000 + 59{,}000 = 86{,}000.$$

Because 87,000 units were actually produced by the sector, that left a surplus of $87,000 − 86,000 = 1,000$ units for export. We could compute the surplus from the refining sector similarly. (The two calculations actually come out slightly different, because we rounded the intermediate results.) The calculation in Example 2 below cannot be done as trivially, however.

Input-Output Table

National economic data are often given in the form of an **input-output table**. The ijth entry in the top portion of the table is the number of units that go from Sector i to Sector j. The "Total outputs" are the total numbers of units produced by each sector. We obtain the technology matrix from the input-output table by dividing the Sector 1 column by the Sector 1 total, the Sector 2 column by the Sector 2 total, and so on.

Quick Example

Input-Output Table:

		To	Skateboards	Wood
From	**Skateboards**		20,000*	0
	Wood		100,000	500,000
	Total Output		200,000	5,000,000

Technology Matrix:

$$A = \begin{bmatrix} \dfrac{20{,}000}{200{,}000} & \dfrac{0}{5{,}000{,}000} \\[2mm] \dfrac{100{,}000}{200{,}000} & \dfrac{500{,}000}{5{,}000{,}000} \end{bmatrix} = \begin{bmatrix} 0.1 & 0 \\ 0.5 & 0.1 \end{bmatrix}.$$

---

*The production of skateboards required skateboards due to the fact that skateboard workers tend to commute to work on (what else?) skateboards!

EXAMPLE 2 Rising Demand

Suppose that external demand for refined petroleum rises to $200,000 million, but the demand for crude remains $1,000 million (as in Example 1). How do the production levels of the two sectors considered in Example 1 have to change?

Solution We are being told that now

$$D = \begin{bmatrix} 1{,}000 \\ 200{,}000 \end{bmatrix}$$

and we are asked to find X. Remember that we can calculate X from the formula

$$X = (I - A)^{-1} D.$$

Now

$$I - A = \begin{bmatrix} 1 & 0 \\ 0 & 1 \end{bmatrix} - \begin{bmatrix} 0.31 & 0.42 \\ 0.0086 & 0.11 \end{bmatrix} = \begin{bmatrix} 0.69 & -0.42 \\ -0.0086 & 0.89 \end{bmatrix}.$$

* **NOTE** Because A is accurate to two digits, we should use more than two significant digits in intermediate calculations so as not to lose additional accuracy. We must, of course, round the final answer to two digits.

We take the inverse using our favorite technique and find that, to four significant digits,*

$$(I - A)^{-1} \approx \begin{bmatrix} 1.458 & 0.6880 \\ 0.01409 & 1.130 \end{bmatrix}.$$

Now we can compute X:

$$X = (I - A)^{-1} D = \begin{bmatrix} 1.458 & 0.6880 \\ 0.01409 & 1.130 \end{bmatrix} \begin{bmatrix} 1,000 \\ 200,000 \end{bmatrix} \approx \begin{bmatrix} 140,000 \\ 230,000 \end{bmatrix}.$$

(As in Example 1, we have rounded all the entries in the answer to two significant digits.) Comparing this vector to the production vector used in Example 1, we see that production in the crude sector has to increase from $87,000 million to $140,000 million, while production in the refining sector has to increase from $140,000 million to $230,000 million.

Note Using the matrix $(I - A)^{-1}$, we have a slightly different way of solving Example 2. We are asking for the effect on production of a *change* in the final demand of 0 for crude and $200,000 - 124,000 = $76,000 million for refined products. If we multiply $(I - A)^{-1}$ by the matrix representing this *change,* we obtain

$$\begin{bmatrix} 1.458 & 0.6880 \\ 0.01409 & 1.130 \end{bmatrix} \begin{bmatrix} 0 \\ 76,000 \end{bmatrix} \approx \begin{bmatrix} 53,000 \\ 90,000 \end{bmatrix}.$$

$(I - A)^{-1} \times$ Change in Demand = Change in Production

We see the changes required in production: an increase of $53,000 million in the crude sector and an increase of $90,000 million in the refining sector.

Notice that the increase in external demand for the products of the refining sector requires the crude sector to also increase production, even though there is no increase in the *external* demand for its products. The reason is that, in order to increase production, the refining sector needs to use more crude oil, so that the *internal* demand for crude oil goes up. The inverse matrix $(I - A)^{-1}$ takes these **indirect effects** into account in a nice way.

By replacing the $76,000 by $1 in the computation we just did, we see that a $1 increase in external demand for refined products will require an increase in production of $0.6880 in the crude sector, as well as an increase in production of $1.130 in the refining sector. This is how we interpret the entries in $(I - A)^{-1}$, and this is why it is useful to look at this matrix inverse rather than just solve $(I - A)X = D$ for X using, say, Gauss-Jordan reduction. Looking at $(I - A)^{-1}$, we can also find the effects of an increase of $1 in external demand for crude: an increase in production of $1.458 in the crude sector and an increase of $0.01409 in the refining sector.

Here are some questions to think about: Why are the diagonal entries of $(I - A)^{-1}$ (slightly) larger than 1? Why is the entry in the lower left so small compared to the others? ∎

Interpreting $(I - A)^{-1}$: Indirect Effects

If A is the technology matrix, then the ijth entry of $(I - A)^{-1}$ is the change in the number of units Sector i must produce in order to meet a one-unit increase in external demand for Sector j products. To meet a rising external demand, the necessary change in production for each sector is given by

$$\text{Change in production} = (I - A)^{-1}D^+$$

where D^+ is the change in external demand.

Quick Example

Take Sector 1 to be skateboards, and Sector 2 to be wood, and assume that

$$(I - A)^{-1} = \begin{bmatrix} 1.1 & 0 \\ 0.6 & 1.1 \end{bmatrix}.$$

Then

$a_{11} = 1.1 =$ number of additional units of skateboards that must be produced to meet a one-unit increase in the demand for skateboards (Why is this number larger than 1?)

$a_{12} = 0 =$ number of additional units of skateboards that must be produced to meet a one-unit increase in the demand for wood (Why is this number 0?)

$a_{21} = 0.6 =$ number of additional units of wood that must be produced to meet a one-unit increase in the demand for skateboards

$a_{22} = 1.1 =$ number of additional units of wood that must be produced to meet a one-unit increase in the demand for wood.

To meet an increase in external demand of 100 skateboards and 400 units of wood, the necessary change in production is

$$(I - A)^{-1}D^+ = \begin{bmatrix} 1.1 & 0 \\ 0.6 & 1.1 \end{bmatrix} \begin{bmatrix} 100 \\ 400 \end{bmatrix} = \begin{bmatrix} 110 \\ 500 \end{bmatrix}$$

so 110 additional skateboards and 500 additional units of wood will need to be produced.

In the preceding examples, we used only two sectors of the economy. The data used in Examples 1 and 2 were taken from an input-output table published by the U.S. Department of Commerce, in which the whole U.S. economy was broken down into 85 sectors. This in turn was a simplified version of a model in which the economy was broken into about 500 sectors. Obviously, computers are required to make a realistic input-output analysis possible. Many governments collect and publish input-output data as part of their national planning. The United Nations collects these data and publishes collections of national statistics. The United Nations also has a useful set of links to government statistics at the following URL:

www.un.org/Depts/unsd/sd_natstat.htm

EXAMPLE 3 Kenya Economy

Consider four sectors of the economy of Kenya*: (1) the traditional economy, (2) agriculture, (3) manufacture of metal products and machinery, and (4) wholesale and retail trade. The input-output table for these four sectors for 1976 looks like this (all numbers are thousands of K£):

	To	1	2	3	4
From	1	8,600	0	0	0
	2	0	20,000	24	0
	3	1,500	530	15,000	660
	4	810	8,500	5,800	2,900
Total Output		87,000	530,000	110,000	180,000

Suppose that external demand for agriculture increased by K£50,000,000 and that external demand for metal products and machinery increased by K£10,000,000. How would production in these four sectors have to change to meet this rising demand?

Solution To find the change in production necessary to meet the rising demand, we need to use the formula

$$\text{Change in production} = (I - A)^{-1} D^+$$

where A is the technology matrix and D^+ is the change in demand:

$$D^+ = \begin{bmatrix} 0 \\ 50,000 \\ 10,000 \\ 0 \end{bmatrix}.$$

With entries shown rounded to two significant digits, the matrix A is

$$A = \begin{bmatrix} 0.099 & 0 & 0 & 0 \\ 0 & 0.038 & 0.00022 & 0 \\ 0.017 & 0.001 & 0.14 & 0.0037 \\ 0.0093 & 0.016 & 0.053 & 0.016 \end{bmatrix}.$$

Entries shown are rounded to two significant digits.

The next calculation is best done using technology:

$$\text{Change in production} = (I - A)^{-1} D^+ = \begin{bmatrix} 0 \\ 52,000 \\ 12,000 \\ 1,500 \end{bmatrix}.$$

Entries shown are rounded to two significant digits.

Looking at this result, we see that the changes in external demand will leave the traditional economy unaffected, production in agriculture will rise by K£52 million, production in the manufacture of metal products and machinery will rise by K£12 million, and activity in wholesale and retail trade will rise by K£1.5 million.

---

* Figures are rounded. Source: *Input-Output Tables for Kenya 1976,* Central Bureau of Statistics of the Ministry of Economic Planning and Community Affairs, Kenya.

using Technology

Technology can be used to do the computations in Example 3. Here is an outline for part (a) (see the Technology Guides at the end of the chapter for additional details on using a TI-83/84 Plus or Excel):

TI-83/84 Plus
Enter the matrices A and D using MATRX ; EDIT. (For A type the entries as quotients: Column entry/ Column total.) Home Screen:
(identity(4)-[A])^-1[D]
[More details on page 256.]

Excel
Obtain the technology matrix as in Example 1.
Insert the 4×4 identity matrix and then use MINVERSE and MMULT to compute $(I - A)^{-1} D$.
[More details on page 261.]

Web Site
www.FiniteandCalc.org
  Student Home
    → Online Utilities
    → Matrix Algebra Tool
Enter the matrices A and D. (For A type the entries as quotients: Column entry/ Column total.)
Type (I-A)^(-1)*D in the formula box and press "Compute."

➡ **Before we go on...** Can you see why the traditional economy was unaffected in Example 3? Although it takes inputs from other parts of the economy, it is not itself an input to any other part. In other words, there is no intermediate demand for the products of the traditional economy coming from any other part of the economy, and so an increase in production in any other sector of the economy will require no increase from the traditional economy. On the other hand, the wholesale and retail trade sector does provide input to the agriculture and manufacturing sectors, so increases in those sectors do require an increase in the trade sector.

One more point: If you calculate $(I - A)^{-1}$ you will notice how small the off-diagonal entries are. This says that increases in each sector have relatively small effects on the other sectors. We say that these sectors are **loosely coupled**. Regional economies, where many products are destined to be shipped out to the rest of the country, tend to show this phenomenon even more strongly. Notice in Example 2 that those two sectors are **strongly coupled**, because a rise in demand for refined products requires a comparable rise in the production of crude. ■

3.5 **EXERCISES**

▼ more advanced   ◆ challenging
⊤ indicates exercises that should be solved using technology

1. Let A be the technology matrix $A = \begin{bmatrix} 0.2 & 0.05 \\ 0.8 & 0.01 \end{bmatrix}$, where

Sector 1 is paper and Sector 2 is wood. Fill in the missing quantities.

a. ___ units of wood are needed to produce one unit of paper.

b. ___ units of paper are used in the production of one unit of paper.

c. The production of each unit of wood requires the use of ___ units of paper.

2. Let A be the technology matrix $A = \begin{bmatrix} 0.01 & 0.001 \\ 0.2 & 0.004 \end{bmatrix}$,

where Sector 1 is computer chips and Sector 2 is silicon. Fill in the missing quantities.

a. ___ units of silicon are required in the production of one unit of silicon.

b. ___ units of computer chips are used in the production of one unit of silicon.

c. The production of each unit of computer chips requires the use of ___ units of silicon.

3. Each unit of television news requires 0.2 units of television news and 0.5 units of radio news. Each unit of radio news requires 0.1 units of television news and no radio news. With Sector 1 as television news and Sector 2 as radio news, set up the technology matrix A.

4. Production of one unit of cologne requires no cologne and 0.5 units of perfume. Into one unit of perfume go 0.1 units of cologne and 0.3 units of perfume. With Sector 1 as cologne and Sector 2 as perfume, set up the technology matrix A.

In each of Exercises 5–12, you are given a technology matrix A and an external demand vector D. Find the corresponding production vector X. HINT [See Quick Example on page 236.]

5. $A = \begin{bmatrix} 0.5 & 0.4 \\ 0 & 0.5 \end{bmatrix}$, $D = \begin{bmatrix} 10,000 \\ 20,000 \end{bmatrix}$

6. $A = \begin{bmatrix} 0.5 & 0.4 \\ 0 & 0.5 \end{bmatrix}$, $D = \begin{bmatrix} 20,000 \\ 10,000 \end{bmatrix}$

7. $A = \begin{bmatrix} 0.1 & 0.4 \\ 0.2 & 0.5 \end{bmatrix}$, $D = \begin{bmatrix} 25,000 \\ 15,000 \end{bmatrix}$

8. $A = \begin{bmatrix} 0.1 & 0.2 \\ 0.4 & 0.5 \end{bmatrix}$, $D = \begin{bmatrix} 24,000 \\ 14,000 \end{bmatrix}$

9. $A = \begin{bmatrix} 0.5 & 0.1 & 0 \\ 0 & 0.5 & 0.1 \\ 0 & 0 & 0.5 \end{bmatrix}$, $D = \begin{bmatrix} 1,000 \\ 1,000 \\ 2,000 \end{bmatrix}$

10. $A = \begin{bmatrix} 0.5 & 0.1 & 0 \\ 0.1 & 0.5 & 0.1 \\ 0 & 0 & 0.5 \end{bmatrix}$, $D = \begin{bmatrix} 3,000 \\ 3,800 \\ 2,000 \end{bmatrix}$

11. $A = \begin{bmatrix} 0.2 & 0.2 & 0 \\ 0.2 & 0.4 & 0.2 \\ 0 & 0.2 & 0.2 \end{bmatrix}$, $D = \begin{bmatrix} 16,000 \\ 8,000 \\ 8,000 \end{bmatrix}$

12. $A = \begin{bmatrix} 0.2 & 0.2 & 0.2 \\ 0.2 & 0.4 & 0.2 \\ 0.2 & 0.2 & 0.2 \end{bmatrix}$, $D = \begin{bmatrix} 7,000 \\ 14,000 \\ 7,000 \end{bmatrix}$

13. Given $A = \begin{bmatrix} 0.1 & 0.4 \\ 0.2 & 0.5 \end{bmatrix}$, find the changes in production required to meet an increase in demand of 50 units of Sector 1 products and 30 units of Sector 2 products.

14. Given $A = \begin{bmatrix} 0.5 & 0.4 \\ 0 & 0.5 \end{bmatrix}$, find the changes in production required to meet an increase in demand of 20 units of Sector 1 products and 10 units of Sector 2 products.

15. Let $(I - A)^{-1} = \begin{bmatrix} 1.5 & 0.1 & 0 \\ 0.2 & 1.2 & 0.1 \\ 0.1 & 0.7 & 1.6 \end{bmatrix}$ and assume that the external demand for the products in Sector 1 increases by 1 unit. By how many units should each sector increase production? What do the columns of the matrix $(I - A)^{-1}$ tell you? HINT [See Quick Example on page 230.]

16. Let $(I - A)^{-1} = \begin{bmatrix} 1.5 & 0.1 & 0 \\ 0.1 & 1.1 & 0.1 \\ 0 & 0 & 1.3 \end{bmatrix}$, and assume that the external demand for the products in each of the sectors increases by 1 unit. By how many units should each sector increase production?

In Exercises 17 and 18, obtain the technology matrix from the given input-output table. HINT [See Example 1.]

17.

From \ To	A	B	C
A	1,000	2,000	3,000
B	0	4,000	0
C	0	1,000	3,000
Total Output	5,000	5,000	6,000

18.

From \ To	A	B	C
A	0	100	300
B	500	400	300
C	0	0	600
Total Output	1,000	2,000	3,000

APPLICATIONS

19. *Campus Food* The two campus cafeterias, the Main Dining Room and Bits & Bytes, typically use each other's food in doing business on campus. One weekend, the input-output table was as follows.[30]

From \ To	Main DR	Bits & Bytes
Main DR	$10,000	$20,000
Bits & Bytes	5,000	0
Total Output	50,000	40,000

Given that the demand for food on campus last weekend was $45,000 from the Main Dining Room and $30,000 from Bits & Bytes, how much did the two cafeterias have to produce to meet the demand last weekend? HINT [See Example 1.]

20. *Plagiarism* Two student groups at Enormous State University, the Choral Society and the Football Club, maintain files of term papers that they write and offer to students for research purposes. Some of these papers they use themselves in generating more papers. In order to avoid suspicion of plagiarism by faculty members (who seem to have astute memories), each paper is given to students or used by the clubs only once (no copies are kept). The number of papers that were used in the production of new papers last year is shown in the following input-output table:

From \ To	Choral Soc.	Football Club
Choral Soc.	20	10
Football Club	10	30
Total Output	100	200

Given that 270 Choral Society papers and 810 Football Club papers will be used by students outside of these two clubs next year, how many new papers do the two clubs need to write?

21. ⊤ *Communication Equipment*[31] Two sectors of the U.S. economy are (1) audio, video, and communication equipment and (2) electronic components and accessories. In 1998, the input-output table involving these two sectors was as follows (all figures are in millions of dollars):

From \ To	Equipment	Components
Equipment	6,000	500
Components	24,000	30,000
Total Output	90,000	140,000

Determine the production levels necessary in these two sectors to meet an external demand for $80,000 million of communication equipment and $90,000 million of electronic components. Round answers to two significant digits.

22. ⊤ *Wood and Paper*[32] Two sectors of the U.S. economy are (1) lumber and wood products and (2) paper and allied products. In 1998 the input-output table involving these two sectors was as follows (all figures are in millions of dollars).

From \ To	Wood	Paper
Wood	36,000	7,000
Paper	100	17,000
Total Output	120,000	120,000

---

[30]For some reason, the Main Dining Room consumes a lot of its own food!

[31]The data have been rounded. Source: *Survey of Current Business*, December, 2001, U.S. Department of Commerce.

[32]Ibid.

If external demand for lumber and wood products rises by $10,000 million and external demand for paper and allied products rises by $20,000 million, what increase in output of these two sectors is necessary? Round answers to two significant digits.

23. *Australia Economy*[33] Two sectors of the Australian economy are (1) textiles and (2) clothing and footwear. The 1977 input-output table involving these two sectors results in the following value for $(I - A)^{-1}$:

$$(I - A)^{-1} = \begin{bmatrix} 1.228 & 0.182 \\ 0.006 & 1.1676 \end{bmatrix}.$$

Complete the following sentences.

a. _____ additional dollars worth of clothing and footwear must be produced to meet a $1 increase in the demand for textiles.

b. 0.182 additional dollars worth of _____ must be produced to meet a one-dollar increase in the demand for _____.

24. *Australia Economy*[34] Two sectors of the Australian economy are (1) community services and (2) recreation services. The 1978–79 input-output table involving these two sectors results in the following value for $(I - A)^{-1}$:

$$(I - A)^{-1} = \begin{bmatrix} 1.0066 & 0.00576 \\ 0.00496 & 1.04206 \end{bmatrix}.$$

Complete the following sentences.

a. 0.00496 additional dollars worth of _____ must be produced to meet a $1 increase in the demand for _____.

b. _____ additional dollars worth of community services must be produced to meet a one-dollar increase in the demand for community services.

T *Exercises 25–28 require the use of technology.*

25. **T** *United States Input-Output Table*[35] Four sectors of the U.S. economy are (1) livestock and livestock products, (2) other agricultural products, (3) forestry and fishery products, and (4) agricultural, forestry, and fishery services. In 1977 the input-output table involving these four sectors was as follows (all figures are in millions of dollars):

	To	1	2	3	4
From	1	11,937	9	109	855
	2	26,649	4,285	0	4,744
	3	0	0	439	61
	4	5,423	10,952	3,002	216
Total Output		97,795	120,594	14,642	47,473

[33]Source: *Australian National Accounts and Input-Output Tables 1978–1979*, Australian Bureau of Statistics.

[34]Ibid.

[35]Source: *Survey of Current Business,* December 2001, U.S. Department of Commerce.

Determine how these four sectors would react to an increase in demand for livestock (Sector 1) of $1,000 million, how they would react to an increase in demand for other agricultural products (Sector 2) of $1,000 million, and so on.

26. **T** *United States Input-Output Table*[36] Four sectors of the U.S. economy are (1) motor vehicles, (2) truck and bus bodies, trailers, and motor vehicle parts, (3) aircraft and parts, and (4) other transportation equipment. In 1998 the input-output table involving these four sectors was (all figures in millions of dollars):

	To	1	2	3	4
From	1	75	1,092	0	1,207
	2	64,858	13,081	7	1,070
	3	0	0	21,782	0
	4	0	0	0	1,375
Total Output		230,676	135,108	129,376	44,133

Determine how these four sectors would react to an increase in demand for motor vehicles (Sector 1) of $1,000 million, how they would react to an increase in demand for truck and bus bodies (Sector 2) of $1,000 million, and so on.

27. ▼ *Australia Input-Output Table* Four sectors of the Australian economy are (1) agriculture, (2) forestry, fishing, and hunting, (3) meat and milk products, and (4) other food products. In 1978–79 the input-output table involving these four sectors was as follows (all figures are in millions of Australian dollars).[37]

	To	1	2	3	4
From	1	678.4	3.7	3,341.5	1,023.5
	2	15.5	6.9	17.1	124.5
	3	47.3	4.3	893.1	145.8
	4	312.5	22.1	83.2	693.5
Total Output		9,401.3	685.8	6,997.3	4,818.3

a. How much additional production by the meat and milk sector is necessary to accommodate a $100 increase in the demand for agriculture?

b. Which sector requires the most of its own product in order to meet a $1 increase in external demand for that product?

28. ▼ *Australia Input-Output Table* Four sectors of the Australian economy are (1) petroleum and coal products, (2) nonmetallic mineral products, (3) basic metals and products, and (4) fabricated metal products. In 1978–79 the input-output table

[36]Ibid.

[37]Source: *Australian National Accounts and Input-Output Tables 1978–1979,* Australian Bureau of Statistics.

involving these four sectors was as follows (all figures are in millions of Australian dollars).[38]

	To	1	2	3	4
From	1	174.1	30.5	120.3	14.2
	2	0	190.1	55.8	12.6
	3	2.1	40.2	1,418.7	1,242.0
	4	0.1	7.3	40.4	326.0
Total Output		3,278.0	2,188.8	6,541.7	4,065.8

a. How much additional production by the petroleum and coal products sector is necessary to accommodate a $1,000 increase in the demand for fabricated metal products?

b. Which sector requires the most of the product of some other sector in order to meet a $1 increase in external demand for that product?

---

[38]Source: *Australian National Accounts and Input-Output Tables 1978–1979*, Australian Bureau of Statistics.

COMMUNICATION AND REASONING EXERCISES

29. What would it mean if the technology matrix A were the zero matrix?

30. Can an external demand be met by an economy whose technology matrix A is the identity matrix? Explain.

31. ▼ What would it mean if the total output figure for a particular sector of an input-output table were equal to the sum of the figures in the row for that sector?

32. ▼ What would it mean if the total output figure for a particular sector of an input-output table were less than the sum of the figures in the row for that sector?

33. ▼ What does it mean if an entry in the matrix $(I - A)^{-1}$ is zero?

34. ▼ Why do we expect the diagonal entries in the matrix $(I - A)^{-1}$ to be slightly larger than 1?

35. ▼ Why do we expect the off-diagonal entries of $(I - A)^{-1}$ to be less than 1?

36. ▼ Why do we expect all the entries of $(I - A)^{-1}$ to be non-negative?

KEY CONCEPTS

Web Site www.FiniteandCalc.org
Go to the student Web site at
www.FiniteandCalc.org to find a
comprehensive and interactive
Web-based summary of Chapter 3.

3.1 Matrix Addition and Scalar Multiplication

$m \times n$ matrix, dimensions, entries
p. 182
Referring to the entries of a matrix
p. 183
Matrix equality p. 183
Row, column, and square matrices
p. 184
Addition and subtraction of matrices
p. 184
Scalar multiplication p. 185
Properties of matrix addition and scalar
multiplication p. 187
The transpose of a matrix p. 188
Properties of transposition p. 188

3.2 Matrix Multiplication

Multiplying a row by a column
p. 192
Linear equation as a matrix
equation p. 194

The product of two matrices: general
case p. 194
Identity matrix p. 198
Properties of matrix addition and
multiplication p. 199
Properties of transposition and
multiplication p. 200
A system of linear equations can be
written as a single matrix equation
p. 201

3.3 Matrix Inversion

The inverse of a matrix, singular matrix
pp. 206, 207
Procedure for finding the inverse of a
matrix p. 209
Formula for the inverse of a 2×2
matrix; determinant of a 2×2
matrix p. 209
Using an inverse matrix to solve a system
of equations p. 210

3.4 Game Theory

Two-person zero sum game, payoff
matrix p. 218
A strategy specifies how a player chooses
a move p. 218
The expected value of a game for given
mixed strategies R and C p. 219

An optimal strategy, according to the
minimax criterion, is one that minimizes the maximum damage your
opponent can cause you. p. 222
The Fundamental Principle of Game
Theory p. 222
Procedure for reducing by dominance
p. 223
Procedure for solving a 2×2 game
p. 223
The expected value of a game is its
expected value when the players use
their optimal strategies. p. 226
A strictly determined game is one with a
saddle point. p. 226
Steps to follow in solving a game
p. 228

3.5 Input-Output Models

An input-output model divides an
economy into sectors. The technology
matrix records the interactions of
these sectors and allows us to relate
external demand to the production
vector. p. 235
Procedure for finding a technology
matrix from an input-output table
p. 236
The entries of $(I - A)^{-1}$ p. 239

REVIEW EXERCISES

For Exercises 1–10, let

$$A = \begin{bmatrix} 1 & 2 & 3 \\ 4 & 5 & 6 \end{bmatrix}, B = \begin{bmatrix} 1 & -1 \\ 0 & 1 \end{bmatrix},$$

$$C = \begin{bmatrix} -1 & 0 \\ 1 & 1 \\ 0 & 1 \end{bmatrix}, \text{ and } D = \begin{bmatrix} -3 & -2 & -1 \\ 1 & 2 & 3 \end{bmatrix}.$$

*Determine whether the expression is defined, and if it is,
evaluate it.*

1. $A + B$

2. $A - D$

3. $2A^T + C$

4. AB

5. $A^T B$

6. A^2

7. B^2

8. B^3

9. $AC + B$

10. $CD + B$

*For each matrix in Exercises 11–16, find the inverse or deter-
mine that the matrix is singular.*

11. $\begin{bmatrix} 1 & -1 \\ 0 & 1 \end{bmatrix}$

12. $\begin{bmatrix} 1 & 2 \\ 0 & 0 \end{bmatrix}$

13. $\begin{bmatrix} 1 & 2 & 3 \\ 0 & 4 & 1 \\ 0 & 0 & 1 \end{bmatrix}$

14. $\begin{bmatrix} 1 & 2 & 3 & 4 \\ 1 & 3 & 4 & 2 \\ 0 & 1 & 2 & 3 \\ 0 & 0 & 1 & 2 \end{bmatrix}$

15. $\begin{bmatrix} 1 & 2 & 3 & 4 \\ 2 & 3 & 3 & 3 \\ 0 & 1 & 2 & 3 \\ 0 & 0 & 1 & 2 \end{bmatrix}$

16. $\begin{bmatrix} 0 & 1 & 0 & 0 \\ 1 & 0 & 0 & 0 \\ 0 & 0 & 0 & 1 \\ 0 & 0 & 1 & 0 \end{bmatrix}$

*Write each system of linear equations in Exercises 17–20 as
a matrix equation, and solve by inverting the coefficient matrix.*

17. $\begin{aligned} x + 2y &= 0 \\ 3x + 4y &= 2 \end{aligned}$

18. $\begin{aligned} x + y + z &= 3 \\ y + 2z &= 4 \\ y - z &= 1 \end{aligned}$

19. $\begin{aligned} x + y + z &= 2 \\ x + 2y + z &= 3 \\ x + y + 2z &= 1 \end{aligned}$

20. $\begin{aligned} x + y &= 0 \\ y + z &= 1 \\ z + w &= 0 \\ x - w &= 3 \end{aligned}$

In each of Exercises 21–24, solve the game with the given matrix and give the expected value of the game.

21. $P = \begin{bmatrix} 2 & 1 & 3 & 2 \\ -1 & 0 & -2 & 1 \\ 2 & 0 & 1 & 3 \end{bmatrix}$ **22.** $P = \begin{bmatrix} 3 & -3 & -2 \\ -1 & 3 & 0 \\ 2 & 2 & 1 \end{bmatrix}$

23. $P = \begin{bmatrix} -1 & -3 & -2 \\ -1 & 3 & 0 \\ 3 & 3 & -1 \end{bmatrix}$ **24.** $P = \begin{bmatrix} 1 & 4 & 3 & 3 \\ 0 & -1 & 2 & 3 \\ 2 & 0 & -1 & 2 \end{bmatrix}$

In each of Exercises 25–28, find the production vector X corresponding to the given technology matrix A and external demand vector D.

25. $A = \begin{bmatrix} 0.3 & 0.1 \\ 0 & 0.3 \end{bmatrix}, D = \begin{bmatrix} 700 \\ 490 \end{bmatrix}$

26. $A = \begin{bmatrix} 0.7 & 0.1 \\ 0.1 & 0.7 \end{bmatrix}, D = \begin{bmatrix} 1,000 \\ 2,000 \end{bmatrix}$

27. $A = \begin{bmatrix} 0.2 & 0.2 & 0.2 \\ 0 & 0.2 & 0.2 \\ 0 & 0 & 0.2 \end{bmatrix}, D = \begin{bmatrix} 32,000 \\ 16,000 \\ 8,000 \end{bmatrix}$

28. $A = \begin{bmatrix} 0.5 & 0.1 & 0 \\ 0.1 & 0.5 & 0.1 \\ 0 & 0.1 & 0.5 \end{bmatrix}, D = \begin{bmatrix} 23,000 \\ 46,000 \\ 23,000 \end{bmatrix}$

APPLICATIONS

It is now July 1 and online sales of romance, science fiction, and horror novels at OHaganBooks.com were disappointingly slow over the past month. Exercises 29–34 are based on the following tables:

Inventory of books in stock on June 1 at the OHaganBooks.com warehouses in Texas and Nevada:

Books in Stock (June 1)

	Romance	Sci Fi	Horror
Texas	2,500	4,000	3,000
Nevada	1,500	3,000	1,000

Online sales during June:

June Sales

	Romance	Sci Fi	Horror
Texas	300	500	100
Nevada	100	600	200

New books purchased each month:

Monthly Purchases

	Romance	Sci Fi	Horror
Texas	400	400	300
Nevada	200	400	300

July Sales (Projected)

	Romance	Sci Fi	Horror
Texas	280	550	100
Nevada	50	500	120

29. Inventory Use matrix algebra to compute the inventory at each warehouse at the end of June.

30. Inventory Use matrix algebra to compute the change in inventory at each warehouse during June.

31. Inventory Assuming that sales continue at the level projected for July for the next few months, write down a matrix equation showing the inventory N at each warehouse x months after July 1. How many months from now will OHaganBooks.com run out of Sci Fi novels at the Nevada warehouse?

32. Inventory Assuming that sales continue at the level projected for July for the next few months, write down a matrix equation showing the change in inventory N at each warehouse x months after July 1. How many months from now will OHaganBooks.com have 1,000 more horror novels in stock in Texas than currently?

33. Revenue It is now the end of July and OHaganBooks.com's e-commerce manager bursts into the CEO's office. "I thought you might want to know, John, that our sales figures are exactly what I projected a month ago. Is that good market analysis or what?" OHaganBooks.com has charged an average of $5 for romance novels, $6 for science fiction novels, and $5.50 for horror novels. Use the projected July sales figures from above and matrix arithmetic to compute the total revenue OHaganBooks.com earned at each warehouse in July.

34. Cost OHaganBooks.com pays an average of $2 for romance novels, $3.50 for science fiction novels, and $1.50 for horror novels. Use this information together with the monthly purchasing information to compute the monthly purchasing cost.

Acting on a "tip" from Marjory Duffin, John O'Hagan decided that his company should invest a significant sum in shares of Duffin House Publishers (DHP) and Duffin Subprime Ventures (DSV). Exercises 35–38 are based on the following table, which shows what information he pieced together later, after some of the records had been deleted by an angry student intern.

Date	Number of Shares: DHP	Price per Share: DHP	Number of Shares: DSV	Price per Share: DSV
July 1	?	$20	?	$10
August 1	?	$10	?	$20
September 1	?	$5	?	$40
Total	5,000		7,000	

35. *Investments* Over the three months shown, the company invested a total of $50,000 in DHP stock, and, on August 15, was paid dividends of 10¢ per share held on that date, for a total of $300. Use matrix inversion to determine how many shares of DHP OHaganBooks.com purchased on each of the three dates shown.

36. *Investments* Over the three months shown, the company invested a total of $150,000 in DSV stock, and, on July 15, was paid dividends of 20¢ per share held on that date, for a total of $600. Use matrix inversion to determine how many shares of DSV OHaganBooks.com purchased on each of the three dates shown.

37. *Investments* (Refer to Exercise 35.) On October 1, the shares of DHP purchased on July 1 were sold at $3 per share. The remaining shares were sold one month later at $1 per share. Use matrix algebra to determine the total loss (taking into account the dividends paid on August 15) incurred as a result of the Duffin stock fiasco.

38. *Investments* (Refer to Exercise 36.) On September 15, DSV announced a two-for-one stock split, so that each share originally purchased was converted into two shares. On October 1, the company paid an additional special dividend of 10¢ per share. On October 15, OHaganBooks.com sold 3,000 shares at $20 per share. One week later (after the subprime fund manager had been awarded a $10 million bonus) the subprime market crashed, Duffin Subprime Ventures declared bankruptcy, and DSV stock became worthless. Use matrix algebra to determine the total loss (taking into account the dividends paid on July 15) incurred as a result of the Duffin stock fiasco.

OHaganBooks.com has two main competitors: JungleBooks.com and FarmerBooks.com, and no other competitors of any significance on the horizon. Exercises 39–42 are based on the following table, which shows the movement of customers during July.[39] (Thus, for instance, the first row tells us that 80% of OHaganBooks.com's customers remained loyal, 10% of them went to JungleBooks.com, and the remaining 10% went to FarmerBooks.com.)

	To OHagan	To Jungle	To Farmer
From OHagan	0.8	0.1	0.1
From Jungle	0.4	0.6	0
From Farmer	0.2	0	0.8

At the beginning of July, OHaganBooks.com had an estimated 2,000 customers, while its two competitors had 4,000 each.

39. *Competition* Set up the July 1 customer numbers in a row matrix, and use matrix arithmetic to estimate the number of customers each company has at the end of July.

40. *Competition* Assuming the July trends continue in August, predict the number of customers each company will have at the end of August.

41. *Competition* Assuming the July trends continue in August, why is it not possible for a customer of FarmerBooks.com on July 1 to have ended up as a JungleBooks.com customer two months later without having ever been an OHaganBooks.com customer?

42. *Competition* Name one or more important factors that the model we have used does not take into account.

Publisher Marjory Duffin reveals that JungleBooks may be launching a promotional scheme in which it will offer either two books for the price of one, or three books for the price of two (Marjory can't quite seem to remember which, and is not certain whether they will go with the scheme at all). John O'Hagan's marketing advisers Flood and O'Lara seem to have different ideas as to how to respond. Flood suggests that the company counter by offering three books for the price of one, while O'Lara suggests that it offer instead a free copy of the "Finite Mathematics Student Solutions Manual" with every purchase. After a careful analysis, O'Hagan comes up with the following payoff matrix, where the payoffs represent the number of customers, in thousands, he expects to gain from JungleBooks.

	JungleBooks		
	No Promo	2 for Price of 1	3 for Price of 2
O'Hagan No Promo	0	−60	−40
3 for Price of 1	30	20	10
Finite Math	20	0	15

Use the above information in Exercises 43–48.

43. *Competition* After a very expensive dinner at an exclusive restaurant, Marjory suddenly "remembers" that the JungleBooks CEO mentioned to her (at a less expensive restaurant) that there is only a 20% chance JungleBooks will launch a "2 for the price of 1" promotion, and a 40% chance that it will launch a "3 for the price of 2" promotion. What should OHaganBooks.com do in view of this information, and what will the expected effect be on its customer base?

44. *Competition* JungleBooks CEO François Dubois has been told by someone with personal ties to OHaganBooks.com staff that OHaganBooks is in fact 80% certain to opt for the "3 for the price of 1" option and will certainly go with one of the two possible promos. What should JungleBooks.com do in view of this information, and what will the expected effect be on its customer base?

45. *Corporate Spies* One of John O'Hagan's trusted marketing advisers has, without knowing it, accidentally sent him a copy of the following e-mail:

> To: René, JungleBooks Marketing Department
>
> From: O'Lara
>
> Hey René somehow the CEO here says he has learned that there is a 20% chance that you will opt for the "2 for the price of 1" promotion, and a 40% chance that you will opt for the "3 for the price of 2" promotion. Thought you might want to know. So when do I get my "commission?"—Jim

---

[39] By a "customer" of one of the three e-commerce sites, we mean someone who purchases more at that site than at either of the two competitors.

What will each company do in view of this new information, and what will the expected effect be on its customer base?

46. **More Corporate Spies** The next day, everything changes: OHaganBooks.com's mole at JungleBooks, Davíde DuPont, is found unconscious in the coffee room at JungleBooks.com headquarters, clutching in his hand the following correspondence he had apparently received moments earlier:

> To: Davíde
> From: John O'Hagan
> Subject: Re: Urgent Information
>
> Davíde: This information is much appreciated and definitely changes my plans—J
>
> >
> >To: John O
> >From: Davíde
> >Subject: Urgent Information
> >Thought you might want to know that JungleBooks
> >thinks you are 80% likely to opt for 3 for 1 and 20%
> >likely to opt for FiniteMath.
> >—D

What will each company do in view of this information, and what will the expected effect be on its customer base?

47. **Things Unravel** John O'Hagan is about to go with the option chosen in Exercise 45 when he hears word about an exposé in the *Publisher Enquirer* on corporate spying in the two companies. Each company now knows that no information about the others' intentions can be trusted. Now what should OHaganBooks.com do, and how many customers should it expect to gain or lose?

48. **Competition** It is now apparent as a result of the *Publisher Enquirer* exposé that, not only can each company make no assumptions about the strategies the other might be using, but the payoff matrix they have been using is wrong: A crack investigative reporter at the *Enquirer* publishes the following revised matrix:

$$P = \begin{bmatrix} 0 & -60 & -40 \\ 30 & 20 & 10 \\ 20 & 0 & 20 \end{bmatrix}.$$

Now what should JungleBooks.com do, and how many customers should it expect to gain or lose?

Some of the books sold by OHaganBooks.com are printed at Bruno Mills, Inc., a combined paper mill and printing company. Exercises 49–52 are based on the following typical monthly input-output table for Bruno Mills' paper and book printing sectors.

	To	Paper	Books
From	Paper	$20,000	$50,000
	Books	2,000	5,000
	Total Output	200,000	100,000

49. **Production** Find the technology matrix for Bruno Mills' paper and book printing sectors.

50. **Production** Compute $(I - A)^{-1}$. What is the significance of the $(1, 2)$ entry?

51. **Production** Approximately $1,700 worth of the books sold each month by OHaganBooks.com are printed at Bruno Mills, Inc., and OHaganBooks.com uses approximately $170 worth of Bruno Mills' paper products each month. What is the total value of paper and books that must be produced by Bruno Mills, Inc. in order to meet demand from OHaganBooks.com?

52. **Production** Currently, Bruno Mills, Inc. has a monthly capacity of $500,000 of paper products and $200,000 of books. What level of external demand would cause Bruno to meet the capacity for both products?

Case Study   Projecting Market Share

You are the sales director at Selular, a cell-phone provider, and things are not looking good for your company: The recently launched *iClone* competitor is beginning to chip away at Selular's market share. Particularly disturbing are rumors of fierce brand loyalty by iClone customers, with several bloggers suggesting that iClone retains close to 100% of their customers. Worse, you will shortly be presenting a sales report to the board of directors, and the CEO has "suggested" that your report include 2-, 5-, and 10-year projections of Selular's market share given the recent impact on the market by iClone, and also a "worst-case" scenario projecting what would happen if iClone customers are so loyal that none of them ever switch services.

The sales department has conducted two market surveys, taken one quarter apart, of the major cell-phone providers, which are iClone, Selular, AB&C, and some smaller companies lumped together as "Other," and has given you the data shown in Figure 4, which shows the percentages of subscribers who switched from one service to another during the quarter.

If you go on to study probability theory in Chapter 7 you will see how this scenario can be interpreted as a Markov System and will revisit the analysis below in that context.

Figure 4

The percentages in the figure and market shares below reflect actual data for several cell-phone services in the United States during a single quarter of 2003. (See the exercises for Section 7.7.)

For example, by the end of the quarter 0.5% of iClone's customers had switched to Selular, 0.5% to AB&C, and 0.9% to Other. The current market shares are as follows: iClone: 29.7%, Selular: 19.3%, AB&C: 18.1%, Other: 32.9%.

"This is simple," you tell yourself. "Since I know the current market shares and percentage movements over one quarter, I can easily calculate the market shares next quarter (assuming the percentages that switch services remain the same), then repeat the calculation for the following quarter, and so on, until I get the long-term prediction I am seeking." So you begin your calculations by computing the market shares next quarter. First you note that, since a total of $0.5 + 0.5 + 0.9 = 1.9\%$ of iClone users switched to other brands, the rest, 98.1%, stayed with iClone. Similarly, 97.2% of Selular users, 97.3% of AB&C, and 98.1% of Other stayed with their respective brands. Then you compute:

iClone share after one quarter

$= 98.1\%$ of iClone $+1.0\%$ of Selular $+1.0\%$ of AB&C $+ 0.8\%$ of Other

$= (0.981)(0.297) + (0.010)(0.193) + (0.010)(0.181) + (0.008)(0.329)$

$= 0.297729$, or 29.7729%.

Similarly,

Selular share:

$= (0.005)(0.297) + (0.972)(0.193) + (0.006)(0.181) + (0.006)(0.329)$
$= 0.192141$

AB&C share:

$= (0.005)(0.297) + (0.006)(0.193) + (0.973)(0.181) + (0.005)(0.329)$
$= 0.180401$

Other share:

$= (0.009)(0.297) + (0.012)(0.193) + (0.011)(0.181) + (0.981)(0.329)$
$= 0.329729$.

So, you project the market shares after one quarter to be: iClone: 29.7729%, Selular: 19.2141%, AB&C: 18.0401%, Other: 32.9729%. You now begin to realize that repeating this kind of calculation for the large number of quarters required for long-term projections will be tedious. You call in your student intern (who happens to be a mathematics major) to see if she can help. After taking one look at the calculations, she makes the observation that all you have really done is compute the product of two matrices:

$$[0.297729 \quad 0.192141 \quad 0.180401 \quad 0.329729]$$

$$= [0.297 \quad 0.193 \quad 0.181 \quad 0.329] \begin{bmatrix} .981 & .005 & .005 & .009 \\ .010 & .972 & .006 & .012 \\ .010 & .006 & .973 & .011 \\ .008 & .006 & .005 & .981 \end{bmatrix}$$

Market shares after one quarter = Market shares at start of quarter × A.

The 4×4 matrix A is organized as follows:

		To			
		iClone	Selular	AB&C	Other
	iClone	.981	.005	.005	.009
	Selular	.010	.972	.006	.012
From	**AB&C**	.010	.006	.973	.011
	Other	.008	.006	.005	.981

Since the market shares one quarter later can be obtained from the shares at the start of the quarter, you realize that you can now obtain the shares *two* quarters later by multiplying the result by A—and at this point you start using technology (such as the Matrix Algebra Tool at www.FiniteandCalc.org) to continue the calculation:

Market shares after two quarters = Market shares after one quarter × A

$$= [0.297729 \quad 0.192141 \quad 0.180401 \quad 0.329729] \begin{bmatrix} .981 & .005 & .005 & .009 \\ .010 & .972 & .006 & .012 \\ .010 & .006 & .973 & .011 \\ .008 & .006 & .005 & .981 \end{bmatrix}$$

$$\approx [0.298435 \quad 0.191310 \quad 0.179820 \quad 0.330434].$$

Although the use of matrices has simplified your work, continually multiplying the result by A over and over again to get the market shares for successive months is still tedious. Would it not be possible to get, say, the market share after 10 years (40 quarters) with a single calculation? To explore this, you decide to use symbols for the various market shares:

m_0 = Starting market shares = $[0.297 \quad 0.193 \quad 0.181 \quad 0.329]$

m_1 = Market shares after 1 quarter
    = $[0.297729 \quad 0.192141 \quad 0.180401 \quad 0.329729]$

m_2 = Market shares after 2 quarters

$\cdots$

m_n = Market share after n quarters.

You then rewrite the relationships above as

$m_1 = m_0 A$ Shares after one quarter = Shares at start of quarter × A

$m_2 = m_1 A$ Shares after two quarters = Shares after one quarter × A.

On an impulse, you substitute the first equation in the second:

$$m_2 = m_1 A = (m_0 A)A = m_0 A^2.$$

Continuing,

$$m_3 = m_2 A = (m_0 A^2)A = m_0 A^3$$

$$\ldots$$

$$m_n = m_0 A^n,$$

which is exactly the formula you need! You can now obtain the 2-, 5-, and 10-year projections each in a single step (with the aid of technology):

2-year projection: $m_8 = m_0 A^8$

$$= [0.297 \quad 0.193 \quad 0.181 \quad 0.329] \begin{bmatrix} .981 & .005 & .005 & .009 \\ .010 & .972 & .006 & .012 \\ .010 & .006 & .973 & .011 \\ .008 & .006 & .005 & .981 \end{bmatrix}^8$$

$$\approx [0.302237 \quad 0.186875 \quad 0.176691 \quad 0.334198].$$

5-year projection: $m_{20} = m_0 A^{20} \approx [0.307992 \quad 0.180290 \quad 0.171938 \quad 0.33978].$
10-year projection: $m_{40} = m_0 A^{40} \approx [0.313857 \quad 0.173809 \quad 0.167074 \quad 0.34526].$

In particular, Selular's market shares are projected to decline slightly: 2-year projection: 18.7%, 5-year projection: 18.0%, 10-year projection: 17.4%.

You now move on to the "worst-case" scenario, which you represent by assuming 100% loyalty by iClone users with the remaining percentages staying the same (Figure 5).

Figure 5

The matrix A corresponding to this diagram is $\begin{bmatrix} 1 & 0 & 0 & 0 \\ .010 & .972 & .006 & .012 \\ .010 & .006 & .973 & .011 \\ .008 & .006 & .005 & .981 \end{bmatrix}$, and you

find:

2-year projection: $m_8 = m_0 A^8 \approx [0.346335 \quad 0.175352 \quad 0.165200 \quad 0.313113]$
5-year projection: $m_{20} = m_0 A^{20} \approx [0.413747 \quad 0.152940 \quad 0.144776 \quad 0.288536]$
10-year projection: $m_{40} = m_0 A^{40} \approx [0.510719 \quad 0.123553 \quad 0.117449 \quad 0.248279].$

Thus, in the worst-case scenario, Selular's market shares are projected to decline more rapidly: 2-year projection: 17.5%, 5-year projection: 15.3%, 10-year projection: 12.4%.

EXERCISES

1. Project Selular's market share 20 and 30 years from now based on the original data shown in Figure 4. (Round all figures to the nearest 0.1%.)

2. Using the original data, what can you say about each company's share in 60 and 80 years (assuming current trends continue)? (Round all figures to the nearest 0.1%.)

3. Obtain a sequence of projections several hundreds of years into the future using the scenarios in both Figure 4 and Figure 5. What do you notice?

4. Compute a sequence of larger and larger powers of the matrix A for both scenarios with all figures rounded to four decimal places. What do you notice?

5. Suppose the trends noted in the market survey were in place for several quarters *before* the current quarter. Using the scenario in Figure 4, determine what the companies' market shares were one quarter before the present and one year before the present (to the nearest 0.1%). Do the same for the scenario in Figure 5.

6. If A is the matrix from the scenario in Figure 4, compute A^{-1}. In light of the preceding exercise, what do the entries in A^{-1} mean?

TECHNOLOGY GUIDE

TI-83/84 Plus   Technology Guide

Section 3.1

Example 2 (page 185)   The A-Plus auto parts store chain has two outlets, one in Vancouver and one in Quebec. Among other things, it sells wiper blades, windshield cleaning fluid, and floor mats. The monthly sales of these items at the two stores for two months are given in the following tables:

January Sales

	Vancouver	Quebec
Wiper Blades	20	15
Cleaning Fluid (bottles)	10	12
Floor Mats	8	4

February Sales

	Vancouver	Quebec
Wiper Blades	23	12
Cleaning Fluid (bottles)	8	12
Floor Mats	4	5

Use matrix arithmetic to calculate the change in sales of each product in each store from January to February.

Solution with Technology

On the TI-83/84 Plus, matrices are referred to as [A], [B], and so on through [J]. To enter a matrix, press MATRX to bring up the matrix menu, select EDIT, select a matrix, and press ENTER. Then enter the dimensions of the matrix followed by its entries. When you want to use a matrix, press MATRX, select the matrix and press ENTER.

On the TI-83/84 Plus, adding matrices is similar to adding numbers. The sum of the matrices [A] and [B] is [A]+[B]; their difference, of course, is [A]−[B]. As in the text, for this example,

1. Create two matrices, [J] and [F].
2. Compute their difference, [F]−[J] using [F]−[J] → [D].

Note that we have stored the difference in the matrix [D] in case we need it for later use.

Section 3.2

Example 3(a) (page 195)   Calculate

$$\begin{bmatrix} 2 & 0 & -1 & 3 \\ 1 & -1 & 2 & -2 \end{bmatrix} \begin{bmatrix} 1 & 1 & -8 \\ 1 & 0 & 0 \\ 0 & 5 & 2 \\ -2 & 8 & -1 \end{bmatrix}.$$

Solution with Technology

On the TI-83/84 Plus, the format for multiplying matrices is the same as for multiplying numbers: [A][B] or [A]∗[B] will give the product. We enter the matrices and then multiply them. (Note that, while editing, you can see only three columns of [A] at a time.)

Note that if you try to multiply two matrices whose product is not defined, you will get the error "DIM MISMATCH" (dimension mismatch).

TECHNOLOGY GUIDE

Example 6 (page 198)—Identity Matrix   On the TI-83/84 Plus, the function `identity(n)` (in the MATRX MATH menu) returns the $n \times n$ identity matrix.

Section 3.3

Example 2(b) (page 208)   Find the inverse of

$$Q = \begin{bmatrix} 1 & 0 & 1 \\ 2 & -2 & -1 \\ 3 & 0 & 0 \end{bmatrix}.$$

Solution with Technology

On a TI-83/84 Plus, you can invert the square matrix [A] by entering [A] X⁻¹ ENTER.

(Note that you can use the right and left arrow keys to scroll the answer, which cannot be shown on the screen all at once.) You could also use the calculator to help you go through the row reduction, as described in Chapter 2.

Example 4 (page 212)   Solve the following three systems of equations.

a. $2x \qquad + z = 1$
    $2x + y - z = 1$
    $3x + y - z = 1$

b. $2x \qquad + z = 0$
    $2x + y - z = 1$
    $3x + y - z = 2$

c. $2x \qquad + z = 0$
    $2x + y - z = 0$
    $3x + y - z = 0$

Solution with Technology

1. Enter the four matrices A, B, C, and D:

2. Compute the solutions $A^{-1}B$, $A^{-1}C$, and $A^{-1}D$:

Section 3.5

Example 1 (page 236)   Recall that the input-output table in Example 1 looks like this:

		Crude	**Refining**
	To		
From	**Crude**	27,000	59,000
	Refining	750	15,000
	Total Output	87,000	140,000

What was the technology matrix for these two sectors? What was left over from each of these sectors for use by other parts of the economy or for export?

Solution with Technology

There are several ways to use these data to create the technology matrix in your TI-83/84 Plus. For small matrices like this, the most straightforward is to use the matrix editor, where you can give each entry as the appropriate quotient:

and so on. Once we have the technology matrix [A] and the production vector [B] (remember that we can't use [X] as a matrix name), we can calculate the external demand vector:

Of course, when interpreting these numbers, we must remember to round to two significant digits, because our original data were accurate to only that many digits.

Here is an alternative way to calculate the technology matrix that may be better for examples with more sectors.

1. Begin by entering the columns of the input-output table as lists in the list editor ($\boxed{\text{STAT}}$ EDIT).

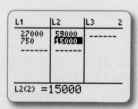

2. We now want to divide each column by the total output of its sector and assemble the results into a matrix. We

can do this using the List $\blacktriangleright$ matr function (under the $\boxed{\text{MATRX}}$ MATH menu) as follows:

Example 3 (page 241) Consider four sectors of the economy of Kenya[40]: (1) the traditional economy, (2) agriculture, (3) manufacture of metal products and machinery, and (4) wholesale and retail trade. The input-output table for these four sectors for 1976 looks like this (all numbers are thousands of K£):

	To	1	2	3	4
From	1	8,600	0	0	0
	2	0	20,000	24	0
	3	1,500	530	15,000	660
	4	810	8,500	5,800	2,900
Total Output		87,000	530,000	110,000	180,000

Suppose that external demand for agriculture increased by K£50,000,000 and that external demand for metal products and machinery increased by K£10,000,000. How would production in these four sectors have to change to meet this rising demand?

Solution with Technology

1. Enter the technology matrix [A] using one of the techniques above.

MATRIX[A] 4 ×4
```
- 0       0      0      0     ]
- .03774  2.2E-4 0      0     ]
- .001    .13636 .00367 ]
- .01604  .05273 .0161111 ]

4,4=.0161111111...
```

---

[40] Figures are rounded. Source: *Input-Output Tables for Kenya 1976,* Central Bureau of Statistics of the Ministry of Economic Planning and Community Affairs, Kenya.

TECHNOLOGY GUIDE

2. Enter the matrix D^+ as [D].

3. You can then compute the change in production with the following formula:

$$(\text{identity}(4)-[A])^{-1}\ [D].$$

```
(identity(4)-[A]
)-1[D]
  [[0          ]
   [51963.42476]
   [11645.36129]
   [1471.104956]]
■
```

EXCEL Technology Guide

Section 3.1

Example 2 (page 185) The A-Plus auto parts store chain has two outlets, one in Vancouver and one in Quebec. Among other things, it sells wiper blades, windshield cleaning fluid, and floor mats. The monthly sales of these items at the two stores for two months are given in the following tables:

January Sales

	Vancouver	Quebec
Wiper Blades	20	15
Cleaning Fluid (bottles)	10	12
Floor Mats	8	4

February Sales

	Vancouver	Quebec
Wiper Blades	23	12
Cleaning Fluid (bottles)	8	12
Floor Mats	4	5

Use matrix arithmetic to calculate the change in sales of each product in each store from January to February.

Solution with Technology

To enter a matrix in a spreadsheet, we put its entries in any convenient block of cells. For example, the matrix A

in the first Quick Example of this section might look like this:

	A	B	C
1	2	0	1
2	33	-22	0

Excel refers to such blocks of data as **arrays**, which it can handle in much the same way as it handles single cells of data. For instance, when typing a formula, just as clicking on a cell creates a reference to that cell, selecting a whole array of cells will create a reference to that array. An array is referred to using an **array range** consisting of the top-left and bottom-right cell coordinates, separated by a colon. For example, the array range A1:C2 refers to the 2×3 matrix above, with top-left corner A1 and bottom-right corner C2.

1. To add or subtract two matrices in Excel, first input their entries in two separate arrays in the spreadsheet (we've also added labels as in the previous tables, which you might do if you wanted to save the spreadsheet for later use):

	A	B	C
1	January Sales		
2		Vancouver	Quebec
3	wiper blades	20	15
4	cleaning fluid (bottles)	10	12
5	floor mats	8	4
6			
7	February Sales		
8		Vancouver	Quebec
9	wiper blades	23	12
10	cleaning fluid (bottles)	8	12
11	floor mats	4	5

2. Select (highlight) a block of the same size (3×2 in this case) where you would like the answer, $F - J$, to appear, enter the formula =B9:C11-B3:C5, and then type

Control+Shift+Enter. The easiest way to do this is as follows:

- Highlight cells B15:C17.   Where you want the answer to appear

- Type "=".
- Highlight the matrix **F**.   Cells B9 through C11
- Type "-".
- Highlight the matrix **J**.   Cells B3 through C5
- Press Control+Shift+Enter.   Not just Enter

	A	B	C
1	January Sales		
2		Vancouver	Quebec
3	wiper blades	20	15
4	cleaning fluid (bottles)	10	12
5	floor mats	8	4
6			
7	February Sales		
8		Vancouver	Quebec
9	wiper blades	23	12
10	cleaning fluid (bottles)	8	12
11	floor mats	4	5
12			
13	Change in Sales		
14		Vancouver	Quebec
15	wiper blades	=B9:C11-B3:C5	
16	cleaning fluid (bottles)		
17	floor mats		

Typing Control+Shift+Enter (instead of Enter) tells Excel that your formula is an *array formula,* one that returns a matrix rather than a single number.[41] Once entered, the formula bar will show the formula you entered enclosed in "curly braces," indicating that it is an array formula. Note that you must use Control+Shift+Enter to delete any array you create: select the block you wish to delete and press Delete followed by Control+Shift+Enter.

Example 3 (page 186)   The revenue generated by sales in the Vancouver and Quebec branches of the A-Plus auto parts store was as follows:

January Sales in Canadian Dollars

	Vancouver	Quebec
Wiper Blades	140.00	105.00
Cleaning Fluid (bottles)	30.00	36.00
Floor Mats	96.00	48.00

If the Canadian dollar was worth \$0.65U.S. at the time, compute the revenue in U.S. dollars.

Solution with Technology

Scalar multiplication is done in Excel in much the same way we did matrix addition above:

	A	B	C
1	January Sales (Can \$)		
2		Vancouver	Quebec
3	wiper blades	140	105
4	cleaning fluid (bottles)	30	36
5	floor mats	96	48
6			
7			
8	January Sales (US \$)		
9		Vancouver	Quebec
10	wiper blades	=0.65*B3:C5	
11	cleaning fluid (bottles)		
12	floor mats		

As with matrix addition, we use Control+Shift+Enter to evaluate scalar multiplication (or to evaluate any formula that uses an array).

Transposition   To transpose a matrix in Excel, first highlight the block where you would like the transpose to appear (shaded in the spreadsheet below). (Note that it should have the correct dimensions for the transpose: 3×2 in the case shown below.) Then type the formula =TRANSPOSE (A1:C2) (use the array range appropriate for the matrix you want to transpose) in the formula bar and press Control+Shift+Enter. The easiest way to do this is as follows:

1. Highlight Cells A4:B6.   The 3×2 block for the answer
2. Type " =TRANSPOSE (" .
3. Highlight the matrix you want to transpose.   Cells A1:C2
4. Type ") " .
5. Type Control+Shift+Enter.   Not just Enter

The transpose will appear in the region you highlighted.

	A	B	C
1	2	0	1
2	33	-22	0
3			
4	=TRANSPOSE(A1:C2)		
5			
6			

---

[41]Note that on a Macintosh, Command-Enter has the same effect as Control+Shift+Enter.

Section 3.2

Example 3(a) (page 195)　Calculate the product

$$\begin{bmatrix} 2 & 0 & -1 & 3 \\ 1 & -1 & 2 & -2 \end{bmatrix}\begin{bmatrix} 1 & 1 & -8 \\ 1 & 0 & 0 \\ 0 & 5 & 2 \\ -2 & 8 & -1 \end{bmatrix}.$$

Solution with Technology

In Excel, the function we use for matrix multiplication is MMULT. (Ordinary multiplication, *, will *not* work.)

1. Enter the two matrices as shown in the spreadsheet and highlight a block where you want the answer to appear. (Note that it should have the correct dimensions for the product: 2×3.)

	A	B	C	D	E	F	G	H
1	2	0	-1	3		1	1	-8
2	1	-1	2	-2		1	0	0
3						0	5	2
4	=MMULT(A1:D2,F1:H4)					-2	8	-1
5								

2. Enter the formula =MMULT(A1:D2,F1:H4) (using the mouse to avoid typing the array ranges if you like) and press Control+Shift+Enter. The product will appear in the region you highlighted. If you try to multiply two matrices whose product is not defined, you will get the error "!VALUE#".

	A	B	C	D	E	F	G	H
1	2	0	-1	3		1	1	-8
2	1	-1	2	-2		1	0	0
3						0	5	2
4	-4	21	-21			-2	8	-1
5	4	-5	-2					

Example 6 (page 198)—Identity Matrix　There is no function in Excel that returns an identity matrix. If you need a small identity matrix, it's simplest to just enter the 1s and 0s by hand. If you need a large identity matrix, here is one way to get it quickly.

1. Say we want a 4×4 identity matrix in the cells B1:E4. Enter the following formula in cell B1:

```
=IF(ROW(B1)-ROW($B$1)
=COLUMN(B1)-COLUMN($B$1),1,0)
```

	A	B	C	D	E
1		=IF(ROW(B1)-ROW($B$1)=COLUMN(B1)-COLUMN($B$1),1,0)			
2					
3					
4					

2. Press Enter, then copy cell B1 to cells B1:E4. The formula will return 1s along the diagonal of the matrix and 0s elsewhere, giving you the identity matrix. Why does this formula work?

	A	B	C	D	E
1		1	0	0	0
2		0	1	0	0
3		0	0	1	0
4		0	0	0	1

Section 3.3

Example 2(b) (page 208)　Find the inverse of

$$Q = \begin{bmatrix} 1 & 0 & 1 \\ 2 & -2 & -1 \\ 3 & 0 & 0 \end{bmatrix}.$$

Solution with Technology

In Excel, the function MINVERSE computes the inverse of a matrix.

1. Enter Q somewhere convenient, for example, in cells A1:C3.
2. Choose the block where you would like the inverse to appear, highlight the whole block.
3. Enter the formula =MINVERSE(A1:C3) and press Control+Shift+Enter.

	A	B	C	D	E	F	G
1	1	0	1		=MINVERSE(A1:C3)		
2	2	-2	-1				
3	3	0	0				

The inverse will appear in the region you highlighted. (To convert the answer to fractions, format the cells as fractions.)

	A	B	C	D	E	F	G
1	1	0	1		0	0	0.3333333
2	2	-2	-1		-0.5	-0.5	0.5
3	3	0	0		1	0	-0.3333333

If a matrix is singular, Excel will register an error by showing #NUM! in each cell.

Although Excel appears to invert the matrix in one step, it is going through the procedure in the text or some variation of it to find the inverse. Of course, you could also use Excel to help you go through the row reduction, just as in Chapter 2.

Online, follow

Chapter 3 → Excel Tutorials → 3.3 Matrix Inversion

for a downloadable Excel tutorial that covers this and other examples in this section.

Example 4 (page 212)   Solve the following three systems of equations.

a.
$$2x \quad\;\; + z = 1$$
$$2x + y - z = 1$$
$$3x + y - z = 1$$

b.
$$2x \quad\;\; + z = 0$$
$$2x + y - z = 1$$
$$3x + y - z = 2$$

c.
$$2x \quad\;\; + z = 0$$
$$2x + y - z = 0$$
$$3x + y - z = 0$$

Solution with Technology

Spreadsheets like Excel instantly update calculated results every time the contents of a cell are changed. We can take advantage of this to solve the three systems of equations given above using the same worksheet as follows.

1. Enter the matrices A and B from the matrix equation $AX = B$.

2. Select a 3×1 block of cells for the matrix X.

3. The Excel formula we can use to calculate X is:

`=MMULT(MINVERSE(A1:C3),E1:E3)` $A^{-1}B$

	A	B	C	D	E
1	2	0	1		1
2	2	1	-1		1
3	3	1	-1		1
4		A			B
5					
6	=MMULT(MINVERSE(A1:C3),E1:E3)				
7					
8					
9	A⁻¹B				

(As usual, use the mouse to select the ranges for A and B while typing the formula, and don't forget to press Control+Shift+Enter.) Having obtained the solution to part (a), you can now simply modify the entries in Column E to see the solutions for parts (b) and (c).

Note   Your spreadsheet for part (a) may look like this:

	A	B	C	D	E
1	2	0	1		1
2	2	1	-1		1
3	3	1	-1		1
4		A			B
5					
6	1.11022E-16				
7	2				
8	1				
9	A⁻¹B				

What is that strange number doing in cell A6? "E-16" represents "$\times 10^{-16}$", so the entry is really

$$1.11022 \times 10^{-16} = 0.000\,000\,000\,000\,000\,111022 \approx 0.$$

Mathematically, it is supposed to be *exactly* zero (see the solution to part (a) in the text) but Excel made a small error in computing the inverse of A, resulting in this spurious value. Note, however, that it is accurate (agrees with zero) to 15 decimal places! In practice, when we see numbers arise in matrix calculations that are far smaller than all the other entries, we can usually assume they are supposed to be zero. ∎

Section 3.5

Example 1 (page 236)   Recall that the input-output table in Example 1 looks like this:

	To	Crude	Refining
From **Crude**		27,000	59,000
Refining		750	15,000
Total Output		87,000	140,000

What was the technology matrix for these two sectors? What was left over from each of these sectors for use by other parts of the economy or for export?

Solution with Technology

1. Enter the input-output table in a spreadsheet:

	A	B	C	D
1			To	
2			Crude	Refining
3	From	Crude	27000	59000
4		Refining	750	15000
5		Total Output	87000	140000

2. To obtain the technology matrix, we divide each column by the total output of its sector:

	A	B	C	D
1			To	
2			Crude	Refining
3	From	Crude	27000	59000
4		Refining	750	15000
5		Total Output	87000	140000
6				
7			=C3/C$5	
8				

The formula =C3/C$5 is copied into the shaded 2×2 block shown on the left. (The $ sign in front of the 5 forces the program to always divide by the total in Row 5 even when the formula is copied from Row 7 to Row 8. The result is the technology matrix shown on the right.

3. Using the techniques discussed in the second section, we can now compute $D = X - AX$ to find the demand vector.

Example 3 (page 241) Consider four sectors of the economy of Kenya[42]: (1) the traditional economy, (2) agriculture, (3) manufacture of metal products and machinery, and (4) wholesale and retail trade. The input-output table for these four sectors for 1976 looks like this (all numbers are thousands of K£):

	To	1	2	3	4
From	1	8,600	0	0	0
	2	0	20,000	24	0
	3	1,500	530	15,000	660
	4	810	8,500	5,800	2,900
Total Output		87,000	530,000	110,000	180,000

Suppose that external demand for agriculture increased by K£50,000,000 and that external demand for metal products and machinery increased by K£10,000,000. How would production in these four sectors have to change to meet this rising demand?

Solution with Technology

1. Enter the input-output table in the spreadsheet.

2. Compute the technology matrix by dividing each column by the column total.

---

[42]Figures are rounded. Source: *Input-Output Tables for Kenya 1976*, Central Bureau of Statistics of the Ministry of Economic Planning and Community Affairs, Kenya.

3. Insert the identity matrix I in preparation for the next step.

4. To see how each sector reacts to rising external demand, you must calculate the inverse matrix $(I - A)^{-1}$, as shown below. (Remember to use Control+Shift+Enter each time.)

5. To compute $(I - A)^{-1}D^{+}$, enter D^{+} as a column and use the MMULT operation. (See Example 3 in Section 3.2.)

Note Here is one of the beauties of spreadsheet programs: Once you are done with the calculation, you can use the spreadsheet as a template for any 4×4 input-output table by just changing the entries of the input-output matrix and/or D^{+}. The rest of the computation will then be done automatically as the spreadsheet is updated. In other words, you can use it do your homework! You can download a version of this spreadsheet by following

Chapter 3 → Excel Tutorials → 3.5 Input-Output Models.

■

4

Linear Programming

Case Study The Diet Problem

The Galaxy Nutrition health-food mega-store chain provides free online nutritional advice and support to its customers. As Web site technical consultant, you are planning to construct an interactive Web page to assist customers prepare a diet tailored to their nutritional and budgetary requirements. Ideally, the customer would select foods to consider and specify nutritional and/or budgetary constraints, and the tool should return the optimal diet meeting those requirements. You would also like the Web page to allow the customer to decide whether, for instance, to find the cheapest possible diet meeting the requirements, the diet with the lowest number of calories, or the diet with the least total carbohydrates. **How do you go about constructing such a Web page?**

Web Site
www.FiniteandCalc.org
At the Web site you will find:

- Section by section tutorials
- A detailed chapter summary
- A true/false quiz
- Additional review exercises
- A linear programming grapher
- A pivot and Gauss-Jordan tool
- A simplex method tool

Image Studios/UpperCut Images/Getty Images

Introduction

In this chapter we begin to look at one of the most important types of problems for business and the sciences: finding the largest or smallest possible value of some quantity (such as profit or cost) under certain constraints (such as limited resources). We call such problems **optimization** problems because we are trying to find the best, or optimum, value. The optimization problems we look at in this chapter involve linear functions only and are known as **linear programming** (LP) problems. One of the main purposes of calculus, which you may study later, is to solve nonlinear optimization problems.

Linear programming problems involving only two unknowns can usually be solved by a graphical method that we discuss in Sections 4.1 and 4.2. When there are three or more unknowns, we must use an algebraic method, as we had to do for systems of linear equations. The method we use is called the **simplex method**. Invented in 1947 by George B. Dantzig* (1914–2005), the simplex method is still the most commonly used technique to solve LP problems in real applications, from finance to the computation of trajectories for guided missiles.

The simplex method can be used for hand calculations when the numbers are fairly small and the unknowns are few. Practical problems often involve large numbers and many unknowns, however. Problems such as routing telephone calls or airplane flights, or allocating resources in a manufacturing process can involve tens of thousands of unknowns. Solving such problems by hand is obviously impractical, and so computers are regularly used. Although computer programs most often use the simplex method, mathematicians are always seeking faster methods. The first radically different method of solving LP problems was the **ellipsoid algorithm** published in 1979 by the Soviet mathematician Leonid G. Khachiyan[2] (1952–2005). In 1984, Narendra Karmarkar (1957–), a researcher at Bell Labs, created a more efficient method now known as **Karmarkar's algorithm**. Although these methods (and others since developed) can be shown to be faster than the simplex method in the worst cases, it seems to be true that the simplex method is still the fastest in the applications that arise in practice.

Calculators and spreadsheets are very useful aids in the simplex method. In practice, software packages do most of the work, so you can think of what we teach you here as a peek inside a "black box." What the software cannot do for you is convert a real situation into a mathematical problem, so the most important lessons to get out of this chapter are (1) how to recognize and set up a linear programming problem, and (2) how to interpret the results.

∗ NOTE Dantzig is the real-life source of the story of the student who, walking in late to a math class, copies down two problems on the board, thinking they're homework. After much hard work he hands in the solutions, only to discover that he's just solved two famous unsolved problems. This actually happened to Dantzig in graduate school in 1939.[1]

4.1 Graphing Linear Inequalities

By the end of the next section, we will be solving linear programming (LP) problems with two unknowns. We use inequalities to describe the constraints in a problem, such as limitations on resources. Recall the basic notation for inequalities.

---

[1] Sources: D. J. Albers and C. Reid, "An Interview of George B. Dantzig: The Father of Linear Programming," *College Math. Journal*, v. 17 (1986), pp. 293–314. Quoted and discussed in the context of the urban legends it inspired at www.snopes.com/college/homework/unsolvable.asp.

[2] Dantzig and Khachiyan died approximately two weeks apart in 2005. The *New York Times* ran their obituaries together on May 23, 2005.

Nonstrict Inequalities	**Quick Examples**
$a \leq b$ means that a is **less than or equal to** b.	$3 \leq 99, -2 \leq -2, 0 \leq 3$
$a \geq b$ means that a is **greater than or equal to** b.	$3 \geq 3, 1.78 \geq 1.76, \dfrac{1}{3} \geq \dfrac{1}{4}$

There are also the inequalities $<$ and $>$, called **strict** inequalities because they do not permit equality. We do not use them in this chapter.

Following are some of the basic rules for manipulating inequalities. Although we illustrate all of them with the inequality $\leq$, they apply equally well to inequalities with $\geq$ and to the strict inequalities $<$ and $>$.

Rules for Manipulating Inequalities	**Quick Examples**
1. The same quantity can be added to or subtracted from both sides of an inequality: If $x \leq y$, then $x + a \leq y + a$ for any real number a.	$x \leq y$ implies $x - 4 \leq y - 4$
2. Both sides of an inequality can be multiplied or divided by a positive constant: If $x \leq y$ and a is positive, then $ax \leq ay$.	$x \leq y$ implies $3x \leq 3y$
3. Both sides of an inequality can be multiplied or divided by a negative constant if the inequality is *reversed*: If $x \leq y$ and a is negative, then $ax \geq ay$.	$x \leq y$ implies $-3x \geq -3y$
4. The left and right sides of an inequality can be switched if the inequality is *reversed*: If $x \leq y$, then $y \geq x$; if $y \geq x$, then $x \leq y$.	$3x \geq 5y$ implies $5y \leq 3x$

Here are the particular kinds of inequalities in which we're interested:

Linear Inequalities and Solving Inequalities

An **inequality in the unknown x** is the statement that one expression involving x is less than or equal to (or greater than or equal to) another. Similarly, we can have an **inequality in x and y**, which involves expressions that contain x and y; an **inequality in x, y, and z;** and so on. A **linear inequality** in one or more unknowns is an inequality of the form

$$ax \leq b \text{ (or } ax \geq b), \quad a \text{ and } b \text{ real constants}$$
$$ax + by \leq c \text{ (or } ax + by \geq c), \quad a, b, \text{ and } c \text{ real constants}$$
$$ax + by + cz \leq d, \quad a, b, c, \text{ and } d \text{ real constants}$$
$$ax + by + cz + dw \leq e, \quad a, b, c, d, \text{ and } e \text{ real constants}$$

and so on.

Quick Examples

$2x + 8 \geq 89$	Linear inequality in x
$2x^3 \leq x^3 + y$	Nonlinear inequality in x and y
$3x - 2y \geq 8$	Linear inequality in x and y
$x^2 + y^2 \leq 19z$	Nonlinear inequality in x, y, and z
$3x - 2y + 4z \leq 0$	Linear inequality in x, y, and z

A **solution** of an inequality in the unknown x is a value for x that makes the inequality true. For example, $2x + 8 \geq 89$ has a solution $x = 50$ because $2(50) + 8 \geq 89$. Of course, it has many other solutions as well. Similarly, a solution of an inequality in x and y is a pair of values (x, y) making the inequality true. For example, $(5, 1)$ is a solution of $3x - 2y \geq 8$ because $3(5) - 2(1) \geq 8$. To **solve** an inequality is to find the set of *all* solutions.

Solving Linear Inequalities in Two Variables

Our first goal is to solve linear inequalities in two variables—that is, inequalities of the form $ax + by \leq c$. As an example, let's solve

$$2x + 3y \leq 6.$$

We already know how to solve the *equation* $2x + 3y = 6$. As we saw in Chapter 1, the solution of this equation may be pictured as the set of all points (x, y) on the straight-line graph of the equation. This straight line has x-intercept 3 (obtained by putting $y = 0$ in the equation) and y-intercept 2 (obtained by putting $x = 0$ in the equation) and is shown in Figure 1.

Notice that, if (x, y) is any point on the line, then x and y not only satisfy the *equation* $2x + 3y = 6$, but they also satisfy the *inequality* $2x + 3y \leq 6$, because being equal to 6 qualifies as being less than or equal to 6.

Figure 1

Q: *Do the points on the line give all possible solutions to the inequality?*

A: No. For example, try the origin, $(0, 0)$. Because $2(0) + 3(0) = 0 \leq 6$, the point $(0, 0)$ is a solution that does not lie on the line. In fact, here is a possibly surprising fact: The solution to any linear inequality in two unknowns is represented by an entire **half plane**: the set of all points on one side of the line (including the line itself). Thus, because $(0, 0)$ is a solution of $2x + 3y \leq 6$ and is not on the line, every point on the same side of the line as $(0, 0)$ is a solution as well (the colored region below the line in Figure 2 shows which half plane constitutes the solution set).

Figure 2

To see why the solution set of $2x + 3y \leq 6$ is the entire half plane shown, start with any point P on the line $2x + 3y = 6$. We already know that P is a solution of $2x + 3y \leq 6$. If we choose any point Q directly below P, the x-coordinate of Q will be the same as that of P, and the y-coordinate will be smaller. So the value of $2x + 3y$ at Q will be smaller than the value at P, which is 6. Thus, $2x + 3y < 6$ at Q, and so Q is another solution of the inequality. (See Figure 3.) In other words, *every point beneath the line is a solution of* $2x + 3y \leq 6$.

On the other hand, any point above the line is directly above a point on the line, and so $2x + 3y > 6$ for such a point. Thus, *no point above the line is a solution of* $2x + 3y \leq 6$.

Figure 3

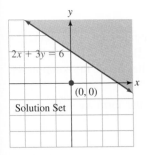

Figure 4

The same kind of argument can be used to show that the solution set of every inequality of the form $ax + by \leq c$ or $ax + by \geq c$ consists of the half plane above or below the line $ax + by = c$. The "test-point" procedure we describe below gives us an easy method for deciding whether the solution set includes the region above or below the corresponding line.

Now we are going to do something that will appear backward at first (but makes it simpler to sketch sets of solutions of *systems* of linear inequalities). For our standard drawing of the region of solutions of $2x + 3y \leq 6$, we are going to *shade only the part that we do not want and leave the solution region blank*. Think of covering over or "blocking out" the unwanted points, leaving those that we do want in full view (but remember that the points on the boundary line are also points that we want). The result is Figure 4. The reason we do this should become clear in Example 2.

Sketching the Region Represented by a Linear Inequality in Two Variables

1. Sketch the straight line obtained by replacing the given inequality with an equality.
2. Choose a test point not on the line; $(0, 0)$ is a good choice if the line does not pass through the origin.
3. If the test point satisfies the inequality, then the set of solutions is the entire region on the same side of the line as the test point. Otherwise, it is the region on the other side of the line. In either case, shade (block out) the side that does *not* contain the solutions, leaving the solution set unshaded.

Quick Example

Here are the three steps used to graph the inequality $x + 2y \geq 5$.

1. Sketch the line $x + 2y = 5$.

2. Test the point $(0, 0)$
$$0 + 2(0) \not\geq 5$$
Inequality is not satisfied.

3. Because the inequality is not satisfied, shade the region containing the test point.

EXAMPLE 1 Graphing Single Inequalities

Sketch the regions determined by each of the following inequalities:

a. $3x - 2y \leq 6$ **b.** $6x \leq 12 + 4y$ **c.** $x \leq -1$ **d.** $y \geq 0$ **e.** $x \geq 3y$

using Technology

Technology can be used to graph inequalities. Here is an outline (see the Technology Guides at the end of the chapter for additional details on using a TI-83/84 Plus or Excel):

TI-83/84 Plus

Solve the inequality for *y* and enter the resulting function of *x*; for example,

Y₁=-(2/3)*X+2.

Position the cursor on the icon to the left of Y₁ and press
ENTER until you see the kind of shading desired (above or below the line).
[More details on page 343.]

Excel

Solve the inequality for *y* and create a scattergraph using two points on the line. Then use the drawing palette to create a polygon to provide the shading.
[More details on page 345.]

Web Site
www.FiniteandCalc.org
→ Online Utilities
  → Linear Programming Grapher
Type "graph" and enter one or more inequalities (each one on a new line) as shown:

Adjust the graph window settings, and click "Graph."

Solution

a. The boundary line $3x - 2y = 6$ has *x*-intercept 2 and *y*-intercept -3 (Figure 5). We use $(0, 0)$ as a test point (because it is not on the line). Because $3(0) - 2(0) \leq 6$, the inequality is satisfied by the test point $(0, 0)$, and so it lies inside the solution set. The solution set is shown in Figure 5.

b. The given inequality, $6x \leq 12 + 4y$, can be rewritten in the form $ax + by \leq c$ by subtracting $4y$ from both sides:

$$6x - 4y \leq 12.$$

Dividing both sides by 2 gives the inequality $3x - 2y \leq 6$, which we considered in part (a). Now, *applying the rules for manipulating inequalities does not affect the set of solutions.* Thus, the inequality $6x \leq 12 + 4y$ has the same set of solutions as $3x - 2y \leq 6$. (See Figure 5.)

Figure 5

Figure 6

c. The region $x \leq -1$ has as boundary the vertical line $x = -1$. The test point $(0, 0)$ is not in the solution set, as shown in Figure 6.

d. The region $y \geq 0$ has as boundary the horizontal line $y = 0$ (that is, the *x*-axis). We cannot use $(0, 0)$ for the test point because it lies on the boundary line. Instead, we choose a convenient point not on the line $y = 0$—say, $(0, 1)$. Because $1 \geq 0$, this point is in the solution set, giving us the region shown in Figure 7.

e. The line $x \geq 3y$ has as boundary the line $x = 3y$ or, solving for *y*,

$$y = \frac{1}{3}x.$$

This line passes through the origin with slope $1/3$, so again we cannot choose the origin as a test point. Instead, we choose $(0, 1)$. Substituting these coordinates in $x \geq 3y$ gives $0 \geq 3(1)$, which is false, so $(0, 1)$ is not in the solution set, as shown in Figure 8.

Figure 7

Figure 8

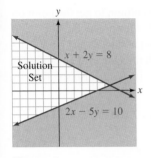

Figure 9

✱ TECHNOLOGY NOTE
Although these graphs are quite easy to do by hand, the more lines we have to graph the more difficult it becomes to get everything in the right place, and this is where graphing technology can become important. This is especially true when, for instance, three or more lines intersect in points that are very close together and hard to distinguish in hand-drawn graphs.

EXAMPLE 2 Graphing Simultaneous Inequalities

Sketch the region of points that satisfy both inequalities:

$$2x - 5y \leq 10$$
$$x + 2y \leq 8.$$

Solution Each inequality has a solution set that is a half plane. If a point is to satisfy *both* inequalities, it must lie in both sets of solutions. Put another way, if we cover the points that are not solutions to $2x - 5y \leq 10$ and then also cover the points that are not solutions to $x + 2y \leq 8$, the points that remain uncovered must be the points we want, those that are solutions to both inequalities. The result is shown in Figure 9, where the unshaded region is the set of solutions.✱

As a check, we can look at points in various regions in Figure 9. For example, our graph shows that $(0, 0)$ should satisfy both inequalities, and it does;

$$2(0) - 5(0) = 0 \leq 10 \qquad ✔$$
$$0 + 2(0) = 0 \leq 8. \qquad ✔$$

On the other hand, $(0, 5)$ should fail to satisfy one of the inequalities.

$$2(0) - 5(5) = -25 \leq 10 \qquad ✔$$
$$0 + 2(5) = 10 > 8 \qquad ✗$$

One more: $(5, -1)$ should fail one of the inequalities:

$$2(5) - 5(-1) = 15 > 10 \qquad ✗$$
$$5 + 2(-1) = 3 \leq 8. \qquad ✔$$

EXAMPLE 3 Corner Points

Sketch the region of solutions of the following system of inequalities and list the coordinates of all the corner points.

$$3x - 2y \leq 6$$
$$x + y \geq -5$$
$$y \leq 4$$

Solution Shading the regions that we do not want leaves us with the triangle shown in Figure 10. We label the corner points A, B, and C as shown.

Each of these corner points lies at the intersection of two of the bounding lines. So, to find the coordinates of each corner point, we need to solve the system of equations given by the two lines. To do this systematically, we make the following table:

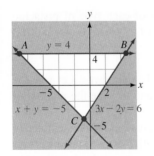

Figure 10

Point	Lines through Point	Coordinates
A	$y = 4$ $x + y = -5$	$(-9, 4)$
B	$y = 4$ $3x - 2y = 6$	$\left(\dfrac{14}{3}, 4\right)$
C	$x + y = -5$ $3x - 2y = 6$	$\left(-\dfrac{4}{5}, -\dfrac{21}{5}\right)$

✳ TECHNOLOGY NOTE
Using the trace feature makes it easy to locate corner points graphically. Remember to zoom in for additional accuracy when appropriate. Of course, you can also use technology to help solve the systems of equations, as we discussed in Chapter 2.

Here, we have solved each system of equations in the middle column to get the point on the right, using the techniques of Chapter 2. You should do this for practice.✳

As a partial check that we have drawn the correct region, let us choose any point in its interior—say, $(0, 0)$. We can easily check that $(0, 0)$ satisfies all three given inequalities. It follows that all of the points in the triangular region containing $(0, 0)$ are also solutions.

Take another look at the regions of solutions in Examples 2 and 3 (Figure 11).

(a) Example 2 Solution Set　　　(b) Example 3 Solution Set

Figure 11

Notice that the solution set in Figure 11(a) extends infinitely far to the left, whereas the one in Figure 11(b) is completely enclosed by a boundary. Sets that are completely enclosed are called **bounded**, and sets that extend infinitely in one or more directions are **unbounded**. For example, all the solution sets in Example 1 are unbounded.

EXAMPLE 4 Resource Allocation

Socaccio Pistachio Inc. makes two types of pistachio nuts: Dazzling Red and Organic. Pistachio nuts require food color and salt, and the following table shows the amount of food color and salt required for a 1-kilogram batch of pistachios, as well as the total amount of these ingredients available each day.

	Dazzling Red	*Organic*	*Total Available*
Food Color (g)	2	1	20
Salt (g)	10	20	220

Use a graph to show the possible numbers of batches of each type of pistachio Socaccio can produce each day. This region (the solution set of a system of inequalities) is called the **feasible region**.

Solution As we did in Chapter 2, we start by identifying the unknowns: Let x be the number of batches of Dazzling Red manufactured per day and let y be the number of batches of Organic manufactured each day.

Now, because of our experience with systems of linear equations, we are tempted to say: For food color $2x + y = 20$ and for salt, $10x + 20y = 220$. However, no one is saying that Socaccio has to use all available ingredients; the company might choose to use fewer than the total available amounts if this proves more profitable. Thus, $2x + y$ can be anything *up to a total of* 20. In other words,

$$2x + y \leq 20.$$

Similarly,

$$10x + 20y \leq 220.$$

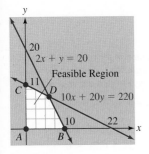

Figure 12

There are two more restrictions not explicitly mentioned: Neither x nor y can be negative. (The company cannot produce a negative number of batches of nuts.) Therefore, we have the additional restrictions

$$x \geq 0 \quad y \geq 0.$$

These two inequalities tell us that the feasible region (solution set) is restricted to the first quadrant, because in the other quadrants, either x or y or both x and y are negative. So instead of shading out all other quadrants, we can simply restrict our drawing to the first quadrant.

The (bounded) feasible region shown in Figure 12 is a graphical representation of the limitations the company faces.

➡ **Before we go on...** Every point in the feasible region in Example 4 represents a value for x and a value for y that do not violate any of the company's restrictions. For example, the point $(5, 6)$ lies well inside the region, so the company can produce five batches of Dazzling Red nuts and six batches of Organic without exceeding the limitations on ingredients [that is, $2(5) + 6 = 16 \leq 20$ and $10(5) + 20(6) = 170 \leq 220$]. The corner points A, B, C, and D are significant if the company wishes to realize the greatest profit, as we will see in Section 4.2. We can find the corners as in the following table:

Point	Lines through Point	Coordinates
A		$(0, 0)$
B		$(10, 0)$
C		$(0, 11)$
D	$2x + y = 20$ $10x + 20y = 220$	$(6, 8)$

(We have not listed the lines through the first three corners because their coordinates can be read easily from the graph.) Points on the line segment DB represent use of all the food color (because the segment lies on the line $2x + y = 20$), and points on the line segment CD represent use of all the salt (because the segment lies on the line $10x + 20y = 220$). Note that the point D is the only solution that uses all of both ingredients. ■

FAQs

Recognizing Whether to Use a Linear Inequality or a Linear Equation

Q : *How do I know whether to model a situation by a linear inequality like $3x + 2y \leq 10$ or by a linear equation like $3x + 2y = 10$?*

A : Here are some key phrases to look for: *at most, up to, no more than, at least, or more, exactly.* Suppose, for instance, that nuts cost 3¢, bolts cost 2¢, x is the number of nuts you can buy, and y is the number of bolts you can buy.

- If you have *up to* 10¢ to spend, then $3x + 2y \leq 10$.
- If you must spend *exactly* 10¢, then $3x + 2y = 10$.
- If you plan to spend *at least* 10¢, then $3x + 2y \geq 10$.

The use of inequalities to model a situation is often more realistic than the use of equations; for instance, one cannot always expect to exactly fill all orders, spend the exact amount of one's budget, or keep a plant operating at exactly 100% capacity.

4.1 EXERCISES

▼ more advanced   ◆ challenging

Ⓣ indicates exercises that should be solved using technology

In Exercises 1–26, sketch the region that corresponds to the given inequalities, say whether the region is bounded or unbounded, and find the coordinates of all corner points (if any). HINT [See Example 1.]

1. $2x + y \leq 10$

2. $4x - y \leq 12$

3. $-x - 2y \leq 8$

4. $-x + 2y \geq 4$

5. $3x + 2y \geq 5$

6. $2x - 3y \leq 7$

7. $x \leq 3y$

8. $y \geq 3x$

9. $\dfrac{3x}{4} - \dfrac{y}{4} \leq 1$

10. $\dfrac{x}{3} + \dfrac{2y}{3} \geq 2$

11. $x \geq -5$

12. $y \leq -4$

13. $4x - y \leq 8$

$x + 2y \leq 2$

HINT [See Examples 2 and 3.]

14. $2x + y \leq 4$

$x - 2y \geq 2$

HINT [See Examples 2 and 3.]

15. $3x + 2y \geq 6$

$3x - 2y \leq 6$

$x \qquad \geq 0$

16. $3x + 2y \leq 6$

$3x - 2y \geq 6$

$-y \geq 2$

17. $x + y \geq 5$

$x \qquad \leq 10$

$y \leq 8$

$x \geq 0, y \geq 0$

18. $2x + 4y \geq 12$

$x \qquad \leq 5$

$y \leq 3$

$x \geq 0, y \geq 0$

19. $20x + 10y \leq 100$

$10x + 20y \leq 100$

$10x + 10y \leq 60$

$x \geq 0, y \geq 0$

20. $30x + 20y \leq 600$

$10x + 40y \leq 400$

$20x + 30y \leq 450$

$x \geq 0, y \geq 0$

21. $20x + 10y \geq 100$

$10x + 20y \geq 100$

$10x + 10y \geq 80$

$x \geq 0, y \geq 0$

22. $30x + 20y \geq 600$

$10x + 40y \geq 400$

$20x + 30y \geq 600$

$x \geq 0, y \geq 0$

23. $-3x + 2y \leq 5$

$3x - 2y \leq 6$

$x \qquad \leq 2y$

$x \geq 0, y \geq 0$

24. $-3x + 2y \leq 5$

$3x - 2y \geq 6$

$y \leq x/2$

$x \geq 0, y \geq 0$

25. $2x - y \geq 0$

$x - 3y \leq 0$

$x \geq 0, y \geq 0$

26. $-x + y \geq 0$

$4x - 3y \geq 0$

$x \geq 0, y \geq 0$

Ⓣ *In Exercises 27–32, we suggest you use technology. Graph the regions corresponding to the inequalities, and find the coordinates of all corner points (if any) to two decimal places:*

27. $2.1x - 4.3y \geq 9.7$

28. $-4.3x + 4.6y \geq 7.1$

29. $-0.2x + 0.7y \geq 3.3$

$1.1x + 3.4y \geq 0$

30. $0.2x + 0.3y \geq 7.2$

$2.5x - 6.7y \leq 0$

31. $4.1x - 4.3y \leq 4.4$

$7.5x - 4.4y \leq 5.7$

$4.3x + 8.5y \leq 10$

32. $2.3x - 2.4y \leq 2.5$

$4.0x - 5.1y \leq 4.4$

$6.1x + 6.7y \leq 9.6$

APPLICATIONS

33. *Resource Allocation* You manage an ice cream factory that makes two flavors: Creamy Vanilla and Continental Mocha. Into each quart of Creamy Vanilla go 2 eggs and 3 cups of cream. Into each quart of Continental Mocha go 1 egg and 3 cups of cream. You have in stock 500 eggs and 900 cups of cream. Draw the feasible region showing the number of quarts of vanilla and number of quarts of mocha that can be produced. Find the corner points of the region. HINT [See Example 4.]

34. *Resource Allocation* Podunk Institute of Technology's Math Department offers two courses: Finite Math and Applied Calculus. Each section of Finite Math has 60 students, and each section of Applied Calculus has 50. The department is allowed to offer a total of up to 110 sections. Furthermore, no more than 6,000 students want to take a math course. (No student will take more than one math course.) Draw the feasible region that shows the number of sections of each class that can be offered. Find the corner points of the region. HINT [See Example 4.]

35. *Nutrition* Ruff Inc. makes dog food out of chicken and grain. Chicken has 10 grams of protein and 5 grams of fat per ounce, and grain has 2 grams of protein and 2 grams of fat per ounce. A bag of dog food must contain at least 200 grams of protein and at least 150 grams of fat. Draw the feasible region that shows the number of ounces of chicken and number of ounces of grain Ruff can mix into each bag of dog food. Find the corner points of the region.

36. *Purchasing* Enormous State University's Business School is buying computers. The school has two models to choose from: the Pomegranate and the iZac. Each Pomegranate comes with 400 MB of memory and 80 GB of disk space, and each iZac has 300 MB of memory and 100 GB of disk space. For reasons related to its accreditation, the school would like to be able to say that it has a total of at least 48,000 MB of memory and at least 12,800 GB of disk space. Draw the feasible region that shows the number of each kind of computer it can buy. Find the corner points of the region.

37. *Nutrition* Each serving of Gerber Mixed Cereal for Baby contains 60 calories and 11 grams of carbohydrates, and each serving of Gerber Mango Tropical Fruit Dessert contains 80 calories and 21 grams of carbohydrates.[3] You want to provide your child with at least 140 calories and at least 32 grams of carbohydrates. Draw the feasible region that shows the number of servings of cereal and number of servings of dessert that you can give your child. Find the corner points of the region.

38. *Nutrition* Each serving of Gerber Mixed Cereal for Baby contains 60 calories, 11 grams of carbohydrates, and no vitamin C. Each serving of Gerber Apple Banana Juice contains 60 calories, 15 grams of carbohydrates, and 120 percent of the U.S. Recommended Daily Allowance (RDA) of vitamin C for infants.[4] You want to provide your child with at least 120 calories, at least 26 grams of carbohydrates, and at least 50 percent of the U.S. RDA of vitamin C for infants. Draw the feasible region that shows the number of servings of cereal and number of servings of juice that you can give your child. Find the corner points of the region.

39. *Municipal Bond Funds* The Pimco New York Municipal Bond Fund (PNF) and the Fidelity Spartan Mass Fund (FDMMX) are tax-exempt municipal bond funds. In 2003, the Pimco fund yielded 6% while the Fidelity fund yielded 5%.[5] You would like to invest a total of up to $80,000 and earn at least $4,200 in interest in the coming year (based on the given yields). Draw the feasible region that shows how much money you can invest in each fund. Find the corner points of the region.

40. *Municipal Bond Funds* In 2003, the Fidelity Spartan Mass Fund (FDMMX) yielded 5%, and the Fidelity Spartan Florida Fund (FFLIX) yielded 7%.[6] You would like to invest a total of up to $60,000 and earn at least $3,500 in interest. Draw the feasible region that shows how much money you can invest in each fund (based on the given yields). Find the corner points of the region.

41. ▼ *Investments* Your portfolio manager has suggested two high-yielding stocks: **Consolidated Edison** (ED) and **General Electric** (GE). ED shares cost $40 and yield 6% in dividends. GE shares cost $16 and yield 7.5% in dividends.[7] You have up to $10,000 to invest, and would like to earn at least $600 in dividends. Draw the feasible region that shows how many shares in each company you can buy. Find the corner points of the region. (Round each coordinate to the nearest whole number.)

42. ▼ *Investments* Your friend's portfolio manager has suggested two energy stocks: **Exxon Mobil** (XOM) and **British Petroleum** (BP). XOM shares cost $80 and yield 2% in dividends. BP shares cost $50 and yield 7% in dividends.[8] Your friend has up to $40,000 to invest, and would like to earn at least $1,400 in dividends. Draw the feasible region that shows how many shares in each company she can buy. Find the corner points of the region. (Round each coordinate to the nearest whole number.)

43. ▼ *Advertising* You are the marketing director for a company that manufactures bodybuilding supplements and you are planning to run ads in *Sports Illustrated* and *GQ Magazine*. Based on readership data, you estimate that each one-page ad in *Sports Illustrated* will be read by 650,000 people in your target group, while each one-page ad in *GQ* will be read by 150,000.[9] You would like your ads to be read by at least three million people in the target group and, to ensure the broadest possible audience, you would like to place at least three full-page ads in each magazine. Draw the feasible region that shows how many pages you can purchase in each magazine. Find the corner points of the region. (Round each coordinate to the nearest whole number.)

44. ▼ *Advertising* You are the marketing director for a company that manufactures bodybuilding supplements and you are planning to run ads in *Sports Illustrated* and *Muscle and Fitness*. Based on readership data, you estimate that each one-page ad in *Sports Illustrated* will be read by 650,000 people in your target group, while each one-page ad in *Muscle and Fitness* will be read by 250,000 people in your target group.[10] You would like your ads to be read by at least four million people in the target group and, to ensure the broadest possible audience, you would like to place at least three full-page ads in each magazine during the year. Draw the feasible region showing how many pages you can purchase in each magazine. Find the corner points of the region. (Round each coordinate to the nearest whole number.)

COMMUNICATION AND REASONING EXERCISES

45. Find a system of inequalities whose solution set is unbounded.

46. Find a system of inequalities whose solution set is empty.

47. How would you use linear inequalities to describe the triangle with corner points (0, 0), (2, 0), and (0, 1)?

48. Explain the advantage of shading the region of points that do not satisfy the given inequalities. Illustrate with an example.

49. Describe at least one drawback to the method of finding the corner points of a feasible region by drawing its graph, when the feasible region arises from real-life constraints.

[3] Source: Nutrition information printed on the jar.

[4] Ibid.

[5] Yields are rounded. Sources: www.pimcofunds.com, www.fidelity.com. January 18, 2004.

[6] Yields are rounded. Source: www.fidelity.com. January 18, 2004.

[7] Share prices and yields are approximate (2008). Source: http://finance.google.com.

[8] Ibid.

[9] The readership data for *Sports Illustrated* is based, in part, on the results of a readership survey taken in March 2000. The readership data for *GQ* is fictitious. Source: Mediamark Research Inc./*New York Times*, May 29, 2000, p. C1.

[10] The readership data for both magazines are based on the results of a readership survey taken in March 2000. Source: Mediamark Research Inc./*New York Times*, May 29, 2000, p. C1.

50. Draw several bounded regions described by linear inequalities. For each region you draw, find the point that gives the greatest possible value of $x + y$. What do you notice?

In Exercises 51–54, you are mixing x grams of ingredient A and y grams of ingredient B. Choose the equation or inequality that models the given requirement.

51. There should be at least 3 more grams of ingredient A than ingredient B.

(A) $3x - y \leq 0$　　　　　　(B) $x - 3y \geq 0$
(C) $x - y \geq 3$　　　　　　(D) $3x - y \geq 0$

52. The mixture should contain at least 25% of ingredient A by weight.

(A) $4x - y \leq 0$　　　　　　(B) $x - 4y \geq 0$
(C) $x - y \geq 4$　　　　　　(D) $3x - y \geq 0$

53. ▼ There should be at least 3 parts (by weight) of ingredient A to 2 parts of ingredient B.

(A) $3x - 2y \geq 0$　　　　　(B) $2x - 3y \geq 0$
(C) $3x + 2y \geq 0$　　　　　(D) $2x + 3y \geq 0$

54. ▼ There should be no more of ingredient A (by weight) than ingredient B.

(A) $x - y = 0$　　　　　　　(B) $x - y \leq 0$
(C) $x - y \geq 0$　　　　　　(D) $x + y \geq y$

55. ▼ You are setting up a system of inequalities in the unknowns x and y. The inequalities represent constraints faced by Fly-by-Night Airlines, where x represents the number of first-class tickets it should issue for a specific flight and y represents the number of business-class tickets it should issue for that flight. You find that the feasible region is empty. How do you interpret this?

56. ▼ In the situation described in the preceding exercise, is it possible instead for the feasible region to be unbounded? Explain your answer.

57. ▼ Create an interesting scenario that leads to the following system of inequalities:

$$20x + 40y \leq 1{,}000$$
$$30x + 20y \leq 1{,}200$$
$$x \geq 0, y \geq 0.$$

58. ▼ Create an interesting scenario that leads to the following system of inequalities:

$$20x + 40y \geq 1{,}000$$
$$30x + 20y \geq 1{,}200$$
$$x \geq 0, y \geq 0.$$

4.2 Solving Linear Programming Problems Graphically

As we saw in Example 4 in Section 4.1, in some scenarios the possibilities are restricted by a system of linear inequalities. In that example, it would be natural to ask which of the various possibilities gives the company the largest profit. This is a kind of problem known as a *linear programming problem* (commonly referred to as an LP problem).

Linear Programming (LP) Problems

A **linear programming problem** in two unknowns x and y is one in which we are to find the maximum or minimum value of a linear expression

$$ax + by$$

called the **objective function**, subject to a number of linear **constraints** of the form

$$cx + dy \leq e \quad \text{or} \quad cx + dy \geq e.$$

The largest or smallest value of the objective function is called the **optimal value**, and a pair of values of x and y that gives the optimal value constitutes an **optimal solution**.

Quick Example

Maximize $p = x + y$ Objective function

subject to $\left. \begin{aligned} x + 2y &\le 12 \\ 2x + y &\le 12 \\ x \ge 0, \; y &\ge 0. \end{aligned} \right\}$ Constraints

See Example 1 for a method of solving this LP problem (that is, finding an optimal solution and value).

The set of points (x, y) satisfying all the constraints is the **feasible region** for the problem. Our methods of solving LP problems rely on the following facts:

Fundamental Theorem of Linear Programming

- If an LP problem has optimal solutions, then at least one of these solutions occurs at a corner point of the feasible region.
- Linear programming problems with bounded, nonempty feasible regions always have optimal solutions.

Let's see how we can use this to solve an LP problem, and then we'll discuss why it's true.

EXAMPLE 1 Solving an LP Problem

Maximize $p = x + y$

subject to $x + 2y \le 12$

$2x + y \le 12$

$x \ge 0, \; y \ge 0.$

Solution We begin by drawing the feasible region for the problem. We do this using the techniques of Section 4.1, and we get Figure 13.

Each **feasible point** (point in the feasible region) gives an x and a y satisfying the constraints. The question now is, which of these points gives the largest value of the objective function $p = x + y$? The Fundamental Theorem of Linear Programming tells us that the largest value must occur at one (or more) of the corners of the feasible region. In the following table, we list the coordinates of each corner point and we compute the value of the objective function at each corner.

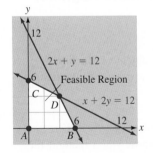

Figure 13

Corner Point	Lines through Point	Coordinates	$p = x + y$
A		$(0, 0)$	0
B		$(6, 0)$	6
C		$(0, 6)$	6
D	$x + 2y = 12$ $2x + y = 12$	$(4, 4)$	8

Now we simply pick the one that gives the largest value for p, which is D. Therefore, the optimal value of p is 8, and an optimal solution is $(4, 4)$.

Figure 14

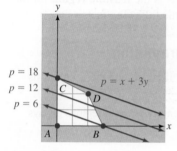

Figure 15

Now we owe you an explanation of why one of the corner points should be an optimal solution. The question is, which point in the feasible region gives the largest possible value of $p = x + y$?

Consider first an easier question: Which points result in a *particular value* of p? For example, which points result in $p = 2$? These would be the points on the line $x + y = 2$, which is the line labeled $p = 2$ in Figure 14.

Now suppose we want to know which points make $p = 4$: These would be the points on the line $x + y = 4$, which is the line labeled $p = 4$ in Figure 14. Notice that this line is parallel to but higher than the line $p = 2$. (If p represented profit in an application, we would call these **isoprofit lines**, or **constant-profit lines**.) Imagine moving this line up or down in the picture. As we move the line down, we see smaller values of p, and as we move it up, we see larger values. Several more of these lines are drawn in Figure 14. Look, in particular, at the line labeled $p = 10$. This line does not meet the feasible region, meaning that no feasible point makes p as large as 10. Starting with the line $p = 2$, as we move the line up, increasing p, there will be a last line that meets the feasible region. In the figure it is clear that this is the line $p = 8$, and this meets the feasible region in only one point, which is the corner point D. Therefore, D gives the greatest value of p of all feasible points.

If we had been asked to maximize some other objective function, such as $p = x + 3y$, then the optimal solution might be different. Figure 15 shows some of the isoprofit lines for this objective function. This time, the last point that is hit as p increases is C, not D. This tells us that the optimal solution is $(0, 6)$, giving the optimal value $p = 18$.

This discussion should convince you that the optimal value in an LP problem will always occur at one of the corner points. By the way, it is possible for the optimal value to occur at *two* corner points and at all points along an edge connecting them. (Do you see why?) We will see this in Example 3(b).

Here is a summary of the method we have just been using.

Graphical Method for Solving Linear Programming Problems in Two Unknowns (Bounded Feasible Regions)

1. Graph the feasible region and check that it is bounded.

2. Compute the coordinates of the corner points.

3. Substitute the coordinates of the corner points into the objective function to see which gives the maximum (or minimum) value of the objective function.

4. Any such corner point is an optimal solution.

Note If the feasible region is unbounded, this method will work only if there are optimal solutions; otherwise, it will not work. We will show you a method for deciding this on page 280. ∎

APPLICATIONS

EXAMPLE 2 Resource Allocation

Acme Babyfoods mixes two strengths of apple juice. One quart of Beginner's juice is made from 30 fluid ounces of water and 2 fluid ounces of apple juice concentrate. One quart of Advanced juice is made from 20 fluid ounces of water and 12 fluid ounces of concentrate. Every day Acme has available 30,000 fluid ounces of water and 3,600 fluid ounces of concentrate. Acme makes a profit of 20¢ on each quart of Beginner's juice and 30¢ on each quart of Advanced juice. How many quarts of each should Acme make each day to get the largest profit? How would this change if Acme made a profit of 40¢ on Beginner's juice and 20¢ on Advanced juice?

Solution Looking at the question that we are asked, we see that our unknown quantities are

$$x = \text{number of quarts of Beginner's juice made each day}$$
$$y = \text{number of quarts of Advanced juice made each day.}$$

(In this context, x and y are often called the **decision variables**, because we must decide what their values should be in order to get the largest profit.) We can write down the data given in the form of a table (the numbers in the first two columns are amounts per quart of juice):

	Beginner's, x	Advanced, y	Available
Water (ounces)	30	20	30,000
Concentrate (ounces)	2	12	3,600
Profit (¢)	20	30	

Because nothing in the problem says that Acme must use up all the water or concentrate, just that it can use no more than what is available, the first two rows of the table give us two inequalities:

$$30x + 20y \le 30,000$$
$$2x + 12y \le 3,600.$$

Dividing the first inequality by 10 and the second by 2 gives

$$3x + 2y \le 3,000$$
$$x + 6y \le 1,800.$$

We also have that $x \ge 0$ and $y \ge 0$ because Acme can't make a negative amount of juice. To finish setting up the problem, we are asked to maximize the profit, which is

$$p = 20x + 30y. \qquad \text{Expressed in ¢}$$

This gives us our LP problem:

$$\text{Maximize} \quad p = 20x + 30y$$
$$\text{subject to} \quad 3x + 2y \le 3,000$$
$$x + 6y \le 1,800$$
$$x \ge 0, y \ge 0.$$

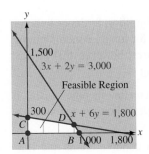

Figure 16

The (bounded) feasible region is shown in Figure 16.

The corners and the values of the objective function are listed in the following table:

Point	Lines through Point	Coordinates	p = 20x + 30y
A		(0, 0)	0
B		(1,000, 0)	20,000
C		(0, 300)	9,000
D	3x + 2y = 3,000 x + 6y = 1,800	(900, 150)	22,500

We are seeking to maximize the objective function p, so we look for corner points that give the maximum value for p. Because the maximum occurs at the point D, we conclude that the (only) optimal solution occurs at D. Thus, the company should make 900 quarts of Beginner's juice and 150 quarts of Advanced juice, for a largest possible profit of 22,500¢, or $225.

If, instead, the company made a profit of 40¢ on each quart of Beginner's juice and 20¢ on each quart of Advanced juice, then we would have $p = 40x + 20y$. This gives the following table:

Point	Lines through Point	Coordinates	$p = 40x + 20y$
A		$(0, 0)$	0
B		$(1,000, 0)$	40,000
C		$(0, 300)$	6,000
D	$3x + 2y = 3,000$ $x + 6y = 1,800$	$(900, 150)$	39,000

We can see that, in this case, Acme should make 1,000 quarts of Beginner's juice and no Advanced juice, for a largest possible profit of 40,000¢, or $400.

➡ **Before we go on...** Notice that, in the first version of the problem in Example 2, the company used all the water and juice concentrate:

Water: $30(900) + 20(150) = 30,000$
Concentrate: $2(900) + 12(150) = 3,600.$

In the second version, it used all the water but not all the concentrate:

Water: $30(100) + 20(0) = 30,000$
Concentrate: $2(100) + 12(0) = 200 < 3,600.$ ∎

EXAMPLE 3 **Investments**

The Solid Trust Savings & Loan Company has set aside $25 million for loans to home buyers. Its policy is to allocate at least $10 million annually for luxury condominiums. A government housing development grant it receives requires, however, that at least one-third of its total loans be allocated to low-income housing.

a. Solid Trust's return on condominiums is 12% and its return on low-income housing is 10%. How much should the company allocate for each type of housing to maximize its total return?

b. Redo part (a), assuming that the return is 12% on both condominiums and low-income housing.

Solution

a. We first identify the unknowns: Let x be the annual amount (in millions of dollars) allocated to luxury condominiums, and let y be the annual amount allocated to low-income housing.

We now look at the constraints. The first constraint is mentioned in the first sentence: The total the company can invest is $25 million. Thus,

$$x + y \leq 25.$$

Renaud Visage/age fotostock/PhotoLibrary

(The company is not required to invest all of the $25 million; rather, it can invest *up to* $25 million.) Next, the company has allocated at least $10 million to condos. Rephrasing this in terms of the unknowns, we get

The amount allocated to condos is at least $10 million.

The phrase "is at least" means ≥. Thus, we obtain a second constraint:

$$x \geq 10.$$

The third constraint is that at least one-third of the total financing must be for low-income housing. Rephrasing this, we say:

The amount allocated to low-income housing is at least one-third of the total.

Because the total investment will be $x + y$, we get

$$y \geq \frac{1}{3}(x + y).$$

We put this in the standard form of a linear inequality as follows:

$$3y \geq x + y \qquad \text{Multiply both sides by 3.}$$
$$-x + 2y \geq 0. \qquad \text{Subtract } x + y \text{ from both sides.}$$

There are no further constraints.

Now, what about the return on these investments? According to the data, the annual return is given by

$$p = 0.12x + 0.10y.$$

We want to make this quantity p as large as possible. In other words, we want to

$$\begin{aligned}
\text{Maximize} \quad & p = 0.12x + 0.10y \\
\text{subject to} \quad & x + y \leq 25 \\
& x \geq 10 \\
& -x + 2y \geq 0 \\
& x \geq 0, \, y \geq 0.
\end{aligned}$$

(Do you see why the inequalities $x \geq 0$ and $y \geq 0$ are slipped in here?) The feasible region is shown in Figure 17.

We now make a table that gives the return on investment at each corner point:

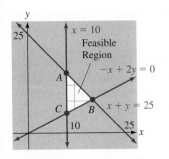

Figure 17

Point	Lines through Point	Coordinates	$p = 0.12x + 0.10y$
A	$x = 10$ $x + y = 25$	$(10, 15)$	2.7
B	$x + y = 25$ $-x + 2y = 0$	$(50/3, 25/3)$	2.833
C	$x = 10$ $-x + 2y = 0$	$(10, 5)$	1.7

From the table, we see that the values of x and y that maximize the return are $x = 50/3$ and $y = 25/3$, which give a total return of $2.833 million. In other words, the most profitable course of action is to invest $16.667 million in loans for condominiums and $8.333 million in loans for low-income housing, giving a maximum annual return of $2.833 million.

b. The LP problem is the same as for part (a) except for the objective function:

$$\text{Maximize} \quad p = 0.12x + 0.12y$$
$$\text{subject to}$$
$$x + y \le 25$$
$$x \ge 10$$
$$-x + 2y \ge 0$$
$$x \ge 0, y \ge 0.$$

Here are the values of p at the three corners:

Point	Coordinates	$p = 0.12x + 0.12y$
A	(10, 15)	3
B	(50/3, 25/3)	3
C	(10, 5)	1.8

Looking at the table, we see that a curious thing has happened: We get the same maximum annual return at both A and B. Thus, we could choose either option to maximize the annual return. In fact, any point along the line segment AB will yield an annual return of $3 million. For example, the point (12, 13) lies on the line segment AB and also yields an annual revenue of $3 million. This happens because the "isoreturn" lines are parallel to that edge.

➡ **Before we go on...** What breakdowns of investments would lead to the *lowest* return for parts (a) and (b)? ∎

The preceding examples all had bounded feasible regions. If the feasible region is unbounded, then, *provided there are optimal solutions,* the fundamental theorem of linear programming guarantees that the above method will work. The following procedure determines whether or not optimal solutions exist and finds them when they do.

Solving Linear Programming Problems in Two Unknowns (Unbounded Feasible Regions)

If the feasible region of an LP problem is unbounded, proceed as follows:

1. Draw a rectangle large enough so that all the corner points are inside the rectangle (and not on its boundary):

Corner points: A, B, C

Corner points inside the rectangle

2. Shade the outside of the rectangle so as to define a new bounded feasible region, and locate the new corner points:

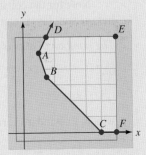

New corner points: D, E, and F

3. Obtain the optimal solutions using this bounded feasible region.

4. If any optimal solutions occur at one of the original corner points (A, B, and C in the figure), then the LP problem has that corner point as an optimal solution. Otherwise, the LP problem has no optimal solutions. When the latter occurs, we say that the **objective function is unbounded**, because it can assume arbitrarily large (positive or negative) values.

In the next two examples, we work with unbounded feasible regions.

EXAMPLE 4 Cost

You are the manager of a small store that specializes in hats, sunglasses, and other accessories. You are considering a sales promotion of a new line of hats and sunglasses. You will offer the sunglasses only to those who purchase two or more hats, so you will sell at least twice as many hats as pairs of sunglasses. Moreover, your supplier tells you that, due to seasonal demand, your order of sunglasses cannot exceed 100 pairs. To ensure that the sale items fill out the large display you have set aside, you estimate that you should order at least 210 items in all.

a. Assume that you will lose $3 on every hat and $2 on every pair of sunglasses sold. Given the constraints above, how many hats and pairs of sunglasses should you order to lose the least amount of money in the sales promotion?

b. Suppose instead that you lose $1 on every hat sold but make a profit of $5 on every pair of sunglasses sold. How many hats and pairs of sunglasses should you order to make the largest profit in the sales promotion?

c. Now suppose that you make a profit of $1 on every hat sold but lose $5 on every pair of sunglasses sold. How many hats and pairs of sunglasses should you order to make the largest profit in the sales promotion?

Solution

a. The unknowns are:

$x =$ number of hats you order
$y =$ number of pairs of sunglasses you order.

The objective is to minimize the total loss:

$$c = 3x + 2y.$$

Now for the constraints. The requirement that you will sell at least twice as many hats as sunglasses can be rephrased as:

The number of hats is at least twice the number of pairs of sunglasses,

or

$$x \geq 2y$$

which, in standard form, is

$$x - 2y \geq 0.$$

Next, your order of sunglasses cannot exceed 100 pairs, so

$$y \leq 100.$$

Finally, you would like to sell at least 210 items in all, giving

$$x + y \geq 210.$$

Thus, the LP problem is the following:

Minimize $c = 3x + 2y$
subject to $x - 2y \geq 0$
$y \leq 100$
$x + y \geq 210$
$x \geq 0, y \geq 0.$

Figure 18

The feasible region is shown in Figure 18. This region is unbounded, so there is no guarantee that there are any optimal solutions. Following the procedure described above, we enclose the corner points in a rectangle as shown in Figure 19. (There are infinitely many possible rectangles we could have used. We chose one that gives convenient coordinates for the new corners.)

We now list all the corners of this bounded region along with the corresponding values of the objective function c:

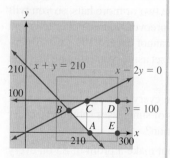

Figure 19

Point	Lines through Point	Coordinates	$c = 3x + 2y$ ($)
A		(210, 0)	630
B	$x + y = 210$ $x - 2y = 0$	(140, 70)	560
C	$x - 2y = 0$ $y = 100$	(200, 100)	800
D		(300, 100)	1,100
E		(300, 0)	900

The corner point that gives the minimum value of the objective function c is B. Because B is one of the corner points of the original feasible region, we conclude that our linear programming problem has an optimal solution at B. Thus, the combination that gives the smallest loss is 140 hats and 70 pairs of sunglasses.

b. The LP problem is the following:

$$\text{Maximize} \quad p = -x + 5y$$
$$\text{subject to} \quad x - 2y \geq 0$$
$$y \leq 100$$
$$x + y \geq 210$$
$$x \geq 0, y \geq 0.$$

Because most of the work is already done for us in part (a), all we need to do is change the objective function in the table that lists the corner points:

Point	Lines through Point	Coordinates	$p = -x + 5y$ ($)
A		(210, 0)	−210
B	$x + y = 210$ $x - 2y = 0$	(140, 70)	210
C	$x - 2y = 0$ $y = 100$	(200, 100)	300
D		(300, 100)	200
E		(300, 0)	−300

The corner point that gives the maximum value of the objective function p is C. Because C is one of the corner points of the original feasible region, we conclude that our LP problem has an optimal solution at C. Thus, the combination that gives the largest profit ($300) is 200 hats and 100 pairs of sunglasses.

c. The objective function is now $p = x - 5y$, which is the negative of the objective function used in part (b). Thus, the table of values of p is the same as in part (b), except that it has opposite signs in the p column. This time we find that the maximum value of p occurs at E. However, E is not a corner point of the original feasible region, so the LP problem has no optimal solution. Referring to Figure 18, we can make the objective p as large as we like by choosing a point far to the right in the unbounded feasible region. Thus, the objective function is unbounded; that is, it is possible to make an arbitrarily large profit.

EXAMPLE 5   Resource Allocation

You are composing a very avant-garde ballade for violins and bassoons. In your ballade, each violinist plays a total of two notes and each bassoonist only one note. To make your ballade long enough, you decide that it should contain at least 200 instrumental notes. Furthermore, after playing the requisite two notes, each violinist will sing one soprano note, while each bassoonist will sing three soprano notes.* To make the ballade sufficiently interesting, you have decided on a minimum of 300 soprano notes. To give your composition a sense of balance, you wish to have no more than three times as many bassoonists as violinists. Violinists charge $200 per performance and bassoonists $400 per performance. How many of each should your ballade call for in order to minimize personnel costs?

---

* Whether or not these musicians are capable of singing decent soprano notes will be left to chance. You reason that a few bad notes will add character to the ballade.

Solution First, the unknowns are x = number of violinists and y = number of bassoonists. The constraint on the number of instrumental notes implies that

$$2x + y \geq 200$$

because the total number is to be *at least* 200. Similarly, the constraint on the number of soprano notes is

$$x + 3y \geq 300.$$

The next one is a little tricky. As usual, we reword it in terms of the quantities x and y.

The number of bassoonists should be no more than three times the number of violinists.

Thus, $y \leq 3x$

or $3x - y \geq 0.$

Finally, the total cost per performance will be

$$c = 200x + 400y.$$

We wish to minimize total cost. So, our linear programming problem is as follows:

Minimize $c = 200x + 400y$
subject to $2x + \ \ y \geq 200$
$x + 3y \geq 300$
$3x - \ \ y \geq 0$
$x \geq 0, y \geq 0.$

Figure 20

Figure 21

✱ **NOTE** In Figure 20 you can see how graphing technology would help in determining the corner points: Unless you are very confident in the accuracy of your sketch, how do you know that the line $y = 3x$ falls to the left of the point B? If it were to fall to the right, then B would not be a corner point and the solution would be different. You could (and should) check that B satisfies the inequality $3x - y \geq 0$, so that the line falls to the left of B as shown. However, if you use a graphing calculator or computer, you can be fairly confident of the picture produced without doing further calculations.

We get the feasible region shown in Figure 20.✱ The feasible region is unbounded, and so we add a convenient rectangle as before (Figure 21).

Point	Lines through Point	Coordinates	$c = 200x + 400y$
A	$2x + y = 200$ $3x - y = 0$	(40, 120)	56,000
B	$2x + \ \ y = 200$ $x + 3y = 300$	(60, 80)	44,000
C		(300, 0)	60,000
D	$3x - y = 0$ $y = 150$	(50, 150)	70,000
E		(400, 150)	140,000
F		(400, 0)	80,000

From the table we see that the minimum cost occurs at B, a corner point of the original feasible region. The linear programming problem thus has an optimal solution, and the minimum cost is $44,000 per performance, employing 60 violinists and 80 bassoonists. (Quite a wasteful ballade, one might say.)

FAQs

Recognizing a Linear Programming Problem, Setting Up Inequalities, and Dealing with Unbounded Regions

Q : *How do I recognize when an application leads to an LP problem as opposed to a system of linear equations?*

A : Here are some cues that suggest an LP problem:

- Key phrases suggesting inequalities rather than equalities, like *at most, up to, no more than, at least,* and *or more*.
- A quantity that is being maximized or minimized (this will be the objective). Key phrases are *maximum, minimum, most, least, largest, greatest, smallest, as large as possible,* and *as small as possible.*

Q : *How do I deal with tricky phrases like "there should be no more than twice as many nuts as bolts" or "at least 50% of the total should be bolts"?*

A : The easiest way to deal with phrases like this is to use the technique we discussed in Chapter 2: reword the phrases using "the number of . . . ", as in

The number of nuts (x) is no more than twice the number of bolts (y) $x \leq 2y$
The number of bolts is at least 50% of the total $y \geq 0.50(x + y)$

Q : *Do I always have to add a rectangle to deal with unbounded regions?*

A : Under some circumstances, you can tell right away whether optimal solutions exist, even when the feasible region is unbounded.

Note that the following apply only when we have the constraints $x \geq 0$ and $y \geq 0$.

1. If you are minimizing $c = ax + by$ with a and b non-negative, then optimal solutions always exist. (Examples 4(a) and 5 are of this type.)
2. If you are maximizing $p = ax + by$ with a and b non-negative (and not both zero), then there is no optimal solution unless the feasible region is bounded.

Do you see why statements (1) and (2) are true?

4.2 EXERCISES

▼ more advanced   ◆ challenging

T indicates exercises that should be solved using technology

In Exercises 1–20, solve the LP problems. If no optimal solution exists, indicate whether the feasible region is empty or the objective function is unbounded. HINT [See Example 1.]

1. Maximize $p = x + y$
   subject to $x + 2y \leq 9$
   $2x + y \leq 9$
   $x \geq 0, y \geq 0.$

2. Maximize $p = x + 2y$
   subject to $x + 3y \leq 24$
   $2x + y \leq 18$
   $x \geq 0, y \geq 0.$

3. Minimize $c = x + y$
   subject to $x + 2y \geq 6$
   $2x + y \geq 6$
   $x \geq 0, y \geq 0.$

4. Minimize $c = x + 2y$
   subject to $x + 3y \geq 30$
   $2x + y \geq 30$
   $x \geq 0, y \geq 0.$

5. Maximize $p = 3x + y$
   subject to $3x - 7y \leq 0$
   $7x - 3y \geq 0$
   $x + y \leq 10$
   $x \geq 0, y \geq 0.$

6. Maximize $p = x - 2y$
   subject to $x + 2y \leq 8$
   $x - 6y \leq 0$
   $3x - 2y \geq 0$
   $x \geq 0, y \geq 0.$

7. Maximize $p = 3x + 2y$

subject to $0.2x + 0.1y \leq 1$

$0.15x + 0.3y \leq 1.5$

$10x + 10y \leq 60$

$x \geq 0, y \geq 0.$

8. Maximize $p = x + 2y$

subject to $30x + 20y \leq 600$

$0.1x + 0.4y \leq 4$

$0.2x + 0.3y \leq 4.5$

$x \geq 0, y \geq 0.$

9. Minimize $c = 0.2x + 0.3y$

subject to $0.2x + 0.1y \geq 1$

$0.15x + 0.3y \geq 1.5$

$10x + 10y \geq 80$

$x \geq 0, y \geq 0.$

10. Minimize $c = 0.4x + 0.1y$

subject to $30x + 20y \geq 600$

$0.1x + 0.4y \geq 4$

$0.2x + 0.3y \geq 4.5$

$x \geq 0, y \geq 0.$

11. Maximize and minimize $p = x + 2y$

subject to $x + y \geq 2$

$x + y \leq 10$

$x - y \leq 2$

$x - y \geq -2.$

12. Maximize and minimize $p = 2x - y$

subject to $x + y \geq 2$

$x - y \leq 2$

$x - y \geq -2$

$x \leq 10, y \leq 10.$

13. Maximize $p = 2x + 3y$

subject to $0.1x + 0.2y \geq 1$

$2x + \quad y \geq 10$

$x \geq 0, y \geq 0.$

14. Maximize $p = 3x + 2y$

subject to $0.1x + 0.1y \geq 0.2$

$y \leq 10$

$x \geq 0, y \geq 0.$

15. Minimize $c = 2x + 4y$

subject to $0.1x + 0.1y \geq 1$

$x + 2y \geq 14$

$x \geq 0, y \geq 0.$

16. Maximize $p = 2x + 3y$

subject to $-x + \quad y \geq 10$

$x + 2y \leq 12$

$x \geq 0, y \geq 0.$

17. ▼ Minimize $c = 3x - 3y$

subject to $\dfrac{x}{4} \leq y$

$y \leq \dfrac{2x}{3}$

$x + \quad y \geq 5$

$x + 2y \leq 10$

$x \geq 0, y \geq 0.$

18. ▼ Minimize $c = -x + 2y$

subject to $y \leq \dfrac{2x}{3}$

$x \leq 3y$

$y \geq 4$

$x \geq 6$

$x + y \leq 16.$

19. ▼ Maximize $p = x + y$

subject to $x + 2y \geq 10$

$2x + 2y \leq 10$

$2x + \quad y \geq 10$

$x \geq 0, y \geq 0.$

20. ▼ Minimize $c = 3x + y$

subject to $10x + 20y \geq 100$

$0.3x + 0.1y \geq 1$

$x \geq 0, y \geq 0.$

APPLICATIONS

21. *Resource Allocation* You manage an ice cream factory that makes two flavors: Creamy Vanilla and Continental Mocha. Into each quart of Creamy Vanilla go 2 eggs and 3 cups of cream. Into each quart of Continental Mocha go 1 egg and 3 cups of cream. You have in stock 500 eggs and 900 cups of cream. You make a profit of $3 on each quart of Creamy Vanilla and $2 on each quart of Continental Mocha. How many quarts of each flavor should you make in order to earn the largest profit? HINT [See Example 2.]

22. *Resource Allocation* Podunk Institute of Technology's Math Department offers two courses: Finite Math and Applied Calculus. Each section of Finite Math has 60 students, and each section of Applied Calculus has 50. The department is allowed to offer a total of up to 110 sections. Furthermore, no more than 6,000 students want to take a math course (no student will take more than one math course). Suppose the university makes a profit of $100,000 on each section of Finite Math and $50,000 on each section of Applied Calculus (the profit is the difference between what the students are charged and what the professors are paid). How many sections of each course should the department offer to make the largest profit? HINT [See Example 2.]

23. **Nutrition** Ruff, Inc. makes dog food out of chicken and grain. Chicken has 10 grams of protein and 5 grams of fat per ounce, and grain has 2 grams of protein and 2 grams of fat per ounce. A bag of dog food must contain at least 200 grams of protein and at least 150 grams of fat. If chicken costs 10¢ per ounce and grain costs 1¢ per ounce, how many ounces of each should Ruff use in each bag of dog food in order to minimize cost? HINT [See Example 4.]

24. **Purchasing** Enormous State University's Business School is buying computers. The school has two models from which to choose, the Pomegranate and the iZac. Each Pomegranate comes with 400 MB of memory and 80 GB of disk space; each iZac has 300 MB of memory and 100 GB of disk space. For reasons related to its accreditation, the school would like to be able to say that it has a total of at least 48,000 MB of memory and at least 12,800 GB of disk space. If the Pomegranate and the iZac cost $2,000 each, how many of each should the school buy to keep the cost as low as possible? HINT [See Example 4.]

25. **Nutrition** Each serving of Gerber Mixed Cereal for Baby contains 60 calories and 11 grams of carbohydrates. Each serving of Gerber Mango Tropical Fruit Dessert contains 80 calories and 21 grams of carbohydrates.[11] If the cereal costs 30¢ per serving and the dessert costs 50¢ per serving, and you want to provide your child with at least 140 calories and at least 32 grams of carbohydrates, how can you do so at the least cost? (Fractions of servings are permitted.)

26. **Nutrition** Each serving of Gerber Mixed Cereal for Baby contains 60 calories, 10 grams of carbohydrates, and no vitamin C. Each serving of Gerber Apple Banana Juice contains 60 calories, 15 grams of carbohydrates, and 120 percent of the U.S. Recommended Daily Allowance (RDA) of vitamin C for infants. The cereal costs 10¢ per serving and the juice costs 30¢ per serving. If you want to provide your child with at least 120 calories, at least 25 grams of carbohydrates, and at least 60 percent of the U.S. RDA of vitamin C for infants, how can you do so at the least cost? (Fractions of servings are permitted.)

27. **Energy Efficiency** You are thinking of making your home more energy efficient by replacing some of the light bulbs with compact fluorescent bulbs, and insulating part or all of your exterior walls. Each compact fluorescent light bulb costs $4 and saves you an average of $2 per year in energy costs, and each square foot of wall insulation costs $1 and saves you an average of $0.20 per year in energy costs.[12] Your home has 60 light fittings and 1,100 sq. ft. of uninsulated exterior wall. You can spend no

more than $1,200 and would like to save as much per year in energy costs as possible. How many compact fluorescent light bulbs and how many square feet of insulation should you purchase? How much will you save in energy costs per year?

28. **Energy Efficiency** (Compare with the preceding exercise.) You are thinking of making your mansion more energy efficient by replacing some of the light bulbs with compact fluorescent bulbs, and insulating part or all of your exterior walls. Each compact fluorescent light bulb costs $4 and saves you an average of $2 per year in energy costs, and each square foot of wall insulation costs $1 and saves you an average of $0.20 per year in energy costs.[13] Your mansion has 200 light fittings and 3,000 sq. ft. of uninsulated exterior wall. To impress your friends, you would like to spend as much as possible, but save no more than $800 per year in energy costs (you are proud of your large utility bills). How many compact fluorescent light bulbs and how many square feet of insulation should you purchase? How much will you save in energy costs per year?

Creatine Supplements Exercises 29 and 30 are based on the following data on three bodybuilding supplements. (Figures shown correspond to a single serving.)[14]

	Creatine (g)	Carbohydrates (g)	Taurine (g)	Alpha Lipoic Acid (mg)	Cost ($)
Cell-Tech® (MuscleTech)	10	75	2	200	2.20
RiboForce HP® (EAS)	5	15	1	0	1.60
Creatine Transport® (Kaizen)	5	35	1	100	0.60

29. You are thinking of combining Cell-Tech and RiboForce HP to obtain a 10-day supply that provides at least 80 grams of creatine and at least 10 grams of taurine, but no more than 750 grams of carbohydrates and no more than 1,000 milligrams of alpha lipoic acid. How many servings of each supplement should you combine to meet your specifications at the least cost?

30. You are thinking of combining Cell-Tech and Creatine Transport to obtain a 10-day supply that provides at least 80 grams of creatine and at least 10 grams of taurine, but no more than 600 grams of carbohydrates and no more than 2,000 milligrams of alpha lipoic acid. How many servings of each supplement should you combine to meet your specifications at the least cost?

31. **Resource Allocation** Your salami manufacturing plant can order up to 1,000 pounds of pork and 2,400 pounds of beef per day for use in manufacturing its two specialties: "Count Dracula Salami" and "Frankenstein Sausage." Production of

---

[11] Source: Nutrition information printed on the containers.

[12] Source: American Council for an Energy-Efficient Economy/*New York Times*, December 1, 2003, p. C6.

[13] Ibid.

[14] Source: Nutritional information supplied by the manufacturers (www.netrition.com). Cost per serving is approximate.

the Count Dracula variety requires 1 pound of pork and 3 pounds of beef for each salami, while the Frankenstein variety requires 2 pounds of pork and 2 pounds of beef for every sausage. In view of your heavy investment in advertising Count Dracula Salami, you have decided that at least one-third of the total production should be Count Dracula. On the other hand, due to the health-conscious consumer climate, your Frankenstein Sausage (sold as having less beef) is earning your company a profit of $3 per sausage, while sales of the Count Dracula variety are down and it is earning your company only $1 per salami. Given these restrictions, how many of each kind of sausage should you produce to maximize profits, and what is the maximum possible profit? HINT [See Example 3.]

32. ***Project Design*** The Megabuck Hospital Corp. is to build a state-subsidized nursing home catering to homeless patients as well as high-income patients. State regulations require that every subsidized nursing home must house a minimum of 1,000 homeless patients and no more than 750 high-income patients in order to qualify for state subsidies. The overall capacity of the hospital is to be 2,100 patients. The board of directors, under pressure from a neighborhood group, insists that the number of homeless patients should not exceed twice the number of high-income patients. Due to the state subsidy, the hospital will make an average profit of $10,000 per month for every homeless patient it houses, whereas the profit per high-income patient is estimated at $8,000 per month. How many of each type of patient should it house in order to maximize profit? HINT [See Example 3.]

33. ***Television Advertising*** In February 2008, each episode of "American Idol" was typically seen by 28.5 million viewers, while each episode of "Back to You" was seen by 12.3 million viewers.[15] Your marketing services firm has been hired to promote Bald No More's hair replacement process by buying at least 30 commercial spots during episodes of "American Idol" and "Back to You." The cable company running "American Idol" has quoted a price of $3,000 per spot, while the cable company showing "Back to You" has quoted a price of $1,000 per spot. Bald No More's advertising budget for TV commercials is $120,000, and it would like no more than 50% of the total number of spots to appear on "Back to You." How many spots should you purchase on each show to reach the most viewers?

34. ***Television Advertising*** In February 2002, each episode of "Boston Public" was typically seen in 7.0 million homes, while each episode of "NYPD Blue" was seen in 7.8 million homes.[16] Your marketing services firm has been hired to promote Gauss Jordan Sneakers by buying at least 30 commercial spots during episodes of "Boston Public" and "NYPD

Blue." The cable company running "Boston Public" has quoted a price of $2,000 per spot, while the cable company showing "NYPD Blue" has quoted a price of $3,000 per spot. Gauss Jordan Sneakers' advertising budget for TV commercials is $70,000, and it would like at least 75% of the total number of spots to appear on "Boston Public." How many spots should you purchase on each show to reach the most homes?

Investing *Exercises 35 and 36 are based on the following data on four stocks.*[17]

	Price	Dividend Yield	Earnings per Share
ATRI (Atrion)	$90	1%	$7.50
BBY (Best Buy)	20	2	3.20
IMCL (ImClone Systems)	70	0	−0.70
TR (Tootsie Roll)	25	1	0.80

35. ▼ You are planning to invest up to $10,000 in ATRI and BBY shares. You want your investment to yield at least $120 in dividends and you want to maximize the total earnings. How many shares of each company should you purchase?

36. ▼ You are planning to invest up to $43,000 in IMCL and TR shares. For tax reasons, you want your investment to yield no more than $10 in dividends. You want to maximize the total earnings. How many shares of each company should you purchase?

37. ▼ ***Investments*** Your portfolio manager has suggested two high-yielding stocks: **Consolidated Edison** (ED) and **General Electric** (GE). ED shares cost $40, yield 6% in dividends, and have a risk index of 2.0 per share. GE shares cost $16, yield 7.5% in dividends, and have a risk index of 3.0 per share.[18] You have up to $10,000 to invest, and would like to earn at least $600 in dividends. How many shares (to the nearest tenth of a unit) of each stock should you purchase to meet your requirements and minimize the total risk index for your portfolio? What is the minimum total risk index?

38. ▼ ***Investments*** Your friend's portfolio manager has suggested two energy stocks: **Exxon Mobil** (XOM) and **British Petroleum** (BP). XOM shares cost $80, yield 2% in dividends, and have a risk index of 2.5. BP shares cost $50, yield 7% in dividends, and have a risk index of 4.5.[19] Your friend has up to $40,000

---

[15] Ratings are for February 26, 2008. Source: Nielsen Media Research (www.tvbythenumbers.com).

[16] Ratings are for February 18–24, 2002. Source: Nielsen Media Research (www.ptd.net) February 28, 2002.

[17] Approximate trading price in fourth quarter of 2008 based on 50-day averages. Earnings per share are rounded. Source: http://finance.google.com.

[18] Share prices and yields are approximate (2008). Source: http://finance.google.com.

[19] Ibid.

to invest, and would like to earn at least $1,400 in dividends. How many shares (to the nearest tenth of a unit) of each stock should she purchase to meet your requirements and minimize the total risk index for your portfolio? What is the minimum total risk index?

39. ▼ *Planning* My friends: I, the mighty Brutus, have decided to prepare for retirement by instructing young warriors in the arts of battle and diplomacy. For each hour spent in battle instruction, I have decided to charge 50 ducats. For each hour in diplomacy instruction I shall charge 40 ducats. Due to my advancing years, I can spend no more than 50 hours per week instructing the youths, although the great Jove knows that they are sorely in need of instruction! Due to my fondness for physical pursuits, I have decided to spend no more than one-third of the total time in diplomatic instruction. However, the present border crisis with the Gauls is a sore indication of our poor abilities as diplomats. As a result, I have decided to spend at least 10 hours per week instructing in diplomacy. Finally, to complicate things further, there is the matter of Scarlet Brew: I have estimated that each hour of battle instruction will require 10 gallons of Scarlet Brew to quench my students' thirst, and that each hour of diplomacy instruction, being less physically demanding, requires half that amount. Because my harvest of red berries has far exceeded my expectations, I estimate that I'll have to use at least 400 gallons per week in order to avoid storing the fine brew at great expense. Given all these restrictions, how many hours per week should I spend in each type of instruction to maximize my income?

40. ▼ *Planning* Repeat the preceding exercise with the following changes: I would like to spend no more than half the total time in diplomatic instruction, and I must use at least 600 gallons of Scarlet Brew.

41. ▼ *Resource Allocation* One day, Gillian the magician summoned the wisest of her women. "Devoted followers," she began, "I have a quandary: As you well know, I possess great expertise in sleep spells and shock spells, but unfortunately, these are proving to be a drain on my aural energy resources; each sleep spell costs me 500 pico-shirleys of aural energy, while each shock spell requires 750 pico-shirleys. Clearly, I would like to hold my overall expenditure of aural energy to a minimum, and still meet my commitments in protecting the Sisterhood from the ever-present threat of trolls. Specifically, I have estimated that each sleep spell keeps us safe for an average of two minutes, while every shock spell protects us for about three minutes. We certainly require enough protection to last 24 hours of each day, and possibly more, just to be safe. At the same time, I have noticed that each of my sleep spells can immobilize three trolls at once, while one of my typical shock spells (having a narrower range) can immobilize only two trolls at once. We are faced, my sisters, with an onslaught of 1,200 trolls per day! Finally, as you are no doubt aware, the bylaws dictate that for a Magician of the Order to remain in good standing, the number of shock

spells must be between one-quarter and one-third the number of shock and sleep spells combined. What do I do, oh Wise Ones?"

42. ▼ *Risk Management* The Grand Vizier of the Kingdom of Um is being blackmailed by numerous individuals and is having a very difficult time keeping his blackmailers from going public. He has been keeping them at bay with two kinds of payoff: gold bars from the Royal Treasury and political favors. Through bitter experience, he has learned that each payoff in gold gives him peace for an average of about 1 month, while each political favor seems to earn him about a month and a half of reprieve. To maintain his flawless reputation in the Court, he feels he cannot afford any revelations about his tainted past to come to light within the next year. Thus it is imperative that his blackmailers be kept at bay for 12 months. Furthermore, he would like to keep the number of gold payoffs at no more than one-quarter of the combined number of payoffs because the outward flow of gold bars might arouse suspicion on the part of the Royal Treasurer. The Grand Vizier feels that he can do no more than seven political favors per year without arousing undue suspicion in the Court. The gold payoffs tend to deplete his travel budget. (The treasury has been subsidizing his numerous trips to the Himalayas.) He estimates that each gold bar removed from the treasury will cost him four trips. On the other hand because the administering of political favors tends to cost him valuable travel time, he suspects that each political favor will cost him about two trips. Now, he would obviously like to keep his blackmailers silenced and lose as few trips as possible. What is he to do? How many trips will he lose in the next year?

43. ◆ *Management*[20] You are the service manager for a supplier of closed-circuit television systems. Your company can provide up to 160 hours per week of technical service for your customers, although the demand for technical service far exceeds this amount. As a result, you have been asked to develop a model to allocate service technicians' time between new customers (those still covered by service contracts) and old customers (whose service contracts have expired). To ensure that new customers are satisfied with your company's service, the sales department has instituted a policy that at least 100 hours per week be allocated to servicing new customers. At the same time, your superiors have informed you that the company expects your department to generate at least $1,200 per week in revenues. Technical service time for new customers generates an average of $10 per hour (because much of the service is still under warranty) and for old customers generates $30 per hour. How many hours per week should you allocate to each type of customer to generate the most revenue?

---

[20]Loosely based on a similiar problem in *An Introduction to Management Science* (6th Ed.) by D. R. Anderson, D. J. Sweeny and T. A. Williams (West, 1991).

44. ◆ *Scheduling*[21] The Scottsville Textile Mill produces several different fabrics on eight dobby looms which operate 24 hours per day and are scheduled for 30 days in the coming month. The Scottsville Textile Mill will produce only Fabric 1 and Fabric 2 during the coming month. Each dobby loom can turn out 4.63 yards of either fabric per hour. Assume that there is a monthly demand of 16,000 yards of Fabric 1 and 12,000 yards of Fabric 2. Profits are calculated as 33¢ per yard for each fabric produced on the dobby looms.

a. Will it be possible to satisfy total demand?

b. In the event that total demand is not satisfied, the Scottsville Textile Mill will need to purchase the fabrics from another mill to make up the shortfall. Its profits on resold fabrics ordered from another mill amount to 20¢ per yard for Fabric 1 and 16¢ per yard for Fabric 2. How many yards of each fabric should it produce to maximize profits?

COMMUNICATION AND REASONING EXERCISES

45. If a linear programming problem has a bounded, nonempty feasible region, then optimal solutions

(A) must exist   **(B)** may or may not exist   **(C)** cannot exist

46. If a linear programming problem has an unbounded, nonempty feasible region, then optimal solutions

(A) must exist   **(B)** may or may not exist   **(C)** cannot exist

47. What can you say if the optimal value occurs at two adjacent corner points?

48. Describe at least one drawback to using the graphical method to solve a linear programming problem arising from a real-life situation.

49. Create a linear programming problem in two variables that has no optimal solution.

[21]Adapted from *The Calhoun Textile Mill Case* by J. D. Camm, P. M. Dearing, and S. K. Tadisina as presented for case study in *An Introduction to Management Science* (6th Ed.) by D. R. Anderson, D. J. Sweeney, and T. A. Williams (West, 1991). Our exercise uses a subset of the data given in the cited study.

50. Create a linear programming problem in two variables that has more than one optimal solution.

51. Create an interesting scenario leading to the following linear programming problem:

Maximize $p = 10x + 10y$

subject to $20x + 40y \le 1,000$
$30x + 20y \le 1,200$
$x \ge 0, y \ge 0.$

52. Create an interesting scenario leading to the following linear programming problem:

Minimize $c = 10x + 10y$

subject to $20x + 40y \ge 1,000$
$30x + 20y \ge 1,200$
$x \ge 0, y \ge 0.$

53. ▼ Use an example to show why there may be no optimal solution to a linear programming problem if the feasible region is unbounded.

54. ▼ Use an example to illustrate why, in the event that an optimal solution does occur despite an unbounded feasible region, that solution corresponds to a corner point of the feasible region.

55. ▼ You are setting up an LP problem for Fly-by-Night Airlines with the unknowns x and y, where x represents the number of first-class tickets it should issue for a specific flight and y represents the number of business-class tickets it should issue for that flight, and the problem is to maximize profit. You find that there are two different corner points that maximize the profit. How do you interpret this?

56. ▼ In the situation described in the preceding exercise, you find that there are no optimal solutions. How do you interpret this?

57. ◆ Consider the following example of a *nonlinear* programming problem: Maximize $p = xy$ subject to $x \ge 0$, $y \ge 0$, $x + y \le 2$. Show that p is zero on every corner point, but is greater than zero at many noncorner points.

58. ◆ Solve the nonlinear programming problem in Exercise 57.

4.3 The Simplex Method: Solving Standard Maximization Problems

The method discussed in Section 4.2 works quite well for LP problems in two unknowns, but what about three or more unknowns? Because we need an axis for each unknown, we would need to draw graphs in three dimensions (where we have x-, y- and z-coordinates) to deal with problems in three unknowns, and we would have to draw in hyperspace to answer questions involving four or more unknowns. Given the state of technology as this book is being written, we can't easily do this. So we need another method for solving

LP problems that will work for any number of unknowns. One such method, called the **simplex method**, has been the method of choice since it was invented by George Dantzig in 1947. To illustrate it best, we first use it to solve only so-called standard maximization problems.

General Linear Programming (LP) Problem

A **linear program problem in n unknowns** $x_1, x_2, \ldots, x_n$ is one in which we are to find the maximum or minimum value of a linear **objective function**

$$a_1 x_1 + a_2 x_2 + \cdots + a_n x_n,$$

where $a_1, a_2, \ldots, a_n$ are numbers, subject to a number of linear **constraints** of the form

$$b_1 x_1 + b_2 x_2 + \cdots + b_n x_n \leq c \quad \text{or} \quad b_1 x_1 + b_2 x_2 + \cdots + b_n x_n \geq c,$$

where $b_1, b_2, \ldots, b_n, c$ are numbers.

Standard Maximization Problem

A **standard maximization problem** is an LP problem in which we are required to *maximize* (not minimize) an objective function of the form

$$p = a_1 x_1 + a_2 x_2 + \cdots + a_n x_n$$

subject to the constraints

$$x_1 \geq 0, x_2 \geq 0, \ldots, x_n \geq 0.$$

and further constraints of the form

$$b_1 x_1 + b_2 x_2 + \cdots + b_n x_n \leq c$$

with c *non-negative*. It is important that the inequality here be $\leq$, *not* $=$ or $\geq$.

Note As in the chapter on linear equations, we will almost always use $x, y, z, \ldots$ for the unknowns. Subscripted variables $x_1, x_2, \ldots$ are very useful names when you start running out of letters of the alphabet, but we should not find ourselves in that predicament. ■

Quick Examples

1. Maximize $p = 2x - 3y + 3z$
   subject to $2x \quad\quad + \ z \leq 7$
   $$-x + 3y - 6z \leq 6$$
   $$x \geq 0, y \geq 0, z \geq 0.$$

   This is a standard maximization problem.

2. Maximize $p = 2x_1 + x_2 - x_3 + x_4$
   subject to $x_1 - 2x_2 \quad\quad + x_4 \leq 0$
   $$3x_1 \quad\quad\quad\quad \leq 1$$
   $$x_2 + x_3 \quad \leq 2$$
   $$x_1 \geq 0, x_2 \geq 0, x_3 \geq 0, x_4 \geq 0.$$

   This is a standard maximization problem.

3. Maximize $p = 2x - 3y + 3z$
   subject to $2x \quad\quad + z \geq 7$
   $-x + 3y - 6z \leq 6$ This is *not* a standard maximization problem.
   $x \geq 0, y \geq 0, z \geq 0.$

The inequality $2x + z \geq 7$ cannot be written in the required form. If we reverse the inequality by multiplying both sides by -1, we get $-2x - z \leq -7$, but a negative value on the right side is not allowed.

The idea behind the simplex method is this: In any linear programming problem, there is a feasible region. If there are only two unknowns, we can draw the region; if there are three unknowns, it is a solid region in space; and if there are four or more unknowns, it is an abstract higher-dimensional region. But it is a faceted region with corners (think of a diamond), and it is at one of these corners that we will find the optimal solution. Geometrically, what the simplex method does is to start at the corner where all the unknowns are 0 (possible because we are talking of standard maximization problems) and then walk around the region, from corner to adjacent corner, always increasing the value of the objective function, until the best corner is found. In practice, we will visit only a small number of the corners before finding the right one. Algebraically, as we are about to see, this walking around is accomplished by matrix manipulations of the same sort as those used in the chapter on systems of linear equations.

We describe the method while working through an example.

EXAMPLE 1 Meet the Simplex Method

Maximize $p = 3x + 2y + z$
subject to $2x + 2y + z \leq 10$
   $x + 2y + 3z \leq 15$
   $x \geq 0, y \geq 0, z \geq 0.$

Solution

Step 1 *Convert to a system of linear equations.* The inequalities $2x + 2y + z \leq 10$ and $x + 2y + 3z \leq 15$ are less convenient than equations. Look at the first inequality. It says that the left-hand side, $2x + 2y + z$, must have some positive number (or zero) *added to it* if it is to equal 10. Because we don't yet know what $x, y,$ and z are, we are not yet sure what number to add to the left-hand side. So we invent a new unknown, $s \geq 0$, called a **slack variable**, to "take up the slack," so that

$$2x + 2y + z + s = 10.$$

Turning to the next inequality, $x + 2y + 3z \leq 15$, we now add a slack variable to its left-hand side, to get it up to the value of the right-hand side. We might have to add a different number than we did the last time, so we use a new slack variable, $t \geq 0$, and obtain

$$x + 2y + 3z + t = 15.$$ Use a different slack variable for each constraint.

Now we write the system of equations we have (including the one that defines the objective function) in standard form.

$$
\begin{aligned}
2x + 2y + \ z + s \qquad\qquad &= 10 \\
x + 2y + 3z \quad + t \qquad &= 15 \\
-3x - 2y - \ z \qquad\quad + p &= 0
\end{aligned}
$$

Note three things: First, all the variables are neatly aligned in columns, as they were in Chapter 2. Second, in rewriting the objective function $p = 3x + 2y + z$, we have left the coefficient of p as $+1$ and brought the other variables over to the same side of the equation as p. This will be our standard procedure from now on. *Don't* write $3x + 2y + z - p = 0$ (even though it means the same thing) because the negative coefficients will be important in later steps. Third, the above system of equations has fewer equations than unknowns, and hence cannot have a unique solution.

Step 2 *Set up the initial tableau.* We represent our system of equations by the following table (which is simply the augmented matrix in disguise), called **the initial tableau:**

x	y	z	s	t	p	
2	2	1	1	0	0	10
1	2	3	0	1	0	15
-3	-2	-1	0	0	1	0

The labels along the top keep track of which columns belong to which variables.

Now notice a peculiar thing. If we rewrite the matrix using the variables s, t, and p first, we get the following matrix

$$
\begin{array}{cccccc}
s & t & p & x & y & z \\
\left[\begin{array}{cccccc}
1 & 0 & 0 & 2 & 2 & 1 \\
0 & 1 & 0 & 1 & 2 & 3 \\
0 & 0 & 1 & -3 & -2 & -1
\end{array}\right.
&
\left.\begin{array}{c}
10 \\
15 \\
0
\end{array}\right]
\end{array}
$$

Matrix with s, t, and p columns first

which is already in reduced form. We can therefore read off the general solution (see Section 2.2) to our system of equations as

$$
\begin{aligned}
s &= 10 - 2x - 2y - z \\
t &= 15 - \ x - 2y - 3z \\
p &= 0 + \ 3x + 2y + z
\end{aligned}
$$

x, y, z arbitrary.

Thus, we get a whole family of solutions, one for each choice of x, y, and z. One possible choice is to set x, y, and z all equal to 0. This gives the particular solution

$$
s = 10, t = 15, p = 0, x = 0, y = 0, z = 0. \qquad \text{Set } x = y = z = 0 \text{ above.}
$$

This solution is called the **basic solution** associated with the tableau. The variables s and t are called the **active** variables, and x, y, and z are the **inactive** variables. (Other terms used are **basic** and **nonbasic** variables.)

We can obtain the basic solution directly from the tableau as follows.

- The active variables correspond to the cleared columns (columns with only one nonzero entry).
- The values of the active variables are calculated as shown following.
- All other variables are inactive, and set equal to zero.

	Inactive $x = 0$	Inactive $y = 0$	Inactive $z = 0$	Active $s = \frac{10}{1}$	Active $t = \frac{15}{1}$	Active $p = \frac{0}{1}$	
	x	y	z	s	t	p	
	2	2	1	1	0	0	10
	1	2	3	0	1	0	15
	−3	−2	−1	0	0	1	0

As an additional aid to recognizing which variables are active and which are inactive, we label each row with the name of the corresponding active variable. Thus, the complete initial tableau looks like this.

	x	y	z	s	t	p	
s	2	2	1	1	0	0	10
t	1	2	3	0	1	0	15
p	−3	−2	−1	0	0	1	0

This basic solution represents our starting position $x = y = z = 0$ in the feasible region in xyz space.

We now need to move to another corner point. To do so, we choose a pivot* in one of the first three columns of the tableau and clear its column. Then we will get a different basic solution, which corresponds to another corner point. Thus, in order to move from corner point to corner point, all we have to do is choose suitable pivots and clear columns in the usual manner.

The next two steps give the procedure for choosing the pivot.

Step 3 *Select the pivot column* (the column that contains the pivot we are seeking).

✳ **NOTE** Also see Section 2.2 for a discussion of pivots and pivoting.

Selecting the Pivot Column

Choose the negative number with the largest magnitude on the left-hand side of the bottom row (that is, don't consider the last number in the bottom row). Its column is the pivot column. (If there are two or more candidates, choose any one.) If all the numbers on the left-hand side of the bottom row are zero or positive, then we are done, and the basic solution is the optimal solution.

Simple enough. The most negative number in the bottom row is −3, so we choose the x column as the pivot column:

	x	y	z	s	t	p	
s	2	2	1	1	0	0	10
t	1	2	3	0	1	0	15
p	−3	−2	−1	0	0	1	0

↑
Pivot column

Q: *Why choose the pivot column this way?*

A: The variable labeling the pivot column is going to be increased from 0 to something positive. In the equation $p = 3x + 2y + z$, the fastest way to increase p is to increase x

because p would increase by 3 units for every 1-unit increase in x. (If we chose to increase y, then p would increase by only 2 units for every 1-unit increase in y, and if we increased z instead, p would grow even more slowly.) In short, choosing the pivot column this way makes it likely that we'll increase p as much as possible.

Step 4 *Select the pivot in the pivot column.*

Selecting the Pivot

1. The pivot must always be a positive number. (This rules out zeros and negative numbers, such as the -3 in the bottom row.)
2. For each positive entry b in the pivot column, compute the ratio a/b, where a is the number in the rightmost column in that row. We call this a **test ratio**.
3. Of these ratios, choose the smallest one. (If there are two or more candidates, choose any one.) The corresponding number b is the pivot.

In our example, the test ratio in the first row is $10/2 = 5$, and the test ratio in the second row is $15/1 = 15$. Here, 5 is the smallest, so the 2 in the upper left is our pivot.

	x	y	z	s	t	p		Test Ratios
s	$\boxed{2}$	2	1	1	0	0	10	$10/2 = 5$
t	1	2	3	0	1	0	15	$15/1 = 15$
p	-3	-2	-1	0	0	1	0	

Q : *Why select the pivot this way?*

A : The rule given above guarantees that, after pivoting, all variables will be non-negative in the basic solution. In other words, it guarantees that we will remain in the feasible region. We will explain further after finishing this example.

Step 5 *Use the pivot to clear the column in the normal manner and then relabel the pivot row with the label from the pivot column.* It is important to follow the exact prescription described in Section 2.2 for formulating the row operations:

$$a R_c \pm b R_p. \qquad \text{\textit{a} and \textit{b} both positive}$$

    ↑   ↑

   Row to change   Pivot row

All entries in the last column should remain non-negative after pivoting. Furthermore, because the x column (and no longer the s column) will be cleared, x will become an active variable. In other words, the s on the left of the pivot will be replaced by x. We call s the **departing**, or **exiting variable** and x the **entering variable** for this step.

Entering variable

↓

		x	y	z	s	t	p		
Departing variable →	s	$\boxed{2}$	2	1	1	0	0	10	
	t	1	2	3	0	1	0	15	$2R_2 - R_1$
	p	-3	-2	-1	0	0	1	0	$2R_3 + 3R_1$

This gives

	x	y	z	s	t	p	
x	2	2	1	1	0	0	10
t	0	2	5	−1	2	0	20
p	0	2	1	3	0	2	30

This is the second tableau.

Step 6 *Go to Step 3.* But wait! According to Step 3, we are finished because there are no negative numbers in the bottom row. Thus, we can read off the answer. Remember, though, that the solution for x, the first active variable, is not just $x = 10$, but is $x = 10/2 = 5$ because the pivot has not been reduced to a 1. Similarly, $t = 20/2 = 10$ and $p = 30/2 = 15$. All the other variables are zero because they are inactive. Thus, the solution is as follows: p has a maximum value of 15, and this occurs when $x = 5$, $y = 0$ and $z = 0$. (The slack variables then have the values $s = 0$ and $t = 10$.)

Q : *Why can we stop when there are no negative numbers in the bottom row? Why does this tableau give an optimal solution?*

A : The bottom row corresponds to the equation $2y + z + 3s + 2p = 30$, or

$$p = 15 - y - \frac{1}{2}z - \frac{3}{2}s.$$

Think of this as part of the general solution to our original system of equations, with y, z, and s as the parameters. Because these variables must be non-negative, *the largest possible value of p in any feasible solution of the system comes when all three of the parameters are 0.* Thus, the current basic solution must be an optimal solution.*

---

* **NOTE** Calculators or spreadsheets could obviously be a big help in the calculations here, just as in Chapter 2. We'll say more about that after the next couple of examples.

We owe some further explanation for Step 4 of the simplex method. After Step 3, we knew that x would be the entering variable, and we needed to choose the departing variable. In the next basic solution, x was to have some positive value and we wanted this value to be as large as possible (to make p as large as possible) without making any other variables negative. Look again at the equations written in Step 2:

$$s = 10 - 2x - 2y - z$$
$$t = 15 - x - 2y - 3z.$$

We needed to make either s or t into an inactive variable and hence zero. Also, y and z were to remain inactive. If we had made s inactive, then we would have had $0 = 10 - 2x$, so $x = 10/2 = 5$. This would have made $t = 15 - 5 = 10$, which would be fine. On the other hand, if we had made t inactive, then we would have had $0 = 15 - x$, so $x = 15$, and this would have made $s = 10 - 2 \cdot 15 = -20$, which would *not* be fine, because slack variables must be non-negative. In other words, we had a choice of making $x = 10/2 = 5$ or $x = 15/1 = 15$, but making x larger than 5 would have made another variable negative. We were thus compelled to choose the smaller ratio, 5, and make s the departing variable. Of course, we do not have to think it through this way every time. We just use the rule stated in Step 4. (For a graphical explanation, see Example 3.)

EXAMPLE 2 Simplex Method

Find the maximum value of $p = 12x + 15y + 5z$, subject to the constraints:

$$2x + 2y + z \leq 8$$
$$x + 4y - 3z \leq 12$$
$$x \geq 0,\ y \geq 0,\ z \geq 0.$$

Solution Following Step 1, we introduce slack variables and rewrite the constraints and objective function in standard form:

$$2x + 2y + z + s \qquad\qquad = 8$$
$$x + 4y - 3z \quad + t \qquad = 12$$
$$-12x - 15y - 5z \qquad + p = 0.$$

We now follow with Step 2, setting up the initial tableau:

	x	y	z	s	t	p	
s	2	2	1	1	0	0	8
t	1	4	-3	0	1	0	12
p	-12	-15	-5	0	0	1	0

For Step 3, we select the column over the negative number with the largest magnitude in the bottom row, which is the y column. For Step 4, finding the pivot, we see that the test ratios are 8/2 and 12/4, the smallest being $12/4 = 3$. So we select the pivot in the t row and clear its column:

	x	y	z	s	t	p		
s	2	2	1	1	0	0	8	$2R_1 - R_2$
t	1	[4]	-3	0	1	0	12	
p	-12	-15	-5	0	0	1	0	$4R_3 + 15R_2$

The departing variable is t and the entering variable is y. This gives the second tableau.

	x	y	z	s	t	p	
s	3	0	5	2	-1	0	4
y	1	4	-3	0	1	0	12
p	-33	0	-65	0	15	4	180

We now go back to Step 3. Because we still have negative numbers in the bottom row, we choose the one with the largest magnitude (which is –65), and thus our pivot column is the z column. Because negative numbers can't be pivots, the only possible choice for the pivot is the 5. (We need not compute the test ratios because there would only be one from which to choose.) We now clear this column, remembering to take care of the departing and entering variables.

	x	y	z	s	t	p		
s	3	0	[5]	2	-1	0	4	
y	1	4	-3	0	1	0	12	$5R_2 + 3R_1$
p	-33	0	-65	0	15	4	180	$R_3 + 13R_1$

This gives

	x	y	z	s	t	p	
z	3	0	5	2	-1	0	4
y	14	20	0	6	2	0	72
p	6	0	0	26	2	4	232

Notice how the value of p keeps climbing: It started at 0 in the first tableau, went up to $180/4 = 45$ in the second, and is currently at $232/4 = 58$. Because there are no more negative numbers in the bottom row, we are done and can write down the solution: p has a maximum value of $232/4 = 58$, and this occurs when

$$x = 0$$

$$y = \frac{72}{20} = \frac{18}{5} \quad \text{and}$$

$$z = \frac{4}{5}.$$

The slack variables are both zero.

As a partial check on our answer, we can substitute these values into the objective function and the constraints:

$$58 = 12(0) + 15(18/5) + 5(4/5) \qquad \checkmark$$

$$2(0) + 2(18/5) + (4/5) = 8 \le 8 \qquad \checkmark$$

$$0 + 4(18/5) - 3(4/5) = 12 \le 12. \qquad \checkmark$$

We say that this is only a partial check, because it shows only that our solution is feasible, and that we have correctly calculated p. It does not show that we have the optimal solution. This check will *usually* catch any arithmetic mistakes we make, but it is not foolproof.

APPLICATIONS

In the next example (further exploits of Acme Baby Foods—compare Example 2 in Section 2) we show how the simplex method relates to the graphical method.

EXAMPLE 3 Resource Allocation

Acme Baby Foods makes two puddings, vanilla and chocolate. Each serving of vanilla pudding requires 2 teaspoons of sugar and 25 fluid ounces of water, and each serving of chocolate pudding requires 3 teaspoons of sugar and 15 fluid ounces of water. Acme has available each day 3,600 teaspoons of sugar and 22,500 fluid ounces of water. Acme makes no more than 600 servings of vanilla pudding because that is all that it can sell each day. If Acme makes a profit of 10¢ on each serving of vanilla pudding and 7¢ on each serving of chocolate, how many servings of each should it make to maximize its profit?

Solution We first identify the unknowns. Let

$x =$ the number of servings of vanilla pudding

$y =$ the number of servings of chocolate pudding.

The objective function is the profit $p = 10x + 7y$, which we need to maximize. For the constraints, we start with the fact that Acme will make no more than 600 servings of vanilla: $x \le 600$. We can put the remaining data in a table as follows:

	Vanilla	Chocolate	Total Available
Sugar (teaspoons)	2	3	3,600
Water (ounces)	25	15	22,500

Because Acme can use no more sugar and water than is available, we get the two constraints:

$$2x + 3y \le 3,600$$
$$25x + 15y \le 22,500. \qquad \text{Note that all the terms are divisible by 5.}$$

Thus our linear programming problem is this:

Maximize $p = 10x + 7y$

subject to $x \le 600$
$2x + 3y \le 3,600$
$5x + 3y \le 4,500$ We divided $25x + 15y \le 22,500$ by 5.
$x \ge 0, \ y \ge 0.$

Next, we introduce the slack variables and set up the initial tableau.

$$x \qquad\quad + s \qquad\qquad\qquad = 600$$
$$2x + 3y \quad + t \qquad\qquad = 3,600$$
$$5x + 3y \qquad\quad + u \qquad = 4,500$$
$$-10x - 7y \qquad\qquad + p = 0$$

Note that we have had to introduce a third slack variable, u. There need to be as many slack variables as there are constraints (other than those of the $x \ge 0$ variety).

Q: What do the slack variables say about Acme puddings?

A: The first slack variable, s, represents the number you must add to the number of servings of vanilla pudding actually made to obtain the maximum of 600 servings. The second slack variable, t, represents the amount of sugar that is left over once the puddings are made, and u represents the amount of water left over.

We now use the simplex method to solve the problem:

	x	y	s	t	u	p		
s	$\boxed{1}$	0	1	0	0	0	600	
t	2	3	0	1	0	0	3,600	$R_2 - 2R_1$
u	5	3	0	0	1	0	4,500	$R_3 - 5R_1$
p	-10	-7	0	0	0	1	0	$R_4 + 10R_1$

	x	y	s	t	u	p		
x	1	0	1	0	0	0	600	
t	0	3	-2	1	0	0	2,400	$R_2 - R_3$
u	0	$\boxed{3}$	-5	0	1	0	1,500	
p	0	-7	10	0	0	1	6,000	$3R_4 + 7R_3$

using Technology

See the Technology Guides at the end of the chapter for a discussion of using a TI-83/84 Plus or Excel to help with the simplex method in Example 3. Or, go to the Web site at www.FiniteandCalc.org and follow the path

→ Online Utilities
→ Pivot and Gauss-Jordan Tool

to find a utility that allows you to avoid doing the calculations in each pivot step: Just highlight the entry you wish to use as a pivot, and press "Pivot on Selection."

	x	y	s	t	u	p		
x	1	0	1	0	0	0	600	$3R_1 - R_2$
t	0	0	$\boxed{3}$	1	−1	0	900	
y	0	3	−5	0	1	0	1,500	$3R_3 + 5R_2$
p	0	0	−5	0	7	3	28,500	$3R_4 + 5R_2$

	x	y	s	t	u	p	
x	3	0	0	−1	1	0	900
s	0	0	3	1	−1	0	900
y	0	9	0	5	−2	0	9,000
p	0	0	0	5	16	9	90,000

Thus, the solution is as follows: The maximum value of p is $90,000/9 = 10,000¢ = \$100$, which occurs when $x = 900/3 = 300$, and $y = 9,000/9 = 1,000$. (The slack variables are $s = 900/3 = 300$ and $t = u = 0$.)

➡ **Before we go on...** Because the problem in Example 3 had only two variables, we could have solved it graphically. It is interesting to think about the relationship between the two methods. Figure 22 shows the feasible region. Each tableau in the simplex method corresponds to a corner of the feasible region, given by the corresponding basic solution. In this example, the sequence of basic solutions is

$$(x, y) = (0, 0), (600, 0), (600, 500), (300, 1,000).$$

This is the sequence of corners shown in Figure 23. In general, we can think of the simplex method as walking from corner to corner of the feasible region, until it locates the optimal solution. In problems with many variables and many constraints, the simplex method usually visits only a small fraction of the total number of corners.

We can also explain again, in a different way, the reason we use the test ratios when choosing the pivot. For example, when choosing the first pivot we had to choose among the test ratios 600, 1,800, and 900 (look at the first tableau). In Figure 22, you can see that those are the three x-intercepts of the lines that bound the feasible region. If we had chosen 1,800 or 900, we would have jumped along the x-axis to a point outside of the feasible region, which we do not want to do. In general, the test ratios measure the distance from the current corner to the constraint lines, and we must choose the smallest such distance to avoid crossing any of them into the unfeasible region.

It is also interesting in an application like this to think about the values of the slack variables. We said above that s is the difference between the maximum 600 servings of vanilla that might be made and the number that is actually made. In the optimal solution, $s = 300$, which says that 300 fewer servings of vanilla were made than the maximum possible. Similarly, t was the amount of sugar left over. In the optimal solution, $t = 0$, which tells us that all of the available sugar is used. Finally, $u = 0$, so all of the available water is used as well. ■

Figure 22

Figure 23

Web Site

www.FiniteandCalc.org

On the

→ Online Utilities

page you will find utilities that automate the simplex method to varying extents:

- Pivot and Gauss-Jordan Tool (Pivots and does row operations)
- Simplex Method Tool (Solves entire LP problems; shows all tableaux)

Summary: The Simplex Method for Standard Maximization Problems

To solve a standard maximization problem using the simplex method, we take the following steps:

1. Convert to a system of equations by introducing **slack variables** to turn the constraints into equations and by rewriting the objective function in standard form.
2. Write down the initial **tableau**.
3. Select the pivot column: Choose the negative number with the largest magnitude in the left-hand side of the bottom row. Its column is the pivot column. (If there are two or more candidates, choose any one.) If all the numbers in the left-hand side of the bottom row are zero or positive, then we are finished, and the basic solution maximizes the objective function. (See below for the basic solution.)
4. Select the pivot in the pivot column: The pivot must always be a positive number. For each positive entry b in the pivot column, compute the ratio a/b, where a is the number in the last column in that row. Of these **test ratios**, choose the smallest one. (If there are two or more candidates, choose any one.) The corresponding number b is the pivot.
5. Use the pivot to clear the column in the normal manner (taking care to follow the exact prescription for formulating the row operations described in Chapter 2) and then relabel the pivot row with the label from the pivot column. The variable originally labeling the pivot row is the **departing**, or **exiting**, **variable**, and the variable labeling the column is the **entering variable**.
6. Go to step 3.

To get the **basic solution** corresponding to any tableau in the simplex method, set to zero all variables that do not appear as row labels. The value of a variable that does appear as a row label (an **active variable**) is the number in the rightmost column in that row divided by the number in that row in the column labeled by the same variable.

FAQs

Troubleshooting the Simplex Method

Q : *What if there is no candidate for the pivot in the pivot column? For example, what do we do with a tableau like the following?*

	x	y	z	s	t	p	
z	0	0	5	2	0	0	4
y	−8	20	0	6	5	0	72
p	−20	0	0	26	15	4	232

A : Here, the pivot column is the x column, but there is no suitable entry for a pivot (because zeros and negative numbers can't be pivots). This happens when the feasible region is unbounded and there is also no optimal solution. In other words, p can be made as large as we like without violating the constraints.

Q: *What should we do if there is a negative number in the rightmost column?*

A: A negative number will not appear above the bottom row in the rightmost column if we follow the procedure correctly. (The bottom right entry is allowed to be negative if the objective takes on negative values as in a negative profit, or loss.) Following are the most likely errors leading to this situation:

- The pivot was chosen incorrectly. (Don't forget to choose the *smallest* test ratio.) When this mistake is made, one or more of the variables will be negative in the corresponding basic solution.
- The row operation instruction was written backwards or performed backwards (for example, instead of $R_2 - R_1$, it was $R_1 - R_2$). This mistake can be corrected by multiplying the row by -1.
- An arithmetic error occurred. (We all make those annoying errors from time to time.)

Q: *What about zeros in the rightmost column?*

A: Zeros are permissible in the rightmost column. For example, the constraint $x - y \leq 0$ will lead to a zero in the rightmost column.

Q: *What happens if we choose a pivot column other than the one with the most negative number in the bottom row?*

A: There is no harm in doing this as long as we choose the pivot in that column using the smallest test ratio. All it might do is slow the whole calculation by adding extra steps.

One last suggestion: If it is possible to do a simplification step (dividing a row by a positive number) *at any stage*, we should do so. As we saw in Chapter 2, this can help prevent the numbers from getting out of hand.

4.3 EXERCISES

▼ more advanced   ◆ challenging
T indicates exercises that should be solved using technology

1. Maximize $p = 2x + y$
subject to $x + 2y \leq 6$
$-x + y \leq 4$
$x + y \leq 4$
$x \geq 0, y \geq 0.$

HINT [See Examples 1 and 2.]

2. Maximize $p = x$
subject to $x - y \leq 4$
$-x + 3y \leq 4$
$x \geq 0, y \geq 0.$

HINT [See Examples 1 and 2.]

3. Maximize $p = x - y$
subject to $5x - 5y \leq 20$
$2x - 10y \leq 40$
$x \geq 0, y \geq 0.$

4. Maximize $p = 2x + 3y$
subject to $3x + 8y \leq 24$
$6x + 4y \leq 30$
$x \geq 0, y \geq 0.$

5. Maximize $p = 5x - 4y + 3z$
subject to $5x + 5z \leq 100$
$5y - 5z \leq 50$
$5x - 5y \leq 50$
$x \geq 0, y \geq 0, z \geq 0.$

6. Maximize $p = 6x + y + 3z$
subject to $3x + y \leq 15$
$2x + 2y + 2z \leq 20$
$x \geq 0, y \geq 0, z \geq 0.$

7. Maximize $p = 7x + 5y + 6z$
subject to $x + y - z \leq 3$
$x + 2y + z \leq 8$
$x + y \leq 5$
$x \geq 0, y \geq 0, z \geq 0.$

8. Maximize $p = 3x + 4y + 2z$
   subject to $3x + y + z \le 5$
             $x + 2y + z \le 5$
             $x + y + z \le 4$
             $x \ge 0, y \ge 0, z \ge 0.$

9. Maximize $z = 3x_1 + 7x_2 + 8x_3$
   subject to $5x_1 - x_2 + x_3 \le 1{,}500$
             $2x_1 + 2x_2 + x_3 \le 2{,}500$
             $4x_1 + 2x_2 + x_3 \le 2{,}000$
             $x_1 \ge 0, x_2 \ge 0, x_3 \ge 0.$

10. Maximize $z = 3x_1 + 4x_2 + 6x_3$
   subject to $5x_1 - x_2 + x_3 \le 1{,}500$
             $2x_1 + 2x_2 + x_3 \le 2{,}500$
             $4x_1 + 2x_2 + x_3 \le 2{,}000$
             $x_1 \ge 0, x_2 \ge 0, x_3 \ge 0.$

11. Maximize $p = x + y + z + w$
   subject to $x + y + z \le 3$
             $y + z + w \le 4$
             $x + z + w \le 5$
             $x + y + w \le 6$
             $x \ge 0, y \ge 0, z \ge 0, w \ge 0.$

12. Maximize $p = x - y + z + w$
   subject to $x + y + z \le 3$
             $y + z + w \le 3$
             $x + z + w \le 4$
             $x + y + w \le 4$
             $x \ge 0, y \ge 0, z \ge 0, w \ge 0.$

13. ▼ Maximize $p = x + y + z + w + v$
   subject to $x + y \le 1$
             $y + z \le 2$
             $z + w \le 3$
             $w + v \le 4$
             $x \ge 0, y \ge 0, z \ge 0, w \ge 0, v \ge 0.$

14. ▼ Maximize $p = x + 2y + z + 2w + v$
   subject to $x + y \le 1$
             $y + z \le 2$
             $z + w \le 3$
             $w + v \le 4$
             $x \ge 0, y \ge 0, z \ge 0, w \ge 0, v \ge 0.$

🖳 *In Exercises 15–20 we suggest the use of technology. Round all answers to two decimal places.*

15. Maximize $p = 2.5x + 4.2y + 2z$
   subject to $0.1x + y - 2.2z \le 4.5$
             $2.1x + y + z \le 8$
             $x + 2.2y \le 5$
             $x \ge 0, y \ge 0, z \ge 0.$

16. Maximize $p = 2.1x + 4.1y + 2z$
   subject to $3.1x + 1.2y + z \le 5.5$
             $x + 2.3y + z \le 5.5$
             $2.1x + y + 2.3z \le 5.2$
             $x \ge 0, y \ge 0, z \ge 0.$

17. Maximize $p = x + 2y + 3z + w$
   subject to $x + 2y + 3z \le 3$
             $y + z + 2.2w \le 4$
             $x + z + 2.2w \le 5$
             $x + y + 2.2w \le 6$
             $x \ge 0, y \ge 0, z \ge 0, w \ge 0.$

18. Maximize $p = 1.1x - 2.1y + z + w$
   subject to $x + 1.3y + z \le 3$
             $1.3y + z + w \le 3$
             $x + z + w \le 4.1$
             $x + 1.3y + w \le 4.1$
             $x \ge 0, y \ge 0, z \ge 0, w \ge 0.$

19. Maximize $p = x - y + z - w + v$
   subject to $x + y \le 1.1$
             $y + z \le 2.2$
             $z + w \le 3.3$
             $w + v \le 4.4$
             $x \ge 0, y \ge 0, z \ge 0, w \ge 0, v \ge 0.$

20. Maximize $p = x - 2y + z - 2w + v$
   subject to $x + y \le 1.1$
             $y + z \le 2.2$
             $z + w \le 3.3$
             $w + v \le 4.4$
             $x \ge 0, y \ge 0, z \ge 0, w \ge 0, v \ge 0.$

APPLICATIONS

21. *Purchasing* You are in charge of purchases at the student-run used-book supply program at your college, and you must decide how many introductory calculus, history, and marketing texts should be purchased from students for resale. Due to budget limitations, you cannot purchase more than 650 of these textbooks each semester. There are also shelf-space limitations: Calculus texts occupy 2 units of shelf space each, history books 1 unit each, and marketing texts 3 units each, and you can spare at most 1,000 units of shelf space for the texts. If the used book program makes a profit of $10 on each calculus text, $4 on each history text, and $8 on each marketing text, how many of each type of text should you purchase to maximize profit? What is the maximum profit the program can make in a semester? HINT [See Example 3.]

22. *Sales* The Marketing Club at your college has decided to raise funds by selling three types of T-shirt: one with a single-color "ordinary" design, one with a two-color "fancy" design, and one with a three-color "very fancy" design. The club feels that it can sell up to 300 T-shirts. "Ordinary" T-shirts will cost the club $6 each, "fancy" T-shirts $8 each, and "very fancy" T-shirts $10 each, and the club has a total purchasing budget of $3,000. It will sell "ordinary" T-shirts at a profit of $4 each, "fancy" T-shirts at a profit of $5 each, and "very fancy" T-shirts at a profit of $4 each. How many of each kind of T-shirt should the club order to maximize profit? What is the maximum profit the club can make? HINT [See Example 3.]

23. *Resource Allocation* Arctic Juice Company makes three juice blends: PineOrange, using 2 portions of pineapple juice and 2 portions of orange juice per gallon; PineKiwi, using 3 portions of pineapple juice and 1 portion of kiwi juice per gallon; and OrangeKiwi, using 3 portions of orange juice and 1 portion of kiwi juice per gallon. Each day the company has 800 portions of pineapple juice, 650 portions of orange juice, and 350 portions of kiwi juice available. Its profit on PineOrange is $1 per gallon, its profit on PineKiwi is $2 per gallon, and its profit on OrangeKiwi is $1 per gallon. How many gallons of each blend should it make each day to maximize profit? What is the largest possible profit the company can make?

24. *Purchasing* Trans Global Tractor Trailers has decided to spend up to $1,500,000 on a fleet of new trucks, and it is considering three models: the Gigahaul, which has a capacity of 6,000 cubic feet and is priced at $60,000; the Megahaul, with a capacity of 5,000 cubic feet and priced at $50,000; and the Picohaul, with a capacity of 2,000 cubic feet, priced at $40,000. The anticipated annual revenues are $500,000 for each new truck purchased (regardless of size). Trans Global would like a total capacity of up to 130,000 cubic feet, and feels that it cannot provide drivers and maintenance for more than 30 trucks. How many of each should it purchase to maximize annual revenue? What is the largest possible revenue it can make?

25. *Resource Allocation* The Enormous State University History Department offers three courses, Ancient, Medieval, and Modern History, and the department chairperson is trying to decide how many sections of each to offer this semester. They may offer up to 45 sections total, up to 5,000 students would like to take a course, and there are 60 professors to teach them (no student will take more than one history course, and no professor will teach more than one section). Sections of Ancient History have 100 students each, sections of Medieval History have 50 students each, and sections of Modern History have 200 students each. Modern History sections are taught by a team of two professors, while Ancient and Medieval History need only one professor per section. Ancient History nets the university $10,000 per section, Medieval nets $20,000, and Modern History nets $30,000 per section. How many sections of each course should the department offer in order to generate the largest profit? What is the largest profit possible? Will there be any unused time slots, any students who did not get into classes, or any professors without anything to teach?

26. *Resource Allocation* You manage an ice cream factory that makes three flavors: Creamy Vanilla, Continental Mocha,

and Succulent Strawberry. Into each batch of Creamy Vanilla go 2 eggs, 1 cup of milk, and 2 cups of cream. Into each batch of Continental Mocha go 1 egg, 1 cup of milk, and 2 cups of cream. Into each batch of Succulent Strawberry go 1 egg, 2 cups of milk, and 2 cups of cream. You have in stock 200 eggs, 120 cups of milk, and 200 cups of cream. You make a profit of $3 on each batch of Creamy Vanilla, $2 on each batch of Continental Mocha and $4 on each batch of Succulent Strawberry.

a. How many batches of each flavor should you make to maximize your profit?

b. In your answer to part (a), have you used all the ingredients?

c. Due to the poor strawberry harvest this year, you cannot make more than 10 batches of Succulent Strawberry. Does this affect your maximum profit?

27. *Agriculture* Your small farm encompasses 100 acres, and you are planning to grow tomatoes, lettuce, and carrots in the coming planting season. Fertilizer costs per acre are: $5 for tomatoes, $4 for lettuce, and $2 for carrots. Based on past experience, you estimate that each acre of tomatoes will require an average of 4 hours of labor per week, while tending to lettuce and carrots will each require an average of 2 hours per week. You estimate a profit of $2,000 for each acre of tomatoes, $1,500 for each acre of lettuce, and $500 for each acre of carrots. You can afford to spend no more than $400 on fertilizer, and your farm laborers can supply up to 500 hours per week. How many acres of each crop should you plant to maximize total profits? In this event, will you be using all 100 acres of your farm?

28. *Agriculture* Your farm encompasses 500 acres, and you are planning to grow soybeans, corn, and wheat in the coming planting season. Fertilizer costs per acre are: $5 for soybeans, $2 for corn, and $1 for wheat. You estimate that each acre of soybeans will require an average of 5 hours of labor per week, while tending to corn and wheat will each require an average of 2 hours per week. Based on past yields and current market prices, you estimate a profit of $3,000 for each acre of soybeans, $2,000 for each acre of corn, and $1,000 for each acre of wheat. You can afford to spend no more than $3,000 on fertilizer, and your farm laborers can supply 3,000 hours per week. How many acres of each crop should you plant to maximize total profits? In this event, will you be using all the available labor?

29. *Resource Allocation* (Note that the following exercise is very similar to Exercise 36 on page 169, except for one important detail. Refer back to your solution of that problem—if you did it—and then attempt this one.) The Enormous State University Choral Society is planning its annual Song Festival, when it will serve three kinds of delicacies: granola treats, nutty granola treats, and nuttiest granola treats. The following table shows some of the ingredients required (in ounces) for a single serving of each delicacy, as well as the total amount of each ingredient available.

	Granola	Nutty Granola	Nuttiest Granola	Total Available
Toasted Oats	1	1	5	1,500
Almonds	4	8	8	10,000
Raisins	2	4	8	4,000

The society makes a profit of $6 on each serving of granola, $8 on each serving of nutty granola, and $3 on each serving of nuttiest granola. Assuming that the Choral Society can sell all that they make, how many servings of each will maximize profits? How much of each ingredient will be left over?

30. Resource Allocation Repeat the preceding exercise, but this time assume that the Choral Society makes a $3 profit on each of its delicacies.

31. Recycling Safety-Kleen operates the world's largest oil re-refinery at Elgin, Illinois. You have been hired by the company to determine how to allocate its intake of up to 50 million gallons of used oil to its three refinery processes: A, B, and C. You are told that electricity costs for process A amount to $150,000 per million gallons treated, while for processes B and C, the costs are respectively $100,000 and $50,000 per million gallons treated. Process A can recover 60 percent of the used oil, process B can recover 55 percent, and process C can recover only 50 percent. Assuming a revenue of $4 million per million gallons of recovered oil and an annual electrical budget of $3 million, how much used oil would you allocate to each process in order to maximize total revenues?[22]

32. Recycling Repeat the preceding exercise, but this time assume that process C can handle only up to 20 million gallons per year.

Creatine Supplements Exercises 33 and 34 are based on the following data on four popular bodybuilding supplements. (Figures shown correspond to a single serving.)[23]

	Creatine (g)	Carbohydrates (g)	Taurine (g)	Alpha Lipoic Acid (mg)
Cell-Tech® (MuscleTech)	10	75	2	200
RiboForce HP® (EAS)	5	15	1	0
Creatine Transport® (Kaizen)	5	35	1	100
Pre-Load Creatine (Optimum)	6	35	1	25

33. You are thinking of combining the first three supplements in the previous table to obtain a 10-day supply that gives you the maximum possible amount of creatine, but no more than 1,000 milligrams of alpha lipoic acid and 225 grams of carbohydrates. How many servings of each supplement should you combine to meet your specifications, and how much creatine will you get?

34. Repeat Exercise 33, but use the last three supplements in the table instead.

Investing Exercises 35 and 36 are based on the following data on three stocks.[24]

	Price	Dividend Yield	Earnings per Share
MON (Monsanto)	$80	1%	$4
SNE (Sony Corp.)	$20	2%	$3
IMCL (ImClone)	$70	0%	−$1

35. ▼ You are planning to invest up to $10,000 in MON, SNE, and IMCL shares. You desire to maximize your share of the companies' earnings but, for tax reasons, want to earn no more than $200 in dividends. Your broker suggests that because IMCL stock pays no dividends, you should invest only in IMCL. Is she right?

36. ▼ Repeat Exercise 35 under the assumption that MON stock has climbed to $120 on speculation, but its dividend yield and EPS (earnings per share) are unchanged.

37. ▌▼ **Loan Planning**[25] Enormous State University's employee credit union has $5 million available for loans in the coming year. As VP in charge of finances, you must decide how much capital to allocate to each of four different kinds of loans, as shown in the following table.

Type of Loan	Annual Rate of Return
Automobile	8%
Furniture	10%
Signature	12%
Other secured	10%

State laws and credit union policies impose the following restrictions:

• Signature loans may not exceed 10 percent of the total investment of funds.

---

[22] These figures are realistic: Safety-Kleen's actual 1993 capacity was 50 million gallons, its recycled oil sold for approximately $4 per gallon, its recycling process could recover approximately 55 percent of the used oil, and its electrical bill was $3 million. Source: (Oil Recycler Greases Rusty City's Economy), *Chicago Tribune*, May 30, 1993, Section 7, p.1.

[23] Source: Nutritional information supplied by the manufacturers (www.netrition.com). Cost per serving is approximate.

[24] Approximate trading price in fourth quarter of 2008 based on 50-day averages. Earnings per share are rounded to the nearest $1. Source: http://finance.google.com.

[25] Adapted from an exercise in *An Introduction to Management Science* (6th. ed.) by D. R. Anderson, D. J. Sweeny, and T. A. Williams (West).

- Furniture loans plus other secured loans may not exceed automobile loans.
- Other secured loans may not exceed 200 percent of automobile loans.

How much should you allocate to each type of loan to maximize the annual return?

38. ▣ ▼ *Investments* You have $100,000 which you are considering investing in three dividend-yielding stocks: **Banco Santander**, **ConAgra Foods**, and **Dillard's**. You have the following data:[26]

Company	Yield
STD (Banco Santander)	7%
CAG (ConAgra Foods)	5%
DDS (Dillard's)	4%

Your broker has made the following suggestions:

- At least 50 percent of your total investment should be in DDS.
- No more than 10 percent of your total investment should be in STD.

How much should you invest in each stock to maximize your anticipated dividends while following your broker's advice?

39. ▼ *Portfolio Management* If x dollars are invested in a company that controls, say, 30 percent of the market with five brand-names, then $0.30x$ is a measure of market exposure and $5x$ is a measure of brand-name exposure. Now suppose you are a broker at a large securities firm, and one of your clients would like to invest up to $100,000 in recording industry stocks. You decide to recommend a combination of stocks in four of the world's largest companies: **Warner Music**, **Universal Music**, **Sony**, and **EMI**. (See the table.)[27]

	Warner Music	Universal Music	Sony	EMI
Market Share	12%	20%	20%	15%
Number of Labels (Brands)	8	20	10	15

You would like your client's brand-name exposure to be as large as possible but his total market exposure to be $15,000 or less. (This would reflect an average of 15 percent.) Furthermore, you would like at least 20 percent of the investment to be in **Universal** because you feel that its control of the DGG and Phillips labels is advantageous for its classical music operations. How much should you advise your client to invest in each company?

40. ▼ *Portfolio Management* Referring to Exercise 39, suppose instead that you wanted your client to maximize his total market exposure but limit his brand-name exposure to 1.5 million or less (representing an average of 15 labels or fewer per company), and still invest at least 20 percent of the total in **Universal**. How much should you advise your client to invest in each company?

41. ▣ ▼ *Transportation Scheduling* (This exercise is almost identical to Exercise 26 in Section 2.3 but is more realistic; one cannot always expect to fill all orders exactly, and keep all plants operating at 100 percent capacity.) The Tubular Ride Boogie Board Company has manufacturing plants in Tucson, Arizona, and Toronto, Ontario. You have been given the job of coordinating distribution of the latest model, the Gladiator, to their outlets in Honolulu and Venice Beach. The Tucson plant, when operating at full capacity, can manufacture 620 Gladiator boards per week, while the Toronto plant, beset by labor disputes, can produce only 410 boards per week. The outlet in Honolulu orders 500 Gladiator boards per week, while Venice Beach orders 530 boards per week. Transportation costs are as follows: Tucson to Honolulu: $10 per board; Tucson to Venice Beach: $5 per board; Toronto to Honolulu: $20 per board; Toronto to Venice Beach: $10 per board. Your manager has informed you that the company's total transportation budget is $6,550. You realize that it may not be possible to fill all the orders, but you would like the total number of boogie boards shipped to be as large as possible. Given this, how many Gladiator boards should you order shipped from each manufacturing plant to each distribution outlet?

42. ▣ ▼ *Transportation Scheduling* Repeat the preceding exercise, but use a transportation budget of $5,050.

43. ▣ ▼ *Transportation Scheduling* Your publishing company is about to start a promotional blitz for its new book, *Physics for the Liberal Arts*. You have 20 salespeople stationed in Chicago and 10 in Denver. You would like to fly at most 10 into Los Angeles and at most 15 into New York. A round-trip plane flight from Chicago to LA costs $195;[28] from Chicago to NY costs $182; from Denver to LA costs $395; and from Denver to NY costs $166. You want to spend at most $4,520 on plane flights. How many salespeople should you fly from each of Chicago and Denver to each of LA and NY to have the most salespeople on the road?

44. ▣ ▼ *Transportation Scheduling* Repeat the preceding exercise, but this time, spend at most $5,320.

COMMUNICATION AND REASONING EXERCISES

45. Can the following linear programming problem be stated as a standard maximization problem? If so, do it; if not, explain why.

Maximize $p = 3x - 2y$
subject to $x - y + z \geq 0$
$x - y - z \leq 6$
$x \geq 0, y \geq 0, z \geq 0.$

---

[26] Yields are as of January 2004. Source: http://finance.yahoo.com.

[27] The number of labels includes only major labels. Market shares are approximate, and represent the period 2000–2002. Sources: Various, including www.emigroup.com, http://finance.vivendi.com/discover/financial, and http://business2.com, March 2002.

[28] Prices from Travelocity, at www.travelocity.com, for the week of June 3, 2002, as of May 5, 2002.

46. Can the following linear programming problem be stated as a standard maximization problem? If so, do it; if not, explain why.

Maximize $p = -3x - 2y$
subject to $x - y + z \geq 0$
$x - y - z \geq -6$
$x \geq 0, y \geq 0, z \geq 0.$

47. Why is the simplex method useful? (After all, we do have the graphical method for solving LP problems.)

48. Are there any types of linear programming problems that cannot be solved with the methods of this section but that can be solved using the methods of the preceding section? Explain.

49. ▼ Your friend Janet is telling everyone that if there are only two constraints in a linear programming problem, then, in any optimal basic solution, at most two unknowns (other than the objective) will be nonzero. Is she correct? Explain.

50. ▼ Your other friend Jason is telling everyone that if there is only one constraint in a standard linear programming problem,

then you will have to pivot at most once to obtain an optimal solution. Is he correct? Explain.

51. ▼ What is a "basic solution"? How might one find a basic solution of a given system of linear equations?

52. ▼ In a typical simplex method tableau, there are more unknowns than equations, and we know from the chapter on systems of linear equations that this typically implies the existence of infinitely many solutions. How are the following types of solutions interpreted in the simplex method?

a. Solutions in which all the variables are positive.
b. Solutions in which some variables are negative.
c. Solutions in which the inactive variables are zero.

53. ◆ Can the value of the objective function decrease in passing from one tableau to the next? Explain.

54. ◆ Can the value of the objective function remain unchanged in passing from one tableau to the next? Explain.

4.4 The Simplex Method: Solving General Linear Programming Problems

As we saw in Section 4.2, not all LP problems are standard maximization problems. We might have constraints like $2x + 3y \geq 4$ or perhaps $2x + 3y = 4$. Or, you might have to minimize, rather than maximize, the objective function. General problems like this are almost as easy to deal with as the standard kind: There is a modification of the simplex method that works very nicely. The best way to illustrate it is by means of examples. First, we discuss nonstandard maximization problems.

Nonstandard Maximization Problems

EXAMPLE 1 Maximizing with Mixed Constraints

Maximize $p = 4x + 12y + 6z$
subject to $x + y + z \leq 100$
$4x + 10y + 7z \leq 480$
$x + y + z \geq 60$
$x \geq 0, y \geq 0, z \geq 0.$

Solution We begin by turning the first two inequalities into equations as usual because they have the standard form. We get

$$x + y + z + s \qquad = 100$$
$$4x + 10y + 7z \qquad + t = 480.$$

We are tempted to use a slack variable for the third inequality, $x + y + z \geq 60$, but *adding* something positive to the left-hand side will not make it equal to the right: It will get even bigger. To make it equal to 60, we must *subtract* some non-negative number.

We will call this number u (because we have already used s and t) and refer to u as a **surplus variable** rather than a slack variable. Thus, we write

$$x + y + z - u = 60.$$

Continuing with the setup, we have

$$
\begin{aligned}
x + y + z + s \phantom{+ t - u + 0} &= 100 \\
4x + 10y + 7z + t &= 480 \\
x + y + z - u &= 60 \\
-4x - 12y - 6z + p &= 0.
\end{aligned}
$$

This leads to the initial tableau:

	x	y	z	s	t	u	p	
s	1	1	1	1	0	0	0	100
t	4	10	7	0	1	0	0	480
*u	1	1	1	0	0	−1	0	60
p	−4	−12	−6	0	0	0	1	0

We put a star next to the third row because the basic solution corresponding to this tableau is

$$x = y = z = 0, s = 100, t = 480, u = 60/(-1) = -60.$$

Several things are wrong here. First, the values $x = y = z = 0$ do not satisfy the third inequality $x + y + z \geq 60$. Thus, this basic solution is *not feasible*. Second—and this is really the same problem—the surplus variable u is negative, whereas we said that it should be non-negative. The star next to the row labeled u alerts us to the fact that the present basic solution is not feasible and that the problem is located in the starred row, where the active variable u is negative.

Whenever an active variable is negative, we star the corresponding row.

In setting up the initial tableau, we star those rows coming from $\geq$ inequalities.

The simplex method as described in the preceding section assumed that we began in the feasible region, but now we do not. Our first task is to get ourselves into the feasible region. In practice, we can think of this as getting rid of the stars on the rows. Once we get into the feasible region, we go back to the method of the preceding section.

There are several ways to get into the feasible region. The method we have chosen is one of the simplest to state and carry out. (We will see why this method works at the end of the example.)

The Simplex Method for General Linear Programming Problems

Star all rows that give a negative value for the associated active variable (except for the objective variable, which is allowed to be negative). If there are starred rows, you will need to begin with Phase I.

Phase I: Getting into the Feasible Region (Getting Rid of the Stars)
In the first starred row, find the largest positive number. Use test ratios as in Section 4.3 to find the pivot in that column (exclude the bottom row), and then pivot on that entry. (If the lowest ratio occurs both in a starred row and an un-starred row, pivot in a starred row rather than the un-starred one.) Check to see

which rows should now be starred. Repeat until no starred rows remain, and then go on to Phase II.

Phase II: Use the Simplex Method for Standard Maximization Problems

If there are any negative entries on the left side of the bottom row after Phase I, use the method described in the preceding section.

Because there is a starred row, we need to use Phase I. The largest positive number in the starred row is 1, which occurs three times. Arbitrarily select the first, which is in the first column. In that column, the smallest test ratio happens to be given by the 1 in the u row, so this is our first pivot.

Pivot column
↓

	x	y	z	s	t	u	p		
s	1	1	1	1	0	0	0	100	$R_1 - R_3$
t	4	10	7	0	1	0	0	480	$R_2 - 4R_3$
*u	$\boxed{1}$	1	1	0	0	-1	0	60	
p	-4	-12	-6	0	0	0	1	0	$R_4 + 4R_3$

This gives

	x	y	z	s	t	u	p	
s	0	0	0	1	0	1	0	40
t	0	6	3	0	1	4	0	240
x	1	1	1	0	0	-1	0	60
p	0	-8	-2	0	0	-4	1	240

Notice that we removed the star from row 3. To see why, look at the basic solution given by this tableau:

$$x = 60, y = 0, z = 0, s = 40, t = 240, u = 0.$$

None of the variables is negative anymore, so there are no rows to star. The basic solution is therefore feasible—it satisfies all the constraints.

Now that there are no more stars, we have completed Phase I, so we proceed to Phase II, which is just the method of the preceding section.

	x	y	z	s	t	u	p		
s	0	0	0	1	0	1	0	40	
t	0	$\boxed{6}$	3	0	1	4	0	240	
x	1	1	1	0	0	-1	0	60	$6R_3 - R_2$
p	0	-8	-2	0	0	-4	1	240	$3R_4 + 4R_2$

	x	y	z	s	t	u	p	
s	0	0	0	1	0	1	0	40
y	0	6	3	0	1	4	0	240
x	6	0	3	0	-1	-10	0	120
p	0	0	6	0	4	4	3	1,680

And we are finished. Thus the solution is

$$p = 1{,}680/3 = 560,\ x = 120/6 = 20,\ y = 240/6 = 40,\ z = 0.$$

The slack and surplus variables are

$$s = 40,\ t = 0,\ u = 0.$$

➡ **Before we go on...** We owe you an explanation of why this method works. When we perform a pivot in Phase I, one of two things will happen. As in Example 1, we may pivot in a starred row. In that case, the negative active variable in that row will become inactive (hence zero) and some other variable will be made active with a positive value because we are pivoting on a positive entry. Thus, at least one star will be eliminated. (We will not introduce any new stars because pivoting on the entry with the smallest test ratio will keep all non-negative variables non-negative.)

The second possibility is that we may pivot on some row other than a starred row. Choosing the pivot via test ratios again guarantees that no new starred rows are created. A little bit of algebra shows that the value of the negative variable in the first starred row must increase toward zero. (Choosing the *largest* positive entry in the starred row will make it a little more likely that we will increase the value of that variable as much as possible; the rationale for choosing the largest entry is the same as that for choosing the most negative entry in the bottom row during Phase II.) Repeating this procedure as necessary, the value of the variable must eventually become zero or positive, assuming that there are feasible solutions to begin with.

So, one way or the other, we can eventually get rid of all of the stars. ∎

Here is an example that begins with two starred rows.

EXAMPLE 2 **More Mixed Constraints**

Maximize $p = 2x + y$
subject to $x + y \geq 35$
$x + 2y \leq 60$
$2x + y \geq 60$
$x \leq 25$
$x \geq 0,\ y \geq 0.$

Solution We introduce slack and surplus variables, and write down the initial tableau:

$$
\begin{aligned}
x + y - s &= 35 \\
x + 2y + t &= 60 \\
2x + y - u &= 60 \\
x + v &= 25 \\
-2x - y + p &= 0.
\end{aligned}
$$

	x	y	s	t	u	v	p	
*s	1	1	−1	0	0	0	0	35
t	1	2	0	1	0	0	0	60
*u	2	1	0	0	−1	0	0	60
v	1	0	0	0	0	1	0	25
p	−2	−1	0	0	0	0	1	0

We locate the largest positive entry in the first starred row (row 1). There are two to choose from (both 1s); let's choose the one in the x column. The entry with the smallest test ratio in that column is the 1 in the v row, so that is the entry we use as the pivot:

Pivot column
↓

	x	y	s	t	u	v	p		
*s	1	1	−1	0	0	0	0	35	$R_1 - R_4$
t	1	2	0	1	0	0	0	60	$R_2 - R_4$
*u	2	1	0	0	−1	0	0	60	$R_3 - 2R_4$
v	⬚1	0	0	0	0	1	0	25	
p	−2	−1	0	0	0	0	1	0	$R_5 + 2R_4$

	x	y	s	t	u	v	p	
*s	0	1	−1	0	0	−1	0	10
t	0	2	0	1	0	−1	0	35
*u	0	1	0	0	−1	−2	0	10
x	1	0	0	0	0	1	0	25
p	0	−1	0	0	0	2	1	50

Notice that both stars are still there because the basic solutions for s and u remain negative (but less so). The only positive entry in the first starred row is the 1 in the y column, and that entry also has the smallest test ratio in its column. (Actually, it is tied with the 1 in the u column, so we could choose either one.)

	x	y	s	t	u	v	p		
*s	0	⬚1	−1	0	0	−1	0	10	
t	0	2	0	1	0	−1	0	35	$R_2 - 2R_1$
*u	0	1	0	0	−1	−2	0	10	$R_3 - R_1$
x	1	0	0	0	0	1	0	25	
p	0	−1	0	0	0	2	1	50	$R_5 + R_1$

	x	y	s	t	u	v	p	
y	0	1	−1	0	0	−1	0	10
t	0	0	2	1	0	1	0	15
u	0	0	1	0	−1	−1	0	0
x	1	0	0	0	0	1	0	25
p	0	0	−1	0	0	1	1	60

The basic solution is $x = 25$, $y = 10$, $s = 0$, $t = 15$, $u = 0/(−1) = 0$, and $v = 0$. Because there are no negative variables left (even u has become 0), we are in the feasible region, so we can go on to Phase II, shown next. (Filling in the instructions for the row operations is an exercise.)

	x	y	s	t	u	v	p	
y	0	1	−1	0	0	−1	0	10
t	0	0	2	1	0	1	0	15
u	0	0	☐1	0	−1	−1	0	0
x	1	0	0	0	0	1	0	25
p	0	0	−1	0	0	1	1	60

	x	y	s	t	u	v	p	
y	0	1	0	0	−1	−2	0	10
t	0	0	0	1	☐2	3	0	15
s	0	0	1	0	−1	−1	0	0
x	1	0	0	0	0	1	0	25
p	0	0	0	0	−1	0	1	60

	x	y	s	t	u	v	p	
y	0	2	0	1	0	−1	0	35
u	0	0	0	1	2	3	0	15
s	0	0	2	1	0	1	0	15
x	1	0	0	0	0	1	0	25
p	0	0	0	1	0	3	2	135

The optimal solution is

$$x = 25, \ y = 35/2 = 17.5, \ p = 135/2 = 67.5 \quad (s = 7.5, t = 0, u = 7.5).$$

➡ **Before we go on...** Because Example 2 had only two unknowns, we can picture the sequence of basic solutions on the graph of the feasible region. This is shown in Figure 24.

You can see that there was no way to jump from $(0, 0)$ in the initial tableau directly into the feasible region because the first jump must be along an axis. (Why?) Also notice that the third jump did not move at all. To which step of the simplex method does this correspond? ∎

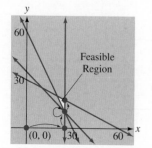

Figure 24

Minimization Problems

Now that we know how to deal with nonstandard constraints, we consider **minimization problems**, problems in which we have to minimize, rather than maximize, the objective function. The idea is to *convert a minimization problem into a maximization problem*, which we can then solve as usual.

Suppose, for instance, we want to minimize $c = 10x - 30y$ subject to some constraints. The technique is as follows: Define a new variable p by taking p to be the negative of c, so that $p = -c$. Then, the larger we make p, the smaller c becomes. For example, if we can make p increase from -10 to -5, then c will decrease from 10 to 5. So, if we are looking for the smallest value of c, we might as well look for the largest value of p instead. More concisely,

Minimizing c is the same as maximizing $p = -c$.

Now because $c = 10x - 30y$, we have $p = -10x + 30y$, and the requirement that we "minimize $c = 10x - 30y$" is now replaced by "maximize $p = -10x + 30y$."

Minimization Problems

We convert a minimization problem into a maximization problem by taking the negative of the objective function. All the constraints remain unchanged.

Quick Example

| **Minimization Problem** | $\rightarrow$ | **Maximization Problem** |

Minimization Problem

Minimize $c = 10x - 30y$
subject to $2x + y \leq 160$
$x + 3y \geq 120$
$x \geq 0, y \geq 0.$

$\rightarrow$

Maximization Problem

Maximize $p = -10x + 30y$
subject to $2x + y \leq 160$
$x + 3y \geq 120$
$x \geq 0, y \geq 0.$

EXAMPLE 3   Purchasing

You are in charge of ordering furniture for your company's new headquarters. You need to buy at least 200 tables, 500 chairs, and 300 computer desks. Wall-to-Wall Furniture (WWF) is offering a package of 20 tables, 25 chairs, and 18 computer desks for $2,000, whereas rival Acme Furniture (AF) is offering a package of 10 tables, 50 chairs, and 24 computer desks for $3,000. How many packages should you order from each company to minimize your total cost?

Solution The unknowns here are

x = number of packages ordered from WWF
y = number of packages ordered from AF.

We can put the information about the various kinds of furniture in a table:

	WWF	*AF*	*Needed*
Tables	20	10	200
Chairs	25	50	500
Computer Desks	18	24	300
Cost ($)	2,000	3,000	

From this table we get the following LP problem:

Minimize $c = 2,000x + 3,000y$
subject to $20x + 10y \geq 200$
$25x + 50y \geq 500$
$18x + 24y \geq 300$
$x \geq 0, y \geq 0.$

Before we start solving this problem, notice that all the inequalities may be simplified. The first is divisible by 10, the second by 25, and the third by 6. (However, this affects the meaning of the surplus variables; see *Before we go on* below.) Dividing gives the following simpler problem:

Minimize $c = 2,000x + 3,000y$
subject to $2x + y \geq 20$
$x + 2y \geq 20$
$3x + 4y \geq 50$
$x \geq 0, y \geq 0.$

Following the discussion that preceded this example, we convert to a maximization problem:

$$\text{Maximize} \quad p = -2{,}000x - 3{,}000y$$
$$\text{subject to} \quad 2x + y \geq 20$$
$$x + 2y \geq 20$$
$$3x + 4y \geq 50$$
$$x \geq 0, y \geq 0.$$

We introduce surplus variables.

$$2x + \quad y - s \qquad\qquad = 20$$
$$x + \quad 2y \quad - t \qquad = 20$$
$$3x + \quad 4y \qquad - u \quad = 50$$
$$2{,}000x + 3{,}000y \qquad\qquad + p = 0.$$

The initial tableau is then

	x	y	s	t	u	p	
*s	2	1	-1	0	0	0	20
*t	1	2	0	-1	0	0	20
*u	3	4	0	0	-1	0	50
p	2,000	3,000	0	0	0	1	0

The largest entry in the first starred row is the 2 in the upper left, which happens to give the smallest test ratio in its column.

	x	y	s	t	u	p		
*s	$\boxed{2}$	1	-1	0	0	0	20	
*t	1	2	0	-1	0	0	20	$2R_2 - R_1$
*u	3	4	0	0	-1	0	50	$2R_3 - 3R_1$
p	2,000	3,000	0	0	0	1	0	$R_4 - 1{,}000R_1$

	x	y	s	t	u	p		
x	2	1	-1	0	0	0	20	$3R_1 - R_2$
*t	0	$\boxed{3}$	1	-2	0	0	20	
*u	0	5	3	0	-2	0	40	$3R_3 - 5R_2$
p	0	2,000	1,000	0	0	1	$-20{,}000$	$3R_4 - 2{,}000R_2$

	x	y	s	t	u	p		
x	6	0	-4	2	0	0	40	$5R_1 - R_3$
y	0	3	1	-2	0	0	20	$5R_2 + R_3$
*u	0	0	4	$\boxed{10}$	-6	0	20	
p	0	0	1,000	4,000	0	3	$-100{,}000$	$R_4 - 400R_3$

	x	y	s	t	u	p		
x	30	0	-24	0	6	0	180	$R_1/6$
y	0	15	9	0	-6	0	120	$R_2/3$
t	0	0	4	10	-6	0	20	$R_3/2$
p	0	0	-600	0	2,400	3	$-108{,}000$	$R_4/3$

This completes Phase I. We are not yet at the optimal solution, so after performing the simplifications indicated we proceed with Phase II.

	x	y	s	t	u	p		
x	5	0	−4	0	1	0	30	$R_1 + 2R_3$
y	0	5	3	0	−2	0	40	$2R_2 - 3R_3$
t	0	0	②	5	−3	0	10	
p	0	0	−200	0	800	1	−36,000	$R_4 + 100R_3$

	x	y	s	t	u	p	
x	5	0	0	10	−5	0	50
y	0	10	0	−15	5	0	50
s	0	0	2	5	−3	0	10
p	0	0	0	500	500	1	−35,000

The optimal solution is

$$x = 50/5 = 10, \ y = 50/10 = 5, \ p = -35{,}000, \text{ so } c = 35{,}000 \ (s = 5, t = 0, u = 0).$$

You should buy 10 packages from Wall-to-Wall Furniture and 5 from Acme Furniture, for a minimum cost of $35,000.

➡ **Before we go on...** The surplus variables in the preceding example represent pieces of furniture over and above the minimum requirements. The order you place will give you 50 extra tables ($s = 5$, but s was introduced after we divided the first inequality by 10, so the actual surplus is $10 \times 5 = 50$), the correct number of chairs ($t = 0$), and the correct number of computer desks ($u = 0$). ∎

The preceding LP problem is an example of a **standard minimization problem**—in a sense the opposite of a standard maximization problem: We are *minimizing* an objective function, where all the constraints have the form $Ax + By + Cz + \cdots \geq N$. We will discuss standard minimization problems more fully in Section 4.5, as well as another method of solving them.

FAQs

When to Switch to Phase II, Equality Constraints, and Troubleshooting

Q : *How do I know when to switch to Phase II?*

A : After each step, check the basic solution for starred rows. You are not ready to proceed with Phase II until all the stars are gone.

Q : *How do I deal with an equality constraint, such as $2x + 7y - z = 90$?*

A : Although we haven't given examples of equality constraints, they can be treated by the following trick: Replace an equality by two inequalities. For example, replace the equality $2x + 7y - z = 90$ by the two inequalities $2x + 7y - z \leq 90$ and $2x + 7y - z \geq 90$. A little thought will convince you that these two inequalities amount to the same thing as the original equality!

> **Q** : *What happens if it is impossible to choose a pivot using the instructions in Phase I?*
>
> **A** : In that case, the LP problem has no solution. In fact, the feasible region is empty. If it is impossible to choose a pivot in phase II, then the feasible region is unbounded and there is no optimal solution.

4.4 EXERCISES

▼ more advanced   ◆ challenging

T indicates exercises that should be solved using technology

1. Maximize $p = x + y$
subject to $x + 2y \geq 6$
$-x + y \leq 4$
$2x + y \leq 8$
$x \geq 0, y \geq 0.$ HINT [See Examples 1 and 2.]

2. Maximize $p = 3x + 2y$
subject to $x + 3y \geq 6$
$-x + y \leq 4$
$2x + y \leq 8$
$x \geq 0, y \geq 0.$ HINT [See Examples 1 and 2.]

3. Maximize $p = 12x + 10y$
subject to $x + y \leq 25$
$x \geq 10$
$-x + 2y \geq 0$
$x \geq 0, y \geq 0.$

4. Maximize $p = x + 2y$
subject to $x + y \leq 25$
$y \geq 10$
$2x - y \geq 0$
$x \geq 0, y \geq 0.$

5. Maximize $p = 2x + 5y + 3z$
subject to $x + y + z \leq 150$
$x + y + z \geq 100$
$x \geq 0, y \geq 0, z \geq 0.$

6. Maximize $p = 3x + 2y + 2z$
subject to $x + y + 2z \leq 38$
$2x + y + z \geq 24$
$x \geq 0, y \geq 0, z \geq 0.$

7. Maximize $p = 2x + 3y + z + 4w$
subject to $x + y + z + w \leq 40$
$2x + y - z - w \geq 10$
$x + y + z + w \geq 10$
$x \geq 0, y \geq 0, z \geq 0, w \geq 0.$

8. Maximize $p = 2x + 2y + z + 2w$
subject to $x + y + z + w \leq 50$
$2x + y - z - w \geq 10$
$x + y + z + w \geq 20$
$x \geq 0, y \geq 0, z \geq 0, w \geq 0.$

9. Minimize $c = 6x + 6y$
subject to $x + 2y \geq 20$
$2x + y \geq 20$
$x \geq 0, y \geq 0.$ HINT [See Example 3.]

10. Minimize $c = 3x + 2y$
subject to $x + 2y \geq 20$
$2x + y \geq 10$
$x \geq 0, y \geq 0.$ HINT [See Example 3.]

11. Minimize $c = 2x + y + 3z$
subject to $x + y + z \geq 100$
$2x + y \geq 50$
$y + z \geq 50$
$x \geq 0, y \geq 0, z \geq 0.$

12. Minimize $c = 2x + 2y + 3z$
subject to $x + z \geq 100$
$2x + y \geq 50$
$y + z \geq 50$
$x \geq 0, y \geq 0, z \geq 0.$

13. Minimize $c = 50x + 50y + 11z$
subject to $2x + z \geq 3$
$2x + y - z \geq 2$
$3x + y - z \leq 3$
$x \geq 0, y \geq 0, z \geq 0.$

14. Minimize $c = 50x + 11y + 50z$
subject to $3x + z \geq 8$
$3x + y - z \geq 6$
$4x + y - z \leq 8$
$x \geq 0, y \geq 0, z \geq 0.$

15. Minimize $c = x + y + z + w$
subject to $5x - y + w \geq 1,000$
$z + w \leq 2,000$
$x + y \leq 500$
$x \geq 0, y \geq 0, z \geq 0, w \geq 0.$

16. Minimize $c = 5x + y + z + w$
subject to $5x - y + w \geq 1,000$
$z + w \leq 2,000$
$x + y \leq 500$
$x \geq 0, y \geq 0, z \geq 0, w \geq 0.$

T *In Exercises 17–22, we suggest the use of technology. Round all answers to two decimal places.*

17. Maximize $p = 2x + 3y + 1.1z + 4w$
subject to
$$1.2x + y + z + \quad w \le 40.5$$
$$2.2x + y - z - \quad w \ge 10$$
$$1.2x + y + z + 1.2w \ge 10.5$$
$$x \ge 0, y \ge 0, z \ge 0, w \ge 0.$$

18. Maximize $p = 2.2x + 2y + 1.1z + 2w$
subject to
$$x + 1.5y + 1.5z + \quad w \le 50.5$$
$$2x + 1.5y - \quad z - \quad w \ge 10$$
$$x + 1.5y + \quad z + 1.5w \ge 21$$
$$x \ge 0, y \ge 0, z \ge 0, w \ge 0.$$

19. Minimize $c = 2.2x + y + 3.3z$
subject to
$$x + 1.5y + 1.2z \ge 100$$
$$2x + 1.5y \quad\quad \ge 50$$
$$1.5y + 1.1z \ge 50$$
$$x \ge 0, y \ge 0, z \ge 0.$$

20. Minimize $c = 50.3x + 10.5y + 50.3z$
subject to
$$3.1x \quad\quad + 1.1z \ge 28$$
$$3.1x + y - 1.1z \ge 23$$
$$4.2x + y - 1.1z \ge 28$$
$$x \ge 0, y \ge 0, z \ge 0.$$

21. Minimize $c = 1.1x + y + 1.5z - w$
subject to
$$5.12x - y \quad\quad + w \le 1,000$$
$$z + w \ge 2,000$$
$$1.22x + y \quad\quad \le 500$$
$$x \ge 0, y \ge 0, z \ge 0, w \ge 0.$$

22. Minimize $c = 5.45x + y + 1.5z + w$
subject to
$$5.12x - y \quad\quad + w \ge 1,000$$
$$z + w \ge 2,000$$
$$1.12x + y \quad\quad \le 500$$
$$x \ge 0, y \ge 0, z \ge 0, w \ge 0.$$

APPLICATIONS

23. Agriculture[29] Your small farm encompasses 100 acres, and you are planning to grow tomatoes, lettuce, and carrots in the coming planting season. Fertilizer costs per acre are: $5 for tomatoes, $4 for lettuce, and $2 for carrots. Based on past experience, you estimate that each acre of tomatoes will require an average of 4 hours of labor per week, while tending to lettuce and carrots will each require an average of 2 hours per week. You estimate a profit of $2,000 for each acre of tomatoes, $1,500 for each acre of lettuce and $500 for each acre of carrots. You would like to spend at least $400 on fertilizer (your niece owns the company that manufactures it) and your farm laborers can supply up to 500 hours per week. How many acres of each crop should you plant to maximize total profits? In this event, will you be using all 100 acres of your farm? HINT [See Example 3.]

24. Agriculture[30] Your farm encompasses 900 acres, and you are planning to grow soybeans, corn, and wheat in the coming planting season. Fertilizer costs per acre are: $5 for soybeans, $2 for corn, and $1 for wheat. You estimate that each acre of soybeans will require an average of 5 hours of labor per week, while tending to corn and wheat will each require an average of 2 hours per week. Based on past yields and current market prices, you estimate a profit of $3,000 for each acre of soybeans, $2,000 for each acre of corn, and $1,000 for each acre of wheat. You can afford to spend no more than $3,000 on fertilizer, but your labor union contract stipulates at least 2,000 hours per week of labor. How many acres of each crop should you plant to maximize total profits? In this event, will you be using more than 2,000 hours of labor?

25. Politics The political pollster Canter is preparing for a national election. It would like to poll at least 1,500 Democrats and 1,500 Republicans. Each mailing to the East Coast gets responses from 100 Democrats and 50 Republicans. Each mailing to the Midwest gets responses from 100 Democrats and 100 Republicans. And each mailing to the West Coast gets responses from 50 Democrats and 100 Republicans. Mailings to the East Coast cost $40 each to produce and mail, mailings to the Midwest cost $60 each, and mailings to the West Coast cost $50 each. How many mailings should Canter send to each area of the country to get the responses it needs at the least possible cost? What will it cost?

26. Purchasing Bingo's Copy Center needs to buy white paper and yellow paper. Bingo's can buy from three suppliers. Harvard Paper sells a package of 20 reams of white and 10 reams of yellow for $60, Yale Paper sells a package of 10 reams of white and 10 reams of yellow for $40, and Dartmouth Paper sells a package of 10 reams of white and 20 reams of yellow for $50. If Bingo's needs 350 reams of white and 400 reams of yellow, how many packages should it buy from each supplier to minimize the cost? What is the least possible cost?

27. Resource Allocation Succulent Citrus produces orange juice and orange concentrate. This year the company anticipates a demand of at least 10,000 quarts of orange juice and 1,000 quarts of orange concentrate. Each quart of orange juice requires 10 oranges, and each quart of concentrate requires 50 oranges. The company also anticipates using at least 200,000 oranges for these products. Each quart of orange juice costs the company 50¢ to produce, and each quart of concentrate costs $2.00 to produce. How many quarts of each product should Succulent Citrus produce to meet the demand and minimize total costs?

28. Resource Allocation Fancy Pineapple produces pineapple juice and canned pineapple rings. This year the company anticipates a demand of at least 10,000 pints of pineapple juice and 1,000 cans of pineapple rings. Each pint of pineapple juice requires 2 pineapples, and each can of pineapple rings requires 1 pineapple. The company anticipates using at least 20,000 pineapples for these products. Each pint of pineapple juice

---

[29] Compare Exercise 27 in Section 4.3.

[30] Compare Exercise 28 in Section 4.3.

costs the company 20¢ to produce, and each can of pineapple rings costs 50¢ to produce. How many pints of pineapple juice and cans of pineapple rings should Fancy Pineapple produce to meet the demand and minimize total costs?

29. *Music CD Sales* In the year 2000, industry revenues from sales of recorded music amounted to $3.6 billion for rock music, $1.8 billion for rap music, and $0.4 billion for classical music.[31] You would like the selection of music in your music store to reflect, in part, this national trend, so you have decided to stock at least twice as many rock music CDs as rap CDs. Your store has an estimated capacity of 20,000 CDs, and, as a classical music devotee, you would like to stock at least 5,000 classical CDs. Rock music CDs sell for $12 on average, rap CDs for $15, and classical CDs for $12. How many of each type of CD should you stock to get the maximum retail value?

30. *Music CD Sales* Your music store's main competitor, Nuttal Hip Hop Classic Store, also wishes to stock at most 20,000 CDs, with at least half as many rap CDs as rock CDs and at least 2,000 classical CDs. It anticipates an average sale price of $15/rock CD, $10/rap CD and $10/classical CD. How many of each type of CD should it stock to get the maximum retail value, and what is the maximum retail value?

31. ☐ *Nutrition* Each serving of Gerber Mixed Cereal for Baby contains 60 calories and no vitamin C. Each serving of Gerber Mango Tropical Fruit Dessert contains 80 calories and 45 percent of the U.S. Recommended Daily Allowance (RDA) of vitamin C for infants. Each serving of Gerber Apple Banana Juice contains 60 calories and 120 percent of the RDA of vitamin C for infants.[32] The cereal costs 10¢/serving, the dessert costs 53¢/serving, and the juice costs 27¢/serving. If you want to provide your child with at least 120 calories and at least 120 percent of the RDA of vitamin C, how can you do so at the least cost?

32. ☐ *Nutrition* Each serving of Gerber Mixed Cereal for Baby contains 60 calories, no vitamin C, and 11 grams of carbohydrates. Each serving of Gerber Mango Tropical Fruit Dessert contains 80 calories, 45 percent of the RDA of vitamin C for infants, and 21 grams of carbohydrates. Each serving of Gerber Apple Banana Juice contains 60 calories, 120 percent of the RDA of vitamin C for infants, and 15 grams of carbohydrates.[33] Assume that the cereal costs 11¢/serving, the dessert costs 50¢/serving, and the juice costs 30¢/serving. If you want to provide your child with at least 180 calories, at least 120 percent of the RDA of vitamin C, and at least 37 grams of carbohydrates, how can you do so at the least cost?

33. ☐ *Purchasing* Cheapskate Electronics Store needs to update its inventory of stereos, TVs, and DVD players. There are

three suppliers it can buy from: Nadir offers a bundle consisting of 5 stereos, 10 TVs, and 15 DVD players for $3,000. Blunt offers a bundle consisting of 10 stereos, 10 TVs, and 10 DVD players for $4,000. Sonny offers a bundle consisting of 15 stereos, 10 TVs, and 10 DVD players for $5,000. Cheapskate Electronics needs at least 150 stereos, 200 TVs, and 150 DVD players. How can it update its inventory at the least possible cost? What is the least possible cost?

34. ☐ *Purchasing* Federal Rent-a-Car is putting together a new fleet. It is considering package offers from three car manufacturers. Fred Motors is offering 5 small cars, 5 medium cars, and 10 large cars for $500,000. Admiral Motors is offering 5 small, 10 medium, and 5 large cars for $400,000. Chrysalis is offering 10 small, 5 medium, and 5 large cars for $300,000. Federal would like to buy at least 550 small cars, at least 500 medium cars, and at least 550 large cars. How many packages should it buy from each car maker to keep the total cost as small as possible? What will be the total cost?

☐ ***Creatine Supplements*** *Exercises 35 and 36 are based on the following data on four bodybuilding supplements. (Figures shown correspond to a single serving.)[34]*

	Creatine (g)	Carbohydrates (g)	Taurine (g)	Alpha Lipoic Acid (mg)	Cost ($)
Cell-Tech® (MuscleTech)	10	75	2	200	2.20
RiboForce HP® (EAS)	5	15	1	0	1.60
Creatine Transport® (Kaizen)	5	35	1	100	0.60
Pre-Load Creatine (Optimum)	6	35	1	25	0.50

35. (Compare Exercise 29 in Section 4.2.) You are thinking of combining Cell-Tech, RiboForce HP, and Creatine Transport to obtain a 10-day supply that provides at least 80 grams of creatine and at least 10 grams of taurine, but no more than 750 grams of carbohydrates and 1,000 milligrams of alpha lipoic acid. How many servings of each supplement should you combine to meet your specifications for the least cost?

36. (Compare Exercise 30 in Section 4.2.) You are thinking of combining RiboForce HP, Creatine Transport, and Pre-Load Creatine to obtain a 10-day supply that provides at least 80 grams of creatine and at least 10 grams of taurine, but no more than 600 grams of carbohydrates and 2,000 milligrams of alpha lipoic acid. How many servings of each supplement should you combine to meet your specifications for the least cost?

37. ▼ *Subsidies* The Miami Beach City Council has offered to subsidize hotel development in Miami Beach, and it is hoping for at least two hotels with a total capacity of at least 1,400.

[31]"Rap" includes "Hip Hop." Revenues are based on total manufacturers' shipments at suggested retail prices and are rounded to the nearest $0.1 billion. Source: Recording Industry Association of America, www.riaa.com, March 2002.

[32] Source: Nutrition information supplied by Gerber.
[33]Ibid.

[34] Source: Nutritional information supplied by the manufacturers (www.netrition.com). Cost per serving is approximate.

Suppose that you are a developer interested in taking advantage of this offer by building a small group of hotels in Miami Beach. You are thinking of three prototypes: a convention-style hotel with 500 rooms costing $100 million, a vacation-style hotel with 200 rooms costing $20 million, and a small motel with 50 rooms costing $4 million. The City Council will approve your plans, provided you build at least one convention-style hotel and no more than two small motels.

a. How many of each type of hotel should you build to satisfy the city council's wishes and stipulations while minimizing your total cost?

b. Now assume that the city council will give developers 20 percent of the cost of building new hotels in Miami Beach, up to $50 million.[35] Will the city's $50 million subsidy be sufficient to cover 20 percent of your total costs?

38. ▼ *Subsidies* Refer back to the preceding exercise. You are about to begin the financial arrangements for your new hotels when the city council informs you that it has changed its mind and now requires at least two vacation-style hotels and no more than four small motels.

a. How many of each type of hotel should you build to satisfy the city council's wishes and stipulations while minimizing your total costs?

b. Will the city's $50 million subsidy limit still be sufficient to cover 20 percent of your total costs?

39. ▼ *Transportation Scheduling* We return to your exploits coordinating distribution for the Tubular Ride Boogie Board Company.[36] You will recall that the company has manufacturing plants in Tucson, Arizona and Toronto, Ontario, and you have been given the job of coordinating distribution of their latest model, the Gladiator, to their outlets in Honolulu and Venice Beach. The Tucson plant can manufacture up to 620 boards per week, while the Toronto plant, beset by labor disputes, can produce no more than 410 Gladiator boards per week. The outlet in Honolulu orders 500 Gladiator boards per week, while Venice Beach orders 530 boards per week. Transportation costs are as follows: Tucson to Honolulu: $10/board; Tucson to Venice Beach: $5/board; Toronto to Honolulu: $20/board; Toronto to Venice Beach: $10/board. Your manager has said that you are to be sure to fill all orders and ship the boogie boards at a minimum total transportation cost. How will you do it?

40. ▼ *Transportation Scheduling* In the situation described in the preceding exercise, you have just been notified that workers at the Toronto boogie board plant have gone on strike, resulting in a total work stoppage. You are to come up with a revised delivery schedule by tomorrow with the understanding that the Tucson plant can push production to a maximum of 1,000 boards per week. What should you do?

41. ▼ *Finance* Senator Porkbarrel habitually overdraws his three bank accounts, at the Congressional Integrity Bank, Citizens' Trust, and Checks R Us. There are no penalties because the overdrafts are subsidized by the taxpayer. The Senate Ethics Committee tends to let slide irregular banking activities as long as they are not flagrant. At the moment (due to Congress' preoccupation with a Supreme Court nominee), a total overdraft of up to $10,000 will be overlooked. Porkbarrel's conscience makes him hesitate to overdraw accounts at banks whose names include expressions like "integrity" and "citizens' trust." The effect is that his overdrafts at the first two banks combined amount to no more than one-quarter of the total. On the other hand, the financial officers at Integrity Bank, aware that Senator Porkbarrel is a member of the Senate Banking Committee, "suggest" that he overdraw at least $2,500 from their bank. Find the amount he should overdraw from each bank in order to avoid investigation by the Ethics Committee and overdraw his account at Integrity by as much as his sense of guilt will allow.

42. ▼ *Scheduling* Because Joe Slim's brother was recently elected to the State Senate, Joe's financial advisement concern, Inside Information Inc., has been doing a booming trade, even though the financial counseling he offers is quite worthless. (None of his seasoned clients pays the slightest attention to his advice.) Slim charges different hourly rates to different categories of individuals: $5,000/hour for private citizens, $50,000/hour for corporate executives, and $10,000/hour for presidents of universities. Due to his taste for leisure, he feels that he can spend no more than 40 hours/week in consultation. On the other hand, Slim feels that it would be best for his intellect were he to devote at least 10 hours of consultation each week to university presidents. However, Slim always feels somewhat uncomfortable dealing with academics, so he would prefer to spend no more than half his consultation time with university presidents. Furthermore, he likes to think of himself as representing the interests of the common citizen, so he wishes to offer at least 2 more hours of his time each week to private citizens than to corporate executives and university presidents combined. Given all these restrictions, how many hours each week should he spend with each type of client in order to maximize his income?

43. ⬛ ▼ *Transportation Scheduling* Your publishing company is about to start a promotional blitz for its new book, *Physics for the Liberal Arts*. You have 20 salespeople stationed in Chicago and 10 in Denver. You would like to fly at least 10 into Los Angeles and at least 15 into New York. A round-trip plane flight from Chicago to LA costs $195;[37] from Chicago to NY costs $182; from Denver to LA costs $395; and from Denver to

[35] The Miami Beach City Council made such an offer in 1993. (*Chicago Tribune*, June 20, 1993, Section 7, p.8).

[36] See Exercise 26 in Section 2.3 and also Exercise 41 in Section 4.3. This time, we will use the simplex method to solve the version of this problem we first considered in the chapter on systems of equations.

[37] Prices from Travelocity, at www.travelocity.com, for the week of June 3, 2002, as of May 5, 2002.

NY costs $166. How many salespeople should you fly from each of Chicago and Denver to each of LA and NY to spend the least amount on plane flights?

44. 🔲 ▼ *Transportation Scheduling* Repeat Exercise 43, but now suppose that you would like at least 15 salespeople in Los Angeles.

45. 🔲 ▼ *Hospital Staffing* As the staff director of a new hospital, you are planning to hire cardiologists, rehabilitation specialists, and infectious disease specialists. According to recent data, each cardiology case averages $12,000 in revenue, each physical rehabilitation case $19,000, and each infectious disease case, $14,000.[38] You judge that each specialist you employ will expand the hospital caseload by about 10 patients per week. You already have 3 cardiologists on staff, and the hospital is equipped to admit up to 200 patients per week. Based on past experience, each cardiologist and rehabilitation specialist brings in one government research grant per year, while each infectious disease specialist brings in three. Your board of directors would like to see a total of at least 30 grants per year and would like your weekly revenue to be as large as possible. How many of each kind of specialist should you hire?

46. 🔲 ▼ *Hospital Staffing* Referring to Exercise 45, you completely misjudged the number of patients each type of specialist would bring to the hospital per week. It turned out that each cardiologist brought in 120 new patients per *year*, each rehabilitation specialist brought in 90 per year, and each infectious disease specialist brought in 70 per year.[39] It also turned out that your hospital could deal with no more than 1,960 new patients per year. Repeat the preceding exercise in the light of this corrected data.

---

[38] These (rounded) figures are based on an Illinois survey of 1.3 million hospital admissions (*Chicago Tribune,* March 29, 1993, Section 4, p.1). Source: Lutheran General Health System, Argus Associates, Inc.

[39] These (rounded) figures were obtained from the survey referenced in the preceding exercise by dividing the average hospital revenue per physician by the revenue per case.

COMMUNICATION AND REASONING EXERCISES

47. Explain the need for Phase I in a nonstandard LP problem.

48. Explain the need for Phase II in a nonstandard LP problem.

49. Explain briefly why we would need to use Phase I in solving a linear programming problem with the constraint $x + 2y - z \geq 3$.

50. Which rows do we star, and why?

51. Consider the following linear programming problem:

$$\begin{aligned}
\text{Maximize} \quad & p = x + y \\
\text{subject to} \quad & x - 2y \geq 0 \\
& 2x + y \leq 10 \\
& x \geq 0, y \geq 0.
\end{aligned}$$

This problem

(A) must be solved using the techniques of Section 4.4.
(B) must be solved using the techniques of Section 4.3.
(C) can be solved using the techniques of either section.

52. Consider the following linear programming problem:

$$\begin{aligned}
\text{Maximize} \quad & p = x + y \\
\text{subject to} \quad & x - 2y \geq 1 \\
& 2x + y \leq 10 \\
& x \geq 0, y \geq 0.
\end{aligned}$$

This problem

(A) must be solved using the techniques of Section 4.4.
(B) must be solved using the techniques of Section 4.3.
(C) can be solved using the techniques of either section.

53. ▼ Find a linear programming problem in three variables that requires one pivot in Phase I.

54. ▼ Find a linear programming problem in three variables that requires two pivots in Phase I.

55. ▼ Find a linear programming problem in two or three variables with no optimal solution, and show what happens when you try to solve it using the simplex method.

56. ▼ Find a linear programming problem in two or three variables with more than one optimal solution, and investigate which solution is found by the simplex method.

4.5 The Simplex Method and Duality

We mentioned **standard minimization problems** in the last section. These problems have the following form.

Standard Minimization Problem

A **standard minimization problem** is an LP problem in which we are required to *minimize* (not maximize) a linear objective function

$$c = as + bt + cu + \cdots$$

of the variables $s, t, u, \ldots$ (in this section, we will always use the letters $s, t, u, \ldots$ for the unknowns in a standard minimization problem) subject to the constraints

$$s \geq 0, t \geq 0, u \geq 0, \ldots$$

and further constraints of the form

$$As + Bt + Cu + \cdots \geq N$$

where $A, B, C, \ldots$ and N are numbers with N non-negative.

A **standard linear programming problem** is an LP problem that is either a standard maximization problem or a standard minimization problem. An LP problem satisfies the **non-negative objective condition** if all the coefficients in the objective function are non-negative.

Quick Examples

Standard Minimization and Maximization Problems

1. Minimize $\quad c = 2s + 3t + 3u$
   subject to $\quad 2s \qquad + \: u \geq 10$ This is a standard minimization problem
   $\qquad\qquad\quad\; s + 3t - 6u \geq 5$ satisfying the non-negative objective
   $\qquad\qquad\quad\; s \geq 0, t \geq 0, u \geq 0.$ condition.

2. Maximize $\quad p = 2x + 3y + 3z$
   subject to $\quad 2x \qquad + \: z \leq 7$ This is a standard maximization problem
   $\qquad\qquad\quad\; x + 3y - 6z \leq 6$ satisfying the non-negative objective
   $\qquad\qquad\quad\; x \geq 0, y \geq 0, z \geq 0.$ condition.

3. Minimize $\quad c = 2s - 3t + 3u$
   subject to $\quad 2s \qquad + \: u \geq 10$ This is a standard minimization problem
   $\qquad\qquad\quad\; s + 3t - 6u \geq 5$ that does *not* satisfy the non-negative
   $\qquad\qquad\quad\; s \geq 0, t \geq 0, u \geq 0.$ objective condition.

We saw a way of solving minimization problems in Section 4.4, but a mathematically elegant relationship between maximization and minimization problems gives us another way of solving minimization problems that satisfy the non-negative objective condition. This relationship is called **duality**.

To describe duality, we must first represent an LP problem by a matrix. This matrix is *not* the first tableau but something simpler: Pretend you forgot all about slack variables and also forgot to change the signs of the objective function.[40] As an example, consider the following two standard* problems.

✱ NOTE Although duality does not require the problems to be standard, it does require them to be written in so-called *standard form*: In the case of a maximization problem all constraints need to be (re)written using $\leq$, while for a minimization problem all constraints need to be (re)written using $\geq$. It is least confusing to stick with standard problems, which is what we will do in this section.

Problem 1

$$\text{Maximize} \quad p = 20x + 20y + 50z$$
$$\text{subject to} \quad 2x + \; y + 3z \leq 2{,}000$$
$$\qquad\qquad\quad\; x + 2y + 4z \leq 3{,}000$$
$$\qquad\qquad\quad\; x \geq 0, y \geq 0, z \geq 0.$$

---

[40] Forgetting these things is exactly what happens to many students under test conditions!

We represent this problem by the matrix

$$\begin{bmatrix} 2 & 1 & 3 & | & 2{,}000 \\ 1 & 2 & 4 & | & 3{,}000 \\ 20 & 20 & 50 & | & 0 \end{bmatrix} \quad \begin{matrix} \text{Constraint 1} \\ \text{Constraint 2} \\ \text{Objective} \end{matrix}$$

Notice that the coefficients of the objective function go in the bottom row, and we place a zero in the bottom right corner.

Problem 2 (from Example 3 in Section 4.4)

$$\begin{aligned} \text{Minimize} \quad & c = 2{,}000s + 3{,}000t \\ \text{subject to} \quad & 2s + t \ge 20 \\ & s + 2t \ge 20 \\ & 3s + 4t \ge 50 \\ & s \ge 0, t \ge 0. \end{aligned}$$

Problem 2 is represented by

$$\begin{bmatrix} 2 & 1 & | & 20 \\ 1 & 2 & | & 20 \\ 3 & 4 & | & 50 \\ 2{,}000 & 3{,}000 & | & 0 \end{bmatrix} \quad \begin{matrix} \text{Constraint 1} \\ \text{Constraint 2} \\ \text{Constraint 3} \\ \text{Objective} \end{matrix}$$

These two problems are related: The matrix for Problem 1 is the transpose of the matrix for Problem 2. (Recall that the transpose of a matrix is obtained by writing its rows as columns; see Section 3.1.) When we have a pair of LP problems related in this way, we say that the two are *dual* LP problems.

Dual Linear Programming Problems

Two LP problems, one a maximization and one a minimization problem, are **dual** if the matrix that represents one is the transpose of the matrix that represents the other.

Finding the Dual of a Given Problem

Given an LP problem, we find its dual as follows:

1. Represent the problem as a matrix (see above).
2. Take the transpose of the matrix.
3. Write down the dual, which is the LP problem corresponding to the new matrix. If the original problem was a maximization problem, its dual will be a minimization problem, and vice versa.

The original problem is called the **primal problem**, and its dual is referred to as the **dual problem**.

Quick Examples

Primal problem

$$\begin{aligned} \text{Minimize} \quad & c = s + 2t \\ \text{subject to} \quad & 5s + 2t \ge 60 \\ & 3s + 4t \ge 80 \\ & s + t \ge 20 \\ & s \ge 0, t \ge 0. \end{aligned} \quad \overset{1}{\to} \quad \begin{bmatrix} 5 & 2 & 60 \\ 3 & 4 & 80 \\ 1 & 1 & 20 \\ 1 & 2 & 0 \end{bmatrix}$$

$$\begin{array}{c} \mathbf{2} \\ \rightarrow \end{array} \begin{bmatrix} 5 & 3 & 1 & 1 \\ 2 & 4 & 1 & 2 \\ 60 & 80 & 20 & 0 \end{bmatrix} \qquad \begin{array}{c} \mathbf{3} \\ \rightarrow \end{array}$$

Dual problem

Maximize $p = 60x + 80y + 20z$
subject to $5x + 3y + z \le 1$
$2x + 4y + z \le 2$
$x \ge 0, y \ge 0, z \ge 0.$

The following theorem justifies what we have been doing, and says that solving the dual problem of an LP problem is equivalent to solving the original problem.

Fundamental Theorem of Duality

a. If an LP problem has an optimal solution, then so does its dual. Moreover, the primal problem and the dual problem have the same optimal value for their objective functions.

b. Contained in the final tableau of the simplex method applied to an LP problem is the solution to its dual problem: It is given by the bottom entries in the columns associated with the slack variables, divided by the entry under the objective variable.

The theorem[41] gives us an alternative way of solving minimization problems that satisfy the non-negative objective condition. Let's illustrate by solving Problem 2 above.

EXAMPLE 1 Solving by Duality

Minimize $c = 2,000s + 3,000t$
subject to $2s + t \ge 20$
$s + 2t \ge 20$
$3s + 4t \ge 50$
$s \ge 0, t \ge 0.$

Solution

Step 1 *Find the dual problem.* Write the primal problem in matrix form and take the transpose:

$$\begin{bmatrix} 2 & 1 & 20 \\ 1 & 2 & 20 \\ 3 & 4 & 50 \\ 2,000 & 3,000 & 0 \end{bmatrix} \rightarrow \begin{bmatrix} 2 & 1 & 3 & 2,000 \\ 1 & 2 & 4 & 3,000 \\ 20 & 20 & 50 & 0 \end{bmatrix}.$$

The dual problem is:

Maximize $p = 20x + 20y + 50z$
subject to $2x + y + 3z \le 2,000$
$x + 2y + 4z \le 3,000$
$x \ge 0, y \ge 0, z \ge 0.$

---

[41] The proof of the theorem is beyond the scope of this book but can be found in a textbook devoted to linear programming, like *Linear Programming* by Vašek Chvátal (San Francisco: W. H. Freeman and Co., 1983) which has a particularly well-motivated discussion.

Step 2 *Use the simplex method to solve the dual problem.* Because we have a standard maximization problem, we do not have to worry about Phase I but go straight to Phase II.

	x	y	z	s	t	p	
s	2	1	③	1	0	0	2,000
t	1	2	4	0	1	0	3,000
p	−20	−20	−50	0	0	1	0

	x	y	z	s	t	p	
z	2	1	3	1	0	0	2,000
t	−5	②	0	−4	3	0	1,000
p	40	−10	0	50	0	3	100,000

	x	y	z	s	t	p	
z	9	0	6	6	−3	0	3,000
y	−5	2	0	−4	3	0	1,000
p	15	0	0	30	15	3	105,000

Note that the maximum value of the objective function is $p = 105,000/3 = 35,000$. By the theorem, this is also the optimal value of c in the primal problem!

Step 3 *Read off the solution to the primal problem by dividing the bottom entries in the columns associated with the slack variables by the entry in the p column.* Here is the final tableau again with the entries in question highlighted.

	x	y	z	s	t	p	
z	9	0	6	6	−3	0	3,000
y	−5	2	0	−4	3	0	1,000
p	15	0	0	30	15	3	105,000

The solution to the primal problem is

$$s = 30/3 = 10, t = 15/3 = 5, c = 105,000/3 = 35,000.$$

(Compare this with the method we used to solve Example 3 in the preceding section. Which method seems more efficient?)

➡ **Before we go on...** Can you now see the reason for using the variable names $s, t, u, \ldots$ in standard minimization problems? ■

Q: *Is the theorem also useful for solving problems that do not satisfy the non-negative objective condition?*

A: Consider a standard minimization problem that does not satisfy the non-negative objective condition, such as

Minimize $c = 2s - t$
subject to $2s + 3t \geq 2$
$s + 2t \geq 2$
$s \geq 0, t \geq 0.$

Its dual would be

Maximize $p = 2x + 2y$
subject to $2x + \ y \le 2$
$\qquad\qquad 3x + 2y \le -1$
$\qquad\qquad x \ge 0, y \ge 0.$

This is not a standard maximization problem because the right-hand side of the second constraint is negative. In general, if a problem does not satisfy the non-negative condition, its dual is not standard. Therefore, to solve the dual by the simplex method will require using Phase I as well as Phase II, and we may as well just solve the primal problem that way to begin with. Thus, duality helps us solve problems only when the primal problem satisfies the non-negative objective condition.

In many economic applications, the solution to the dual problem also gives us useful information about the primal problem, as we will see in the following example.

EXAMPLE 2 Shadow Costs

You are trying to decide how many vitamin pills to take. SuperV brand vitamin pills each contain 2 milligrams of vitamin X, 1 milligram of vitamin Y, and 1 milligram of vitamin Z. Topper brand vitamin pills each contain 1 milligram of vitamin X, 1 milligram of vitamin Y, and 2 milligrams of vitamin Z. You want to take enough pills daily to get at least 12 milligrams of vitamin X, 10 milligrams of vitamin Y, and 12 milligrams of vitamin Z. However, SuperV pills cost 4¢ each and Toppers cost 3¢ each, and you would like to minimize the total cost of your daily dosage. How many of each brand of pill should you take? How would changing your daily vitamin requirements affect your minimum cost?

Solution This is a straightforward minimization problem. The unknowns are

s = number of SuperV brand pills
t = number of Topper brand pills.

The linear programming problem is

Minimize $c = 4s + 3t$
subject to $2s + \ t \ge 12$
$\qquad\qquad s + \ t \ge 10$
$\qquad\qquad s + 2t \ge 12$
$\qquad\qquad s \ge 0, t \ge 0.$

We solve this problem by using the simplex method on its dual, which is

Maximize $p = 12x + 10y + 12z$
subject to $2x + y + \ z \le 4$
$\qquad\qquad x + y + 2z \le 3$
$\qquad\qquad x \ge 0, y \ge 0, z \ge 0.$

After pivoting three times, we arrive at the final tableau:

	x	y	z	s	t	p	
x	6	0	−6	6	−6	0	6
y	0	1	3	−1	2	0	2
p	0	0	6	2	8	1	32

Therefore, the answer to the original problem is that you should take two SuperV vitamin pills and eight Toppers at a cost of 32¢ per day.

Now, the key to answering the last question, which asks you to determine how changing your daily vitamin requirements would affect your minimum cost, is to look at the solution to the dual problem. From the tableau we see that $x = 1$, $y = 2$, and $z = 0$. To see what x, y, and z might tell us about the original problem, let's look at their units. In the inequality $2x + y + z \leq 4$, the coefficient 2 of x has units "mg of vitamin X/SuperV pill," and the 4 on the right-hand side has units "¢/SuperV pill." For $2x$ to have the same units as the 4 on the right-hand side, x must have units "¢/mg of vitamin X." Similarly, y must have units "¢/mg of vitamin Y" and z must have units "¢/mg of vitamin Z." One can show (although we will not do it here) that x gives the amount that would be added to the minimum cost for each increase* of 1 milligram of vitamin X in our daily requirement. For example, if we were to increase our requirement from 12 milligrams to 14 milligrams, an increase of 2 milligrams, the minimum cost would change by $2x = 2$¢, from 32¢ to 34¢. (Try it; you'll end up taking four SuperV pills and six Toppers.) Similarly, each increase of 1 milligram of vitamin Y in the requirements would increase the cost by $y = 2$¢. These costs are called the **marginal costs** or the **shadow costs** of the vitamins.

What about $z = 0$? The shadow cost of vitamin Z is 0¢/mg, meaning that you can increase your requirement of vitamin Z without changing your cost. In fact, the solution $s = 2$ and $t = 8$ provides you with 18 milligrams of vitamin Z, so you can increase the required amount of vitamin Z up to 18 milligrams without changing the solution at all.

We can also interpret the shadow costs as the effective cost to you of each milligram of each vitamin in the optimal solution. You are paying 1¢/milligram of vitamin X, 2¢/milligram of vitamin Y, and getting the vitamin Z for free. This gives a total cost of $1 \times 12 + 2 \times 10 + 0 \times 12 = 32$¢, as we know. Again, if you change your requirements slightly, these are the amounts you will pay per milligram of each vitamin.

---

*To be scrupulously correct, this works only for relatively small changes in the requirements, not necessarily for very large ones.

Game Theory

We return to a topic we discussed in Section 3.4: solving two-person zero-sum games. In that section, we described how to solve games that could be reduced to 2×2 games or smaller. It turns out that we can solve larger games using linear programming and duality. We summarize the procedure, work through an example, and then discuss why it works.

Solving a Matrix Game

Step 1 Reduce the payoff matrix by dominance.

Step 2 Add a fixed number k to each of the entries so that they all become nonnegative and no column is all zero.

Step 3 Write 1s to the right of and below the matrix, and then write down the associated standard maximization problem. Solve this primal problem using the simplex method.

Step 4 Find the optimal strategies and the expected value as follows:

Column Strategy

1. Express the solution to the primal problem as a column vector.
2. Normalize by dividing each entry of the solution vector by p (which is also the sum of all the entries).
3. Insert zeros in positions corresponding to the columns deleted during reduction.

Row Strategy

1. Express the solution to the dual problem as a row vector.
2. Normalize by dividing each entry by p, which will once again be the sum of all the entries.
3. Insert zeros in positions corresponding to the rows deleted during reduction.

Value of the Game: $e = \dfrac{1}{p} - k$

EXAMPLE 3 **Restaurant Inspector**

You manage two restaurants, Tender Steaks Inn (TSI) and Break for a Steak (BFS). Even though you run the establishments impeccably, the Department of Health has been sending inspectors to your restaurants on a daily basis and fining you for minor infractions. You've found that you can head off a fine if you're present, but you can cover only one restaurant at a time. The Department of Health, on the other hand, has two inspectors, who sometimes visit the same restaurant and sometimes split up, one to each restaurant. The average fines you have been getting are shown in the following matrix.

		Health Inspectors		
		Both at BFS	**Both at TSI**	**One at Each**
You go to	**TSI**	$8,000	0	$2,000
	BFS	0	$10,000	$4,000

How should you choose which restaurant to visit to minimize your expected fine?

Solution This matrix is not quite the payoff matrix because fines, being penalties, should be negative payoffs. Thus, the payoff matrix is the following:

$$P = \begin{bmatrix} -8,000 & 0 & -2,000 \\ 0 & -10,000 & -4,000 \end{bmatrix}.$$

We follow the steps above to solve the game using the simplex method.

Step 1 There are no dominated rows or columns, so this game does not reduce.

Step 2 We add $k = 10,000$ to each entry so that none are negative, getting the following new matrix (with no zero column):

$$\begin{bmatrix} 2,000 & 10,000 & 8,000 \\ 10,000 & 0 & 6,000 \end{bmatrix}.$$

Step 3 We write 1s to the right and below this matrix:

$$\begin{bmatrix} 2{,}000 & 10{,}000 & 8{,}000 & 1 \\ 10{,}000 & 0 & 6{,}000 & 1 \\ 1 & 1 & 1 & 0 \end{bmatrix}.$$

The corresponding standard maximization problem is the following:

Maximize $p = x + y + z$
subject to $2{,}000x + 10{,}000y + 8{,}000z \le 1$
                $10{,}000x \qquad\qquad + 6{,}000z \le 1$
                $x \ge 0,\, y \ge 0,\, z \ge 0.$

Step 4 We use the simplex method to solve this problem. After pivoting twice, we arrive at the final tableau:

	x	y	z	s	t	p	
y	0	50,000	34,000	5	−1	0	4
x	10,000	0	6,000	0	1	0	1
p	0	0	14,000	5	4	50,000	9

Column Strategy The solution to the primal problem is

$$\begin{bmatrix} x \\ y \\ z \end{bmatrix} = \begin{bmatrix} \frac{1}{10{,}000} \\ \frac{4}{50{,}000} \\ 0 \end{bmatrix}.$$

We divide each entry by $p = 9/50{,}000$, which is also the sum of the entries. This gives the optimal column strategy:

$$C = \begin{bmatrix} \frac{5}{9} \\ \frac{4}{9} \\ 0 \end{bmatrix}.$$

Thus, the inspectors' optimal strategy is to stick together, visiting BFS with probability 5/9 and TSI with probability 4/9.

Row Strategy The solution to the dual problem is

$$[s \quad t] = \begin{bmatrix} \dfrac{5}{50{,}000} & \dfrac{4}{50{,}000} \end{bmatrix}.$$

Once again, we divide by $p = 9/50{,}000$ to find the optimal row strategy:

$$R = \begin{bmatrix} \dfrac{5}{9} & \dfrac{4}{9} \end{bmatrix}.$$

Thus, you should visit TSI with probability 5/9 and BFS with probability 4/9.

Value of the Game Your expected average fine is

$$e = \frac{1}{p} - k = \frac{50{,}000}{9} - 10{,}000 = -\frac{40{,}000}{9} \approx -\$4{,}444.$$

➡ **Before we go on...** We owe you an explanation of why the procedure we used in Example 3 works. The main point is to understand how we turn a game into a linear programming problem. It's not hard to see that adding a fixed number k to all the payoffs will change only the payoff, increasing it by k, and not change the optimal strategies. So let's pick up Example 3 from the point where we were considering the following game:

$$P = \begin{bmatrix} 2{,}000 & 10{,}000 & 8{,}000 \\ 10{,}000 & 0 & 6{,}000 \end{bmatrix}.$$

We are looking for the optimal strategies R and C for the row and column players, respectively; if e is the value of the game, we will have $e = RPC$. Let's concentrate first on the column player's strategy $C = [u \ v \ w]^T$, where u, v, and w are the unknowns we want to find. Because e is the value of the game, if the column player uses the optimal strategy C and the row player uses any old strategy S, the expected value with these strategies has to be e or better for the column player, so $SPC \le e$. Let's write that out for two particular choices of S. First, consider $S = [1 \ 0]$:

$$[1 \ 0] \begin{bmatrix} 2{,}000 & 10{,}000 & 8{,}000 \\ 10{,}000 & 0 & 6{,}000 \end{bmatrix} \begin{bmatrix} u \\ v \\ w \end{bmatrix} \le e.$$

Multiplied out, this gives

$$2{,}000u + 10{,}000v + 8{,}000w \le e.$$

Next, do the same thing for $S = [0 \ 1]$:

$$[0 \ 1] \begin{bmatrix} 2{,}000 & 10{,}000 & 8{,}000 \\ 10{,}000 & 0 & 6{,}000 \end{bmatrix} \begin{bmatrix} u \\ v \\ w \end{bmatrix} \le e$$

$$10{,}000u + 6{,}000w \le e.$$

It turns out that if these two inequalities are true, then $SPC \le e$ for any S at all, which is what the column player wants. These are starting to look like constraints in a linear programming problem, but the e appearing on the right is in the way. We get around this by dividing by e, which we know to be positive because all of the payoffs are nonnegative and no column is all zero (so the column player can't force the value of the game to be 0; here is where we need these assumptions). We get the following inequalities:

$$2{,}000 \left(\frac{u}{e}\right) + 10{,}000 \left(\frac{v}{e}\right) + 8{,}000 \left(\frac{w}{e}\right) \le 1$$

$$10{,}000 \left(\frac{u}{e}\right) + 6{,}000 \left(\frac{w}{e}\right) \le 1.$$

Now we're getting somewhere. To make these look even more like linear constraints, we replace our unknowns u, v, and w with new unknowns, $x = u/e$, $y = v/e$, and $z = w/e$. Our inequalities then become:

$$2{,}000x + 10{,}000y + 8{,}000z \le 1$$

$$10{,}000x + 6{,}000z \le 1.$$

What about an objective function? From the point of view of the column player, the objective is to find a strategy that will minimize the expected value e. In order to write e in terms of our new variables x, y, and z, we use the fact that our original variables, being the entries in the column strategy, have to add up to 1: $u + v + w = 1$. Dividing by e gives

$$\frac{u}{e} + \frac{v}{e} + \frac{w}{e} = \frac{1}{e}$$

or

$$x + y + z = \frac{1}{e}.$$

Now we notice that, if we *maximize* $p = x + y + z = 1/e$, it will have the effect of minimizing e, which is what we want. So, we get the following linear programming problem:

Maximize $p = x + y + z$
subject to $2{,}000x + 10{,}000y + 8{,}000z \leq 1$
$10{,}000x \qquad\qquad + 6{,}000z \leq 1$
$x \geq 0,\ y \geq 0,\ z \geq 0.$

Why can we say that x, y, and z should all be non-negative? Because the unknowns u, v, w, and e must all be non-negative.

So now, if we solve this linear programming problem to find x, y, z, and p, we can find the column player's optimal strategy by computing $u = xe = x/p$, $v = y/p$, and $w = z/p$. Moreover, the value of the game is $e = 1/p$. (If we added k to all the payoffs, we should now adjust by subtracting k again to find the correct value of the game.)

Turning now to the row player's strategy, if we repeat the above type of argument from the row player's viewpoint, we'll end up with the following linear programming problem to solve:

Minimize $c = s + t$
subject to $2{,}000s + 10{,}000t \geq 1$
$10{,}000s \qquad\qquad \geq 1$
$8{,}000s + \ \ 6{,}000t \geq 1$
$s \geq 0,\ t \geq 0.$

This is, of course, the dual to the problem we solved to find the column player's strategy, so we know that we can read its solution off of the same final tableau. The optimal value of c will be the same as the value of p, so $c = 1/e$ also. The entries in the optimal row strategy will be s/c and t/c. ∎

FAQs

When to Use Duality

Q: *Given a minimization problem, when should I use duality, and when should I use the two-phase method in Section 4.4?*

A: If the original problem satisfies the non-negative objective condition (none of the coefficients in the objective function are negative), then you can use duality to convert the problem to a standard maximization one, which can be solved with the one-phase method. If the original problem does not satisfy the non-negative objective condition, then dualizing results in a nonstandard LP problem, so dualizing may not be worthwhile.

Q: *When is it absolutely necessary to use duality?*

A: Never. Duality gives us an efficient but not necessary alternative for solving standard minimization problems.

4.5 EXERCISES

▼ more advanced　◆ challenging

T indicates exercises that should be solved using technology

In Exercises 1–8, write down (without solving) the dual LP problem. HINT [See the Quick Example on page 322.]

1. Maximize　$p = 2x + y$
subject to　$x + 2y \le 6$
$-x + y \le 2$
$x \ge 0, y \ge 0.$

2. Maximize　$p = x + 5y$
subject to　$x + y \le 6$
$-x + 3y \le 4$
$x \ge 0, y \ge 0.$

3. Minimize　$c = 2s + t + 3u$
subject to　$s + t + u \ge 100$
$2s + t \quad \ge 50$
$s \ge 0, t \ge 0, u \ge 0.$

4. Minimize　$c = 2s + 2t + 3u$
subject to　$s \quad + u \ge 100$
$2s + t \quad \ge 50$
$s \ge 0, t \ge 0, u \ge 0.$

5. Maximize　$p = x + y + z + w$
subject to　$x + y + z \quad \le 3$
$y + z + w \le 4$
$x + z + w \le 5$
$x + y + w \le 6$
$x \ge 0, y \ge 0, z \ge 0, w \ge 0.$

6. Maximize　$p = x + y + z + w$
subject to　$x + y + z \quad \le 3$
$y + z + w \le 3$
$x + z + w \le 4$
$x + y + w \le 4$
$x \ge 0, y \ge 0, z \ge 0, w \ge 0.$

7. Minimize　$c = s + 3t + u$
subject to　$5s - t \quad + v \ge 1{,}000$
$u - v \ge 2{,}000$
$s + t \quad \ge 500$
$s \ge 0, t \ge 0, u \ge 0, v \ge 0.$

8. Minimize　$c = 5s + 2u + v$
subject to　$s - t \quad + 2v \ge 2{,}000$
$u + v \ge 3{,}000$
$s + t \quad \ge 500$
$s \ge 0, t \ge 0, u \ge 0, v \ge 0.$

In Exercises 9–22, solve the standard minimization problems using duality. (You may already have seen some of them in earlier sections, but now you will be solving them using a different method.) HINT [See Example 1.]

9. Minimize　$c = s + t$
subject to　$s + 2t \ge 6$
$2s + t \ge 6$
$s \ge 0, t \ge 0.$

10. Minimize　$c = s + 2t$
subject to　$s + 3t \ge 30$
$2s + t \ge 30$
$s \ge 0, t \ge 0.$

11. Minimize　$c = 6s + 6t$
subject to　$s + 2t \ge 20$
$2s + t \ge 20$
$s \ge 0, t \ge 0.$

12. Minimize　$c = 3s + 2t$
subject to　$s + 2t \ge 20$
$2s + t \ge 10$
$s \ge 0, t \ge 0.$

13. Minimize　$c = 0.2s + 0.3t$
subject to　$0.2s + 0.1t \ge 1$
$0.15s + 0.3t \ge 1.5$
$10s + 10t \ge 80$
$s \ge 0, t \ge 0.$

14. Minimize　$c = 0.4s + 0.1t$
subject to　$30s + 20t \ge 600$
$0.1s + 0.4t \ge 4$
$0.2s + 0.3t \ge 4.5$
$s \ge 0, t \ge 0.$

15. Minimize　$c = 2s + t$
subject to　$3s + t \ge 30$
$s + t \ge 20$
$s + 3t \ge 30$
$s \ge 0, t \ge 0.$

16. Minimize　$c = s + 2t$
subject to　$4s + t \ge 100$
$2s + t \ge 80$
$s + 3t \ge 150$
$s \ge 0, t \ge 0.$

17. Minimize　$c = s + 2t + 3u$
subject to　$3s + 2t + u \ge 60$
$2s + t + 3u \ge 60$
$s \ge 0, t \ge 0, u \ge 0.$

18. Minimize $c = s + t + 2u$

subject to $s + 2t + 2u \geq 60$

$2s + t + 3u \geq 60$

$s \geq 0, t \geq 0, u \geq 0.$

19. Minimize $c = 2s + t + 3u$

subject to $s + t + u \geq 100$

$2s + t \quad \geq 50$

$t + u \geq 50$

$s \geq 0, t \geq 0, u \geq 0.$

20. Minimize $c = 2s + 2t + 3u$

subject to $s \quad + u \geq 100$

$2s + t \quad \geq 50$

$t + u \geq 50$

$s \geq 0, t \geq 0, u \geq 0.$

21. Minimize $c = s + t + u$

subject to $3s + 2t + u \geq 60$

$2s + t + 3u \geq 60$

$s + 3t + 2u \geq 60$

$s \geq 0, t \geq 0, u \geq 0.$

22. Minimize $c = s + t + 2u$

subject to $s + 2t + 2u \geq 60$

$2s + t + 3u \geq 60$

$s + 3t + 6u \geq 60$

$s \geq 0, t \geq 0, u \geq 0.$

In Exercises 23–28, solve the games with the given payoff matrices. HINT [See Example 3.]

23. $P = \begin{bmatrix} -1 & 1 & 2 \\ 2 & -1 & -2 \end{bmatrix}$

24. $P = \begin{bmatrix} 1 & -1 & 2 \\ 1 & 2 & 0 \end{bmatrix}$

25. $P = \begin{bmatrix} -1 & 1 & 2 \\ 2 & -1 & -2 \\ 1 & 2 & 0 \end{bmatrix}$

26. $P = \begin{bmatrix} 1 & -1 & 2 \\ 1 & 2 & 0 \\ 0 & 1 & 1 \end{bmatrix}$

27. $P = \begin{bmatrix} -1 & 1 & 2 & -1 \\ 2 & -1 & -2 & -3 \\ 1 & 2 & 0 & 1 \\ 0 & 2 & 3 & 3 \end{bmatrix}$

28. $P = \begin{bmatrix} 1 & -1 & 2 & 0 \\ 1 & 2 & 0 & 1 \\ 0 & 1 & 1 & 0 \\ 2 & 0 & -2 & 2 \end{bmatrix}$

APPLICATIONS

The following applications are similar to ones in preceding exercise sets. Use duality to answer them.

29. *Resource Allocation* Meow makes cat food out of fish and cornmeal. Fish has 8 grams of protein and 4 grams of fat per ounce, and cornmeal has 4 grams of protein and 8 grams of fat. A jumbo can of cat food must contain at least 48 grams of

protein and 48 grams of fat. If fish and cornmeal both cost 5¢/ounce, how many ounces of each should Meow use in each can of cat food to minimize costs? What are the shadow costs of protein and of fat? HINT [See Example 2.]

30. *Resource Allocation* Oz makes lion food out of giraffe and gazelle meat. Giraffe meat has 18 grams of protein and 36 grams of fat per pound, while gazelle meat has 36 grams of protein and 18 grams of fat per pound. A batch of lion food must contain at least 36,000 grams of protein and 54,000 grams of fat. Giraffe meat costs $2/pound and gazelle meat costs $4/pound. How many pounds of each should go into each batch of lion food in order to minimize costs? What are the shadow costs of protein and fat? HINT [See Example 2.]

31. *Nutrition* Ruff makes dog food out of chicken and grain. Chicken has 10 grams of protein and 5 grams of fat/ounce, and grain has 2 grams of protein and 2 grams of fat/ounce. A bag of dog food must contain at least 200 grams of protein and at least 150 grams of fat. If chicken costs 10¢/ounce and grain costs 1¢/ounce, how many ounces of each should Ruff use in each bag of dog food in order to minimize cost? What are the shadow costs of protein and fat?

32. *Purchasing* The Enormous State University's Business School is buying computers. The school has two models to choose from, the Pomegranate and the iZac. Each Pomegranate comes with 400 MB of memory and 80 GB of disk space, while each iZac has 300 MB of memory and 100 GB of disk space. For reasons related to its accreditation, the school would like to be able to say that it has a total of at least 48,000 MB of memory and at least 12,800 GB of disk space. If both the Pomegranate and the iZac cost $2,000 each, how many of each should the school buy to keep the cost as low as possible? What are the shadow costs of memory and disk space?

33. *Nutrition* Each serving of Gerber Mixed Cereal for Baby contains 60 calories and no vitamin C. Each serving of Gerber Mango Tropical Fruit Dessert contains 80 calories and 45 percent of the U.S. Recommended Daily Allowance (RDA) of vitamin C for infants. Each serving of Gerber Apple Banana Juice contains 60 calories and 120 percent of the U.S. RDA of vitamin C for infants.[42] The cereal costs 10¢/serving, the dessert costs 53¢/serving, and the juice costs 27¢/serving. If you want to provide your child with at least 120 calories and at least 120 percent of the U.S. RDA of vitamin C, how can you do so at the least cost? What are your shadow costs for calories and vitamin C?

34. *Nutrition* Each serving of Gerber Mixed Cereal for Baby contains 60 calories, no vitamin C, and 11 grams of carbohydrates. Each serving of Gerber Mango Tropical Fruit Dessert contains 80 calories, 45 percent of the U.S. Recommended Daily Allowance (RDA) of vitamin C for infants, and 21 grams of carbohydrates. Each serving of Gerber Apple Banana Juice contains 60 calories, 120 percent of the U.S. RDA of vitamin C for infants, and 15 grams of carbohydrates.[43] Assume that the cereal costs 11¢/serving, the dessert

[42] Source: Nutrition information provided by Gerber.

[43] Ibid.

costs 50¢/serving, and the juice costs 30¢/serving. If you want to provide your child with at least 180 calories, at least 120 percent of the U.S. RDA of vitamin C, and at least 37 grams of carbohydrates, how can you do so at the least cost? What are your shadow costs for calories, vitamin C, and carbohydrates?

35. *Politics* The political pollster Canter is preparing for a national election. It would like to poll at least 1,500 Democrats and 1,500 Republicans. Each mailing to the East Coast gets responses from 100 Democrats and 50 Republicans. Each mailing to the Midwest gets responses from 100 Democrats and 100 Republicans. And each mailing to the West Coast gets responses from 50 Democrats and 100 Republicans. Mailings to the East Coast cost $40 each to produce and mail, mailings to the Midwest cost $60 each, and mailings to the West Coast cost $50 each. How many mailings should Canter send to each area of the country to get the responses it needs at the least possible cost? What will it cost? What are the shadow costs of a Democratic response and a Republican response?

36. *Purchasing* Bingo's Copy Center needs to buy white paper and yellow paper. Bingo's can buy from three suppliers. Harvard Paper sells a package of 20 reams of white and 10 reams of yellow for $60; Yale Paper sells a package of 10 reams of white and 10 reams of yellow for $40, and Dartmouth Paper sells a package of 10 reams of white and 20 reams of yellow for $50. If Bingo's needs 350 reams of white and 400 reams of yellow, how many packages should it buy from each supplier so as to minimize the cost? What is the lowest possible cost? What are the shadow costs of white paper and yellow paper?

37. ▼ *Resource Allocation* One day Gillian the Magician summoned the wisest of her women. "Devoted followers," she began, "I have a quandary: As you well know, I possess great expertise in sleep spells and shock spells, but unfortunately, these are proving to be a drain on my aural energy resources; each sleep spell costs me 500 pico-shirleys of aural energy, while each shock spell requires 750 pico-shirleys. Clearly, I would like to hold my overall expenditure of aural energy to a minimum, and still meet my commitments in protecting the Sisterhood from the ever-present threat of trolls. Specifically, I have estimated that each sleep spell keeps us safe for an average of 2 minutes, while every shock spell protects us for about 3 minutes. We certainly require enough protection to last 24 hours of each day, and possibly more, just to be safe. At the same time, I have noticed that each of my sleep spells can immobilize 3 trolls at once, while one of my typical shock spells (having a narrower range) can immobilize only 2 trolls at once. We are faced, my sisters, with an onslaught of 1,200 trolls per day! Finally, as you are no doubt aware, the bylaws dictate that for a Magician of the Order to remain in good standing, the number of shock spells must be between one-quarter and one-third the number of shock and sleep spells combined. What do I do, oh Wise Ones?"

38. ▼ *Risk Management* The Grand Vizier of the Kingdom of Um is being blackmailed by numerous individuals and is having a very difficult time keeping his blackmailers from going public.

He has been keeping them at bay with two kinds of payoff: gold bars from the Royal Treasury and political favors. Through bitter experience, he has learned that each payoff in gold gives him peace for an average of about one month, and each political favor seems to earn him about a month and a half of reprieve. To maintain his flawless reputation in the court, he feels he cannot afford any revelations about his tainted past to come to light within the next year. Thus, it is imperative that his blackmailers be kept at bay for 12 months. Furthermore, he would like to keep the number of gold payoffs at no more than one-quarter of the combined number of payoffs because the outward flow of gold bars might arouse suspicion on the part of the Royal Treasurer. The gold payoffs tend to deplete the Grand Vizier's travel budget. (The treasury has been subsidizing his numerous trips to the Himalayas.) He estimates that each gold bar removed from the treasury will cost him four trips. On the other hand, because the administering of political favors tends to cost him valuable travel time, he suspects that each political favor will cost him about two trips. Now, he would obviously like to keep his blackmailers silenced and lose as few trips as possible. What is he to do? How many trips will he lose in the next year?

39. ▼ *Game Theory—Politics* Incumbent Tax N. Spend and challenger Trick L. Down are running for county executive, and polls show them to be in a dead heat. The election hinges on three cities: Littleville, Metropolis, and Urbantown. The candidates have decided to spend the last weeks before the election campaigning in those three cities; each day each candidate will decide in which city to spend the day. Pollsters have determined the following payoff matrix, where the payoff represents the number of votes gained or lost for each one-day campaign trip.

		T. N. Spend		
		Littleville	*Metropolis*	*Urbantown*
	Littleville	−200	−300	300
T. L. Down	**Metropolis**	−500	500	−100
	Urbantown	−500	0	0

What percentage of time should each candidate spend in each city in order to maximize votes gained? If both candidates use their optimal strategies, what is the expected vote?

40. ▼ *Game Theory—Marketing* Your company's new portable phone/music player/PDA/bottle washer, the RunMan, will compete against the established market leader, the iNod, in a saturated market. (Thus, for each device you sell, one fewer iNod is sold.) You are planning to launch the RunMan with a traveling road show, concentrating on two cities, New York and Boston. The makers of the iNod will do the same to try to maintain their sales. If, on a given day, you both go to New York, you will lose 1,000 units in sales to the iNod. If you both go to Boston, you will lose 750 units in sales. On the other hand, if you go to New York and your competitor to Boston, you will gain 1,500 units in sales from them. If you

go to Boston and they to New York, you will gain 500 units in sales. What percentage of time should you spend in New York and what percentage in Boston, and how do you expect your sales to be affected?

41. ▼ *Game Theory—Morra Games* A three-finger Morra game is a game in which two players simultaneously show one, two, or three fingers at each round. The outcome depends on a predetermined set of rules. Here is an interesting example: If the number of fingers shown by A and B differ by 1, then A loses one point. If they differ by more than 1, the round is a draw. If they show the same number of fingers, A wins an amount equal to the sum of the fingers shown. Determine the optimal strategy for each player and the expected value of the game.

42. ▼ *Game Theory—Morra Games* Referring to the preceding exercise, consider the following rules for a three-finger Morra game: If the sum of the fingers shown is odd, then A wins an amount equal to that sum. If the sum is even, B wins the sum. Determine the optimal strategy for each player and the expected value of the game.

43. 🔳 ◆ *Game Theory—Military Strategy* Colonel Blotto is a well-known game in military strategy.[44] Here is a version of this game: Colonel Blotto has four regiments under his command, while his opponent, Captain Kije, has three. The armies are to try to occupy two locations, and each commander must decide how many regiments to send to each location. The army that sends more regiments to a location captures that location as well as the other army's regiments. If both armies send the same number of regiments to a location, then there is a draw. The payoffs are one point for each location captured and one point for each regiment captured. Find the optimum strategy for each commander and also the value of the game.

44. 🔳 ◆ *Game Theory—Military Strategy* Referring to the preceding exercise, consider the version of Colonel Blotto with the same payoffs given there except that Captain Kije earns two points for each location captured, while Colonel Blotto continues to earn only one point. Find the optimum strategy for each commander and also the value of the game.

---

[44] See Samuel Karlin, *Mathematical Methods and Theory in Games, Programming and Economics* (Addison-Wesley, 1959).

COMMUNICATION AND REASONING EXERCISES

45. Give one possible advantage of using duality to solve a standard minimization problem.

46. To ensure that the dual of a minimization problem will result in a standard maximization problem,

   (A) the primal problem should satisfy the non-negative objective condition.

   (B) the primal problem should be a standard minimization problem.

   (C) the primal problem should not satisfy the non-negative objective condition.

47. Give an example of a standard minimization problem whose dual is *not* a standard maximization problem. How would you go about solving your problem?

48. Give an example of a nonstandard minimization problem whose dual is a standard maximization problem.

49. ▼ Solve the following nonstandard minimization problem using duality. Recall from a footnote in the text that to find the dual you must first rewrite all of the constraints using "≥." The Miami Beach City Council has offered to subsidize hotel development in Miami Beach, and is hoping for at least two hotels with a total capacity of at least 1,400. Suppose that you are a developer interested in taking advantage of this offer by building a small group of hotels in Miami Beach. You are thinking of three prototypes: a convention-style hotel with 500 rooms costing $100 million, a vacation-style hotel with 200 rooms costing $20 million, and a small motel with 50 rooms costing $4 million. The city council will approve your plans provided you build at least one convention-style hotel and no more than two small motels. How many of each type of hotel should you build to satisfy the city council's wishes and stipulations while minimizing your total cost?

50. ▼ Given a minimization problem, when would you solve it by applying the simplex method to its dual, and when would you apply the simplex method to the minimization problem itself?

51. ▼ Create an interesting application that leads to a standard maximization problem. Solve it using the simplex method and note the solution to its dual problem. What does the solution to its dual tell you about your application?

KEY CONCEPTS

Web Site www.FiniteandCalc.org
Go to the student Web site at
www.FiniteandCalc.org to find a
comprehensive and interactive
Web-based summary of Chapter 4.

4.1 Graphing Linear Inequalities

Inequalities, strict and nonstrict *p. 265*
Linear inequalities *p. 265*
Solution of an inequality *p. 266*
Sketching the region represented by a
linear inequality in two variables *p. 267*
Bounded and unbounded regions *p. 270*
Feasible region *p. 270*

4.2 Solving Linear Programming Problems Graphically

Linear programming (LP) problem in
two unknowns; objective function;
constraints; optimal value; optimal
solution *p. 274*
Feasible region *p. 275*
Fundamental Theorem of Linear
Programming *p. 275*

Graphical method for solving an
LP problem *p. 276*
Decision variables *p. 277*
Procedure for solving an LP problem
with an unbounded feasible
region *p. 280*

4.3 The Simplex Method: Solving Standard Maximization Problems

General linear programming problem in
n unknowns *p. 291*
Standard maximization problem *p. 291*
Slack variable *p. 292*
Tableau *p. 293*
Active (or basic) variables; inactive
(or nonbasic) variables; basic
solution *p. 293*
Rules for selecting the pivot
column *p. 294*
Rules for selecting the pivot; test
ratios *p. 295*
Departing or exiting variable, entering
variable *p. 295*

4.4 The Simplex Method: Solving General Linear Programming Problems

Surplus variable *p. 308*
Phase I and Phase II for solving
general LP problems *pp. 308–309*
Using the simplex method to solve
a minimization problem *p. 313*

4.5 The Simplex Method and Duality

Standard minimization problem *p. 320*
Standard LP problem *p. 321*
Non-negative objective condition
p. 321
Dual LP problems; primal problem;
dual problem *p. 322*
Fundamental Theorem of Duality
p. 323
Shadow costs *p. 325*
Game Theory: The LP problem
associated to a two-person zero-sum
game *p. 326*

REVIEW EXERCISES

In each of Exercises 1–4, sketch the region corresponding to the given inequalities, say whether it is bounded, and give the coordinates of all corner points.

1. $2x - 3y \le 12$

2. $x \le 2y$

3. $x + 2y \le 20$
$3x + 2y \le 30$
$x \ge 0, y \ge 0$

4. $3x + 2y \ge 6$
$2x - 3y \le 6$
$3x - 2y \ge 0$
$x \ge 0, y \ge 0$

In each of Exercises 5–8, solve the given linear programming problem graphically.

5. Maximize $p = 2x + y$
subject to $3x + y \le 30$
$x + y \le 12$
$x + 3y \le 30$
$x \ge 0, y \ge 0.$

6. Maximize $p = 2x + 3y$
subject to $x + y \ge 10$
$2x + y \ge 12$
$x + y \le 20$
$x \ge 0, y \ge 0.$

7. Minimize $c = 2x + y$
subject to $3x + y \ge 30$
$x + 2y \ge 20$
$2x - y \ge 0$
$x \ge 0, y \ge 0.$

8. Minimize $c = 3x + y$
subject to $3x + 2y \ge 6$
$2x - 3y \le 0$
$3x - 2y \ge 0$
$x \ge 0, y \ge 0.$

In each of Exercises 9–16, solve the given linear programming problem using the simplex method. If no optimal solution exists, indicate whether the feasible region is empty or the objective function is unbounded.

9. Maximize $p = x + y + 2z$
subject to $x + 2y + 2z \le 60$
$2x + y + 3z \le 60$
$x \ge 0, y \ge 0, z \ge 0.$

10. Maximize $p = x + y + 2z$
subject to $x + 2y + 2z \le 60$
$2x + y + 3z \le 60$
$x + 3y + 6z \le 60$
$x \ge 0, y \ge 0, z \ge 0.$

11. Maximize $p = x + y + 3z$
subject to $x + y + z \ge 100$
$y + z \le 80$
$x \quad + z \le 80$
$x \ge 0, y \ge 0, z \ge 0.$

12. Maximize $p = 2x + y$
subject to $x + 2y \ge 12$
$2x + y \le 12$
$x + y \le 5$
$x \ge 0, y \ge 0.$

13. Minimize $c = x + 2y + 3z$
subject to $3x + 2y + z \geq 60$
$2x + y + 3z \geq 60$
$x \geq 0, y \geq 0, z \geq 0.$

14. Minimize $c = x + y - z$
subject to $3x + 2y + z \geq 60$
$2x + y + 3z \geq 60$
$x + 3y + 2z \geq 60$
$x \geq 0, y \geq 0, z \geq 0.$

15. Minimize $c = x + y + z + w$
subject to $x + y \qquad \geq 30$
$x \quad + z \qquad \geq 20$
$x + y \quad - w \leq 10$
$y + z - w \leq 10$
$x \geq 0, y \geq 0, z \geq 0, w \geq 0.$

16. Minimize $c = 4x + y + z + w$
subject to $x + y \qquad \geq 30$
$y - z \qquad \leq 20$
$z - w \leq 10$
$x \geq 0, y \geq 0, z \geq 0, w \geq 0.$

In each of Exercises 17–20, solve the given linear programming problem using duality.

17. Minimize $c = 2x + y$
subject to $3x + 2y \geq 60$
$2x + y \geq 60$
$x + 3y \geq 60$
$x \geq 0, y \geq 0.$

18. Minimize $c = 2x + y + 2z$
subject to $3x + 2y + z \geq 100$
$2x + y + 3z \geq 200$
$x \geq 0, y \geq 0, z \geq 0.$

19. Minimize $c = 2x + y$
subject to $3x + 2y \geq 10$
$2x - y \leq 30$
$x + 3y \geq 60$
$x \geq 0, y \geq 0.$

20. Minimize $c = 2x + y + 2z$
subject to $3x - 2y + z \geq 100$
$2x + y - 3z \leq 200$
$x \geq 0, y \geq 0, z \geq 0.$

In each of Exercises 21–24, solve the game with the given payoff matrix.

21. $P = \begin{bmatrix} -1 & 2 & -1 \\ 1 & -2 & 1 \\ 3 & -1 & 0 \end{bmatrix}$ **22.** $P = \begin{bmatrix} -3 & 0 & 1 \\ -4 & 0 & 0 \\ 0 & -1 & -2 \end{bmatrix}$

23. $P = \begin{bmatrix} -3 & -2 & 3 \\ 1 & 0 & 0 \\ -2 & 2 & 1 \end{bmatrix}$ **24.** $P = \begin{bmatrix} -4 & -2 & -3 \\ 1 & -3 & -2 \\ -3 & 1 & -4 \end{bmatrix}$

Exercises 25–28 are adapted from the Actuarial Exam on Operations Research.

25. You are given the following linear programming problem:

Minimize $c = x + 2y$
subject to $-2x + y \geq 1$
$x - 2y \geq 1$
$x \geq 0, y \geq 0.$

Which of the following is true?

(A) The problem has no feasible solutions.
(B) The objective function is unbounded.
(C) The problem has optimal solutions.

26. Repeat the preceding exercise with the following linear programming problem:

Maximize $p = x + y$
subject to $-2x + y \leq 1$
$x - 2y \leq 2$
$x \geq 0, y \geq 0.$

27. Determine the optimal value of the objective function. You are given the following linear programming problem.

Maximize $Z = x_1 + 4x_2 + 2x_3 - 10$
subject to $4x_1 + x_2 + x_3 \leq 45$
$-x_1 + x_2 + 2x_3 \leq 0$
$x_1, x_2, x_3 \geq 0.$

28. Determine the optimal value of the objective function. You are given the following linear programming problem.

Minimize $Z = x_1 + 4x_2 + 2x_3 + x_4 + 40$
subject to $4x_1 + x_2 + x_3 \leq 45$
$-x_1 + 2x_2 + x_4 \geq 40$
$x_1, x_2, x_3 \geq 0.$

APPLICATIONS

Purchases In Exercises 29–32, you are the buyer for OHaganBooks.com and are considering increasing stocks of romance and horror novels at the new OHaganBooks.com warehouse in Texas. You have offers from several publishers: Duffin House, Higgins Press, McPhearson Imprints, and O'Conell Books. Duffin offers a package of 5 horror novels and 5 romance novels for $50, Higgins offers a package of 5 horror and 10 romance novels for $80, McPhearson offers a package of 10 horror novels and 5 romance novels for $80, and O'Conell offers a package of 10 horror novels and 10 romance novels for $90.

29. How many packages should you purchase from Duffin House and Higgins Press to obtain at least 4,000 horror novels and 6,000 romance novels at minimum cost? What is the minimum cost?

30. How many packages should you purchase from McPhearson Imprints and O'Conell Books to obtain at least 5,000 horror novels and 4,000 romance novels at minimum cost? What is the minimum cost?

31. Refer to the scenario in Exercise 29. As it turns out, John O'Hagan promised Marjory Duffin that OHaganBooks.com would buy at least 20 percent more packages from Duffin as from Higgins, but you still want to obtain at least 4,000 horror novels and 6,000 romance novels at minimum cost.

a. *Without solving the problem,* say which of the following statements are possible:

(A) The cost will stay the same.
(B) The cost will increase.
(C) The cost will decrease.
(D) It will be impossible to meet all the conditions.
(E) The cost will become unbounded.

b. If you wish to meet all the requirements in part (a) at minimum cost, how many packages should you purchase from each publisher? What is the minimum cost?

32. Refer to Exercise 30. You are about to place the order meeting the requirements of Exercise 30 when you are told that you can order no more than a total of 500 packages, and that at least half of the packages should be from McPhearson. Explain why this is impossible by referring to the feasible region for Exercise 30.

33. *Investments* Marjory Duffin's portfolio manager has suggested two high-yielding stocks: European Emerald Emporium (EEE) and Royal Ruby Retailers (RRR). EEE shares cost $50, yield 4.5% in dividends, and have a risk index of 2.0 per share. RRR shares cost $55, yield 5% in dividends, and have a risk index of 3.0 per share. Marjory has up to $12,100 to invest and would like to earn at least $550 in dividends. How many shares of each stock should she purchase to meet her requirements and minimize the total risk index for her portfolio? What is the minimum total risk index?

34. *Investments* Marjory Duffin's other portfolio manager has suggested another two high-yielding stocks: Countrynarrow Mortgages (CNM) and Scotland Subprime (SS). CNM shares cost $40, yield 5.5% in dividends, and have a risk index of 1.0 per share. SS shares cost $25, yield 7.5% in dividends, and have a risk index of 1.5 per share. Marjory can invest up to $30,000 in these stocks and would like to earn at least $1,650 in dividends. How many shares of each stock should she purchase in order to meet her requirements and minimize the total risk index for your portfolio?

35. *Resource Allocation* Billy-Sean O'Hagan has joined the Physics Society at Suburban State University, and the group is planning to raise money to support the dying space program by making and selling umbrellas. The society intends to make three models: the Sprinkle, the Storm, and the Hurricane. The amounts of cloth, metal, and wood used in making each model are given in this table:

	Sprinkle	Storm	Hurricane	Total Available
Cloth (sq. yd)	1	2	2	600
Metal (lbs)	2	1	3	600
Wood (lbs)	1	3	6	600
Profit ($)	1	1	2	

The table also shows the amounts of each material available in a given day and the profits to be made from each model. How many of each model should the society make in order to maximize its profit?

36. *Profit* Duffin Press, which is now the largest publisher of books sold at the OHaganBooks.com site, prints three kinds of books: paperback, quality paperback, and hardcover. The amounts of paper, ink, and time on the presses required for each kind of book are given in this table:

	Paperback	Quality Paperback	Hardcover	Total Available
Paper (pounds)	3	2	1	6,000
Ink (gallons)	2	1	3	6,000
Time (minutes)	10	10	10	22,000
Profit ($)	1	2	3	

The table also lists the total amounts of paper, ink, and time available in a given day and the profits made on each kind of book. How many of each kind of book should Duffin print to maximize profit?

37. *Purchases* You are just about to place book orders from Duffin and Higgins (see Exercise 29) when everything changes: Duffin House informs you that, due to a global romance crisis, its packages now each will contain 5 horror novels but only 2 romance novels and still cost $50 per package. Packages from Higgins will now contain 10 of each type of novel, but now cost $150 per package. Ewing Books enters the fray and offers its own package of 5 horror and 5 romance novels for $100. The sales manager now tells you that at least 50% of the packages must come from Higgins Press and, as before, you want to obtain at least 4,000 horror novels and 6,000 romance novels at minimum cost. Taking all of this into account, how many packages should you purchase from each publisher? What is the minimum cost?

38. *Purchases* You are about to place book orders from McPhearson and O'Conell (see Exercise 30) when you get an e-mail from McPhearson Imprints saying that, sorry, but they have stopped publishing romance novels due to the global romance crisis and can now offer only packages of 10 horror novels for $50. O'Conell is still offering packages of 10 horror novels and 10 romance novels for $90, and now the United States Treasury, in an attempt to bolster the floundering romance industry, is offering its own package of 20 romance novels for $120. Furthermore, Congress, in approving this measure, has passed legislation dictating that at least 2/3 of the packages in every order must come from the U.S. Treasury. As before, you wish to obtain at least 5,000 horror novels and 4,000 romance novels at minimum cost. Taking all of this into account, how many packages should you purchase from each supplier? What is the minimum cost?

39. *Degree Requirements* During his lunch break, John O'Hagan decides to devote some time to assisting his son Billy-Sean, who continues to have a terrible time planning his college

course schedule. The latest Bulletin of Suburban State University claims to have added new flexibility to its course requirements, but it remains as complicated as ever. It reads as follows:

All candidates for the degree of Bachelor of Arts at SSU must take at least 120 credits from the Sciences, Fine Arts, Liberal Arts and Mathematics combined, including at least as many Science credits as Fine Arts credits, and at most twice as many Mathematics credits as Science credits, but with Liberal Arts credits exceeding Mathematics credits by no more than one-third of the number of Fine Arts credits.

Science and fine arts credits cost $300 each, and liberal arts and mathematics credits cost $200 each. John would like to have Billy-Sean meet all the requirements at a minimum total cost.

a. Set up (without solving) the associated linear programming problem.

b. ▉ Use technology to determine how many of each type of credit Billy-Sean should take. What will the total cost be?

40. *Degree Requirements* No sooner had the "new and flexible" course requirement been released than the English Department again pressured the University Senate to include their vaunted "Verbal Expression" component in place of the fine arts requirement in all programs (including the sciences):

All candidates for the degree of Bachelor of Science at SSU must take at least 120 credits from the Liberal Arts, Sciences, Verbal Expression, and Mathematics, including at most as many Science credits as Liberal Arts credits, and at least twice as many Verbal Expression credits as Science credits and Liberal Arts credits combined, with Liberal Arts credits exceeding Mathematics credits by at least a quarter of the number of Verbal Expression credits.

Science credits cost $300 each, while each credit in the remaining subjects now costs $400. John would like to have Billy-Sean meet all the requirements at a minimum total cost.

a. Set up (without solving) the associated linear programming problem.

b. ▉ Use technology to determine how many of each type of credit Billy-Sean should take. What will the total cost be?

41. *Shipping* On the same day that the sales department at Duffin House received an order for 600 packages from the OHaganBooks.com Texas headquarters, it received an additional order for 200 packages from FantasyBooks.com, based in California. Duffin House has warehouses in New York and Illinois. The New York warehouse has 600 packages in stock, but the Illinois warehouse is closing down and has only 300 packages in stock. Shipping costs per package of books are as follows: New York to Texas: $20; New York to California: $50; Illinois to Texas: $30; Illinois to California: $40. What is the lowest total shipping cost for which Duffin House can fill the orders? How many packages should be sent from each warehouse to each online bookstore at a minimum shipping cost?

42. *Transportation Scheduling* Duffin Press is about to start a promotional blitz for its new book, *Physics for the Liberal Arts*. The company has 20 salespeople stationed in Chicago and 10 in Denver, and would like to fly at least 15 to sales fairs in each of Los Angeles and New York. A round-trip plane flight from Chicago to LA costs $200; from Chicago to NY costs $150; from Denver to LA costs $400; and from Denver to NY costs $200. How many salespeople should the company fly from each of Chicago and Denver to each of LA and NY for the lowest total cost in air fare?

43. *Marketing* Marjory Duffin, head of Duffin House, reveals to John O'Hagan that FantasyBooks.com is considering several promotional schemes: It may offer two books for the price of one, three books for the price of two, or possibly a free copy of *Brain Surgery for Klutzes* with each order. OHaganBooks.com's marketing advisers Floody and O'Lara seem to have different ideas as to how to respond. Floody suggests offering *three* books for the price of one, while O'Lara suggests instead offering a free copy of the *Finite Mathematics Student Solutions Manual* with every purchase. After a careful analysis, O'Hagan comes up with the following payoff matrix, where the payoffs represent the number of customers, in thousands, O'Hagan expects to gain from FantasyBooks.com.

		FantasyBooks.com			
		No Promo	2 for Price of 1	3 for Price of 2	Brain Surgery
OHaganBooks.com	No Promo	0	−60	−40	10
	3 for Price of 1	30	20	10	15
	Finite Math	20	0	15	10

Find the optimal strategies for both companies and the expected shift in customers.

44. *Study Techniques* Billy-Sean's friend Pat from college has been spending all of his time in fraternity activities, and thus knows absolutely nothing about any of the three topics on tomorrow's math test. He has turned to Billy-Sean for advice as to how to spend his "all-nighter." The table below shows the scores Pat could expect to earn if the entire test were to be in a specific subject. (Because he knows no linear programming or matrix algebra, the table shows, for instance, that studying game theory all night will not be much use in preparing him for this topic.)

	Test		
Pat's Strategies ↓	Game Theory	Linear Programming	Matrix Algebra
Study Game Theory	30	0	20
Study Linear Programming	0	70	0
Study Matrix Algebra	0	0	70

What percentage of the night should Pat spend on each topic, assuming the principles of game theory, and what score can he expect to get?

Case Study   The Diet Problem

The Galaxy Nutrition health-food mega-store chain provides free online nutritional advice and support to its customers. As Web site technical consultant, you are planning to construct an interactive Web page to assist customers in preparing a diet tailored to their nutritional and budgetary requirements. Ideally, the customer would select foods to consider and specify nutritional and/or budgetary constraints, and the tool should return the optimal diet meeting those requirements. You would also like the Web page to allow the customer to decide whether, for instance, to find the cheapest possible diet meeting the requirements, the diet with the lowest number of calories, or the diet with the least total carbohydrates.

After doing a little research, you notice that the kind of problem you are trying is solve is quite well known and referred to as the *diet problem*, and that solving the diet problem is a famous example of linear programming. Indeed, there are already some online pages that solve versions of the problem that minimize total cost, so you have adequate information to assist you as you plan the page.*

NOTE See, for instance, the Diet Problem page at the Argonne National Laboratory Web site: http://www-neos.mcs.anl.gov/CaseStudies/dietpy/WebForms/index.html

You decide to start on a relatively small scale, starting with a program that uses a list of 10 foods, and minimizes either total caloric intake or total cost and satisfies a small list of requirements. Following is a small part of a table of nutritional information from the Argonne National Laboratory Web site (all the values shown are for a single serving) as well as approximate minimum daily requirements:

	Price per Serving	Calories	Total Fat g	Carbs g	Dietary Fiber g	Protein g	Vit C IU
Tofu	$0.31	88.2	5.5	2.2	1.4	9.4	0.1
Roast Chicken	$0.84	277.4	10.8	0	0	42.2	0
Spaghetti w/Sauce	$0.78	358.2	12.3	58.3	11.6	8.2	27.9
Tomato	$0.27	25.8	0.4	5.7	1.4	1.0	23.5
Oranges	$0.15	61.6	0.2	15.4	3.1	1.2	69.7
Wheat Bread	$0.05	65.0	1.0	12.4	1.3	2.2	0
Cheddar Cheese	$0.25	112.7	9.3	0.4	0	7.0	0
Oatmeal	$0.82	145.1	2.3	25.3	4.0	6.1	0
Peanut Butter	$0.07	188.5	16.0	6.9	2.1	7.7	0
White Tuna in Water	$0.69	115.6	2.1	0	0	22.7	0
Minimum requirements		2,200	20	80	25	60	90

Source: www-neos.mcs.anl.gov/CaseStudies/dietpy/WebForms/complete_table.html

Now you get to work. As always, you start by identifying the unknowns. Since the output of the Web page will consist of a recommended diet, the unknowns should logically be the number of servings of each item of food selected by the user. In your first trial run, you decide to include all the 10 food items listed, so you take

$$x_1 = \text{Number of servings of tofu}$$
$$x_2 = \text{Number of servings of roast chicken}$$
$$\vdots$$
$$x_{10} = \text{Number of servings of white tuna in water.}$$

You now set up a linear programming problem for two sample scenarios:

Scenario 1 (Minimum Cost): Satisfy all minimum nutritional requirements at a minimum cost. Here the linear programming problem is:

Minimize

$$c = 0.31x_1 + 0.84x_2 + 0.78x_3 + 0.27x_4 + 0.15x_5 + 0.05x_6 + 0.25x_7$$
$$+ 0.82x_8 + 0.07x_9 + 0.69x_{10}$$

Subject to

$$88.2x_1 + 277.4x_2 + 358.2x_3 + 25.8x_4 + 61.6x_5 + 65x_6 + 112.7x_7$$
$$+ 145.1x_8 + 188.5x_9 + 115.6x_{10} \geq 2{,}200$$
$$5.5x_1 + 10.8x_2 + 12.3x_3 + 0.4x_4 + 0.2x_5 + 1x_6 + 9.3x_7 + 2.3x_8$$
$$+ 16x_9 + 2.1x_{10} \geq 20$$
$$2.2x_1 + 58.3x_3 + 5.7x_4 + 15.4x_5 + 12.4x_6 + 0.4x_7 + 25.3x_8 + 6.9x_9 \geq 80$$
$$1.4x_1 + 11.6x_3 + 1.4x_4 + 3.1x_5 + 1.3x_6 + 4x_8 + 2.1x_9 \geq 25$$
$$9.4x_1 + 42.2x_2 + 8.2x_3 + 1x_4 + 1.2x_5 + 2.2x_6 + 7x_7 + 6.1x_8 + 7.7x_9$$
$$+ 22.7x_{10} \geq 60$$
$$0.1x_1 + 27.9x_3 + 23.5x_4 + 69.7x_5 \geq 90.$$

This is clearly the kind of linear programming problem no one in their right mind would like to do by hand (solving it requires 16 tableaus!) so you decide to use the online simplex method tool at the Web site (www.FiniteandCalc.org → Student Web Site → Online Utilities → Simplex Method Tool).

Here is a picture of the input, entered almost exactly as written above (you need to enter each constraint on a new line, and "Minimize c = 0.31x1 + · · · Subject to" must be typed on a single line):

```
Type your linear programming problem below. (Press "Example" to see how to set it up.)
Minimize   c =
0.31x1+0.84x2+0.78x3+0.27x4+0.15x5+0.05x6+0.25x7+0.82x8+0.07x9+0.69x10 Subject to
88.2x1+277.4x2+358.2x3+25.8x4+61.6x5+65x6+112.7x7+145.1x8+188.5x9+115.6x10 >= 2200
5.5x1+10.8x2+12.3x3+0.4x4+0.2x5+1x6+9.3x7+2.3x8+16x9+2.1x10 >= 20
2.2x1+58.3x3+5.7x4+15.4x5+12.4x6+0.4x7+25.3x8+6.9x9 >= 80
1.4x1+11.6x3+1.4x4+3.1x5+1.3x6+4x8+2.1x9 >= 25
9.4x1+42.2x2+8.2x3+1x4+1.2x5+2.2x6+7x7+6.1x8+7.7x9+22.7x10 >= 60
0.1x1+0x2+27.9x3+23.5x4+69.7x5 >= 90
```

Clicking "Solve" results in the following solution:

$$c = 0.981126; \; x_1 = 0, \, x_2 = 0, \, x_3 = 0, \, x_4 = 0, \, x_5 = 1.29125, \, x_6 = 0, \, x_7 = 0,$$
$$x_8 = 0, \, x_9 = 11.2491, \, x_{10} = 0.$$

This means that you can satisfy all the daily requirements for less than $1 on a diet of 1.3 servings of orange juice and 11.2 servings of peanut butter! Although you enjoy peanut butter, 11.2 servings seems a little over the top, so you modify the LP problem by adding a new constraint (which also suggests to you that some kind of flexibility needs to be built into the site to allow users to set limits on the number of servings of any one item):

$$x_9 \leq 3.$$

This new constraint results in the following solution:

$$c = 1.59981; x_1 = 0, x_2 = 0, x_3 = 0, x_4 = 0, x_5 = 1.29125, x_6 = 23.9224,$$
$$x_7 = 0, x_8 = 0, x_9 = 3, x_{10} = 0.$$

Because wheat bread is cheap and, in large enough quantities, supplies ample protein, the program has now substituted 23.9 servings of wheat bread for the missing peanut butter for a total cost of $1.60.

Unfettered, you now add

$$x_6 \leq 4$$

and obtain the following spaghetti, bread, and peanut butter diet for $3.40 per day:

$$c = 3.40305; x_1 = 0, x_2 = 0, x_3 = 3.83724, x_4 = 0, x_5 = 0, x_6 = 4, x_7 = 0,$$
$$x_8 = 0, x_9 = 3, x_{10} = 0.$$

Scenario 2 (Minimum Calories): Minimize total calories and satisfy all minimum nutritional requirements (except for caloric intake).

Here, the linear programming problem is

Minimize
$$c = 88.2x_1 + 277.4x_2 + 358.2x_3 + 25.8x_4 + 61.6x_5 + 65x_6 + 112.7x_7$$
$$+ 145.1x_8 + 188.5x_9 + 115.6x_{10}$$

Subject to
$$5.5x_1 + 10.8x_2 + 12.3x_3 + 0.4x_4 + 0.2x_5 + 1x_6 + 9.3x_7 + 2.3x_8 + 16x_9$$
$$+ 2.1x_{10} \geq 20$$
$$2.2x_1 + 58.3x_3 + 5.7x_4 + 15.4x_5 + 12.4x_6 + 0.4x_7 + 25.3x_8 + 6.9x_9 \geq 80$$
$$1.4x_1 + 11.6x_3 + 1.4x_4 + 3.1x_5 + 1.3x_6 + 4x_8 + 2.1x_9 \geq 25$$
$$9.4x_1 + 42.2x_2 + 8.2x_3 + 1x_4 + 1.2x_5 + 2.2x_6 + 7x_7 + 6.1x_8 + 7.7x_9$$
$$+ 22.7x_{10} \geq 60$$
$$0.1x_1 + 27.9x_3 + 23.5x_4 + 69.7x_5 \geq 90.$$

You obtain the following 716-calorie tofu, tomato, and tuna diet:

$$x_1 = 2.07232, x_2 = 0, x_3 = 0, x_4 = 15.7848, x_5 = 0, x_6 = 0, x_7 = 0, x_8 = 0,$$
$$x_9 = 0, x_{10} = 1.08966.$$

As 16 servings of tomatoes seems a little over the top, you add the new constraint $x_4 \leq 3$ and obtain a 783-calorie tofu, tomato, orange, and tuna diet:

$$x_1 = 2.81682, x_2 = 0, x_3 = 0, x_4 = 3, x_5 = 5.43756, x_6 = 0, x_7 = 0, x_8 = 0,$$
$$x_9 = 0, x_{10} = 1.05713.$$

What the trial runs have shown you is that your Web site will need to allow the user to set reasonable upper bounds for the number of servings of each kind of food considered. You now get to work writing the algorithm, which appears here:

www.FiniteandCalc.org → Student Web Site → Online Utilities → Diet Problem Solver

EXERCISES

1. Briefly explain why roast chicken, which supplies protein more cheaply than either tofu or tuna, does not appear in the optimal solution in either scenario.

2. Consider the optimal solution obtained in Scenario 1 when peanut butter and bread were restricted. Experiment on the Simplex Method tool by increasing the protein requirement 10 grams at a time until chicken appears in the optimal diet. At what level of protein does the addition of chicken first become necessary?

3. What constraints would you add for a person who wants to eat at most two servings of chicken a day and is allergic to tomatoes and peanut butter? What is the resulting diet for Scenario 2?

4. What is the linear programming problem for someone who wants as much protein as possible at a cost of no more than $6 per day with no more than 50 g of carbohydrates per day assuming they want to satisfy the minimum requirements for all the remaining nutrients. What is the resulting diet?

5. Is it possible to obtain a diet with no bread or peanut butter in Scenario 1 costing less than $4 per day?

TI-83/84 Plus   Technology Guide

Section 4.1

Some calculators, including the TI-83/84 Plus, will shade one side of a graph, but you need to tell the calculator which side to shade. For instance, to obtain the solution set of $2x + 3y \le 6$ shown in Figure 4:

1. Solve the corresponding equation $2x + 3y = 6$ for y and use the following input:

2. The icon to the left of "Y_1" tells the calculator to shade above the line. You can cycle through the various shading options by positioning the cursor to the left of Y_1 and pressing ENTER until you see the one you want. Here's what the graph will look like:

Section 4.3

Example 3 (page 298)   The Acme Baby Foods example in the text leads to the following linear programming problem:

$$\text{Maximize} \quad p = 10x + 7y$$
$$\text{subject to} \quad x \qquad \le 600$$
$$2x + 3y \le 3{,}600$$
$$5x + 3y \le 4{,}500$$
$$x \ge 0, \ y \ge 0.$$

Solve it using technology.

Solution with Technology

When we introduce slack variables, we get the following system of equations:

$$\begin{aligned}
x \qquad\quad + s \qquad\qquad\quad &= 600 \\
2x + 3y \quad\quad + t \qquad\quad &= 3{,}600 \\
5x + 3y \qquad\qquad + u \quad &= 4{,}500 \\
-10x - 7y \qquad\qquad\quad + p &= 0.
\end{aligned}$$

We use the PIVOT program for the TI-83/84 Plus to help with the simplex method. This program is available at the Web site by following

Everything for Finite Math → Math Tools for Chapter 4.

Because the calculator handles decimals as easily as integers, there is no need to avoid them, except perhaps to save limited screen space. If we don't need to avoid decimals, we can use the traditional Gauss-Jordan method (see the discussion at the end of Section 2.2): After selecting your pivot, and prior to clearing the pivot column, *divide the pivot row by the value of the pivot, thereby turning the pivot into a 1*.

The main drawback to using the TI-83/84 Plus is that we can't label the rows and columns. We can mentally label them as we go, but we can do without labels entirely if we wish. We begin by entering the initial tableau as the matrix [A]. (Another drawback to using the TI-83/84 Plus is that it can't show the whole tableau at once. Here and below we show tableaux across several screens. Use the TI-83/84 Plus's arrow keys to scroll a matrix left and right so you can see all of it.)

The following is the sequence of tableaux we get while using the simplex method with the help of the PIVOT program.

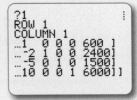

After determining that the next pivot is in the third row and second column, we divide the third row by the pivot, 3, and then pivot:

```
?2
DIVIDE ROW 3
BY 3
[[1  0  1       ...
 [0  3  -2      ...
 [0  1  -1.66666...
 [0  -7 10      ...
```

```
?2
DIVIDE ROW 3
BY 3
...      0  0      ...
...      1  0      ...
...667   0  .3333333...
...      0  0      ...
```

```
?2
DIVIDE ROW 3
BY 3
...      0  600 ]
...      0  2400]
...333333 0  500 ]
...      1  6000]]
```

```
?1
ROW 3
COLUMN 2
[[1  0  1       ...
 [0  0  3       ...
 [0  1  -1.666666...
 [0  0  -1.666666...
```

```
?1
ROW 3
COLUMN 2
...      0  0      ...
...      1  -1     ...
...667   0  .3333333...
...667   0  2.333333...
```

```
?1
ROW 3
COLUMN 2
...      0  600 ]
...      0  900 ]
...333333 0  500 ]
...333333 1  9500]]
```

The next pivot is the 3 in the second row, third column. We divide its row by 3 and pivot:

```
?2
DIVIDE ROW 2
BY 3
[[1  0  1       ...
 [0  0  1       ...
 [0  1  -1.666666...
 [0  0  -1.666666...
```

```
?2
DIVIDE ROW 2
BY 3
...      0         ...
...      .33333333...
...6667  0         ...
...6667  0         ...
```

```
?2
DIVIDE ROW 2
BY 3
...      0     ...
...33    -.333333333...
...      .333333333...
...      2.333333333...
```

```
?2
DIVIDE ROW 2
BY 3
...      0  600 ]
...333333 0  300 ]
...33333  0  500 ]
...33333  1  9500]]
```

```
?1
ROW 2
COLUMN 3
[[1  0  0  -.33333...
 [0  0  1  .333333...
 [0  1  0  .555555...
 [0  0  0  .555555...
```

```
?1
ROW 2
COLUMN 3
...3333  .33333333...
...333   -.3333333...
...556   -.2222222...
...556   1.7777777...
```

```
?1
ROW 2
COLUMN 3
...3333  0  300  ]
...33333 0  300  ]
...22222 0  1000 ]
...7778  1  10000]]
```

There are no negative numbers in the bottom row, so we're finished. How do we read off the optimal solutions if we don't have labels, though? Look at the columns containing one 1 and three 0s. They are the x column, the y column, the s column, and the p column. Think of the 1 that appears in each of these columns as a pivot whose column has been cleared. If we had labels, the row containing a pivot would have the same label as the column containing that pivot. We can now read off the solution as follows:

x column: The pivot is in the first row, so row 1 would have been labeled with x. We look at the rightmost column to read off the value $x = 300$.

y column: The pivot is in row 3, so we look at the rightmost column to read off the value $y = 1,000$.

s column: The pivot is in row 2, so we look at the rightmost column to read off the value $s = 300$.

p column: The pivot is in row 3, so we look at the rightmost column to read off the value $p = 10,000$.

Thus, the maximum value of p is $10,000¢ = \$100$, which occurs when $x = 300$ and $y = 1,000$. The values of the slack variables are $s = 300$ and $t = u = 0$. (Look at the t and u columns to see that they must be inactive.)

EXCEL Technology Guide

Section 4.1

Excel is not a particularly good tool for graphing linear inequalities because it cannot easily shade one side of a line. One solution is to use the "error bar" feature to indicate which side of the line *should* be shaded. For example, here is how we might graph the inequality $2x + 3y \leq 6$.

1. Create a scatter graph using two points to construct a line segment (as in Chapter 1). (Notice that we had to solve the equation $2x + 3y = 6$ for y.)

▲	A	B
1	x	y
2	-10	=-(2/3)*A2 + 2
3	10	

2. Double-click on the line-segment, and use the "X-Error Bars" feature to obtain a diagram similar to the one below, where the error bars indicate the direction of shading.

Alternatively, you can use the Drawing Palette to create a polygon with a semi-transparent fill, as shown above.

Section 4.3

Example 3 (page 298) The Acme Baby Foods example in the text leads to the following linear programming problem:

$$\begin{aligned} \text{Maximize} \quad & p = 10x + 7y \\ \text{subject to} \quad & x \leq 600 \\ & 2x + 3y \leq 3,600 \\ & 5x + 3y \leq 4,500 \\ & x \geq 0, \ y \geq 0. \end{aligned}$$

Solve it using technology.

Solution with Technology

When we introduce slack variables, we get the following system of equations:

$$
\begin{aligned}
x && +\,s && &&&= 600 \\
2x + 3y && +\,t &&&&= 3{,}600 \\
5x + 3y &&&& +\,u &&= 4{,}500 \\
-10x - 7y &&&&&& +\,p &= 0.
\end{aligned}
$$

We use the Excel Row Operation and Pivoting Utility to help with the simplex method. This spreadsheet is available at the Web site by following

Everything for Finite Math → Math Tools for Chapter 4.

Because Excel handles decimals as easily as integers, there is no need to avoid them. If we don't need to avoid decimals, we can use the traditional Gauss-Jordan method (see the discussion at the end of Section 2.2): After selecting your pivot, and prior to clearing the pivot column, *divide the pivot row by the value of the pivot, thereby turning the pivot into a 1.*

The main drawback to using a tool like Excel is that it will not automatically keep track of row and column labels. We could enter and modify labels by hand as we go, or we can do without them entirely if we wish. The following is the sequence of tableaux we get while using the simplex method with the help of the pivoting tool.

1	0	1	0	0	0	600
2	3	0	1	0	0	3600
5	3	0	0	1	0	4500
-10	-7	0	0	0	1	0

1	0	1	0	0	0	600
0	3	-2	1	0	0	2400
0	3	-5	0	1	0	1500
0	-7	10	0	0	1	6000

After determining that the next pivot is in the third row and second column, we divide the third row by the pivot, 3, before actually pivoting:

1	0	1	0	0	0	600
0	3	-2	1	0	0	2400
0	1	-1.6666667	0	0.33333333	0	500
0	-7	10	0	0	1	6000

1	0	1	0	0	0	600
0	0	3	1	-1	0	900
0	1	-1.6666667	0	0.33333333	0	500
0	0	-1.6666667	0	2.33333333	1	9500

Again, we divide by the pivot, this time in the second row, third column.

1	0	1	0	0	0	600
0	0	1	0.33333333	-0.3333333	0	300
0	1	-1.6666667	0	0.33333333	0	500
0	0	-1.6666667	0	2.33333333	1	9500

1	0	0	-0.3333333	0.33333333	0	300
0	0	1	0.33333333	-0.3333333	0	300
0	1	0	0.55555556	-0.2222222	0	1000
0	0	0	0.55555556	1.77777778	1	10000

There are no negative numbers in the bottom row, so we're finished. How do we read off the optimal solutions if we don't have labels, though? Look at the columns containing one 1 and three 0s. They are the x column, the y column, the s column, and the p column. Think of the 1 that appears in each of these columns as a pivot whose column has been cleared. If we had labels, the row containing a pivot would have the same label as the column containing that pivot. We can now read off the solution as follows:

x column: The pivot is in the first row, so row 1 would have been labeled with x. We look at the rightmost column to read off the value $x = 300$.

y column: The pivot is in row 3, so we look at the rightmost column to read off the value $y = 1{,}000$.

s column: The pivot is in row 2, so we look at the rightmost column to read off the value $s = 300$.

p column: The pivot is in row 3, so we look at the rightmost column to read off the value $p = 10{,}000$.

Thus, the maximum value of p is $10{,}000\cent = \$100$, which occurs when $x = 300$ and $y = 1{,}000$. The values of the slack variables are $s = 300$ and $t = u = 0$. (Look at the t and u columns to see that they must be inactive.)

6

Sets and Counting

Case Study Designing a Puzzle

As Product Design Manager for Cerebral Toys, Inc., you are constantly on the lookout for ideas for intellectually stimulating yet inexpensive toys. Your design team recently came up with an idea for a puzzle consisting of a number of plastic cubes. Each cube will have two faces colored red, two white, and two blue, and there will be exactly two cubes with each possible configuration of colors. The goal of the puzzle is to seek out the matching pairs, thereby enhancing a child's geometric intuition and three-dimensional manipulation skills. **If the kit is to include every possible configuration of colors, how many cubes will the kit contain?**

Image Source/Getty Images

Web Site

www.FiniteandCalc.org

At the Web site you will find:

- A detailed chapter summary

- A true/false quiz

- A utility to compute factorials, permutations, and combinations

- Additional review exercises

Introduction

The theory of sets is the foundation for most of mathematics. It also has direct applications—for example, in searching computer databases. We will use set theory extensively in the chapter on probability, and thus much of this chapter revolves around the idea of a **set of outcomes** of a procedure such as rolling a pair of dice or choosing names from a database. Also important in probability is the theory of **counting** the number of elements in a set, which is called **combinatorics**.

Counting elements is not a trivial proposition; for example, the betting game Lotto (used in many state lotteries) has you pick six numbers from some range—say, 1–55. If your six numbers match the six numbers chosen in the "official drawing," you win the top prize. How many Lotto tickets would you need to buy to guarantee that you will win? That is, how many Lotto tickets are possible? By the end of this chapter, we will be able to answer these questions.

6.1   Sets and Set Operations

In this section we review the basic ideas of set theory with examples in applications that recur throughout the rest of the chapter.

Sets

Sets and Elements

A **set** is a collection of items, referred to as the **elements** of the set.

Visualizing a Set

Set

Elements of the Set

	Quick Examples
We usually use a capital letter to name a set and braces to enclose the elements of a set.	$W = \{$Amazon, eBay, Apple$\}$ $N = \{1, 2, 3, \ldots\}$
$x \in A$ means that x **is an element of** the set A. If x is not an element of A, we write $x \notin A$.	Amazon $\in W$ (W as above) Microsoft $\notin W$ $2 \in N$
$B = A$ means that A and B have the same elements. The order in which the elements are listed does not matter.	$\{5, -9, 1, 3\} = \{-9, 1, 3, 5\}$ $\{1, 2, 3, 4\} \neq \{1, 2, 3, 6\}$
$B \subseteq A$ means that B is a **subset** of A; every element of B is also an element of A.	$\{$eBay, Apple$\} \subseteq W$ $\{1, 2, 3, 4\} \subseteq \{1, 2, 3, 4\}$
$B \subset A$ means that B is a **proper subset** of A: $B \subseteq A$, but $B \neq A$.	$\{$eBay, Apple$\} \subset W$ $\{1, 2, 3\} \subset \{1, 2, 3, 4\}$ $\{1, 2, 3\} \subset N$ (N as above)

> Ø is the **empty set**, the set containing no elements. It is a subset of every set.
>
> A **finite** set has finitely many elements. An **infinite** set does not have finitely many elements.

> $\emptyset \subseteq W$
> $\emptyset \subset W$
>
> $W = \{$Amazon, eBay, Apple$\}$ is a finite set.
> $N = \{1, 2, 3, \ldots\}$ is an infinite set.

One type of set we'll use often is the **set of outcomes** of some activity or experiment. For example, if we toss a coin and observe which side faces up, there are two possible outcomes, heads (H) and tails (T). The set of outcomes of tossing a coin once can be written

$S = \{$H, T$\}.$

As another example, suppose we roll a die that has faces numbered 1 through 6, as usual, and observe which number faces up. The set of outcomes *could* be represented as

$$ S = \left\{ \boxdot, \boxdot, \boxdot, \boxdot, \boxdot, \boxdot \right\}. $$

However, we can much more easily write

$S = \{1, 2, 3, 4, 5, 6\}.$

EXAMPLE 1 Two Dice: Distinguishable vs. Indistinguishable

a. Suppose we have two dice that we can distinguish in some way—say, one is blue and one is green. If we roll both dice, what is the set of outcomes?

b. Describe the set of outcomes if the dice are indistinguishable.

Solution

a. A systematic way of laying out the set of outcomes for a distinguishable pair of dice is shown in Figure 1.

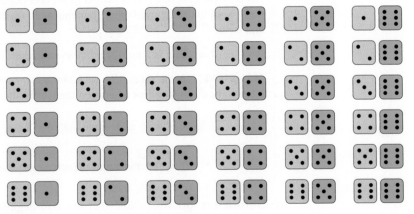

Figure 1

In the first row all the blue dice show a 1, in the second row a 2, in the third row a 3, and so on. Similarly, in the first column all the green dice show a 1, in the second column a 2, and so on. The diagonal pairs (top left to bottom right) show all the "doubles." Using the picture as a guide, we can write the set of 36 outcomes as follows.

$$S = \left\{ \begin{array}{llllll} (1,1), & (1,2), & (1,3), & (1,4), & (1,5), & (1,6), \\ (2,1), & (2,2), & (2,3), & (2,4), & (2,5), & (2,6), \\ (3,1), & (3,2), & (3,3), & (3,4), & (3,5), & (3,6), \\ (4,1), & (4,2), & (4,3), & (4,4), & (4,5), & (4,6), \\ (5,1), & (5,2), & (5,3), & (5,4), & (5,5), & (5,6), \\ (6,1), & (6,2), & (6,3), & (6,4), & (6,5), & (6,6) \end{array} \right\} \qquad \text{Distinguishable dice}$$

Notice that S is also the set of outcomes if we roll a single die twice, if we take the first number in each pair to be the outcome of the first roll and the second number the outcome of the second roll.

b. If the dice are truly indistinguishable, we will have no way of knowing which die is which once they are rolled. Think of placing two identical dice in a closed box and then shaking the box. When we look inside afterward, there is no way to tell which die is which. (If we make a small marking on one of the dice or somehow keep track of it as it bounces around, we are *distinguishing* the dice.) We regard two dice as **indistinguishable** if we make no attempt to distinguish them. Thus, for example, the two different outcomes (1,3) and (3,1) from part (a) would represent the same outcome in part (b) (one die shows a 3 and the other a 1). Because the set of outcomes should contain each outcome only once, we can remove (3,1). Following this approach gives the following smaller set of outcomes:

$$S = \left\{ \begin{array}{llllll} (1,1), & (1,2), & (1,3), & (1,4), & (1,5), & (1,6), \\ & (2,2), & (2,3), & (2,4), & (2,5), & (2,6), \\ & & (3,3), & (3,4), & (3,5), & (3,6), \\ & & & (4,4), & (4,5), & (4,6), \\ & & & & (5,5), & (5,6), \\ & & & & & (6,6) \end{array} \right\} \qquad \text{Indistinguishable dice}$$

EXAMPLE 2 Set-Builder Notation

Let $B = \{0, 2, 4, 6, 8\}$. B is the set of all non-negative even integers less than 10. If we don't want to list the individual elements of B, we can instead use "set-builder notation," and write

$$B = \{n \mid n \text{ is a non-negative even integer less than 10}\}.$$

This is read "*B is the set of all n such that n is a non-negative even integer less than 10.*" Here is the correspondence between the words and the symbols:

B is the set of all n such that n is a non-negative even integer less than 10

$$B = \{n \mid n \text{ is a non-negative even integer less than 10}\}.$$

➡ **Before we go on...** Note that the **non-negative** integers *include* 0, whereas the **positive** integers *exclude* 0. ∎

Figure 2

Venn Diagrams

We can visualize sets and relations between sets using **Venn diagrams**. In a Venn diagram, we represent a set as a region, often a disk (Figure 2).

The elements of A are the points inside the region. The following Venn diagrams illustrate the relations we've discussed so far.

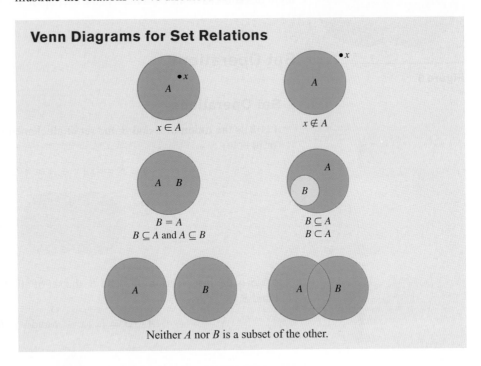

Venn Diagrams for Set Relations

$x \in A$ $x \notin A$

$B = A$
$B \subseteq A$ and $A \subseteq B$ $B \subseteq A$
$B \subset A$

Neither A nor B is a subset of the other.

Note Although the diagram for $B \subseteq A$ suggests a proper subset, it is customary to use the same diagram for both subsets and proper subsets. ■

EXAMPLE 3 Customer Interests

NobelBooks.com (a fierce competitor of OHaganBooks.com) maintains a database of customers and the types of books they have purchased. In the company's database is the set of customers

$S = \{$Einstein, Bohr, Millikan, Heisenberg, Schrödinger, Dirac$\}$.

A search of the database for customers who have purchased cookbooks yields the subset

$A = \{$Einstein, Bohr, Heisenberg, Dirac$\}$.

Another search, this time for customers who have purchased mysteries, yields the subset

$B = \{$Bohr, Heisenberg, Schrödinger$\}$.

NobelBooks.com wants to promote a new combination mystery/cookbook, and wants to target two subsets of customers: those who have purchased either cookbooks or mysteries (or both) and, for additional promotions, those who have purchased both cookbooks and mysteries. Name the customers in each of these subsets.

Figure 3

Solution We can picture the database and the two subsets using the Venn diagram in Figure 3.

The set of customers who have purchased either cookbooks or mysteries (or both) consists of the customers who are in A or B or both: Einstein, Bohr, Heisenberg, Schrödinger, and Dirac. The set of customers who have purchased both cookbooks and mysteries consists of the customers in the overlap of A and B, Bohr and Heisenberg.

Set Operations

Set Operations

$A \cup B$ is the **union** of A and B, the set of all elements that are either in A or in B (or in both).

$$A \cup B = \{x \mid x \in A \text{ or } x \in B\}$$

$A \cap B$ is the **intersection** of A and B, the set of all elements that are common to A and B.

$$A \cap B = \{x \mid x \in A \text{ and } x \in B\}$$

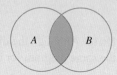

Logical Equivalents

Union: For an element to be in $A \cup B$, it must be in A **or** in B.
Intersection: For an element to be in $A \cap B$, it must be in A **and** in B.

Quick Examples

If $A = \{a, b, c, d\}$, and $B = \{c, d, e, f\}$ then

$A \cup B = \{a, b, c, d, e, f\}$

$A \cap B = \{c, d\}.$

Note Mathematicians always use "or" in its *inclusive* sense: one thing or another *or both*. ■

There is one other operation we use, called the **complement** of a set A, which, roughly speaking, is the set of things *not* in A.

Q : *Why only "roughly"? Why not just form the set of things not in A?*

A : This would amount to assuming that there is a set of *all things*. (It would be the complement of the empty set.) Although tempting, talking about entities such as the "set of all things" leads to paradoxes.* Instead, we first need to fix a set S of all objects under consideration, or the *universe of discourse*, which we generally call the **universal set** for the discussion. For example, when we search the Web, we take S to be the set of all Web pages. When talking about integers, we take S to be the set of all integers. In other words, our choice of universal set depends on the context. The complement of a set $A \subseteq S$ is then the set of *things in S that are not in A.*

∗ NOTE The most famous such paradox is called "Russell's Paradox," after the mathematical logician (and philosopher and pacifist) Bertrand Russell. It goes like this: If there were a set of all things, then there would also be a (smaller) set of all sets. Call it S. Now, because S is the *set* of *all* sets, it must contain itself as a member. In other words, $S \in S$. Let P be the subset of S consisting of all sets that are *not* members of themselves. Now we pose the following question: Is P a member of itself? If it is, then, because it is the set of all sets that are *not* members of themselves, it is not a member of itself. On the other hand, if it is *not* a member of itself, then it qualifies as an element of P. In other words, it *is* a member of itself! Because neither can be true, something is wrong. What is wrong is the assumption that there is such a thing as the set of all sets or the set of all things.

Complement

If S is the universal set and $A \subseteq S$, then A' is the **complement** of A (in S), the set of all elements of S not in A.

$$A' = \{x \in S \,|\, x \notin A\} = \text{Green Region Below}$$

Logical Equivalent
For an element to be in A', it must be in S but **not** in A.

Quick Example
If $S = \{a, b, c, d, e, f, g\}$ and $A = \{a, b, c, d\}$ then

$$A' = \{e, f, g\}.$$

In the following example we use set operations to describe the sets we found in Example 3, as well as some others.

EXAMPLE 4 **Customer Interests**

NobelBooks.com maintains a database of customers and the types of books they have purchased. In the company's database is the set of customers

$$S = \{\text{Einstein, Bohr, Millikan, Heisenberg, Schrödinger, Dirac}\}.$$

A search of the database for customers who have purchased cookbooks yields the subset

$$A = \{\text{Einstein, Bohr, Heisenberg, Dirac}\}.$$

Another search, this time for customers who have purchased mysteries, yields the subset

$$B = \{\text{Bohr, Heisenberg, Schrödinger}\}.$$

Figure 4

Figure 5

A third search, for customers who had registered with the site but not used their first-time customer discount yields the subset

$$C = \{\text{Millikan}\}.$$

Use set operations to describe the following subsets:

a. The subset of customers who have purchased either cookbooks or mysteries

b. The subset of customers who have purchased both cookbooks and mysteries

c. The subset of customers who have not purchased cookbooks

d. The subset of customers who have purchased cookbooks but have not used their first-time customer discount

Solution Figure 4 shows two alternative Venn diagram representations of the database. Although the second version shows C overlapping A and B, the placement of the names inside shows that there are no customers in those overlaps.

a. The subset of customers who have bought either cookbooks *or* mysteries is

$$A \cup B = \{\text{Einstein, Bohr, Heisenberg, Schrödinger, Dirac}\}.$$

b. The subset of customers who have bought both cookbooks *and* mysteries is

$$A \cap B = \{\text{Bohr, Heisenberg}\}.$$

c. The subset of customers who have *not* bought cookbooks is

$$A' = \{\text{Millikan, Schrödinger}\}.$$

Note that, for the universal set, we are using the set S of all customers in the database.

d. The subset of customers who have bought cookbooks but have not used their first-time purchase discount is the empty set

$$A \cap C = \emptyset.$$

When the intersection of two sets is empty, we say that the two sets are **disjoint**. In a Venn diagram, disjoint sets are drawn as regions that don't overlap, as in Figure 5.*

* **NOTE** People new to set theory sometimes find it strange to consider the empty set a valid set. Here is one of the times where it is very useful to do so. If we did not, we would have to say that $A \cap C$ was defined only when A and C had something in common. Having to deal with the fact that this set operation was not always defined would quickly get tiresome.

➡ **Before we go on...** Computer databases and the Web can be searched using so-called "Boolean searches." These are search requests using "and," "or," and "not." Using "and" gives the intersection of separate searches, using "or" gives the union, and using "not" gives the complement. In the next section we'll see how Web search engines allow such searches. ■

Cartesian Product

There is one more set operation we need to discuss.

Cartesian Product

The **Cartesian product** of two sets, A and B, is the set of all ordered pairs (a, b) with $a \in A$ and $b \in B$.

$$A \times B = \{(a, b) \mid a \in A \text{ and } b \in B\}$$

In words, $A \times B$ is the set of all ordered pairs whose first component is in A and whose second component is in B.

Quick Examples

1. If $A = \{a, b\}$ and $B = \{1, 2, 3\}$, then

$$A \times B = \{(a, 1), (a, 2), (a, 3), (b, 1), (b, 2), (b, 3)\}.$$

Visualizing A × B

2. If $S = \{H, T\}$, then

$$S \times S = \{(H, H), (H, T), (T, H), (T, T)\}.$$

In other words, if S is the set of outcomes of tossing a coin once, then $S \times S$ is the set of outcomes of tossing a coin twice.

3. If $S = \{1, 2, 3, 4, 5, 6\}$, then

$$S \times S = \begin{cases} (1, 1), & (1, 2), & (1, 3), & (1, 4), & (1, 5), & (1, 6), \\ (2, 1), & (2, 2), & (2, 3), & (2, 4), & (2, 5), & (2, 6), \\ (3, 1), & (3, 2), & (3, 3), & (3, 4), & (3, 5), & (3, 6), \\ (4, 1), & (4, 2), & (4, 3), & (4, 4), & (4, 5), & (4, 6), \\ (5, 1), & (5, 2), & (5, 3), & (5, 4), & (5, 5), & (5, 6), \\ (6, 1), & (6, 2), & (6, 3), & (6, 4), & (6, 5), & (6, 6) \end{cases}.$$

In other words, if S is the set of outcomes of rolling a die once, then $S \times S$ is the set of outcomes of rolling a die twice (or rolling two distinguishable dice).

4. If $A = \{$red, yellow$\}$ and $B = \{$Mustang, Firebird$\}$ then

$A \times B = \{$(red, Mustang), (red, Firebird), (yellow, Mustang), (yellow, Firebird)$\}$ which we might also write as

$A \times B = \{$red Mustang, red Firebird, yellow Mustang, yellow Firebird$\}$.

EXAMPLE 5 Representing Cartesian Products

The manager of an automobile dealership has collected data on the number of preowned Acura, Infiniti, Lexus, and Mercedes cars the dealership has from the 2009, 2010, and 2011 model years. In entering this information on a spreadsheet, the manager would like to have each spreadsheet cell represent a particular year and make. Describe this set of cells.

Solution Because each cell represents a year and a make, we can think of the cell as a pair (year, make), as in (2009, Acura). Thus, the set of cells can be thought of as a Cartesian product:

$Y = \{2009, 2010, 2011\}$ Year of car

$M = \{$Acura, Infiniti, Lexus, Mercedes$\}$ Make of car

$$Y \times M = \left\{ \begin{array}{llll} (2009, \text{Acura}) & (2009, \text{Infiniti}) & (2009, \text{Lexus}) & (2009, \text{Mercedes}) \\ (2010, \text{Acura}) & (2010, \text{Infiniti}) & (2010, \text{Lexus}) & (2010, \text{Mercedes}) \\ (2011, \text{Acura}) & (2011, \text{Infiniti}) & (2011, \text{Lexus}) & (2011, \text{Mercedes}) \end{array} \right\} .$$ Cells

Thus, the manager might arrange the spreadsheet as follows:

	A	B	C	D	E
1		**Acura**	**Infiniti**	**Lexus**	**Mercedes**
2	**2009**	(2009 Acura)	(2009 Infiniti)	(2009 Lexus)	(2009 Mercedes)
3	**2010**	(2010 Acura)	(2010 Infiniti)	(2010 Lexus)	(2010 Mercedes)
4	**2011**	(2011 Acura)	(2011 Infiniti)	(2011 Lexus)	(2011 Mercedes)

The highlighting shows the 12 cells to be filled in, representing the numbers of cars of each year and make. For example, in cell B2 should go the number of 2009 Acuras the dealership has.

➡ **Before we go on...** The arrangement in the spreadsheet in Example 5 is consistent with the matrix notation in Chapter 2. We could also have used the elements of Y as column labels along the top and the elements of M as row labels down the side. Along those lines, we can also visualize the Cartesian product $Y \times M$ as a set of points in the xy-plane ("Cartesian plane") as shown in Figure 6.

Figure 6

FAQs

The Many Meanings of "And"

Q: *Suppose A is the set of actors and B is the set of all baseball players. Then the set of all actors and baseball players is A ∩ B, right?*

A: Wrong. The fact that the word "and" appears in the description of a set does not always mean that the set is an intersection; the word "and" can mean different things in different contexts. $A \cap B$ refers to the set of elements that are in both A and B, hence to actors who are also baseball players. On the other hand, the set of all actors and baseball players is the set of people who are either actors or baseball players (or both), which is $A \cup B$. We can use the word "and" to describe both sets:

$A \cap B = \{$people who are both actors *and* baseball players$\}$

$A \cup B = \{$people who are actors *or* baseball players$\}$

$\qquad = \{$all actors *and* baseball players$\}$.

6.1 EXERCISES

▼ more advanced   ◆ challenging
Ⓣ indicates exercises that should be solved using technology

List the elements in each of the sets in Exercises 1–16.

1. The set F consisting of the four seasons.

2. The set A consisting of the authors of this book.

3. The set I of all positive integers no greater than 6.

4. The set N of all negative integers greater than -3.

5. $A = \{n \mid n$ is a positive integer and $0 \le n \le 3\}$.
HINT [See Example 2.]

6. $A = \{n \mid n$ is a positive integer and $0 < n < 8\}$.
HINT [See Example 2.]

7. $B = \{n \mid n$ is an even positive integer and $0 \le n \le 8\}$.

8. $B = \{n \mid n$ is an odd positive integer and $0 \le n \le 8\}$.

9. The set of all outcomes of tossing a pair of **(a)** distinguishable coins **(b)** indistinguishable coins. HINT [See Example 1.]

10. The set of outcomes of tossing three **(a)** distinguishable coins **(b)** indistinguishable coins. HINT [See Example 1.]

11. The set of all outcomes of rolling two distinguishable dice such that the numbers add to 6.

12. The set of all outcomes of rolling two distinguishable dice such that the numbers add to 8.

13. The set of all outcomes of rolling two indistinguishable dice such that the numbers add to 6.

14. The set of all outcomes of rolling two indistinguishable dice such that the numbers add to 8.

15. The set of all outcomes of rolling two distinguishable dice such that the numbers add to 13.

16. The set of all outcomes of rolling two distinguishable dice such that the numbers add to 1.

In each of Exercises 17–20, draw a Venn diagram that illustrates the relationships among the given sets. HINT [See Example 3.]

17. $S = \{$eBay, Google™, Amazon, OHaganBooks, Hotmail$\}$, $A = \{$Amazon, OHaganBooks$\}$, $B = \{$eBay, Amazon$\}$, $C = \{$Amazon, Hotmail$\}$

18. $S = \{$Apple, Dell, Gateway, Pomegranate, Compaq$\}$, $A = \{$Gateway, Pomegranate, Compaq$\}$, $B = \{$Dell, Gateway, Pomegranate, Compaq$\}$, $C = \{$Apple, Dell, Compaq$\}$

19. $S = \{$eBay, Google™, Amazon, OHaganBooks, Hotmail$\}$, $A = \{$Amazon, Hotmail$\}$, $B = \{$eBay, Google™, Amazon, Hotmail$\}$, $C = \{$Amazon, Hotmail$\}$

20. $S = \{$Apple, Dell, Gateway, Pomegranate, Compaq$\}$, $A = \{$Apple, Dell, Pomegranate, Compaq$\}$, $B = \{$Pomegranate$\}$, $C = \{$Pomegranate$\}$

Let $A = \{$June, Janet, Jill, Justin, Jeffrey, Jello$\}$, $B = \{$Janet, Jello, Justin$\}$, and $C = \{$Sally, Solly, Molly, Jolly, Jello$\}$. Find each set in Exercises 21–34. HINT [See Quick Examples on page 400.]

21. $A \cup B$ **22.** $A \cup C$

23. $A \cup \varnothing$ **24.** $B \cup \varnothing$

25. $A \cup (B \cup C)$ **26.** $(A \cup B) \cup C$

27. $C \cap B$ **28.** $C \cap A$

29. $A \cap \varnothing$ **30.** $\varnothing \cap B$

31. $(A \cap B) \cap C$ **32.** $A \cap (B \cap C)$

33. $(A \cap B) \cup C$ **34.** $A \cup (B \cap C)$

In Exercises 35–42, $A = \{$small, medium, large$\}$, $B = \{$blue, green$\}$, and $C = \{$triangle, square$\}$. HINT [See Quick Examples on page 403.]

35. List the elements of $A \times C$.

36. List the elements of $B \times C$.

37. List the elements of $A \times B$.

38. The elements of $A \times B \times C$ are the ordered triples (a, b, c) with $a \in A$, $b \in B$, and $c \in C$. List all the elements of $A \times B \times C$.

39. Represent $B \times C$ as cells in a spreadsheet. HINT [See Example 5.]

40. Represent $A \times C$ as cells in a spreadsheet. HINT [See Example 5.]

41. Represent $A \times B$ as cells in a spreadsheet.

42. Represent $A \times A$ as cells in a spreadsheet.

Let $A = \{H, T\}$ be the set of outcomes when a coin is tossed, and let $B = \{1, 2, 3, 4, 5, 6\}$ be the set of outcomes when a die is rolled. Write each set in Exercises 43–46 in terms of A and/or B and list its elements.

43. The set of outcomes when a die is rolled and then a coin tossed.

44. The set of outcomes when a coin is tossed twice.

45. The set of outcomes when a coin is tossed three times.

46. The set of outcomes when a coin is tossed twice and then a die is rolled.

Let S be the set of outcomes when two distinguishable dice are rolled, let E be the subset of outcomes in which at least one die shows an even number, and let F be the subset of outcomes in which at least one die shows an odd number. List the elements in each subset given in Exercises 47–52.

47. E' **48.** F'

49. $(E \cup F)$ **50.** $(E \cap F)'$

51. $E' \cup F'$ **52.** $E' \cap F'$

Use Venn diagrams to illustrate the following identities for subsets A, B, and C of S.

53. ▼ $(A \cup B)' = A' \cap B'$ De Morgan's Law

54. ▼ $(A \cap B)' = A' \cup B'$ De Morgan's Law

55. ▼ $(A \cap B) \cap C = A \cap (B \cap C)$ Associative Law

56. ▼ $(A \cup B) \cup C = A \cup (B \cup C)$ Associative Law

57. ▼ $A \cup (B \cap C) = (A \cup B) \cap (A \cup C)$ Distributive Law

58. ▼ $A \cap (B \cup C) = (A \cap B) \cup (A \cap C)$ Distributive Law

59. ▼ $S' = \emptyset$ **60.** ▼ $\emptyset' = S$

APPLICATIONS

Databases A freelance computer consultant keeps a database of her clients, which contains the names

$S = \{$Acme, Brothers, Crafts, Dion, Effigy, Floyd, Global, Hilbert$\}$.

The following clients owe her money:

$A = \{$Acme, Crafts, Effigy, Global$\}$.

The following clients have done at least $10,000 worth of business with her:

$B = \{$Acme, Brothers, Crafts, Dion$\}$.

The following clients have employed her in the last year:

$C = \{$Acme, Crafts, Dion, Effigy, Global, Hilbert$\}$.

In Exercises 61–68, a subset of clients is described that the consultant could find using her database. Write each subset in terms of A, B, and C and list the clients in that subset. HINT [See Example 4.]

61. The clients who owe her money and have done at least $10,000 worth of business with her.

62. The clients who owe her money or have done at least $10,000 worth of business with her.

63. The clients who have done at least $10,000 worth of business with her or have employed her in the last year.

64. The clients who have done at least $10,000 worth of business with her and have employed her in the last year.

65. The clients who do not owe her money and have employed her in the last year.

66. The clients who do not owe her money or have employed her in the last year.

67. ▼ The clients who owe her money, have not done at least $10,000 worth of business with her, and have not employed her in the last year.

68. ▼ The clients who either do not owe her money, have done at least $10,000 worth of business with her, or have employed her in the last year.

69. ***Boat Sales*** You are given data on revenues from sales of sail boats, motor boats, and yachts for each of the years 2003 through 2006. How would you represent these data in a spreadsheet? The cells in your spreadsheet represent elements of which set?

70. ***Health-Care Spending*** Spending in most categories of health care in the United States increased dramatically in the last 30 years of the 1900s.[1] You are given data showing total spending on prescription drugs, nursing homes, hospital care, and professional services for each of the last three decades of the 1900s. How would you represent these data in a spreadsheet? The cells in your spreadsheet represent elements of which set?

COMMUNICATION AND REASONING EXERCISES

71. You sell iPods® and jPods. Let I be the set of all iPods you sold last year, and let J be the set of all jPods you sold last year. What set represents the collection of all iPods and jPods you sold combined?

72. You sell two models of music players: the *yoVaina Grandote* and the *yoVaina Minúsculito,* and each comes in three colors: Infraroja, Ultravioleta, and Radiografía. Let M be the set of models and let C be the set of colors. What set represents the different choices a customer can make?

73. You are searching online for techno music that is neither European nor Dutch. In set notation, which set of music files are you searching for?

  (A) Techno $\cap$ (European $\cap$ Dutch)$'$
  (B) Techno $\cap$ (European $\cup$ Dutch)$'$
  (C) Techno $\cup$ (European $\cap$ Dutch)$'$
  (D) Techno $\cup$ (European $\cup$ Dutch)$'$

74. You would like to see either a World War II movie, or one that is based on a comic book character but does not feature aliens. Which set of movies are you interested in seeing?

  (A) WWII $\cap$ (Comix $\cap$ Aliens$'$)
  (B) WWII $\cap$ (Comix $\cup$ Aliens$'$)
  (C) WWII $\cup$ (Comix $\cap$ Aliens$'$)
  (D) WWII $\cup$ (Comix $\cup$ Aliens$'$)

75. ▼ Explain, illustrating by means of an example, why $(A \cap B) \cup C \neq A \cap (B \cup C)$.

76. ▼ Explain, making reference to operations on sets, why the statement "He plays soccer or rugby and cricket" is ambiguous.

77. ▼ Explain the meaning of a universal set, and give two different universal sets that could be used in a discussion about sets of positive integers.

78. ▼ Is the set of outcomes when two indistinguishable dice are rolled (Example 1) a Cartesian product of two sets? If so, which two sets; if not, why not?

---

[1] Source: Department of Health and Human Services/*New York Times,* January 8, 2002, p. A14.

79. ▼ Design a database scenario that leads to the following statement: To keep the factory operating at maximum capacity, the plant manager should select the suppliers in $A \cap (B \cup C')$.

80. ▼ Design a database scenario that leads to the following statement: To keep her customers happy, the bookstore owner should stock periodicals in $A \cup (B \cap C')$.

81. ▼ Rewrite in set notation: She prefers movies that are not violent, are shorter than two hours, and have neither a tragic ending nor an unexpected ending.

82. ▼ Rewrite in set notation: He will cater for any event as long as there are no more than 1,000 people, it lasts for at least three hours, and it is within a 50 mile radius of Toronto.

6.2   Cardinality

In this section, we begin to look at a deceptively simple idea: the size of a set, which we call its **cardinality**.

Cardinality

If A is a finite set, then its **cardinality** is

$$n(A) = \text{number of elements in } A.$$

Visualizing Cardinality

$n(A) = 6$

Quick Examples

1. Let $S = \{a, b, c\}$. Then $n(S) = 3$.

2. Let S be the set of outcomes when two distinguishable dice are rolled. Then $n(S) = 36$ (see Example 1 in Section 6.1).

3. $n(\emptyset) = 0$ because the empty set has no elements.

Counting the elements in a small, simple set is straightforward. To count the elements in a large, complicated set, we try to describe the set as built of simpler sets using the set operations. We then need to know how to calculate the number of elements in, for example, a union, based on the number of elements in the simpler sets whose union we are taking.

The Cardinality of a Union

How can we calculate $n(A \cup B)$ if we know $n(A)$ and $n(B)$? Our first guess might be that $n(A \cup B)$ is $n(A) + n(B)$. But consider a simple example. Let

$$A = \{a, b, c\}$$

and

$$B = \{b, c, d\}.$$

Then $A \cup B = \{a, b, c, d\}$ so $n(A \cup B) = 4$, but $n(A) + n(B) = 3 + 3 = 6$. The calculation $n(A) + n(B)$ gives the wrong answer because the elements b and c are counted twice, once for being in A and again for being in B. To correct for this overcounting, we need to subtract the number of elements that get counted twice, which is the number of elements that A and B have in common, or $n(A \cap B) = 2$ in this case. So, we get the right number for $n(A \cup B)$ from the following calculation:

$$n(A) + n(B) - n(A \cap B) = 3 + 3 - 2 = 4.$$

This argument leads to the following general formula.

Cardinality of a Union

If A and B are finite sets, then

$$n(A \cup B) = n(A) + n(B) - n(A \cap B).$$

In particular, if A and B are disjoint (meaning that $A \cap B = \emptyset$), then

$$n(A \cup B) = n(A) + n(B).$$

(When A and B are disjoint we say that $A \cup B$ is a **disjoint union**.)

Visualizing Cardinality of a Union

Disjoint Sets

$n(A \cup B) = n(A) + n(B)$
$= 3 + 1$

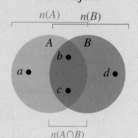

Not Disjoint

$n(A \cup B) = n(A) + n(B) - n(A \cap B)$
$= 3 + 3 - 2$

Quick Examples

1. If $A = \{a, b, c, d\}$ and $B = \{b, c, d, e, f\}$, then

$$n(A \cup B) = n(A) + n(B) - n(A \cap B) = 4 + 5 - 3 = 6.$$

In fact, $A \cup B = \{a, b, c, d, e, f\}$.

2. If $A = \{a, b, c\}$ and $B = \{d, e, f\}$, then $A \cap B = \emptyset$, so

$$n(A \cup B) = n(A) + n(B) = 3 + 3 = 6.$$

EXAMPLE 1 Web Searches

In January 2009, a search on Google™ for "Lt. William Burrows" yielded 64 Web sites containing that phrase, and a search for "unmanned Romulan probe" yielded 4 sites. A search for sites containing both phrases yielded 3 Web sites. How many Web sites contained either "Lt. William Burrows," "unmanned Romulan probe," or both?

Solution Let A be the set of sites containing "Lt. William Burrows" and let B be the set of sites containing "unmanned Romulan probe." We are told that

$$n(A) = 64$$

$$n(B) = 4$$

$$n(A \cap B) = 3. \quad \text{"Lt. William Burrows" AND "unmanned Romulan probe"}$$

The formula for the cardinality of the union tells us that

$$n(A \cup B) = n(A) + n(B) - n(A \cap B) = 64 + 4 - 3 = 65.$$

So, 65 sites in the Google™ database contained one or both of the phrases "Lt. William Burrows" or "Unmanned Romulan probe."

➡ **Before we go on...** Each search engine has a different way of specifying a search for a union or an intersection. At Google™ or AltaVista, you can use "OR" for the union and "AND" for the intersection.

Although the formula $n(A \cup B) = n(A) + n(B) - n(A \cap B)$ always holds mathematically, you may sometimes find that, in an actual search, the numbers don't add up. The reason? Search engines are not perfect. AltaVista, for example, explains that the number reported may be only an estimate of the actual number of sites in their database containing the search words.[2] ∎

Q: *Is there a similar formula for n(A ∩ B)?*

A: The formula for the cardinality of a union can also be thought of as a formula for the cardinality of an intersection. We can solve for $n(A \cap B)$ to get

$$n(A \cap B) = n(A) + n(B) - n(A \cup B).$$

In fact, we can think of this formula as an equation relating four quantities. If we know any three of them, we can use the equation to find the fourth. (See Example 2 on next page).

Q: *Is there a similar formula for n(A′)?*

A: We can get a formula for the cardinality of a complement as follows: If S is our universal set and $A \subseteq S$, then S is the disjoint union of A and its complement. That is,

$$S = A \cup A' \quad \text{and} \quad A \cap A' = \emptyset.$$

Applying the cardinality formula for a disjoint union, we get

$$n(S) = n(A) + n(A').$$

We can solve for $n(A')$ or for $n(A)$ to get the following formulas.

Cardinality of a Complement

If S is a finite universal set and A is a subset of S, then

$$n(A') = n(S) - n(A)$$

and

$$n(A) = n(S) - n(A').$$

---

[2] E-mail correspondence with the authors, January 2002.

Visualizing Cardinality of a Complement

$$n(A') = n(S) - n(A)$$
$$= 6 - 4$$

Quick Example

If $S = \{a, b, c, d, e, f\}$ and $A = \{a, b, c, d\}$, then

$$n(A') = n(S) - n(A) = 6 - 4 = 2.$$

In fact, $A' = \{e, f\}$.

EXAMPLE 2 Cookbooks

In January 2009, a search at Amazon.com found 355,000 books on cooking.* Of these, 15,000 were on American cooking, 5,000 were on vegetarian cooking, and 19,000 were on either American or vegetarian cooking (or both). How many of these books were not on both American and vegetarian cooking?

Solution Let S be the set of all 355,000 books on cooking, let A be the set of books on American cooking, and let B be the set of books on vegetarian cooking. We wish to find the size of the complement of the set of books on both American and vegetarian cooking— that is, $n((A \cap B)')$. Using the formula for the cardinality of a complement, we have

$$n((A \cap B)') = n(S) - n(A \cap B) = 355,000 - n(A \cap B).$$

To find $n(A \cap B)$, we use the formula for the cardinality of a union:

$$n(A \cup B) = n(A) + n(B) - n(A \cap B).$$

Substituting the values we were given, we find

$$19,000 = 15,000 + 5,000 - n(A \cap B)$$

which we can solve to get

$$n(A \cap B) = 1,000.$$

Therefore,

$$n((A \cap B)') = 355,000 - n(A \cap B) = 355,000 - 1,000 = 354,000.$$

So, 354,000 of the books on cooking were not on both American and vegetarian cooking.

_____

*Precisely, it found that many books under the subject "cooking." Figures are rounded to the nearest 1,000.

EXAMPLE 3 iPods, iPhones, and Macs

The following table shows sales, in millions of units, of iPods, iPhones, and Macintosh computers in the last three quarters of 2008.*

	iPods	iPhones	Macs	Total
2008 Q2	10.6	1.7	2.3	14.6
2008 Q3	11.0	0.7	2.5	14.2
2008 Q4	11.1	6.9	2.6	20.6
Total	32.7	9.3	7.4	49.4

Let S be the set of all these iPods, iPhones, and Macs. Let D be the set of iPods sold during the stated quarters, let M be the set of Macs sold during the stated quarters, and let A be the set of all items sold in the second quarter of 2008. Describe the following sets and compute their cardinality:

a. A' **b.** $D \cap A'$ **c.** $(D \cap A)'$ **d.** $M \cup A$

Solution Because all the figures are stated in millions of units, we'll give our calculations and results in millions of units as well.

a. A' is the set of all items not sold in the second quarter of 2008. To compute its cardinality, we could add the totals for all the other quarters listed in the rightmost column:

$$n(A') = 14.2 + 20.6 = 34.8 \text{ million items.}$$

Alternatively, we can use the formula for the cardinality of a complement (referring again to the totals in the table):

$$n(A') = n(S) - n(A) = 49.4 - 14.6 = 34.8 \text{ million items.}$$

b. $D \cap A'$ is the intersection of the set of all iPods and the set of all items not sold in 2008 Q2. In other words, it is the set of all iPods not sold in the second quarter of 2008. Here is the table with the corresponding sets D and A' shaded ($D \cap A'$ is the overlap):

	iPods	iPhones	Macs	Total
2008 Q2	10.6	1.7	2.3	14.6
2008 Q3	11.0	0.7	2.5	14.2
2008 Q4	11.1	6.9	2.6	20.6
Total	32.7	9.3	7.4	49.4

From the figure:

$$n(D \cap A') = 11.0 + 11.1 = 22.1 \text{ million iPods.}$$

c. $D \cap A$ is the set of all iPods sold in 2008 Q2, and so $(D \cap A)'$ is the set of all items remaining if we exclude iPods sold in 2008 Q2:

---

*Figures are rounded. Source: Company reports (www.apple.com/investor/).

	iPods	iPhones	Macs	Total
2008 Q2	10.6	1.7	2.3	14.6
2008 Q3	11.0	0.7	2.5	14.2
2008 Q4	11.1	6.9	2.6	20.6
Total	32.7	9.3	7.4	49.4

From the formula for the cardinality of a complement:

$$n((D \cap A)') = n(S) - n(D \cap A)$$
$$= 49.4 - 10.6 = 38.8 \text{ million items.}$$

d. $M \cup A$ is the set of items that were either Macs or sold in 2008 Q2:

	iPods	iPhones	Macs	Total
2008 Q2	10.6	1.7	2.3	14.6
2008 Q3	11.0	0.7	2.5	14.2
2008 Q4	11.1	6.9	2.6	20.6
Total	32.7	9.3	7.4	49.4

To compute it, we can use the formula for the cardinality of a union:

$$n(M \cup A) = n(M) + n(A) - n(M \cap A)$$
$$= 7.4 + 14.6 - 2.3 = 19.7 \text{ million items.}$$

To determine the cardinality of a union of three or more sets, like $n(A \cup B \cup C)$, we can think of $A \cup B \cup C$ as a union of two sets, $(A \cup B)$ and C, and then analyze each piece using the techniques we already have. Alternatively, there are formulas for the cardinalities of unions of any number of sets, but these formulas get more and more complicated as the number of sets grows. In many applications, like the following example, we can use Venn diagrams instead.

EXAMPLE 4 Reading Lists

A survey of 300 college students found that 100 had read *War and Peace,* 120 had read *Crime and Punishment,* and 100 had read *The Brothers Karamazov.* It also found that 40 had read only *War and Peace,* 70 had read *War and Peace* but not *The Brothers Karamazov,* and 80 had read *The Brothers Karamazov* but not *Crime and Punishment.* Only 10 had read all three novels. How many had read none of these three novels?

Solution There are four sets mentioned in the problem: the universe S consisting of the 300 students surveyed, the set W of students who had read *War and Peace,* the set C of students who had read *Crime and Punishment,* and the set K of students who had read *The Brothers Karamazov.* Figure 7 shows a Venn diagram representing these sets.

We have put labels in the various regions of the diagram to represent the number of students in each region. For example, x represents the number of students in $W \cap C \cap K$,

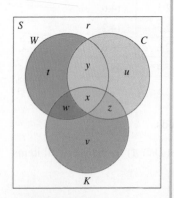

Figure 7

which is the number of students who have read all three novels. We are told that this number is 10, so

$$x = 10.$$

(You should draw the diagram for yourself and fill in the numbers as we go along.) We are also told that 40 students had read only *War and Peace,* so

$$t = 40.$$

We are given none of the remaining regions directly. However, because 70 had read *War and Peace* but not *The Brothers Karamazov,* we see that t and y must add up to 70. Because we already know that $t = 40$, it follows that $y = 30$. Further, because a total of 100 students had read *War and Peace,* we have

$$x + y + t + w = 100.$$

Substituting the known values of x, y, and t gives

$$10 + 30 + 40 + w = 100$$

so $w = 20$. Because 80 students had read *The Brothers Karamazov* but not *Crime and Punishment,* we see that $v + w = 80$, so $v = 60$ (because we know $w = 20$). We can now calculate z using the fact that a total of 100 students had read *The Brothers Karamazov:*

$$60 + 20 + 10 + z = 100$$

giving $z = 10$. Similarly, we can now get u using the fact that 120 students had read *Crime and Punishment:*

$$10 + 30 + 10 + u = 120$$

giving $u = 70$. Of the 300 students surveyed, we've now found $x + y + z + w + t + u + v = 240$. This leaves

$$r = 60$$

who had read none of the three novels.

The Cardinality of a Cartesian Product

We've covered all the operations except Cartesian product. To find a formula for $n(A \times B)$, consider the following simple example:

$$A = \{H, T\}$$
$$B = \{1, 2, 3, 4, 5, 6\}$$

so that

$$A \times B = \{H1, H2, H3, H4, H5, H6, T1, T2, T3, T4, T5, T6\}.$$

As we saw in Example 5 in Section 6.1, the elements of $A \times B$ can be arranged in a table or spreadsheet with $n(A) = 2$ rows and $n(B) = 6$ elements in each row.

	A	B	C	D	E	F	G
1		1	2	3	4	5	6
2	**H**	H1	H2	H3	H4	H5	H6
3	**T**	T1	T2	T3	T4	T5	T6

In a region with 2 rows and 6 columns, there are $2 \times 6 = 12$ cells. So,

$$n(A \times B) = n(A)n(B)$$

in this case. There is nothing particularly special about this example, however, and that formula holds true in general.

Cardinality of a Cartesian Product

If A and B are finite sets, then

$$n(A \times B) = n(A)n(B).$$

Quick Example

If $A = \{a, b, c\}$ and $B = \{x, y, z, w\}$, then

$$n(A \times B) = n(A)n(B) = 3 \times 4 = 12.$$

EXAMPLE 5 Coin Tosses

a. If we toss a coin twice and observe the sequence of heads and tails, how many possible outcomes are there?

b. If we toss a coin three times, how many possible outcomes are there?

c. If we toss a coin ten times, how many possible outcomes are there?

Solution

a. Let $A = \{H, T\}$ be the set of possible outcomes when a coin is tossed once. The set of outcomes when a coin is tossed twice is $A \times A$, which has

$$n(A \times A) = n(A)n(A) = 2 \times 2 = 4$$

possible outcomes.

b. When a coin is tossed three times, we can think of the set of outcomes as the product of the set of outcomes for the first two tosses, which is $A \times A$, and the set of outcomes for the third toss, which is just A. The set of outcomes for the three tosses is then $(A \times A) \times A$, which we usually write as $A \times A \times A$ or A^3. The number of outcomes is

$$n((A \times A) \times A) = n(A \times A)n(A) = (2 \times 2) \times 2 = 8.$$

c. Considering the result of part (b), we can easily see that the set of outcomes here is $A^{10} = A \times A \times \cdots \times A$ (10 copies of A), or the set of ordered sequences of ten Hs and Ts. It's also easy to see that

$$n(A^{10}) = [n(A)]^{10} = 2^{10} = 1,024.$$

➡ **Before we go on...** We can start to see the power of these formulas for cardinality. In Example 5, we were able to calculate that there are 1,024 possible outcomes when we toss a coin 10 times without writing out all 1,024 possibilities and counting them. ∎

6.2 EXERCISES

▼ more advanced   ◆ challenging

⊤ indicates exercises that should be solved using technology

Let A = {Dirk, Johan, Frans, Sarie}, B = {Frans, Sarie, Tina, Klaas, Henrika}, C = {Hans, Frans}. Find the numbers indicated in Exercises 1–6. HINT [See Quick Examples on page 408.]

1. $n(A) + n(B)$ **2.** $n(A) + n(C)$ **3.** $n(A \cup B)$

4. $n(A \cup C)$ **5.** $n(A \cup (B \cap C))$ **6.** $n(A \cap (B \cup C))$

7. Verify that $n(A \cup B) = n(A) + n(B) - n(A \cap B)$ with A and B as above.

8. Verify that $n(A \cup C) = n(A) + n(C) - n(A \cap C)$ with A and C as above.

Let A = {H, T}, B = {1, 2, 3, 4, 5, 6}, and C = {red, green, blue}. Find the numbers indicated in Exercises 9–14. HINT [See Example 5.]

9. $n(A \times A)$ **10.** $n(B \times B)$ **11.** $n(B \times C)$

12. $n(A \times C)$ **13.** $n(A \times B \times B)$ **14.** $n(A \times B \times C)$

15. If $n(A) = 43$, $n(B) = 20$, and $n(A \cap B) = 3$, find $n(A \cup B)$.

16. If $n(A) = 60$, $n(B) = 20$, and $n(A \cap B) = 1$, find $n(A \cap B)$.

17. If $n(A \cup B) = 100$ and $n(A) = n(B) = 60$, find $n(A \cap B)$.

18. If $n(A) = 100$, $n(A \cup B) = 150$, and $n(A \cap B) = 40$, find $n(B)$.

Let S = {Barnsley, Manchester United, Southend, Sheffield United, Liverpool, Maroka Swallows, Witbank Aces, Royal Tigers, Dundee United, Lyon} be a universal set, A = {Southend, Liverpool, Maroka Swallows, Royal Tigers}, and B = {Barnsley, Manchester United, Southend}. Find the numbers indicated in Exercises 19–24. HINT [See Quick Example on page 410.]

19. $n(A')$ **20.** $n(B')$ **21.** $n((A \cap B)')$

22. $n((A \cup B)')$ **23.** $n(A' \cap B')$ **24.** $n(A' \cup B')$

25. With S, A, and B as above, verify that $n((A \cap B)') = n(A') + n(B') - n((A \cup B)')$.

26. With S, A, and B as above, verify that $n(A' \cap B') + n(A \cup B) = n(S)$.

In Exercises 27–30, use the given information to complete the solution of each partially solved Venn diagram. HINT [See Example 4.]

27.

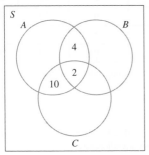

$n(A) = 20$, $n(B) = 20$, $n(C) = 28$, $n(B \cap C) = 8$, $n(S) = 50$

28.

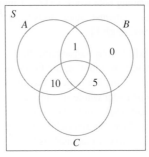

$n(A) = 16$, $n(B) = 11$, $n(C) = 30$, $n(S) = 40$

29. ▼

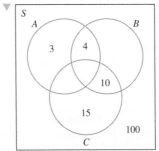

$n(A) = 10$, $n(B) = 19$, $n(S) = 140$

30. ▼

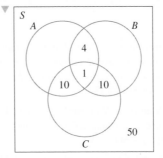

$n(A \cup B) = 30$, $n(B \cup C) = 30$, $n(A \cup C) = 35$

APPLICATIONS

31. *Web Searches* In January 2009, a search using the Web search engine Google™ for "costenoble" yielded 93,000 Web sites containing that word. A search for "waner" yielded 428,000 sites. A search for sites containing both words yielded 25,000 sites.[3] How many Web sites contained either "costenoble" or "waner" or both? HINT [See Example 1.]

---

[3] Figures are rounded to the nearest 1,000.

32. Web Searches In January 2009, a search using the Web search engine Google™ for "foreclosure" yielded 55 million Web sites containing that word. A search for "meltdown" yielded 17 million sites. A search for sites containing both words yielded 1 million sites.[4] How many Web sites contained either "foreclosure" or "meltdown" or both? HINT [See Example 1.]

33. Amusement On a particularly boring transatlantic flight, one of the authors amused himself by counting the heads of the people in the seats in front of him. He noticed that all 37 of them either had black hair or had a whole row to themselves (or both). Of this total, 33 had black hair and 6 were fortunate enough to have a whole row of seats to themselves. How many black-haired people had whole rows to themselves?

34. Restaurant Menus Your favorite restaurant offers a total of 14 desserts, of which 8 have ice cream as a main ingredient and 9 have fruit as a main ingredient. Assuming that all of them have either ice cream or fruit or both as a main ingredient, how many have both?

Publishing Exercises 35–40 are based on the following table, which shows the results of a survey of authors by a fictitious publishing company.

	New Authors	Established Authors	Total
Successful	5	25	30
Unsuccessful	15	55	70
Total	20	80	100

Consider the following subsets of the set S of all authors represented in the table: C, the set of successful authors; U, the set of unsuccessful authors; N, the set of new authors; and E, the set of established authors. HINT [See Example 3.]

35. Describe the sets $C \cap N$ and $C \cup N$ in words. Use the table to compute $n(C)$, $n(N)$, $n(C \cap N)$ and $n(C \cup N)$. Verify that $n(C \cup N) = n(C) + n(N) - n(C \cap N)$.

36. Describe the sets $N \cap U$ and $N \cup U$ in words. Use the table to compute $n(N)$, $n(U)$, $n(N \cap U)$ and $n(N \cup U)$. Verify that $n(N \cup U) = n(N) + n(U) - n(N \cap U)$.

37. Describe the set $C \cap N'$ in words, and find the number of elements it contains.

38. Describe the set $U \cup E'$ in words, and find the number of elements it contains.

39. ▼ What percentage of established authors are successful? What percentage of successful authors are established?

40. ▼ What percentage of new authors are unsuccessful? What percentage of unsuccessful authors are new?

Home Sales Exercises 41–46 are based on the following table, which shows the number of sales of existing homes, in millions, in the different regions of the United States during 2006–2008.[5] Take S to be the set of all home sales represented in the table and label the sets representing the home sales in each row and column as shown (so that, for example, N is the set of all sales of existing homes in the Northeast during 2006–2008)

	Northeast N	Midwest M	South T	West W	Total
2006 A	1.1	1.5	2.6	1.3	6.5
2007 B	1.0	1.3	2.2	1.1	5.6
2008 C	0.8	1.1	1.8	1.1	4.8
Total	2.9	3.9	6.6	3.5	16.9

In Exercises 41–46, use symbols to describe each set, and compute its cardinality.

41. The set of sales of existing homes in the Midwest in 2008

42. The set of sales of existing homes either in the West or in 2006

43. The set of sales of existing homes in 2007 excluding sales in the South

44. The set of sales of existing homes in the Northeast after 2006

45. ▼ The set of sales of existing homes in 2007 in the West and Midwest

46. ▼ The set of sales of existing homes in the South and West in years other than 2006

Exercises 47–52 are based on the following table, which shows the performance of a selection of 100 stocks after one year. (Take S to be the set of all stocks represented in the table.)

	Companies			
	Pharmaceutical P	Electronic E	Internet I	Total
Increased V	10	5	15	30
Unchanged* N	30	0	10	40
Decreased D	10	5	15	30
Total	50	10	40	100

* If a stock stayed within 20% of its original value, it is classified as "unchanged."

---

[4] Figures are rounded to the nearest million.

[5] Figures are rounded (2008 figure is an estimate based on sales through November). Source: Realtor.org (www.realtor.org).

47. Use symbols to describe the set of non-Internet stocks that increased. How many elements are in this set?

48. Use symbols to describe the set of Internet stocks that did not increase. How many elements are in this set?

49. Compute $n(P' \cup N)$. What does this number represent?

50. Compute $n(P \cup N')$. What does this number represent?

51. Calculate $\dfrac{n(V \cap I)}{n(I)}$. What does the answer represent?

52. Calculate $\dfrac{n(D \cap I)}{n(D)}$. What does the answer represent?

53. ▼ *Medicine* In a study of Tibetan children,[6] a total of 1,556 children were examined. Of these, 1,024 had rickets. Of the 243 urban children in the study, 93 had rickets.

  a. How many children living in nonurban areas had rickets?

  b. How many children living in nonurban areas did not have rickets?

54. ▼ *Medicine* In a study of Tibetan children,[7] a total of 1,556 children were examined. Of these, 615 had caries (cavities). Of the 1,313 children living in nonurban areas, 504 had caries.

  a. How many children living in urban areas had caries?

  b. How many children living in urban areas did not have caries?

55. *Entertainment* According to a survey of 100 people regarding their movie attendance in the last year, 40 had seen a science fiction movie, 55 had seen an adventure movie, and 35 had seen a horror movie. Moreover, 25 had seen a science fiction movie and an adventure movie, 5 had seen an adventure movie and a horror movie, and 15 had seen a science fiction movie and a horror movie. Only 5 people had seen a movie from all three categories.

  a. Use the given information to set up a Venn diagram and solve it. HINT [See Example 4.]

  b. Complete the following sentence: The survey suggests that __ % of science fiction movie fans are also horror movie fans.

56. *Athletics* Of the 4,700 students at Medium Suburban College (MSC), 50 play collegiate soccer, 60 play collegiate lacrosse, and 96 play collegiate football. Only 4 students play both collegiate soccer and lacrosse, 6 play collegiate soccer and football, and 16 play collegiate lacrosse and football. No students play all three sports.

  a. Use the given information to set up a Venn diagram and solve it. HINT [See Example 4.]

  b. Complete the following sentence: __ % of the college soccer players also play one of the other two sports at the collegiate level.

57. *Entertainment* In a survey of 100 Enormous State University students, 21 enjoyed classical music, 22 enjoyed rock music, and 27 enjoyed house music. Five of the students enjoyed both classical and rock. How many of those that enjoyed rock did not enjoy classical music?

58. *Entertainment* Refer back to the preceding exercise. You are also told that 5 students enjoyed all three kinds of music while 53 enjoyed music in none of these categories. How many students enjoyed both classical and rock but disliked house music?

COMMUNICATION AND REASONING EXERCISES

59. If A and B are finite sets with $A \subset B$, how are $n(A)$ and $n(B)$ related?

60. If A and B are subsets of the finite set S with $A \subset B$, how are $n(A')$ and $n(B')$ related?

61. Why is the Cartesian product referred to as a "product"? [*Hint:* Think about cardinality.]

62. Refer back to your answer to Exercise 61. What set operation could one use to represent the *sum* of two disjoint sets A and B? Why?

63. Formulate an interesting application whose answer is $n(A \cap B) = 20$.

64. Formulate an interesting application whose answer is $n(A \times B) = 120$.

65. ▼ When is $n(A \cup B) \neq n(A) + n(B)$?

66. ▼ When is $n(A \times B) = n(A)$?

67. ▼ When is $n(A \cup B) = n(A)$?

68. ▼ When is $n(A \cap B) = n(A)$?

69. ◆ Use a Venn diagram or some other method to obtain a formula for $n(A \cup B \cup C)$ in terms of $n(A), n(B), n(C)$, $n(A \cap B), n(A \cap C), n(B \cap C)$ and $n(A \cap B \cap C)$.

70. ◆ Suppose that A and B are nonempty sets with $A \subset B$ and $n(A)$ at least two. Arrange the following numbers from smallest to largest (if two numbers are equal, say so): $n(A)$, $n(A \times B), n(A \cap B), n(A \cup B), n(B \times A), n(B), n(B \times B)$.

---

[6] Source: N. S. Harris et al., Nutritional and Health Status of Tibetan Children Living at High Altitudes, *New England Journal of Medicine,* 344(5), February 1, 2001, pp. 341–347.

[7] Ibid.

6.3 The Addition and Multiplication Principles

Let's start with a really simple example. You walk into an ice cream parlor and find that you can choose between ice cream, of which there are 15 flavors, and frozen yogurt, of which there are 5 flavors. How many different selections can you make? Clearly, you have $15 + 5 = 20$ different desserts from which to choose. Mathematically, this is an example of the formula for the cardinality of a disjoint union: If we let A be the set of ice creams you can choose from, and B the set of frozen yogurts, then $A \cap B = \emptyset$ and we want $n(A \cup B)$. But the formula for the cardinality of a disjoint union is $n(A \cup B) = n(A) + n(B)$, which gives $15 + 5 = 20$ in this case.

This example illustrates a very useful general principle.

Addition Principle

When choosing among r disjoint alternatives, if

  alternative 1 has n_1 possible outcomes,

  alternative 2 has n_2 possible outcomes,

  . . .

  alternative r has n_r possible outcomes,

then you have a total of $n_1 + n_2 + \cdots + n_r$ possible outcomes.

Quick Example

At a restaurant you can choose among 8 chicken dishes, 10 beef dishes, 4 seafood dishes, and 12 vegetarian dishes. This gives a total of $8 + 10 + 4 + 12 = 34$ different dishes to choose from.

Here is another simple example. In that ice cream parlor, not only can you choose from 15 flavors of ice cream, but you can also choose from 3 different sizes of cone. How many different ice cream cones can you select from? If we let A again be the set of ice cream flavors and now let C be the set of cone sizes, we want to pick a flavor *and* a size. That is, we want to pick an element of $A \times C$, the Cartesian product. To find the number of choices we have, we use the formula for the cardinality of a Cartesian product: $n(A \times C) = n(A)n(C)$. In this case, we get $15 \times 3 = 45$ different ice cream cones we can select.

This example illustrates another general principle.

Multiplication Principle

When making a sequence of choices with r steps, if

  step 1 has n_1 possible outcomes

  step 2 has n_2 possible outcomes

  . . .

  step r has n_r possible outcomes

then you have a total of $n_1 \times n_2 \times \cdots \times n_r$ possible outcomes.

> **Quick Example**
>
> At a restaurant you can choose among 5 appetizers, 34 main dishes, and 10 desserts. This gives a total of $5 \times 34 \times 10 = 1,700$ different meals (each including one appetizer, one main dish, and one dessert) from which you can choose.

Things get more interesting when we have to use the addition and multiplication principles in tandem.

EXAMPLE 1 Desserts

You walk into an ice cream parlor and find that you can choose between ice cream, of which there are 15 flavors, and frozen yogurt, of which there are 5 flavors. In addition, you can choose among 3 different sizes of cones for your ice cream or 2 different sizes of cups for your yogurt. How many different desserts can you choose from?

Solution It helps to think about a definite procedure for deciding which dessert you will choose. Here is one we can use:

Alternative 1: An ice cream cone
   Step 1 Choose a flavor.
   Step 2 Choose a size.

Alternative 2: A cup of frozen yogurt
   Step 1 Choose a flavor.
   Step 2 Choose a size.

That is, we can choose between alternative 1 and alternative 2. If we choose alternative 1, we have a sequence of two choices to make: flavor and size. The same is true of alternative 2. We shall call a procedure in which we make a sequence of decisions a **decision algorithm**.* Once we have a decision algorithm, we can use the addition and multiplication principles to count the number of possible outcomes.

✳ **NOTE** An algorithm is a procedure with definite rules for what to do at every step.

Alternative 1: An ice cream cone
   Step 1 Choose a flavor; 15 choices
   Step 2 Choose a size; 3 choices
   There are $15 \times 3 = 45$ possible choices in alternative 1.   Multiplication Principle

Alternative 2: A cup of frozen yogurt
   Step 1 Choose a flavor; 5 choices
   Step 2 Choose a size; 2 choices
   There are $5 \times 2 = 10$ possible choices in alternative 2.   Multiplication Principle

   So, there are $45 + 10 = 55$ possible choices of desserts.   Addition Principle

➡ **Before we go on...** Decision algorithms can be illustrated by **decision trees**. To simplify the picture, suppose we had fewer choices in Example 1—say, only two choices of ice cream flavor: vanilla and chocolate, and two choices of yogurt flavor: banana and raspberry. This gives us a total of $2 \times 3 + 2 \times 2 = 10$ possible desserts. We can illustrate the decisions we need to make when choosing what to buy in the diagram in Figure 8, called a decision tree.

Choose Type	Choose Flavor	Choose Size	
	Vanilla	Small	Small vanilla cone
		Medium	Medium vanilla cone
Ice cream		Large	Large vanilla cone
	Chocolate	Small	Small chocolate cone
		Medium	Medium chocolate cone
		Large	Large chocolate cone
	Banana	Small	Small banana cup
		Large	Large banana cup
Yogurt	Raspberry	Small	Small raspberry cup
		Large	Large raspberry cup

Figure 8

We do not use decision trees much in this chapter because, while they provide a good way of thinking about decision algorithms, they're not really practical for counting large sets. Similar diagrams will be very useful, however, in the chapter on probability. ■

To count the number of possible gadgets, pretend you are *designing* a gadget, and list the decisions to be made at each stage.

Decision Algorithm

A **decision algorithm** is a procedure in which we make a sequence of decisions. We can use decision algorithms to determine the number of possible items by pretending we are *designing* such an item (for example, an ice-cream cone) and listing the decisions or choices we should make at each stage of the process.

Quick Example

An iPod is available in two sizes. The larger size comes in two colors and the smaller size (the Mini) comes in four colors. A decision algorithm for "designing" an iPod is:

Alternative 1: Select Large:
Step 1 Choose a color: Two choices
(so, there are two choices for Alternative 1)

Alternative 2: Select a Mini:
Step 1 Choose a color: Four choices
(so, there are four choices for Alternative 2)

Thus, there are $2 + 4 = 6$ possible choices of iPods.

Caution

For a decision algorithm to give the correct number of possible items, it must be the case that *changing one or more choices results in a different item.* (See Example 3.)

EXAMPLE 2 **Exams**

An exam is broken into two parts, Part A and Part B, both of which you are required to do. In Part A you can choose between answering 10 true-false questions or answering 4 multiple-choice questions, each of which has 5 answers to choose from. In Part B you can choose between answering 8 true-false questions and answering 5 multiple-choice questions, each of which has 4 answers to choose from. How many different collections of answers are possible?

Solution While deciding what answers to write down, we use the following decision algorithm:

Step 1 Do Part A.

    Alternative 1: Answer the 10 true-false questions.
        Steps 1–10 Choose true or false for each question; 2 choices each.
        There are $2 \times 2 \times \cdots \times 2 = 2^{10} = 1{,}024$ choices in alternative 1.

    Alternative 2: Answer the 4 multiple-choice questions.
        Steps 1–4 Choose one answer for each question; 5 choices each.
        $5 \times 5 \times 5 \times 5 = 5^4 = 625$ choices in alternative 2.
    $1{,}024 + 625 = 1{,}649$ choices in step 1

Step 2 Do Part B.

    Alternative 1: Answer the 8 true-false questions; 2 choices each.
        $2^8 = 256$ choices in alternative 1

    Alternative 2: Answer the 5 multiple-choice questions, 4 choices each.
        $4^5 = 1{,}024$ choices in alternative 2
    $256 + 1{,}024 = 1{,}280$ choices in step 2

There are $1{,}649 \times 1{,}280 = 2{,}110{,}720$ different collections of answers possible.

The next example illustrates the need to select your decision algorithm with care.

EXAMPLE 3 **Scrabble**

You are playing Scrabble and have the following letters to work with: k, e, r, e. Because you are losing the game, you would like to use all your letters to make a single word, but you can't think of any four-letter words using all these letters. In desperation, you decide to list *all* the four-letter sequences possible to see if there are any valid words among them. How large is your list?

Solution It may first occur to you to try the following decision algorithm.

Step 1 Select the first letter; 4 choices.
Step 2 Select the second letter; 3 choices.
Step 3 Select the third letter; 2 choices.
Step 4 Select the last letter; 1 choice.

This gives $4 \times 3 \times 2 \times 1 = 24$ choices. However, something is wrong with the algorithm.

✱ NOTE Consider the following extreme case: If all four letters were "e," then there would be only a single sequence: "eeee" and not the 24 predicted by the decision algorithm.

Q: *What is wrong with this decision algorithm?*

A: We didn't take into account the fact that there are two "e"s;✱ different decisions in Steps 1–4 can produce the same sequence. Suppose, for example, that we selected the first "e" in Step 1, the second "e" in Step 2, and then the "k" and the "r." This would produce the sequence "eekr." If we selected the *second* "e" in Step 1, the *first* "e" in Step 2, and then the "k" and "r," we would obtain the *same* sequence: "eekr." In other words, the decision algorithm produces two copies of the sequence "eekr" in the associated decision tree. (In fact, it produces two copies of each possible sequence of the letters.)

For a decision algorithm to be valid, each sequence of choices must produce a different result.

Because our original algorithm is not valid, we need a new one. Here is a strategy that works nicely for this example. Imagine, as before, that we are going to construct a sequence of four letters. This time we are going to imagine that we have a sequence of four empty slots: ☐☐☐☐, and instead of selecting letters to fill the slots from left to right, we are going to select *slots* in which to place each of the letters. Remember that we have to use these letters: k, e, r, e. We proceed as follows, leaving the "e"s until last.

Step 1 Select an empty slot for the k; 4 choices (e.g., ☐☐k☐)
Step 2 Select an empty slot for the r; 3 choices (e.g., r☐k☐).
Step 3 Place the "e"s in the remaining two slots; 1 choice!

Thus the multiplication principle yields $4 \times 3 \times 1 = 12$ choices.

➡ **Before we go on...** You should try constructing a decision tree for Example 3, and you will see that each sequence of four letters is produced exactly once when we use the correct (second) decision algorithm. ∎

FAQs

Creating and Testing a Decision Algorithm

Q: *How do I set up a decision algorithm to count how many items there are in a given scenario?*

A: Pretend that you are *designing* such an item (for example, pretend that you are designing an ice-cream cone) and come up with a step-by-step procedure for doing so, listing the decisions you should make at each stage.

Q: *Once I have my decision algorithm, how do I check if it is valid?*

A: Ask yourself the following question: "Is it possible to get the same item (the exact same ice-cream cone, say) by making different decisions when applying the algorithm?" If the answer is "yes," then your decision algorithm is invalid. Otherwise, it is valid.

6.3 EXERCISES

▼ more advanced   ◆ challenging
⊺ indicates exercises that should be solved using technology

1. An experiment requires a choice among three initial setups. The first setup can result in two possible outcomes, the second in three possible outcomes, and the third in five possible outcomes. What is the total number of outcomes possible? HINT [See Quick Example on page 418.]

2. A surgical procedure requires choosing among four alternative methodologies. The first can result in four possible outcomes, the second in three possible outcomes, and the remaining methodologies can each result in two possible outcomes. What is the total number of outcomes possible? HINT [See Quick Example on page 418.]

3. An experiment requires a sequence of three steps. The first step can result in two possible outcomes, the second in three possible outcomes, and the third in five possible outcomes. What is the total number of outcomes possible? HINT [See Quick Example on page 419.]

4. A surgical procedure requires four steps. The first can result in four possible outcomes, the second in three possible outcomes, and the remaining two can each result in two possible outcomes. What is the total number of outcomes possible? HINT [See Quick Example on page 419.]

For the decision algorithms in Exercises 5–12, find how many outcomes are possible. HINT [See Example 1.]

5. Alternative 1: Alternative 2:
  Step 1: 1 outcome   Step 1: 2 outcomes
  Step 2: 2 outcomes   Step 2: 2 outcomes
          Step 3: 1 outcome

6. Alternative 1: Alternative 2:
  Step 1: 1 outcome   Step 1: 2 outcomes
  Step 2: 2 outcomes   Step 2: 2 outcomes
  Step 3: 2 outcomes

7. Step 1: Step 2:
  Alternative 1: 1 outcome   Alternative 1: 2 outcomes
  Alternative 2: 2 outcomes   Alternative 2: 2 outcomes
          Alternative 3: 1 outcome

8. Step 1: Step 2:
  Alternative 1: 1 outcome   Alternative 1: 2 outcomes
  Alternative 2: 2 outcomes   Alternative 2: 2 outcomes
  Alternative 3: 2 outcomes

9. Alternative 1: Alternative 2: 5 outcomes
  Step 1:
    Alternative 1: 3 outcomes
    Alternative 2: 1 outcome
  Step 2: 2 outcomes

10. Alternative 1: 2 outcomes Alternative 2:
          Step 1:
            Alternative 1: 4 outcomes
            Alternative 2: 1 outcome
          Step 2: 2 outcomes

11. Step 1: Step 2: 5 outcomes
  Alternative 1:
    Step 1: 3 outcomes
    Step 2: 1 outcome
  Alternative 2: 2 outcomes

12. Step 1: 2 outcomes Step 2:
          Alternative 1:
            Step 1: 4 outcomes
            Step 2: 1 outcome
          Alternative 2: 2 outcomes

13. How many different four-letter sequences can be formed from the letters a, a, a, b? HINT [See Example 3.]

14. How many different five-letter sequences can be formed from the letters a, a, a, b, c? HINT [See Example 3.]

APPLICATIONS

15. *Ice Cream* When **Baskin-Robbins** was founded in 1945, it made 31 different flavors of ice cream.[8] If you had a choice of having your ice cream in a cone, a cup, or a sundae, how many different desserts could you have?

16. *Ice Cream* At the beginning of 2002, **Baskin-Robbins** claimed to have "nearly 1,000 different ice cream flavors."[9] Assuming that you could choose from 1,000 different flavors, that you could have your ice cream in a cone, a cup, or a sundae, and that you could choose from a dozen different toppings, how many different desserts could you have?

17. *Binary Codes* A binary digit, or "bit," is either 0 or 1. A nybble is a four-bit sequence. How many different nybbles are possible?

18. *Ternary Codes* A ternary digit is either 0, 1, or 2. How many sequences of six ternary digits are possible?

19. *Ternary Codes* A ternary digit is either 0, 1, or 2. How many sequences of six ternary digits containing a single 1 and a single 2 are possible?

20. *Binary Codes* A binary digit, or "bit," is either 0 or 1. A nybble is a four-bit sequence. How many different nybbles containing a single 1 are possible?

21. *Reward* While selecting candy for students in his class, Professor Murphy must choose between gummy candy and licorice nibs. Gummy candy packets come in three sizes, while packets of licorice nibs come in two. If he chooses gummy candy, he must select gummy bears, gummy worms, or gummy dinos. If he chooses licorice nibs, he must choose between red and black. How many choices does he have? HINT [See Example 2.]

---

[8] Source: Company Web site (www.baskinrobbins.com).
[9] Ibid.

22. *Productivity* Professor Oger must choose between an extra writing assignment and an extra reading assignment for the upcoming spring break. For the writing assignment, there are two essay topics to choose from and three different mandatory lengths (30 pages, 35 pages, or 40 pages). The reading topic would consist of one scholarly biography combined with one volume of essays. There are five biographies and two volumes of essays to choose from. How many choices does she have? HINT [See Example 2.]

23. *CD Discs* CD discs at your local computer store are available in two types (CD-R and CD-RW), packaged singly, in spindles of 50, or in spindles of 100. When purchasing singly, you can choose from five colors; when purchasing in spindles of 50 or 100 you have two choices, silver or an assortment of colors. If you are purchasing CD discs, how many possibilities do you have to choose from?

24. *Radar Detectors* Radar detectors are either powered by their own battery or plug into the cigarette lighter socket. All radar detectors come in two models: no-frills and fancy. In addition, detectors powered by their own batteries detect either radar or laser, or both, whereas the plug-in types come in models that detect either radar or laser, but not both. How many different radar detectors can you buy?

25. *Multiple-Choice Tests* Professor Easy's final examination has 10 true-false questions followed by 2 multiple-choice questions. In each of the multiple-choice questions, you must select the correct answer from a list of five. How many answer sheets are possible?

26. *Multiple-choice Tests* Professor Tough's final examination has 20 true-false questions followed by 3 multiple-choice questions. In each of the multiple-choice questions, you must select the correct answer from a list of six. How many answer sheets are possible?

27. *Tests* A test requires that you answer either Part A or Part B. Part A consists of eight true-false questions, and Part B consists of five multiple-choice questions with one correct answer out of five. How many different completed answer sheets are possible?

28. *Tests* A test requires that you answer first Part A and then either Part B or Part C. Part A consists of four true-false questions, Part B consists of four multiple-choice questions with one correct answer out of five, and Part C consists of three questions with one correct answer out of six. How many different completed answer sheets are possible?

29. *Stock Portfolios* Your broker has suggested that you diversify your investments by splitting your portfolio among mutual funds, municipal bond funds, stocks, and precious metals. She suggests four good mutual funds, three municipal bond funds, eight stocks, and three precious metals (gold, silver, and platinum).

   a. Assuming your portfolio is to contain one of each type of investment, how many different portfolios are possible?

   b. Assuming your portfolio is to contain three mutual funds, two municipal bond funds, one stock, and two precious metals, how many different portfolios are possible?

30. *Menus* The local diner offers a meal combination consisting of an appetizer, a soup, a main course, and a dessert. There are five appetizers, two soups, four main courses, and five desserts. Your diet restricts you to choosing between a dessert and an appetizer. (You cannot have both.) Given this restriction, how many three-course meals are possible?

31. *Computer Codes* A computer "byte" consists of eight "bits," each bit being either a 0 or a 1. If characters are represented using a code that uses a byte for each character, how many different characters can be represented?

32. *Computer Codes* Some written languages, like Chinese and Japanese, use tens of thousands of different characters. If a language uses roughly 50,000 characters, a computer code for this language would have to use how many bytes per character? (See Exercise 31.)

33. *Symmetries of a Five-Pointed Star* A five-pointed star will appear unchanged if it is rotated through any one of the angles 0°, 72°, 144°, 216°, or 288°. It will also appear unchanged if it is flipped about the axis shown in the figure. A *symmetry* of the five-pointed star consists of either a rotation, or a rotation followed by a flip. How many different symmetries are there altogether?

34. *Symmetries of a Six-Pointed Star* A six-pointed star will appear unchanged if it is rotated through any one of the angles 0°, 60°, 120°, 180°, 240°, or 300°. It will also appear unchanged if it is flipped about the axis shown in the figure. A *symmetry* of the six-pointed star consists of either a rotation, or a rotation followed by a flip. How many different symmetries are there altogether?

35. *Variables in BASIC*[10] A variable name in the programming language BASIC can be either a letter or a letter followed by a decimal digit—that is, one of the numbers 0, 1, . . . , 9. How many different variables are possible?

36. *Employee IDs* A company assigns to each of its employees an ID code that consists of one, two, or three letters followed by a digit from 0 through 9. How many employee codes does the company have available?

37. *Tournaments* How many ways are there of filling in the blanks for the following (fictitious) soccer tournament?

North Carolina

Central Connecticut

Virginia

Syracuse

38. *Tournaments* How many ways are there of filling in the blanks for a (fictitious) soccer tournament involving the four teams San Diego State, De Paul, Colgate, and Hofstra?

San Diego State

De Paul

Colgate

39. ▼ *Telephone Numbers* A telephone number consists of a sequence of seven digits not starting with 0 or 1.

a. How many telephone numbers are possible?

b. How many of them begin with either 463, 460, or 400?

c. How many telephone numbers are possible if no two adjacent digits are the same? (For example, 235-9350 is permitted, but not 223-6789.)

40. ▼ *Social Security Numbers* A Social Security Number is a sequence of nine digits.

a. How many Social Security Numbers are possible?

b. How many of them begin with either 023 or 003?

c. How many Social Security Numbers are possible if no two adjacent digits are the same? (For example, 235-93-2345 is permitted, but not 126-67-8189.)

41. ▼ *DNA Chains* DNA (deoxyribonucleic acid) is the basic building block of reproduction in living things. A DNA chain is a sequence of chemicals called *bases*. There are four possible bases: thymine (T), cytosine (C), adenine (A), and guanine (G).

a. How many three-element DNA chains are possible?

b. How many n-element DNA chains are possible?

c. A human DNA chain has 2.1×10^{10} elements. How many human DNA chains are possible?

42. ▼ *Credit Card Numbers*[11] Each customer of Mobil Credit Corporation is given a 9-digit number for computer identification purposes.

a. If each digit can be any number from 0 to 9, are there enough different account numbers for 10 million credit-card holders?

b. Would there be if the digits were only 0 or 1?

43. ▼ *HTML* Colors in HTML (the language in which many web pages are written) can be represented by 6-digit hexadecimal codes: sequences of six integers ranging from 0 to 15 (represented as 0, . . . , 9, A, B, . . . , F).

a. How many different colors can be represented?

b. Some monitors can only display colors encoded with pairs of repeating digits (such as 44DD88). How many colors can these monitors display?

c. Grayscale shades are represented by sequences $xyxyxy$ consisting of a repeated pair of digits. How many grayscale shades are possible?

d. The pure colors are pure red: $xy0000$; pure green: $00xy00$; and pure blue: $0000xy$. ($xy = FF$ gives the brightest pure color, while $xy = 00$ gives the darkest: black). How many pure colors are possible?

44. ▼ *Telephone Numbers* In the past, a local telephone number in the United States consisted of a sequence of two letters followed by five digits. Three letters were associated with each number from 2 to 9 (just as in the standard telephone layout shown in the figure) so that each telephone number corresponded to a sequence of seven digits. How many different sequences of seven digits were possible?

45. ▼ *Romeo and Juliet* Here is a list of the main characters in Shakespeare's *Romeo and Juliet*. The first seven characters are male and the last four are female.

Escalus, *prince of Verona*
Paris, *kinsman to the prince*
Romeo, *of Montague Household*

---

[10] From *Applied Combinatorics* by F.S. Roberts (Prentice Hall, New Jersey, 1984).

[11] Ibid.

Mercutio, *friend of Romeo*
Benvolio, *friend of Romeo*
Tybalt, *nephew to Lady Capulet*
Friar Lawrence, *a Franciscan*
Lady Montague, *of Montague Household*
Lady Capulet, *of Capulet Household*
Juliet, *of Capulet Household*
Juliet's Nurse

A total of 10 male and 8 female actors are available to play these roles. How many possible casts are there? (All roles are to be played by actors of the same gender as the character.)

46. ▼ *Swan Lake* The Enormous State University's Accounting Society has decided to produce a version of the ballet *Swan Lake,* in which all the female roles (including all of the swans) will be danced by men, and vice versa. Here are the main characters:

Prince Siegfried
Prince Siegfried's Mother
Princess Odette, *the White Swan*
The Evil Duke Rotbart
Odile, *the Black Swan*
Cygnet #1, *young swan*
Cygnet #2, *young swan*
Cygnet #3, *young swan*

The ESU Accounting Society has on hand a total of 4 female dancers and 12 male dancers who are to be considered for the main roles. How many possible casts are there?

47. ▼ *License Plates* Many U.S. license plates display a sequence of three letters followed by three digits.

a. How many such license plates are possible?
b. In order to avoid confusion of letters with digits, some states do not issue standard plates with the last letter an I, O, or Q. How many license plates are still possible?
c. Assuming that the letter combinations VET, MDZ, and DPZ are reserved for disabled veterans, medical practitioners and disabled persons, respectively, how many license plates are possible, also taking the restriction in part (b) into account?

48. ▼ *License Plates*[12] License plates in Montana have a sequence consisting of: (1) a digit from 1 to 9, (2) a letter, (3) a dot, (4) a letter, and (5) a four-digit number.

a. How many different license plates are possible?
b. How many different license plates are available for citizens if numbers that end with 0 are reserved for official state vehicles?

49. ▼ *Mazes*

a. How many four-letter sequences are possible that contain only the letters R and D, with D occurring only once?

b. Use part (a) to calculate the number of possible routes from Start to Finish in the maze shown in the figure, where each move is either to the right or down.

c. Comment on what would happen if we also allowed left and up moves.

50. ▼ *Mazes*

a. How many six-letter sequences are possible that contain only the letters R and D, with D occurring only once?
b. Use part (a) to calculate the number of possible routes from Start to Finish in the maze shown in the figure, where each move is either to the right or down.

c. Comment on what would happen if we also allowed left and up moves.

51. ▼ *Car Engines*[13] In a six-cylinder V6 engine, the even-numbered cylinders are on the left and the odd-numbered cylinders are on the right. A good firing order is a sequence of the numbers 1 through 6 in which right and left sides alternate.

a. How many possible good firing sequences are there?
b. How many good firing sequences are there that start with a cylinder on the left?

52. ▼ *Car Engines* Repeat the preceding exercise for an eight-cylinder V8 engine.

53. ▼ *Minimalist Art* You are exhibiting your collection of minimalist paintings. Art critics have raved about your paintings, each of which consists of 10 vertical colored lines set against a white background. You have used the following rule to produce your paintings: Every second line, starting with the first, is to be either blue or grey, while the remaining five lines are to be either all light blue, all red, or all purple. Your collection is complete: Every possible combination that satisfies the rules occurs. How many paintings are you exhibiting?

[12] Source: The License Plates of the World Web site (http://servo.oit .gatech.edu/~mk5/).

[13] Adapted from an exercise in *Basic Techniques of Combinatorial Theory* by D.I.A. Cohen (New York: John Wiley, 1978).

54. ▼ *Combination Locks* Dripping wet after your shower, you have clean forgotten the combination of your lock. It is one of those "standard" combination locks, which uses a three-number combination with each number in the range 0 through 39. All you remember is that the second number is either 27 or 37, while the third number ends in a 5. In desperation, you decide to go through all possible combinations using the information you remember. Assuming that it takes about 10 seconds to try each combination, what is the longest possible time you may have to stand dripping in front of your locker?

55. ▼ *Product Design* Your company has patented an electronic digital padlock that a user can program with his or her own four-digit code. (Each digit can be 0 through 9.) The padlock is designed to open if either the correct code is keyed in or—and this is helpful for forgetful people—if exactly one of the digits is incorrect.

a. How many incorrect codes will open a programmed padlock?

b. How many codes will open a programmed padlock?

56. ▼ *Product Design* Your company has patented an electronic digital padlock which has a telephone-style keypad. Each digit from 2 through 9 corresponds to three letters of the alphabet (see the figure for Exercise 44). How many different four-letter sequences correspond to a single four-digit sequence using digits in the range 2 through 9?

57. ▼ *Calendars* The World Almanac[14] features a "perpetual calendar," a collection of 14 possible calendars. Why does this suffice to be sure there is a calendar for every conceivable year?

58. ▼ *Calendars* How many possible calendars are there that have February 12 falling on a Sunday, Monday, or Tuesday?

59. ▼ *Programming in BASIC* (Some programming knowledge assumed for this exercise.) How many iterations will be carried out in the following routine?

```
For i = 1 to 10
    For j = 2 to 20
        For k = 1 to 10
            Print i, j, k
        Next k
    Next j
Next i
```

60. ▼ *Programming in JAVASCRIPT* (Some programming knowledge assumed for this exercise.) How many iterations will be carried out in the following routine?

```
for (i = 1; i <= 2; i++) {
    for (j = 1; j <= 2; j++) {
        for (k = 1; k <= 2; k++)
            sum += i+j+k;
    }
}
```

[14] Source: *The World Almanac and Book of Facts* 1992 (New York: Pharos Books, 1992).

61. ◆ *Building Blocks* Use a decision algorithm to show that a rectangular solid with dimensions $m \times n \times r$ can be constructed with $m \cdot n \cdot r$ cubical $1 \times 1 \times 1$ blocks. (See the figure.)

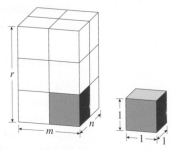

Rectangular Solid Made Up of $1 \times 1 \times 1$ Cubes

62. ◆ *Matrices* (Some knowledge of matrices is assumed for this exercise.) Use a decision algorithm to show that an $m \times n$ matrix must have $m \cdot n$ entries.

63. ◆ *Morse Code* In Morse Code, each letter of the alphabet is encoded by a different sequence of dots and dashes. Different letters may have sequences of different lengths. How long should the longest sequence be in order to allow for every possible letter of the alphabet?

64. ◆ *Numbers* How many odd numbers between 10 and 99 have distinct digits?

COMMUNICATION AND REASONING EXERCISES

65. Complete the following sentences: The multiplication principle is based on the cardinality of the _____ of two sets.

66. Complete the following sentences: The addition principle is based on the cardinality of the _____ of two disjoint sets.

67. You are packing for a short trip and want to take 2 of the 10 shirts you have hanging in your closet. Critique the following decision algorithm and calculation of how many different ways you can choose two shirts to pack: Step 1, choose one shirt, 10 choices. Step 2, choose another shirt, 9 choices. Hence there are 90 possible choices of two shirts.

68. You are designing an advertising logo that consists of a tower of five squares. Three are yellow, one is blue, and one is green. Critique the following decision algorithm and calculation of the number of different five-square sequences: Step 1: choose the first square, 5 choices. Step 2: choose the second square, 4 choices. Step 3: choose the third square: 3 choices. Step 4: choose the fourth square, 2 choices. Step 5: choose the last square: 1 choice. Hence there are 120 possible five-square sequences.

69. ▼ Construct a decision algorithm that gives the correct number of five-square sequences in Exercise 68.

70. ▼ Find an interesting application that requires a decision algorithm with two steps in which each step has two alternatives.

6.4   **Permutations and Combinations**

Certain classes of counting problems come up frequently, and it is useful to develop formulas to deal with them.

EXAMPLE 1 **Casting**

Ms. Birkitt, the English teacher at Brakpan Girls High School, wanted to stage a production of R. B. Sheridan's play, *The School for Scandal*. The casting was going well until she was left with five unfilled characters and five seniors who were yet to be assigned roles. The characters were Lady Sneerwell, Lady Teazle, Mrs. Candour, Maria, and Snake; while the unassigned seniors were April, May, June, Julia and Augusta. How many possible assignments are there?

Solution To decide on a specific assignment, we use the following algorithm:

> **Step 1** Choose a senior to play Lady Sneerwell; 5 choices.
>
> **Step 2** Choose one of the remaining seniors to play Lady Teazle; 4 choices.
>
> **Step 3** Choose one of the now remaining seniors to play Mrs. Candour; 3 choices.
>
> **Step 4** Choose one of the now remaining seniors to play Maria; 2 choices.
>
> **Step 5** Choose the remaining senior to play Snake; 1 choice.

Thus, there are $5 \times 4 \times 3 \times 2 \times 1 = 120$ possible assignments of seniors to roles.

What the situation in Example 1 has in common with many others is that we start with a set—here the set of seniors—and we want to know how many ways we can put the elements of that set in order in a list. In this example, an ordered list of the five seniors—say,

1. May

2. Augusta

3. June

4. Julia

5. April

corresponds to a particular casting:

Cast

Lady Sneerwell	May
Lady Teazle	Augusta
Mrs. Candour	June
Maria	Julia
Snake	April

We call an ordered list of items a **permutation** of those items.

If we have *n* items, how many permutations of those items are possible? We can use a decision algorithm similar to the one we used in the preceding example to select a permutation.

Step 1 Select the first item; n choices.
Step 2 Select the second item; $n - 1$ choices.
Step 3 Select the third item; $n - 2$ choices.
. . .
Step $n - 1$ Select the next-to-last item; 2 choices.
Step n Select the last item; 1 choice.
Thus, there are $n \times (n - 1) \times (n - 2) \times \cdots \times 2 \times 1$ possible permutations. We call this number ***n* factorial,** which we write as $n!$.

Permutations

A **permutation of *n* items** is an ordered list of those items. The number of possible permutations of n items is given by ***n* factorial,** which is

$$n! = n \times (n - 1) \times (n - 2) \times \cdots \times 2 \times 1$$

for n a positive integer, and

$$0! = 1.$$

Visualizing Permutations

Permutations of 3 colors in a flag:

$3! = 3 \times 2 \times 1 = 6$ Possible Flags

Quick Examples

1. The number of permutations of five items is $5! = 5 \times 4 \times 3 \times 2 \times 1 = 120$.
2. The number of ways four CDs can be played in sequence is
   $4! = 4 \times 3 \times 2 \times 1 = 24$.
3. The number of ways three cars can be matched with three drivers is $3! = 6$.

Sometimes, instead of constructing an ordered list of *all* the items of a set, we might want to construct a list of only *some* of the items, as in the next example.

using Technology

Technology can be used to compute factorials. For instance, to compute 5!:

TI-83/84 Plus
Home screen: $5\,!$
(To obtain the $!$ symbol, press
MATH , choose PRB, and
select $4 : !$.)

Excel
Use the formula
=FACT(5)

Web Site
www.FiniteandCalc.org
→ Online Utilities
→ Pop-up Factorials,
  Permutations and
  Combinations
  Computer
Screenshot:

EXAMPLE 2 **Corporations***

At the end of 2008, the 10 largest companies (by market capitalization) listed on the New York Stock Exchange were, in alphabetical order, AT&T Inc., Berkshire Hathaway Inc., Chevron Corporation, China Mobile Ltd. (ADR), Exxon Mobil Corporation, Johnson & Johnson, PetroChina Company Limited (ADR), Royal Dutch Shell plc (ADR), The Procter & Gamble Company, and Wal-Mart Stores, Inc. You would like to apply to six of these companies for a job and you would like to list them in order of job preference. How many such ordered lists are possible?

---

* Source: New York Stock Exchange Web site (www.nyse.com).

Scott Barrow, Inc./SuperStock

Solution We want to count ordered lists, but we can't use the permutation formula because we don't want all 10 companies in the list, just 6 of them. So we fall back to a decision algorithm.

Step 1 Choose the first company; 10 choices.

Step 2 Choose the second company; 9 choices.

Step 3 Choose the third one; 8 choices;

Step 4 Choose the fourth one; 7 choices.

Step 5 Choose the fifth one; 6 choices.

Step 6 Choose the sixth one; 5 choices.

Thus, there are $10 \times 9 \times 8 \times 7 \times 6 \times 5 = 151,200$ possible lists of six. We call this number the **number of permutations of 6 items chosen from 10**, or the **number of permutations of 10 items taken 6 at a time**.

➡ **Before we go on...** We wrote the answer as the product $10 \times 9 \times 8 \times 7 \times 6 \times 5$. But it is useful to notice that we can write this number in a more compact way:

$$10 \times 9 \times 8 \times 7 \times 6 \times 5 = \frac{10 \times 9 \times 8 \times 7 \times 6 \times 5 \times 4 \times 3 \times 2 \times 1}{4 \times 3 \times 2 \times 1}$$

$$= \frac{10!}{4!} = \frac{10!}{(10-6)!}$$ ∎

So, we can generalize our definition of permutation to allow for the case in which we use only some of the items, not all. Check that, if $r = n$ below, this is the same definition we gave above.

using Technology

Technology can be used to compute permutations. For instance, to compute $P(6, 2)$:

TI-83/84 Plus
Home screen: `6 nPr 2`
(To obtain the nPr symbol, press [MATH], choose PRB, and select 2:nPr.)

Excel
Use the formula
`=PERMUT(6,2)`

Web Site
www.FiniteandCalc.org
→ Online Utilities
→ Pop-up Factorials, Permutations and Combinations Computer

Screenshot:

To compute $P(n, r)$, enter values for n and r and press "Compute."

$n =$ 6 , $r =$ 2

(Compute) (Clear)

$P(6, 2) = 30$

Permutations of *n* items taken *r* at a time

A **permutation of *n* items taken *r* at a time** is an ordered list of r items chosen from a set of n items. The number of permutations of n items taken r at a time is given by

$$P(n, r) = n \times (n-1) \times (n-2) \times \cdots \times (n-r+1)$$

(there are r terms multiplied together). We can also write

$$P(n, r) = \frac{n!}{(n-r)!}.$$

Quick Example

The number of permutations of six items taken two at a time is

$$P(6, 2) = 6 \times 5 = 30$$

which we could also calculate as

$$P(6, 2) = \frac{6!}{(6-2)!} = \frac{6!}{4!} = \frac{720}{24} = 30.$$

What if we don't care about the order of the items we're choosing? Consider the following example:

EXAMPLE 3 **Corporations**

Suppose we simply wanted to pick two of the 10 companies listed in Example 2 to apply to, without regard to order. How many possible choices do we have? What if we wanted to choose six to apply to, without regard to order?

Solution Our first guess might be $P(10, 2) = 10 \times 9 = 90$. However, that is the number of *ordered lists* of two companies. We said that we don't care which is first and which second. For example, we consider the list

1. Merck   **2.** Pfizer

to be the same as

1. Pfizer   **2.** Merck.

Because every set of two companies occurs twice in the 90 lists, once in one order and again in the reverse order, we would count every set of two twice. Thus, there are $90/2 = 45$ possible choices of two companies.

Now, if we wish to pick six companies, again we might start with $P(10, 6) = 151,200$. But now, every set of six companies appears as many times as there are different orders in which they could be listed. Six things can be listed in $6! = 720$ different orders, so the number of ways of choosing six companies is $151,200/720 = 210$.

In Example 3 we were concerned with counting not the number of ordered lists, but the number of *unordered sets* of companies. For ordered lists we used the word *permutation*; for unordered sets we use the word **combination**.

Permutations and Combinations

A **permutation** of n items taken r at a time is an *ordered list* of r items chosen from n. A **combination** of n items taken r at a time is an *unordered set* of r items chosen from n.

Visualizing

1. ○
2. ●
3. ○

Permutation   Combination

Note Because lists are usually understood to be ordered, when we refer to a list of items, we will always mean an *ordered* list. Similarly, because sets are understood to be unordered, when we refer to a set of items we will always mean an *unordered* set. In short:

Lists are ordered. Sets are unordered. ∎

Quick Example

There are six permutations of the three letters a, b, c taken two at a time:

1. a, b;   **2.** b, a;   **3.** a, c;   **4.** c, a;   **5.** b, c;   **6.** c, b.

There are six lists containing two of the letters a, b, c.

There are three combinations of the three letters a, b, c taken two at a time:

1. {a, b};   **2.** {a, c};   **3.** {b, c}.

There are three sets containing two of the letters a, b, c.

How do we count the number of possible combinations of n items taken r at a time? We generalize the calculation done in Example 3. The number of permutations is $P(n, r)$, but each set of r items occurs $r!$ times because this is the number of ways in which those r items can be ordered. So, the number of combinations is $P(n, r)/r!$.

Combinations of _n_ items taken _r_ at a time

The number of **combinations of _n_ items taken _r_ at a time** is given by

$$C(n, r) = \frac{P(n, r)}{r!} = \frac{n \times (n-1) \times (n-2) \times \cdots \times (n-r+1)}{r!}.$$

We can also write

$$C(n, r) = \frac{n!}{r!(n-r)!}.$$

Quick Examples

1. The number of combinations of six items taken two at a time is

$$C(6, 2) = \frac{6 \times 5}{2 \times 1} = 15$$

which we can also calculate as

$$C(6, 2) = \frac{6!}{2!(6-2)!} = \frac{6!}{2!4!} = \frac{720}{2 \times 24} = 15.$$

2. The number of sets of four marbles chosen from six is

$$C(6, 4) = \frac{6 \times 5 \times 4 \times 3}{4 \times 3 \times 2 \times 1} = 15.$$

Note   There are other common notations for $C(n, r)$. Calculators often have $_nC_r$. In mathematics we often write $\binom{n}{r}$ which is also known as a **binomial coefficient**. Because $C(n, r)$ is the number of ways of choosing a set of r items from n, it is often read "n choose r." ■

EXAMPLE 4 Calculating Combinations

Calculate   **a.** $C(11, 3)$ **b.** $C(11, 8)$.

Solution The easiest way to calculate $C(n, r)$ by hand is to use the formula

$$C(n, r) = \frac{n \times (n - 1) \times (n - 2) \times \cdots \times (n - r + 1)}{r!}$$

$$= \frac{n \times (n - 1) \times (n - 2) \times \cdots \times (n - r + 1)}{r \times (r - 1) \times (r - 2) \times \cdots \times 1}.$$

Both the numerator and the denominator have r factors, so we can begin with n/r and then continue multiplying by decreasing numbers on the top and the bottom until we hit 1 in the denominator. When calculating, it helps to cancel common factors from the numerator and denominator before doing the multiplication in either one.

a. $C(11, 3) = \dfrac{11 \times 10 \times 9}{3 \times 2 \times 1} = \dfrac{11 \times \overset{5}{\cancel{10}} \times \overset{3}{\cancel{9}}}{\cancel{3} \times \cancel{2} \times 1} = 165$

b. $C(11, 8) = \dfrac{11 \times 10 \times 9 \times 8 \times 7 \times 6 \times 5 \times 4}{8 \times 7 \times 6 \times 5 \times 4 \times 3 \times 2 \times 1}$

$= \dfrac{11 \times \overset{5}{\cancel{10}} \times \overset{3}{\cancel{9}}}{\cancel{3} \times \cancel{2} \times 1} = 165$

➡ **Before we go on...** It is no coincidence that the answers for parts (a) and (b) of Example 4 are the same. Consider what each represents. $C(11, 3)$ is the number of ways of choosing 3 items from 11—for example, electing 3 trustees from a slate of 11. Electing those 3 is the same as choosing the 8 who do not get elected. Thus, there are exactly as many ways to choose 3 items from 11 as there are ways to choose 8 items from 11. So, $C(11, 3) = C(11, 8)$. In general,

$$C(n, r) = C(n, n - r).$$

We can also see this equality by using the formula

$$C(n, r) = \frac{n!}{r!(n - r)!}.$$

If we substitute $n - r$ for r, we get exactly the same formula.

Use the equality $C(n, r) = C(n, n - r)$ to make your calculations easier. Choose the one with the smaller denominator to begin with. ∎

EXAMPLE 5 Calculating Combinations

Calculate **a.** $C(11, 11)$ **b.** $C(11, 0)$.

Solution

a. $C(11, 11) = \dfrac{11 \times 10 \times 9 \times 8 \times 7 \times 6 \times 5 \times 4 \times 3 \times 2 \times 1}{11 \times 10 \times 9 \times 8 \times 7 \times 6 \times 5 \times 4 \times 3 \times 2 \times 1} = 1$

b. What do we do with that 0? What does it mean to multiply 0 numbers together? We know from above that $C(11, 0) = C(11, 11)$, so we must have $C(11, 0) = 1$. How does this fit with the formulas? Go back to the calculation of $C(11, 11)$:

$$1 = C(11, 11) = \frac{11!}{11!(11 - 11)!} = \frac{11!}{11!0!}.$$

This equality is true only if we agree that $0! = 1$, which we do. Then

$$C(11, 0) = \frac{11!}{0!11!} = 1.$$

➡ **Before we go on...** There is nothing special about 11 in the calculation in Example 5. In general,

$$C(n, n) = C(n, 0) = 1.$$

After all, there is only one way to choose n items out of n: choose them all. Similarly, there is only one way to choose 0 items out of n: choose none of them. ∎

Now for a few more complicated examples that illustrate the applications of the counting techniques we've discussed.

EXAMPLE 6 **Lotto**

In the betting game Lotto, used in many state lotteries, you choose six different numbers in the range 1–55 (the upper number varies). The order in which you choose them is irrelevant. If your six numbers match the six numbers chosen in the "official drawing," you win the top prize. If Lotto tickets cost $1 for two sets of numbers and you decide to buy tickets that cover every possible combination, thereby guaranteeing that you will win the top prize, how much money will you have to spend?

Solution We first need to know how many sets of numbers are possible. Because order does not matter, we are asking for the number of combinations of 55 numbers taken 6 at a time. This is

$$C(55, 6) = \frac{55 \times 54 \times 53 \times 52 \times 51 \times 50}{6 \times 5 \times 4 \times 3 \times 2 \times 1} = 28{,}989{,}675.$$

Because $1 buys you two of these, you need to spend $28{,}989{,}675/2 = \$14{,}494{,}838$ (rounding up to the nearest dollar) to be assured of a win!

➡ **Before we go on...** The calculation in Example 6 shows that you should not bother buying all these tickets if the winning prize is less than about $14.5 million. Even if the prize is higher, you need to account for the fact that many people will play and the prize may end up split among several winners, not to mention the impracticality of filling out millions of betting slips. ∎

EXAMPLE 7 **Marbles**

A bag contains three red marbles, three blue ones, three green ones, and two yellow ones (all distinguishable from one another).

a. How many sets of four marbles are possible?

b. How many sets of four are there such that each one is a different color?

c. How many sets of four are there in which at least two are red?

d. How many sets of four are there in which none are red, but at least one is green?

Solution

a. We simply need to find the number of ways of choosing 4 marbles out of 11, which is

$$C(11, 4) = 330 \text{ possible sets of 4 marbles}$$

b. We use a decision algorithm for choosing such a set of marbles.

Step 1 Choose one red one from the three red ones; $C(3, 1) = 3$ choices.
Step 2 Choose one blue one from the three blue ones; $C(3, 1) = 3$ choices.
Step 3 Choose one green one from the three green ones; $C(3, 1) = 3$ choices.
Step 4 Choose one yellow one from the two yellow ones; $C(2, 1) = 2$ choices.

This gives a total of $3 \times 3 \times 3 \times 2 = 54$ possible sets.

c. We need another decision algorithm. To say that at least two must be red means that either two are red or three are red (with a total of three red ones). In other words, we have two *alternatives*.

Alternative 1: Exactly two red marbles
Step 1 Choose two red ones; $C(3, 2) = 3$ choices.
Step 2 Choose two nonred ones. There are eight of these, so we get $C(8, 2) = 28$ possible choices.

Thus, the total number of choices for this alternative is $3 \times 28 = 84$.

Alternative 2: Exactly three red marbles.
Step 1 Choose the three red ones; $C(3, 3) = 1$ choice.
Step 2 Choose one nonred one; $C(8, 1) = 8$ choices.

Thus, the total number of choices for this alternative is $1 \times 8 = 8$.

By the addition principle, we get a total of $84 + 8 = 92$ sets.

d. The phrase "at least one green" tells us that we again have some alternatives.

Alternative 1: One green marble
Step 1 Choose one green marble from the three; $C(3, 1) = 3$ choices.
Step 2 Choose three nongreen, nonred marbles; $C(5, 3) = 10$ choices.

Thus, the total number of choices for alternative 1 is $3 \times 10 = 30$.

Alternative 2: Two green marbles
Step 1 Choose two green marbles from the three; $C(3, 2) = 3$ choices.
Step 2 Choose two nongreen, nonred marbles; $C(5, 2) = 10$ choices.

Thus, the total number of choices for alternative 2 is $3 \times 10 = 30$.

Alternative 3: Three green marbles
Step 1 Choose three green marbles from the three; $C(3, 3) = 1$ choice.
Step 2 Choose one nongreen, nonred marble; $C(5, 1) = 5$ choices.

Thus, the total number of choices for alternative 3 is $1 \times 5 = 5$.

The addition principle now tells us that the number of sets of four marbles with none red, but at least one green, is $30 + 30 + 5 = 65$.

➡ **Before we go on...** Here is an easier way to answer part (d) of Example 7. First, the total number of sets having *no* red marbles is $C(8, 4) = 70$. Next, of those, the number containing no green marbles is $C(5, 4) = 5$. This leaves $70 - 5 = 65$ sets that contain no red marbles but have at least one green marble. (We have really used here the formula for the cardinality of the complement of a set.) ∎

The last example concerns poker hands. For those unfamiliar with playing cards, here is a short description. A standard deck consists of 52 playing cards. Each card is in one of 13 denominations: ace, 2, 3, 4, 5, 6, 7, 8, 9, 10, jack (J), queen (Q), and king (K), and in one of four suits: hearts (♥), diamonds (♦), clubs (♣), and spades (♠). Thus, for instance, the jack of spades, J♠, refers to the denomination of jack in the suit of spades. The entire deck of cards is thus

A♥	2♥	3♥	4♥	5♥	6♥	7♥	8♥	9♥	10♥	J♥	Q♥	K♥
A♦	2♦	3♦	4♦	5♦	6♦	7♦	8♦	9♦	10♦	J♦	Q♦	K♦
A♣	2♣	3♣	4♣	5♣	6♣	7♣	8♣	9♣	10♣	J♣	Q♣	K♣
A♠	2♠	3♠	4♠	5♠	6♠	7♠	8♠	9♠	10♠	J♠	Q♠	K♠.

EXAMPLE 8   Poker Hands

In the card game poker, a hand consists of a set of five cards from a standard deck of 52. A **full house** is a hand consisting of three cards of one denomination ("three of a kind"—e.g., three 10s) and two of another ("two of a kind"—e.g., two queens). Here is an example of a full house: 10♣, 10♦, 10♠, Q♥, Q♣.

a. How many different poker hands are there?

b. How many different full houses are there that contain three 10s and two queens?

c. How many different full houses are there altogether?

Solution

a. Because the order of the cards doesn't matter, we simply need to know the number of ways of choosing a set of 5 cards out of 52, which is

$$C(52, 5) = 2{,}598{,}960 \text{ hands.}$$

b. Here is a decision algorithm for choosing a full house with three 10s and two queens.

Step 1 Choose three 10s. Because there are four 10s to choose from, we have $C(4, 3) = 4$ choices.

Step 2 Choose two queens; $C(4, 2) = 6$ choices.

Thus, there are $4 \times 6 = 24$ possible full houses with three 10s and two queens.

c. Here is a decision algorithm for choosing a full house.

Step 1 Choose a denomination for the three of a kind; 13 choices.

Step 2 Choose three cards of that denomination. Because there are four cards of each denomination (one for each suit), we get $C(4, 3) = 4$ choices.

Step 3 Choose a different denomination for the two of a kind. There are only 12 denominations left, so we have 12 choices.

Step 4 Choose two of that denomination; $C(4, 2) = 6$ choices.

Thus, by the multiplication principle, there are a total of $13 \times 4 \times 12 \times 6 = 3{,}744$ possible full houses.

FAQs

Recognizing When to Use Permutations or Combinations

Q: *How can I tell whether a given application calls for permutations or combinations?*

A: Decide whether the application calls for ordered lists (as in situations where order is implied) or for unordered sets (as in situations where order is not relevant). Ordered lists are permutations, whereas unordered sets are combinations.

6.4 EXERCISES

▼ more advanced   ◆ challenging

Ⓣ indicates exercises that should be solved using technology

Evaluate each number in Exercises 1–16. HINT [See Quick Examples on pages 430 and 432.]

1. 6!

2. 7!

3. 8!/6!

4. 10!/8!

5. $P(6, 4)$

6. $P(8, 3)$

7. $P(6, 4)/4!$

8. $P(8, 3)/3!$

9. $C(3, 2)$

10. $C(4, 3)$

11. $C(10, 8)$

12. $C(11, 9)$

13. $C(20, 1)$

14. $C(30, 1)$

15. $C(100, 98)$

16. $C(100, 97)$

17. How many ordered lists are there of four items chosen from six?

18. How many ordered sequences are possible that contain three objects chosen from seven?

19. How many unordered sets are possible that contain three objects chosen from seven?

20. How many unordered sets are there of four items chosen from six?

21. How many five-letter sequences are possible that use the letters b, o, g, e, y once each?

22. How many six-letter sequences are possible that use the letters q, u, a, k, e, s once each?

23. How many three-letter sequences are possible that use the letters q, u, a, k, e, s at most once each?

24. How many three-letter sequences are possible that use the letters b, o, g, e, y at most once each?

25. How many three-letter (unordered) sets are possible that use the letters q, u, a, k, e, s at most once each?

26. How many three-letter (unordered) sets are possible that use the letters b, o, g, e, y at most once each?

27. ▼ How many six-letter sequences are possible that use the letters a, u, a, a, u, k? [Hint: Use the decision algorithm discussed in Example of Section 6.3.]

28. ▼ How many six-letter sequences are possible that use the letters f, f, a, a, f, f? [See the hint for the preceding exercise.]

Marbles For Exercises 29–42, a bag contains three red marbles, two green ones, one lavender one, two yellows, and two orange marbles. HINT [See Example 7.]

29. How many possible sets of four marbles are there?

30. How many possible sets of three marbles are there?

31. How many sets of four marbles include all the red ones?

32. How many sets of three marbles include all the yellow ones?

33. How many sets of four marbles include none of the red ones?

34. How many sets of three marbles include none of the yellow ones?

35. How many sets of four marbles include one of each color other than lavender?

36. How many sets of five marbles include one of each color?

37. How many sets of five marbles include at least two red ones?

38. How many sets of five marbles include at least one yellow one?

39. How many sets of five marbles include at most one of the yellow ones?

40. How many sets of five marbles include at most one of the red ones?

41. ▼ How many sets of five marbles include either the lavender one or exactly one yellow one but not both colors?

42. ▼ How many sets of five marbles include at least one yellow one but no green ones?

Dice If a die is rolled 30 times, there are 6^{30} different sequences possible. Exercises 43–46 ask how many of these sequences satisfy certain conditions. HINT [Use the decision algorithm discussed in Example 3 of Section 6.3.]

43. ▼ What fraction of these sequences have exactly five 1s?

44. ▼ What fraction of these sequences have exactly five ones and five 2s?

45. ▼ What fraction of these sequences have exactly 15 even numbers?

46. ▼ What fraction of these sequences have exactly 10 numbers less than or equal to 2?

APPLICATIONS

47. *Itineraries* Your international diplomacy trip requires stops in Thailand, Singapore, Hong Kong, and Bali. How many possible itineraries are there? HINT [See Examples 1 and 2.]

48. *Itineraries* Refer back to the preceding exercise. How many possible itineraries are there in which the last stop is Thailand?

Poker Hands A poker hand consists of five cards from a standard deck of 52. (See the chart preceding Example 8.) In Exercises 49–54, find the number of different poker hands of the specified type. HINT [See Example 8.]

49. Two pairs (two of one denomination, two of another denomination, and one of a third)

50. Three of a kind (three of one denomination, one of another denomination, and one of a third)

51. Two of a kind (two of one denomination and three of different denominations)

52. Four of a kind (all four of one denomination and one of another)

53. ▼ Straight (five cards of consecutive denominations: A, 2, 3, 4, 5 up through 10, J, Q, K, A, not all of the same suit) (Note that the ace counts either as a 1 or as the denomination above king.)

54. ▼ Flush (five cards all of the same suit, but not consecutive denominations)

Dogs of the Dow *The "Dogs of the Dow" refer to the stocks listed on the Dow with the highest dividend yield. Exercises 55 and 56 are based on the following table, which shows the top ten stocks of the "Dogs of the Dow" list in January, 2009:*[15]

Symbol	Company	Price	Yield
BAC	Bank of America	14.08	9.09%
GE	General Electric	16.20	7.65%
PFE	Pfizer	17.71	7.23%
DD	DuPont	25.30	6.48%
AA	Alcoa	11.26	6.04%
T	AT&T	28.50	5.75%
VZ	Verizon	33.90	5.43%
MRK	Merck	30.40	5.00%
JPM	JP Morgan Chase	31.53	4.82%
KFT	Kraft	26.85	4.32%

55. You decide to make a small portfolio consisting of a collection of five of the top ten Dogs of the Dow.

   a. How many portfolios are possible?
   b. How many of these portfolios contain BAC and KFT but neither GE nor DD?
   c. How many of these portfolios contain at least four stocks with yields above 6%?

56. You decide to make a small portfolio consisting of a collection of six of the top ten Dogs of the Dow.

   a. How many portfolios are possible?
   b. How many of these portfolios contain MRK but not BAC?
   c. How many of these portfolios contain at most one stock priced above $30?

---
[15] Source: www.dogsofthedow.com.

Day Trading *Day traders typically buy and sell stocks (or other investment instruments) during the trading day and sell all investments by the end of the day. Exercises 57 and 58 are based on the following table, which shows the closing prices on January 9, 2009, of 12 stocks selected by your broker, Prudence Swift, as well as the change that day.*

Tech Stocks	Close	Change
AAPL (Apple)	$90.58	−2.12
MSFT (Microsoft)	$19.52	−0.60
NOK (Nokia)	$15.21	−0.16
NT (Nortel)	$0.39	0.10
RIMM (Research in Motion)	$47.99	1.49
S (Sprint Nextel)	$2.59	0.01
Non-Tech Stocks		
DIS (Walt Disney)	$22.31	−0.59
DUK (Duke)	$15.27	−0.14
ED (Con Ed)	$39.66	0.20
FE (First Energy)	$48.90	1.14
MO (Altria Group)	$15.48	0.38
NVS (Novarnis)	$48.16	−1.46

57. On the morning of January 9, 2009, Swift advised you to purchase a collection of three tech stocks and two non-tech stocks, all chosen at random from those listed in the table. You were to sell all the stocks at the end of the trading day.

   a. How many possible collections are possible?
   b. You tend to have bad luck with stocks—they usually start going down the moment you buy them. How many of the collections in part (a) consist entirely of stocks that declined in value by the end of the day?
   c. Using the answers to parts (a) and (b), what would you say your chances were of choosing a collection consisting entirely of stocks that declined in value by the end of the day?

58. On the morning of January 9, 2009, Swift advised your friend to purchase a collection of three stocks chosen at random from those listed in the table. Your friend was to sell all the stocks at the end of the trading day.

   a. How many possible collections are possible?
   b. How many of the collections in part (a) included exactly two tech stocks that increased in value by the end of the day?
   c. Using the answers to parts (a) and (b), what would you say the chances were that your friend chose a collection that included exactly two tech stocks that increased in value by the end of the day?

Movies Exercises 59 and 60 are based on the following list of top DVD rentals (based on revenue) for the weekend ending January 4, 2009:[16]

Name	Rental Index
Eagle Eye	100.00
Burn After Reading	74.62
Mamma Mia!	63.30
The Dark Knight	62.43
Death Race	61.50
The Mummy: Tomb of the Dragon Emperor	60.72
Traitor	52.57
Wanted	49.22
Step Brothers	46.81
Horton Hears a Who!	43.91

59. ▼ Rather than study for math, you and your buddies decide to get together for a marathon movie-watching popcorn-guzzling event on Saturday night. You decide to watch four movies selected at random from the above list.

   a. How many sets of four movies are possible?
   b. Your best friends, the Lara twins, refuse to see *Horton Hears a Who!* on the grounds that it is "for girlie men" and also insist that at least one of *Death Race* or *Eagle Eye* be among the movies selected. How many of the possible groups of four will satisfy the twins?
   c. Comparing the answers in parts (a) and (b), would you say the Lara twins are more likely than not to be satisfied with your random selection?

60. ▼ Rather than study for astrophysics, you and your friends decide to get together for a marathon movie-watching gummy-bear-munching event on Saturday night. You decide to watch three movies selected at random from the above list.

   a. How many sets of three movies are possible?
   b. Your best friends, the Pelogrande twins, refuse to see either *Mamma Mia!* or *The Mummy* on the grounds that they are "for idiots" and also insist that no more than one of *Traitor* and *Death Race* should be among the movies selected. How many of the possible groups of three will satisfy the twins?
   c. Comparing the answers in parts (a) and (b), would you say the Pelogrande twins are more likely than not to be satisfied with your random selection?

61. ▼ *Traveling Salesperson* Suppose you are a salesperson who must visit the following 23 cities: Dallas, Tampa, Orlando, Fairbanks, Seattle, Detroit, Chicago, Houston, Arlington, Grand Rapids, Urbana, San Diego, Aspen, Little Rock, Tuscaloosa, Honolulu, New York, Ithaca, Charlottesville, Lynchville, Raleigh, Anchorage, and Los Angeles. Leave all your answers in factorial form.

   a. How many possible itineraries are there that visit each city exactly once?
   b. Repeat part (a) in the event that the first five stops have already been determined.
   c. Repeat part (a) in the event that your itinerary must include the sequence Anchorage, Fairbanks, Seattle, Chicago, and Detroit, in that order.

62. ▼ *Traveling Salesperson* Refer back to the preceding exercise (and leave all your answers in factorial form).

   a. How many possible itineraries are there that start and end at Detroit, and visit every other city exactly once?
   b. How many possible itineraries are there that start and end at Detroit, visit Chicago twice and every other city once?
   c. Repeat part (a) in the event that your itinerary must include the sequence Anchorage, Fairbanks, Seattle, Chicago, and New York, in that order.

In Exercises 63–68, calculate how many different sequences can be formed that use the letters of each given word. [Decide where, for example, all the s's will go, rather than what will go in each position. Leave your answer as a product of terms of the form C(n, r).]

63. ▼ Mississippi   64. ▼ Mesopotamia

65. ▼ Megalomania   66. ▼ Schizophrenia

67. ▼ Casablanca   68. ▼ Desmorelda

69. ▼ *(From the GMAT)* Ben and Ann are among seven contestants from which four semifinalists are to be selected. Of the different possible selections, how many contain neither Ben nor Ann?

   (A) 5   (B) 6   (C) 7   (D) 14   (E) 21

70. ▼ *(Based on a Question from the GMAT)* Ben and Ann are among seven contestants from which four semifinalists are to be selected. Of the different possible selections, how many contain Ben but not Ann?

   (A) 5   (B) 8   (C) 9   (D) 10   (E) 20

71. ◆ *(From the GMAT exam)* If 10 persons meet at a reunion and each person shakes hands exactly once with each of the others, what is the total number of handshakes?

   (A) $10 \cdot 9 \cdot 8 \cdot 7 \cdot 6 \cdot 5 \cdot 4 \cdot 3 \cdot 2 \cdot 1$ (B) $10 \cdot 10$
   (C) $10 \cdot 9$ (D) 45   (E) 36

---

[16] Source: Home Media Magazine (www.imdb.com/Charts/videolast).

72. ◆ (*Based on a question from the GMAT exam*) If 12 businesspeople have a meeting and each pair exchanges business cards, how many business cards, total, get exchanged?

(A) $12 \cdot 11 \cdot 10 \cdot 9 \cdot 8 \cdot 7 \cdot 6 \cdot 5 \cdot 4 \cdot 3 \cdot 2 \cdot 1$ (B) $12 \cdot 12$
(C) $12 \cdot 11$ (D) 66   (E) 72

73. ◆ *Product Design* The Honest Lock Company plans to introduce what it refers to as the "true combination lock." The lock will open if the correct set of three numbers from 0 through 39 is entered in any order.

a. How many different combinations of three different numbers are possible?
b. If it is allowed that a number appear twice (but not three times), how many more possibilities are created?
c. If it is allowed that any or all of the numbers may be the same, what is the total number of combinations that will open the lock?

74. ◆ *Product Design* Repeat Exercise 73 for a lock based on selecting from the numbers 0 through 19.

75. ◆ *Theory of Linear Programming* (Some familiarity with linear programming is assumed for this exercise.) Suppose you have a linear programming problem with two unknowns and 20 constraints. You decide that graphing the feasible region would take a lot of work, but then you recall that corner points are obtained by solving a system of two equations in two unknowns obtained from two of the constraints. Thus, you decide that it might pay instead to locate all the possible corner points by solving all possible combinations of two equations and then checking whether each solution is a feasible point.

a. How many systems of two equations in two unknowns will you be required to solve?
b. Generalize this to n constraints.

76. ◆ *More Theory of Linear Programming* (Some familiarity with linear programming is assumed for this exercise.) Before the advent of the simplex method for solving linear programming problems, the following method was used: Suppose you have a linear programming problem with three unknowns and 20 constraints. You locate corner points as follows: Selecting three of the constraints, you turn them into equations (by replacing the inequalities with equalities), solve the resulting system of three equations in three unknowns, and then check to see whether the solution is feasible.

a. How many systems of three equations in three unknowns will you be required to solve?
b. Generalize this to n constraints.

COMMUNICATION AND REASONING EXERCISES

77. If you were hard pressed to study for an exam on counting and had only enough time to study one topic, would you choose the formula for the number of permutations or the multiplication principle? Give reasons for your choice.

78. The formula for $C(n, r)$ is written as a ratio of two whole numbers. Can $C(n, r)$ ever be a fraction and not a whole number? Explain (without actually discussing the formula itself).

79. Which of the following represent permutations?

(A) An arrangement of books on a shelf
(B) A group of 10 people in a bus
(C) A committee of 5 senators chosen from 100
(D) A presidential cabinet of 5 portfolios chosen from 20

80. Which of the following represent combinations?

(A) A portfolio of five stocks chosen from the S&P Top Ten
(B) A group of 5 tenors for a choir chosen from 12 singers
(C) A new company CEO and a new CFO chosen from five
(D) The *New York Times* Top Ten Bestseller list

81. When you click on "Get Driving Directions" on Mapquest.com do you get a permutation or a combination of driving instructions? Explain, and give a simple example to illustrate why the answer is important.

82. If you want to know how many possible lists, arranged in alphabetical order, there are of five students selected from your class, you would use the formula for permutations, right? (Explain your answer.)

83. You are tutoring your friend for a test on sets and counting and she asks the question: "How do I know what formula to use for a given problem?" What is a good way to respond?

84. Complete the following. If a counting procedure has five alternatives, each of which has four steps of two choices each, then there are ___ outcomes. On the other hand, if there are five steps, each of which has four alternatives of two choices each, then there are ___ outcomes.

85. ▼ A textbook has the following exercise. "Three students from a class of 50 are selected to take part in a play. How many casts are possible?" Comment on this exercise.

86. ▼ Explain why the coefficient of $a^2 b^4$ in $(a + b)^6$ is $C(6, 2)$ (this is a consequence of the **binomial theorem**). HINT [In the product $(a + b)(a + b) \cdots (a + b)$ (six times), in how many different ways can you pick two a's and four b's to multiply together?]

CHAPTER 6 REVIEW

KEY CONCEPTS

Web Site www.FiniteandCalc.org
Go to the student Web site at www.FiniteandCalc.org to find a comprehensive and interactive Web-based summary of Chapter 6.

6.1 Sets and Set Operations

Sets, elements, subsets, proper subsets, empty set, finite and infinite sets *pp. 396 & 397*

Visualizing sets and relations between sets using Venn diagrams *p. 399*

Union:
$$A \cup B = \{x \mid x \in A \text{ or } x \in B\}$$
p. 400

Intersection: $A \cap B = \{x \mid x \in A \text{ and } x \in B\}$ *p. 400*

Universal sets, complements *p. 401*

Disjoint sets: $A \cap B = \emptyset$ *p. 402*

Cartesian product: $A \times B = \{(a, b) \mid a \in A \text{ and } b \in B\}$ *p. 402*

6.2 Cardinality

Cardinality: $n(A) = $ number of elements in A. *p. 407*

If A and B are finite sets, then $n(A \cup B) = n(A) + n(B) - n(A \cap B)$. *p. 408*

If A and B are disjoint finite sets, then $n(A \cup B) = n(A) + n(B)$. In this case, we say that $A \cup B$ is a **disjoint union**. *p. 408*

If S is a finite universal set and A is a subset of S, then $n(A') = n(S) - n(A)$ and $n(A) = n(S) - n(A')$. *p. 409*

If A and B are finite sets, then $n(A \times B) = n(A)n(B)$. *p. 414*

6.3 The Addition and Multiplication Principles

Addition Principle *p. 418*

Multiplication Principle *p. 418*

Decision Algorithm: a procedure for making a sequence of decisions to choose an element of a set *p. 419*

6.4 Permutations and Combinations

n factorial:
$$n! = n \times (n - 1) \times (n - 2) \times \cdots \times 2 \times 1$$
p. 429

Permutation of n items taken r at a time:
$$P(n, r) = \frac{n!}{(n - r)!} \quad p. 430$$

Combination of n items taken r at a time:
$$C(n, r) = P(n, r)/r! = \frac{n!}{r!(n - r)!}$$
p. 431

Using the equality $C(n, r) = C(n, n - r)$ to simplify calculations of combinations. *p. 433*

REVIEW EXERCISES

In each of Exercises 1–5, list the elements of the given set.

1. The set N of all negative integers greater than or equal to -3

2. The set of all outcomes of tossing a coin five times

3. The set of all outcomes of tossing two distinguishable dice such that the numbers are different

4. The sets $(A \cap B) \cup C$ and $A \cap (B \cup C)$ where $A = \{1, 2, 3, 4, 5\}$, $B = \{3, 4, 5\}$ and $C = \{1, 2, 5, 6, 7\}$

5. The sets $A \cup B'$ and $A \times B'$ where $A = \{a, b\}$, $B = \{b, c\}$ and $S = \{a, b, c, d\}$

In each of Exercises 6–9, write the indicated set in terms of the given sets A and B.

6. S: the set of all customers; A: the set of all customers who owe money; B: the set of all customers who owe at least $1,000. The set of all customers who owe money but owe less than $1,000

7. A: the set of outcomes when a day in August is selected; B: the set of outcomes when a time of day is selected. The set of outcomes when a day in August and a time of that day are selected

8. S: the set of outcomes when two dice are rolled; E: those outcomes in which at most one die shows an even number, F: those outcomes in which the sum of the numbers is 7. The set of outcomes in which both dice show an even number or sum to seven

9. S: the set of all integers; P: the set of all positive integers; E: the set of all even integers; Q: the set of all integers that are perfect squares ($Q = \{0, 1, 4, 9, 16, 25, \ldots\}$). The set of all integers that are not positive odd perfect squares

In each of Exercises 10–13, give a formula for the cardinality rule or rules needed to answer the question, and then give the solution.

10. There are 32 students in categories A and B combined; 24 are in A and 24 are in B. How many are in both A and B?

11. You have read 150 of the 400 novels in your home, but your sister Roslyn has read 200, of which only 50 are novels you have read as well. How many have neither of you read?

12. The *Apple iMac* comes in three models, each with five colors to choose from. How many combinations are possible?

13. You roll two dice, one red and one green. Losing combinations are doubles (both dice show the same number) and outcomes in which the green die shows an odd number and the red die shows an even number. The other combinations are winning ones. How many winning combinations are there?

Recall that a poker hand consists of 5 cards from a standard deck of 52. In each of Exercises 14–17, find the number of different poker hands of the specified type. Leave your answer in terms of combinations.

14. A full house with either two kings and three queens or two queens and three kings

441

15. Two of a kind with no aces

16. Three of a kind with no aces

17. Straight Flush (five cards of the same suit with consecutive denominations: A, 2, 3, 4, 5 up through 10, J, Q, K, A)

In each of Exercises 18–22, consider a bag containing four red marbles, two green ones, one transparent one, three yellow ones, and two orange ones.

18. How many possible sets of five marbles are there?

19. How many sets of five marbles include all the red ones?

20. How many sets of five marbles do not include all the red ones?

21. How many sets of five marbles include at least two yellow ones?

22. How many sets of five marbles include at most one of the red ones but no yellow ones?

APPLICATIONS

OHaganBooks.com currently operates three warehouses: one in Washington, one in California, and the new one in Texas. Book inventories are shown in the following table:

	Sci Fi	Horror	Romance	Other	Total
Washington	10,000	12,000	12,000	30,000	64,000
California	8,000	12,000	6,000	16,000	42,000
Texas	15,000	15,000	20,000	44,000	94,000
Total	33,000	39,000	38,000	90,000	200,000

Take the first letter of each category to represent the corresponding set of books; for instance, S is the set of sci fi books in stock, W is the set of books in the Washington warehouse, and so on. In each of Exercises 23–28, describe the given set in words and compute its cardinality.

23. $S \cup T$

24. $H \cap C$

25. $C \cup S'$

26. $(R \cap T) \cup H$

27. $R \cap (T \cup H)$

28. $(S \cap W) \cup (H \cap C')$

OHaganBooks.com has two main competitors: JungleBooks .com, and FarmerBooks.com. At the beginning of August, OHaganBooks.com had 3,500 customers. Of these, a total of 2,000 customers were shared with JungleBooks.com and 1,500 with FarmerBooks.com. Furthermore, 1,000 customers were shared with both. JungleBooks.com has a total of 3,600 customers, FarmerBooks.com has 3,400, and they share 1,100 customers between them. Use these data for Exercises 29–34,

29. How many of all these customers are exclusive OHaganBooks .com customers?

30. How many customers of the other two companies are not customers of OHaganBooks.com?

31. Which of the three companies has the largest number of exclusive customers?

32. Which of the three companies has the smallest number of exclusive customers?

33. OHaganBooks.com is interested in merging with one of its two competitors. Which merger would give it the largest combined customer base, and how large would that be?

34. Referring to the preceding exercise, which merger would give OHaganBooks.com the largest *exclusive* customer base, and how large would that be?

As the customer base at OHaganBooks.com grows, software manager Ruth Nabarro is thinking of introducing identity codes for all the online customers. Help her with the questions in Exercises 35–38.

35. If she uses 3-letter codes, how many different customers can be identified?

36. If she uses codes with three different letters, how many different customers can be identified?

37. It appears that Nabarro has finally settled on codes consisting of two letters followed by two digits. For technical reasons, the letters must be different and the first digit cannot be a zero. How many different customers can be identified?

38. The CEO sends Nabarro the following memo:

```
To: Ruth Nabarro, Software Manager
From: John O'Hagan, CEO
Subject: Customer Identity Codes

I have read your proposal for the cus-
tomer ID codes. However, due to our am-
bitious expansion plans, I would like
our system software to allow for at
least 500,000 customers. Please adjust
your proposal accordingly.
```

Nabarro is determined to have a sequence of letters followed by some digits, and, for reasons too complicated to explain, there cannot be more than two letters, the letters must be different, the digits must all be different, and the first digit cannot be a zero. What is the form of the shortest code she can use to satisfy the CEO, and how many different customers can be identified?

After an exhausting day at the office (you are CEO of OHagan Books.com), you return home and find yourself having to assist your son Billy-Sean, who continues to have a terrible time planning his first-year college course schedule. The latest Bulletin of Suburban State University reads as follows:

All candidates for the degree of Bachelor of Arts at SSU must take, in their first year, at least 10 courses in the Sciences, Fine Arts, Liberal Arts and Mathematics combined, of which at least 2 must be in each of the Sciences and Fine Arts, and exactly 3 must be in each of the Liberal Arts and Mathematics.

Help him with the answers to Exercises 39–41.

39. If the Bulletin lists exactly five first-year-level science courses and six first-year-level courses in each of the other categories, how many course combinations are possible that meet the minimum requirements?

40. Reading through the course descriptions in the bulletin a second time, you notice that Calculus I (listed as one of the mathematics courses) is a required course for many of the other courses, and you decide that it would be best if Billy-Sean included Calculus I. Further, two of the Fine Arts courses cannot both be taken in the first year. How many

course combinations are possible that meet the minimum requirements and include Calculus I?

41. To complicate things further, in addition to the requirement in Exercise 40, Physics II has Physics I as a prerequisite (both are listed as first-year science courses, but it is not necessary to take both). How many course combinations are possible that include Calculus I and meet the minimum requirements?

Case Study   Designing a Puzzle

As Product Design Manager for Cerebral Toys Inc., you are constantly on the lookout for ideas for intellectually stimulating yet inexpensive toys. You recently received the following memo from Felix Frost, the developmental psychologist on your design team.

> To: Felicia
> From: Felix
> Subject: Crazy Cubes
>
> We've hit on an excellent idea for a new educational puzzle (which we are calling "Crazy Cubes" until Marketing comes up with a better name). Basically, Crazy Cubes will consist of a set of plastic cubes. Two faces of each cube will be colored red, two will be colored blue, and two white, and there will be exactly two cubes with each possible configuration of colors. The goal of the puzzle is to seek out the matching pairs, thereby enhancing a child's geometric intuition and three-dimensional manipulation skills. The kit will include every possible configuration of colors. We are, however, a little stumped on the following question: How many cubes will the kit contain? In other words, how many possible ways can one color the faces of a cube so that two faces are red, two are blue, and two are white?

Looking at the problem, you reason that the following three-step decision algorithm ought to suffice:

Step 1 Choose a pair of faces to color red; $C(6, 2) = 15$ choices.

Step 2 Choose a pair of faces to color blue; $C(4, 2) = 6$ choices.

Step 3 Choose a pair of faces to color white; $C(2, 2) = 1$ choice.

This algorithm appears to give a total of $15 \times 6 \times 1 = 90$ possible cubes. However, before sending your reply to Felix, you realize that something is wrong, because there are different choices that result in the same cube. To describe some of these choices, imagine a cube oriented so that four of its faces are facing the four compass directions (Figure 9). Consider choice 1 with the top and bottom faces blue, north and south faces white, and east and west faces red and choice 2 with the top and bottom faces blue, north and south faces red, and east and west faces white. These cubes are actually the same, as you see by rotating the second cube 90 degrees (Figure 10).

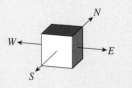

Figure 9

You therefore decide that you need a more sophisticated decision algorithm. Here is one that works.

Alternative 1: Faces with the same color opposite each other. Place one of the blue faces down. Then the top face is also blue. The cube must look like the one drawn in Figure 10. Thus there is only one choice here.

Figure 10

Figure 11

Figure 12

Alternative 2: Red faces opposite each other and the other colors on adjacent pairs of faces. Again there is only one choice, as you can see by putting the red faces on the top and bottom and then rotating.

Alternative 3: White faces opposite each other and the other colors on adjacent pairs of faces; one possibility.

Alternative 4: Blue faces opposite each other and the other colors on adjacent pairs of faces; one possibility.

Alternative 5: Faces with the same color adjacent to each other. Look at the cube so that the edge common to the two red faces is facing you and horizontal (Figure 11). Then the faces on the left and right must be of different colors because they are opposite each other. Assume that the face on the right is white. (If it's blue, then rotate the die with the red edge still facing you to move it there, as in Figure 12.) This leaves two choices for the other white face, on the upper or the lower of the two back faces. This alternative gives two choices.

It follows that there are $1 + 1 + 1 + 1 + 2 = 6$ choices. Because the Crazy Cubes kit will feature two of each cube, the kit will require 12 different cubes.[17]

EXERCISES

In all of the following exercises, there are three colors to choose from: red, white, and blue.

1. In order to enlarge the kit, Felix suggests including two each of two-colored cubes (using two of the colors red, white, and blue) with three faces one color and three another. How many additional cubes will be required?

2. If Felix now suggests adding two each of cubes with two faces one color, one face another color, and three faces the third color, how many additional cubes will be required?

3. Felix changes his mind and suggests the kit use tetrahedral blocks with two colors instead (see the figure). How many of these would be required?

4. Once Felix finds the answer to the preceding exercise, he decides to go back to the cube idea, but this time insists that all possible combinations of up to three colors should be included. (For instance, some cubes will be all one color, others will be two colors.) How many cubes should the kit contain?

A tetrahedron

---

[17]There is a beautiful way of calculating this and similar numbers, called Pólya enumeration, but it requires a discussion of topics well outside the scope of this book. Take this as a hint that counting techniques can use some of the most sophisticated mathematics.

7

Probability

Case Study The Monty Hall Problem

On the game show *Let's Make a Deal*, you are shown three doors, A, B, and C, and behind one of them is the Big Prize. After you select one of them—say, door A—to make things more interesting the host (Monty Hall) opens one of the other doors—say, door B—revealing that the Big Prize is not there. He then offers you the opportunity to change your selection to the remaining door, door C. Should you switch or stick with your original guess? **Does it make any difference?**

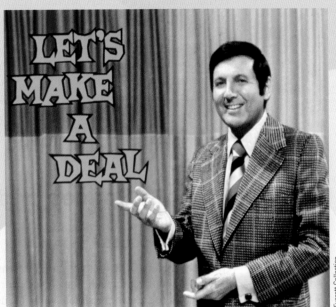

Everett Collection

Web Site
www.FiniteandCalc.org
At the Web site you will find:

- Section by section tutorials, including game tutorials with randomized quizzes

- A detailed chapter summary

- A true/false quiz

- A Markov system simulation and matrix algebra tool

- Additional review exercises

Introduction

What is the probability of winning the lottery twice? What are the chances that a college athlete whose drug test is positive for steroid use is actually using steroids? You are playing poker and have been dealt two jacks. What is the likelihood that one of the next three cards you are dealt will also be a jack? These are all questions about probability.

Understanding probability is important in many fields, ranging from risk management in business through hypothesis testing in psychology to quantum mechanics in physics. Historically, the theory of probability arose in the sixteenth and seventeenth centuries from attempts by mathematicians such as Gerolamo Cardano, Pierre de Fermat, Blaise Pascal, and Christiaan Huygens to understand games of chance. Andrey Nikolaevich Kolmogorov set forth the foundations of modern probability theory in his 1933 book *Foundations of the Theory of Probability.*

The goal of this chapter is to familiarize you with the basic concepts of modern probability theory and to give you a working knowledge that you can apply in a variety of situations. In the first two sections, the emphasis is on translating real-life situations into the language of sample spaces, events, and probability. Once we have mastered the language of probability, we spend the rest of the chapter studying some of its theory and applications. The last section gives an interesting application of both probability and matrix arithmetic.

7.1 Sample Spaces and Events

Sample Spaces

At the beginning of a football game, to ensure fairness, the referee tosses a coin to decide who will get the ball first. When the ref tosses the coin and observes which side faces up, there are two possible results: heads (H) and tails (T). These are the *only* possible results, ignoring the (remote) possibility that the coin lands on its edge. The act of tossing the coin is an example of an **experiment**. The two possible results, H and T, are possible **outcomes** of the experiment, and the set $S = \{H, T\}$ of all possible outcomes is the **sample space** for the experiment.

Experiments, Outcomes, and Sample Spaces

An **experiment** is an occurrence with a result, or **outcome**, that is uncertain before the experiment takes place. The set of all possible outcomes is called the **sample space** for the experiment.

Quick Examples

1. *Experiment:* Flip a coin and observe the side facing up.
   Outcomes: H, T
   Sample Space: $S = \{H,\ T\}$
2. *Experiment:* Select a student in your class.
   Outcomes: The students in your class
   Sample Space: The set of students in your class

3. *Experiment:* Select a student in your class and observe the color of his or her hair.
   Outcomes: red, black, brown, blond, green, ...
   Sample Space: {red, black, brown, blond, green, ...}

4. *Experiment:* Cast a die and observe the number facing up.
   Outcomes: 1, 2, 3, 4, 5, 6
   Sample Space: $S = \{1, 2, 3, 4, 5, 6\}$

5. *Experiment:* Cast two distinguishable dice (see Example 1(a) of Section 6.1) and observe the numbers facing up.
   Outcomes: $(1, 1), (1, 2), \ldots, (6, 6)$ (36 outcomes)

$$\text{Sample Space: } S = \begin{cases} (1,1), & (1,2), & (1,3), & (1,4), & (1,5), & (1,6), \\ (2,1), & (2,2), & (2,3), & (2,4), & (2,5), & (2,6), \\ (3,1), & (3,2), & (3,3), & (3,4), & (3,5), & (3,6), \\ (4,1), & (4,2), & (4,3), & (4,4), & (4,5), & (4,6), \\ (5,1), & (5,2), & (5,3), & (5,4), & (5,5), & (5,6), \\ (6,1), & (6,2), & (6,3), & (6,4), & (6,5), & (6,6) \end{cases}$$

$n(S) =$ the number of outcomes in $S = 36$

6. *Experiment:* Cast two indistinguishable dice (see Example 1(b) of Section 6.1) and observe the numbers facing up.
   Outcomes: $(1, 1), (1, 2), \ldots, (6, 6)$ (21 outcomes)

$$\text{Sample Space: } S = \begin{cases} (1,1), & (1,2), & (1,3), & (1,4), & (1,5), & (1,6), \\ & (2,2), & (2,3), & (2,4), & (2,5), & (2,6), \\ & & (3,3), & (3,4), & (3,5), & (3,6), \\ & & & (4,4), & (4,5), & (4,6), \\ & & & & (5,5), & (5,6), \\ & & & & & (6,6) \end{cases}$$

$n(S) = 21$

7. *Experiment:* Cast two dice and observe the *sum* of the numbers facing up.
   Outcomes: 2, 3, 4, 5, 6, 7, 8, 9, 10, 11, 12
   Sample Space: $S = \{2, 3, 4, 5, 6, 7, 8, 9, 10, 11, 12\}$

8. *Experiment:* Choose 2 cars (without regard to order) at random from a fleet of 10.
   Outcomes: Collections of 2 cars chosen from 10
   Sample Space: The set of all collections of 2 cars chosen from 10

   $n(S) = C(10, 2) = 45$

The following example introduces a sample space that we'll use in several other examples.

EXAMPLE 1 **School and Work**

In a survey conducted by the Bureau of Labor Statistics,* the high school graduating class of 2007 was divided into those who went on to college and those who did not. Those who went on to college were further divided into those who went to two-year colleges and those who went to four-year colleges. All graduates were also asked whether they were working or not. Find the sample space for the experiment "Select a member of the high school graduating class of 2007 and classify his or her subsequent school and work activity."

Solution The tree in Figure 1 shows the various possibilities.

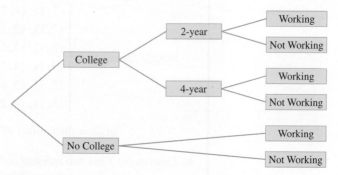

Figure 1

The sample space is

$$S = \{\text{2-year college \& working, 2-year college \& not working,}$$
$$\text{4-year college \& working, 4-year college \& not working,}$$
$$\text{no college \& working, no college \& not working}\}.$$

---

* "College Enrollment and Work Activity of High School Graduates News Release," U.S. Bureau of Labor Statistics, April 2008, available at www.bls.gov/news.release/hsgec.htm.

Events

In Example 1, suppose we are interested in the event that a 2003 high school graduate was working. In mathematical language, we are interested in the *subset* of the sample space consisting of all outcomes in which the graduate was working.

Events

Given a sample space *S*, an **event** *E* is a subset of *S*. The outcomes in *E* are called the **favorable** outcomes. We say that *E* **occurs** in a particular experiment if the outcome of that experiment is one of the elements of *E*—that is, if the outcome of the experiment is favorable.

Visualizing an Event

In the following figure, the favorable outcomes (events in E) are shown in green.

Sample Space S

Quick Examples

1. *Experiment:* Roll a die and observe the number facing up.

   $S = \{1, 2, 3, 4, 5, 6\}$

   Event: E: The number observed is odd.

   $E = \{1, 3, 5\}$

2. *Experiment:* Roll two distinguishable dice and observe the numbers facing up.

   $S = \{(1, 1), (1, 2), \ldots, (6, 6)\}$

   Event: F: The dice show the same number.

   $F = \{(1, 1), (2, 2), (3, 3), (4, 4), (5, 5), (6, 6)\}$

3. *Experiment:* Roll two distinguishable dice and observe the numbers facing up.

   $S = \{(1, 1), (1, 2), \ldots, (6, 6)\}$

   Event: G: The sum of the numbers is 1.

   $G = \emptyset$ There are no favorable outcomes.

4. *Experiment:* Select a city beginning with "J."
   Event: E: The city is Johannesburg.

   $E = \{\text{Johannesburg}\}$ An event can consist of a single outcome.

5. *Experiment:* Roll a die and observe the number facing up.
   Event: E: The number observed is either even or odd.

   $E = S = \{1, 2, 3, 4, 5, 6\}$ An event can consist of all possible outcomes.

6. *Experiment:* Select a student in your class.
   Event: E: The student has red hair.

   $E = \{\text{red-haired students in your class}\}$

7. *Experiment:* Draw a hand of two cards from a deck of 52.
   Event: H: Both cards are diamonds.

   H is the set of all hands of 2 cards chosen from 52 such that both cards are diamonds.

Here are some more examples of events.

EXAMPLE 2 Dice

We roll a red die and a green die and observe the numbers facing up. Describe the following events as subsets of the sample space.

a. E: The sum of the numbers showing is 6.

b. F: The sum of the numbers showing is 2.

Solution Here (again) is the sample space for the experiment of throwing two dice.

$$S = \begin{cases} (1,1), & (1,2), & (1,3), & (1,4), & (1,5), & (1,6), \\ (2,1), & (2,2), & (2,3), & (2,4), & (2,5), & (2,6), \\ (3,1), & (3,2), & (3,3), & (3,4), & (3,5), & (3,6), \\ (4,1), & (4,2), & (4,3), & (4,4), & (4,5), & (4,6), \\ (5,1), & (5,2), & (5,3), & (5,4), & (5,5), & (5,6), \\ (6,1), & (6,2), & (6,3), & (6,4), & (6,5), & (6,6) \end{cases}$$

a. In mathematical language, E is the subset of S that consists of all those outcomes in which the sum of the numbers showing is 6. Here is the sample space once again, with the outcomes in question shown in color:

$$S = \begin{cases} (1,1), & (1,2), & (1,3), & (1,4), & (1,5), & (1,6), \\ (2,1), & (2,2), & (2,3), & (2,4), & (2,5), & (2,6), \\ (3,1), & (3,2), & (3,3), & (3,4), & (3,5), & (3,6), \\ (4,1), & (4,2), & (4,3), & (4,4), & (4,5), & (4,6), \\ (5,1), & (5,2), & (5,3), & (5,4), & (5,5), & (5,6), \\ (6,1), & (6,2), & (6,3), & (6,4), & (6,5), & (6,6) \end{cases}$$

Thus, $E = \{(1,5), (2,4), (3,3), (4,2), (5,1)\}$.

b. The only outcome in which the numbers showing add to 2 is $(1, 1)$. Thus,

$$F = \{(1, 1)\}.$$

EXAMPLE 3 School and Work

Let S be the sample space of Example 1. List the elements in the following events:

a. The event E that a 2007 high school graduate was working.

b. The event F that a 2007 high school graduate was not going to a two-year college.

Solution

a. We had this sample space:

$S = \{$2-year college & working, two-year college & not working,
    4-year college & working, four-year college & not working,
    no college & working, no college & not working$\}$.

We are asked for the event that a graduate was working. Whenever we encounter a phrase involving "the event that . . . ," we mentally translate this into mathematical language by changing the wording.

Replace the phrase "the event that . . . " by the phrase "the subset of the sample space consisting of all outcomes in which . . . "

Thus we are interested in the subset of the sample space consisting of all outcomes in which the graduate was working. This gives

$E = \{$two-year college & working, four-year college & working, no college & working$\}$.

The outcomes in E are illustrated by the shaded cells in Figure 2.

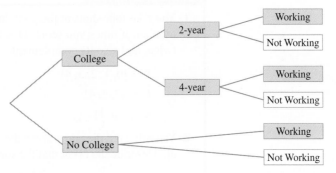

Figure 2

b. We are looking for the event that a graduate was not going to a two-year college, that is, the subset of the sample space consisting of all outcomes in which the graduate was not going to a two-year college. Thus,

$F = \{$four-year college & working, four-year college & not working, no college & working, no college & not working$\}$.

The outcomes in F are illustrated by the shaded cells in Figure 3.

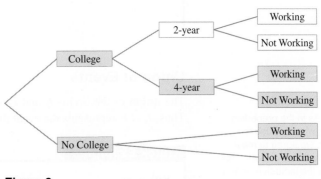

Figure 3

Complement, Union, and Intersection of Events

Events may often be described in terms of other events, using set operations such as complement, union, and intersection.

Complement of an Event

The **complement** of an event E is the set of outcomes not in E. Thus, the complement of E represents the event that E *does not occur*.

Visualizing the Complement

Sample Space S

E E'

Quick Examples

1. You take four shots at the goal during a soccer game and record the number of times you score. Describe the event that you score at least twice, and also its complement.

   $S = \{0, 1, 2, 3, 4\}$ Set of outcomes

   $E = \{2, 3, 4\}$ Event that you score at least twice

   $E' = \{0, 1\}$ Event that you do not score at least twice

2. You roll a red die and a green die and observe the two numbers facing up. Describe the event that the sum of the numbers is not 6.

   $S = \{(1, 1), (1, 2), \ldots, (6, 6)\}$

   $F = \{(1, 5), (2, 4), (3, 3), (4, 2), (5, 1)\}$ Sum of numbers is 6.

   $$F' = \begin{Bmatrix} (1, 1), & (1, 2), & (1, 3), & (1, 4), & & (1, 6), \\ (2, 1), & (2, 2), & (2, 3), & & (2, 5), & (2, 6), \\ (3, 1), & (3, 2), & & (3, 4), & (3, 5), & (3, 6), \\ (4, 1), & & (4, 3), & (4, 4), & (4, 5), & (4, 6), \\ & (5, 2), & (5, 3), & (5, 4), & (5, 5), & (5, 6), \\ (6, 1), & (6, 2), & (6, 3), & (6, 4), & (6, 5), & (6, 6) \end{Bmatrix}$$

   Sum of numbers is not 6.

Union of Events

The **union** of the events E and F is the set of all outcomes in E or F (or both). Thus, $E \cup F$ represents the event that E occurs *or* F occurs (or both).*

Quick Example

Roll a die.

   E: The outcome is a 5; $E = \{5\}$.

   F: The outcome is an even number; $F = \{2, 4, 6\}$.

   $E \cup F$: The outcome is either a 5 *or* an even number;
   $E \cup F = \{2, 4, 5, 6\}$.

Intersection of Events

The **intersection** of the events E and F is the set of all outcomes common to E and F. Thus, $E \cap F$ represents the event that both E *and* F occur.

Quick Example

Roll two dice; one red and one green.

E: The red die is 2.

F: The green die is odd.

$E \cap F$: The red die is 2 and the green die is odd;
$$E \cap F = \{(2, 1), (2, 3), (2, 5)\}.$$

EXAMPLE 4 **Weather**

Let R be the event that it will rain tomorrow, let P be the event that it will be pleasant, let C be the event that it will be cold, and let H be the event that it will be hot.

a. Express in words: $R \cap P'$, $R \cup (P \cap C)$.

b. Express in symbols: Tomorrow will be either a pleasant day or a cold and rainy day; it will not, however, be hot.

Solution The key here is to remember that intersection corresponds to *and* and union to *or*.

a. $R \cap P'$ is the event that it will rain *and* it will not be pleasant.
$R \cup (P \cap C)$ is the event that either it will rain, or it will be pleasant and cold.

b. If we rephrase the given statement using *and* and *or* we get "Tomorrow will be either a pleasant day or a cold and rainy day, and it will not be hot."

$$[P \cup (C \cap R)] \cap H' \qquad \text{Pleasant, or cold and rainy, and not hot.}$$

The nuances of the English language play an important role in this formulation. For instance, the effect of the pause (comma) after "rainy day" suggests placing the preceding clause $P \cup (C \cap R)$ in parentheses. In addition, the phrase "cold and rainy" suggests that C and R should be grouped together in their own parentheses.

EXAMPLE 5 **iPods, iPhones, and Macs**

(Compare Example 3 in Section 6.2.) The following table shows sales, in millions of units, of iPods, iPhones, and Macintosh computers in the last three quarters of 2008.*

	iPods	iPhones	Macs	Total
2008 Q2	10.6	1.7	2.3	14.6
2008 Q3	11.0	0.7	2.5	14.2
2008 Q4	11.1	6.9	2.6	20.6
Total	32.7	9.3	7.4	49.4

---

*Figures are rounded. Source: Company reports (www.apple.com/investor/).

Consider the experiment in which a device is selected at random from those represented in the table. Let D be the event that it was an iPod, let M be the event that it was a Mac, and let A be the event that it was sold in the second quarter of 2008. Describe the following events and compute their cardinality.

a. A' **b.** $D \cap A$ **c.** $M \cup A'$

Solution Before we answer the questions, note that S is the set of all items represented in the table, so S has a total of 49.4 million outcomes.

a. A' is the event that the item was not sold in the second quarter of 2008. Its cardinality is

$$n(A') = n(S) - n(A) = 49.4 - 14.6 = 34.8 \text{ million items.}$$

b. $D \cap A$ is the event that it was an iPod sold in the second quarter of 2008. Referring to the table, we find

$$n(D \cap A) = 10.6 \text{ million items.}$$

c. $M \cup A'$ is the event that either it was a Mac or it was not sold in the second quarter of 2008:

	iPods	iPhones	Macs	Total
2008 Q2	10.6	1.7	2.3	14.6
2008 Q3	11.0	0.7	2.5	14.2
2008 Q4	11.1	6.9	2.6	20.6
Total	32.7	9.3	7.4	49.4

To compute its cardinality, we use the formula for the cardinality of a union:

$$n(M \cup A') = n(M) + n(A') - n(M \cap A')$$
$$= 7.4 + 34.8 - (2.5 + 2.6) = 37.1 \text{ million items.}$$

➡ **Before we go on...** We could shorten the calculation in part (c) of Example 5 even further using De Morgan's law to write $n(M \cup A') = n((M' \cap A)') = 49.4 - (10.6 + 1.7) = 37.1$ million items, a calculation suggested by looking at the table. ∎

The case where $E \cap F$ is empty is interesting, and we give it a name.

Mutually Exclusive Events

If E and F are events, then E and F are said to be **disjoint** or **mutually exclusive** if $E \cap F$ is empty. (Hence, they have no outcomes in common.)

Visualizing Mutually Exclusive Events

Sample Space S

Interpretation
It is impossible for mutually exclusive events to occur simultaneously.

Quick Examples

In each of the following examples, E and F are mutually exclusive events.

1. Roll a die and observe the number facing up. E: The outcome is even; F: The outcome is odd.

$$E = \{2, 4, 6\}, F = \{1, 3, 5\}$$

2. Toss a coin three times and record the sequence of heads and tails. E: All three tosses land the same way up, F: One toss shows heads and the other two show tails.

$$E = \{HHH, TTT\}, F = \{HTT, THT, TTH\}$$

3. Observe tomorrow's weather. E: It is raining; F: There is not a cloud in the sky.

FAQs

Specifying the Sample Space

Q : *How do I determine the sample space in a given application?*

A : Strictly speaking, an experiment should include a description of what kinds of objects are in the sample space, as in:

Cast a die and observe the number facing up.
Sample space: the possible numbers facing up, {1, 2, 3, 4, 5, 6}.

Choose a person at random and record her social security number and whether she is blonde.
Sample space: pairs (9-digit number, Y/N).

However, in many of the scenarios discussed in this chapter and the next, an experiment is specified more vaguely, as in "Select a student in your class." In cases like this, the nature of the sample space should be determined from the context. For example, if the discussion is about grade-point averages and gender, the sample space can be taken to consist of pairs (grade-point average, M/F).

7.1 EXERCISES

▼ more advanced   ◆ challenging
T indicates exercises that should be solved using technology

In Exercises 1–18, describe the sample space S of the experiment and list the elements of the given event. (Assume that the coins are distinguishable and that what is observed are the faces or numbers that face up.) HINT [See Examples 1–3.]

1. Two coins are tossed; the result is at most one tail.

2. Two coins are tossed; the result is one or more heads.

3. Three coins are tossed; the result is at most one head.

4. Three coins are tossed; the result is more tails than heads.

5. Two distinguishable dice are rolled; the numbers add to 5.

6. Two distinguishable dice are rolled; the numbers add to 9.

7. Two indistinguishable dice are rolled; the numbers add to 4.

8. Two indistinguishable dice are rolled; one of the numbers is even and the other is odd.

9. Two indistinguishable dice are rolled; both numbers are prime.[1]

10. Two indistinguishable dice are rolled; neither number is prime.

11. A letter is chosen at random from those in the word *Mozart*; the letter is a vowel.

12. A letter is chosen at random from those in the word *Mozart*; the letter is neither *a* nor *m*.

13. A sequence of two different letters is randomly chosen from those of the word *sore*; the first letter is a vowel.

14. A sequence of two different letters is randomly chosen from those of the word *hear*; the second letter is not a vowel.

15. A sequence of two different digits is randomly chosen from the digits 0–4; the first digit is larger than the second.

16. A sequence of two different digits is randomly chosen from the digits 0–4; the first digit is twice the second.

17. You are considering purchasing either a domestic car, an imported car, a van, an antique car, or an antique truck; you do not buy a car.

18. You are deciding whether to enroll for Psychology 1, Psychology 2, Economics 1, General Economics, or Math for Poets; you decide to avoid economics.

19. A packet of gummy candy contains four strawberry gums, four lime gums, two black currant gums, and two orange gums. April May sticks her hand in and selects four at random. Complete the following sentences:
    a. The sample space is the set of . . .
    b. April is particularly fond of combinations of two strawberry and two black currant gums. The event that April will get the combination she desires is the set of . . .

20. A bag contains three red marbles, two blue ones, and four yellow ones, and Alexandra pulls out three of them at random. Complete the following sentences:
    a. The sample space is the set of . . .
    b. The event that Alexandra gets one of each color is the set of . . .

21. ▼ President Barack H. Obama's cabinet consisted of the Secretaries of Agriculture, Commerce, Defense, Education, Energy, Health and Human Services, Homeland Security, Housing and Urban Development, Interior, Labor, State, Transportation, Treasury, Veterans Affairs, and the Attorney General.[2] Assuming that President Obama had 20 candidates, including Hillary Clinton, to fill these posts (and wished to assign no one to more than one post), complete the following sentences:
    a. The sample space is the set of . . .
    b. The event that Hillary Clinton is the Secretary of State is the set of . . .

22. ▼ A poker hand consists of a set of 5 cards chosen from a standard deck of 52 playing cards. You are dealt a poker hand. Complete the following sentences:
    a. The sample space is the set of . . .
    b. The event "a full house" is the set of . . . (Recall that a full house is three cards of one denomination and two of another.)

Suppose two dice (one red, one green) are rolled. Consider the following events. A: the red die shows 1; B: the numbers add to 4; C: at least one of the numbers is 1; and D: the numbers do not add to 11. In Exercises 23–30, express the given event in symbols and say how many elements it contains. HINT [See Example 5.]

23. The red die shows 1 and the numbers add to 4.

24. The red die shows 1 but the numbers do not add to 11.

25. The numbers do not add to 4.

26. The numbers add to 11.

27. The numbers do not add to 4, but they do add to 11.

28. Either the numbers add to 11 or the red die shows a 1.

29. At least one of the numbers is 1 or the numbers add to 4.

30. Either the numbers add to 4, or they add to 11, or at least one of them is 1.

Let W be the event that you will use the Web site tonight, let I be the event that your math grade will improve, and let E be the event that you will use the Web site every night. In Exercises 31–38, express the given event in symbols.

31. You will use the Web site tonight and your math grade will improve.

32. You will use the Web site tonight or your math grade will not improve.

33. Either you will use the Web site every night, or your math grade will not improve.

34. Your math grade will not improve even though you use the Web site every night.

35. ▼ Either your math grade will improve, or you will use the Web site tonight but not every night.

36. ▼ You will use the Web site either tonight or every night, and your grade will improve.

37. ▼ (Compare Exercise 35.) Either your math grade will improve or you will use the Web site tonight, but you will not use it every night.

38. ▼ (Compare Exercise 36.) You will either use the Web site tonight, or you will use it every night and your grade will improve.

APPLICATIONS

Housing Prices *Exercises 39–44 are based on the following map, which shows the percentage increase in housing prices*

---

[1] A positive integer is **prime** if it is neither 1 nor a product of smaller integers.

[2] Source: The White House Web site (www.whitehouse.gov).

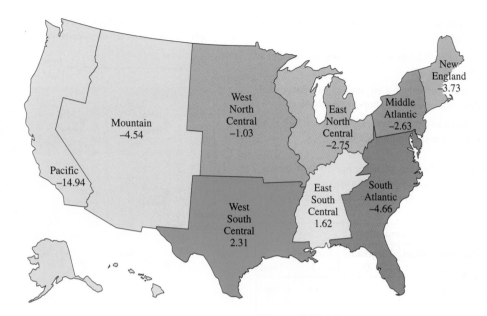

from September 30, 2007 to September 30, 2008 in each of nine regions (U.S. Census divisions)[3].

39. You are choosing a region of the country to move to. Describe the event E that the region you choose saw a decrease in housing prices of 4% or more.

40. You are choosing a region of the country to move to. Describe the event E that the region you choose saw an increase in housing prices.

41. You are choosing a region of the country to move to. Let E be the event that the region you choose saw a decrease in housing prices of 4% or more, and let F be the event that the region you choose is on the east coast. Describe the events $E \cup F$ and $E \cap F$ both in words and by listing the outcomes of each.

42. You are choosing a region of the country to move to. Let E be the event that the region you choose saw an increase in housing prices, and let F be the event that the region you choose is not on the east coast. Describe the events $E \cup F$ and $E \cap F$ both in words and by listing the outcomes of each.

43. ▼ You are choosing a region of the country to move to. Which of the following pairs of events are mutually exclusive?

a. E: You choose a region from among the two with the highest percentage decrease in housing prices.
F: You choose a region that is not on the east or west coast.

b. E: You choose a region from among the two with the highest percentage decrease in housing prices.
F: You choose a region that is not on the west coast.

---

[3] Source: Third Quarter 2008 House Price Index, Office of Federal Housing Enterprise Oversight; available online at www.ofheo.gov/media/pdf/3q08hpi.pdf.

44. ▼ You are choosing a region of the country to move to. Which of the following pairs of events are mutually exclusive?

a. E: You choose a region from among the three best performing in terms of housing prices.
F: You choose a region from among the central divisions.

b. E: You choose a region from among the three best performing in terms of housing prices.
F: You choose a region from among the noncentral divisions.

Publishing Exercises 45–52 are based on the following table, which shows the results of a survey of authors by a (fictitious) publishing company. HINT [See Example 5.]

	New Authors	Established Authors	Total
Successful	5	25	30
Unsuccessful	15	55	70
Total	20	80	100

Consider the following events: S: an author is successful; U: an author is unsuccessful; N: an author is new; and E: an author is established.

45. Describe the events $S \cap N$ and $S \cup N$ in words. Use the table to compute $n(S \cap N)$ and $n(S \cup N)$.

46. Describe the events $N \cap U$ and $N \cup U$ in words. Use the table to compute $n(N \cap U)$ and $n(N \cup U)$.

47. Which of the following pairs of events are mutually exclusive: N and E; N and S; S and E?

48. Which of the following pairs of events are mutuall¹· U and E; U and S; S and N?

49. Describe the event $S \cap N'$ in words and find the number of elements it contains.

50. Describe the event $U \cup E'$ in words and find the number of elements it contains.

51. ▼ What percentage of established authors are successful? What percentage of successful authors are established?

52. ▼ What percentage of new authors are unsuccessful? What percentage of unsuccessful authors are new?

Exercises 53–60 are based on the following table, which shows the performance of a selection of 100 stocks after one year. (Take S to be the set of all stocks represented in the table.)

	Companies			
	Pharmaceutical P	**Electronic** E	**Internet** I	**Total**
Increased V	10	5	15	30
Unchanged[*] N	30	0	10	40
Decreased D	10	5	15	30
Total	50	10	40	100

[*] If a stock stayed within 20% of its original value, it is classified as "unchanged."

53. Use symbols to describe the event that a stock's value increased but it was not an Internet stock. How many elements are in this event?

54. Use symbols to describe the event that an Internet stock did not increase. How many elements are in this event?

55. Compute $n(P' \cup N)$. What does this number represent?

56. Compute $n(P \cup N')$. What does this number represent?

57. Find all pairs of mutually exclusive events among the events $P, E, I, V, N,$ and D.

58. Find all pairs of events that are not mutually exclusive among the events $P, E, I, V, N,$ and D.

59. ▼ Calculate $\dfrac{n(V \cap I)}{n(I)}$. What does the answer represent?

60. ▼ Calculate $\dfrac{n(D \cap I)}{n(D)}$. What does the answer represent?

Animal Psychology *Exercises 61–66 concern the following chart, which shows the way in which a dog moves its facial muscles when torn between the drives of fight and flight.[4] The "fight" drive increases from left to right; the "flight" drive increases from top to bottom. (Notice that an increase in the*

"fight" drive causes its upper lip to lift, while an increase in the "flight" drive draws its ears downward.)

61. ▼ Let E be the event that the dog's flight drive is the strongest, let F be the event that the dog's flight drive is weakest, let G be the event that the dog's fight drive is the strongest, and let H be the event that the dog's fight drive is weakest. Describe the following events in terms of $E, F, G,$ and H using the symbols $\cap, \cup,$ and $'$.

a. The dog's flight drive is not strongest and its fight drive is weakest.

b. The dog's flight drive is strongest or its fight drive is weakest.

c. Neither the dog's flight drive nor its fight drive is strongest.

62. ▼ Let E be the event that the dog's flight drive is the strongest, let F be the event that the dog's flight drive is weakest, let G be the event that the dog's fight drive is the strongest, and let H be the event that the dog's fight drive is weakest. Describe the following events in terms of $E, F, G,$ and H using the symbols $\cap, \cup,$ and $'$.

a. The dog's flight drive is weakest and its fight drive is not weakest.

b. The dog's flight drive is not strongest or its fight drive is weakest.

c. Either the dog's flight drive or its fight drive fails to be strongest.

63. ▼ Describe the following events explicitly (as subsets of the sample space):

a. The dog's fight and flight drives are both strongest.

b. The dog's fight drive is strongest, but its flight drive is neither weakest nor strongest.

64. ▼ Describe the following events explicitly (as subsets of the sample space):

a. Neither the dog's fight drive nor its flight drive is strongest.

b. The dog's fight drive is weakest, but its flight drive is neither weakest nor strongest.

Source: *On Aggression* by Konrad Lorenz (Fakenham, Norfolk: Univer-, Paperback Edition, Cox & Wyman Limited, 1967).

65. ▼ Describe the following events in words:

   a. {1, 4, 7}

   b. {1, 9}

   c. {3, 6, 7, 8, 9}

66. ▼ Describe the following events in words:

   a. {7, 8, 9}

   b. {3, 7}

   c. {1, 2, 3, 4, 7}

Exercises 67–74 use counting arguments from the preceding chapter.

67. ▼ *Gummy Bears* A bag contains six gummy bears. Noel picks four at random. How many possible outcomes are there? If one of the gummy bears is raspberry, how many of these outcomes include the raspberry gummy bear?

68. ▼ *Chocolates* My couch potato friend enjoys sitting in front of the TV and grabbing handfuls of 5 chocolates at random from his snack jar. Unbeknownst to him, I have replaced one of the 20 chocolates in his jar with a cashew. (He hates cashews with a passion.) How many possible outcomes are there the first time he grabs 5 chocolates? How many of these include the cashew?

69. ▼ *Horse Races* The seven contenders in the fifth horse race at Aqueduct on February 18, 2002, were: Pipe Bomb, Expect a Ship, All That Magic, Electoral College, Celera, Cliff Glider, and Inca Halo.[5] You are interested in the first three places (winner, second place, and third place) for the race.

   a. Find the cardinality $n(S)$ of the sample space S of all possible finishes of the race. (A finish for the race consists of a first, second, and third place winner.)

   b. Let E be the event that Electoral College is in second or third place, and let F be the event that Celera is the winner. Express the event $E \cap F$ in words, and find its cardinality.

70. ▼ *Intramurals* The following five teams will be participating in Urban University's hockey intramural tournament: the Independent Wildcats, the Phi Chi Bulldogs, the Gate Crashers, the Slide Rule Nerds, and the City Slickers. Prizes will be awarded for the winner and runner-up.

   a. Find the cardinality $n(S)$ of the sample space S of all possible outcomes of the tournament. (An outcome of the tournament consists of a winner and a runner-up.)

   b. Let E be the event that the City Slickers are runners-up, and let F be the event that the Independent Wildcats are neither the winners nor runners-up. Express the event $E \cup F$ in words, and find its cardinality.

---

[5] Source: *Newsday*, Feb. 18, 2002, p. A36.

In Exercises 71–74, Pablo randomly picks three marbles from a bag of eight marbles (four red ones, two green ones, and two yellow ones).

71. ▼ How many outcomes are there in the sample space?

72. ▼ How many outcomes are there in the event that Pablo grabs three red marbles?

73. ▼ How many outcomes are there in the event that Pablo grabs one marble of each color?

74. ▼ How many outcomes are there in the event that Pablo's marbles are not all the same color?

COMMUNICATION AND REASONING EXERCISES

75. Complete the following sentence. An event is a ____.

76. Complete the following sentence. Two events E and F are mutually exclusive if their intersection is ____.

77. If E and F are events, then $(E \cap F)'$ is the event that ____.

78. If E and F are events, then $(E' \cap F')$ is the event that ____.

79. Let E be the event that you meet a tall dark stranger. Which of the following could reasonably represent the experiment and sample space in question?

   (A) You go on vacation and lie in the sun; S is the set of cloudy days.

   (B) You go on vacation and spend an evening at the local dance club; S is the set of people you meet.

   (C) You go on vacation and spend an evening at the local dance club; S is the set of people you do not meet.

80. Let E be the event that you buy a Porsche. Which of the following could reasonably represent the experiment and sample space in question?

   (A) You go to an auto dealership and select a Mustang; S is the set of colors available.

   (B) You go to an auto dealership and select a red car; S is the set of cars you decide not to buy.

   (C) You go to an auto dealership and select a red car; S is the set of car models available.

81. ▼ True or false? Every set S is the sample space for some experiment. Explain.

82. ▼ True or false? Every sample space S is a finite set. Explain.

83. ▼ Describe an experiment in which a die is cast and the set of outcomes is {0, 1}.

84. ▼ Describe an experiment in which two coins are flipped and the set of outcomes is {0, 1, 2}.

85. ▼ Two distinguishable dice are rolled. Could there be two mutually exclusive events that both contain outcomes in which the numbers facing up add to 7?

86. ▼ Describe an experiment in which two dice are rolled and describe two mutually exclusive events that both contain outcomes in which both dice show a 1.

7.2 **Relative Frequency**

Suppose you have a coin that you think is not fair and you would like to determine the likelihood that heads will come up when it is tossed. You could estimate this likelihood by tossing the coin a large number of times and counting the number of times heads comes up. Suppose, for instance, that in 100 tosses of the coin, heads comes up 58 times. The fraction of times that heads comes up, $58/100 = .58$, is the **relative frequency**, or **estimated probability** of heads coming up when the coin is tossed. In other words, saying that the relative frequency of heads coming up is .58 is the same as saying that heads came up 58% of the time in your series of experiments.

Now let's think about this example in terms of sample spaces and events. First of all, there is an experiment that has been repeated $N = 100$ times: Toss the coin and observe the side facing up. The sample space for this experiment is $S = \{H, T\}$. Also, there is an event E in which we are interested: the event that heads comes up, which is $E = \{H\}$. The number of times E has occurred, or the **frequency** of E, is $fr(E) = 58$. The relative frequency of the event E is then

$$P(E) = \frac{fr(E)}{N} \qquad \frac{\text{Frequency of event } E}{\text{Number of repetitions } N}$$

$$= \frac{58}{100} = .58.$$

Notes

1. The relative frequency gives us an *estimate* of the likelihood that heads will come up when that particular coin is tossed. This is why statisticians often use the alternative term *estimated probability* to describe it.

2. The larger the number of times the experiment is performed, the more accurate an estimate we expect this estimated probability to be. ■

Relative Frequency

When an experiment is performed a number of times, the **relative frequency** or **estimated probability** of an event E is the fraction of times that the event E occurs. If the experiment is performed N times and the event E occurs $fr(E)$ times, then the relative frequency is given by

$$P(E) = \frac{fr(E)}{N}. \qquad \text{Fraction of times } E \text{ occurs}$$

The number $fr(E)$ is called the **frequency** of E. N, the number of times that the experiment is performed, is called the number of **trials** or the **sample size**. If E consists of a single outcome s, then we refer to $P(E)$ as the relative frequency or estimated probability of the outcome s, and we write $P(s)$.

Visualizing Relative Frequency

$$P(E) = \frac{fr(E)}{N} = \frac{4}{10} = .4$$

The collection of the estimated probabilities of *all* the outcomes is the **relative frequency distribution** or **estimated probability distribution**.

Quick Examples

1. **Experiment:** Roll a pair of dice and add the numbers that face up.

   Event: E: The sum is 5.

   If the experiment is repeated 100 times and E occurs on 10 of the rolls, then the relative frequency of E is

   $$P(E) = \frac{fr(E)}{N} = \frac{10}{100} = .10.$$

2. If 10 rolls of a single die resulted in the outcomes 2, 1, 4, 4, 5, 6, 1, 2, 2, 1, then the associated relative frequency distribution is shown in the following table:

Outcome	1	2	3	4	5	6
Rel. Frequency	.3	.3	0	.2	.1	.1

3. **Experiment:** Note the cloud conditions on a particular day in April.

   If the experiment is repeated a number of times, and it is clear 20% of those times, partly cloudy 30% of those times, and overcast the rest of those times, then the relative frequency distribution is:

Outcome	Clear	Partly Cloudy	Overcast
Rel. Frequency	.20	.30	.50

EXAMPLE 1 Sales of Hybrid SUVs

In a survey of 120 hybrid SUVs sold in the United States, 48 were Toyota Highlanders, 28 were Lexus RX 400s, 38 were Ford Escapes, and 6 were other brands.* What is the relative frequency that a hybrid SUV sold in the United States is not a Toyota Highlander?

Solution The experiment consists of choosing a hybrid SUV sold in the United States and determining its type. The sample space suggested by the information given is

$$S = \{\text{Toyota Highlander, Lexus RX 400, Ford Escape, Other}\}$$

and we are interested in the event

$$E = \{\text{Lexus RX 400, Ford Escape, Other}\}.$$

The sample size is $N = 120$ and the frequency of E is $fr(E) = 28 + 38 + 6 = 72$. Thus, the relative frequency of E is

$$P(E) = \frac{fr(E)}{N} = \frac{72}{120} = .6.$$

---

* The proportions are based on actual U.S. sales in February 2008. Source: www.hybridsuv.com/hybrid-resources/hybrid-suv-sales.

David Young-Wolff/PhotoEdit

➡ **Before we go on...** In Example 1, you might ask how accurate the estimate of .6 is or how well it reflects *all* of the hybrid SUVs sold in the United States absent any information about national sales figures. The field of statistics provides the tools needed to say to what extent this estimated probability can be trusted. ■

EXAMPLE 2 Auctions on eBay

The following chart shows the results of a survey of 50 paintings on eBay whose listings were close to expiration, examining the number of bids each had received.*

Bids	0	1	2–10	>10
Frequency	31	9	7	3

Consider the experiment in which a painting whose listing is close to expiration is chosen and the number of bids is observed.

a. Find the relative frequency distribution.

b. Find the relative frequency that a painting whose listing was close to expiration had received no more than 10 bids.

Solution

a. The following table shows the relative frequency of each outcome, which we find by dividing each frequency by the sum $N = 50$:

Relative Frequency Distribution

Bids	0	1	2–10	>10
Rel. Frequency	$\frac{31}{50} = .62$	$\frac{9}{50} = .18$	$\frac{7}{50} = .14$	$\frac{3}{50} = .06$

b. Method 1: Computing Directly
$E = \{0 \text{ bids}, 1 \text{ bid}, 2\text{–}10 \text{ bids}\}$; thus,

$$P(E) = \frac{fr(E)}{N} = \frac{31 + 9 + 7}{50} = \frac{47}{50} = .94.$$

Method 2: Using the Relative Frequency Distribution
Notice that we can obtain the same answer from the distribution in part (a) by simply adding the relative frequencies of the outcomes in E:

$$P(E) = .62 + .18 + .14 = .94.$$

---

* The 50 paintings whose listings were closest to expiration in the category "Art-Direct from Artist" on January 13, 2009 (www.eBay.com).

➡ **Before we go on...**

Q : *Why did we get the same result in part (b) of Example 2 by simply adding the relative frequencies of the outcomes in E?*

A : The reason can be seen by doing the calculation in the first method a slightly different way:

$$P(E) = \frac{fr(E)}{N} = \frac{31 + 9 + 7}{50}$$

$$= \frac{31}{50} + \frac{9}{50} + \frac{7}{50} \qquad \text{Sum of rel. frequencies of the individual outcomes}$$

$$= .62 + .18 + .14 = .94.$$

This property of relative frequency distributions is discussed below.

■

Following are some important properties of estimated probability that we can observe in Example 2.

Some Properties of Relative Frequency Distributions

Let $S = \{s_1, s_2, \ldots, s_n\}$ be a sample space and let $P(s_i)$ be the relative frequency of the event $\{s_i\}$. Then

1. $0 \le P(s_i) \le 1$
2. $P(s_1) + P(s_2) + \cdots + P(s_n) = 1$
3. If $E = \{e_1, e_2, \ldots, e_r\}$, then $P(E) = P(e_1) + P(e_2) + \cdots + P(e_r)$.

In words:

1. The relative frequency of each outcome is a number between 0 and 1 (inclusive).
2. The relative frequencies of all the outcomes add up to 1.
3. The relative frequency of an event E is the sum of the relative frequencies of the individual outcomes in E.

Relative Frequency and Increasing Sample Size

using Technology

See the Technology Guides at the end of the chapter to see how to use a TI-83/84 Plus or Excel to simulate experiments.

A "fair" coin is one that is as likely to come up heads as it is to come up tails. In other words, we expect heads to come up 50% of the time if we toss such a coin many times. Put more precisely, we expect the relative frequency to approach .5 as the number of trials gets larger. Figure 4 shows how the relative frequency behaved for one sequence of coin tosses. For each N we have plotted what fraction of times the coin came up heads in the first N tosses.

Figure 4

Notice that the relative frequency graph meanders as N increases, sometimes getting closer to .5, and sometimes drifting away again. However, the graph tends to meander within smaller and smaller distances of .5 as N increases.*

＊ NOTE This can be made more precise by the concept of "limit" used in calculus.

In general, this is how relative frequency seems to behave; as N gets large, the relative frequency appears to approach some fixed value. Some refer to this value as the "actual" probability, whereas others point out that there are difficulties with this this notion. For instance, how can we actually determine this limit to any accuracy by experiment? How exactly is the experiment conducted? Technical and philosophical issues aside, the relative frequencies do approach a fixed value and, in the next section, we will talk about how we use probability models to predict this limiting value.

7.2 EXERCISES

▼ more advanced   ◆ challenging
⊤ indicates exercises that should be solved using technology

In Exercises 1–6, calculate the relative frequency $P(E)$ using the given information.

1. $N = 100,\ fr(E) = 40$ **2.** $N = 500,\ fr(E) = 300$

3. Eight hundred adults are polled and 640 of them support universal health-care coverage. E is the event that an adult supports universal health coverage. HINT [See Example 1.]

4. Eight Hundred adults are polled and 640 of them support universal health-care coverage. E is the event that an adult does not support universal health coverage. HINT [See Example 1.]

5. A die is rolled 60 times with the following result: 1, 2, and 3 each come up 8 times, and 4, 5, and 6 each come up 12 times. E is the event that the number that comes up is at most 4.

6. A die is rolled 90 times with the following result: 1 and 2 never come up, 3 and 4 each come up 30 times, and 5 and 6 each come up 15 times. E is the event that the number that comes up is at least 4.

Exercises 7–12 are based on the following table, which shows the frequency of outcomes when two distinguishable coins were tossed 4,000 times and the uppermost faces were observed. HINT [See Example 2.]

Outcome	HH	HT	TH	TT
Frequency	1,100	950	1,200	750

7. Determine the relative frequency distribution.

8. What is the relative frequency that heads comes up at least once?

9. What is the relative frequency that the second coin lands with heads up?

10. What is the relative frequency that the first coin lands with heads up?

11. Would you judge the second coin to be fair? Give a reason for your answer.

12. Would you judge the first coin to be fair? Give a reason for your answer.

In Exercises 13–18, say whether the given distribution can be a relative frequency distribution. If your answer is no, indicate why not. HINT [See the properties of relative frequency distributions on page 463.]

13.

Outcome	1	2	3	5
Rel. Frequency	.4	.6	0	0

14.

Outcome	A	B	C	D
Rel. Frequency	.2	.1	.2	.1

15.

Outcome	HH	HT	TH	TT
Rel. Frequency	.5	.4	.5	−.4

16.

Outcome	2	4	6	8
Rel. Frequency	25	25	25	25

17.

Outcome	−3	−2	−1	0
Rel. Frequency	.2	.3	.2	.3

18.

Outcome	HH	HT	TH	TT
Rel. Frequency	0	0	0	1

In Exercises 19 and 20, complete the given relative frequency distribution and compute the stated relative frequencies. HINT [See the properties of relative frequency distributions on page 463.]

19.

Outcome	1	2	3	4	5
Rel. Frequency	.2	.3	.1	.1	

   a. $P(\{1, 3, 5\})$ **b.** $P(E')$ where $E = \{1, 2, 3\}$

20.

Outcome	1	2	3	4	5
Rel. Frequency	.4		.3	.1	.1

   a. $P(\{2, 3, 4\})$ **b.** $P(E')$ where $E = \{3, 4\}$

▮ *Exercises 21–24 require the use of a calculator or computer with a random number generator.*

21. Simulate 100 tosses of a fair coin, and compute the estimated probability that heads comes up.

22. Simulate 100 throws of a fair die, and calculate the estimated probability that the result is a 6.

23. Simulate 50 tosses of two coins, and compute the estimated probability that the outcome is one head and one tail (in any order).

24. Simulate 100 throws of two fair dice, and calculate the estimated probability that the result is a double 6.

APPLICATIONS

25. *Music Sales* In a survey of 500 music downloads, 160 were rock music, 55 were hip-hop, and 20 were classical, while the remainder were other genres.[6] Calculate the following relative frequencies:

  a. That a music download was rock music.
  b. That a music download was either classical music or hip-hop.
  c. That a music download was not rock music. HINT [See Example 1.]

26. *Music Sales* In a survey of 400 music downloads, 45 were country music, 16 were religious music, and 16 were jazz, while the remainder were other genres.[7] Calculate the following relative frequencies:

  a. That a music download was jazz.
  b. That a music download was either religious music or jazz.
  c. That a music download was not country music. HINT [See Example 1.]

27. *Subprime Mortgages* The following chart shows the results of a survey of the status of subprime home mortgages in Texas in November 2008:[8]

Mortgage Status	Current	Past Due	In Foreclosure	Repossessed
Frequency	134	52	9	5

(The four categories are mutually exclusive; for instance, "Past Due" refers to a mortgage whose payment status is past due but is not in foreclosure, and "In Foreclosure" refers to a mortgage that is in the process of being foreclosed but not yet repossessed.)

  a. Find the relative frequency distribution for the experiment of randomly selecting a subprime mortgage in Texas and determining its status.

  b. What is the relative frequency that a randomly selected subprime mortgage in Texas was not current? HINT [See Example 2.]

28. *Subprime Mortgages* The following chart shows the results of a survey of the status of subprime home mortgages in Florida in November 2008:[9]

Mortgage Status	Current	Past Due	In Foreclosure	Repossessed
Frequency	110	65	60	15

(The four categories are mutually exclusive; for instance, "Past Due" refers to a mortgage whose payment status is past due but is not in foreclosure, and "In Foreclosure" refers to a mortgage that is in the process of being foreclosed but not yet repossessed.)

  a. Find the relative frequency distribution for the experiment of randomly selecting a subprime mortgage in Florida and determining its status.

  b. What is the relative frequency that a randomly selected subprime mortgage in Florida was neither in foreclosure nor repossessed? HINT [See Example 2.]

29. *Employment in Mexico by Age* The following table shows the results of a survey of employed adult (age 18 and higher) residents of Mexico:[10]

Age	18–25	26–35	36–45	46–55	>55
Percentage	29	47	20	3	1

  a. Find the associated relative frequency distribution. HINT [See Quick Example 3 page 461.]
  b. Find the relative frequency that an employed adult resident of Mexico is *not* between 26 and 45.

30. *Unemployment in Mexico by Age* The following table shows the results of a survey of unemployed adult (age 18 and higher) residents of Mexico:[11]

Age	18–25	26–35	36–45	46–55	>55
Percentage	40	37	13	7	3

  a. Find the associated relative frequency distribution. HINT [See Quick Example 3 page 461.]
  b. Find the relative frequency that an employed adult resident of Mexico is either younger than 26 or older than 55.

---

[6] Based on actual sales in 2007. Source: The Recording Industry Association of America (www.riaa.com).

[7] Ibid.

[8] Based on actual data in 2008. Source: Federal Reserve Bank of New York (www.newyorkfed.org/regional/subprime.html).

[9] Ibid.

[10] Source: Profeco/*Empresas y Empresarios*, April 23, 2007, p. 2.

[11] Ibid.

31. *Motor Vehicle Safety* The following table shows crashworthiness ratings for 10 small SUVs.[12] (3 = Good, 2 = Acceptable, 1 = Marginal, 0 = Poor)

Frontal Crash Test Rating	3	2	1	0
Frequency	1	4	4	1

a. Find the relative frequency distribution for the experiment of choosing a small SUV at random and determining its frontal crash rating.

b. What is the relative frequency that a randomly selected small SUV will have a crash test rating of "Acceptable" or better?

32. *Motor Vehicle Safety* The following table shows crashworthiness ratings for 16 small cars.[13] (3 = Good, 2 = Acceptable, 1 = Marginal, 0 = Poor)

Frontal Crash Test Rating	3	2	1	0
Frequency	1	11	2	2

a. Find the relative frequency distribution for the experiment of choosing a small car at random and determining its frontal crash rating.

b. What is the relative frequency that a randomly selected small car will have a crash test rating of "Marginal" or worse?

33. *Internet Connections* The following pie chart shows the relative frequency distribution resulting from a survey of 2000 U.S. households with Internet connections back in 2003.[14]

Determine the **frequency distribution**; that is, the total number of households with each type of Internet connection in the survey.

[12] Ratings by the Insurance Institute for Highway Safety. Sources: Oak Ridge National Laboratory: "An Analysis of the Impact of Sport Utility Vehicles in the United States" Stacy C. Davis, Lorena F. Truett (August 2000) Insurance Institute for Highway Safety (www-cta.ornl.gov/Publications/Final SUV report.pdf).

[13] Ratings by the Insurance Institute for Highway Safety. Sources: Oak Ridge National Laboratory: "An Analysis of the Impact of Sport Utility Vehicles in the United States" Stacy C. Davis, Lorena F. Truett (August 2000) Insurance Institute for Highway Safety (www-cta.ornl.gov/Publications/Final SUV report.pdf www.highwaysafety.org/vehicle_ratings/).

[14] Based on a 2003 survey. Source: "A Nation Online: Entering the Broadband Age," U.S. Department of Commerce, September 2004 (www.ntia.doc.gov/reports/anol/index.html).

34. *Internet Connections* The following pie chart shows the relative frequency distribution resulting from a survey of 3,000 U.S. rural households with Internet connections back in 2003.[15]

Determine the **frequency distribution**; that is, the total number of households with each type of Internet connection in the survey.

35. ▼ *Stock Market Gyrations* The following chart shows the day-by-day change in the Dow Jones Industrial Average during 20 successive business days in October 2008:[16]

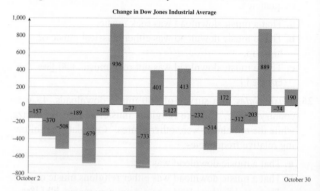

Use the chart to construct the relative frequency distribution using the following three outcomes. Surge: The Dow was up by more than 300 points; Plunge: The Dow was down by more than 300 points; Steady: The Dow changed by 300 points or less.

36. ▼ *Stock Market Gyrations* Repeat Exercise 35 using the following chart for November–December 2008:[17]

[15] Ibid.

[16] Source: http://finance.google.com.

[17] Ibid.

Publishing Exercises 37–46 are based on the following table, which shows the results of a survey of 100 authors by a publishing company.

	New Authors	**Established Authors**	**Total**
Successful	5	25	30
Unsuccessful	15	55	70
Total	20	80	100

Compute the relative frequencies of the given events if an author as specified is chosen at random.

37. ▼ An author is established and successful.

38. ▼ An author is unsuccessful and new.

39. ▼ An author is a new author.

40. ▼ An author is successful.

41. ▼ An author is unsuccessful.

42. ▼ An author is established.

43. ▼ A successful author is established.

44. ▼ An unsuccessful author is established.

45. ▼ An established author is successful.

46. ▼ A new author is unsuccessful.

47. ▼ *Public Health* A random sampling of chicken in supermarkets revealed that approximately 80% was contaminated with the organism *Campylobacter*.[18] Of the contaminated chicken, 20% had the strain resistant to antibiotics. Construct a relative frequency distribution showing the following outcomes when chicken is purchased at a supermarket: *U:* the chicken is not infected with *Campylobacter*; *C:* the chicken is infected with nonresistant *Campylobacter*; *R:* the chicken is infected with resistant *Campylobacter*.

48. ▼ *Public Health* A random sampling of turkey in supermarkets found 58% to be contaminated with *Campylobacter*, and 84% of those to be resistant to antibiotics.[19] Construct a relative frequency distribution showing the following outcomes when turkey is purchased at a supermarket: *U:* the turkey is not infected with *Campylobacter*; *C:* the turkey is infected with nonresistant *Campylobacter*; and *R:* the turkey is infected with resistant *Campylobacter*.

49. ▼ *Organic Produce* A 2001 Agriculture Department study of more than 94,000 samples from more than 20 crops showed that 73% of conventionally grown foods had residues from at least one pesticide. Moreover, conventionally grown foods were six times as likely to contain multiple pesticides as organic foods. Of the organic foods tested, 23% had pesticide residues, which includes 10% with multiple pesticide residues.[20] Compute two estimated probability distributions: one for conventional produce and one for organic produce, showing the relative frequencies that a randomly selected product has no pesticide residues, has residues from a single pesticide, and has residues from multiple pesticides.

50. ▼ *Organic Produce* Repeat Exercise 49 using the following information for produce from California: 31% of conventional food and 6.5% of organic food had residues from at least one pesticide. Assume that, as in Exercise 49, conventionally grown foods were six times as likely to contain multiple pesticides as organic foods. Also assume that 3% of the organic food has residues from multiple pesticides.

51. ▼ *Steroids Testing* A pharmaceutical company is running trials on a new test for anabolic steroids. The company uses the test on 400 athletes known to be using steroids and 200 athletes known not to be using steroids. Of those using steroids, the new test is positive for 390 and negative for 10. Of those not using steroids, the test is positive for 10 and negative for 190. What is the relative frequency of a **false negative** result (the probability that an athlete using steroids will test negative)? What is the relative frequency of a **false positive** result (the probability that an athlete not using steroids will test positive)?

52. ▼ *Lie Detectors* A manufacturer of lie detectors is testing its newest design. It asks 300 subjects to lie deliberately and another 500 to tell the truth. Of those who lied, the lie detector caught 200. Of those who told the truth, the lie detector accused 200 of lying. What is the relative frequency of the machine wrongly letting a liar go, and what is the probability that it will falsely accuse someone who is telling the truth?

53. ▣ ◆ *Public Health* Refer back to Exercise 47. Simulate the experiment of selecting chicken at a supermarket and determining the following outcomes: *U:* The chicken is not infected with *campylobacter*; *C:* The chicken is infected with nonresistant *campylobacter*; *R:* The chicken is infected with resistant *campylobacter*. [*Hint*: Generate integers in the range 1–100. The outcome is determined by the range. For instance if the number is in the range 1–20, regard the outcome as *U*, etc.]

54. ▣ ◆ *Public Health* Repeat the preceding exercise, but use turkeys and the data given in Exercise 48.

COMMUNICATION AND REASONING EXERCISES

55. Complete the following. The relative frequency of an event *E* is defined to be _____.

56. If two people each flip a coin 100 times and compute the relative frequency that heads comes up, they will both obtain the same result, right?

---

[18] *Campylobacter* is one of the leading causes of food poisoning in humans. Thoroughly cooking the meat kills the bacteria. Source: *The New York Times*, October 20, 1997, p. A1. Publication of this article first brought *Campylobacter* to the attention of a wide audience.

[19] Ibid.

[20] The 10% figure is an estimate. Source: *New York Times*, May 8, 2002, p. A29.

57. How many different answers are possible if you flip a coin 100 times and compute the relative frequency that heads comes up? What are the possible answers?

58. Interpret the popularity rating of the student council president as a relative frequency by specifying an appropriate experiment and also what is observed.

59. ▼ Ruth tells you that when you roll a pair of fair dice, the probability of obtaining a pair of matching numbers is 1/6. To test this claim, you roll a pair of fair dice 20 times, and never once get a pair of matching numbers. This proves that either Ruth is wrong or the dice are not fair, right?

60. ▼ Juan tells you that when you roll a pair of fair dice, the probability that the numbers add up to 7 is 1/6. To test this claim, you roll a pair of fair dice 24 times, and the numbers add up to 7 exactly four times. This proves that Juan is right, right?

61. ▼ How would you measure the relative frequency that the weather service accurately predicts the next day's high temperature?

62. ▼ Suppose that you toss a coin 100 times and get 70 heads. If you continue tossing the coin, the estimated probability of heads overall should approach 50% if the coin is fair. Will you have to get more tails than heads in subsequent tosses to "correct" for the 70 heads you got in the first 100 tosses?

7.3 **Probability and Probability Models**

It is understandable if you are a little uncomfortable with using relative frequency as the estimated probability because it does not always agree with what you intuitively feel to be true. For instance, if you toss a fair coin (one as likely to come up heads as tails) 100 times and heads happen to come up 62 times, the experiment seems to suggest that the probability of heads is .62, even though you *know* that the "actual" probability is .50 (because the coin is fair).

Q : *So what do we mean by "actual" probability?*

A : There are various philosophical views as to exactly what we should mean by "actual" probability. For example, (finite) *frequentists* say that there is no such thing as "actual probability"—all we should really talk about is what we can actually measure, the relative frequency. *Propensitists* say that the actual probability p of an event is a (often physical) property of the event that makes its relative frequency tend to p in the long run; that is, p will be the limiting value of the relative frequency as the number of trials in a repeated experiment gets larger and larger. (See Figure 4 in the preceding section.) *Bayesians*, on the other hand, argue that the actual probability of an event is the degree to which we *expect* it to occur, given our knowledge about the nature of the experiment. These and other viewpoints have been debated in considerable depth in the literature.[21]

Mathematicians tend to avoid the whole debate, and talk instead about *abstract* probability, or **probability distributions**, based purely on the properties of relative frequency listed in Section 7.2. Specific probability distributions can then be used as models of probability in real life situations, such as flipping a coin or tossing a die, to predict (or model) relative frequency.

---

[21] The interested reader should consult references in the philosophy of probability. For an online summary, see, for example, the Stanford Encyclopedia of Philosophy (http://plato.stanford.edu/contents.html).

Probability Distribution; Probability

(Compare page 463.) A (finite) **probability distribution** is an assignment of a number $P(s_i)$, the **probability of** s_i, to each outcome of a finite sample space $S = \{s_1, s_2, \ldots, s_n\}$. The probabilities must satisfy

1. $0 \leq P(s_i) \leq 1$

and

2. $P(s_1) + P(s_2) + \cdots + P(s_n) = 1$.

We find the **probability of an event** E, written $P(E)$, by adding up the probabilities of the outcomes in E.

If $P(E) = 0$, we call E an **impossible event**. The empty event $\emptyset$ is always impossible, since *something* must happen.

Quick Examples

1. All the examples of relative frequency distributions in Section 7.2 are examples of probability distributions. (See page 463.)

2. Let us take $S = \{H, T\}$ and make the assignments $P(H) = .5$, $P(T) = .5$. Because these numbers are between 0 and 1 and add to 1, they specify a probability distribution.

3. In Quick Example 2, we can instead make the assignments $P(H) = .2$, $P(T) = .8$. Because these numbers are between 0 and 1 and add to 1, they, too, specify a probability distribution.

4. With $S = \{H, T\}$ again, we could also take $P(H) = 1$, $P(T) = 0$, so that $\{T\}$ is an impossible event.

5. The following table gives a probability distribution for the sample space

$S = \{1, 2, 3, 4, 5, 6\}$.

Outcome	1	2	3	4	5	6
Probability	.3	.3	0	.1	.2	.1

It follows that

$$P(\{1, 6\}) = .3 + .1 = .4$$
$$P(\{2, 3\}) = .3 + 0 = .3$$
$$P(3) = 0. \qquad \text{\{3\} is an impossible event.}$$

The above Quick Examples included models for the experiments of flipping fair and unfair coins. In general:

Probability Models

A **probability model** for a particular experiment is a probability distribution that predicts the relative frequency of each outcome if the experiment is performed a large number of times (see Figure 4 at the end of the preceding section).* Just as we think of relative frequency as *estimated probability*, we can think of modeled probability as *theoretical probability*.

* NOTE Just how large is a "large number of times"? That depends on the nature of the experiment. For example, if you toss a fair coin 100 times, then the relative frequency of heads will be between .45 and .55 about 73% of the time. If an outcome is extremely unlikely (such as winning the lotto) one might need to repeat the experiment billions or trillions of times before the relative frequencies approaches any specific number.

Quick Examples

1. **Fair Coin Model:** (See Quick Example 2 on the previous page.) Flip a fair coin and observe the side that faces up. Because we expect that heads is as likely to come up as tails, we model this experiment with the probability distribution specified by $S = \{H, T\}$, $P(H) = .5$, $P(T) = .5$. Figure 4 on p. 463 suggests that the relative frequency of heads approaches .5 as the number of coin tosses gets large, so the fair coin model predicts the relative frequency for a large number of coin tosses quite well.

2. **Unfair Coin Model:** (See Quick Example 3 on the previous page.) Take $S = \{H, T\}$ and $P(H) = .2$, $P(T) = .8$. We can think of this distribution as a model for the experiment of flipping an unfair coin that is four times as likely to land with tails uppermost than heads.

3. **Fair Die Model:** Roll a fair die and observe the uppermost number. Because we expect to roll each specific number one sixth of the time, we model the experiment with the probability distribution specified by $S = \{1, 2, 3, 4, 5, 6\}$, $P(1) = 1/6$, $P(2) = 1/6, \ldots, P(6) = 1/6$. This model predicts for example, that the relative frequency of throwing a 5 approaches $1/6$ as the number of times you roll the die gets large.

4. Roll a pair of fair dice (recall that there are a total of 36 outcomes if the dice are distinguishable). Then an appropriate model of the experiment has

$$S = \begin{Bmatrix} (1,1), & (1,2), & (1,3), & (1,4), & (1,5), & (1,6), \\ (2,1), & (2,2), & (2,3), & (2,4), & (2,5), & (2,6), \\ (3,1), & (3,2), & (3,3), & (3,4), & (3,5), & (3,6), \\ (4,1), & (4,2), & (4,3), & (4,4), & (4,5), & (4,6), \\ (5,1), & (5,2), & (5,3), & (5,4), & (5,5), & (5,6), \\ (6,1), & (6,2), & (6,3), & (6,4), & (6,5), & (6,6) \end{Bmatrix}$$

with each outcome being assigned a probability of $1/36$.

5. In the experiment in Quick Example 4, take E to be the event that the sum of the numbers that face up is 5, so

$$E = \{(1,4), (2,3), (3,2), (4,1)\}.$$

By the properties of probability distributions,

$$P(E) = \frac{1}{36} + \frac{1}{36} + \frac{1}{36} + \frac{1}{36} = \frac{4}{36} = \frac{1}{9}.$$

Notice that, in all of the Quick Examples above except for the unfair coin, all the outcomes are equally likely, and each outcome s has a probability of

$$P(s) = \frac{1}{\text{Total number of outcomes}} = \frac{1}{n(S)}.$$

More generally, in the last Quick Example we saw that adding the probabilities of the individual outcomes in an event E amounted to computing the ratio (Number of favorable outcomes)/(Total number of outcomes):

$$P(E) = \frac{\text{Number of favorable outcomes}}{\text{Total number of outcomes}} = \frac{n(E)}{n(S)}.$$

Probability Model for Equally Likely Outcomes

In an experiment in which all outcomes are equally likely, we model the experiment by taking the probability of an event E to be

$$P(E) = \frac{\text{Number of favorable outcomes}}{\text{Total number of outcomes}} = \frac{n(E)}{n(S)}.$$

Visualizing Probability for Equally Likely Outcomes

Sample Space S

$$P(E) = \frac{n(E)}{n(S)} = \frac{6}{10} = .6$$

Note

Remember that this formula will work *only* when the outcomes are equally likely. If, for example, a die is *weighted*, then the outcomes may not be equally likely, and the formula above will not give an appropriate probability model.

Quick Examples

1. Toss a fair coin three times, so $S = \{$HHH, HHT, HTH, HTT, THH, THT, TTH, TTT$\}$. The probability that we throw exactly two heads is

$$P(E) = \frac{n(E)}{n(S)} = \frac{3}{8}.$$ There are eight equally likely outcomes and $E = \{$HHT, HTH, THH$\}$.

2. Roll a pair of fair dice. The probability that we roll a double (both dice show the same number) is

$$P(E) = \frac{n(E)}{n(S)} = \frac{6}{36} = \frac{1}{6}.$$ $E = \{(1, 1), (2, 2), (3, 3), (4, 4), (5, 5), (6, 6)\}$

3. Randomly choose a person from a class of 40, in which 6 have red hair. If E is the event that a randomly selected person in the class has red hair, then

$$P(E) = \frac{n(E)}{n(S)} = \frac{6}{40} = .15.$$

EXAMPLE 1 Sales of Hybrid SUVs

(Compare Example 1 in Section 7.2.) In February 2008 total sales of hybrid SUVs amounted to only 4,840 vehicles. Of these, 1,940 were Toyota Highlanders, 1,150 were Lexus RX 400s, 1,510 were Ford Escapes, and 240 were other brands.*

a. What is the probability that a randomly selected hybrid SUV sold in the United States during February 2008 was either a Lexus RX 400 or a Ford Escape?

b. What is the probability that a randomly selected hybrid SUV sold in the United States during February 2008 was not a Toyota Highlander?

---

*Figures are rounded. Source: www.hybridsuv.com/hybrid-resources/hybrid-suv-sales.

Solution

a. The experiment suggested by the question consists of randomly choosing a hybrid SUV sold in the United States during February 2008 and determining its make. We are interested in the event E that the hybrid SUV was either a Lexus RX 400 or a Ford Escape. So,

$$S = \text{the set of hybrid SUVs sold in February 2008}; \; n(S) = 4{,}840$$

$$E = \text{the set of Lexus RX 400s and Ford Escapes sold in February 2008};$$
$$n(E) = 1{,}150 + 1{,}510 = 2{,}660.$$

Are the outcomes equally likely in this experiment? Yes, because we are as likely to choose one SUV as another. Thus,

$$P(E) = \frac{n(E)}{n(S)} = \frac{2{,}660}{4{,}840} \approx .55.$$

b. Let the event F consist of those hybrid SUVs sold in February 2008 that were not Toyota Highlanders.

$$n(F) = 4{,}840 - 1{,}940 = 2{,}900$$

Hence,

$$P(F) = \frac{n(F)}{n(S)} = \frac{2{,}900}{4{,}840} \approx .60.$$

Q : *In Example 1 of Section 7.2 we had a similar example about hybrid SUVs, but we called the probabilities calculated there relative frequencies. Here they are probabilities. What is the difference?*

A : In Example 1 of Section 7.2, the data were based on the results of a survey, or sample, of only 120 hybrid SUVs (out of a total of about 4,840 sold in the United States during February 2008), and were therefore incomplete. (A statistician would say that we were given *sample data*.) It follows that any inference we draw from the 120 surveyed, such as the probability that a hybrid SUV sold in the United States is not a Toyota Highlander, is uncertain, and this is the cue that tells us that we are working with relative frequency, or estimated probability. Think of the survey as an experiment (choosing a hybrid SUV) repeated 120 times—exactly the setting for estimated probability.

In Example 1 above, on the other hand, the data do not describe how *some* hybrid SUV sales are broken down into the categories described, but they describe how *all* 4,840 hybrid SUV sales in the United States are broken down. (The statistician would say that we were given *population data* in this case, because the data describe the entire "population" of hybrid SUVs sold in the United States during February.)

EXAMPLE 2   **Indistinguishable Dice**

We recall from Section 7.1 that the sample space when we roll a pair of indistinguishable dice is

$$S = \left\{ \begin{array}{l} (1,1),\ (1,2),\ (1,3),\ (1,4),\ (1,5),\ (1,6), \\ \quad (2,2),\ (2,3),\ (2,4),\ (2,5),\ (2,6), \\ \quad\quad (3,3),\ (3,4),\ (3,5),\ (3,6), \\ \quad\quad\quad (4,4),\ (4,5),\ (4,6), \\ \quad\quad\quad\quad (5,5),\ (5,6), \\ \quad\quad\quad\quad\quad (6,6) \end{array} \right\}.$$

Construct a probability model for this experiment.

Solution Because there are 21 outcomes, it is tempting to say that the probability of each outcome should be taken to be 1/21. However, the outcomes are not all equally likely. For instance, the outcome (2, 3) is twice as likely as (2, 2), because (2, 3) can occur in two ways (it corresponds to the event {(2, 3), (3, 2)} for distinguishable dice). For purposes of calculating probability, it is easiest to use calculations for distinguishable dice.* Here are some examples.

✱ NOTE Note that any pair of real dice can be distinguished in principle because they possess slight differences, although we may regard them as indistinguishable by not attempting to distinguish them. Thus, the probabilities of events must be the same as for the corresponding events for distinguishable dice.

Outcome (indistinguishable dice)	(1, 1)	(1, 2)	(2, 2)	(1, 3)	(2, 3)	(3, 3)
Corresponding event (distinguishable dice)	{(1, 1)}	{(1, 2), (2, 1)}	{(2, 2)}	{(1, 3), (3, 1)}	{(2, 3), (3, 2)}	{(3, 3)}
Probability	$\frac{1}{36}$	$\frac{2}{36} = \frac{1}{18}$	$\frac{1}{36}$	$\frac{2}{36} = \frac{1}{18}$	$\frac{2}{36} = \frac{1}{18}$	$\frac{1}{36}$

If we continue this process for all 21 outcomes, we will find that they add to 1. Figure 5 illustrates the complete probability distribution:

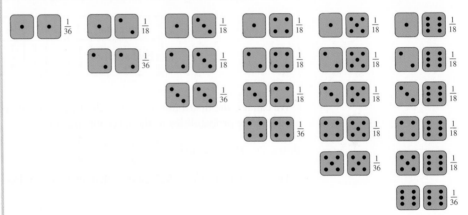

Figure 5

EXAMPLE 3 Weighted Dice

In order to impress your friends with your die-rolling skills, you have surreptitiously weighted your die in such a way that 6 is three times as likely to come up as any one of the other numbers. (All the other outcomes are equally likely.) Obtain a probability distribution for a roll of the die and use it to calculate the probability of an even number coming up.

Solution Let us label our unknowns (there appear to be two of them):

x = probability of rolling a 6

y = probability of rolling any one of the other numbers

We are first told that "6 is three times as likely to come up as any one of the other numbers." If we rephrase this in terms of our unknown probabilities we get, "the probability of rolling a 6 is three times the probability of rolling any one of the other numbers." In symbols,

$x = 3y.$

We must also use a piece of information not given to us, but one we know must be true: The sum of the probabilities of all the outcomes is 1:

$$x + y + y + y + y + y = 1$$

or

$$x + 5y = 1.$$

We now have two linear equations in two unknowns, and we solve for x and y. Substituting the first equation ($x = 3y$) in the second ($x + 5y = 1$) gives

$$8y = 1$$

or

$$y = \frac{1}{8}.$$

To get x, we substitute the value of y back into either equation and find

$$x = \frac{3}{8}.$$

Thus, the probability model we seek is the one shown in the following table.

Outcome	1	2	3	4	5	6
Probability	$\frac{1}{8}$	$\frac{1}{8}$	$\frac{1}{8}$	$\frac{1}{8}$	$\frac{1}{8}$	$\frac{3}{8}$

We can use the distribution to calculate the probability of an even number coming up by adding the probabilities of the favorable outcomes.

$$P(\{2,\ 4,\ 6\}) = \frac{1}{8} + \frac{1}{8} + \frac{3}{8} = \frac{5}{8}.$$

Thus there is a $5/8 = .625$ chance that an even number will come up.

➡ **Before we go on...** We should check that the probability distribution in Example 3 satisfies the requirements: 6 is indeed three times as likely to come up as any other number. Also, the probabilities we calculated do add up to 1:

$$\frac{1}{8} + \frac{1}{8} + \frac{1}{8} + \frac{1}{8} + \frac{1}{8} + \frac{3}{8} = 1. \ \blacksquare$$

Probability of Unions, Intersections, and Complements

So far, all we know about computing the probability of an event E is that $P(E)$ is the sum of the probabilities of the individual outcomes in E. Suppose, though, that we do not know the probabilities of the individual outcomes in E but we do know that $E = A \cup B$, where we happen to know $P(A)$ and $P(B)$. How do we compute the probability of $A \cup B$? We might be tempted to say that $P(A \cup B)$ is $P(A) + P(B)$, but let us look at an example using the probability distribution in Quick Example 5 at the beginning of this section:

Outcome	1	2	3	4	5	6
Probability	.3	.3	0	.1	.2	.1

For A let us take the event $\{2, 4, 5\}$, and for B let us take $\{2, 4, 6\}$. $A \cup B$ is then the event $\{2, 4, 5, 6\}$. We know that we can find the probabilities $P(A)$, $P(B)$, and $P(A \cup B)$ by adding the probabilities of all the outcomes in these events, so

$$P(A) = P(\{2, 4, 5\}) = .3 + .1 + .2 = .6$$
$$P(B) = P(\{2, 4, 6\}) = .3 + .1 + .1 = .5, \text{ and}$$
$$P(A \cup B) = P(\{2, 4, 5, 6\}) = .3 + .1 + .2 + .1 = .7.$$

Our first guess was wrong: $P(A \cup B) \neq P(A) + P(B)$. Notice, however, that the outcomes in $A \cap B$ are counted twice in computing $P(A) + P(B)$, but only once in computing $P(A \cup B)$:

$$P(A) + P(B) = P(\{2, 4, 5\}) + P(\{2, 4, 6\}) \qquad A \cap B = \{2, 4\}$$
$$= (.3 + .1 + .2) + (.3 + .1 + .1) \qquad P(A \cap B) \text{ counted twice}$$
$$= 1.1$$

whereas

$$P(A \cup B) = P(\{2, 4, 5, 6\}) = .3 + .1 + .2 + .1 \qquad P(A \cap B) \text{ counted once}$$
$$= .7.$$

Thus, if we take $P(A) + P(B)$ and then subtract the surplus $P(A \cap B)$, we get $P(A \cup B)$. In symbols,

$$P(A \cup B) = P(A) + P(B) - P(A \cap B)$$
$$.7 = .6 + .5 - .4.$$

(see Figure 6). We call this formula the **addition principle**. One more thing: Notice that our original guess $P(A \cup B) = P(A) + P(B)$ would have worked if we had chosen A and B with no outcomes in common; that is, if $A \cap B = \emptyset$. When $A \cap B = \emptyset$, recall that we say that A and B are mutually exclusive.

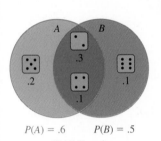

$P(A) = .6 \qquad P(B) = .5$

$P(A \cap B) = .4$

$P(A \cup B) = .6 + .5 - .4$

Figure 6

Addition Principle

If A and B are any two events, then

$$P(A \cup B) = P(A) + P(B) - P(A \cap B).$$

Visualizing the Addition Principle

In the figure, the area of the union is obtained by adding the areas of A and B and then subtracting the overlap (because it is counted twice when we add the areas).

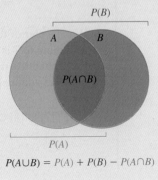

$$P(A \cup B) = P(A) + P(B) - P(A \cap B)$$

Addition Principle for Mutually Exclusive Events

If $A \cap B = \emptyset$, we say that A and B are **mutually exclusive**, and we have

$$P(A \cup B) = P(A) + P(B). \qquad \text{Because } P(A \cap B) = 0$$

Visualizing the Addition Principle for Mutually Exclusive Events

If A and B do not overlap, then the area of the union is obtained by adding the areas of A and B.

$$P(A \cup B) = P(A) + P(B)$$

This holds true also for more than two events: If $A_1, A_2, \ldots, A_n$ are mutually exclusive events (that is, the intersection of every pair of them is empty), then

$$P(A_1 \cup A_2 \cup \cdots \cup A_n) = P(A_1) + P(A_2) + \cdots + P(A_n). \qquad \text{Addition principle for many mutually exclusive events}$$

Quick Examples

1. There is a 10% chance of rain (R) tomorrow, a 20% chance of high winds (W), and a 5% chance of both. The probability of either rain or high winds (or both) is

$$P(R \cup W) = P(R) + P(W) - P(R \cap W)$$
$$= .10 + .20 - .05 = .25.$$

2. The probability that you will be in Cairo at 6:00 AM tomorrow (C) is .3, while the probability that you will be in Alexandria at 6:00 AM tomorrow (A) is .2. Thus, the probability that you will be either in Cairo or Alexandria at 6:00 AM tomorrow is

$$P(C \cup A) = P(C) + P(A) \qquad \text{A and C are mutually exclusive.}$$
$$= .3 + .2 = .5.$$

3. When a pair of fair dice is rolled, the probability of the numbers that face up adding to 7 is 6/36, the probability of their adding to 8 is 5/36, and the probability of their adding to 9 is 4/36. Thus, the probability of the numbers adding to 7, 8, or 9 is

$$P(\{7\} \cup \{8\} \cup \{9\}) = P(7) + P(8) + P(9) \qquad \text{The events are mutually exclusive.*}$$
$$= \frac{6}{36} + \frac{5}{36} + \frac{4}{36} = \frac{15}{36} = \frac{5}{12}.$$

＊ NOTE The sum of the numbers that face up cannot equal two different numbers at the same time.

You can use the formula $P(A \cup B) = P(A) + P(B) - P(A \cap B)$ to calculate any of the four quantities in the formula if you know the other three.

EXAMPLE 4 School and Work

A survey conducted by the Bureau of Labor Statistics found that 67% of the high school graduating class of 2007 went on to college the following year, while 44% of the class was working.* Furthermore, 92% were either in college or working, or both.

a. What percentage went on to college and work at the same time?

b. What percentage went on to college but not work?

Solution We can think of the experiment of choosing a member of the high school graduating class of 2007 at random. The sample space is the set of all these graduates.

a. We are given information about two events:

A: A graduate went on to college; $P(A) = .67$

B: A graduate went on to work; $P(B) = .44$

We are also told that $P(A \cup B) = .92$. We are asked for the probability that a graduate went on to both college and work, $P(A \cap B)$. To find $P(A \cap B)$, we take advantage of the fact that the formula

$$P(A \cup B) = P(A) + P(B) - P(A \cap B)$$

can be used to calculate any one of the four quantities that appear in it as long as we know the other three. Substituting the quantities we know, we get

$$.92 = .67 + .44 - P(A \cap B)$$

so

$$P(A \cap B) = .67 + .44 - .92 = .19.$$

Thus, 19% of the graduates went on to college and work at the same time.

b. We are asked for the probability of a new event:

C: A graduate went on to college but not work.

C is the part of A outside of $A \cap B$, so $C \cup (A \cap B) = A$, and C and $A \cap B$ are mutually exclusive. (See Figure 7.)

Thus, applying the addition principle, we have

$$P(C) + P(A \cap B) = P(A).$$

From part (a), we know that $P(A \cap B) = .19$, so

$$P(C) + .19 = .67$$

giving

$$P(C) = .48.$$

In other words, 48% of the graduates went on to college but not work.

B: Went to Work

$P(C)$ = ? $P(A \cap B)$ = .19

A: Went to College
$P(A) = .67$

Figure 7

---

* "College Enrollment and Work Activity of 2007 High School Graduates," U.S. Bureau of Labor Statistics, April 2008, available at www.bls.gov/schedule/archives/all_nr.htm.

We can use the addition principle to deduce other useful properties of probability distributions.

More Principles of Probability Distributions

The following rules hold for any sample space S and any event A:

$P(S) = 1$ The probability of *something* happening is 1.

$P(\emptyset) = 0$ The probability of *nothing* happening is 0.

$P(A') = 1 - P(A).$ The probability of A *not* happening is 1 minus the probability of A.

Note

We can also write the third equation as

$$P(A) = 1 - P(A')$$

or

$$P(A) + P(A') = 1. \quad \blacksquare$$

Visualizing the Rule for Complements

Think of A' as the portion of S outside of A. Adding the two areas gives the area of all of S, equal to 1.

Sample Space S

A A'

$P(A) + P(A') = 1$

Quick Examples

1. There is a 10% chance of rain (R) tomorrow. Therefore, the probability that it will *not* rain is

$$P(R') = 1 - P(R) = 1 - .10 = .90.$$

2. The probability that Eric Ewing will score at least two goals is .6. Therefore, the probability that he will score at most one goal is $1 - .6 = .4$.

Q: *Can you persuade me that all of these principles are true?*

A: Let us take them one at a time.

We know that $S = \{s_1, s_2, \ldots, s_n\}$ is the set of all outcomes, and so

$$P(S) = P(\{s_1, s_2, \ldots, s_n\})$$

We add the probabilities of the outcomes to obtain the probability of an event.

$$= P(s_1) + P(s_2) + \cdots + P(s_n)$$

$$= 1.$$

By the definition of a probability distribution

Now, note that $S \cap \emptyset = \emptyset$, so that S and $\emptyset$ are mutually exclusive. Applying the addition principle gives

$$P(S) = P(S \cup \emptyset) = P(S) + P(\emptyset).$$

Subtracting $P(S)$ from both sides gives $0 = P(\emptyset)$.

If A is any event in S, then we can write

$$S = A \cup A'$$

where A and A' are mutually exclusive. (Why?) Thus, by the addition principle,

$$P(S) = P(A) + P(A').$$

Because $P(S) = 1$, we get

$$1 = P(A) + P(A')$$

or $P(A') = 1 - P(A).$

EXAMPLE 5 Subprime Mortgages

A home loan is either current, 30–59 days past due, 60–89 days past due, 90 or more days past due, in foreclosure, or repossessed by the lender. In November 2008, the probability that a randomly selected subprime home mortgage in California was not current was .51. The probability that a mortgage was not current, but neither in foreclosure nor repossessed, was .28.* Calculate the probabilities of the following events.

a. A California home mortgage was current.

b. A California home mortgage was in foreclosure or repossessed.

Solution

a. Let us write C for the event that a randomly selected subprime home mortgage in California was current. The event that the home mortgage was *not* current is its complement C', and we are given that $P(C') = .51$. We have

$$P(C) + P(C') = 1$$
$$P(C) + .51 = 1,$$
so $P(C) = 1 - .51 = .49.$

b. Take

> F: A mortgage was in foreclosure or repossessed.
>
> N: A mortgage was neither current, in foreclosure, nor repossessed.

We are given $P(N) = .28$. Further, the events F and N are mutually exclusive with union C', the set of all non-current mortgages. Hence,

$$P(C') = P(F) + P(N)$$
$$.51 = P(F) + .28$$

giving

$$P(F) = .51 - .28 = .23.$$

Thus, there was a 23% chance that a subprime home mortgage was either in foreclosure or repossessed.

---

* Source: Federal Reserve Bank of New York (www.newyorkfed.org/regional/subprime.html).

EXAMPLE 6 iPods, iPhones, and Macs

The following table shows sales, in millions of units, of iPods, iPhones, and Macintosh computers in the last three quarters of 2008.*

	iPods	iPhones	Macs	Total
2008 Q2	10.6	1.7	2.3	14.6
2008 Q3	11.0	0.7	2.5	14.2
2008 Q4	11.1	6.9	2.6	20.6
Total	32.7	9.3	7.4	49.4

If one of the items sold is selected at random, find the probabilities of the following events:

a. It is an iPod.

b. It was sold in the third quarter of 2008.

c. It is an iPod sold in the third quarter of 2008.

d. It is either an iPod or was sold in the third quarter of 2008.

e. It is not an iPod.

Solution

a. The sample space S is the set of all these items, and the outcomes consist of all the items sold in the given quarters. Because an item is being selected at random, all the outcomes are equally likely. If D is the event that the selected item is an iPod, then

$$P(D) = \frac{n(D)}{n(S)} = \frac{32.7}{49.4} \approx .662.$$

The event D is represented by the pink shaded region in the table:

	iPods	iPhones	Macs	Total
2008 Q2	10.6	1.7	2.3	14.6
2008 Q3	11.0	0.7	2.5	14.2
2008 Q4	11.1	6.9	2.6	20.6
Total	32.7	9.3	7.4	49.4

b. If A is the event that the selected item was sold in the third quarter of 2008, then

$$P(A) = \frac{n(A)}{n(S)} = \frac{14.2}{49.4} \approx .287.$$

In the table, A is represented as shown:

	iPods	iPhones	Macs	Total
2008 Q2	10.6	1.7	2.3	14.6
2008 Q3	11.0	0.7	2.5	14.2
2008 Q4	11.1	6.9	2.6	20.6
Total	32.7	9.3	7.4	49.4

---

* Figures are rounded. Source: Company reports (www.apple.com/investor/).

c. The event that the selected item is an iPod sold in the third quarter of 2008 is the event $D \cap A$.

$$P(D \cap A) = \frac{n(D \cap A)}{n(S)} = \frac{11.0}{49.4} \approx .223$$

In the table, $D \cap A$ is represented by the overlap of the regions representing D and A:

	iPods	iPhones	Macs	Total
2008 Q2	10.6	1.7	2.3	14.6
2008 Q3	11.0	0.7	2.5	14.2
2008 Q4	11.1	6.9	2.6	20.6
Total	32.7	9.3	7.4	49.4

d. The event that the selected item is either an iPod or was sold in the third quarter of 2008 is the event $D \cup A$, and is represented by the pink shaded area in the table:

	iPods	iPhones	Macs	Total
2008 Q2	10.6	1.7	2.3	14.6
2008 Q3	11.0	0.7	2.5	14.2
2008 Q4	11.1	6.9	2.6	20.6
Total	32.7	9.3	7.4	49.4

We can compute its probability in two ways:

1. Directly from the table:

$$P(D \cup A) = \frac{n(D \cup A)}{n(S)} = \frac{14.2 + 32.7 - 11.0}{49.4} \approx .727.$$

2. Using the addition principle:

$$P(D \cup A) = P(D) + P(A) - P(D \cap A)$$
$$\approx .662 + .287 - .223 = .726.$$

(The discrepancy in the third decimal place is due to rounding error.)

e. The event that the selected item is not an iPod is the event D'. Its probability may be computed using the formula for the probability of the complement:

$$P(D') = 1 - P(D) \approx 1 - .662 = .338.$$

FAQs

Distinguishing Probability from Relative Frequency

Q: *Relative frequency and modeled probability using equally likely outcomes have essentially the same formula: (Number of favorable outcomes)/(Total number of outcomes). How do I know whether a given probability is one or the other?*

A: Ask yourself this: Has the probability been arrived at experimentally, by performing a number of trials and counting the number of times the event occurred? If so, the probability is estimated; that is, relative frequency. If, on the other hand, the probability was computed by analyzing the experiment under consideration rather than by performing actual trials of the experiment, it is a probability model.

Q: *Out of every 100 homes, 22 have broadband Internet service. Thus, the probability that a house has broadband service is .22. Is this probability estimated (relative frequency) or theoretical (a probability model)?*

A: That depends on how the ratio 22 out of 100 was arrived at. If it is based on a poll of *all* homes, then the probability is theoretical. If it is based on a survey of only a *sample* of homes, it is estimated (see the Q/A following Example 1).

7.3 EXERCISES

▼ more advanced   ◆ challenging
T indicates exercises that should be solved using technology

1. Complete the following probability distribution table and then calculate the stated probabilities. HINT [See Quick Example 5, page 469.]

Outcome	a	b	c	d	e
Probability	.1	.05	.6	.05	

a. $P(\{a, c, e\})$
b. $P(E \cup F)$, where $E = \{a, c, e\}$ and $F = \{b, c, e\}$
c. $P(E')$, where E is as in part (b)
d. $P(E \cap F)$, where E and F are as in part (b)

2. Repeat the preceding exercise using the following table. HINT [See Quick Example 5, page 469.]

Outcome	a	b	c	d	e
Probability	.1		.65	.1	.05

In Exercises 3–8, calculate the (modeled) probability $P(E)$ using the given information, assuming that all outcomes are equally likely. HINT [See Quick Examples on page 471.]

3. $n(S) = 20$, $n(E) = 5$ 4. $n(S) = 8$, $n(E) = 4$
5. $n(S) = 10$, $n(E) = 10$ 6. $n(S) = 10$, $n(E) = 0$
7. $S = \{a, b, c, d\}$, $E = \{a, b, d\}$
8. $S = \{1, 3, 5, 7, 9\}$, $E = \{3, 7\}$

In Exercises 9–18, an experiment is given together with an event. Find the (modeled) probability of each event, assuming that the coins and dice are distinguishable and fair, and that what is observed are the faces or numbers uppermost. (Compare with Exercises 1–10 in Section 7.1.)

9. Two coins are tossed; the result is at most one tail.
10. Two coins are tossed; the result is one or more heads.
11. Three coins are tossed; the result is at most one head.
12. Three coins are tossed; the result is more tails than heads.
13. Two dice are rolled; the numbers add to 5.
14. Two dice are rolled; the numbers add to 9.
15. Two dice are rolled; the numbers add to 1.
16. Two dice are rolled; one of the numbers is even, the other is odd.
17. Two dice are rolled; both numbers are prime.[22]
18. Two dice are rolled; neither number is prime.
19. If two indistinguishable dice are rolled, what is the probability of the event $\{(4, 4), (2, 3)\}$? What is the corresponding event for a pair of distinguishable dice? HINT [See Example 2.]
20. If two indistinguishable dice are rolled, what is the probability of the event $\{(5, 5), (2, 5), (3, 5)\}$? What is the corresponding event for a pair of distinguishable dice? HINT [See Example 2.]

---

[22] A positive integer is prime if it is neither 1 nor a product of smaller integers.

21. A die is weighted in such a way that each of 2, 4, and 6 is twice as likely to come up as each of 1, 3, and 5. Find the probability distribution. What is the probability of rolling less than 4? HINT [See Example 3.]

22. Another die is weighted in such a way that each of 1 and 2 is three times as likely to come up as each of the other numbers. Find the probability distribution. What is the probability of rolling an even number?

23. A tetrahedral die has four faces, numbered 1–4. If the die is weighted in such a way that each number is twice as likely to land facing down as the next number (1 twice as likely as 2, 2 twice as likely as 3, and so on) what is the probability distribution for the face landing down?

24. A dodecahedral die has 12 faces, numbered 1–12. If the die is weighted in such a way that 2 is twice as likely to land facing up as 1, 3 is three times as likely to land facing up as 1, and so on, what is the probability distribution for the face landing up?

In Exercises 25–40, use the given information to find the indicated probability. HINT [See Quick Examples, page 476.]

25. $P(A) = .1$, $P(B) = .6$, $P(A \cap B) = .05$. Find $P(A \cup B)$.

26. $P(A) = .3$, $P(B) = .4$, $P(A \cap B) = .02$. Find $P(A \cup B)$.

27. $A \cap B = \emptyset$, $P(A) = .3$, $P(A \cup B) = .4$. Find $P(B)$.

28. $A \cap B = \emptyset$, $P(B) = .8$, $P(A \cup B) = .8$. Find $P(A)$.

29. $A \cap B = \emptyset$, $P(A) = .3$, $P(B) = .4$. Find $P(A \cup B)$.

30. $A \cap B = \emptyset$, $P(A) = .2$, $P(B) = .3$. Find $P(A \cup B)$.

31. $P(A \cup B) = .9$, $P(B) = .6$, $P(A \cap B) = .1$. Find $P(A)$.

32. $P(A \cup B) = 1.0$, $P(A) = .6$, $P(A \cap B) = .1$. Find $P(B)$.

33. $P(A) = .75$. Find $P(A')$.

34. $P(A) = .22$. Find $P(A')$.

35. A, B, and C are mutually exclusive. $P(A) = .3$, $P(B) = .4$, $P(C) = .3$. Find $P(A \cup B \cup C)$.

36. A, B, and C are mutually exclusive. $P(A) = .2$, $P(B) = .6$, $P(C) = .1$. Find $P(A \cup B \cup C)$.

37. A and B are mutually exclusive. $P(A) = .3$, $P(B) = .4$. Find $P((A \cup B)')$.

38. A and B are mutually exclusive. $P(A) = .4$, $P(B) = .4$. Find $P((A \cup B)')$.

39. $A \cup B = S$ and $A \cap B = \emptyset$. Find $P(A) + P(B)$.

40. $P(A \cup B) = .3$ and $P(A \cap B) = .1$. Find $P(A) + P(B)$.

In Exercises 41–46, determine whether the information shown is consistent with a probability distribution. If not, say why.

41. $P(A) = .2$; $P(B) = .1$; $P(A \cup B) = .4$

42. $P(A) = .2$; $P(B) = .4$; $P(A \cup B) = .2$

43. $P(A) = .2$; $P(B) = .4$; $P(A \cap B) = .2$

44. $P(A) = .2$; $P(B) = .4$; $P(A \cap B) = .3$

45. $P(A) = .1$; $P(B) = 0$; $P(A \cup B) = 0$

46. $P(A) = .1$; $P(B) = 0$; $P(A \cap B) = 0$

APPLICATIONS

47. *Subprime Mortgages* (Compare Exercise 27 in Section 7.2.) The following chart shows the (approximate) total number of subprime home mortgages in Texas in November 2008, broken down into four categories:[23]

Mortgage Status	Current	Past Due	In Foreclosure	Repossessed	Total
Number	136,330	53,310	8,750	5,090	203,480

(The four categories are mutually exclusive; for instance, "Past Due" refers to a mortgage whose payment status is past due but is not in foreclosure, and "In Foreclosure" refers to a mortgage that is in the process of being foreclosed but not yet repossessed.)

a. Find the probability that a randomly selected subprime mortgage in Texas during November 2008 was neither in foreclosure nor repossessed. HINT [See Example 1.]

b. What is the probability that a randomly selected subprime mortgage in Texas during November 2008 was not current?

48. *Subprime Mortgages* (Compare Exercise 28 in Section 7.2.) The following chart shows the (approximate) total number of subprime home mortgages in Florida in November 2008, broken down into four categories:[24]

Mortgage Status	Current	Past Due	In Foreclosure	Repossessed	Total
Number	130,400	73,260	72,380	17,000	293,040

(The four categories are mutually exclusive; for instance, "Past Due" refers to a mortgage whose payment status is past due but is not in foreclosure, and "In Foreclosure" refers to a mortgage that is in the process of being foreclosed but not yet repossessed.)

a. Find the probability that a randomly selected subprime mortgage in Florida during November 2008 was either in foreclosure or repossessed. HINT [See Example 1.]

b. What is the probability that a randomly selected subprime mortgage in Florida during November 2008 was not repossessed?

49. *Ethnic Diversity* The following pie chart shows the ethnic makeup of California schools in the 2006–2007 academic year.[25]

---

[23] Data are rounded to the nearest 10 units. Source: Federal Reserve Bank of New York (www.newyorkfed.org/regional/subprime.html).

[24] Ibid.

[25] Source: CBEDS data collection, Educational Demographics, October 2006 (www.cde.ca.gov/resrc/factbook/).

Write down the probability distribution showing the probability that a randomly selected California student in 2006–2007 belonged to one of the ethnic groups named. What is the probability that a student is neither white nor Asian?

50. *Ethnic Diversity* (Compare Exercise 49.) The following pie chart shows the ethnic makeup of California schools in the 1981–1982 academic year.[26]

Write down the probability distribution showing the probability that a randomly selected California student in 1981–1982 belonged to one of the ethnic groups named. What is the probability that a student is neither Hispanic, Latino, nor African American?

51. ▼ *Internet Investments in the 90s* The following excerpt is from an article in *The New York Times* in July, 1999.[27]

> While statistics are not available for Web entrepreneurs who fail, the venture capitalists that finance such Internet start-up companies have a rule of thumb. For every 10 ventures that receive financing—and there are plenty who do not—2 will be stock market successes, which means spectacular profits for early investors; 3 will be sold to other concerns, which translates into more modest profits; and the rest will fail.

a. What is a sample space for the scenario?
b. Write down the associated probability distribution.
c. What is the probability that a start-up venture that receives financing will realize profits for early investors?

52. ◆ *Internet Investments in the 90s* The following excerpt is from an article in *The New York Times* in July, 1999.[28]

[26] Source: CBEDS data collection, Educational Demographics, October 2006 (www.cde.ca.gov/resrc/factbook/).

[27] Article: "Not All Hit It Rich in the Internet Gold Rush," *The New York Times*, July 20, 1999, p. A1.

[28] Article: Ibid. Source for data: Comm-Scan/*The New York Times*, July 20, 1999, p. A1.

> Right now, the market for Web stocks is sizzling. Of the 126 initial public offerings of Internet stocks priced this year, 73 are trading above the price they closed on their first day of trading.... Still, 53 of the offerings have failed to live up to their fabulous first-day billings, and 17 [of these] are below the initial offering price.

Assume that, on the first day of trading, all stocks closed higher than their initial offering price.

a. What is a sample space for the scenario?
b. Write down the associated probability distribution. (Round your answers to two decimal places.)
c. What is the probability that an Internet stock purchased during the period reported ended either below its initial offering price or above the price it closed on its first day of trading? **HINT** [See Example 3.]

53. *Market Share: Light Vehicles* In 2003, 25% of all light vehicles sold (SUVs, pickups, passenger cars, and minivans) in the United States were SUVs and 15% were pickups. Moreover, a randomly chosen vehicle sold that year was five times as likely to be a passenger car as a minivan.[29] Find the associated probability distribution.

54. *Market Share: Light Vehicles* In 2000, 15% of all light vehicles (SUVs, pickups, passenger cars, and minivans) sold in the United States were pickups and 55% were passenger cars. Moreover, a randomly chosen vehicle sold that year was twice as likely to be an SUV as a minivan.[30] Find the associated probability distribution.

Gambling In Exercises 55–62 are detailed some of the nefarious dicing practices of the Win Some/Lose Some Casino. In each case, find the probabilities of all the possible outcomes and also the probability that an odd number or an odd sum faces up. **HINT** [See Example 3.]

55. Some of the dice are specially designed so that 1 and 6 never come up, and all the other outcomes are equally likely.

56. Other dice are specially designed so that 1 comes up half the time, 6 never comes up, and all the other outcomes are equally likely.

[29] Source: Environmental Protection Agency/*The New York Times*, June 28, 2003.

[30] Ibid.

57. Some of the dice are cleverly weighted so that each of 2, 3, 4, and 5 is twice as likely to come up as 1 is, and 1 and 6 are equally likely.

58. Other dice are weighted so that each of 2, 3, 4, and 5 is half as likely to come up as 1 is, and 1 and 6 are equally likely.

59. ▼ Some pairs of dice are magnetized so that each pair of mismatching numbers is twice as likely to come up as each pair of matching numbers.

60. ▼ Other pairs of dice are so strongly magnetized that mismatching numbers never come up.

61. ▼ Some dice are constructed in such a way that deuce (2) is five times as likely to come up as 4 and three times as likely to come up as each of 1, 3, 5, and 6.

62. ▼ Other dice are constructed in such a way that deuce is six times as likely to come up as 4 and four times as likely to come up as each of 1, 3, 5, and 6.

63. *Astrology* The astrology software package, Turbo Kismet,[31] works by first generating random number sequences and then interpreting them numerologically. When I ran it yesterday, it informed me that there was a 1/3 probability that I would meet a tall dark stranger this month, a 2/3 probability that I would travel this month, and a 1/6 probability that I would meet a tall dark stranger and also travel this month. What is the probability that I will either meet a tall dark stranger or that I will travel this month? HINT [See Quick Example 1, page 476 and Example 4.]

64. *Astrology* Another astrology software package, Java Kismet, is designed to help day traders choose stocks based on the position of the planets and constellations. When I ran it yesterday, it informed me that there was a .5 probability that Amazon.com will go up this afternoon, a .2 probability that Yahoo.com will go up this afternoon, and a .2 chance that both will go up this afternoon. What is the probability that either Amazon.com or Yahoo.com will go up this afternoon? HINT [See Quick Example 1 on page 476 and Example 4.]

65. *Polls* According to a *New York Times*/CBS poll released in March 2005, 61% of those polled ranked jobs or health care as the top domestic priority.[32] What is the probability that a randomly selected person polled did not rank either as the top domestic priority? HINT [See Example 5.]

66. *Polls* According to the *New York Times*/CBS poll of March 2005, referred to in Exercise 65, 72% of those polled ranked neither Iraq nor North Korea as the top foreign policy issue.[33] What is the probability that a randomly selected person polled ranked either Iraq or North Korea as the top foreign policy issue? HINT [See Example 5.]

67. *Auto Sales* In April 2008, the probability that a randomly chosen new automobile was manufactured by **General Motors** was .21, while the probability that it was manufactured by **Toyota** was .18.[34] What is the probability that a randomly chosen new automobile was manufactured by neither company?

68. *Auto Sales* In April 2008, the probability that a randomly chosen new automobile was manufactured by **Ford** was .15, while the probability that it was manufactured by **Chrysler** was .12.[35] What is the probability that a randomly chosen new automobile was manufactured by neither company?

Student Admissions Exercises 69–84 are based on the following table, which shows the profile, by Math SAT I scores, of admitted students at UCLA for the Fall 2008 semester.[36]

Math SAT I

	700–800	600–699	500–599	400–499	200–399	Total
Admitted	5,919	3,822	1,470	425	49	11,685
Not admitted	6,313	14,237	10,797	4,755	1,273	37,375
Total applicants	12,232	18,059	12,267	5,180	1,322	49,060

Determine the probabilities of the following events. (Round your answers to the nearest .01.) HINT [Example 6.]

69. An applicant was admitted.

70. An applicant had a Math SAT below 400.

71. An applicant had a Math SAT below 400 and was admitted.

72. An applicant had a Math SAT of 700 or above and was admitted.

73. An applicant was not admitted.

74. An applicant did not have a Math SAT below 400.

75. An applicant had a Math SAT in the range 500–599 or was admitted.

76. An applicant had a Math SAT of 700 or above or was admitted.

77. An applicant neither was admitted nor had a Math SAT in the range 500–599.

78. An applicant neither had a Math SAT of 700 or above nor was admitted.

79. ▼ An applicant who had a Math SAT below 400 was admitted.

80. ▼ An applicant who had a Math SAT of 700 or above was admitted.

81. ▼ An admitted student had a Math SAT of 700 or above.

82. ▼ An admitted student had a Math SAT below 400.

---

[31] The name and concept were borrowed from a hilarious (as yet unpublished) novel by the science-fiction writer William Orr, who also happens to be a faculty member at Hofstra University.

[32] Source: *New York Times*, March 3, 2005, p. A20.

[33] Ibid.

[34] Source: *New York Times*, May 2, 2008. (www.nytimes.com/imagepages/2008/05/02/business/02autosgraphic.ready.html).

[35] Ibid.

[36] Source: University of California (www.admissions.ucla.edu/Prospect/Adm_fr/Frosh_Prof08.htm).

83. ▼ A rejected applicant had a Math SAT below 600.

84. ▼ A rejected applicant had a Math SAT of at least 600.

85. ▼ *Social Security* According to the *New York Times*/CBS poll of March, 2005, referred to in Exercise 65, 79% agreed that it should be the government's responsibility to provide a decent standard of living for the elderly, and 43% agreed that it would be a good idea to invest part of their Social Security taxes on their own.[37] What is the smallest percentage of people who could have agreed with both statements? What is the largest percentage of people who could have agreed with both statements?

86. ▼ *Social Security* According to the *New York Times*/CBS poll of March, 2005, referred to in Exercise 65, 49% agreed that Social Security taxes should be raised if necessary to keep the system afloat, and 43% agreed that it would be a good idea to invest part of their Social Security taxes on their own.[38] What is the largest percentage of people who could have agreed with at least one of these statements? What is the smallest percentage of people who could have agreed with at least one of these statements?

87. ▼ *Greek Life* The TΦΦ Sorority has a tough pledging program—it requires its pledges to master the Greek alphabet forward, backward, and "sideways." During the last pledge period, two-thirds of the pledges failed to learn it backward and three quarters of them failed to learn it sideways; 5 of the 12 pledges failed to master it either backward or sideways. Because admission into the sisterhood requires both backward and sideways mastery, what fraction of the pledges were disqualified on this basis?

88. ▼ *Swords and Sorcery* Lance the Wizard has been informed that tomorrow there will be a 50% chance of encountering the evil Myrmidons and a 20% chance of meeting up with the dreadful Balrog. Moreover, Hugo the Elf has predicted that there is a 10% chance of encountering both tomorrow. What is the probability that Lance will be lucky tomorrow and encounter neither the Myrmidons nor the Balrog?

89. ▼ *Public Health* A study shows that 80% of the population has been vaccinated against the Venusian flu, but 2% of the vaccinated population gets the flu anyway. If 10% of the total population gets this flu, what percent of the population either gets the vaccine or gets the disease?

90. ▼ *Public Health* A study shows that 75% of the population has been vaccinated against the Martian ague, but 4% of this group gets this disease anyway. If 10% of the total population gets this disease, what is the probability that a randomly selected person has been neither vaccinated nor has contracted Martian ague?

---

[37] Source: *New York Times*, March 3, 2005, p. A20.
[38] Ibid.

COMMUNICATION AND REASONING EXERCISES

91. Design an experiment based on rolling a fair die for which there are exactly three outcomes with the same probabilities.

92. Design an experiment based on rolling a fair die for which there are at least three outcomes with different probabilities.

93. ▼ Tony has had a "losing streak" at the casino—the chances of winning the game he is playing are 40%, but he has lost five times in a row. Tony argues that, because he should have won two times, the game must obviously be "rigged." Comment on his reasoning.

94. ▼ Maria is on a winning streak at the casino. She has already won four times in a row and concludes that her chances of winning a fifth time are good. Comment on her reasoning.

95. Complete the following sentence. The probability of the union of two events is the sum of the probabilities of the two events if _____.

96. A friend of yours asserted at lunch today that, according to the weather forecast for tomorrow, there is a 52% chance of rain and a 60% chance of snow. "But that's impossible!" you blurted out, "the percentages add up to more than 100%." Explain why you were wrong.

97. ▼ A certain experiment is performed a large number of times, and the event E has relative frequency equal to zero. This means that it should have modeled probability zero, right? HINT [See the definition of a probability model on p. 469.]

98. ▼ (Refer to the preceding exercise.) How can the modeled probability of winning the lotto be nonzero if you have never won it, despite playing 600 times? HINT [See the definition of a probability model on p. 469.]

99. ▼ Explain how the addition principle for mutually exclusive events follows from the general addition principle.

100. ▼ Explain how the property $P(A') = 1 - P(A)$ follows directly from the properties of a probability distribution.

101. ◆ It is said that lightning never strikes twice in the same spot. Assuming this to be the case, what should be the modeled probability that lightning will strike a given spot during a thunderstorm? Explain. HINT [See the definition of a probability model on p. 469.]

102. ◆ A certain event has modeled probability equal to zero. This means it will never occur, right? HINT [See the definition of a probability model on p. 469.]

103. ◆ Find a formula for the probability of the union of three (not necessarily mutually exclusive) events A, B, and C.

104. ◆ Four events A, B, C, and D have the following property: If any two events have an outcome in common, that outcome is common to all four events. Find a formula for the probability of their union.

7.4 Probability and Counting Techniques

We saw in the preceding section that, when all outcomes in a sample space are equally likely, we can use the following formula to model the probability of each event:

Modeling Probability: Equally Likely Outcomes

In an experiment in which all outcomes are equally likely, the probability of an event E is given by

$$P(E) = \frac{\text{Number of favorable outcomes}}{\text{Total number of outcomes}} = \frac{n(E)}{n(S)}.$$

This formula is simple, but calculating $n(E)$ and $n(S)$ may not be. In this section, we look at some examples in which we need to use the counting techniques discussed in Chapter 6.

EXAMPLE 1 Marbles

A bag contains four red marbles and two green ones. Upon seeing the bag, Suzan (who has compulsive marble-grabbing tendencies) sticks her hand in and grabs three at random. Find the probability that she will get both green marbles.

Solution According to the formula, we need to know these numbers:

• The number of elements in the sample space S.

• The number of elements in the event E.

S is the set of all outcomes that can occur, and has nothing to do with having green marbles.

First of all, what is the sample space? The sample space is the set of all possible outcomes, and each outcome consists of a set of three marbles (in Suzan's hand). So, the set of outcomes is the set of all sets of three marbles chosen from a total of six marbles (four red and two green). Thus,

$$n(S) = C(6, 3) = 20.$$

Now what about E? This is the event that Suzan gets both green marbles. We must *rephrase this as a subset of S* in order to deal with it: "E is the collection of sets of three marbles such that one is red and two are green." Thus, $n(E)$ is the *number* of such sets, which we determine using a decision algorithm.

Step 1 Choose a red marble; $C(4, 1) = 4$ possible outcomes.

Step 2 Choose the two green marbles; $C(2, 2) = 1$ possible outcome.

We get $n(E) = 4 \times 1 = 4$. Now,

$$P(E) = \frac{n(E)}{n(S)} = \frac{4}{20} = \frac{1}{5}.$$

Thus, there is a one in five chance of Suzan's getting both the green marbles.

EXAMPLE 2 Investment Lottery

In order to "spice up" your investment portfolio, you decided to ignore your broker's cautious advice and select three stocks at random from the six most active stocks listed on the New York Stock Exchange shortly after the start of trading on January 23, 2009:*

Company	Symbol	Price	Change
General Electric	GE	$12.74	−$0.74
Bank of America	BAC	$5.63	−$0.03
SPDR S&P 500	SPY	$82.75	$0.00
Ultra Financials Pro	UYG	$2.86	−$0.16
Citigroup	C	$3.11	$0.00
Wyeth	WYE	$42.81	+$4.15

Find the probabilities of the following events:

a. Your portfolio included GE and BAC.

b. At most two of the stocks in your portfolio declined in value.

Solution First, the sample space is the set of all collections of three stocks chosen from the six. Thus,

$$n(S) = C(6, 3) = 20.$$

a. The event E of interest is the event that your portfolio includes GE and BAC. Thus, E is the set of all groups of three stocks that include GE and BAC. Because there is only one more stock left to choose,

$$n(E) = C(4, 1) = 4.$$

We now have

$$P(E) = \frac{n(E)}{n(S)} = \frac{4}{20} = \frac{1}{5} = .2.$$

b. Let F be the event that at most two of the stocks in your portfolio declined in value. Thus, F is the set of all portfolios of three stocks of which at most two declined in value. To calculate $n(F)$, we use the following decision algorithm, noting that three of the stocks declined in value and three did not.

Alternative 1: None of the stocks declined in value.
  Step 1 Choose three stocks that did not decline in value; $C(3, 3) = 1$ possibility.

Alternative 2: One of the stocks declined in value.
  Step 1 Choose one stock that declined in value; $C(3, 1) = 3$ possibilities.
  Step 2 Choose two stocks that did not decline in value; $C(3, 2) = 3$ possibilities. This gives $3 \times 3 = 9$ possibilities for this alternative.

Alternative 3: Two of the stocks declined in value.
  Step 1 Choose two stocks that declined in value; $C(3, 2) = 3$ possibilities.
  Step 2 Choose one stock that did not decline in value; $C(3, 1) = 3$ possibilities. This gives $3 \times 3 = 9$ possibilities for this alternative.

---

*Prices shortly after the market opened on January 23, 2009. Source: Yahoo! Finance (http://finance.yahoo.com).

So, we have a total of $1 + 9 + 9 = 19$ possible portfolios. Thus,

$$n(F) = 19$$

and

$$P(F) = \frac{n(F)}{n(S)} = \frac{19}{20} = .95.$$

➡ **Before we go on...** When counting the number of outcomes in an event, the calculation is sometimes easier if we look at the *complement* of that event. In the case of part (b) of Example 2, the complement of the event F is

F': At least three of the stocks in your portfolio declined in value.

Because there are only three stocks in your portfolio, this is the same as the event that all three stocks in your portfolio declined in value. The decision algorithm for $n(F')$ is far simpler:

Step 1 Choose three stocks that declined in value: $C(3, 3) = 1$ possibility.

So, $n(F') = 1$, giving

$$n(F) = n(S) - n(F') = 20 - 1 = 19$$

as we calculated above. ■

At most two of the stocks declined in value.

Complementary Events

At least three of the stocks declined in value.

EXAMPLE 3 **Poker Hands**

You are dealt 5 cards from a well-shuffled standard deck of 52. Find the probability that you have a full house. (Recall that a full house consists of 3 cards of one denomination and 2 of another.)

Solution The sample space S is the set of all possible 5-card hands dealt from a deck of 52. Thus,

$$n(S) = C(52, 5) = 2{,}598{,}960.$$

If the deck is thoroughly shuffled, then each of these 5-card hands is equally likely. Now consider the event E, the set of all possible 5-card hands that constitute a full house. To calculate $n(E)$, we use a decision algorithm, which we show in the following compact form.

1. Choose first denomination.
2. Choose three cards of that denomination.
3. Choose second denomination.
4. Choose two cards of that denomination.

$$n(E) = C(13, 1) \times C(4, 3) \times C(12, 1) \times C(4, 2) = 3{,}744$$

Thus,

$$P(E) = \frac{n(E)}{n(S)} = \frac{3{,}744}{2{,}598{,}960} \approx .00144.$$

In other words, there is an approximately 0.144% chance that you will be dealt a full house.

Chris Ware/The Image Works

EXAMPLE 4 **More Poker Hands**

You are playing poker, and you have been dealt the following hand:

$$J\spadesuit, J\diamondsuit, J\heartsuit, 2\clubsuit, 10\spadesuit.$$

You decide to exchange the last two cards. The exchange works as follows: The two cards are discarded (not replaced in the deck), and you are dealt two new cards.

a. Find the probability that you end up with a full house.

b. Find the probability that you end up with four jacks.

c. What is the probability that you end up with either a full house or four jacks?

Solution

a. In order to get a full house, you must be dealt two of a kind. The sample space S is the set of all pairs of cards selected from what remains of the original deck of 52. You were dealt 5 cards originally, so there are $52 - 5 = 47$ cards left in the deck. Thus, $n(S) = C(47, 2) = 1,081$. The event E is the set of all pairs of cards that constitute two of a kind. Note that you cannot get two jacks because only one is left in the deck. Also, only three 2s and three 10s are left in the deck. We have

1. Choose a denomination other than Jacks, 2s, and 10s.   **1.** Choose either 2s or 10s.

OR

$$n(E) = C(10, 1) \times C(4, 2) \qquad + \qquad C(2, 1) \times C(3, 2) = 66$$

2. Choose two cards of that denomination.   **2.** Choose two cards of that denomination.

Thus,

$$P(E) = \frac{n(E)}{n(S)} = \frac{66}{1,081} \approx .0611.$$

b. We have the same sample space as in part (a). Let F be the set of all pairs of cards that include the missing jack of clubs. So,

1. Choose the jack of clubs.

2. Choose 1 card from the remaining 46.

$$n(F) = C(1, 1) \times C(46, 1) = 46.$$

Thus,

$$P(F) = \frac{n(F)}{n(S)} = \frac{46}{1,081} \approx .0426.$$

c. We are asked to calculate the probability of the event $E \cup F$. From the addition principle, we have

$$P(E \cup F) = P(E) + P(F) - P(E \cap F).$$

Because $E \cap F$ means "E and F," $E \cap F$ is the event that the pair of cards you are dealt are two of a kind and include the jack of clubs. But this is impossible because only one jack is left. Thus $E \cap F = \emptyset$, and so $P(E \cap F) = 0$. This gives us

$$P(E \cup F) = P(E) + P(F) \approx .0611 + .0426 = .1037.$$

In other words, there is slightly better than a one in ten chance that you will wind up with either a full house or four of a kind, given the original hand.

➡ **Before we go on...** A more accurate answer to part (c) of Example 4 is $(66 + 46)/1{,}081 \approx .1036$; we lost some accuracy in rounding the answers to parts (a) and (b). ∎

EXAMPLE 5 Committees

The University Senate bylaws at Hofstra University state the following:*

> The Student Affairs Committee shall consist of one elected faculty senator, one faculty senator-at-large, one elected student senator, five student senators-at-large (including one from the graduate school), two delegates from the Student Government Association, the President of the Student Government Association or his/her designate, and the President of the Graduate Student Organization. It shall be chaired by the elected student senator on the Committee and it shall be advised by the Dean of Students or his/her designate.

You are an undergraduate student and, even though you are not an elected student senator, you would very much like to serve on the Student Affairs Committee. The senators-at-large as well as the Student Government delegates are chosen by means of a random drawing from a list of candidates. There are already 13 undergraduate candidates for the position of senator-at-large, and 6 candidates for Student Government delegates, and you have been offered a position on the Student Government Association by the President (who happens to be a good friend of yours), should you wish to join it. (This would make you ineligible for a senator-at-large position.) What should you do?

Solution You have two options. Option 1 is to include your name on the list of candidates for the senator-at-large position. Option 2 is to join the Student Government Association (SGA) and add your name to its list of candidates. Let us look at the two options separately.

Option 1: Add your name to the senator-at-large list.
This will result in a list of 14 undergraduates for 4 undergraduate positions. The sample space is the set of all possible outcomes of the random drawing. Each outcome consists of a set of 4 lucky students chosen from 14. Thus,

$$n(S) = C(14, 4) = 1{,}001.$$

We are interested in the probability that you are among the chosen four. Thus, E is the set of sets of four that include you.

1. Choose yourself.

2. Choose 3 from the remaining 13.

$$n(E) = C(1, 1) \times C(13, 3) = 286.$$

---

* As of 2009. Source: Hofstra University Senate Bylaws.

So,

$$P(E) = \frac{n(E)}{n(S)} = \frac{286}{1,001} = \frac{2}{7} \approx .2857.$$

Option 2: Join the SGA and add your name to its list.
This results in a list of seven candidates from which two are selected. For this case, the sample space consists of all sets of two chosen from seven, so

$$n(S) = C(7, 2) = 21$$

and

1. Choose yourself.

2. Choose one from the remaining six.

$$n(E) = C(1, 1) \times C(6, 1) = 6.$$

Thus,

$$P(E) = \frac{n(E)}{n(S)} = \frac{6}{21} = \frac{2}{7} \approx .2857.$$

In other words, the probability of being selected is exactly the same for Option 1 as it is for Option 2! Thus, you can choose either option, and you will have slightly less than a 29% chance of being selected.

7.4 **EXERCISES**

▼ more advanced   ◆ challenging
 Ⓣ indicates exercises that should be solved using technology

Recall from Example 1 that whenever Suzan sees a bag of marbles, she grabs a handful at random. In Exercises 1–10, she has seen a bag containing four red marbles, three green ones, two white ones, and one purple one. She grabs five of them. Find the probabilities of the following events, expressing each as a fraction in lowest terms. HINT [See Example 1.]

1. She has all the red ones.

2. She has none of the red ones.

3. She has at least one white one.

4. She has at least one green one.

5. She has two red ones and one of each of the other colors.

6. She has two green ones and one of each of the other colors.

7. She has at most one green one.

8. She has no more than one white one.

9. She does not have all the red ones.

10. She does not have all the green ones.

Dogs of the Dow The phrase "Dogs of the Dow" refers to the stocks listed on the Dow with the highest dividend yield. Exercises 11–16 are based on the following table, which shows the top ten stocks of the "Dogs of the Dow" list in January 2009:[39] HINT [See Example 2.]

Symbol	Company	Yield
BAC	Bank of America	9.09%
GE	General Electric	7.65%
PFE	Pfizer	7.23%
DD	DuPont	6.48%
AA	Alcoa	6.04%
T	AT&T	5.75%
VZ	Verizon	5.43%
MRK	Merck	5.00%
JPM	JP Morgan Chase	4.82%
KFT	Kraft	4.32%

---
[39] Source: www.dogsofthedow.com.

11. If you selected two of these stocks at random, what is the probability that both the stocks in your selection had yields of 7% or more?

12. If you selected three of these stocks at random, what is the probability that all three of the stocks in your selection had yields of 7% or more?

13. If you selected four of these stocks at random, what is the probability that your selection included the company with the highest yield and excluded the company with the lowest yield?

14. If you selected four of these stocks at random, what is the probability that your selection included BAC and GE but excluded PFE and DD?

15. ▼ If your portfolio included 100 shares of PFE and you then purchased 100 shares each of any two companies on the list at random, find the probability that you ended up with a total of 200 shares of PFE.

16. ▼ If your portfolio included 100 shares of PFE and you then purchased 100 shares each of any three companies on the list at random, find the probability that you ended up with a total of 200 shares of PFE.

17. *Tests* A test has three parts. Part A consists of eight true-false questions, Part B consists of five multiple choice questions with five choices each, and Part C requires you to match five questions with five different answers one-to-one. Assuming that you make random guesses in filling out your answer sheet, what is the probability that you will earn 100% on the test? (Leave your answer as a formula.)

18. *Tests* A test has three parts. Part A consists of four true-false questions, Part B consists of four multiple choice questions with five choices each, and Part C requires you to match six questions with six different answers one-to-one. Assuming that you make random choices in filling out your answer sheet, what is the probability that you will earn 100% on the test? (Leave your answer as a formula.)

Poker In Exercises 19–24, you are asked to calculate the probability of being dealt various poker hands. (Recall that a poker player is dealt 5 cards at random from a standard deck of 52.) Express each of your answers as a decimal rounded to four decimal places, unless otherwise stated. HINT [See Example 3.]

19. **Two of a kind:** Two cards with the same denomination and three cards with other denominations (different from each other and that of the pair). Example: K♣, K♥, 2♠, 4♦, J♠

20. **Three of a kind:** Three cards with the same denomination and two cards with other denominations (different from each other and that of the three). Example: Q♣, Q♥, Q♠, 4♦, J♠

21. **Two pair:** Two cards with one denomination, two with another, and one with a third. Example: 3♣, 3♥, Q♠, Q♥, 10♠

22. **Straight Flush:** Five cards of the same suit with consecutive denominations but not a royal flush (a royal flush consists of the 10, J, Q, K, and A of one suit). Round the answer to one significant digit. Examples: A♣, 2♣, 3♣, 4♣, 5♣, or

9♦, 10♦, J♦, Q♦, K♦, or A♥, 2♥, 3♥, 4♥, 5♥, but *not* 10♦, J♦, Q♦, K♦, A♦

23. **Flush:** Five cards of the same suit, but not a straight flush or royal flush. Example: A♣, 5♣, 7♣, 8♣, K♣

24. **Straight:** Five cards with consecutive denominations, but not all of the same suit. Examples: 9♦, 10♦, J♣, Q♥, K♦, and 10♥, J♦, Q♦, K♦, A♠.

25. *The Monkey at the Typewriter* Suppose that a monkey is seated at a computer keyboard and randomly strikes the 26 letter keys and the space bar. Find the probability that its first 39 characters (including spaces) will be "to be or not to be that is the question". (Leave your answer as a formula.)

26. *The Cat on the Piano* A standard piano keyboard has 88 different keys. Find the probability that a cat, jumping on 4 keys in sequence and at random (possibly with repetition), will strike the first four notes of Beethoven's Fifth Symphony. (Leave your answer as a formula.)

27. *(Based on a question from the GMAT)* Tyler and Gebriella are among seven contestants from which four semifinalists are to be selected at random. Find the probability that neither Tyler nor Gebriella is selected.

28. *(Based on a question from the GMAT)* Tyler and Gebriella are among seven contestants from which four semifinalists are to be selected at random. Find the probability that Tyler but not Gebriella is selected.

29. ▼ *Lotteries* The Sorry State Lottery requires you to select five different numbers from 0 through 49. (Order is not important.) You are a Big Winner if the five numbers you select agree with those in the drawing, and you are a Small-Fry Winner if four of your five numbers agree with those in the drawing. What is the probability of being a Big Winner? What is the probability of being a Small-Fry Winner? What is the probability that you are either a Big Winner or a Small-Fry winner?

30. ▼ *Lotto* The Sad State Lottery requires you to select a sequence of three different numbers from 0 through 49. (Order is important.) You are a winner if your sequence agrees with that in the drawing, and you are a booby prize winner if your selection of numbers is correct, but in the wrong order. What is the probability of being a winner? What is the probability of being a booby prize winner? What is the probability that you are either a winner or a booby prize winner?

31. ▼ *Transfers* Your company is considering offering 400 employees the opportunity to transfer to its new headquarters in Ottawa and, as personnel manager, you decide that it would be fairest if the transfer offers are decided by means of a lottery. Assuming that your company currently employs 100 managers, 100 factory workers, and 500 miscellaneous staff, find the following probabilities, leaving the answers as formulas:

  a. All the managers will be offered the opportunity.
  b. You will be offered the opportunity.

32. ▼ *Transfers* (Refer back to the preceding exercise.) After thinking about your proposed method of selecting employees for the opportunity to move to Ottawa, you decide it might be a better idea to select 50 managers, 50 factory workers, and 300 miscellaneous staff, all chosen at random. Find the probability that you will be offered the opportunity. (Leave your answer as a formula.)

33. ▼ *Lotteries* In a New York State daily lottery game, a sequence of three digits (not necessarily different) in the range 0–9 are selected at random. Find the probability that all three are different.

34. ▼ *Lotteries* Refer back to the preceding exercise. Find the probability that two of the three digits are the same.

35. ▼ *Sports* The following table shows the results of the Big Eight Conference for the 1988 college football season.[40]

Team	Won	Lost
Nebraska (NU)	7	0
Oklahoma (OU)	6	1
Oklahoma State (OSU)	5	2
Colorado (CU)	4	3
Iowa State (ISU)	3	4
Missouri (MU)	2	5
Kansas (KU)	1	6
Kansas State (KSU)	0	7

This is referred to as a "perfect progression." Assuming that the "Won" score for each team is chosen at random in the range 0–7, find the probability that the results form a perfect progression.[41] (Leave your answer as a formula.)

36. ▼ *Sports* Refer back to Exercise 35. Find the probability of a perfect progression with Nebraska scoring seven wins and zero losses. (Leave your answer as a formula.)

37. ▼ *Graph Searching* A graph consists of a collection of **nodes** (the dots in the figure) connected by **edges** (line segments from one node to another). A **move on a graph** is a move from one node to another along a single edge. Find the probability of going from Start to Finish in a sequence of two random moves in the graph shown. (All directions are equally likely.)

38. ▼ *Graph Searching* Refer back to Exercise 37. Find the probability of going from Start to one of the Finish nodes in a sequence of two random moves in the following figure. (All directions are equally likely.)

39. ▼ *Tournaments* What is the probability that North Carolina will beat Central Connecticut but lose to Virginia in the following (fictitious) soccer tournament? (Assume that all outcomes are equally likely.)

40. ▼ *Tournaments* In a (fictitious) soccer tournament involving the four teams San Diego State, De Paul, Colgate, and Hofstra, find the probability that Hofstra will play Colgate in the finals and win. (Assume that all outcomes are equally likely and that the teams not listed in the first round slots are placed at random.)

41. ◆ *Product Design* Your company has patented an electronic digital padlock which a user can program with his or her own four-digit code. (Each digit can be 0 through 9, and repetitions are allowed.) The padlock is designed to open either if the correct code is keyed in or—and this is helpful for forgetful people—if exactly one of the digits is incorrect. What is the probability that a randomly chosen sequence of four digits will open a programmed padlock?

---

[40] Source: On the probability of a perfect progression, *The American Statistician,* August 1991, vol. 45, no. 3, p. 214.

[41] Even if all the teams are equally likely to win each game, the chances of a perfect progression actually coming up are a little more difficult to estimate, because the number of wins by one team impacts directly on the number of wins by the others. For instance, it is impossible for all eight teams to show a score of seven wins and zero losses at the end of the season—someone must lose! It is, however, not too hard to come up with a counting argument to estimate the total number of win-loss scores actually possible.

42. ◆ *Product Design* Assume that you already know the first digit of the combination for the lock described in Exercise 41. Find the probability that a random guess of the remaining three digits will open the lock. HINT [See Example 5.]

43. ◆ *Committees* An investigatory Committee in the Kingdom of Utopia consists of a chief investigator (a Royal Party member), an assistant investigator (a Birthday Party member), two at-large investigators (either party), and five ordinary members (either party). Royal Party member Larry Sifford is hoping to avoid serving on the committee, unless he is the Chief Investigator and Otis Taylor, a Birthday Party member, is the Assistant Investigator. The committee is to be selected at random from a pool of 12 candidates (including Larry Sifford and Otis Taylor), half of whom are Royal Party and half of whom are Birthday Party.

a. How many different committees are possible? HINT [See Example 5.]

b. How many committees are possible in which Larry's hopes are fulfilled? (This includes the possibility that he's not on the committee at all.)

c. What is the probability that he'll be happy with a randomly selected committee?

44. ◆ *Committees* A committee is to consist of a chair, three hagglers, and four do-nothings. The committee is formed by choosing randomly from a pool of 10 people and assigning them to the various "jobs."

a. How many different committees are possible? HINT [See Example 5.]

b. Norman is eager to be the chair of the committee. What is the probability that he will get his wish?

c. Norman's girlfriend Norma is less ambitious and would be happy to hold any position on the committee provided Norman is also selected as a committee member. What is the probability that she will get her wish and serve on the committee?

d. Norma does not get along with Oona (who is also in the pool of prospective members) and would be most unhappy if Oona were to chair the committee. Find the probability that all her wishes will be fulfilled: she and Norman are on the committee and it is not chaired by Oona.

COMMUNICATION AND REASONING EXERCISES

45. What is wrong with the following argument? A bag contains two blue marbles and two red ones; two are drawn at random. Because there are four possibilities—(red, red), (blue, blue), (red, blue) and (blue, red)—the probability that both are red is 1/4.

46. What is wrong with the following argument? When we roll two indistinguishable dice, the number of possible outcomes (unordered groups of two not necessarily distinct numbers) is 21 and the number of outcomes in which both numbers are the same is 6. Hence, the probability of throwing a double is 6/21 = 2/7.

47. ▼ Suzan grabs two marbles out of a bag of five red marbles and four green ones. She could do so in two ways: She could take them out one at a time, so that there is a first and a second marble, or she could grab two at once so that there is no order. Does the method she uses to grab the marbles affect the probability that she gets two red marbles?

48. ▼ If Suzan grabs two marbles, one at a time, out of a bag of five red marbles and four green ones, find an event with a probability that depends on the order in which the two marbles are drawn.

49. Create an interesting application whose solution requires finding a probability using combinations.

50. Create an interesting application whose solution requires finding a probability using permutations.

7.5 Conditional Probability and Independence

Cyber Video Games, Inc., ran a television ad in advance of the release of its latest game, "Ultimate Hockey." As Cyber Video's director of marketing, you would like to assess the ad's effectiveness, so you ask your market research team to survey video game players. The results of its survey of 2000 video game players are summarized in the following table:

	Saw Ad	Did Not See Ad	Total
Purchased Game	100	200	300
Did Not Purchase Game	200	1,500	1,700
Total	300	1,700	2,000

The market research team concludes in its report that the ad is highly persuasive, and recommends using the company that produced the ad for future projects.

But wait, how could the ad possibly have been persuasive? Only 100 people who saw the ad purchased the game, while 200 people purchased the game without seeing the ad at all! At first glance, it looks as though potential customers are being *put off* by the ad. But let us analyze the figures a little more carefully.

First, let us restrict attention to those players who saw the ad (first column of data: "Saw Ad") and compute the estimated probability that a player *who saw the ad* purchased Ultimate Hockey.

	Saw Ad
Purchased Game	100
Did Not Purchase Game	200
Total	300

To compute this probability, we calculate

Probability that someone who saw the ad purchased the game

$$= \frac{\text{Number of people who saw the ad and bought the game}}{\text{Total number of people who saw the ad}} = \frac{100}{300} \approx .33.$$

In other words, 33% of game players who saw the ad went ahead and purchased the game. Let us compare this with the corresponding probability for those players who did *not* see the ad (second column of data "Did Not See Ad"):

	Did Not See Ad
Purchased Game	200
Did Not Purchase Game	1,500
Total	1,700

Probability that someone who did not see the ad purchased the game

$$= \frac{\text{Number of people who did not see the ad and bought the game}}{\text{Total number of people who did not see the ad}} = \frac{200}{1,700} \approx .12.$$

In other words, only 12% of game players who did not see the ad purchased the game, whereas 33% of those who *did* see the ad purchased the game. Thus, it appears that the ad *was* highly persuasive.

Here's some terminology. In this example there were two related events of importance:

A: A video game player purchased Ultimate Hockey.

B: A video game player saw the ad.

The first probability we computed was the estimated probability that a video game player purchased Ultimate Hockey *given that* he or she saw the ad. We call the latter probability the (estimated) **probability of *A*, given *B***, and we write it as $P(A \mid B)$. We call $P(A \mid B)$ a **conditional probability**—it is the probability of *A* under the condition that B occurred. Put another way, it is the probability of A occurring if the sample space is reduced to just those outcomes in B.

$$P(\text{Purchased game } given \ that \text{ saw the ad}) = P(A \mid B) \approx .33$$

The second probability we computed was the estimated probability that a video game player purchased Ultimate Hockey *given that* he or she did not see the ad, or the **probability of A, given B'**.

$$P(\text{Purchased game } given \ that \text{ did not see the ad}) = P(A \mid B') \approx .12$$

Calculating Conditional Probabilities

How do we calculate conditional probabilities? In the example above we used the ratio

$$P(A \mid B) = \frac{\text{Number of people who saw the ad and bought the game}}{\text{Total number of people who saw the ad}}.$$

The numerator is the frequency of $A \cap B$, and the denominator is the frequency of B:

$$P(A \mid B) = \frac{fr(A \cap B)}{fr(B)}.$$

Now, we can write this formula in another way:

$$P(A \mid B) = \frac{fr(A \cap B)}{fr(B)} = \frac{fr(A \cap B)/N}{fr(B)/N} = \frac{P(A \cap B)}{P(B)}.$$

We therefore have the following definition, which applies to general probability distributions.

Conditional Probability

If A and B are events with $P(B) \neq 0$, then the probability of A given B is

$$P(A \mid B) = \frac{P(A \cap B)}{P(B)}.$$

Visualizing Conditional Probability
In the figure, $P(A \mid B)$ is represented by the fraction of B that is covered by A.

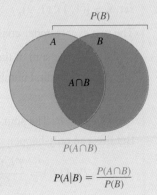

$$P(A|B) = \frac{P(A \cap B)}{P(B)}$$

Quick Examples

1. If there is a 50% chance of rain (R) and a 10% chance of both rain and lightning (L), then the probability of lightning, given that it rains, is

$$P(L \mid R) = \frac{P(L \cap R)}{P(R)} = \frac{.10}{.50} = .20.$$

Here are two more ways to express the result:

- If it rains, the probability of lightning is .20.
- Assuming that it rains, there is a 20% chance of lightning.

2. Referring to the Cyber Video data at the beginning of this section, the probability that a video game player did not purchase the game (A'), given that she did not see the ad (B'), is

$$P(A' \mid B') = \frac{P(A' \cap B')}{P(B')} = \frac{1,500/2,000}{1,700/2,000} = \frac{15}{17} \approx .88.$$

Q : *Returning to the video game sales survey, how do we compute the* ordinary proba-bility *of A, not "given" anything?*

A : We look at the event A that a randomly chosen game player purchased Ultimate Hockey *regardless of whether or not he or she saw the ad.* In the "Purchased Game" row we see that a total of 300 people purchased the game out of a total of 2,000 surveyed. Thus, the (estimated) probability of A is

$$P(A) = \frac{fr(A)}{N} = \frac{300}{2,000} = .15.$$

We sometimes refer to $P(A)$ as the **unconditional** probability of A to distinguish it from conditional probabilities like $P(A|B)$ and $P(A|B')$.

Now, let's see some more examples involving conditional probabilities.

EXAMPLE 1 Dice

If you roll a fair die twice and observe the numbers that face up, find the probability that the sum of the numbers is 8, given that the first number is 3.

Solution We begin by recalling that the sample space when we roll a fair die twice is the set $S = \{(1, 1), (1, 2), \ldots, (6, 6)\}$ containing the 36 different equally likely outcomes.

The two events under consideration are

A: The sum of the numbers is 8.

B: The first number is 3.

We also need

$A \cap B$: The sum of the numbers is 8 and the first number is 3.

But this can only happen in one way: $A \cap B = \{(3, 5)\}$. From the formula, then,

$$P(A \mid B) = \frac{P(A \cap B)}{P(B)} = \frac{1/36}{6/36} = \frac{1}{6}.$$

➡ **Before we go on...** There is another way to think about Example 1. When we say that the first number is 3, we are restricting the sample space to the six outcomes (3, 1), (3, 2), . . . , (3, 6), all still equally likely. Of these six, only one has a sum of 8, so the probability of the sum being 8, given that the first number is 3, is 1/6. ■

Notes

1. Remember that, in the expression $P(A \mid B)$, A is the event whose probability you want, given that you know the event B has occurred.

2. From the formula, notice that $P(A \mid B)$ is not defined if $P(B) = 0$. Could $P(A \mid B)$ make any sense if the event B were impossible? ■

EXAMPLE 2 School and Work

A survey of the high school graduating class of 2007,* conducted by the Bureau of Labor Statistics, found that, if a graduate went on to college, there was a 36% chance that he or she would work at the same time. On the other hand, there was a 67% chance that a randomly selected graduate would go on to college. What is the probability that a graduate went to college and work at the same time?

Solution To understand what the question asks and what information is given, it is helpful to rephrase everything using the standard wording "*the probability that ___*" and "*the probability that ___ given that ___.*" Now we have, "The probability that a graduate worked, given that the graduate went on to college, equals .36. (See Figure 8.) The probability that a graduate went on to college is .67." The events in question are as follows:

> W: A high school graduate went on to work.
>
> C: A high school graduate went on to college.

From our rephrasing of the question we can write:

$$P(W \mid C) = .36. \qquad P(C) = .67. \qquad \text{Find } P(W \cap C).$$

The definition

$$P(W \mid C) = \frac{P(W \cap C)}{P(C)}$$

can be used to find $P(W \cap C)$:

$$P(W \cap C) = P(W \mid C)P(C)$$
$$= (.36)(.67) \approx .24.$$

Thus there is a 24% chance that a member of the high school graduating class of 2008 went on to college and work at the same time.

> If a graduate went on to college, there was a 36% chance that he or she would work.
>
> *Rephrase by filling in the blanks:*
>
> *The probability that_____ given that_____ equals____.*
>
> *The probability that* **a graduate worked,** *given that* **the graduate went on to college,** *equals* **.36.**
>
> P(Worked | Went to college) = .36
>
> **Figure 8**

---
*"College Enrollment and Work Activity of 2007 High School Graduates," U.S. Bureau of Labor Statistics, April 2008, available at www.bls.gov/schedule/archives/all_nr.htm.

The Multiplication Principle and Trees

In Example 2, we saw that the formula

$$P(A \mid B) = \frac{P(A \cap B)}{P(B)}$$

can be used to calculate $P(A \cap B)$ if we rewrite the formula in the following form, known as the **multiplication principle for conditional probability**:

Multiplication Principle for Conditional Probability

If A and B are events, then

$$P(A \cap B) = P(A \mid B)P(B).$$

Quick Example

If there is a 50% chance of rain (R) and a 20% chance of a lightning (L) if it rains, then the probability of both rain and lightning is

$$P(R \cap L) = P(L \mid R)P(R) = (.20)(.50) = .10.$$

The multiplication principle is often used in conjunction with **tree diagrams**. Let's return to Cyber Video Games, Inc., and its television ad campaign. Its marketing survey was concerned with the following events:

   A: A video game player purchased Ultimate Hockey.

   B: A video game player saw the ad.

We can illustrate the various possibilities by means of the two-stage "tree" shown in Figure 9.

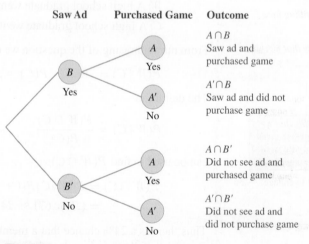

Figure 9

Consider the outcome $A \cap B$. To get there from the starting position on the left, we must first travel up to the B node. (In other words, B must occur.) Then we must travel up the branch from the B node to the A node. We are now going to associate a probability with each branch of the tree: the probability of traveling along that branch *given that we have gotten to its beginning node*. For instance, the probability of traveling up the branch from the starting position to the B node is $P(B) = 300/2{,}000 = .15$ (see the data in the survey). The probability of going up the branch from the B node to the A node is the probability that A occurs, given that B has occurred. In other words, it is the *conditional* probability $P(A \mid B) \approx .33$. (We calculated this probability at the beginning of the section.) The probability of the outcome $A \cap B$ can then be computed using the multiplication principle:

$$P(A \cap B) = P(B)P(A \mid B) \approx (.15)(.33) \approx .05.$$

In other words, *to obtain the probability of the outcome $A \cap B$, we multiply the probabilities on the branches leading to that outcome* (Figure 10).

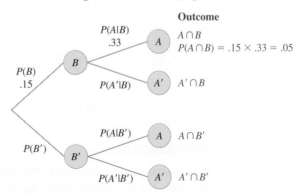

Figure 10

The same argument holds for the remaining three outcomes, and we can use the table given at the beginning of this section to calculate all the conditional probabilities shown in Figure 11.

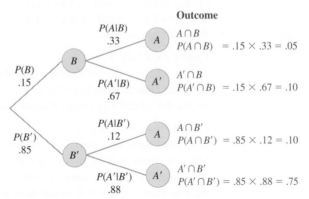

Figure 11

Note The sum of the probabilities on the branches leaving any node is always 1 (why?). This observation often speeds things up because after we have labeled one branch (or, all but one, if a node has more than two branches leaving it), we can easily label the remaining one. ■

EXAMPLE 3 Unfair Coins

An experiment consists of tossing two coins. The first coin is fair, while the second coin is twice as likely to land with heads facing up as it is with tails facing up. Draw a tree diagram to illustrate all the possible outcomes, and use the multiplication principle to compute the probabilities of all the outcomes.

Solution A quick calculation shows that the probability distribution for the second coin is $P(\text{H}) = 2/3$ and $P(\text{T}) = 1/3$. (How did we get that?) Figure 12 shows the tree diagram and the calculations of the probabilities of the outcomes.

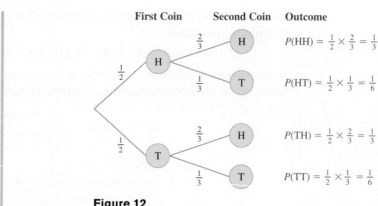

Figure 12

Independence

Let us go back once again to Cyber Video Games, Inc., and its ad campaign. How did we assess the ad's effectiveness? We considered the following events.

  A: A video game player purchased Ultimate Hockey.

  B: A video game player saw the ad.

We used the survey data to calculate $P(A)$, the probability that a video game player purchased Ultimate Hockey, and $P(A \mid B)$, the probability that a video game player *who saw the ad* purchased Ultimate Hockey. When these probabilities are compared, one of three things can happen.

Case 1 $P(A \mid B) > P(A)$
This is what the survey data actually showed: A video game player was more likely to purchase Ultimate Hockey if he or she saw the ad. This indicates that the ad is effective; seeing the ad had a positive effect on a player's decision to purchase the game.

Case 2 $P(A \mid B) < P(A)$
If this had happened, then a video game player would have been *less* likely to purchase Ultimate Hockey if he or she saw the ad. This would have indicated that the ad had "backfired"; it had, for some reason, put potential customers off. In this case, just as in the first case, the event *B* would have had an effect—a negative one—on the event *A*.

Case 3 $P(A \mid B) = P(A)$
In this case seeing the ad would have had absolutely no effect on a potential customer's buying Ultimate Hockey. Put another way, the probability of *A* occurring *does not depend* on whether *B* occurred or not. We say in a case like this that the events *A* and *B* are **independent**.

  In general, we say that two events *A* and *B* are independent if $P(A \mid B) = P(A)$. When this happens, we have

$$P(A) = P(A \mid B) = \frac{P(A \cap B)}{P(B)}$$

so

$$P(A \cap B) = P(A)P(B).$$

✱ NOTE We shall only discuss the independence of two events in cases where their probabilities are both nonzero.

Conversely, if $P(A \cap B) = P(A)P(B)$, then, assuming $P(B) \neq 0$,✱ $P(A) = P(A \cap B)/P(B) = P(A \mid B)$. Thus, saying that $P(A) = P(A \mid B)$ is the same as saying that $P(A \cap B) = P(A)P(B)$. Also, we can switch *A* and *B* in this last formula and conclude that saying that $P(A \cap B) = P(A)P(B)$ is the same as saying that $P(B \mid A) = P(B)$.

Independent Events

The events A and B are **independent** if

$$P(A \cap B) = P(A)P(B).$$

Equivalent formulas (assuming neither A nor B is impossible) are

$$P(A \mid B) = P(A)$$

and $\quad P(B \mid A) = P(B).$

If two events A and B are not independent, then they are **dependent**.

The property $P(A \cap B) = P(A)P(B)$ can be extended to three or more independent events. If, for example, A, B, and C are three mutually independent events (that is, each one of them is independent of each of the other two and of their intersection), then, among other things,

$$P(A \cap B \cap C) = P(A)P(B)P(C).$$

To test for independence, calculate the three quantities $P(A)$, $P(B)$, and $P(A \cap B)$ separately, and then see if $P(A \cap B) = P(A) \cdot P(B)$.

Quick Examples

1. If A and B are independent, and if A has a probability of .2 and B has a probability of .3, then $A \cap B$ has a probability of $(.2)(.3) = .06$.

2. Let us assume that the phase of the moon has no effect on whether or not my newspaper is delivered. The probability of a full moon (M) on a randomly selected day is about .034, and the probability that my newspaper will be delivered (D) on the random day is .20. Therefore, the probability that it is a full moon and my paper is delivered is

$$P(M \cap D) = P(M)P(D) = (.034)(.20) = .0068.$$

Testing for Independence

To check whether two events A and B are independent, we compute $P(A)$, $P(B)$, and $P(A \cap B)$. If $P(A \cap B) = P(A)P(B)$, the events are independent; otherwise, they are dependent. Sometimes it is obvious that two events, by their nature, are independent, so a test is not necessary. For example, the event that a die you roll comes up 1 is clearly independent of whether or not a coin you toss comes up heads.

✱ **NOTE** Two numbers have the **same parity** if both are even or both are odd. Otherwise, they have **opposite parity**.

Quick Examples

1. Roll two distinguishable dice (one red, one green) and observe the numbers that face up.

   A: The red die is even; $P(A) = \dfrac{18}{36} = \dfrac{1}{2}.$

   B: The dice have the same parity*; $P(B) = \dfrac{18}{36} = \dfrac{1}{2}.$

   $A \cap B$: Both dice are even; $P(A \cap B) = \dfrac{9}{36} = \dfrac{1}{4}.$

   $P(A \cap B) = P(A)P(B)$, and so A and B are independent.

2. Roll two distinguishable dice and observe the numbers that face up.

A: The sum of the numbers is 6; $P(A) = \dfrac{5}{36}$.

B: Both numbers are odd; $P(B) = \dfrac{9}{36} = \dfrac{1}{4}$.

$A \cap B$: The sum is 6, and both are odd; $P(A \cap B) = \dfrac{3}{36} = \dfrac{1}{12}$.

$P(A \cap B) \neq P(A)P(B)$, and so A and B are dependent.

EXAMPLE 4 Weather Prediction

According to the weather service, there is a 50% chance of rain in New York and a 30% chance of rain in Honolulu. Assuming that New York's weather is independent of Honolulu's, find the probability that it will rain in at least one of these cities.

Solution We take A to be the event that it will rain in New York and B to be the event that it will rain in Honolulu. We are asked to find the probability of $A \cup B$, the event that it will rain in at least one of the two cities. We use the addition principle:

$$P(A \cup B) = P(A) + P(B) - P(A \cap B).$$

We know that $P(A) = .5$ and $P(B) = .3$. But what about $P(A \cap B)$? Because the events A and B are independent, we can compute

$$P(A \cap B) = P(A)P(B)$$
$$= (.5)(.3) = .15.$$

Thus,

$$P(A \cup B) = P(A) + P(B) - P(A \cap B)$$
$$= .5 + .3 - .15$$
$$= .65.$$

So, there is a 65% chance that it will rain either in New York or in Honolulu (or in both).

EXAMPLE 5 Roulette

You are playing roulette, and have decided to leave all 10 of your $1 chips on black for five consecutive rounds, hoping for a sequence of five blacks which, according to the rules, will leave you with $320. There is a 50% chance of black coming up on each spin, ignoring the complicating factor of zero or double zero. What is the probability that you will be successful?

Solution Because the roulette wheel has no memory, each spin is independent of the others. Thus, if A_1 is the event that black comes up the first time, A_2 the event that it comes up the second time, and so on, then

$$P(A_1 \cap A_2 \cap A_3 \cap A_4 \cap A_5) = P(A_1)P(A_2)P(A_3)P(A_4)P(A_5) = \left(\frac{1}{2}\right)^5 = \frac{1}{32}.$$

The next example is a version of a well known "brain teaser" that forces one to think carefully about conditional probability.

EXAMPLE 6 Legal Argument

A man was arrested for attempting to smuggle a bomb on board an airplane. During the subsequent trial, his lawyer claimed that, by means of a simple argument, she would prove beyond a shadow of a doubt that her client was not only innocent of any crime, but was in fact contributing to the safety of the other passengers on the flight. This was her eloquent argument: "Your Honor, first of all, my client had absolutely no intention of setting off the bomb. As the record clearly shows, the detonator was unarmed when he was apprehended. In addition—and your Honor is certainly aware of this—there is a small but definite possibility that there will be a bomb on any given flight. On the other hand, the chances of there being *two* bombs on a flight are so remote as to be negligible. There is in fact no record of this having *ever* occurred. Thus, because my client had already brought one bomb on board (with no intention of setting it off) and because we have seen that the chances of there being a second bomb on board were vanishingly remote, it follows that the flight was far safer as a result of his action! I rest my case." This argument was so elegant in its simplicity that the judge acquitted the defendant. Where is the flaw in the argument? (Think about this for a while before reading the solution.)

Solution The lawyer has cleverly confused the phrases "two bombs on board" and "a second bomb on board." To pinpoint the flaw, let us take B to be the event that there is one bomb on board a given flight, and let A be the event that there are two independent bombs on board. Let us assume for argument's sake that $P(B) = 1/1,000,000 = .000\,001$. Then the probability of the event A is

$$(.000\,001)(.000\,001) = .000\,000\,000\,001.$$

This *is* vanishingly small, as the lawyer contended. It was at this point that the lawyer used a clever maneuver: She assumed in concluding her argument that the probability of having two bombs on board was the same as the probability of having a *second* bomb on board. But to say that there is a *second* bomb on board is to imply that there already is one bomb on board. This is therefore a *conditional* event: the event that there are two bombs on board, *given that there is already one bomb on board*. Thus, the probability that there is a second bomb on board is the probability that there are two bombs on board, given that there is already one bomb on board, which is

$$P(A \mid B) = \frac{P(A \cap B)}{P(B)} = \frac{.000\,000\,000\,001}{.000\,001} = .000\,001.$$

In other words, it is the same as the probability of there being a single bomb on board to begin with! Thus the man's carrying the bomb onto the plane did not improve the flight's safety at all.*

✳ NOTE If we want to be picky, there was a *slight* decrease in the probability of a second bomb because there was one less seat for a potential second bomb bearer to occupy. In terms of our analysis, this is saying that the event of one passenger with a bomb and the event of a second passenger with a bomb are not completely independent.

FAQ

Probability of what given what?

Q : *How do I tell if a statement in an application is talking about conditional probability or unconditional probability? And if it is talking about conditional probability, how do I determine what to use as A and B in P(A|B)?*

A : Look carefully at the wording of the statement. If there is some kind of qualification or restriction to a smaller set than the entire sample space, then it is probably talking about conditional probability, as in the following examples:

60% of veterans vote Republican while 40% of the entire voting population vote Republican.

Here the sample space can be taken to be the entire voting population.

Reworded (see Example 2): *The probability of voting Republican (R) is 60% given that the person is a veteran (V); $P(R|V) = .60$, whereas the probability of voting Republican is .40: $P(R) = .40$.*

The likelihood of being injured if in an accident is 80% for a driver not wearing a seatbelt but it is 50% for all drivers.

Here, the sample space can be taken to be the set of drivers involved in an accident—these are the only drivers discussed.

Reworded: *The probability of a driver being injured (I) is .80 given that the driver is not wearing a seatbelt (B); $P(I|B) = .80$ whereas, for all drivers, the probability of being injured is .50: $P(I) = .50$.*

7.5 EXERCISES

▼ more advanced   ◆ challenging

T indicates exercises that should be solved using technology

In Exercises 1–10, compute the indicated quantity.

1. $P(B) = .5$, $P(A \cap B) = .2$. Find $P(A | B)$.

2. $P(B) = .6$, $P(A \cap B) = .3$. Find $P(A | B)$.

3. $P(A | B) = .2$, $P(B) = .4$. Find $P(A \cap B)$.

4. $P(A | B) = .1$, $P(B) = .5$. Find $P(A \cap B)$.

5. $P(A | B) = .4$, $P(A \cap B) = .3$. Find $P(B)$.

6. $P(A | B) = .4$, $P(A \cap B) = .1$. Find $P(B)$.

7. $P(A) = .5$, $P(B) = .4$. A and B are independent. Find $P(A \cap B)$.

8. $P(A) = .2$, $P(B) = .2$. A and B are independent. Find $P(A \cap B)$.

9. $P(A) = .5$, $P(B) = .4$. A and B are independent. Find $P(A | B)$.

10. $P(A) = .3$, $P(B) = .6$. A and B are independent. Find $P(B | A)$.

In Exercises 11–14, supply the missing quantities.

11.

Outcome

$P(A \cap C) = \underline{\quad}$

$P(A \cap D) = \underline{\quad}$

$\underline{\quad} = \underline{\quad}$

$\underline{\quad} = \underline{\quad}$

12.

Outcome

$P(A \cap C) = \underline{\quad}$

$\underline{\quad} = \underline{\quad}$

$P(B \cap C) = \underline{\quad}$

$\underline{\quad} = \underline{\quad}$

13.

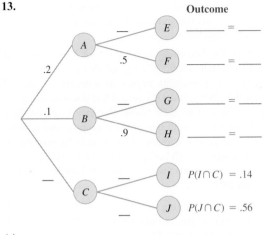

Outcome

$P(I \cap C) = .14$
$P(J \cap C) = .56$

14.

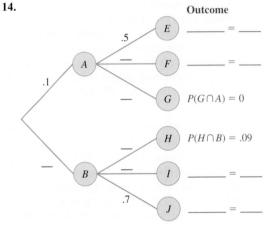

Outcome

$P(G \cap A) = 0$
$P(H \cap B) = .09$

In Exercises 15–20, find the conditional probabilities of the indicated events when two fair dice (one red and one green) are rolled. HINT [See Example 1.]

15. The sum is 5, given that the green one is not a 1.

16. The sum is 6, given that the green one is either 4 or 3.

17. The red one is 5, given that the sum is 6.

18. The red one is 4, given that the green one is 4.

19. The sum is 5, given that the dice have opposite parity.

20. The sum is 6, given that the dice have opposite parity.

Exercises 21–26 require the use of counting techniques from the last chapter. A bag contains three red marbles, two green ones, one fluorescent pink one, two yellow ones, and two orange ones. Suzan grabs four at random. Find the probabilities of the indicated events.

21. She gets all the red ones, given that she gets the fluorescent pink one.

22. She gets all the red ones, given that she does not get the fluorescent pink one.

23. She gets none of the red ones, given that she gets the fluorescent pink one.

24. She gets one of each color other than fluorescent pink, given that she gets the fluorescent pink one.

25. She gets one of each color other than fluorescent pink, given that she gets at least one red one.

26. She gets at least two red ones, given that she gets at least one green one.

In Exercises 27–30, say whether the given pairs of events are independent, mutually exclusive, or neither.

27. *A*: Your new skateboard design is a success.
   B: Your new skateboard design is a failure.

28. *A*: Your new skateboard design is a success.
   B: There is life in the Andromeda galaxy.

29. *A*: Your new skateboard design is a success.
   B: Your competitor's new skateboard design is a failure.

30. *A*: Your first coin flip results in heads.
   B: Your second coin flip results in heads.

In Exercises 31–36, two dice (one red and one green) are rolled, and the numbers that face up are observed. Test the given pairs of events for independence. HINT [See Quick Example on Testing for Independence, page 503.]

31. *A*: The red die is 1, 2, or 3; *B*: The green die is even.

32. *A*: The red die is 1; *B*: The sum is even.

33. *A*: Exactly one die is 1; *B*: The sum is even.

34. *A*: Neither die is 1 or 6; *B*: The sum is even.

35. *A*: Neither die is 1; *B*: Exactly one die is 2.

36. *A*: Both dice are 1; *B*: Neither die is 2.

37. If a coin is tossed 11 times, find the probability of the sequence H, T, T, H, H, H, T, H, H, T, T. HINT [See Example 5.]

38. If a die is rolled four times, find the probability of the sequence 4, 3, 2, 1. HINT [See Example 5.]

In Exercises 39–44, fill in the blanks using the named events. HINT [See Example 2 and also the FAQ on page 506.]

39. 10% of all Anchovians detest anchovies (*D*), whereas 30% of all married Anchovians (*M*) detest them. $P(\_\_) = \_\_$; $P(\_\_ | \_\_) = \_\_$

40. 95% of all music composers can read music (*M*), whereas 99% of all classical music composers (*C*) can read music. $P(\_\_) = \_\_$; $P(\_\_ | \_\_) = \_\_$

41. 30% of all lawyers who lost clients (*L*) were antitrust lawyers (*A*), whereas 10% of all antitrust lawyers lost clients. $P(\_\_ | \_\_) = \_\_$; $P(\_\_ | \_\_) = \_\_$

42. 2% of all items bought on my auction site (B) were works of art (A), whereas only 1% of all works of art on the site were bought. $P(\_\_ \mid \_\_) = \_\_$; $P(\_\_ \mid \_\_) = \_\_$

43. 55% of those who go out in the midday sun (M) are English-men (E) whereas only 5% of those who do not go out in the midday sun are Englishmen. $P(\_\_ \mid \_\_) = \_\_$; $P(\_\_ \mid \_\_) = \_\_$

44. 80% of those who have a Mac now (M) will purchase a Mac next time (X) whereas 20% of those who do not have a Mac now will purchase a Mac next time. $P(\_\_ \mid \_\_) = \_\_$; $P(\_\_ \mid \_\_) = \_\_$

APPLICATIONS

45. *Personal Bankruptcy* In 2004, the probability that a person in the United States would declare personal bankruptcy was .006. The probability that a person in the United States would declare personal bankruptcy and had recently experienced a "big three" event (loss of job, medical problem, or divorce or separation) was .005.[42] What was the probability that a person had recently experienced one of the "big three" events, given that she had declared personal bankruptcy? (Round your an-swer to one decimal place.)

46. *Personal Bankruptcy* In 2004, the probability that a person in the United States would declare personal bankruptcy was .006. The probability that a person in the United States would declare personal bankruptcy and had recently overspent credit cards was .0004.[43] What was the probability that a person had recently overspent credit cards given that he had declared per-sonal bankruptcy?

47. *Listings on* **eBay** During 2008, approximately 2,750 million new listings were posted worldwide on **eBay**, of which 1,130 million were in the United States. A total of 730 million of the worldwide new listings, including 275 million in the United States, were posted during the fourth quarter of 2008.[44]

   a. Find the probability that a new listing on **eBay** was in the United States, given that the item was posted during the fourth quarter.

   b. Find the probability that a new listing on **eBay** was posted in the fourth quarter, given that the item was posted in the United States.

48. *Listings on* **eBay** Refer to the data given in Exercise 41.

   a. Find the probability that a new listing on **eBay** was outside the United States, given that the item was posted during the fourth quarter.

   b. Find the probability that a new listing on **eBay** was posted in the fourth quarter, given that the item was posted out-side the United States.

49. *Social Security* According to a *New York Times*/CBS poll released in March, 2005, 79% agreed that it should be the government's responsibility to provide a decent standard of living for the elderly, and 43% agreed that it would be a good idea to invest part of their Social Security taxes on their own.[45] If agreement with one of these propositions is inde-pendent of agreement with the other, what is the probability that a person agreed with both propositions? (Round your an-swer to two decimal places.) HINT [See Quick Examples on Indepen-dence on page 503.]

50. *Social Security* According to the *New York Times*/CBS poll of March, 2005, referred to in Exercise 43, 49% agreed that Social Security taxes should be raised if necessary to keep the system afloat, and 43% agreed that it would be a good idea to invest part of their Social Security taxes on their own.[46] If agreement with one of these propositions is inde-pendent of agreement with the other, what is the probability that a person agreed with both propositions? (Round your answer to two decimal places.) HINT [See Quick Examples on Inde-pendence on page 503.]

51. *Marketing* A market survey shows that 40% of the population used Brand X laundry detergent last year, 5% of the popula-tion gave up doing its laundry last year, and 4% of the popu-lation used Brand X and then gave up doing laundry last year. Are the events of using Brand X and giving up doing laundry independent? Is a user of Brand X detergent more or less likely to give up doing laundry than a randomly chosen person?

52. *Marketing* A market survey shows that 60% of the population used Brand Z computers last year, 5% of the population quit their jobs last year, and 3% of the population used Brand Z computers and then quit their jobs. Are the events of using Brand Z computers and quitting your job independent? Is a user of Brand Z computers more or less likely to quit a job than a randomly chosen person?

53. *Road Safety* In 1999, the probability that a randomly selected vehicle would be involved in a deadly tire-related accident was approximately 3×10^{-6}, whereas the probability that a tire-related accident would prove deadly was .02.[47] What was the probability that a vehicle would be involved in a tire-related accident?

---

[42] Probabilities are approximate. Source: *New York Times*, March 13, 2005, p, WK3.

[43] Ibid. The .0004 figure is an estimate by the authors.

[44] Source: http://news.ebay.com/about.cfm.

[45] Source: *New York Times*, March 3, 2005, p. A20.

[46] Ibid.

[47] The original data reported three tire-related deaths per million vehicles. Source: *New York Times* analysis of National Traffic Safety Administration crash data/Polk Company vehicle registration data/ *New York Times*, Nov. 22, 2000, p. C5.

54. *Road Safety* In 1998, the probability that a randomly selected vehicle would be involved in a deadly tire-related accident was approximately 2.8×10^{-6}, while the probability that a tire-related accident would prove deadly was .016.[48] What was the probability that a vehicle would be involved in a tire-related accident?

Publishing *Exercises 55–62 are based on the following table, which shows the results of a survey of 100 authors by a publishing company.*

	New Authors	Established Authors	Total
Successful	5	25	30
Unsuccessful	15	55	70
Total	20	80	100

Compute the following conditional probabilities:

55. An author is established, given that she is successful.

56. An author is successful, given that he is established.

57. An author is unsuccessful, given that he is a new author.

58. An author is a new author, given that she is unsuccessful.

59. An author is unsuccessful, given that she is established.

60. An author is established, given that he is unsuccessful.

61. An unsuccessful author is established.

62. An established author is successful.

In Exercises 63–68, draw an appropriate tree diagram and use the multiplication principle to calculate the probabilities of all the outcomes. HINT [See Example 3.]

63. *Sales* Each day, there is a 40% chance that you will sell an automobile. You know that 30% of all the automobiles you sell are two-door models, and the rest are four-door models.

64. *Product Reliability* You purchase Brand X floppy discs one quarter of the time and Brand Y floppies the rest of the time. Brand X floppy discs have a 1% failure rate, while Brand Y floppy discs have a 3% failure rate.

65. *Car Rentals* Your auto rental company rents out 30 small cars, 24 luxury sedans, and 46 slightly damaged "budget" vehicles. The small cars break down 14% of the time, the luxury sedans break down 8% of the time, and the "budget" cars break down 40% of the time.

66. *Travel* It appears that there is only a one in five chance that you will be able to take your spring vacation to the Greek Islands. If you are lucky enough to go, you will visit either Corfu (20% chance) or Rhodes. On Rhodes, there is a 20% chance of meeting a tall dark stranger, while on Corfu, there is no such chance.

67. *Weather Prediction* There is a 50% chance of rain today and a 50% chance of rain tomorrow. Assuming that the event that it rains today is independent of the event that it rains tomorrow, draw a tree diagram showing the probabilities of all outcomes. What is the probability that there will be no rain today or tomorrow?

68. *Weather Prediction* There is a 20% chance of snow today and a 20% chance of snow tomorrow. Assuming that the event that it snows today is independent of the event that it snows tomorrow, draw a tree diagram showing the probabilities of all outcomes. What is the probability that it will snow by the end of tomorrow?

Education and Employment *Exercises 69–78 are based on the following table, which shows U.S. employment figures for 2007, broken down by educational attainment.[49] All numbers are in millions, and represent civilians aged 25 years and over. Those classed as "not in labor force" were not employed nor actively seeking employment. Round all answers to two decimal places.*

	Employed	Unemployed	Not in Labor Force	Total
Less Than High School Diploma	11.5	1.6	14.2	27.3
High School Diploma Only	36.9	1.7	22.4	61.0
Some College or Associate's Degree	34.6	1.3	14.0	49.9
Bachelor's Degree or Higher	44.1	0.9	12.1	57.1
Total	127.1	5.5	62.7	195.3

69. Find the probability that a person was employed, given that the person had a bachelor's degree or higher.

70. Find the probability that a person was employed, given that the person had attained less than a high school diploma.

71. Find the probability that a person had a bachelor's degree or higher, given that the person was employed.

72. Find the probability that a person had attained less than a high school diploma, given that the person was employed.

73. ▼ Find the probability that a person who had not completed a bachelor's degree or higher was not in the labor force.

74. ▼ Find the probability that a person who had completed at least a high school diploma was not in the labor force.

75. ▼ Find the probability that a person who had completed a bachelor's degree or higher and was in the labor force was employed.

---

[48] The original data reported 2.8 tire-related deaths per million vehicles. Source: Ibid.

[49] Source: Bureau of Labor Statistics (www.bls.gov/).

76. ▼ Find the probability that a person who had completed less than a high school diploma and was in the labor force was employed.

77. ▼ Your friend claims that an unemployed person is more likely to have a high school diploma only than an employed person. Respond to this claim by citing actual probabilities.

78. ▼ Your friend claims that a person not in the labor force is more likely to have less than a high school diploma than an employed person. Respond to this claim by citing actual probabilities.

79. ▼ *Airbag Safety* According to a study conducted by the Harvard School of Public Health, a child seated in the front seat who was wearing a seatbelt was 31% more likely to be killed in an accident if the car had an air bag that deployed than if it did not.[50] Let the sample space S be the set of all accidents involving a child seated in the front seat wearing a seatbelt. Let K be the event that the child was killed and let D be the event that the airbag deployed. Fill in the missing terms and quantities: $P(\_\_ \mid \_\_) = \_\_ \times P(\_\_ \mid \_\_)$. HINT [When we say "A is 31% more likely than B" we mean that the probability of A is 1.31 times the probability of B.]

80. ▼ *Airbag Safety* According to the study cited in Exercise 73, a child seated in the front seat not wearing a seatbelt was 84% more likely to be killed in an accident if the car had an air bag that deployed than if it did not.[51] Let the sample space S be the set of all accidents involving a child seated in the front seat not wearing a seatbelt. Fill in the missing terms and quantities: $P(\_\_ \mid \_\_) = \_\_ \times P(\_\_ \mid \_\_)$. HINT [When we say "A is 84% more likely than B" we mean that the probability of A is 1.84 times the probability of B.]

81. ▼ *Productivity* A company wishes to enhance productivity by running a one-week training course for its employees. Let T be the event that an employee participated in the course, and let I be the event that an employee's productivity improved the week after the course was run.

   a. Assuming that the course has a positive effect on productivity, how are $P(I \mid T)$ and $P(I)$ related?
   b. If T and I are independent, what can one conclude about the training course?

82. ▼ *Productivity* Consider the events T and I in the preceding exercise.

   a. Assuming that everyone who improved took the course but that not everyone took the course, how are $P(T \mid I)$ and $P(T)$ related?
   b. If half the employees who improved took the course and half the employees took the course, are T and I independent?

83. ▼ *Internet Use in 2000* The following pie chart shows the percentage of the population that used the Internet in 2000, broken down further by family income, and based on a survey taken in August 2000.[52]

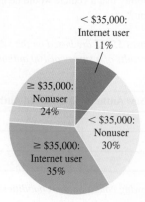

   a. Determine the probability that a randomly chosen person was an Internet user, given that his or her family income was at least $35,000.
   b. Based on the data, was a person more likely to be an Internet user if his or her family income was less than $35,000 or $35,000 or more? (Support your answer by citing the relevant conditional probabilities.)

84. ▼ *Internet Use in 2001* Repeat Exercise 77 using the following pie chart, which shows the results of a similar survey taken in September 2001.[53]

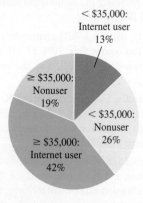

---

[50] The study was conducted by Dr. Segul-Gomez at the Harvard School of Public Health. Source: *New York Times*, December 1, 2000, p. F1.
[51] Ibid.

[52] Source: *Falling Through the Net: Toward Digital Inclusion, A Report on Americans' Access to Technology Tools*, U.S. Department of Commerce, October, 2000. Available at www.ntia.doc.gov/ntiahome/fttn00/contents00.html.

[53] Source: *A Nation Online: How Americans Are Expanding Their Use of the Internet*, U.S. Department of Commerce, February, 2002. Available at www.ntia.doc.gov/ntiahome/dn/index.html.

Auto Theft Exercises 85–90 are based on the following table, which shows the probability that an owner of the given model would report his or her vehicle stolen in a one-year period.[54]

Brand	Jeep Wrangler	Suzuki Sidekick (two-door)	Toyota Land Cruiser	Geo Tracker (two-door)	Acura Integra (two-door)
Probability	.0170	.0154	.0143	.0142	.0123
Brand	Mitsubishi Montero	Acura Integra (four-door)	BMW 3-series (two-door)	Lexus GS300	Honda Accord (two-door)
Probability	.0108	.0103	.0077	.0074	.0070

In an experiment in which a vehicle is selected, consider the following events:

    R: The vehicle was reported stolen.
    J: The vehicle was a Jeep Wrangler.
    A2: The vehicle was an Acura Integra (two-door).
    A4: The vehicle was an Acura Integra (four-door).
    A: The vehicle was an Acura Integra (either two-door or four-door).

85. ▼ Fill in the blanks: $P(\_\_\_ \mid \_\_\_) = .0170$.

86. ▼ Fill in the blanks: $P(\_\_\_ \mid A4) = \_\_\_$.

87. ▼ Which of the following is true?

  (A) There is a 1.43% chance that a vehicle reported stolen was a Toyota Land Cruiser.
  (B) Of all the vehicles reported stolen, 1.43% of them were Toyota Land Cruisers.
  (C) Given that a vehicle was reported stolen, there is a .0143 probability that it was a Toyota Land Cruiser.
  (D) Given that a vehicle was a Toyota Land Cruiser, there was a 1.43% chance that it was reported stolen.

88. ▼ Which of the following is true?

  (A) $P(R \mid A) = .0123 + .0103 = .0226$.
  (B) $P(R' \mid A2) = 1 - .0123 = .9877$.
  (C) $P(A2 \mid A) = .0123/(.0123 + .0103) \approx .544$.
  (D) $P(R \mid A2') = 1 - .0123 = .9877$.

89. ▼ It is now January, and I own a BMW 3-series and a Lexus GS300. Because I house my vehicles in different places, the event that one of my vehicles gets stolen does not depend on the event that the other gets stolen. Compute each probability to six decimal places.

  a. Both my vehicles will get stolen this year.
  b. At least one of my vehicles will get stolen this year.

90. ▼ It is now December, and I own a Mitsubishi Montero and a Jeep Wrangler. Because I house my vehicles in different places, the event that one of my vehicles gets stolen does not depend on the event that the other gets stolen. I have just returned from a one-year trip to the Swiss Alps.

  a. What is the probability that my Montero, but not my Wrangler, has been stolen?

  b. Which is more likely: the event that my Montero was stolen or the event that *only* my Montero was stolen?

91. ▼ *Drug Tests* If 90% of the athletes who test positive for steroids in fact use them, and 10% of all athletes use steroids and test positive, what percentage of athletes test positive?

92. ▼ *Fitness Tests* If 80% of candidates for the soccer team pass the fitness test, and only 20% of all athletes are soccer team candidates who pass the test, what percentage of the athletes are candidates for the soccer team?

93. ▼ *Food Safety* According to a University of Maryland study of 200 samples of ground meats,[55] the probability that a sample was contaminated by salmonella was .20. The probability that a salmonella-contaminated sample was contaminated by a strain resistant to at least three antibiotics was .53. What was the probability that a ground meat sample was contaminated by a strain of salmonella resistant to at least three antibiotics?

94. ▼ *Food Safety* According to the study mentioned in Exercise 87,[56] the probability that a ground meat sample was contaminated by salmonella was .20. The probability that a salmonella-contaminated sample was contaminated by a strain resistant to at least one antibiotic was .84. What was the probability that a ground meat sample was contaminated by a strain of salmonella resistant to at least one antibiotic?

95. ◆ *Food Safety* According to a University of Maryland study of 200 samples of ground meats,[57] the probability that one of the samples was contaminated by salmonella was .20. The probability that a salmonella-contaminated sample was contaminated by a strain resistant to at least one antibiotic was .84, and the probability that a salmonella-contaminated sample was contaminated by a strain resistant to at least three antibiotics was .53. Find the probability that a ground meat sample that was contaminated by an antibiotic-resistant strain was contaminated by a strain resistant to at least three antibiotics.

96. ◆ *Food Safety* According to a University of Maryland study of 200 samples of ground meats,[58] the probability that a ground meat sample was contaminated by a strain of

---

[54] Data are for insured vehicles, for 1995 to 1997 models except Wrangler, which is for 1997 models only. Source: Highway Loss Data Institute/*The New York Times*, March 28, 1999, p. WK3.

[55] As cited in the *New York Times*, October 16, 2001, p. A12.

[56] Ibid.

[57] Ibid.

[58] Ibid.

salmonella resistant to at least three antibiotics was .11. The probability that someone infected with any strain of salmonella will become seriously ill is .10. What is the probability that someone eating a randomly-chosen ground meat sample will not become seriously ill with a strain of salmonella resistant to at least three antibiotics?

COMMUNICATION AND REASONING EXERCISES

97. Name three events, each independent of the others, when a fair coin is tossed four times.

98. Name three pairs of independent events when a pair of distinguishable and fair dice is rolled and the numbers that face up are observed.

99. You wish to ascertain the probability of an event E, but you happen to know that the event F has occurred. Is the probability you are seeking $P(E)$ or $P(E|F)$? Give the reason for your answer.

100. Your television advertising campaign seems to have been very persuasive: 10,000 people who saw the ad purchased your product, while only 2,000 people purchased the product without seeing the ad. Explain how additional data could show that your ad campaign was, in fact, unpersuasive.

101. You are having trouble persuading your friend Iliana that conditional probability is different from unconditional prob-

ability. She just said: "Look here, Saul, the probability of throwing a double-six is 1/36, and that's that! That probability is not affected by anything, including the 'given' that the sum is larger than 7." How do you persuade her otherwise?

102. Your other friend Giuseppe is spreading rumors that the conditional probability $P(E|F)$ is always bigger than $P(E)$. Is he right? (If he is, explain why; if not, give an example to prove him wrong.)

103. ▼ If $A \subseteq B$ and $P(B) \neq 0$, why is $P(A \mid B) = \dfrac{P(A)}{P(B)}$?

104. ▼ If $B \subseteq A$ and $P(B) \neq 0$, why is $P(A \mid B) = 1$?

105. ▼ Your best friend thinks that it is impossible for two mutually exclusive events with nonzero probabilities to be independent. Establish whether or not he is correct.

106. ▼ Another of your friends thinks that two mutually exclusive events with nonzero probabilities can never be dependent. Establish whether or not she is correct.

107. ◆ Show that if A and B are independent, then so are A' and B' (assuming none of these events has zero probability). [Hint: $A' \cap B'$ is the complement of $A \cup B$.]

108. ◆ Show that if A and B are independent, then so are A and B' (assuming none of these events has zero probability). [Hint: $P(B' \mid A) + P(B \mid A) = 1$.]

7.6 Bayes' Theorem and Applications

Should schools test their athletes for drug use? A problem with drug testing is that there are always false positive results, so one can never be certain that an athlete who tests positive is in fact using drugs. Here is a typical scenario.

EXAMPLE 1 Steroids Testing

Gamma Chemicals advertises its anabolic steroid detection test as being 95% effective at detecting steroid use, meaning that it will show a positive result on 95% of all anabolic steroid users. It also states that its test has a false positive rate of 6%. This means that the probability of a nonuser testing positive is .06. Estimating that about 10% of its athletes are using anabolic steroids, Enormous State University (ESU) begins testing its football players. The quarterback, Hugo V. Huge, tests positive and is promptly dropped from the team. Hugo claims that he is not using anabolic steroids. How confident can we be that he is not telling the truth?

Solution There are two events of interest here: the event T that a person tests positive, and the event A that the person tested uses anabolic steroids. Here are the probabilities we are given:

$$P(T \mid A) = .95$$
$$P(T \mid A') = .06$$
$$P(A) = .10$$

We are asked to find $P(A \mid T)$, the probability that someone who tests positive is using anabolic steroids. We can use a tree diagram to calculate $P(A \mid T)$. The trick to setting up the tree diagram is to use as the first branching the events with *unconditional* probabilities we know. Because the only unconditional probability we are given is $P(A)$, we use A and A' as our first branching (Figure 13).

Figure 13

For the second branching, we use the outcomes of the drug test: positive (T) or negative (T'). The probabilities on these branches are conditional probabilities because they depend on whether or not an athlete uses steroids. (See Figure 14.) (We fill in the probabilities that are not supplied by remembering that the sum of the probabilities on the branches leaving any node must be 1.)

Figure 14

We can now calculate the probability we are asked to find:

$$P(A \mid T) = \frac{P(A \cap T)}{P(T)} = \frac{P(\text{Uses anabolic steroids and tests positive})}{P(\text{Tests positive})}$$

$$= \frac{P(\text{Using } A \text{ and } T \text{ branches})}{\text{Sum of } P(\text{Using branches ending in } T)}.$$

From the tree diagram, we see that $P(A \cap T) = .095$. To calculate $P(T)$, the probability of testing positive, notice that there are two outcomes on the tree diagram that reflect a positive test result. The probabilities of these events are .095 and .054. Because these two events are mutually exclusive (an athlete either uses steroids or does not, but not both), the probability of a test being positive (ignoring whether or not steroids are used) is the sum of these probabilities, .149. Thus,

$$P(A \mid T) = \frac{.095}{.095 + .054} = \frac{.095}{.149} \approx .64.$$

Thus there is a 64% chance that a randomly selected athlete who tests positive, like Hugo, is using steroids. In other words, we can be 64% confident that Hugo is lying.

➡ **Before we go on...** Note that the correct answer in Example 1 is 64%, *not* the 94% we might suspect from the test's false positive rating. In fact, we can't answer the question asked without knowing the percentage of athletes who actually use steroids. For instance, if *no* athletes at all use steroids, then Hugo must be telling the truth, and so the test result has no significance whatsoever. On the other hand, if *all* athletes use steroids, then Hugo is definitely lying, regardless of the outcome of the test.

False positive rates are determined by testing a large number of samples known not to contain drugs and computing estimated probabilities. False negative rates are computed similarly by testing samples known to contain drugs. However, the accuracy of the tests depends also on the skill of those administering them. False positives were a significant problem when drug testing started to become common, with estimates of false positive rates for common immunoassay tests ranging from 10–30% on the high end,[59] but the accuracy has improved since then. Because of the possibility of false positive results, positive immunoassay tests need to be confirmed by the more expensive and much more reliable gas chromatograph/mass spectrometry (GC/MS) test. See also the NCAA's Drug-Testing Program Handbook, available at www.ncaa.org/. (The section on Institutional Drug Testing addresses the problem of false positives.) ■

Bayes' Theorem

The calculation we used to answer the question in Example 1 can be recast as a formula known as **Bayes' theorem**. Figure 15 shows a general form of the tree we used in Example 1.

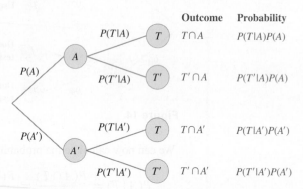

Figure 15

We first calculated

$$P(A \mid T) = \frac{P(A \cap T)}{P(T)}$$

as follows. We first calculated the numerator $P(A \cap T)$ using the multiplication principle:

$$P(A \cap T) = P(T \mid A)P(A).$$

We then calculated the denominator $P(T)$ by using the addition principle for mutually exclusive events together with the multiplication principle:

$$P(T) = P(A \cap T) + P(A' \cap T)$$
$$= P(T \mid A)P(A) + P(T \mid A')P(A').$$

---

[59] *Drug Testing in the Workplace*, ACLU Briefing Paper, 1996.

Substituting gives

$$P(A \mid T) = \frac{P(T \mid A)P(A)}{P(T \mid A)P(A) + P(T \mid A')P(A')}.$$

This is the short form of Bayes' theorem.

Bayes' Theorem (Short Form)

If A and T are events, then

Bayes' Formula

$$P(A \mid T) = \frac{P(T \mid A)P(A)}{P(T \mid A)P(A) + P(T \mid A')P(A')}.$$

Using a Tree

$$P(A \mid T) = \frac{P(\text{Using } A \text{ and } T \text{ branches})}{\text{Sum of } P(\text{Using branches ending in } T)}$$

Quick Example

Let us calculate the probability that an athlete from Example 1 who tests positive is actually using steroids if only 5% of ESU athletes are using steroids. Thus,

$$P(T \mid A) = .95$$
$$P(T \mid A') = .06$$
$$P(A) = .05$$
$$P(A') = .95$$

and so

$$P(A \mid T) = \frac{P(T \mid A)P(A)}{P(T \mid A)P(A) + P(T \mid A')P(A')} = \frac{(.95)(.05)}{(.95)(.05) + (.06)(.95)} \approx .45.$$

In other words, it is actually more likely that such an athlete does *not* use steroids than he does.[*]

---

* NOTE Without knowing the results of the test we would have said that there was a probability of $P(A) = 0.05$ that the athlete is using steroids. The positive test result raises the probability to $P(A \mid T) = 0.45$, but the test gives too many false positives for us to be any more certain than that that the athlete is actually using steroids.

Remembering the Formula

Although the formula looks complicated at first sight, it is not hard to remember if you notice the pattern. Or, you could re-derive it yourself by thinking of the tree diagram.

The next example illustrates that we can use either a tree diagram or the Bayes' theorem formula.

* NOTE The reason for this is that many people show physical signs of distress when asked accusatory questions. Many people are nervous around police officers even if they have done nothing wrong.

EXAMPLE 2 Lie Detectors

The Sherlock Lie Detector Company manufactures the latest in lie detectors, and the Count-Your-Pennies (CYP) store chain is eager to use them to screen their employees for theft. Sherlock's advertising claims that the test misses a lie only once in every 100 instances. On the other hand, an analysis by a consumer group reveals 20% of people who are telling the truth fail the test anyway.[*] The local police department estimates that 1 out of every 200 employees has engaged in theft. When the CYP store first screened its employees, the test indicated Mrs. Prudence V. Good was lying when she claimed that she had never stolen from CYP. What is the probability that she was lying and had in fact stolen from the store?

Solution We are asked for the probability that Mrs. Good was lying, and in the preceding sentence we are told that the lie detector test showed her to be lying. So, we are looking for a conditional probability: the probability that she is lying, given that the lie detector test is positive. Now we can start to give names to the events:

  L: A subject is lying.

  T: The test is positive (indicated that the subject was lying).

We are looking for $P(L \mid T)$. We know that 1 out of every 200 employees engages in theft; let us assume that no employee admits to theft while taking a lie detector test, so the probability $P(L)$ that a test subject is lying is $1/200$. We also know the false negative and false positive rates $P(T' \mid L)$ and $P(T \mid L')$.

Using a tree diagram
Figure 16 shows the tree diagram.

Figure 16

We see that

$$P(L \mid T) = \frac{P(\text{Using } L \text{ and } T \text{ branches})}{\text{Sum of } P(\text{Using branches ending in } T)}$$

$$= \frac{.00495}{.00495 + .199} \approx .024.$$

This means that there was only a 2.4% chance that poor Mrs. Good was lying and had stolen from the store!

Using Bayes' Theorem
We have

  $P(L) = .005$

  $P(T' \mid L) = .01$, from which we obtain

  $P(T \mid L) = .99$

  $P(T \mid L') = .2$

and so

$$P(L \mid T) = \frac{P(T \mid L)P(L)}{P(T \mid L)P(L) + P(T \mid L')P(L')} = \frac{(.99)(.005)}{(.99)(.005) + (.2)(.995)} \approx .024.$$

A and *A'* form a partition of *S*.

Figure 17

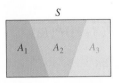

A_1, A_2, and A_3 form a partition of *S*.

Figure 18

Expanded Form of Bayes' Theorem

We have seen the "short form" of Bayes' theorem. What is the "long form?" To motivate an expanded form of Bayes' theorem, look again at the formula we've been using:

$$P(A \mid T) = \frac{P(T \mid A)P(A)}{P(T \mid A)P(A) + P(T \mid A')P(A')}.$$

The events A and A' form a **partition** of the sample space S; that is, their union is the whole of S and their intersection is empty (Figure 17).

The expanded form of Bayes' theorem applies to a partition of S into three or more events, as shown in Figure 18.

By saying that the events A_1, A_2, and A_3 form a partition of S, we mean that their union is the whole of S and the intersection of any two of them is empty, as in the figure. When we have a partition into three events as shown, the formula gives us $P(A_1 \mid T)$ in terms of $P(T \mid A_1)$, $P(T \mid A_2)$, $P(T \mid A_3)$, $P(A_1)$, $P(A_2)$, and $P(A_3)$.

Bayes' Theorem (Expanded Form)

If the events A_1, A_2, and A_3 form a partition of the sample space S, then

$$P(A_1 \mid T) = \frac{P(T \mid A_1)P(A_1)}{P(T \mid A_1)P(A_1) + P(T \mid A_2)P(A_2) + P(T \mid A_3)P(A_3)}$$

As for why this is true, and what happens when we have a partition into *four or more* events, we will wait for the exercises. In practice, as was the case with a partition into two events, we can often compute $P(A_1 \mid T)$ by constructing a tree diagram.

EXAMPLE 3 School and Work

A survey* conducted by the Bureau of Labor Statistics found that approximately 24% of the high school graduating class of 2007 went on to a two-year college, 43% went on to a four-year college, and the remaining 33% did not go on to college. Of those who went on to a two-year college, 49% worked at the same time, 28% of those going on to a four-year college worked, and 61% of those who did not go on to college worked. What percentage of those working had not gone on to college?

Solution We can interpret these percentages as probabilities if we consider the experiment of choosing a member of the high school graduating class of 2007 at random. The events we are interested in are these:

   R_1: A graduate went on to a two-year college.

   R_2: A graduate went on to a four-year college.

   R_3: A graduate did not go to college.

   A: A graduate went on to work.

---

*"College Enrollment and Work Activity of High School Graduates," U.S. Bureau of Labor Statistics (www.bls.gov/news.release/hsgec.htm).

The three events R_1, R_2, and R_3 partition the sample space of all graduates into three events. We are given the following probabilities:

$$P(R_1) = .24 \qquad P(R_2) = .43 \qquad P(R_3) = .33$$
$$P(A \mid R_1) = .49 \quad P(A \mid R_2) = .28 \quad P(A \mid R_3) = .61.$$

We are asked to find the probability that a graduate who went on to work did not go to college, so we are looking for $P(R_3 \mid A)$. Bayes' formula for these events is

$$P(R_3 \mid A) = \frac{P(A \mid R_3)P(R_3)}{P(A \mid R_1)P(R_1) + P(A \mid R_2)P(R_2) + P(A \mid R_3)P(R_3)}$$

$$= \frac{(.61)(.33)}{(.49)(.24) + (.28)(.43) + (.61)(.33)} \approx .46.$$

Thus we conclude that 46% of all those working had not gone on to college.

➡ **Before we go on...** We could also solve Example 3 using a tree diagram. As before, the first branching corresponds to the events with unconditional probabilities that we know: R_1, R_2, and R_3. You should complete the tree and check that you obtain the same result as above. ∎

7.6 EXERCISES

▼ more advanced   ◆ challenging

🎲 indicates exercises that should be solved using technology

In Exercises 1–8, use Bayes' theorem or a tree diagram to calculate the indicated probability. Round all answers to four decimal places. HINT [See Quick Examples on page 515.]

1. $P(A \mid B) = .8$, $P(B) = .2$, $P(A \mid B') = .3$. Find $P(B \mid A)$.

2. $P(A \mid B) = .6$, $P(B) = .3$, $P(A \mid B') = .5$. Find $P(B \mid A)$.

3. $P(X \mid Y) = .8$, $P(Y') = .3$, $P(X \mid Y') = .5$. Find $P(Y \mid X)$.

4. $P(X \mid Y) = .6$, $P(Y') = .4$, $P(X \mid Y') = .3$. Find $P(Y \mid X)$.

5. Y_1, Y_2, Y_3 form a partition of S. $P(X \mid Y_1) = .4$, $P(X \mid Y_2) = .5$, $P(X \mid Y_3) = .6$, $P(Y_1) = .8$, $P(Y_2) = .1$. Find $P(Y_1 \mid X)$.

6. Y_1, Y_2, Y_3 form a partition of S. $P(X \mid Y_1) = .2$, $P(X \mid Y_2) = .3$, $P(X \mid Y_3) = .6$, $P(Y_1) = .3$, $P(Y_2) = .4$. Find $P(Y_1 \mid X)$.

7. Y_1, Y_2, Y_3 form a partition of S. $P(X \mid Y_1) = .4$, $P(X \mid Y_2) = .5$, $P(X \mid Y_3) = .6$, $P(Y_1) = .8$, $P(Y_2) = .1$. Find $P(Y_2 \mid X)$.

8. Y_1, Y_2, Y_3 form a partition of S. $P(X \mid Y_1) = .2$, $P(X \mid Y_2) = .3$, $P(X \mid Y_3) = .6$, $P(Y_1) = .3$, $P(Y_2) = .4$. Find $P(Y_2 \mid X)$.

APPLICATIONS

9. *Music Downloading* According to a study on the effect of music downloading on spending on music, 11% of all Internet users had decreased their spending on music.[60] We estimate that 40% of all music fans used the Internet at the time of the study.[61] If 20% of non-Internet users had decreased their spending on music, what percentage of those who had decreased their spending on music were Internet users? HINT [See Examples 1 and 2.]

10. *Music Downloading* According to the study cited in the preceding exercise, 36% of experienced file-sharers with broadband access had decreased their spending on music. Let us estimate that 3% of all music fans were experienced file-sharers with broadband access at the time of the study.[62] If 20% of the other music fans had decreased their spending on music, what percentage of those who had decreased their spending on music were experienced file-sharers with broadband access? HINT [See Examples 1 and 2.]

11. *Weather* It snows in Greenland an average of once every 25 days, and when it does, glaciers have a 20% chance of growing. When it does not snow in Greenland, glaciers have only a 4% chance of growing. What is the probability that it is snowing in Greenland when glaciers are growing?

---

[60] Regardless of whether they used the Internet to download music. Source: *New York Times*, May 6, 2002, p. C6.

[61] According to the U.S. Department of Commerce, 51% of all U.S. households had computers in 2001.

[62] Around 15% of all online households had broadband access in 2001 according to a *New York Times* article (Dec. 24, 2001, p. C1).

12. **Weather** It rains in Spain an average of once every 10 days, and when it does, hurricanes have a 2% chance of happening in Hartford. When it does not rain in Spain, hurricanes have a 1% chance of happening in Hartford. What is the probability that it rains in Spain when hurricanes happen in Hartford?

13. **Side Impact Hazard** In 2004, 45.4% of all light vehicles were cars, and the rest were pickups or SUVs. The probability that a severe side-impact crash would prove deadly to a driver depended on the type of vehicle he or she was driving at the time, as shown in the table:[63]

Car	1.0
Light Truck or SUV	.3

What is the probability that the victim of a deadly side-impact accident was driving a car?

14. **Side Impact Hazard** In 2004, 27.3% of all light vehicles were light trucks, and the rest were cars or SUVs. The probability that a severe side-impact crash would prove deadly to a driver depended on the type of vehicle he or she was driving at the time, as shown in the table:[64]

Light Truck	.2
Car or SUV	.7

What is the probability that the victim of a deadly side-impact accident was driving a car or SUV?

15. **Athletic Fitness Tests** Any athlete who fails the Enormous State University's women's soccer fitness test is automatically dropped from the team. Last year, Mona Header failed the test, but claimed that this was due to the early hour. (The fitness test is traditionally given at 5 AM on a Sunday morning.) In fact, a study by the ESU Physical Education Department suggested that 50% of athletes fit enough to play on the team would fail the soccer test, although no unfit athlete could possibly pass the test. It also estimated that 45% of the athletes who take the test are fit enough to play soccer. Assuming these estimates are correct, what is the probability that Mona was justifiably dropped?

16. **Academic Testing** Professor Frank Nabarro insists that all senior physics majors take his notorious physics aptitude test. The test is so tough that anyone *not* going on to a career in physics has no hope of passing, whereas 60% of the seniors who do go on to a career in physics still fail the test. Further, 75% of all senior physics majors in fact go on to a career in physics. Assuming that you fail the test, what is the probability that you will not go on to a career in physics? HINT [See Example 3.]

17. **Side Impact Hazard** (Compare Exercise 13.) In 2004, 27.3% of all light vehicles were light trucks, 27.3% were SUVs, and 45.4% were cars. The probability that a severe side-impact crash would prove deadly to a driver depended on the type of vehicle he or she was driving at the time, as shown in the table:[65]

Light Truck	.210
SUV	.371
Car	1.000

What is the probability that the victim of a deadly side-impact accident was driving an SUV?

18. **Side Impact Hazard** In 1986, 23.9% of all light vehicles were pickups, 5.0% were SUVs, and 71.1% were cars. Refer to Exercise 17 for the probabilities that a severe side-impact crash would prove deadly. What is the probability that the victim of a deadly side-impact accident was driving a car? HINT [See Example 3.]

19. **University Admissions** In fall 2008, UCLA admitted 22% of its California resident applicants, 28% of its applicants from other U.S. states, and 22% of its international student applicants. Of all its applicants, 84% were California residents, 10% were from other U.S. states, and 6% were international students.[66] What percentage of all admitted students were California residents? (Round your answer to the nearest 1%.)

20. **University Admissions** In fall 2002, UCLA admitted 26% of its California resident applicants, 18% of its applicants from other U.S. states, and 13% of its international student applicants. Of all its applicants, 86% were California residents, 11% were from other U.S. states, and 3% were international students.[67] What percentage of all admitted students were California residents? (Round your answer to the nearest 1%.)

21. **Internet Use** In 2000, 86% of all Caucasians in the United States, 77% of all African-Americans, 77% of all Hispanics, and 85% of residents not classified into one of these groups used the Internet for e-mail.[68] At that time, the U.S. population was 69% Caucasian, 12% African-American, and 13% Hispanic. What percentage of U.S. residents who used the Internet for e-mail were Hispanic?

---

[63] A "serious" side-impact accident is defined as one in which the driver of a car would be killed. Source: National Highway Traffic Safety Administration/*New York Times*, May 30, 2004, p. BU 9.

[64] Ibid.

[65] Ibid.

[66] Source: University of California (www.admissions.ucla.edu/Prospect/Adm_fr/Frosh_Prof08.htm).

[67] Source: UCLA Web site, May 2002 (www.admissions.ucla.edu/Prospect/Adm_fr/Frosh_Prof.htm).

[68] Source: NTIA and ESA, U.S. Department of Commerce, using August 2000 U.S. Bureau of The Census Current Population Survey Supplement.

22. *Internet Use* In 2000, 59% of all Caucasians in the United States, 57% of all African-Americans, 58% of all Hispanics, and 54% of residents not classified into one of these groups used the Internet to search for information.[69] At that time, the U.S. population was 69% Caucasian, 12% African-American, and 13% Hispanic. What percentage of U.S. residents who used the Internet for information search were African-American?

23. ▼ *Market Surveys* A *New York Times* survey of homeowners showed that 86% of those with swimming pools were married couples, and the other 14% were single.[70] It also showed that 15% of all homeowners had pools.

a. Assuming that 90% of all homeowners without pools are married couples, what percentage of homes owned by married couples have pools?

b. Would it better pay pool manufacturers to go after single homeowners or married homeowners? Explain.

24. ▼ *Crime and Preschool*. Another *New York Times* survey of needy and disabled youths showed that 51% of those who had no preschool education were arrested or charged with a crime by the time they were 19, whereas only 31% who had preschool education wound up in this category.[71] The survey did not specify what percentage of the youths in the survey had preschool education, so let us take a guess at that and estimate that 20% of them had attended preschool.

a. What percentage of the youths arrested or charged with a crime had no preschool education?

b. What would this figure be if 80% of the youths had attended preschool? Would youths who had preschool education be more likely to be arrested or charged with a crime than those who did not? Support your answer by quoting probabilities.

25. ▼ *Grade Complaints* Two of the mathematics professors at Enormous State are Professor A (known for easy grading) and Professor F (known for tough grading). Last semester, roughly three quarters of Professor F's class consisted of former students of Professor A; these students apparently felt encouraged by their (utterly undeserved) high grades. (Professor F's own former students had fled in droves to Professor A's class to try to shore up their grade point averages.) At the end of the semester, as might have been predicted, all of Professor A's former students wound up with a C– or lower. The rest of the students in the class—former students of Professor F who had decided to "stick it out"—fared better, and two-thirds of them earned higher than a C–. After discovering what had befallen them, all the students who earned C– or lower got together and decided to send a delegation to the Department Chair to complain that their grade point averages had been ruined by this callous and heartless beast! The contingent was to consist of 10 representatives selected at random from among them. How many of the 10 would you estimate to have been former students of Professor A?

26. ▼ *Weather Prediction* A local TV station employs Desmorelda, "Mistress of the Zodiac," as its weather forecaster. Now, when it rains, Sagittarius is in the shadow of Jupiter one-third of the time, and it rains on 4 out of every 50 days. Sagittarius falls in Jupiter's shadow on only 1 in every 5 rainless days. The powers that be at the station notice a disturbing pattern to Desmorelda's weather predictions. It seems that she always predicts that it will rain when Sagittarius is in the shadow of Jupiter. What percentage of the time is she correct? Should they replace her?

27. ▼ *Employment in the 1980s* In a 1987 survey of married couples with earnings, 95% of all husbands were employed. Of all employed husbands, 71% of their wives were also employed.[72] Noting that either the husband or wife in a couple with earnings had to be employed, find the probability that the husband of an employed woman was also employed.

28. ▼ *Employment in the 1980s* Repeat the preceding exercise in the event that 50% of all husbands were employed.

29. ▼ *Juvenile Delinquency* According to a study at the Oregon Social Learning Center, boys who had been arrested by age 14 were 17.9 times more likely to become chronic offenders than those who had not.[73] Use these data to estimate the percentage of chronic offenders who had been arrested by age 14 in a city where 0.1% of all boys have been arrested by age 14. (Hint: Use Bayes' formula rather than a tree.) HINT [See Example 3.]

30. ▼ *Crime* According to the same study at the Oregon Social Learning Center, chronic offenders were 14.3 times more likely to commit violent offenses than people who were not chronic offenders.[74] In a neighborhood where 2 in every 1,000 residents is a chronic offender, estimate the probability that a violent offender is also a chronic offender. (Hint: Use Bayes' formula rather than a tree.) HINT [See Example 3.]

31. ▼ *Benefits of Exercise* According to a study in *The New England Journal of Medicine*,[75] 202 of a sample of 5,990 middle-aged men had developed diabetes. It also found that men who were very active (burning about 3,500 calories daily) were half as likely to develop diabetes compared with men who were sedentary. Assume that one-third of all middle-aged men are very active, and the rest are classified as sedentary. What is the probability that a middle-aged man with diabetes is very active?

32. ▼ *Benefits of Exercise* Repeat Exercise 31, assuming that only 1 in 10 middle-aged men is very active.

[69] Source: NTIA and ESA, U.S. Department of Commerce, using August 2000 U.S. Bureau of The Census Current Population Survey Supplement.

[70] Source: "All about Swimming Pools," *The New York Times*, September 13, 1992.

[71] Source: "Governors Develop Plan to Help Preschool Children," *The New York Times*, August 2, 1992.

[72] Source: *Statistical Abstract of the United States*, 111th Ed., 1991, U.S. Dept. of Commerce/U.S. Bureau of Labor Statistics. Figures rounded to the nearest 1%.

[73] Based on a study, by Marion S. Forgatch, of 319 boys from high-crime neighborhoods in Eugene, Oregon. Source: W. Wayt Gibbs, "Seeking the Criminal Element," *Scientific American*, March 1995, pp. 101–107.

[74] Ibid.

[75] As cited in an article in *The New York Times* on July 18, 1991.

33. ◆ *Airbag Safety* According to a study conducted by the Harvard School of Public Health, a child seated in the front seat who was wearing a seatbelt was 31% more likely to be killed in an accident if the car had an air bag that deployed than if it did not.[76] Airbags deployed in 25% of all accidents. For a child seated in the front seat wearing a seatbelt, what is the probability that the airbag deployed in an accident in which the child was killed? (Round your answer to two decimal places.) HINT [When we say "A is 31% more likely than B" we mean that the probability of A is 1.31 times the probability of B.]

34. ◆ *Airbag Safety* According to the study cited in Exercise 33, a child seated in the front seat who was not wearing a seatbelt was 84% more likely to be killed in an accident if the car had an air bag that deployed than if it did not.[77] Airbags deployed in 25% of all accidents. For a child seated in the front seat not wearing a seatbelt, what is the probability that the airbag deployed in an accident in which the child was killed? (Round your answer to two decimal places.) HINT [When we say "A is 84% more likely than B" we mean that the probability of A is 1.84 times the probability of B.]

COMMUNICATION AND REASONING EXERCISES

35. Your friend claims that the probability of *A* given *B* is the same as the probability of *B* given *A*. How would you convince him that he is wrong?

36. Complete the following sentence. To use Bayes' formula to compute $P(E \mid F)$, you need to be given _____.

37. ▼ Give an example in which a steroids test gives a false positive only 1% of the time, and yet if an athlete tests positive, the chance that he or she has used steroids is under 10%.

38. ▼ Give an example in which a steroids test gives a false positive 30% of the time, and yet if an athlete tests positive, the chance that he or she has used steroids is over 90%.

39. ▼ Use a tree to derive the expanded form of Bayes' Theorem for a partition of the sample space *S* into three events R_1, R_2, and R_3.

40. ▼ Write down an expanded form of Bayes' Theorem that applies to a partition of the sample space *S* into four events R_1, R_2, R_3, and R_4.

41. ◆ *Politics* The following letter appeared in the *New York Times*.[78]

> To the Editor:
>
> It stretches credulity when William Safire contends (column, Jan. 11) that 90 percent of those who agreed with his Jan. 8 column, in which he called the First Lady, Hillary Rodham Clinton, "a congenital liar," were men and 90 percent of those who disagreed were women.
>
> Assuming these percentages hold for Democrats as well as Republicans, only 10 percent of Democratic men disagreed with him. Is Mr. Safire suggesting that 90 percent of Democratic men supported him? How naive does he take his readers to be?
>
> A. D.
> New York, Jan. 12, 1996

Comment on the letter writer's reasoning.

42. ◆ *Politics* Refer back to the preceding exercise. If the letter writer's conclusion was correct, what percentage of all Democrats would have agreed with Safire's column?

---

[76] The study was conducted by Dr. Segul-Gomez at the Harvard School of Public Health. Source: *The New York Times*, December 1, 2000, p. F1.

[77] Ibid.

[78] The original letter appeared in *The New York Times*, January 16, 1996, p. A16. The authors have edited the first phrase of the second paragraph slightly for clarity; the original sentence read: "Assuming the response was equally divided between Democrats and Republicans, . . . "

7.7 Markov Systems

Many real-life situations can be modeled by processes that pass from state to state with given probabilities. A simple example of such a **Markov system** is the fluctuation of a gambler's fortune as he or she continues to bet. Other examples come from the study of trends in the commercial world and the study of neural networks and artificial intelligence. The mathematics of Markov systems is an interesting combination of probability and matrix arithmetic.

Here is a basic example we shall use many times: A market analyst for Gamble Detergents is interested in whether consumers prefer powdered laundry detergents or liquid detergents. Two market surveys taken one year apart revealed that 20% of powdered detergent users had switched to liquid one year later, while the rest were still using powder. Only 10% of liquid detergent users had switched to powder one year later, with the rest still using liquid.

We analyze this example as follows: Every year a consumer may be in one of two possible **states**: He may be a powdered detergent user or a liquid detergent user. Let us number these states: A consumer is in state 1 if he uses powdered detergent and in state 2 if he uses liquid. There is a basic **time step** of one year. If a consumer happens to be in state 1 during a given year, then there is a probability of 20% $= .2$ (the chance that a randomly chosen powder user will switch to liquid) that he will be in state 2 the next year. We write

$$p_{12} = .2$$

to indicate that the probability of going *from* state 1 *to* state 2 in one time step is .2. The other 80% of the powder users are using powder the next year. We write

$$p_{11} = .8$$

to indicate that the probability of *staying* in state 1 from one year to the next is .8.* What if a consumer is in state 2? Then the probability of going to state 1 is given as 10% $= .1$, so the probability of remaining in state 2 is .9. Thus,

$$p_{21} = .1$$

and

$$p_{22} = .9.$$

We can picture this system as in Figure 19, which shows the **state transition diagram** for this example. The numbers p_{ij}, which appear as labels on the arrows, are the **transition probabilities**.

* **NOTE** Notice that these are actually *conditional* probabilities. For instance, p_{12} is the probability that the system (the consumer in this case) will go into state 2, *given that the system* (the consumer) *is in state 1.*

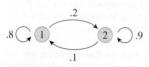

Figure 19

* **NOTE** Named after the Russian mathematician A.A. Markov (1856–1922) who first studied these "non-deterministic" processes.

Markov System, States, and Transition Probabilities

A **Markov system*** (or **Markov process** or **Markov chain**) is a system that can be in one of several specified **states**. There is specified a certain **time step**, and at each step the system will randomly change states or remain where it is. The probability of going from state i to state j is a fixed number p_{ij}, called the **transition probability**.

Quick Example

The Markov system depicted in Figure 19 has two states: state 1 and state 2. The transition probabilities are as follows:

$$p_{11} = \text{Probability of going from state 1 to state 1} = .8$$
$$p_{12} = \text{Probability of going from state 1 to state 2} = .2$$
$$p_{21} = \text{Probability of going from state 2 to state 1} = .1$$
$$p_{22} = \text{Probability of going from state 2 to state 2} = .9.$$

Notice that, because the system must go somewhere at each time step, the transition probabilities originating at a particular state always add up to 1. For example, in the transition diagram above, when we add the probabilities originating at state 1, we get $.8 + .2 = 1$.

The transition probabilities may be conveniently arranged in a matrix.

Transition Matrix

The **transition matrix** associated with a given Markov system is the matrix P whose ijth entry is the transition probability p_{ij}, the transition probability of going *from* state i *to* state j. In other words, the entry in position ij is the *label on the arrow going from state i to state j* in a state transition diagram.

Thus, the transition matrix for a system with two states would be set up as follows:

To:

$$\text{From:} \begin{array}{c} \\ 1 \\ 2 \end{array} \begin{matrix} 1 & 2 \\ \left[\begin{matrix} p_{11} & p_{12} \\ p_{21} & p_{22} \end{matrix} \right] \end{matrix}. \qquad \begin{array}{l} \text{Arrows Originating in State 1} \\ \text{Arrows Originating in State 2} \end{array}$$

Quick Example

In the system pictured in Figure 19, the transition matrix is

$$P = \begin{bmatrix} .8 & .2 \\ .1 & .9 \end{bmatrix}.$$

Note Notice that because the sum of the transition probabilities that originate at any state is 1, *the sum of the entries in any row of a transition matrix is 1.* ∎

Now, let's start doing some calculations.

EXAMPLE 1 Laundry Detergent Switching

Consider the Markov system found by Gamble Detergents at the beginning of this section. Suppose that 70% of consumers are now using powdered detergent, while the other 30% are using liquid.

a. What will be the distribution one year from now? (That is, what percentage will be using powdered and what percentage liquid detergent?)

b. Assuming that the probabilities remain the same, what will be the distribution two years from now? Three years from now?

Solution

a. First, let us think of the statement that 70% of consumers are using powdered detergent as telling us a probability: The probability that a randomly chosen consumer uses powdered detergent is .7. Similarly, the probability that a randomly chosen consumer uses liquid detergent is .3. We want to find the corresponding probabilities one year from now. To do this, consider the tree diagram in Figure 20.

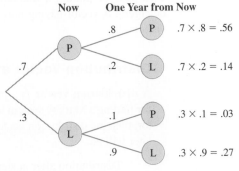

Figure 20

📊 **using Technology**

Technology can be used to compute the distribution vectors in Example 1:

TI-83/84 Plus
Define [A] as the initial distribution and [B] as the transition matrix. Then compute [A]*[B] for the distribution after 1 step. Ans*[B] gives the distribution after successive steps. [More details on page 542.]

Excel
Use the MMULT command to multiply the associated matrices. [More details on page 544.]

Web Site
www.FiniteandCalc.org

Student Home
→ Online Utilities
→ Matrix Algebra Tool

You can enter the transition matrix *P* and the initial distribution vector *v* in the input area, and compute the various distribution vectors using the following formulas:

v*P   1 step
v*P^2   2 steps
v*P^3   3 steps.

The first branching shows the probabilities now, while the second branching shows the (conditional) transition probabilities. So, if we want to know the probability that a consumer is using powdered detergent one year from now, it will be

Probability of using powder after one year $= .7 \times .8 + .3 \times .1 = .59$.

On the other hand, we have:

Probability of using liquid after one year $= .7 \times .2 + .3 \times .9 = .41$.

Now, here's the crucial point: *These are exactly the same calculations as in the matrix product*

$$[.7 \quad .3] \begin{bmatrix} .8 & .2 \\ .1 & .9 \end{bmatrix} = [.59 \quad .41].$$

  ↑   ↑   ↑
Initial distribution   Transition matrix   Distribution after 1 step

Thus, to get the distribution of detergent users after one year, all we have to do is multiply the **initial distribution vector** [.7 .3] by the transition matrix *P*. The result is [.59 .41], the **distribution vector after one step**.

b. Now what about the distribution after *two* years? If we assume that the same fraction of consumers switch or stay put in the second year as in the first, we can simply repeat the calculation we did above, using the new distribution vector:

$$[.59 \quad .41] \begin{bmatrix} .8 & .2 \\ .1 & .9 \end{bmatrix} = [.513 \quad .487].$$

  ↑   ↑   ↑
Distribution after 1 step   Transition matrix   Distribution after 2 steps

Thus, after two years we can expect 51.3% of consumers to be using powdered detergent and 48.7% to be using liquid detergent. Similarly, after three years we have

$$[.513 \quad .487] \begin{bmatrix} .8 & .2 \\ .1 & .9 \end{bmatrix} = [.4591 \quad .5409].$$

So, after three years 45.91% of consumers will be using powdered detergent and 54.09% will be using liquid. Slowly but surely, liquid detergent seems to be winning.

➡ **Before we go on...** Note that the sum of the entries is 1 in each of the distribution vectors in Example 1. In fact, these vectors are giving the probability distributions for each year of finding a randomly chosen consumer using either powdered or liquid detergent. A vector having non-negative entries adding up to 1 is called a **probability vector**. ∎

Distribution Vector after *m* Steps

A **distribution vector** is a probability vector giving the probability distribution for finding a Markov system in its various possible states. If *v* is a distribution vector, then the distribution vector one step later will be *vP*. The distribution *m* steps later will be

Distribution after *m* steps $= v \cdot P \cdot P \cdot \ldots \cdot P$ (*m* times) $= vP^m$.

Quick Example

If $P = \begin{bmatrix} 0 & 1 \\ .5 & .5 \end{bmatrix}$ and $v = [.2 \quad .8]$, then we can calculate the following distribution vectors:

$$vP = [.2 \quad .8]\begin{bmatrix} 0 & 1 \\ .5 & .5 \end{bmatrix} = [.4 \quad .6] \qquad \text{Distribution after one step}$$

$$vP^2 = (vP)P = [.4 \quad .6]\begin{bmatrix} 0 & 1 \\ .5 & .5 \end{bmatrix} = [.3 \quad .7] \qquad \text{Distribution after two steps}$$

$$vP^3 = (vP^2)P = [.3 \quad .7]\begin{bmatrix} 0 & 1 \\ .5 & .5 \end{bmatrix} = [.35 \quad .65]. \quad \text{Distribution after three steps}$$

What about the matrix P^m that appears above? Multiplying a distribution vector v times P^m gives us the distribution m steps later, so we can think of P^m and the m-step transition matrix. More explicitly, consider the following example.

EXAMPLE 2 Powers of the Transition Matrix

Continuing the example of detergent switching, suppose that a consumer is now using powdered detergent. What are the probabilities that the consumer will be using powdered or liquid detergent two years from now? What if the consumer is now using liquid detergent?

Solution To record the fact that we know that the consumer is using powdered detergent, we can take as our initial distribution vector $v = [1 \quad 0]$. To find the distribution two years from now, we compute vP^2. To make a point, we do the calculation slightly differently:

$$vP^2 = [1 \quad 0]\begin{bmatrix} .8 & .2 \\ .1 & .9 \end{bmatrix}\begin{bmatrix} .8 & .2 \\ .1 & .9 \end{bmatrix}$$

$$= [1 \quad 0]\begin{bmatrix} .66 & .34 \\ .17 & .83 \end{bmatrix}$$

$$= [.66 \quad .34].$$

So, the probability that our consumer is using powdered detergent two years from now is .66, while the probability of using liquid detergent is .34. The point to notice is that these are the entries in the first row of P^2. Similarly, if we consider a consumer now using liquid detergent, we should take the initial distribution vector to be $v = [0 \quad 1]$ and compute

$$vP^2 = [0 \quad 1]\begin{bmatrix} .66 & .34 \\ .17 & .83 \end{bmatrix} = [.17 \quad .83].$$

Thus, the bottom row gives the probabilities that a consumer, now using liquid detergent, will be using either powdered or liquid detergent two years from now.

In other words, the ijth entry of P^2 gives the probability that a consumer, starting in state i, will be in state j after two time steps.

What is true in Example 2 for two time steps is true for any number of time steps:

Powers of the Transition Matrix

P^m ($m = 1, 2, 3, \ldots$) is the **m-step transition matrix**. The ijth entry in P^m is the probability of a transition from state i to state j in m steps.

Quick Example

If $P = \begin{bmatrix} 0 & 1 \\ .5 & .5 \end{bmatrix}$ then

$$P^2 = P \cdot P = \begin{bmatrix} .5 & .5 \\ .25 & .75 \end{bmatrix} \qquad \text{2-step transition matrix}$$

$$P^3 = P \cdot P^2 = \begin{bmatrix} .25 & .75 \\ .375 & .625 \end{bmatrix}. \qquad \text{3-step transition matrix}$$

The probability of going from state 1 to state 2 in two steps = (1, 2)-entry of $P^2 = .5$.

The probability of going from state 1 to state 2 in three steps = (1, 2)-entry of $P^3 = .75$.

What happens if we follow our laundry detergent-using consumers for many years?

EXAMPLE 3 Long-Term Behavior

Suppose that 70% of consumers are now using powdered detergent while the other 30% are using liquid. Assuming that the transition matrix remains valid the whole time, what will be the distribution 1, 2, 3, . . . , and 50 years later?

Solution Of course, to do this many matrix multiplications, we're best off using technology. We already did the first three calculations in an earlier example.

Distribution after 1 year: $[.7 \quad .3] \begin{bmatrix} .8 & .2 \\ .1 & .9 \end{bmatrix} = [.59 \quad .41].$

Distribution after 2 years: $[.59 \quad .41] \begin{bmatrix} .8 & .2 \\ .1 & .9 \end{bmatrix} = [.513 \quad .487].$

Distribution after 3 years: $[.513 \quad .487] \begin{bmatrix} .8 & .2 \\ .1 & .9 \end{bmatrix} = [.4591 \quad .5409].$

. . .

Distribution after 48 years: $[.33333335 \quad .66666665].$

Distribution after 49 years: $[.33333334 \quad .66666666].$

Distribution after 50 years: $[.33333334 \quad .66666666].$

Thus, the distribution after 50 years is approximately $[.33333334 \quad .66666666].$

Something interesting seems to be happening in Example 3. The distribution seems to be getting closer and closer to

$$[.333333\ldots \quad .666666\ldots] = \begin{bmatrix} \dfrac{1}{3} & \dfrac{2}{3} \end{bmatrix}.$$

Let's call this distribution vector v_∞. Notice two things about v_∞:

- v_∞ is a probability vector.
- If we calculate $v_\infty P$, we find

$$v_\infty P = \begin{bmatrix} \dfrac{1}{3} & \dfrac{2}{3} \end{bmatrix} \begin{bmatrix} .8 & .2 \\ .1 & .9 \end{bmatrix} = \begin{bmatrix} \dfrac{1}{3} & \dfrac{2}{3} \end{bmatrix} = v_\infty.$$

In other words,

$$v_\infty P = v_\infty.$$

We call a probability vector v with the property that $vP = v$ a **steady-state (probability) vector**.

Q: *Where does the name steady-state vector come from?*

A: If $vP = v$, then v is a distribution that will not change from time step to time step. In the example above, because [1/3 2/3] is a steady-state vector, if 1/3 of consumers use powdered detergent and 2/3 use liquid detergent one year, then the proportions will be the same the next year. Individual consumers may still switch from year to year, but as many will switch from powder to liquid as switch from liquid to powder, so the number using each will remain constant.

But how do we find a steady-state vector?

EXAMPLE 4 Calculating the Steady-State Vector

Calculate the steady-state probability vector for the transition matrix in the preceding examples:

$$P = \begin{bmatrix} .8 & .2 \\ .1 & .9 \end{bmatrix}.$$

Solution We are asked to find

$$v_\infty = [x \quad y].$$

This vector must satisfy the equation

$$v_\infty P = v_\infty$$

or

$$[x \quad y] \begin{bmatrix} .8 & .2 \\ .1 & .9 \end{bmatrix} = [x \quad y].$$

Doing the matrix multiplication gives

$$[.8x + .1y \quad .2x + .9y] = [x \quad y].$$

using Technology

Technology can be used to compute the steady state vector in Example 4.

TI-83/84 Plus
Define [A] as the coefficient matrix of the system of equations being solved, and [B] as the column matrix of the right-hand sides. Then compute [A]$^{-1}$[B] [More details on page 543.]

Excel
Use the MMULT and MINVERSE commands to solve the necessary system of equations. [More details on page 545.]

Web Site
www.FiniteandCalc.org
  Student Home
    → Online Utilities
    → Pivot and Gauss-Jordan
      Tool
You can use the Pivot and Gauss-Jordan Tool to solve the system of equations that gives you the steady-state vector.

Equating corresponding entries gives

$$.8x + .1y = x$$
$$.2x + .9y = y$$

or

$$-.2x + .1y = 0$$
$$.2x - .1y = 0.$$

Now these equations are really the same equation. (Do you see that?) There is one more thing we know, though: Because $[x \ \ y]$ is a probability vector, its entries must add up to 1. This gives one more equation:

$$x + y = 1.$$

Taking this equation together with one of the two equations above gives us the following system:

$$x + \ \ y = 1$$
$$-.2x + .1y = 0.$$

We now solve this system using any of the techniques we learned for solving systems of linear equations. We find that the solution is $x = 1/3$, and $y = 2/3$, so the steady-state vector is

$$v_\infty = [x \ \ y] = \begin{bmatrix} \dfrac{1}{3} & \dfrac{2}{3} \end{bmatrix}$$

as suggested in Example 3.

The method we just used works for any size transition matrix and can be summarized as follows.

Calculating the Steady-State Distribution Vector

To calculate the steady-state probability vector for a Markov System with transition matrix P, we solve the system of equations given by

$$x + y + z + \cdots = 1$$
$$[x \ \ y \ \ z \ ...]P = [x \ \ y \ \ z \ ...]$$

where we use as many unknowns as there are states in the Markov system. The steady-state probability vector is then

$$v_\infty = [x \ \ y \ \ z \ ...].$$

Q: *Is there always a steady-state distribution vector?*

A: Yes, although the explanation why is more involved than we can give here.

Q: *In Example 3, we started with a distribution vector v and found that vP^m got closer and closer to v_∞ as m got larger. Does that always happen?*

A: It does if the Markov system is **regular**, as we define on the next page, but may not for other kinds of systems. Again, we shall not prove this fact here.

Regular Markov Systems

A **regular** Markov system is one for which some power of its transition matrix P has no zero entries. If a Markov system is regular, then

1. It has a unique steady-state probability vector v_∞, and

2. If v is any probability vector whatsoever, then vP^m approaches v_∞ as m gets large. We say that the **long-term behavior** of the system is to have distribution (close to) v_∞.

Interpreting the Steady-State Vector

In a regular Markov system, the entries in the steady-state probability vector give the long-term probabilities that the system will be in the corresponding states, or the fractions of time one can expect to find the Markov system in the corresponding states.

Quick Examples

1. The system with transition matrix $P = \begin{bmatrix} .8 & .2 \\ .1 & .9 \end{bmatrix}$ is regular because $P(= P^1)$ has no zero entries.

2. The system with transition matrix $P = \begin{bmatrix} 0 & 1 \\ .5 & .5 \end{bmatrix}$ is regular because

$P^2 = \begin{bmatrix} .5 & .5 \\ .25 & .75 \end{bmatrix}$ has no zero entries.

3. The system with transition matrix $P = \begin{bmatrix} 0 & 1 \\ 1 & 0 \end{bmatrix}$ is *not* regular:

$P^2 = \begin{bmatrix} 1 & 0 \\ 0 & 1 \end{bmatrix}$ and $P^3 = P$ again, so the powers of P alternate between these two matrices. Thus, every power of P has zero entries. Although this system has a steady-state vector, namely $[.5 \;\; .5]$, if we take $v = [1 \;\; 0]$, then $vP = [0 \;\; 1]$ and $vP^2 = v$, so the distribution vectors vP^m just alternate between these two vectors, not approaching v_∞.

We finish with one more example.

EXAMPLE 5 Gambler's Ruin

A timid gambler, armed with her annual bonus of \$20, decides to play roulette using the following scheme. At each spin of the wheel, she places \$10 on red. If red comes up, she wins an additional \$10; if black comes up, she loses her \$10. For the sake of simplicity, assume that she has a probability of $1/2$ of winning. (In the real game, the probability is slightly lower—a fact that many gamblers forget.) She keeps playing until she has either gotten up to \$30 or lost it all. In either case, she then packs up and leaves. Model this situation as a Markov system and find the associated transition matrix. What can we say about the long-term behavior of this system?

Solution We must first decide on the states of the system. A good choice is the gambler's financial state, the amount of money she has at any stage of the game. According to her rules, she can be broke, have \$10, \$20, or \$30. Thus, there are four states: $1 = \$0$,

2 = \$10, 3 = \$20, and 4 = \$30. Because she bets \$10 each time, she moves down \$10 if she loses (with probability 1/2) and up \$10 if she wins (with probability also 1/2), until she reaches one of the extremes. The transition diagram is shown in Figure 21.

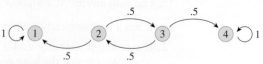

Figure 21

Note that once the system enters state 1 or state 4, it does not leave; with probability 1, it stays in the same state.* We call such states **absorbing states**. We can now write down the transition matrix:

$$P = \begin{bmatrix} 1 & 0 & 0 & 0 \\ .5 & 0 & .5 & 0 \\ 0 & .5 & 0 & .5 \\ 0 & 0 & 0 & 1 \end{bmatrix}.$$

(Notice all the 0 entries, corresponding to possible transitions that we did not draw in the transition diagram because they have 0 probability of occurring. We usually leave out such arrows.) Is this system regular? Take a look at P^2:

$$P^2 = \begin{bmatrix} 1 & 0 & 0 & 0 \\ .5 & .25 & 0 & .25 \\ .25 & 0 & .25 & .5 \\ 0 & 0 & 0 & 1 \end{bmatrix}.$$

Notice that the first and last rows haven't changed. After two steps, there is still no chance of leaving states 1 or 4. In fact, no matter how many powers we take, no matter how many steps we look at, there will still be no way to leave either of those states, and the first and last rows will still have plenty of zeros. This system is not regular.

Nonetheless, we can try to find a steady-state probability vector. If we do this (and you should set up the system of linear equations and solve it), we find that there are infinitely many steady-state probability vectors, namely all vectors of the form $[x \ 0 \ 0 \ 1 - x]$ for $0 \le x \le 1$. (You can check directly that these are all steady-state vectors.) As with a regular system, if we start with any distribution, the system will tend toward one of these steady-state vectors. In other words, eventually the gambler will either lose all her money or leave the table with \$30.

But which outcome is more likely, and with what probability? One way to approach this question is to try computing the distribution after many steps. The distribution that represents the gambler starting with \$20 is $v = [0 \ 0 \ 1 \ 0]$. Using technology, it's easy to compute vP^n for some large values of n:

$$vP^{10} \approx [.333008 \quad 0 \quad .000976 \quad .666016]$$
$$vP^{50} \approx [.333333 \quad 0 \quad 0 \quad .666667].$$

So, it looks like the probability that she will leave the table with \$30 is approximately 2/3, while the probability that she loses it all is 1/3.

---

*These states are like "Roach Motels" ("Roaches check in, but they don't check out")!

Web Site
www.FiniteandCalc.org
Follow the path

Chapter 7
→ Online Utilities
→ Markov Simulation

where you can enter the transition matrix and watch a visual simulation showing the system hopping from state to state. Run the simulation a number of times to get an experimental estimate of the time to absorption. (Take the average time to absorption over many runs.) Also, try varying the transition probabilities to study the effect on the time to absorption.

What if she started with only $10? Then our initial distribution would be $v = [0 \ 1 \ 0 \ 0]$ and

$$vP^{10} \approx [.666016 \quad .000976 \quad 0 \quad .333008]$$
$$vP^{50} \approx [.666667 \quad 0 \quad 0 \quad .333333].$$

So, this time, the probability of her losing everything is about 2/3 while the probability of her leaving with $30 is 1/3. There is a way of calculating these probabilities exactly using matrix arithmetic; however, it would take us too far afield to describe it here.

➡ **Before we go on...** Another interesting question is, how long will it take the gambler in Example 5 to get to $30 or lose it all? This is called the *time to absorption* and can be calculated using matrix arithmetic. ∎

7.7 EXERCISES

▼ more advanced   ◆ challenging
Ⓣ indicates exercises that should be solved using technology

In Exercises 1–10, write down the transition matrix associated with each state transition diagram.

1.

2.

3.

4.

5.

6.

7.

8.

9.

10.

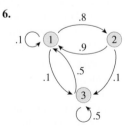

In each of Exercises 11–24, you are given a transition matrix P and initial distribution vector v. Find

(a) *the two-step transition matrix and*
(b) *the distribution vectors after one, two, and three steps.*
    HINT [See Quick Examples on pages 525 and 526.]

11. $P = \begin{bmatrix} .5 & .5 \\ 0 & 1 \end{bmatrix}$, $v = [1 \ 0]$

12. $P = \begin{bmatrix} 1 & 0 \\ .5 & .5 \end{bmatrix}$, $v = [0 \ 1]$

13. $P = \begin{bmatrix} .2 & .8 \\ .4 & .6 \end{bmatrix}$, $v = [.5 \ .5]$

14. $P = \begin{bmatrix} 1/3 & 2/3 \\ 1/2 & 1/2 \end{bmatrix}$, $v = [1/4 \ 3/4]$

15. $P = \begin{bmatrix} 1/2 & 1/2 \\ 1 & 0 \end{bmatrix}$, $v = [2/3 \ 1/3]$

16. $P = \begin{bmatrix} 0 & 1 \\ 1/4 & 3/4 \end{bmatrix}$, $v = [1/5 \ 4/5]$

17. $P = \begin{bmatrix} 3/4 & 1/4 \\ 3/4 & 1/4 \end{bmatrix}$, $v = [1/2 \ 1/2]$

18. $P = \begin{bmatrix} 2/3 & 1/3 \\ 2/3 & 1/3 \end{bmatrix}, v = [1/7 \ \ 6/7]$

19. $P = \begin{bmatrix} .5 & .5 & 0 \\ 0 & 1 & 0 \\ 0 & .5 & .5 \end{bmatrix}, v = [1 \ \ 0 \ \ 0]$

20. $P = \begin{bmatrix} .5 & 0 & .5 \\ 1 & 0 & 0 \\ 0 & .5 & .5 \end{bmatrix}, v = [0 \ \ 1 \ \ 0]$

21. $P = \begin{bmatrix} 0 & 1 & 0 \\ 1/3 & 1/3 & 1/3 \\ 1 & 0 & 0 \end{bmatrix}, v = [1/2 \ \ 0 \ \ 1/2]$

22. $P = \begin{bmatrix} 1/2 & 1/2 & 0 \\ 1/2 & 1/2 & 0 \\ 1/2 & 0 & 1/2 \end{bmatrix}, v = [0 \ \ 0 \ \ 1]$

23. $P = \begin{bmatrix} .1 & .9 & 0 \\ 0 & 1 & 0 \\ 0 & .2 & .8 \end{bmatrix}, v = [.5 \ \ 0 \ \ .5]$

24. $P = \begin{bmatrix} .1 & .1 & .8 \\ .5 & 0 & .5 \\ .5 & 0 & .5 \end{bmatrix}, v = [0 \ \ 1 \ \ 0]$

In each of Exercises 25–36, you are given a transition matrix P. Find the steady-state distribution vector. HINT [See Example 4.]

25. ▼ $P = \begin{bmatrix} 1/2 & 1/2 \\ 1 & 0 \end{bmatrix}$ **26.** ▼ $P = \begin{bmatrix} 0 & 1 \\ 1/4 & 3/4 \end{bmatrix}$

27. ▼ $P = \begin{bmatrix} 1/3 & 2/3 \\ 1/2 & 1/2 \end{bmatrix}$ **28.** ▼ $P = \begin{bmatrix} .2 & .8 \\ .4 & .6 \end{bmatrix}$

29. ▼ $P = \begin{bmatrix} .1 & .9 \\ .6 & .4 \end{bmatrix}$ **30.** ▼ $P = \begin{bmatrix} .2 & .8 \\ .7 & .3 \end{bmatrix}$

31. ▼ $P = \begin{bmatrix} .5 & 0 & .5 \\ 1 & 0 & 0 \\ 0 & .5 & .5 \end{bmatrix}$ **32.** ▼ $P = \begin{bmatrix} 0 & .5 & .5 \\ .5 & .5 & 0 \\ 1 & 0 & 0 \end{bmatrix}$

33. ▼ $P = \begin{bmatrix} 0 & 1 & 0 \\ 1/3 & 1/3 & 1/3 \\ 1 & 0 & 0 \end{bmatrix}$ **34.** ▼ $P = \begin{bmatrix} 1/2 & 1/2 & 0 \\ 1/2 & 1/2 & 0 \\ 1/2 & 0 & 1/2 \end{bmatrix}$

35. ▼ $P = \begin{bmatrix} .1 & .9 & 0 \\ 0 & 1 & 0 \\ 0 & .2 & .8 \end{bmatrix}$ **36.** ▼ $P = \begin{bmatrix} .1 & .1 & .8 \\ .5 & 0 & .5 \\ .5 & 0 & .5 \end{bmatrix}$

APPLICATIONS

37. *Marketing* A market survey shows that half the owners of Sorey State Boogie Boards became disenchanted with the product and switched to C&T Super Professional Boards the next surf season, while the other half remained loyal to Sorey

State. On the other hand, three quarters of the C&T Boogie Board users remained loyal to C&T, while the rest switched to Sorey State. Set these data up as a Markov transition matrix, and calculate the probability that a Sorey State Board user will be using the same brand two seasons later. HINT [See Example 1.]

38. *Major Switching* At Suburban Community College, 10% of all business majors switched to another major the next semester, while the remaining 90% continued as business majors. Of all nonbusiness majors, 20% switched to a business major the following semester, while the rest did not. Set up these data as a Markov transition matrix, and calculate the probability that a business major will no longer be a business major in two semesters' time. HINT [See Example 1.]

39. *Pest Control* In an experiment to test the effectiveness of the latest roach trap, the "Roach Resort," 50 roaches were placed in the vicinity of the trap and left there for an hour. At the end of the hour, it was observed that 30 of them had "checked in," while the rest were still scurrying around. (Remember that "once a roach checks in, it never checks out.")

   a. Set up the transition matrix P for the system with decimal entries, and calculate P^2 and P^3.

   b. If a roach begins outside the "Resort," what is the probability of it "checking in" by the end of 1 hour? 2 hours? 3 hours?

   c. What do you expect to be the long-term impact on the number of roaches? HINT [See Example 5.]

40. *Employment* You have worked for the Department of Administrative Affairs (DAA) for 27 years, and you still have little or no idea exactly what your job entails. To make your life a little more interesting, you have decided on the following course of action. Every Friday afternoon, you will use your desktop computer to generate a random digit from 0 to 9 (inclusive). If the digit is a zero, you will immediately quit your job, never to return. Otherwise, you will return to work the following Monday.

   a. Use the states (1) employed by the DAA and (2) not employed by the DAA to set up a transition probability matrix P with decimal entries, and calculate P^2 and P^3.

   b. What is the probability that you will still be employed by the DAA after each of the next three weeks?

   c. What are your long-term prospects for employment at the DAA? HINT [See Example 5.]

41. ▼ *Risk Analysis* An auto insurance company classifies each motorist as "high-risk" if the motorist has had at least one moving violation during the past calendar year and "low risk" if the motorist has had no violations during the past calendar year. According to the company's data, a high-risk motorist has a 50% chance of remaining in the high-risk category the next year and a 50% chance of moving to the low-risk category. A low-risk motorist has a 10% chance of moving to the high-risk category the next year and a 90% chance of remaining in the low-risk category. In the long term, what percentage of motorists fall in each category?

42. ▼ *Debt Analysis* A credit card company classifies its cardholders as falling into one of two credit ratings: "good" and "poor." Based on its rating criteria, the company finds that a cardholder with a good credit rating has an 80% chance of remaining in that category the following year and a 20% chance of dropping into the poor category. A cardholder with a poor credit rating has a 40% chance of moving into the good rating the following year and a 60% chance of remaining in the poor category. In the long term, what percentage of cardholders fall in each category?

43. ▼ *Textbook Adoptions* College instructors who adopt this book are (we hope!) twice as likely to continue to use the book the following semester as they are to drop it, whereas nonusers are nine times as likely to remain nonusers the following year as they are to adopt this book.

  a. Determine the probability that a nonuser will be a user in two years.
  b. In the long term, what proportion of college instructors will be users of this book?

44. ▼ *Confidence Level* Tommy the Dunker's performance on the basketball court is influenced by his state of mind: If he scores, he is twice as likely to score on the next shot as he is to miss, whereas if he misses a shot, he is three times as likely to miss the next shot as he is to score.

  a. If Tommy has missed a shot, what is the probability that he will score two shots later?
  b. In the long term, what percentage of shots are successful?

45. ▼ *Debt Analysis* As the manager of a large retailing outlet, you have classified all credit customers as falling into one of the following categories: Paid Up, Outstanding 0–90 Days, Bad Debts. Based on an audit of your company's records, you have come up with the following table, which gives the probabilities that a single credit customer will move from one category to the next in the period of 1 month.

		To	
	Paid Up	**0–90 Days**	**Bad Debts**
From **Paid Up**	.5	.5	0
0–90 Days	.5	.3	.2
Bad Debts	0	.5	.5

How do you expect the company's credit customers to be distributed in the long term?

46. ▼ *Debt Analysis* Repeat the preceding exercise using the following table:

		To	
	Paid Up	**0–90 Days**	**Bad Debts**
From **Paid Up**	.8	.2	0
0–90 Days	.5	.3	.2
Bad Debts	0	.5	.5

47. ▼ *Income Brackets* The following diagram shows the movement of U.S. households among three income groups—affluent, middle class, and poor—over the 11-year period 1980–1991.[79]

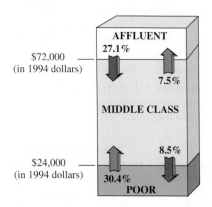

  a. Use the transitions shown in the diagram to construct a transition matrix (assuming zero probabilities for the transitions between affluent and poor).
  b. Assuming that the trend shown was to continue, what percent of households classified as affluent in 1980 were predicted to become poor in 2002? (Give your answer to the nearest 0.1%.)
  c. ▣ According to the model, what percentage of all U.S. households will be in each income bracket in the long term? (Give your answer to the nearest 0.1%.)

48. ▼ *Income Brackets* The following diagram shows the movement of U.S. households among three income groups—affluent, middle class, and poor—over the 12-year period 1967–1979.[80]

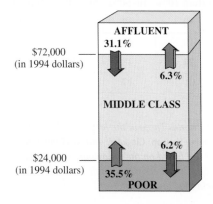

---

[79] The figures were based on household after-tax income. The study was conducted by G. J. Duncan of Northwestern University and T. Smeeding of Syracuse University and based on annual surveys of the personal finances of 5,000 households since the late 1960s. (The surveys were conducted by the University of Michigan.) Source: *The New York Times*, June 4, 1995, p. E4.
[80] Ibid.

a. Use the transitions shown in the diagram to construct a transition matrix (assuming zero probabilities for the transitions between affluent and poor).

b. Assuming that the trend shown had continued, what percent of households classified as affluent in 1967 would have been poor in 1991? (Give your answer to the nearest 0.1%.)

c. ⊞ According to the model, what percentage of all U.S. households will be in each income bracket in the long term? (Give your answer to the nearest 0.1%.)

49. ⊞ ▼ *Income Distribution* A University of Michigan study shows the following one-generation transition probabilities among four major income groups.[81]

Father's Income	Eldest Son's Income			
	Bottom 10%	10–50%	50–90%	Top 10%
Bottom 10%	.30	.52	.17	.01
10–50%	.10	.48	.38	.04
50–90%	.04	.38	.48	.10
Top 10%	.01	.17	.52	.30

In the long term, what percentage of male earners would you expect to find in each category? Why are the long-range figures not necessarily 10% in the lowest 10% income bracket, 40% in the 10–50% range, 40% in the 50–90% range, and 10% in the top 10% range?

50. ⊞ ▼ *Income Distribution* Repeat Exercise 49, using the following data:

Father's Income	Son's income			
	Bottom 10%	10–50%	50–90%	Top 10%
Bottom 10%	.50	.32	.17	.01
10–50%	.10	.48	.38	.04
50–90%	.04	.38	.48	.10
Top 10%	.01	.17	.32	.50

Market Share: Cell Phones *Three of the largest cellular phone companies in 2004 were* **Verizon**, **Cingular**, *and* **AT&T Wireless**. *Exercises 51 and 52 are based on the following figure, which shows percentages of subscribers who switched from one company to another during the third quarter of 2003:*[82]

[81] Source: Gary Solon, University of Michigan/*New York Times*, May 18, 1992, p. D5. We have adjusted some of the figures so that the probabilities add to 1; they did not do so in the original table due to rounding.

[82] Published market shares and "churn rate" (percentage drops for each company) were used to estimate the individual transition percentages. "Other" consists of Sprint, Nextel, and T Mobile. No other cellular companies are included in this analysis. Source: The Yankee Group/*New York Times*, January 21, 2004, p. C1.

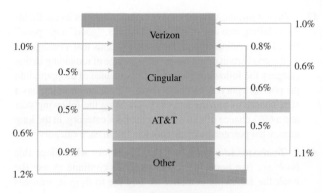

51. a. ⊞ ▼ Use the diagram to set up an associated transition matrix.

b. At the end of the third quarter of 2003, the market shares were: **Verizon**: 29.7%, **Cingular**: 19.3%, **AT&T**: 18.1%, and Other: 32.9%. Use your Markov system to estimate the percentage shares at the *beginning* of the third quarter of 2003.

c. Using the information from part (b), estimate the market shares at the end of 2005. Which company is predicted to gain the most in market share?

52. a. ⊞ ▼ Use the diagram to set up an associated transition matrix.

b. At the end of the third quarter of 2003, the market shares were: **Verizon**: 29.7%, **Cingular**: 19.3%, **AT&T**: 18.1%, Other: 32.9%. Use your Markov system to estimate the percentage shares one year earlier.

c. Using the information from part (b), estimate the market shares at the end of 2010. Which company is predicted to lose the most in market share?

53. ▼ *Dissipation* Consider the following five-state model of one-dimensional dissipation without drift:

Find the steady-state distribution vector.

54. ▼ *Dissipation with Drift* Consider the following five-state model of one-dimensional dissipation with drift:

Find the steady-state distribution vector.

COMMUNICATION AND REASONING EXERCISES

55. ▼ Describe an interesting situation that can be modeled by the transition matrix

$$P = \begin{bmatrix} .2 & .8 & 0 \\ 0 & 1 & 0 \\ .4 & .6 & 0 \end{bmatrix}.$$

56. ▼ Describe an interesting situation that can be modeled by the transition matrix

$$P = \begin{bmatrix} .8 & .1 & .1 \\ 1 & 0 & 0 \\ .3 & .3 & .4 \end{bmatrix}.$$

57. ▼ Describe some drawbacks to using Markov processes to model the behavior of the stock market with states (1) bull market (2) bear market.

58. ▼ Can the repeated toss of a fair coin be modeled by a Markov process? If so, describe a model; if not, explain the reason.

59. ▼ Explain: If Q is a matrix whose rows are steady-state distribution vectors, then $QP = Q$.

60. ▼ Construct a four-state Markov system so that both [.5 .5 0 0] and [0 0 .5 .5] are steady-state vectors. HINT [Try one in which no arrows link the first two states to the last two.]

61. ▼ Refer to the following state transition diagram and explain in words (without doing any calculation) why the steady-state vector has a zero in position 1.

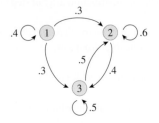

62. ▼ Without doing any calculation, find the steady-state distribution of the following system and explain the reasoning behind your claim.

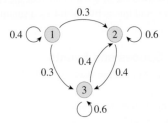

63. ◆ Construct a regular state transition diagram that possesses the steady-state vector [.3 .3 .4].

64. ◆ Construct a regular state transition diagram possessing a steady-state vector [.6 .3 0 .1].

65. ◆ Show that if a Markov system has two distinct steady-state distributions v and w, then $\dfrac{v+w}{2}$ is another steady-state distribution.

66. ◆ If higher and higher powers of P approach a fixed matrix Q, explain why the rows of Q must be steady-state distributions vectors.

KEY CONCEPTS

Web Site www.FiniteandCalc.org

Go to the student Web site at www.FiniteandCalc.org to find a comprehensive and interactive Web-based summary of Chapter 7.

7.1 Sample Spaces and Events

Experiment, outcome, sample space *p. 446*

Event *p. 448*

The complement of an event *p. 452*

Unions of events *p. 452*

Intersections of events *p. 453*

Mutually exclusive events *p. 454*

7.2 Relative Frequency

Relative frequency or estimated probability *p. 460*

Relative frequency distribution *p. 460*

Properties of relative frequency distribution *p. 463*

7.3 Probability and Probability Models

Probability distribution, probability: $0 \leq P(s_i) \leq 1$ and $P(s_1) + \cdots + P(s_n) = 1$ *p. 469*

If $P(E) = 0$, we call E an impossible event *p. 469*

Probability models *p. 469*

Probability models for equally likely outcomes: $P(E) = n(E)/n(S)$ *p. 471*

Addition principle: $P(A \cup B) = P(A) + P(B) - P(A \cap B)$ *p. 475*

If A and B are mutually exclusive, then $P(A \cup B) = P(A) + P(B)$ *p. 476*

If S is the sample space, then $P(S) = 1$, $P(\emptyset) = 0$, and $P(A') = 1 - P(A)$ *p. 478*

7.4 Probability and Counting Techniques

Use counting techniques from Chapter 6 to calculate probability *p. 487*

7.5 Conditional Probability and Independence

Conditional probability: $P(A \mid B) = P(A \cap B)/P(B)$ *p. 497*

Multiplication principle for conditional probability: $P(A \cap B) = P(A \mid B)P(B)$ *p. 500*

Independent events: $P(A \cap B) = P(A)P(B)$ *p. 503*

7.6 Bayes' Theorem and Applications

Bayes' Theorem (short form):

$$P(A \mid T) = \frac{P(T \mid A)P(A)}{P(T \mid A)P(A) + P(T \mid A')P(A')} \quad p.\ 515$$

Bayes' Theorem (partition of sample space into three events):

$$P(A_1 \mid T) = \frac{P(T \mid A_1)P(A_1)}{P(T \mid A_1)P(A_1) + P(T \mid A_2)P(A_2) + P(T \mid A_3)P(A_3)}$$

p. 517

7.7 Markov Systems

Markov system, Markov process, states, transition probabilities *p. 522*

Transition matrix associated with a given Markov system *p. 522*

A vector having non-negative entries adding up to 1 is called a probability vector *p. 524*

A distribution vector is a probability vector giving the probability distribution for finding a Markov system in its various possible states *p. 524*

If v is a distribution vector, then the distribution vector one step later will be vP. The distribution after m steps will be vP^m *p. 524*

P^m is the m-step transition matrix. The ijth entry in P^m is the probability of a transition from state i to state j in m steps *p. 526*

A steady-state (probability) vector is a probability vector v such that $vP = v$ *p. 527*

Calculation of the steady-state distribution vector *p. 528*

A regular Markov system, long-term behavior of a regular Markov system *p. 527*

An absorbing state is one for which the probability of staying in the state is 1 (and the probability of leaving it for any other state is 0) *p. 530*

REVIEW EXERCISES

In each of Exercises 1–6, say how many elements are in the sample space S, list the elements of the given event E, and compute the probability of E.

1. Three coins are tossed; the result is one or more tails.

2. Four coins are tossed; the result is fewer heads then tails.

3. Two distinguishable dice are rolled; the numbers facing up add to 7.

4. Three distinguishable dice are rolled; the number facing up add to 5.

5. A die is weighted so that each of 2, 3, 4, and 5 is half as likely to come up as either 1 or 6; however, 2 comes up.

6. Two indistinguishable dice are rolled; the numbers facing up add to 7.

In each of Exercises 7–10, calculate the relative frequency $P(E)$.

7. Two coins are tossed 50 times, and two heads come up 12 times. E is the event that at least one tail comes up.

8. Ten stocks are selected at random from a portfolio. Seven of them have increased in value since their purchase, and the rest have decreased. Eight of them are Internet stocks and two of those have decreased in value. E is the event that a stock has either increased in value or is an Internet stock.

9. You have read 150 of the 400 novels in your home, but your sister Roslyn has read 200, of which only 50 are novels you have read as well. E is the event that a novel has been read by neither you nor your sister.

10. You roll two dice 10 times. Both dice show the same number 3 times, and on 2 rolls, exactly one number is odd. E is the event that the sum of the numbers is even.

In each of Exercises 11–14, calculate the probability $P(E)$.

11. There are 32 students in categories A and B combined. Some are in both, 24 are in A, and 24 are in B. E is the event that a randomly selected student (among the 32) is in both categories.

12. You roll two dice, one red and one green. Losing combinations are doubles (both dice showing the same number) and outcomes in which the green die shows an odd number and the red die shows an even number. The other combinations are winning ones. E is the event that you roll a winning combination.

13. The *jPlay* portable music/photo/video player and bottle opener comes in three models: A, B, and C, each with five colors to choose from, and there are equal numbers of each combination. E is the event that a randomly selected *jPlay* is either orange (one of the available colors), a Model A, or both.

14. The Heavy Weather Service predicts that for tomorrow there is a 50% chance of tornadoes, a 20% chance of a monsoon, and a 10% chance of both. What is the probability that we will be lucky tomorrow and encounter neither tornadoes nor a monsoon?

A bag contains four red marbles, two green ones, one transparent one, three yellow ones, and two orange ones. You select five at random. In each of Exercises 15–20, compute the probability of the given event.

15. You have selected all the red ones.

16. You have selected all the green ones.

17. All are different colors.

18. At least one is not red.

19. At least two are yellow.

20. None are yellow and at most one is red.

In each of Exercises 21–26, find the probability of being dealt the given type of 5-card hand from a standard deck of 52 cards. (None of these is a recognized poker hand.) Express your answer in terms of combinations.

21. **Kings and Queens:** Each of the five cards is either a king or a queen.

22. **Five Pictures:** Each card is a picture card (J, Q, K).

23. **Fives and Queens:** Three fives, the queen of spades, and one other queen.

24. **Prime Full House:** A full house (three cards of one denomination, two of another) with the face value of each card a prime number (Ace = 1, J = 11, Q = 12, K = 13).

25. **Full House of Commons:** A full house (three cards of one denomination, two of another) with no royal cards (that is, no J, Q, K, or Ace).

26. **Black Two Pair:** Five black cards (spades or clubs), two with one denomination, two with another, and one with a third.

Two dice, one green and one yellow, are rolled. In each of Exercises 27–32, find the conditional probability, and also say whether the indicated pair of events is independent.

27. The sum is 5, given that the green one is not 1 and the yellow one is 1.

28. That the sum is 6, given that the green one is either 1 or 3 and the yellow one is 1.

29. The yellow one is 4, given that the green one is 4.

30. The yellow one is 5, given that the sum is 6.

31. The dice have the same parity, given that both of them are odd.

32. The sum is 7, given that the dice do not have the same parity.

A poll shows that half the consumers who use Brand A switched to Brand B the following year, while the other half stayed with Brand A. Three quarters of the Brand B users stayed with Brand B the following year, while the rest switched to Brand A. Use this information to answer Exercises 33–36.

33. Give the associated Markov state distribution matrix with state 1 representing using Brand A, and state 2 represented by using Brand B.

34. Compute the associated two- and three-step transition matrices. What is the probability that a Brand A user will be using Brand B three years later?

35. If two-thirds of consumers are presently using Brand A and one-third are using Brand B, how are these consumers distributed in three years' time?

36. In the long term, what fraction of the time will a user spend using each of the two brands?

APPLICATIONS

OHaganBooks.com currently operates three warehouses: one in Washington, one in California, and the new one in Texas. Book inventories are shown in the following table.

	Sci-Fi	Horror	Romance	Other	Total
Washington	10,000	12,000	12,000	30,000	64,000
California	8,000	12,000	6,000	16,000	42,000
Texas	15,000	15,000	20,000	44,000	94,000
Total	33,000	39,000	38,000	90,000	200,000

A book is selected at random. In each of Exercises 37–42, compute the probability of the given event.

37. That it is either a sci-fi book or stored in Texas (or both).

38. That it is a sci-fi book stored in Texas.

39. That it is a sci-fi book, given that it is stored in Texas.

40. That it was stored in Texas, given that it was a sci-fi book.

41. That it was stored in Texas, given that it was not a sci-fi book.

42. That it was not stored in Texas, given that it was a sci-fi book.

In order to gauge the effectiveness of the OHaganBooks.com site, you recently commissioned a survey of online shoppers. According to the results, 2% of online shoppers visited OHaganBooks.com during a one-week period, while 5% of them visited at least one of OHaganBooks.com's two main competitors: JungleBooks.com and FarmerBooks.com. Use this information to answer Exercises 43–50.

43. What percentage of online shoppers never visited OHaganBooks.com?

44. What percentage of shoppers never visited either of OHaganBooks.com's main competitors?

45. Assuming that visiting OHaganBooks.com was independent of visiting a competitor, what percentage of online shoppers visited either OHaganBooks.com or a competitor?

46. Assuming that visiting OHaganBooks.com was independent of visiting a competitor, what percentage of online shoppers visited OHaganBooks.com but not a competitor?

47. Under the assumption of Exercise 45, what is the estimated probability that an online shopper will visit none of the three sites during a week?

48. If no one who visited OHaganBooks.com ever visited any of the competitors, what is the estimated probability that an online shopper will visit none of the three sites during a week?

49. Actually, the assumption in Exercise 45 is not what was found by the survey, because an online shopper visiting a competitor was in fact more likely to visit OHaganBooks.com than a randomly selected online shopper. Let H be the event that an online shopper visits OHaganBooks.com, and let C be the event that he visits a competitor. Which is greater: $P(H \cap C)$ or $P(H)P(C)$? Why?

50. What the survey found is that 25% of online shoppers who visited a competitor also visited OHaganBooks.com. Given this information, what percentage of online shoppers visited OHaganBooks.com and neither of its competitors?

Not all visitors to the OHaganBooks.com site actually purchase books, and not all OHaganBooks.com customers buy through the Web site (some phone in their orders and others use a mail-order catalog). According to statistics gathered at the Web site, 8% of online shoppers who visit the site during the course of a

single week will purchase books. However, the survey mentioned prior to Exercise 43 revealed that 2% of online shoppers visited the site during the course of a week. Another survey estimated that 0.5% of online shoppers who did not visit the site during the course of a week nonetheless purchased books at OHaganBooks.com. Use this information to answer Exercises 51–54.

51. Complete the following sentence: Online shoppers who visit the OHaganBooks.com Web site are ___ times as likely to purchase books as shoppers who do not.

52. What is the probability that an online shopper will not visit the site during the course of a week but still purchase books?

53. What is the probability that an online shopper who purchased books during a given week also visited the site?

54. Repeat exercise 53 in the event that 1% of online shoppers visited OHaganBooks.com during the week.

As mentioned earlier, OHaganBooks.com has two main competitors, JungleBooks.com and FarmerBooks.com, and no other competitors of any significance. The following table shows the movement of customers during July.[83] (Thus, for instance, the first row tells us that 80% of OHaganBooks.com's customers remained loyal, 10% of them went to JungleBooks.com and the remaining 10% to FarmerBooks.com.)

		To		
		OHaganBooks	**JungleBooks**	**FarmerBooks**
From	**OHaganBooks**	80%	10%	10%
	JungleBooks	40%	60%	0%
	FarmerBooks	20%	0%	80%

At the beginning of July, OHaganBooks.com had an estimated market share of one-fifth of all customers, while its two competitors had two-fifths each. Use this information to answer Exercises 55–58.

55. Estimate the market shares each company had at the end of July.

56. Assuming the July trends continue in August, predict the market shares of each company at the end of August.

57. Name one or more important factors that the Markov model does not take into account.

58. Assuming the July trend were to continue indefinitely, predict the market share enjoyed by each of the three e-commerce sites.

---

[83] By a "customer" of one of the three e-commerce sites, we mean someone who purchases more at that site than at any of the two competitors' sites.

Case Study

The Monty Hall Problem

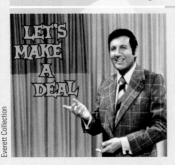

Everett Collection

Here is a famous "paradox" that even mathematicians find counterintuitive. On the game show *Let's Make a Deal*, you are shown three doors, A, B, and C, and behind one of them is the Big Prize. After you select one of them—say, door A—to make things more interesting the host (Monty Hall), who knows what is behind each door, opens one of the other doors—say, door B—to reveal that the Big Prize is not there. He then offers you the opportunity to change your selection to the remaining door, door C. Should you switch or stick with your original guess? Does it make any difference?

Most people would say that the Big Prize is equally likely to be behind door A or door C, so there is no reason to switch.[84] In fact, this is wrong: The prize is more likely to be behind door C! There are several ways of seeing why this is so. Here is how you might work it out using Bayes' theorem.

Let A be the event that the Big Prize is behind door A, B the event that it is behind door B, and C the event that it is behind door C. Let F be the event that Monty has opened door B and revealed that the prize is not there. You wish to find $P(C \mid F)$ using Bayes' theorem. To use that formula you need to find $P(F \mid A)$ and $P(A)$ and similarly for B and C. Now, $P(A) = P(B) = P(C) = 1/3$ because at the outset, the prize is equally likely to be behind any of the doors. $P(F \mid A)$ is the probability that Monty will open door B if the prize is actually behind door A, and this is $1/2$ because we assume that he will choose either B or C randomly in this case. On the other hand, $P(F \mid B) = 0$, because he will never open the door that hides the prize. Also, $P(F \mid C) = 1$ because if the prize is behind door C, he must open door B to keep from revealing that the prize is behind door C. Therefore,

$$P(C \mid F) = \frac{P(F \mid C)P(C)}{P(F \mid A)P(A) + P(F \mid B)P(B) + P(F \mid C)P(C)}$$

$$= \frac{1 \cdot \frac{1}{3}}{\frac{1}{2} \cdot \frac{1}{3} + 0 \cdot \frac{1}{3} + 1 \cdot \frac{1}{3}} = \frac{2}{3}.$$

You conclude from this that you *should* switch to door C because it is more likely than door A to be hiding the Prize.

Here is a more elementary way you might work it out. Consider the tree diagram of possibilities shown in Figure 22. The top two branches of the tree give the cases in which the prize is behind door A, and there is a total probability of 1/3 for that case. The remaining two branches with nonzero probabilities give the cases in which the prize is behind the door that you did not choose, and there is a total probability of 2/3 for that case. Again, you conclude that you should switch your choice of doors because the one you did not choose is twice as likely as door A to be hiding the Big Prize.

---

[84] This problem caused quite a stir in late 1991 when this problem was discussed in Marilyn vos Savant's column in *Parade* magazine. Vos Savant gave the answer that you should switch. She received about 10,000 letters in response, most of them disagreeing with her, including several from mathematicians.

Figure 22

EXERCISES

1. The answer you came up with, to switch to the other door, depends on the strategy Monty Hall uses in picking the door to open. Suppose that he actually picks one of doors B and C at random, so that there is a chance that he will reveal the Big Prize. If he opens door B and it happens that the Prize is not there, should you switch or not?

2. What if you know that Monty's strategy is always to open door B if possible (i.e., it does not hide the Big Prize) after you choose A?

   a. If he opens door B, should you switch?
   b. If he opens door C, should you switch?

3. Repeat the analysis of the original game, but suppose that the game uses four doors instead of three (and still only one prize).

4. Repeat the analysis of the original game, but suppose that the game uses 1,000 doors instead of 3 (and still only one prize).

TI-83/84 Plus Technology Guide

Section 7.2

The TI-83/84 Plus has a random number generator that we can use to simulate experiments. For the following example, recall that a fair coin has probability 1/2 of coming up heads and 1/2 of coming up tails.

Example Use a simulated experiment to check the following.

a. The estimated probability of heads coming up in a toss of a fair coin approaches 1/2 as the number of trials gets large.

b. The estimated probability of heads coming up in two consecutive tosses of a fair coin approaches 1/4 as the number of trials gets large.[85]

Solution with Technology

a. Let us use 1 to represent heads and 0 to represent tails. We need to generate a list of **random binary digits** (0 or 1). One way to do this—and a method that works for most forms of technology—is to generate a random number between 0 and 1 and then round it to the nearest whole number, which will be either 0 or 1.

We generate random numbers on the TI-83/84 Plus using the "rand" function. To round the number X to the nearest whole number on the TI-83/84 Plus, follow [MATH] → NUM, select "round," and enter round(X,0). This instruction rounds X to zero decimal places—that is, to the nearest whole number. Since we wish to round a random number we need to enter

    round(rand,0)   To obtain rand,
                       follow [MATH] → PRB.

The result will be either 0 or 1. Each time you press [ENTER] you will now get another 0 or 1. The TI-83/84 Plus can also generate a random integer directly (without the need for rounding) through the instruction

    randInt(0,1)   To obtain randInt,
                    follow [MATH] → PRB.

In general, the command randInt (m, n) generates a random integer in the range $[m, n]$. The following sequence of 100 random binary digits was produced using technology.[86]

0	1	0	0	1	1	0	1	0	0
0	1	0	0	0	0	0	0	1	0
1	1	0	0	0	1	0	0	1	1
1	1	1	0	1	0	0	0	1	0
1	1	1	1	1	1	1	0	0	1
1	0	1	1	1	0	0	1	1	0
0	1	0	1	1	1	0	1	1	1
1	0	0	0	0	0	0	1	1	1
1	1	1	1	0	0	1	1	1	0
1	1	1	0	1	1	0	1	0	0

If we use only the first row of data (corresponding to the first ten tosses), we find

$$P(\text{H}) = \frac{fr(1)}{N} = \frac{4}{10} = .4.$$

Using the first two rows ($N = 20$) gives

$$P(\text{H}) = \frac{fr(1)}{N} = \frac{6}{20} = .3.$$

Using all ten rows ($N = 100$) gives

$$P(\text{H}) = \frac{fr(1)}{N} = \frac{54}{100} = .54.$$

This is somewhat closer to the theoretical probability of 1/2 and supports our intuitive notion that the larger the number of trials, the more closely the estimated probability should approximate the theoretical value.[87]

b. We need to generate pairs of random binary digits and then check whether they are both 1s. Although the TI-83/84 Plus will generate a pair of random digits if you enter round(rand(2),0), it would be a lot more convenient if the calculator could tell you right away whether both digits are 1s (corresponding to two consecutive heads in a coin toss). Here is a simple way of accomplishing this. Notice that if we *add* the two random binary digits, we obtain either 0, 1, or 2, telling us the number of heads that result from the two consecutive throws. Therefore, all we need to do is add the pairs of random digits and then count the number of times 2 comes up. A formula we can use is

    randInt(0,1)+randInt(0,1)

What would be even *more* convenient is if the result of the calculation would be either 0 or 1, with 1 signifying

---

[85] Since the set of outcomes of a pair of coin tosses is {HH, HT, TH, TT}, we expect HH to come up once in every four trials, on average.

[86] The instruction randInt(0,1,100)→L$_1$ will generate a list of 100 random 0s and 1s and store it in L$_1$, where it can be summed with Sum(L$_1$) (under [2ND] [LIST] →MATH).

[87] Do not expect this to happen every time. Compare, for example, $P(\text{H})$ for the first five rows and for all ten rows.

success (two consecutive heads) and 0 signifying failure. Then, we could simply add up all the results to obtain the number of times two heads occurred. To do this, we first divide the result of the previous calculation above by 2 (obtaining 0, .5, or 1, where now 1 signifies success) and then round *down* to an integer using a function called "int":

```
int(0.5*(randInt(0,1)+randInt(0,1)))
```

Following is the result of 100 such pairs of coin tosses, with 1 signifying success (two heads) and 0 signifying failure (all other outcomes). The last column records the number of successes in each row and the total number at the end.

1	1	0	0	0	0	0	0	0	0	2
0	1	0	0	0	0	0	1	0	1	3
0	1	0	0	1	1	0	0	0	1	4
0	0	0	0	0	0	0	0	1	0	1
0	1	0	0	1	0	0	1	0	0	3
1	0	1	0	0	0	0	0	0	0	2
0	0	0	0	0	0	0	0	0	1	1
0	1	1	1	1	0	0	0	0	1	5
1	1	0	1	0	0	1	1	0	0	5
0	0	0	0	0	0	0	0	1	0	1
										27

Now, as in part (a), we can compute estimated probabilities, with D standing for the outcome "two heads":

First 10 trials: $P(D) = \dfrac{fr(1)}{N} = \dfrac{2}{10} = .2$

First 20 trials: $P(D) = \dfrac{fr(1)}{N} = \dfrac{5}{20} = .25$

First 50 trials: $P(D) = \dfrac{fr(1)}{N} = \dfrac{13}{50} = .26$

100 trials: $P(D) = \dfrac{fr(1)}{N} = \dfrac{27}{100} = .27.$

Q : *What is happening with the data? The probabilities seem to be getting less accurate as N increases!*

A : Quite by chance, exactly 5 of the first 20 trials resulted in success, which matches the theoretical probability. Figure 23 shows an Excel plot of estimated probability versus N (for N a multiple of 10). Notice that, as N increases, the graph seems to meander within smaller distances of .25.

Figure 23

Q : *The previous techniques work fine for simulating coin tosses. What about rolls of a fair die, where we want outcomes between 1 and 6?*

A : We can simulate a roll of a die by generating a random integer in the range 1 through 6. The following formula accomplishes this:

$$1 + \text{int}(5.99999 * \text{rand}).$$

(We used 5.99999 instead of 6 to avoid the outcome 7.)

Section 7.7

Example 1 (page 523) Consider the Markov system found by Gamble Detergents at the beginning of this section. Suppose that 70% of consumers are now using powdered detergent while the other 30% are using liquid. What will be the distribution one year from now? Two years from now? Three years from now?

Solution with Technology

In Chapter 3 we saw how to set up and multiply matrices. For this example, we can use the matrix editor to define [A] as the initial distribution and [B] as the transition matrix (remember that the only names we can use are [A] through [J]).

Entering [A] (obtained by pressing MATRX 1 ENTER) will show you the initial distribution. To obtain the distribution after 1 step, press X MATRX 2 ENTER, which has the effect of multiplying the previous answer by the transition matrix [B]. Now, just press ENTER repeatedly to continue multiplying by the transition matrix and obtain the distribution after any number of steps. The screenshot shows the initial distribution [A] and the distributions after 1, 2, and 3 steps.

```
[A]
          [[.7 .3]]
Ans*[B]
       [[.59 .41]]
     [[.513 .487]]
   [[.4591 .5409]]
```

Example 4 (page 527) Calculate the steady-state probability vector for the transition matrix in the preceding examples.

Solution with Technology

Finding the steady-state probability vector comes down to solving a system of equations. As discussed in Chapters 2 and 3, there are several ways to use a calculator to help. The most straightforward is to use matrix inversion to solve the matrix form of the system. In this case, as in the text, the system of equations we need to solve is

$$x + y = 1$$
$$-.2x + .1y = 0.$$

We write this as the matrix equation $AX = B$ with

$$A = \begin{bmatrix} 1 & 1 \\ -.2 & .1 \end{bmatrix} \qquad B = \begin{bmatrix} 1 \\ 0 \end{bmatrix}.$$

To find $X = A^{-1}B$ using the TI-83/84 Plus, we first use the matrix editor to enter these matrices as [A] and [B], then compute $[A]^{-1}[B]$ on the home screen.

```
[A]-1[B]
    [[.3333333333]
     [.6666666667]]
```

To convert the entries to fractions, we can follow this by the command

➤ Frac   MATH ENTER ENTER

```
[A]-1[B]
    [[.3333333333]
     [.6666666667]]
Ans▶Frac
             [[1/3]
              [2/3]]
```

EXCEL Technology Guide

Section 7.2

Excel has a random number generator that we can use to simulate experiments. For the following example, recall that a fair coin has probability 1/2 of coming up heads and 1/2 of coming up tails.

Example Use a simulated experiment to check the following.

a. The estimated probability of heads coming up in a toss of a fair coin approaches 1/2 as the number of trials gets large.

b. The estimated probability of heads coming up in two consecutive tosses of a fair coin approaches 1/4 as the number of trials gets large.[88]

Solution with Technology

a. Let us use 1 to represent heads and 0 to represent tails. We need to generate a list of **random binary digits** (0 or 1). One way to do this—and a method that works for most forms of technology—is to generate a random number between 0 and 1 and then round it to the nearest whole number, which will be either 0 or 1.

In Excel, the formula RAND() gives a random number between 0 and 1.[89] The function ROUND(X,0) rounds X to zero decimal places—that is, to the nearest integer. Therefore, to obtain a random binary digit in any cell just enter the following formula:

```
=ROUND(RAND(),0)
```

---

[88] Because the set of outcomes of a pair of coin tosses is {HH, HT, TH, TT}, we expect HH to come up once in every four trials, on average.

[89] The parentheses after RAND are necessary even though the function takes no arguments.

Excel can also generate a random integer directly (without the need for rounding) through the formula

```
=RANDBETWEEN(0,1)
```

To obtain a whole array of random numbers, just drag this formula into the cells you wish to use.

b. We need to generate pairs of random binary digits and then check whether they are both 1s. It would be convenient if the spreadsheet could tell you right away whether both digits are 1s (corresponding to two consecutive heads in a coin toss). Here is a simple way of accomplishing this. Notice that if we *add* two random binary digits, we obtain either 0, 1, or 2, telling us the number of heads that result from the two consecutive throws. Therefore, all we need to do is add pairs of random digits and then count the number of times 2 comes up. Formulas we can use are

```
=RANDBETWEEN(0,1)+RANDBETWEEN(0,1)
```

What would be even *more* convenient is if the result of the calculation would be either 0 or 1, with 1 signifying success (two consecutive heads) and 0 signifying failure. Then, we could simply add up all the results to obtain the number of times two heads occurred. To do this, we first divide the result of the calculation above by 2 (obtaining 0, .5, or 1, where now 1 signifies success) and then round *down* to an integer using a function called "int":

```
=INT(0.5*(RANDBETWEEN(0,1)+
RANDBETWEEN(0,1)))
```

Following is the result of 100 such pairs of coin tosses, with 1 signifying success (two heads) and 0 signifying failure (all other outcomes). The last column records the number of successes in each row and the total number at the end.

1	1	0	0	0	0	0	0	0	0	2
0	1	0	0	0	0	0	1	0	1	3
0	1	0	0	1	1	0	0	0	1	4
0	0	0	0	0	0	0	0	1	0	1
0	1	0	0	1	0	0	1	0	0	3
1	0	1	0	0	0	0	0	0	0	2
0	0	0	0	0	0	0	0	0	1	1
0	1	1	1	1	0	0	0	0	1	5
1	1	0	1	0	0	1	1	0	0	5
0	0	0	0	0	0	0	0	1	0	1
										27

Now, as in part (a), we can compute estimated probabilities, with D standing for the outcome "two heads":

First 10 trials: $P(D) = \dfrac{fr(1)}{N} = \dfrac{2}{10} = .2$

First 20 trials: $P(D) = \dfrac{fr(1)}{N} = \dfrac{5}{20} = .25$

First 50 trials: $P(D) = \dfrac{fr(1)}{N} = \dfrac{13}{50} = .26$

100 trials: $P(D) = \dfrac{fr(1)}{N} = \dfrac{27}{100} = .27.$

Q: *What is happening with the data? The probabilities seem to be getting* less *accurate as N increases!*

A: Quite by chance, exactly 5 of the first 20 trials resulted in success, which matches the theoretical probability. Figure 24 shows an Excel plot of estimated probability versus N (for N a multiple of 10). Notice that, as N increases, the graph seems to meander within smaller distances of .25.

Figure 24

Q: *The previous techniques work fine for simulating coin tosses. What about rolls of a fair die, where we want outcomes between 1 and 6?*

A: We can simulate a roll of a die by generating a random integer in the range 1 through 6. The following formula accomplishes this:

```
=1 + INT(5.99999*RAND())
```

(We used 5.99999 instead of 6 to avoid the outcome 7.)

Section 7.7

Example 1 (page 523) Consider the Markov system found by Gamble Detergents at the beginning of this section. Suppose that 70% of consumers are now using powdered detergent while the other 30% are using liquid. What will be the distribution one year from now? Two years from now? Three years from now?

Solution with Technology

In Excel, enter the initial distribution vector in cells A1 and B1 and the transition matrix to the right of that, as shown.

	A	B	C	D	E
1	0.7	0.3		0.8	0.2
2				0.1	0.9

To calculate the distribution after one step, use the array formula

$$=MMULT(A1:B1,\$D\$1:\$E\$2)$$

The absolute cell references (dollar signs) ensure that the formula always refers to the same transition matrix, even if we copy it into other cells. To use the array formula, select cells A2 and B2, where the distribution vector will go, enter this formula, and then press Control+Shift+Enter.[90]

	A	B	C	D	E
1	0.7	0.3		0.8	0.2
2	=MMULT(A1:B1,$D$1:$E$2)			0.1	0.9

The result is the following, with the distribution after one step highlighted.

	A	B	C	D	E
1	0.7	0.3		0.8	0.2
2	0.59	0.41		0.1	0.9

To calculate the distribution after two steps, select cells A2 and B2 and drag the fill handle down to copy the formula to cells A3 and B3. Note that the formula now takes the vector in A2:B2 and multiplies it by the transition matrix to get the vector in A3:B3. To calculate several more steps, drag down as far as desired.

	A	B	C	D	E
1	0.7	0.3		0.8	0.2
2	0.59	0.41		0.1	0.9
3					
4					

	A	B	C	D	E
1	0.7	0.3		0.8	0.2
2	0.59	0.41		0.1	0.9
3	0.513	0.487			
4	0.4591	0.5409			

----

[90] On a Macintosh, you can also use Command+Enter.

Example 4 (page 527) Calculate the steady-state probability vector for the transition matrix in the preceding examples.

Solution with Technology

Finding the steady-state probability vector comes down to solving a system of equations. As discussed in Chapters 2 and 3, there are several ways to use Excel to help. The most straightforward is to use matrix inversion to solve the matrix form of the system. In this case, as in the text, the system of equations we need to solve is

$$x + y = 1$$
$$-.2x + .1y = 0.$$

We write this as the matrix equation $AX = B$ with

$$A = \begin{bmatrix} 1 & 1 \\ -.2 & .1 \end{bmatrix} \qquad B = \begin{bmatrix} 1 \\ 0 \end{bmatrix}.$$

We enter A in cells A1:B2, B in cells D1:D2, and the formula for $X = A^{-1}B$ in a convenient location, say B4:B5.

	A	B	C	D
1	1	1		1
2	-0.2	0.1		0
3				
4		=MMULT(MINVERSE(A1:B2),D1:D2)		
5				

When we press Control+Shift+Enter we see the result:

	A	B	C	D
1	1	1		1
2	-0.2	0.1		0
3				
4		0.3333333		
5		0.6666667		

If we want to see the answer in fraction rather than decimal form, we format the cells as fractions.

	A	B	C	D
1	1	1		1
2	-0.2	0.1		0
3				
4		1/3		
5		2/3		

8

Random Variables and Statistics

Web Site
www.FiniteandCalc.org
At the Web site you will find:

- A detailed chapter summary

- Section by section tutorials

- A true/false quiz

- Additional review exercises

- Histogram, Bernoulli trials, and normal distribution utilities

- The following optional extra sections:

  Sampling Distributions and the Central Limit Theorem

  Confidence Intervals

  Calculus and Statistics

Case Study Spotting Tax Fraud with Benford's Law

You are a tax fraud specialist working for the Internal Revenue Service (IRS), and you have just been handed a portion of the tax return from Colossal Conglomerate. The IRS suspects that the portion you were handed may be fraudulent and would like your opinion. **Is there any mathematical test, you wonder, that can point to a suspicious tax return based on nothing more than the numbers entered?**

age fotostock/SuperStock

Introduction

Statistics is the branch of mathematics concerned with organizing, analyzing, and interpreting numerical data. For example, given the current annual incomes of 1,000 lawyers selected at random, you might wish to answer some questions: If I become a lawyer, what income am I likely to earn? Do lawyers' salaries vary widely? How widely?

To answer questions like these, it helps to begin by organizing the data in the form of tables or graphs. This is the topic of the first section of the chapter. The second section describes an important class of examples that are applicable to a wide range of situations, from tossing a coin to product testing.

Once the data are organized, the next step is to apply mathematical tools for analyzing the data and answering questions like those posed above. Numbers such as the **mean** and the **standard deviation** can be computed to reveal interesting facts about the data. These numbers can then be used to make predictions about future events.

The chapter ends with a section on one of the most important distributions in statistics, the **normal distribution**. This distribution describes many sets of data and also plays an important role in the underlying mathematical theory.

8.1 Random Variables and Distributions

Random Variables

In many experiments we can assign numerical values to the outcomes. For instance, if we roll a die, each outcome has a value from 1 through 6. If you select a lawyer and ascertain his or her annual income, the outcome is again a number. We call a rule that assigns a number to each outcome of an experiment a **random variable**.

Random Variable

A **random variable** X is a rule that assigns a number, or **value**, to each outcome in the sample space of an experiment.*

✳ NOTE In the language of functions (Chapter 1), a random variable is a *real-valued function* whose domain is the sample space.

Visualizing a Random Variable

Quick Examples

1. Roll a die; $X =$ the number facing up.
2. Select a mutual fund; $X =$ the number of companies in the fund portfolio.
3. Select a computer; $X =$ the number of megabytes of memory it has.
4. Survey a group of 20 college students; $X =$ the mean SAT.

Discrete and Continuous Random Variables

A **discrete** random variable can take on only specific, isolated numerical values, like the outcome of a roll of a die, or the number of dollars in a randomly chosen bank account. A **continuous** random variable, on the other hand, can take on any values within a continuum or an interval, like the temperature in Central Park, or the height of an athlete in centimeters. Discrete random variables that can take on only finitely many values (like the outcome of a roll of a die) are called **finite** random variables.

Quick Examples

Random Variable	Values	Type
1. Select a mutual fund; $X =$ the number of companies in the fund portfolio.	$\{1, 2, 3, \ldots\}$	Discrete Infinite
2. Take five shots at the goal during a soccer match; $X =$ the number of times you score.	$\{0, 1, 2, 3, 4, 5\}$	Finite
3. Measure the length of an object; $X =$ its length in centimeters.	Any positive real number	Continuous
4. Roll a die until you get a 6; $X =$ the number of times you roll the die.	$\{1, 2, \ldots\}$	Discrete Infinite
5. Bet a whole number of dollars in a race where the betting limit is $100; $X =$ the amount you bet.	$\{0, 1, \ldots, 100\}$	Finite
6. Bet a whole number of dollars in a race where there is no betting limit; $X =$ the amount you bet.	$\{0, 1, \ldots, 100, 101, \ldots\}$	Discrete Infinite

---

Notes

1. In Chapter 7, the only sample spaces we considered in detail were finite sample spaces. However, in general, sample spaces can be infinite, as in many of the experiments mentioned above.

2. There are some "borderline" situations. For instance, if X is the salary of a factory worker, then X is, strictly speaking, discrete. However, the values of X are so numerous and close together that in some applications it makes sense to model X as a continuous random variable. ■

For the moment, we shall consider only finite random variables.

EXAMPLE 1   Finite Random Variable

Let X be the number of heads that come up when a coin is tossed three times. List the value of X for each possible outcome. What are the possible values of X?

Solution First, we describe X as a random variable.

X is the rule that assigns to each outcome the number of heads that come up.

2 Heads ($X = 2$)

We take as the outcomes of this experiment all possible sequences of three heads and tails. Then, for instance, if the outcome is HTH, the value of X is 2. An easy way to list the values of X for all the outcomes is by means of a table.

Web Site
www.FiniteandCalc.org
Go to the Chapter 8 Topic
Summary to find an interactive
simulation based on Example 1.

Outcome	HHH	HHT	HTH	HTT	THH	THT	TTH	TTT
Value of X	3	2	2	1	2	1	1	0

From the table, we also see that the possible values of X are 0, 1, 2, and 3.

➡ **Before we go on...** Remember that X is just a rule we decide on. In Example 1, we could have taken X to be a different rule, such as the number of tails or perhaps the number of heads minus the number of tails. These different rules are examples of different random variables associated with the same experiment. ∎

EXAMPLE 2 Stock Prices

You have purchased \$10,000 worth of stock in a biotech company whose newest arthritis drug is awaiting approval by the F.D.A. If the drug is approved this month, the value of the stock will double by the end of the month. If the drug is rejected this month, the stock's value will decline by 80%. If no decision is reached this month, its value will decline by 10%. Let X be the value of your investment at the end of this month. List the value of X for each possible outcome.

Solution There are three possible outcomes: the drug is approved this month, it is rejected this month, and no decision is reached. Once again, we express the random variable as a rule.

The random variable X is the rule that assigns to each outcome the value of your investment at the end of this month.

We can now tabulate the values of X as follows:

Outcome	Approved This Month	Rejected This Month	No Decision
Value of X	\$20,000	\$2,000	\$9,000

Probability Distribution of a Finite Random Variable

Given a random variable X, it is natural to look at certain *events*—for instance, the event that $X = 2$. By this, we mean the event consisting of all outcomes that have an assigned X-value of 2. Looking once again at the chart in Example 1, with X being the number of heads that face up when a coin is tossed three times, we find the following events:

The event that $X = 0$ is $\{TTT\}$.
The event that $X = 1$ is $\{HTT, THT, TTH\}$.
The event that $X = 2$ is $\{HHT, HTH, THH\}$.
The event that $X = 3$ is $\{HHH\}$.
The event that $X = 4$ is $\emptyset$.   There are no outcomes with four heads.

Each of these events has a certain probability. For instance, the probability of the event that $X = 2$ is $3/8$ because the event in question consists of three of the eight possible (equally likely) outcomes. We shall abbreviate this by writing

$$P(X = 2) = \frac{3}{8}.$$

The probability that $X = 2$ is $3/8$.

Similarly,

$$P(X = 4) = 0.$$

The probability that $X = 4$ is 0.

When X is a finite random variable, the collection of the probabilities of X equaling each of its possible values is called the **probability distribution** of X. Because the probabilities in a probability distribution can be estimated or theoretical, we shall discuss both *estimated probability distributions* (or *relative frequency distributions*) and *theoretical (modeled) probability distributions* of random variables. (See the next two examples.)

Probability Distribution of a Finite Random Variable

If X is a finite random variable, with values $n_1, n_2, \ldots$ then its **probability distribution** lists the probabilities that $X = n_1, X = n_2, \ldots$ The sum of these probabilities is always 1.

Visualizing the Probability Distribution of a Random Variable

If each outcome in S is equally likely, we get the probability distribution shown for the random variable X.

S

| •0 | •0 | •5 |
| •2 | | •−1 |

Probability Distribution of X

x	−1	0	2	5
$P(X = x)$	$\frac{1}{5} = .2$	$\frac{2}{5} = .4$	$\frac{1}{5} = .2$	$\frac{1}{5} = .2$

Here $P(X = x)$ means "the probability that the random variable X has the specific value x."

Quick Example

Roll a fair die; $X =$ the number facing up. Then, the (theoretical) probability that any specific value of X occurs is $\frac{1}{6}$. So, the probability distribution of X is the following (notice that the probabilities add up to 1):

x	1	2	3	4	5	6
$P(X = x)$	$\frac{1}{6}$	$\frac{1}{6}$	$\frac{1}{6}$	$\frac{1}{6}$	$\frac{1}{6}$	$\frac{1}{6}$

Note The distinction between X (upper case) and x (lower case) in the tables above is important; X stands for the random variable in question, whereas x stands for a specific *value* of X (so that x is always a number). Thus, if, say $x = 2$, then $P(X = x)$ means $P(X = 2)$, the probability that X is 2. Similarly, if Y is a random variable, then $P(Y = y)$ is the probability that Y has the specific value y. ■

$P(X = x)$

Figure 1

 using Technology

Technology can be used to replicate the histogram in Example 3.

TI-83/84 Plus

STAT EDIT values of x in L_1 and probabilities in L_2
WINDOW $0 \le X \le 4$,
$0 \le Y \le 0.5$, Xscl $= 1$
2ND Y= STAT PLOT on,
Histogram icon,
Xlist $= L_1$ Freq $= L_2$, then
GRAPH
[More details on page 612.]

Excel

x-values and probabilities in Columns A and B.
Highlight probabilities (column B only) and insert a column chart.
Right click on resulting graph and use Select Data to set the category labels to be the values of x.
[More details on page 615.]

Web Site
www.FiniteandCalc.org
  Student Home
    → Online Utilities
    → Histogram Utility
Enter the x-values and probabilities as shown:

```
0, 1/8
1, 3/8
2, 3/8
3, 1/8
```

Make sure "Show histogram" is checked, and press "Results."

EXAMPLE 3 **Probability Distribution**

Let X be the number of heads that face up in three tosses of a coin. Give the probability distribution of X.

Solution X is the random variable of Example 1, so its values are 0, 1, 2, and 3. The probability distribution of X is given in the following table:

x	0	1	2	3
$P(X = x)$	$\dfrac{1}{8}$	$\dfrac{3}{8}$	$\dfrac{3}{8}$	$\dfrac{1}{8}$

Notice that the probabilities add to 1, as we might expect.

We can use a bar graph to visualize a probability distribution. Figure 1 shows the bar graph for the probability distribution we obtained. Such a graph is sometimes called a **histogram**.

➡ **Before we go on...** The probabilities in the table in Example 3 are *theoretical* (modeled) probabilities. To obtain a similar table of relative frequencies, we would have to repeatedly toss a coin three times and calculate the fraction of times we got 0, 1, 2, and 3 heads. (See the simulation in the chapter summary at the Web Site.) ■

Note The table of probabilities in Example 3 looks like the probability distribution associated with an experiment, as we studied in Section 7.3. In fact, the probability distribution of a random variable is not really new. Consider the following experiment: toss three coins and count the number of heads. The associated probability distribution (as per Section 7.3) would be this:

Outcome	0	1	2	3
Probability	$\dfrac{1}{8}$	$\dfrac{3}{8}$	$\dfrac{3}{8}$	$\dfrac{1}{8}$

The difference is that in this chapter we are thinking of 0, 1, 2, and 3 not as the outcomes of the experiment, but as values of the random variable X. ■

EXAMPLE 4 **Relative Frequency Distribution**

The following table shows the (fictitious) income brackets of a sample of 1,000 lawyers in their first year out of law school.

Income Bracket	\$20,000–\$29,999	\$30,000–\$39,999	\$40,000–\$49,999	\$50,000–\$59,999	\$60,000–\$69,999	\$70,000–\$79,999	\$80,000–\$89,999
Number	20	80	230	400	170	70	30

Think of the experiment of choosing a first-year lawyer at random (all being equally likely) and assign to each lawyer the number X that is the midpoint of his or her income bracket. Find the relative frequency distribution of X.

Solution Statisticians refer to the income brackets as **measurement classes**. Because the first measurement class contains incomes that are at least \$20,000, but less than

* NOTE One might argue that the midpoint should be $(20,000 + 29,999)/2 = 24,999.50$, but we round this to 25,000. So, technically we are using "rounded" midpoints of the measurement classes.

 using Technology

Technology can be used to automate the calculations in Example 4. Here is an outline.

TI-83/84 Plus

STAT EDIT values of x in L_1 and frequencies in L_2.

Home screen:

L_2/sum(L_2)→L_3

[More details on page 612.]

Excel

Headings x, Fr, and $P(X = x)$ in A1–C1

x-values and frequencies in Columns A2–B8

=B2/SUM(B:B) in C2

Copy down column C.

[More details on page 615.]

Web Site

www.FiniteandCalc.org

Student Home

→ Online Utilities

→ Histogram Utility

Enter the x-values and frequencies as shown:

```
25000, 20
35000, 80
45000, 230
55000, 400
65000, 170
75000, 70
85000, 30
```

Make sure "Show probability distribution" is checked, and press "Results." The relative frequency distribution will appear at the bottom of the page.

$30,000, its midpoint is $25,000.* Similarly the second measurement class has midpoint $35,000, and so on. We can rewrite the table with the midpoints, as follows:

x	25,000	35,000	45,000	55,000	65,000	75,000	85,000
Frequency	20	80	230	400	170	70	30

We have used the term *frequency* rather than *number*, although it means the same thing. This table is called a **frequency table**. It is *almost* the relative frequency distribution for X, except that we must replace frequencies by relative frequencies. (We did this in calculating relative frequencies in the preceding chapter.) We start with the lowest measurement class. Because 20 of the 1,000 lawyers fall in this group, we have

$$P(X = 25,000) = \frac{20}{1,000} = .02.$$

We can calculate the remaining relative frequencies similarly to obtain the following distribution:

x	25,000	35,000	45,000	55,000	65,000	75,000	85,000
$P(X = x)$	.02	.08	.23	.40	.17	.07	.03

Note again the distinction between X and x: X stands for the random variable in question, whereas x stands for a specific value (25,000, 35,000, . . . , or 85,000) of X.

EXAMPLE 5 Probability Distribution: Greenhouse Gases

The following table shows per capita emissions of greenhouse gases for the 30 countries with the highest per capita carbon dioxide emissions. (Emissions are rounded to the nearest 5 metric tons.)*

Country	Per Capita Emissions (metric tons)	Country	Per Capita Emissions (metric tons)
Qatar	70	Estonia	15
Kuwait	40	Faroe Islands	15
United Arab Emirates	40	Saudi Arabia	15
Luxembourg	25	Kazakhstan	15
Trinidad and Tobago	25	Gibraltar	15
Brunei	25	Finland	15
Bahrain	25	Oman	15
Netherlands Antilles	20	Singapore	10
Aruba	20	Palau	10
United States	20	Montserrat	10
Canada	20	Czech Republic	10
Norway	20	Equatorial Guinea	10
Australia	15	New Caledonia	10
Falkland Islands	15	Israel	10
Nauru	15	Russia	10

* Figures are based on 2004 data. Source: United Nations Millennium Development Goals Indicators (http://mdgs.un.org/unsd/mdg/Data.aspx).

Consider the experiment in which a country is selected at random from this list, and let X be the per capita carbon dioxide emissions for that country. Find the probability distribution of X and graph it with a histogram. Use the probability distribution to compute $P(X \geq 20)$ (the probability that X is 20 or more) and interpret the result.

Solution The values of X are the possible emissions figures, which we can take to be $0, 5, 10, 15, \ldots, 70$. In the table below, we first compute the frequency of each value of X by counting the number of countries that produce that per capita level of greenhouse gases. For instance, there are seven countries that have $X = 15$. Then, we divide each frequency by the sample size $N = 30$ to obtain the probabilities.*

* NOTE Even though we are using the term "frequency," we are really calculating *modeled* probability based on the assumption of equally likely outcomes. In this context, the frequencies are the number of favorable outcomes for each value of X. (See the Q&A discussion at the end of Section 7.3.)

x	0	5	10	15	20	25	30	35	40	45	50	55	60	65	70
Frequency	0	0	8	10	5	4	0	0	2	0	0	0	0	0	1
$P(X=x)$	0	0	$\dfrac{8}{30}$	$\dfrac{10}{30}$	$\dfrac{5}{30}$	$\dfrac{4}{30}$	0	0	$\dfrac{2}{30}$	0	0	0	0	0	$\dfrac{1}{30}$

$P(X = x)$

Per Capita Emissions

Figure 2

Figure 2 shows the resulting histogram.

Finally, we compute $P(X \geq 20)$, the probability of the event that X has a value of 20 or more, which is the sum of the probabilities $P(X = 20)$, $P(X = 25)$, and so on. From the table, we obtain

$$P(X \geq 20) = \frac{5}{30} + \frac{4}{30} + \frac{2}{30} + \frac{1}{30} = \frac{12}{30} = .4.$$

Thus, there is a 40% chance that a country randomly selected from the given list produces 20 or more metric tons per capita of carbon dioxide.

FAQs

Recognizing What to Use as a Random Variable and Deciding on Its Values

Q : *In an application, how, exactly, do I decide what to use as a random variable X?*

A : Be as systematic as possible: First, decide what the experiment is and what its sample space is. Then, based on what is asked for in the application, complete the following sentence: "X assigns ___ to each outcome." For instance, "X assigns the number of flavors to each packet of gummy bears selected," or "X assigns the average faculty salary to each college selected."

Q : *Once I have decided what X should be, how do I decide what values to assign it?*

A : Ask yourself: What are the conceivable values I could get for X? Then choose a collection of values that includes all of these. For instance, if X is the number of heads obtained when a coin is tossed five times, then the possible values of X are 0, 1, 2, 3, 4, and 5. If X is the average faculty salary in dollars, rounded to the nearest $5,000, then possible values of X could be 20,000, 25,000, 30,000, and so on, up to the highest salary in your data.

8.1 EXERCISES

▼ more advanced   ◆ challenging
⊤ indicates exercises that should be solved using technology

In Exercises 1–10, classify each random variable X as finite, discrete infinite, or continuous, and indicate the values that X can take. HINT [See Quick Examples on page 549.]

1. Roll two dice; X = the sum of the numbers facing up.

2. Open a 500-page book on a random page; X = the page number.

3. Select a stock at random; X = your profit, to the nearest dollar, if you purchase one share and sell it one year later.

4. Select an electric utility company at random; X = the exact amount of electricity, in gigawatt hours, it supplies in a year.

5. Look at the second hand of your watch; X is the time it reads in seconds.

6. Watch a soccer game; X = the total number of goals scored.

7. Watch a soccer game; X = the total number of goals scored, up to a maximum of 10.

8. Your class is given a mathematics exam worth 100 points; X is the average score, rounded to the nearest whole number.

9. According to quantum mechanics, the energy of an electron in a hydrogen atom can assume only the values $k/1, k/4, k/9, k/16, \ldots$ for a certain constant value k. X = the energy of an electron in a hydrogen atom.

10. According to classical mechanics, the energy of an electron in a hydrogen atom can assume any positive value. X = the energy of an electron in a hydrogen atom.

In Exercises 11–18, (a) say what an appropriate sample space is; (b) complete the following sentence: "X is the rule that assigns to each . . . "; (c) list the values of X for all the outcomes. HINT [See Example 1.]

11. X is the number of tails that come up when a coin is tossed twice.

12. X is the largest number of consecutive times heads comes up in a row when a coin is tossed three times.

13. X is the sum of the numbers that face up when two dice are rolled.

14. X is the value of the larger number when two dice are rolled.

15. X is the number of red marbles that Tonya has in her hand after she selects four marbles from a bag containing four red marbles and two green ones and then notes how many there are of each color.

16. X is the number of green marbles that Stej has in his hand after he selects four marbles from a bag containing three red marbles and two green ones and then notes how many there are of each color.

17. The mathematics final exam scores for the students in your study group are 89%, 85%, 95%, 63%, 92%, and 80%.

18. The capacities of the hard drives of your dormitory suite mates' computers are 10GB, 15GB, 20GB, 25GB, 30GB, and 35GB.

19. The random variable X has this probability distribution table:

x	2	4	6	8	10
$P(X = x)$	.1	.2	–	–	.1

a. Assuming $P(X = 8) = P(X = 6)$, find each of the missing values. HINT [See Quick Example on page 551.]
b. Calculate $P(X \geq 6)$.

20. The random variable X has the probability distribution table shown below:

x	−2	−1	0	1	2
$P(X = x)$	–	–	.4	.1	.1

a. Calculate $P(X \geq 0)$ and $P(X < 0)$. HINT [See Quick Example on page 551.]
b. Assuming $P(X = -2) = P(X = -1)$, find each of the missing values.

In Exercises 21–28, give the probability distribution for the indicated random variable and draw the corresponding histogram. HINT [See Example 3.]

21. A fair die is rolled, and X is the number facing up.

22. A fair die is rolled, and X is the square of the number facing up.

23. Three fair coins are tossed, and X is the square of the number of heads showing.

24. Three fair coins are tossed, and X is the number of heads minus the number of tails.

25. A red and a green die are rolled, and X is the sum of the numbers facing up.

26. A red and a green die are rolled, and
$$X = \begin{cases} 0 & \text{If the numbers are the same} \\ 1 & \text{If the numbers are different.} \end{cases}$$

27. ▼ A red and a green die are rolled, and X is the larger of the two numbers facing up.

28. ▼ A red and a green die are rolled, and X is the smaller of the two numbers facing up.

APPLICATIONS

29. *Income Distribution up to $100,000* The following table shows the distribution of household incomes for a sample of 1,000 households in the United States with incomes up to $100,000.[1]

Income Bracket	0–19,999	20,000–39,999	40,000–59,999	60,000–79,999	80,000–99,999
Households	240	270	220	160	110

a. Let X be the (rounded) midpoint of a bracket in which a household falls. Find the relative frequency distribution of X and graph its histogram. HINT [See Example 4.]

b. Shade the area of your histogram corresponding to the probability that a U.S. household has a value of X of 50,000 or more. What is this probability?

30. *Income Distribution up to $100,000* Repeat Exercise 29, using the following data for a sample of 1,000 Hispanic households in the U.S.[2]

Income Bracket	0–19,999	20,000–39,999	40,000–59,999	60,000–79,999	80,000–99,999
Households	260	310	210	140	80

31. *Employment in Mexico by Age* The following chart shows the ages of 250 working adults surveyed in Mexico:[3]

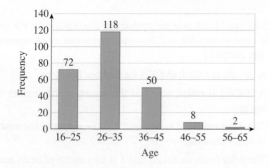

What is the associated random variable? Represent the data as a relative frequency distribution using the (rounded) midpoints of the given measurement classes. HINT [See Example 4.]

32. *Unemployment in Mexico by Age* Repeat the preceding exercise, using the following chart, which shows the ages of 250 unemployed adults surveyed in Mexico:[4]

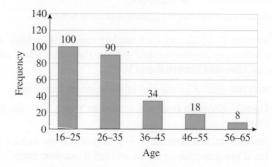

33. *Sport Utility Vehicles—Tow Ratings* The following table shows tow ratings (in pounds) for some popular sports utility vehicles:[5]

Mercedes Grand Marquis V8	2,000
Jeep Wrangler I6	2,000
Ford Explorer V6	3,000
Dodge Dakota V6	4,000
Mitsubishi Montero V6	5,000
Ford Explorer V8	6,000
Dodge Durango V8	6,000
Dodge Ram 1500 V8	8,000
Ford Expedition V8	8,000
Hummer 2-door Hardtop	8,000

Let X be the tow rating of a randomly chosen popular SUV from the list above.

a. What are the values of X?

b. Compute the frequency and probability distributions of X. HINT [See Example 5.]

c. What is the probability that an SUV (from the list above) is rated to tow no more than 5,000 pounds?

34. *Housing Prices* The following table shows the average percentage increase in the price of a house from 1980 to 2001 in nine regions of the United States.[6]

[1] Based on the actual household income distribution in 2007. Source: U.S. Census Bureau, Current Population Survey, 2008 Annual Social and Economic Supplement (http://pubdb3.census.gov/macro/032008/hhinc/new06_000.htm).

[2] Ibid.

[3] Based on data from January 2007. Source for data: Instituto Nacional de Estadística y Geografía (INEGI) (www.inegi.org.mx).

[4] Ibid.

[5] Tow rates are for 2000 models and vary considerably within each model. Figures cited are rounded. For more detailed information, consult www.rvsafety.com/towrate2k.htm.

[6] Percentages are rounded to the nearest 25%. Source: Third Quarter 2001 House Price Index, released November 30, 2001 by the Office of Federal Housing Enterprise Oversight; available online at www.ofheo.gov/house/3q01hpi.pdf.

New England	300
Pacific	225
Middle Atlantic	225
South Atlantic	150
Mountain	150
West North Central	125
West South Central	75
East North Central	150
East South Central	125

Let X be the percentage increase in the price of a house in a randomly selected region.

a. What are the values of X?

b. Compute the frequency and probability distribution of X. HINT [See Example 5.]

c. What is the probability that, in a randomly selected region, the percentage increase in the cost of a house exceeded 200%?

35. Stock Market Gyrations The following chart shows the day-by-day change, rounded to the nearest 100 points, in the Dow Jones Industrial Average during 20 successive business days around the start of the financial crisis in October 2008:[7]

Change in DJIA

October 2   October 30

Let X be the (rounded) change in the Dow on a randomly selected day.

a. What are the values of X?

b. Compute the frequency and probability distribution of X. HINT [See Example 5.]

c. What is the probability that, on a randomly selected day, the Dow decreased by more than 250 points?

36. Stock Market Gyrations Repeat Exercise 35 using the following chart for November–December 2008:[8]

Change in DJIA

November 4   December 2

37. Grade Point Averages The grade point averages of the students in your mathematics class are

3.2, 3.5, 4.0, 2.9, 2.0, 3.3, 3.5, 2.9, 2.5, 2.0,
2.1, 3.2, 3.6, 2.8, 2.5, 1.9, 2.0, 2.2, 3.9, 4.0

Use these raw data to construct a frequency table with the following measurement classes: 1.1–2.0, 2.1–3.0, 3.1–4.0, and find the probability distribution using the (rounded) midpoint values as the values of X. HINT [See Example 5.]

38. Test Scores Your scores for the 20 surprise math quizzes last semester were (out of 10)

4.5, 9.5, 10.0, 3.5, 8.0, 9.5, 7.5, 6.5, 7.0, 8.0,
8.0, 8.5, 7.5, 7.0, 8.0, 9.0, 10.0, 8.5, 7.5, 8.0.

Use these raw data to construct a frequency table with the following brackets: 2.1–4.0, 4.1–6.0, 6.1–8.0, 8.1–10.0, and find the probability distribution using the (rounded) midpoint values as the values of X. HINT [See Example 5.]

39. ▼ Car Purchases To persuade his parents to contribute to his new car fund, Carmine has spent the last week surveying the ages of 2,000 cars on campus. His findings are reflected in the following frequency table:

Age of Car (years)	0	1	2	3	4	5	6	7	8	9	10
Number of Cars	140	350	450	650	200	120	50	10	5	15	10

Carmine's jalopy is 6 years old. He would like to make the following claim to his parents: "x percent of students have cars newer than mine." Use a relative frequency distribution to find x.

[7] Source: http://finance.google.com.

[8] Ibid.

40. ▼ Car Purchases Carmine's parents, not convinced of his need for a new car, produced the following statistics showing the ages of cars owned by students on the Dean's List:

Age of Car (years)	0	1	2	3	4	5	6	7	8	9	10
Number of Cars	0	2	5	5	10	10	15	20	20	20	40

They then claimed that if he kept his 6-year-old car for another year, his chances of getting on the Dean's List would be increased by x percent. Use a relative frequency distribution to find x.

Highway Safety *Exercises 41–50 are based on the following table, which shows crashworthiness ratings for several categories of motor vehicles.[9] In all of these exercises, take X as the crash-test rating of a small car, Y as the crash-test rating for a small SUV, and so on, as shown in the table.*

	Number Tested	**Overall Frontal Crash Test Rating**			
		3 (Good)	2 (Acceptable)	1 (Marginal)	0 (Poor)
Small Cars X	16	1	11	2	2
Small SUVs Y	10	1	4	4	1
Medium SUVs Z	15	3	5	3	4
Passenger Vans U	13	3	0	3	7
Midsize Cars V	15	3	5	0	7
Large Cars W	19	9	5	3	2

41. Compute the relative frequency distribution for X.

42. Compute the relative frequency distribution for Y.

43. Compute $P(X \geq 2)$ and interpret the result.

44. Compute $P(Y \leq 1)$ and interpret the result.

45. Compare $P(Y \geq 2)$ and $P(Z \geq 2)$. What does the result suggest about SUVs?

46. Compare $P(V \geq 2)$ and $P(Z \geq 2)$. What does the result suggest?

47. ▼ Which of the six categories shown has the *lowest* probability of a Good rating?

48. ▼ Which of the six categories shown has the *highest* probability of a Poor rating?

49. ▼ You choose, at random, a small car and a small SUV. What is the probability that both will be rated at least 2?

---

[9] Ratings are by the Insurance Institute for Highway Safety. Sources: Oak Ridge National Laboratory: "An Analysis of the Impact of Sport Utility Vehicles in the United States," Stacy C. Davis, Lorena F. Truett (August 2000)/Insurance Institute for Highway Safety (www-cta.ornl.gov/Publications/Final SUV report.pdf, www.highwaysafety.org/vehicle_ratings).

50. ▼ You choose, at random, a small car and a midsize car. What is the probability that both will be rated at most 1?

Exercises 51 and 52 assume familiarity with counting arguments and probability (Section 7.4).

51. ▼ Camping Kent's Tents has four red tents and three green tents in stock. Karin selects four of them at random. Let X be the number of red tents she selects. Give the probability distribution and find $P(X \geq 2)$.

52. ▼ Camping Kent's Tents has five green knapsacks and four yellow ones in stock. Curt selects four of them at random. Let X be the number of green knapsacks he selects. Give the probability distribution and find $P(X \leq 2)$.

53. ◆ Testing Your Calculator Use your calculator or computer to generate a sequence of 100 random digits in the range 0–9, and test the random number generator for uniformness by drawing the distribution histogram.

54. ◆ Testing Your Dice Repeat Exercise 53, but this time, use a die to generate a sequence of 50 random numbers in the range 1–6.

COMMUNICATION AND REASONING EXERCISES

55. Are all infinite random variables necessarily continuous? Explain.

56. Are all continuous random variables necessarily infinite? Explain.

57. If you are unable to compute the (theoretical) probability distribution for a random variable X, how can you estimate the distribution?

58. What do you expect to happen to the probabilities in a probability distribution as you make the measurement classes smaller?

59. ▼ Give an example of a real-life situation that can be modeled by a random variable with a probability distribution whose histogram is highest on the left.

60. ▼ Give an example of a real-life situation that can be modeled by a random variable with a probability distribution whose histogram is highest on the right.

61. ▼ How wide should the bars in a histogram be so that the area of each bar equals the probability of the corresponding range of values of X?

62. ▼ How wide should the bars in a histogram be so that the probability $P(a \leq X \leq b)$ equals the area of the corresponding portion of the histogram?

63. ▼ Give at least one scenario in which you might prefer to model the number of pages in a randomly selected book using a continuous random variable rather than a discrete random variable.

64. ▼ Give at least one scenario in which you might prefer to model a temperature using a discrete random variable rather than a continuous random variable.

8.2 Bernoulli Trials and Binomial Random Variables

Your electronic production plant produces video game joysticks. Unfortunately, quality control at the plant leaves much to be desired, and 10% of the joysticks the plant produces are defective. A large corporation has expressed interest in adopting your product for its new game console, and today an inspection team will be visiting to test video game joysticks as they come off the assembly line. If the team tests five joysticks, what is the probability that none will be defective? What is the probability that more than one will be defective?

NOTE These are customary names for the two possible outcomes, and often do not indicate actual success or failure at anything. "Success" is the label we give the outcome of interest—in this case, finding a defective joystick.

In this scenario we are interested in the following, which is an example of a particular type of finite random variable called a **binomial random variable**: Think of the experiment as a sequence of five "trials" (in each trial the inspection team chooses one joystick at random and tests it) each with two possible outcomes: "success" (a defective joystick) and "failure" (a non-defective one).* If we now take X to be the number of successes (defective joysticks) the inspection team finds, we can recast the questions above as follows: Find $P(X = 0)$ and $P(X > 1)$.

Bernoulli Trial

† *NOTE* Jakob Bernoulli (1654–1705) was one of the pioneers of probability theory.

A **Bernoulli†** **trial** is an experiment that has two possible outcomes, called **success** and **failure**. If the probability of success is p then the probability of failure is $q = 1 - p$.

Visualizing a Bernoulli Trial

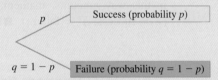

Tossing a coin three times is an example of a **sequence of independent Bernoulli trials**: a sequence of Bernoulli trials in which the outcomes in any one trial are independent (in the sense of the preceding chapter) of those in any other trial, and in which the probability of success is the same for all the trials.

Quick Examples

1. Roll a die, and take success to be the event that you roll a 6. Then $p = 1/6$ and $q = 5/6$. Rolling the die 10 times is then an example of a sequence of 10 independent Bernoulli trials.

2. Provide a property with flood insurance for 20 years, and take success to be the event that the property is flooded during a particular year. Observing whether or not the property is flooded each year for 20 years is then an example of 20 independent Bernoulli trials (assuming that the occurrence of flooding one year is independent of whether there was flooding in earlier years).

✱ NOTE Choosing a "loser" (a fund that will depreciate next year) slightly depletes the pool of "losers" and hence slightly decreases the probability of choosing another one. However, the fact that the pool of funds is very large means that this decrease is extremely small. Hence, *p* is very nearly constant.

3. You know that 60% of all bond funds will depreciate in value next year. Take success to be the event that a randomly chosen fund depreciates next year. Then $p = .6$ and $q = .4$. Choosing five funds at random for your portfolio from a very large number of possible funds is, approximately,✱ an example of five independent Bernolli trials.

4. Suppose that E is an event in an experiment with sample space S. Then we can think of the experiment as a Bernoulli trial with two outcomes; success if E occurs, and failure if E' occurs. The probability of success is then

$$p = P(E) \qquad\qquad \text{Success is the occurrence of } E.$$

and the probability of failure is

$$q = P(E') = 1 - P(E) = 1 - p. \qquad \text{Failure is the occurrence of } E'.$$

Repeating the experiment 30 times, say, is then an example of 30 independent Bernoulli trials.

Note Quick Example 4 above tells us that Bernoulli trials are not very special kinds of experiments; in fact, we are performing a Bernoulli trial every time we repeat *any* experiment and observe whether a specific event E occurs. Thinking of an experiment in this way amounts, mathematically, to thinking of $\{E, E'\}$ as our sample space (E = success, E' = failure). ∎

Binomial Random Variable

A **binomial random variable** is one that counts the number of successes in a sequence of independent Bernoulli trials, where the number of trials is fixed.

Visualizing a Binomial Random Variable

Quick Examples

1. Roll a die ten times; X is the number of times you roll a 6.

2. Provide a property with flood insurance for 20 years; X is the number of years, during the 20-year period, during which the property is flooded (assuming that the occurrence of flooding one year is independent of whether there was flooding in earlier years).

3. You know that 60% of all bond funds will depreciate in value next year, and you randomly select four from a very large number of possible choices; X is the number of bond funds you hold that will depreciate next year. (X is approximately binomial; see the margin note on p. 560.)

EXAMPLE 1 **Probability Distribution of a Binomial Random Variable**

Suppose that we have a possibly unfair coin with the probability of heads p and the probability of tails $q = 1 - p$.

a. Let X be the number of heads you get in a sequence of five tosses. Find $P(X = 2)$.

b. Let X be the number of heads you get in a sequence of n tosses. Find $P(X = x)$.

Solution

a. We are looking for the probability of getting exactly two heads in a sequence of five tosses. Let's start with a simpler question: What is the probability that we will get the sequence HHTTT?

The probability that the first toss will come up heads is p.

The probability that the second toss will come up heads is also p.

The probability that the third toss will come up tails is q.

The probability that the fourth toss will come up tails is q.

The probability that the fifth toss will come up tails is q.

The probability that the first toss will be heads *and* the second will be heads *and* the third will be tails *and* the fourth will be tails *and* the fifth will be tails equals the probability of the *intersection* of these five events. Because these are independent events, the probability of the intersection is the product of the probabilities, which is

$$p \times p \times q \times q \times q = p^2 q^3.$$

Now HHTTT is only one of several outcomes with two heads and three tails. Two others are HTHTT and TTTHH. How many such outcomes are there altogether? This is the number of "words" with two H's and three T's, and we know from Chapter 6 that the answer is $C(5, 2) = 10$.

Each of the 10 outcomes with two H's and three T's has the same probability: $p^2 q^3$. (Why?) Thus, the probability of getting one of these 10 outcomes is the probability of the union of all these (mutually exclusive) events, and we saw in the preceding chapter that this is just the sum of the probabilities. In other words, the probability we are after is

$$P(X = 2) = p^2 q^3 + p^2 q^3 + \cdots + p^2 q^3 \qquad C(5, 2) \text{ times}$$
$$= C(5, 2) p^2 q^3.$$

The structure of this formula is as follows:

Number of heads Number of tails

$$P(X = 2) = C(5, 2)p^2 q^3$$

Number of tosses | | Probability of tails
Number of heads Probability of heads

b. What we did using the numbers 5 and 2 in part (a) works as well in general. For the general case, with n tosses and x heads, replace 5 with n and replace 2 with x to get:

$$P(X = x) = C(n, x)p^x q^{n-x}.$$

(Note that the coefficient of q is the number of tails, which is $n - x$.)

The calculation in Example 1 applies to any binomial random variable, so we can say the following:

Probability Distribution of Binomial Random Variables

If X is the number of successes in a sequence of n independent Bernoulli trials, then

$$P(X = x) = C(n, x)p^x q^{n-x}$$

where

n = number of trials
p = probability of success
q = probability of failure = $1 - p$.

Quick Example

If you roll a fair die five times, the probability of throwing exactly two 6s is

$$P(X = 2) = C(5, 2) \left(\frac{1}{6}\right)^2 \left(\frac{5}{6}\right)^3 = 10 \times \frac{1}{36} \times \frac{125}{216} \approx .1608.$$

Here, we used $n = 5$ and $p = 1/6$, the probability of rolling a 6 on one roll of the die.

EXAMPLE 2 Aging

By 2030, the probability that a randomly chosen resident in the United States will be 65 years old or older is projected to be .2.[*]

a. What is the probability that, in a randomly selected sample of six U.S. residents, exactly four of them will be 65 or older?

b. If X is the number of people aged 65 or older in a sample of six, construct the probability distribution of X and plot its histogram.

---

[*] Source: U.S. Census Bureau, Decennial Census, Population Estimates and Projections (www.agingstats.gov/agingstatsdotnet/Main_Site/Data/2008_Documents/Population.aspx).

c. Compute $P(X \le 2)$.

d. Compute $P(X \ge 2)$.

Solution

a. The experiment is a sequence of Bernoulli trials; in each trial we select a person and ascertain his or her age. If we take "success" to mean selection of a person aged 65 or older, then the probability distribution is

$$P(X = x) = C(n, x)p^x q^{n-x}$$

where n = number of trials = 6

p = probability of success = .2

q = probability of failure = .8

So,

$$P(X = 4) = C(6, 4)(.2)^4(.8)^2$$
$$= 15 \times .0016 \times .64 = .01536$$

b. We have already computed $P(X = 4)$. Here are all the calculations:

$$P(X = 0) = C(6, 0)(.2)^0(.8)^6$$
$$= 1 \times 1 \times .262144 = .262144$$

$$P(X = 1) = C(6, 1)(.2)^1(.8)^5$$
$$= 6 \times .2 \times .32768 = .393216$$

$$P(X = 2) = C(6, 2)(.2)^2(.8)^4$$
$$= 15 \times .04 \times .4096 = .24576$$

$$P(X = 3) = C(6, 3)(.2)^3(.8)^3$$
$$= 20 \times .008 \times .512 = .08192$$

$$P(X = 4) = C(6, 4)(.2)^4(.8)^2$$
$$= 15 \times .0016 \times .64 = .01536$$

$$P(X = 5) = C(6, 5)(.2)^5(.8)^1$$
$$= 6 \times .00032 \times .8 = .001536$$

$$P(X = 6) = C(6, 6)(.2)^6(.8)^0$$
$$= 1 \times .000064 \times 1 = .000064.$$

The probability distribution is therefore as follows:

x	0	1	2	3	4	5	6
$P(X = x)$	.262144	.393216	.24576	.08192	.01536	.001536	.000064

Figure 3 shows its histogram.

c. $P(X \le 2)$—the probability that the number of people selected who are at least 65 years old is either 0, 1, or 2—is the probability of the union of these events and is thus the sum of the three probabilities:

$$P(X \le 2) = P(X = 0) + P(X = 1) + P(X = 2)$$
$$= .262144 + .393216 + .24576$$
$$= .90112.$$

$P(X = x)$

0.4
0.3
0.2
0.1
0

0 1 2 3 4 5 6 x

Figure 3

 using Technology

Technology can be used to replicate the histogram in Example 2.

TI-83/84 Plus

Y= screen: Y_1=6 nCr
X*0.2^X*0.8^(6-X)
2ND TBLSET Set Indpt to Ask.
2ND TABLE Enter *x*-values
0, 1, . . . , 6.

[More details on page 612.]

d. To compute $P(X \geq 2)$, we *could* compute the sum

$$P(X \geq 2) = P(X = 2) + P(X = 3) + P(X = 4) + P(X = 5) + P(X = 6)$$

but it is far easier to compute the probability of the complement of the event:

$$P(X < 2) = P(X = 0) + P(X = 1)$$
$$= .262144 + .393216 = .65536$$

and then subtract the answer from 1:

$$P(X \geq 2) = 1 - P(X < 2)$$
$$= 1 - .65536 = .34464.$$

FAQs

Terminology and Recognizing When to Use the Binomial Distribution

Q: *What is the difference between Bernoulli trials and a binomial random variable?*

A: A Bernoulli trial is a type of experiment, whereas a binomial random variable is the resulting kind of random variable. More precisely, if your experiment consists of performing a sequence of *n* Bernoulli trials (think of throwing a dart *n* times at random points on a dartboard hoping to hit the bull's eye), then the random variable *X* that counts the number of successes (the number of times you actually hit the bull's eye) is a binomial random variable.

Q: *How do I recognize when a situation gives a binomial random variable?*

A: Make sure that the experiment consists of a sequence of independent Bernoulli trials; that is, a sequence of a fixed number of trials of an experiment that has two outcomes, where the outcome of each trial does not depend on the outcomes in previous trials, and where the probability of success is the same for all the trials. For instance, repeatedly throwing a dart at a dartboard hoping to hit the bull's eye does not constitute a sequence of Bernoulli trials if you adjust your aim each time depending on the outcome of your previous attempt. This dart-throwing experiment can be modeled by a sequence of Bernoulli trials if you make no adjustments after each attempt and your aim does not improve (or deteriorate) with time.

8.2 EXERCISES

▼ more advanced   ◆ challenging

🔟 indicates exercises that should be solved using technology

In Exercises 1–10, you are performing 5 independent Bernoulli trials with p = .1 and q = .9. Calculate the probability of each of the stated outcomes. Check your answer using technology. HINT [See Quick Example on page 562.]

1. Two successes

2. Three successes

3. No successes

4. No failures

5. All successes

6. All failures

7. At most two successes

8. At least four successes

9. At least three successes

10. At most three successes

In Exercises 11–18, X is a binomial variable with n = 6 and p = .4. Compute the given probabilities. Check your answer using technology. HINT [See Example 2.]

11. $P(X = 3)$

12. $P(X = 4)$

13. $P(X \leq 2)$

14. $P(X \leq 1)$

15. $P(X \geq 5)$

16. $P(X \geq 4)$

17. $P(1 \leq X \leq 3)$

18. $P(3 \leq X \leq 5)$

In Exercises 19 and 20, graph the histogram of the given binomial distribution. Check your answer using technology.

19. $n = 5, p = \dfrac{1}{4}, q = \dfrac{3}{4}$

20. $n = 5, p = \dfrac{1}{3}, q = \dfrac{2}{3}$

In Exercises 21 and 22, graph the histogram of the given binomial distribution and compute the given quantity, indicating the corresponding region on the graph.

21. $n = 4$, $p = \dfrac{1}{3}$, $q = \dfrac{2}{3}$; $P(X \leq 2)$

22. $n = 4$, $p = \dfrac{1}{4}$, $q = \dfrac{3}{4}$; $P(X \leq 1)$

APPLICATIONS

23. *Internet Addiction* The probability that a randomly chosen person in the Netherlands connects to the Internet immediately upon waking is approximately .25.[10] What is the probability that, in a randomly selected sample of five people, two connect to the Internet immediately upon waking? HINT [See Example 2.]

24. *Alien Retirement* The probability that a randomly chosen citizen-entity of Cygnus is of pension age[11] is approximately .8. What is the probability that, in a randomly selected sample of four citizen-entities, all of them are of pension age? HINT [See Example 2.]

25. *'90s Internet Stock Boom* According to a July, 1999, article in the *New York Times*,[12] venture capitalists had this "rule of thumb": The probability that an Internet start-up company will be a "stock market success" resulting in "spectacular profits for early investors" is .2. If you were a venture capitalist who invested in 10 Internet start-up companies, what was the probability that at least 1 of them would be a stock market success? (Round your answer to four decimal places.)

26. *'90s Internet Stock Boom* According to the article cited in Exercise 25, 13.5% of Internet stocks that entered the market in 1999 ended up trading below their initial offering prices. If you were an investor who purchased five Internet stocks at their initial offering prices, what was the probability that at least four of them would end up trading at or above their initial offering price? (Round your answer to four decimal places.)

27. *Job Training* *(from the GRE Exam in Economics)* In a large on-the-job training program, half of the participants are female and half are male. In a random sample of three participants, what is the probability that an investigator will draw at least one male?

28. *Job Training* *(based on a question from the GRE Exam in Economics)* In a large on-the-job training program, half of the participants are female and half are male. In a random sample of five participants, what is the probability that an investigator will draw at least two males?

29. *Manufacturing* Your manufacturing plant produces air bags, and it is known that 10% of them are defective. Five air bags are tested.

  a. Find the probability that three of them are defective.
  b. Find the probability that at least two of them are defective.

30. *Manufacturing* Compute the probability distribution of the binomial variable described in the preceding exercise, and use it to compute the probability that if five air bags are tested, at least one will be defective and at least one will not.

31. *Teenage Pastimes* According to a study,[13] the probability that a randomly selected teenager watched a rented video at least once during a week was .71. What is the probability that at least 8 teenagers in a group of 10 watched a rented movie at least once last week?

32. *Other Teenage Pastimes* According to the study cited in the preceding exercise, the probability that a randomly selected teenager studied at least once during a week was only .52. What is the probability that less than half of the students in your study group of 10 have studied in the last week?

33. *Subprime Mortgages* In November 2008 the probability that a randomly selected subprime home mortgage in Florida was in foreclosure was .24.[14] Choose 10 subprime home mortgages at random.

  a. What is the probability that exactly five of them were in foreclosure?
  b. ▯ Use technology to generate the probability distribution for the associated binomial random variable.
  c. Fill in the blank: If 10 subprime home mortgages were chosen at random, the number of them most likely to have been in foreclosure was _____.

34. *Subprime Mortgages* In November 2008 the probability that a randomly selected subprime home mortgage in Texas was current in its payments was .67.[15] Choose 10 subprime home mortgages at random.

  a. What is the probability that exactly four of them were current?
  b. ▯ Use technology to generate the probability distribution for the associated binomial random variable.
  c. Fill in the blank: If 10 subprime home mortgages were chosen at random, the number of them most likely to have been current was _____.

35. ▼ *Triple Redundancy* In order to ensure reliable performance of vital computer systems, aerospace engineers sometimes employ the technique of "triple redundancy," in which three identical computers are installed in a space vehicle. If one of the three computers gives results different from the other two,

---

[10] Source: *Webwereld* November 17, 2008 (http://webwereld.nl/article/view/id/53599).

[11] The retirement age in Cygnus is 12,000 bootlags, which is equivalent to approximately 20 minutes Earth time.

[12] "Not All Hit It Rich in the Internet Gold Rush," *The New York Times*, July 20, 1999, p. A1.

[13] Sources: Rand Youth Poll/Teen-age Research Unlimited/*The New York Times*, March 14, 1998, p. D1.

[14] Source: Federal Reserve Bank of New York (www.newyorkfed.org/regional/subprime.html).

[15] Ibid.

it is assumed to be malfunctioning and it is ignored. This technique will work as long as no more than one computer malfunctions. Assuming that an onboard computer is 99% reliable (that is, the probability of its failing is .01), what is the probability that at least two of the three computers will malfunction?

36. ▼ *IQ Scores* Mensa is a club for people who have high IQ scores. To qualify, your IQ must be at least 132, putting you in the top 2% of the general population. If a group of 10 people are chosen at random, what is the probability that at least 2 of them qualify for Mensa?

37. Ⓣ▼ *Standardized Tests* Assume that on a standardized test of 100 questions, a person has a probability of 80% of answering any particular question correctly. Find the probability of answering between 75 and 85 questions, inclusive, correctly. (Assume independence, and round your answer to four decimal places.)

38. Ⓣ▼ *Standardized Tests* Assume that on a standardized test of 100 questions, a person has a probability of 80% of answering any particular question correctly. Find the probability of answering at least 90 questions correctly. (Assume independence, and round your answer to four decimal places.)

39. Ⓣ▼ *Product Testing* It is known that 43% of all the ZeroFat hamburger patties produced by your factory actually contain more than 10 grams of fat. Compute the probability distribution for $n = 50$ Bernoulli trials.
   a. What is the most likely value for the number of burgers in a sample of 50 that contain more than 10 grams of fat?
   b. Complete the following sentence: There is an approximately 71% chance that a batch of 50 ZeroFat patties contains _____ or more patties with more than 10 grams of fat.
   c. Compare the graphs of the distributions for $n = 50$ trials and $n = 20$ trials. What do you notice?

40. Ⓣ▼ *Product Testing* It is known that 65% of all the ZeroCal hamburger patties produced by your factory actually contain more than 1,000 calories. Compute the probability distribution for $n = 50$ Bernoulli trials.
   a. What is the most likely value for the number of burgers in a sample of 50 that contain more than 1,000 calories?
   b. Complete the following sentence: There is an approximately 73% chance that a batch of 50 ZeroCal patties contains _____ or more patties with more than 1,000 calories.
   c. Compare the graphs of the distributions for $n = 50$ trials and $n = 20$ trials. What do you notice?

41. Ⓣ▼ *Quality Control* A manufacturer of light bulbs chooses bulbs at random from its assembly line for testing. If the probability of a bulb's being bad is .01, how many bulbs do they need to test before the probability of finding at least one bad one rises to more than .5? (You may have to use trial and error to solve this.)

42. Ⓣ▼ *Quality Control* A manufacturer of light bulbs chooses bulbs at random from its assembly line for testing. If the probability of a bulb's being bad is .01, how many bulbs do they need to test before the probability of finding at least two bad ones rises to more than .5? (You may have to use trial and error to solve this.)

43. ▼ *Highway Safety* According to a study,[16] a male driver in the United States will average 562 accidents per 100 million miles. Regard an n-mile trip as a sequence of n Bernoulli trials with "success" corresponding to having an accident during a particular mile. What is the probability that a male driver will have an accident in a one-mile trip?

44. ▼ *Highway Safety*: According to the study cited in the preceding exercise, a female driver in the United States will average 611 accidents per 100 million miles. Regard an n-mile trip as a sequence of n Bernoulli trials with "success" corresponding to having an accident during a particular mile. What is the probability that a female driver will have an accident in a one-mile trip?

45. ◆ *Mad Cow Disease* In March 2004, the U.S. Agriculture Department announced plans to test approximately 243,000 slaughtered cows per year for mad cow disease (bovine spongiform encephalopathy).[17] When announcing the plan, the Agriculture Department stated that "by the laws of probability, that many tests should detect mad cow disease even if it is present in only 5 cows out of the 45 million in the nation."[18] Test the Department's claim by computing the probability that, if only 5 out of 45 million cows had mad cow disease, at least 1 cow would test positive in a year (assuming the testing was done randomly).

46. ◆ *Mad Cow Disease* According to the article cited in Exercise 45, only 223,000 of the cows being tested for bovine spongiform encephalopathy were to be "downer cows"; cows unable to walk to their slaughter. Assuming that just one downer cow in 500,000 is infected on average, use a binomial distribution to find the probability that 2 or more cows would test positive in a year. Your associate claims that "by the laws of probability, that many tests should detect at least two cases of mad cow disease even if it is present in only 2 cows out of a million downers." Comment on that claim.

COMMUNICATION AND REASONING EXERCISES

47. A soccer player is more likely to score on his second shot if he was successful on his first. Can we model a succession of shots a player takes as a sequence of Bernoulli trials? Explain.

---

[16] Data are based on a report by National Highway Traffic Safety Administration released in January, 1996. Source for data: U.S. Department of Transportation/*The New York Times*, April 9, 1999, p. F1.

[17] Source: *The New York Times*, March 17, 2004, p. A19.

[18] As stated in the *New York Times* article.

48. A soccer player takes repeated shots on goal. What assumption must we make if we want to model a succession of shots by a player as a sequence of Bernoulli trials?

49. Your friend just told you that "misfortunes always occur in threes." If life is just a sequence of Bernoulli trials, is this possible? Explain.

50. Suppose an experiment consists of repeatedly (every week) checking whether your graphing calculator battery has died. Is this a sequence of Bernoulli trials? Explain.

51. In an experiment with sample space S, a certain event E has a probability p of occurring. What has this scenario to do with Bernoulli trials?

52. An experiment consists of removing a gummy bear from a bag originally containing 10, and then eating it. Regard eating a lime flavored bear as success. Repeating the experiment five times is a sequence of Bernoulli trials, right?

53. ▼ Why is the following not a binomial random variable? Select, without replacement, five marbles from a bag containing six red marbles and two blue ones, and let X be the number of red marbles you have selected.

54. ▼ By contrast with Exercise 53, why can the following be modeled by a binomial random variable? Select, without replacement, 5 electronic components from a batch of 10,000 in which 1,000 are defective, and let X be the number of defective components you select.

8.3 Measures of Central Tendency

Mean, Median, and Mode of a Set of Data

One day you decide to measure the popularity rating of your statistics instructor, Mr. Pelogrande. Ideally, you should poll all of Mr. Pelogrande's students, which is what statisticians would refer to as the **population**. However, it would be difficult to poll all the members of the population in question (Mr. Pelogrande teaches more than 400 students). Instead, you decide to survey 10 of his students, chosen at random, and ask them to rate Mr. Pelogrande on a scale of 0–100. The survey results in the following set of data:

$$60, 50, 55, 0, 100, 90, 40, 20, 40, 70.$$

Such a collection of data is called a **sample**, because the 10 people polled represent only a (small) sample of Mr. Pelogrande's students. We should think of the individual scores $60, 50, 55, \ldots$ as values of a random variable: Choose one of Mr. Pelogrande's students at random and let X be the rating the student gives to Mr. Pelogrande.

How do we distill a single measurement, or **statistic**, from this sample that would describe Mr. Pelogrande's popularity? Perhaps the most commonly used statistic is the **average**, or **mean**, which is computed by adding the scores and dividing the sum by the number of scores in the sample:

$$\text{Sample Mean} = \frac{60 + 50 + 55 + 0 + 100 + 90 + 40 + 20 + 40 + 70}{10} = \frac{525}{10} = 52.5.$$

We might then conclude, based on the sample, that Mr. Pelogrande's average popularity rating is about 52.5. The usual notation for the sample mean is $\bar{x}$, and the formula we use to compute it is

$$\bar{x} = \frac{x_1 + x_2 + \cdots + x_n}{n}$$

where $x_1, x_2, \ldots, x_n$ are the values of X in the sample.

A convenient way of writing the sum that appears in the numerator is to use **summation** or **sigma notation**. We write the sum $x_1 + x_2 + \cdots + x_n$ as

$$\sum_{i=1}^{n} x_i.$$

$\sum_{i=1}^{n}$ by itself stands for "the sum, from $i = 1$ to n."

$\sum_{i=1}^{n} x_i$ stands for "the sum of the x_i, from $i = 1$ to n."

We think of i as taking on the values $1, 2, \ldots, n$ in turn, making x_i equal $x_1, x_2, \ldots, x_n$ in turn, and we then add up these values.

Sample and Mean

A **sample** is a sequence of values (or scores) of a random variable X. (The process of collecting such a sequence is sometimes called **sampling** X.) The **sample mean** is the average of the values, or **scores**, in the sample. To compute the sample mean, we use the following formula:

$$\bar{x} = \frac{x_1 + x_2 + \cdots + x_n}{n} = \frac{\sum_{i=1}^{n} x_i}{n}$$

or simply

$$\bar{x} = \frac{\sum_i x_i}{n}. \qquad \sum_i \text{ stands for "sum over all } i."\ast$$

Here, n is the **sample size** (number of scores), and $x_1, x_2, \ldots, x_n$ are the individual values.

If the sample $x_1, x_2, \ldots, x_n$ consists of all the values of X from the entire population[†] (for instance, the ratings given Mr. Pelogrande by *all* of his students), we refer to the mean as the **population mean**, and write it as μ (Greek "mu") instead of $\bar{x}$.

Visualizing the Mean

$$\bar{x} = \frac{8 + 5 + 2}{3} = 5$$

✳ NOTE In Section 1.4 we simply wrote $\sum x$ for the sum of all the x_i, but here we will use the subscripts to make it easier to interpret formulas in this and the next section.

† NOTE When we talk about *populations*, the understanding is that the underlying experiment consists of selecting a member of a given population and ascertaining the value of X.

Quick Examples

1. The mean of the sample 1, 2, 3, 4, 5 is $\bar{x} = 3$.
2. The mean of the sample $-1, 0, 2$ is $\bar{x} = \dfrac{-1 + 0 + 2}{3} = \dfrac{1}{3}$.
3. The mean of the population $-3, -3, 0, 0, 1$ is
$$\mu = \frac{-3 - 3 + 0 + 0 + 1}{5} = -1.$$

Note: Sample Mean versus Population Mean

Determining a population mean can be difficult or even impossible. For instance, computing the mean household income for the United States would entail recording the income of every single household in the United States. Instead of attempting to do this, we usually use sample means instead. The larger the sample used, the more accurately we expect the sample mean to approximate the population mean. Estimating how accurately a sample mean based on a given sample size approximates the population mean is possible, but we will not go into that in this book. ∎

The mean $\bar{x}$ is an attempt to describe where the "center" of the sample is. It is therefore called a **measure of central tendency**. There are two other common measures of central tendency: the "middle score," or **median**, and the "most frequent score," or **mode**. These are defined as follows.

Median and Mode

The **sample median** m is the middle score (in the case of an odd-size sample), or average of the two middle scores (in the case of an even-size sample) when the scores in a sample are arranged in ascending order.

A **sample mode** is a score that appears most often in the collection. (There may be more than one mode in a sample.)

Visualizing the Median and Mode

Median = Middle Score = 4

Mode = Most Frequent Score = 2

As before, we refer to the **population median** and **population mode** if the sample consists of the data from the entire population.

Quick Examples

1. The sample median of 2, –3, –1, 4, 2 is found by first arranging the scores in ascending order: –3, –1, 2, 2, 4 and then selecting the middle (third) score: $m = 2$. The sample mode is also 2 because this is the score that appears most often.
2. The sample 2, 5, 6, –1, 0, 6 has median $m = (2 + 5)/2 = 3.5$ and mode 6.

The mean tends to give more weight to scores that are further away from the center than does the median. For example, if you take the largest score in a collection of more than two numbers and make it larger, the mean will increase but the median will remain the same. For this reason the median is often preferred for collections that contain a wide range of scores. The mode can sometimes lie far from the center and is thus used less often as an indication of where the "center" of a sample lies.

Heide Benser/CORBIS

EXAMPLE 1 **Teenage Spending in the '90s**

A 10-year survey of spending patterns of U.S. teenagers in the 1990s yielded the following figures (in billions of dollars spent in a year):* 90, 90, 85, 80, 80, 80, 80, 85, 90, 100. Compute and interpret the mean, median, and mode, and illustrate the data on a graph.

Solution The *mean* is given by

$$\bar{x} = \frac{\sum_i x_i}{n}$$

$$= \frac{90 + 90 + 85 + 80 + 80 + 80 + 80 + 85 + 90 + 100}{10} = \frac{860}{10} = 86.$$

Thus, spending by teenagers averaged $86 billion per year.

For the *median*, we arrange the sample data in ascending order:

$$80, 80, 80, 80, 85, 85, 90, 90, 90, 100.$$

We then take the average of the two middle scores:

$$m = \frac{85 + 85}{2} = 85.$$

This means that in half the years in question, teenagers spent $85 billion or less, and in half they spent $85 billion or more.

For the *mode* we choose the score (or scores) that occurs most frequently: $80 billion. Thus, teenagers spent $80 billion per year more often than any other amount.

The frequency histogram in Figure 4 illustrates these three measures.

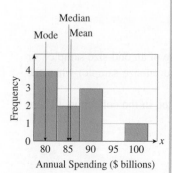

Figure 4

---

*Spending figures are rounded, and cover the years 1988 through 1997. Source: Rand Youth Poll/Teenage Research Unlimited/*The New York Times*, March 14, 1998, p. D1.

➡ **Before we go on...** There is a nice geometric interpretation of the difference between the median and mode: The median line shown in Figure 4 divides the total area of the histogram into two equal pieces, whereas the mean line passes through its "center of gravity"; if you placed the histogram on a knife-edge along the mean line, it would balance. ■

Expected Value of a Finite Random Variable

Now, instead of looking at a sample of values of a given random variable, let us look at the probability distribution of the random variable itself and see if we can predict the sample mean without actually taking a sample. This prediction is what we call the *expected value* of the random variable.

EXAMPLE 2 **Expected Value of a Random Variable**

Suppose you roll a fair die a large number of times. What do you expect to be the average of the numbers that face up?

Solution Suppose we take a sample of n rolls of the die (where n is large). Because the probability of rolling a 1 is 1/6, we would expect that we would roll a 1 one sixth of the time, or $n/6$ times. Similarly, each other number should also appear $n/6$ times. The frequency table should then look like this:

x	1	2	3	4	5	6
Number of Times x Is Rolled (frequency)	$\dfrac{n}{6}$	$\dfrac{n}{6}$	$\dfrac{n}{6}$	$\dfrac{n}{6}$	$\dfrac{n}{6}$	$\dfrac{n}{6}$

Note that we would not really expect the scores to be evenly distributed in practice, although for very large values of n we would expect the frequencies to vary only by a small percentage. To calculate the sample mean, we would add up all the scores and divide by the sample size. Now, the table tells us that there are $n/6$ ones, $n/6$ twos, $n/6$ threes, and so on, up to $n/6$ sixes. Adding these all up gives

$$\sum_i x_i = \frac{n}{6} \cdot 1 + \frac{n}{6} \cdot 2 + \frac{n}{6} \cdot 3 + \frac{n}{6} \cdot 4 + \frac{n}{6} \cdot 5 + \frac{n}{6} \cdot 6.$$

(Notice that we can obtain this number by multiplying the frequencies by the values of X and then adding.) Thus, the mean is

$$\bar{x} = \frac{\sum_i x_i}{n}$$

$$= \frac{\frac{n}{6} \cdot 1 + \frac{n}{6} \cdot 2 + \frac{n}{6} \cdot 3 + \frac{n}{6} \cdot 4 + \frac{n}{6} \cdot 5 + \frac{n}{6} \cdot 6}{n}$$

$$= \frac{1}{6} \cdot 1 + \frac{1}{6} \cdot 2 + \frac{1}{6} \cdot 3 + \frac{1}{6} \cdot 4 + \frac{1}{6} \cdot 5 + \frac{1}{6} \cdot 6 \qquad \text{\small Divide top and bottom by } n.$$

$$= 3.5.$$

This is the average value we expect to get after a large number of rolls or, in short, the **expected value** of a roll of the die. More precisely, we say that this is the expected value of the random variable X whose value is the number we get by rolling a die. Notice that n, the number of rolls, does not appear in the expected value. In fact, we could redo the calculation more simply by dividing the frequencies in the table by n *before* adding. Doing this replaces the frequencies with the *probabilities*, $1/6$. That is, it *replaces the frequency distribution with the probability distribution.*

x	1	2	3	4	5	6
$P(X = x)$	$\dfrac{1}{6}$	$\dfrac{1}{6}$	$\dfrac{1}{6}$	$\dfrac{1}{6}$	$\dfrac{1}{6}$	$\dfrac{1}{6}$

The expected value of X is then the sum of the products $x \cdot P(X = x)$. This is how we shall compute it from now on.

Expected Value of a Finite Random Variable

If X is a finite random variable that takes on the values $x_1, x_2, \ldots, x_n$, then the **expected value** of X, written $E(X)$ or μ, is

$$\mu = E(X) = x_1 \cdot P(X = x_1) + x_2 \cdot P(X = x_2) + \cdots + x_n \cdot P(X = x_n)$$
$$= \sum_i x_i \cdot P(X = x_i).$$

To obtain the expected value, multiply the values of X by their probabilities, and then add the results.

In Words

To compute the expected value from the probability distribution of X, we multiply the values of X by their probabilities and add up the results.

Interpretation

We interpret the expected value of X as a *prediction* of the mean of a large random sample of measurements of X; in other words, it is what we "expect" the mean of a large number of scores to be. (The larger the sample, the more accurate this prediction will tend to be.)

Quick Example

If X has the distribution shown,

x	-1	0	4	5
$P(X = x)$	.3	.5	.1	.1

then $\mu = E(X) = -1(.3) + 0(.5) + 4(.1) + 5(.1) = -.3 + 0 + .4 + .5 = .6$.

EXAMPLE 3 Sports Injuries

According to historical data, the number of injuries that a member of the Enormous State University women's soccer team will sustain during a typical season is given by the following probability distribution table:

Injuries	0	1	2	3	4	5	6
Probability	.20	.20	.22	.20	.15	.01	.02

If X denotes the number of injuries sustained by a player during one season, compute $E(X)$ and interpret the result.

Solution We can compute the expected value using the following tabular approach: take the probability distribution table, add another row in which we compute the product $x P(X = x)$, and then add these products together.

x	0	1	2	3	4	5	6	
$P(X = x)$	.20	.20	.22	.20	.15	.01	.02	**Total:**
$xP(X = x)$	0	.20	.44	.60	.60	.05	.12	2.01

The total of the entries in the bottom row is the expected value. Thus,

$$E(X) = 2.01.$$

We interpret the result as follows: If many soccer players are observed for a season, we predict that the average number of injuries each will sustain is about two.

▦ using Technology

Technology can be used to compute the expected values in Example 3.

TI-83/84 Plus

STAT EDIT values of X in L_1 and probabilities in L_2.
Home screen: sum(L_1*L_2)
[More details on page 613.]

Excel

Headings x and $P(X = x)$ in A1, B1.
x-values and probabilities in A2–B8.
=A2*B2 in C2, copied down to B6.
=SUM(C2:C8) in C9.
[More details on page 616.]

EXAMPLE 4 **Roulette**

A roulette wheel (of the kind used in the United States) has the numbers 1 through 36, 0 and 00. A bet on a single number pays 35 to 1. This means that if you place a $1 bet on a single number and win (your number comes up), you get your $1 back plus $35 (that is, you gain $35). If your number does not come up, you lose the $1 you bet. What is the expected gain from a $1 bet on a single number?

Solution The probability of winning is 1/38, so the probability of losing is 37/38. Let X be the gain from a $1 bet. X has two possible values: $X = -1$ if you lose and $X = 35$ if you win. $P(X = -1) = 37/38$ and $P(X = 35) = 1/38$. This probability distribution and the calculation of the expected value are given in the following table:

x	-1	35	
$P(X = x)$	$\frac{37}{38}$	$\frac{1}{38}$	**Total:**
$xP(X = x)$	$-\frac{37}{38}$	$\frac{35}{38}$	$-\frac{2}{38}$

So, we expect to average a small loss of $2/38 \approx \$0.0526$ on each spin of the wheel.

➡ **Before we go on...** Of course, you cannot actually lose the expected $0.0526 on one spin of the roulette wheel in Example 4. However, if you play many times, this is what you expect your *average* loss per bet to be. For example, if you played 100 times, you could expect to lose about $100 \times 0.0526 = \$5.26$. ∎

A betting game in which the expected value is zero is called a **fair game**. For example, if you and I flip a coin, and I give you $1 each time it comes up heads but you give me $1 each time it comes up tails, then the game is fair. Over the long run, we expect to come out even. On the other hand, a game like roulette in which the expected value is not zero is **biased**. Most casino games are slightly biased in favor of the house.* Thus, most gamblers will lose only a small amount and many gamblers will actually win something (and return to play some more). However, when the earnings are averaged over the huge numbers of people playing, the house is guaranteed to come out ahead. This is how casinos make (lots of) money.

∗ NOTE Only rarely are games not biased in favor of the house. However, blackjack played without continuous shuffle machines can be beaten by card counting.

Expected Value of a Binomial Random Variable

Suppose you guess all the answers to the questions on a multiple-choice test. What score can you expect to get? This scenario is an example of a sequence of Bernoulli trials (see the preceding section), and the number of correct guesses is therefore a binomial random variable whose expected value we wish to know. There is a simple formula for the expected value of a binomial random variable.

Expected Value of Binomial Random Variable

If X is the binomial random variable associated with n independent Bernoulli trials, each with probability p of success, then the expected value of X is

$$\mu = E(X) = np.$$

Quick Examples

1. If X is the number of successes in 20 Bernoulli trials with $p = .7$, then the expected number of successes is $\mu = E(X) = (20)(.7) = 14$.
2. If an event F in some experiment has $P(F) = .25$, the experiment is repeated 100 times, and X is the number of times F occurs, then $E(X) = (100)(.25) = 25$ is the number of times we expect F to occur.

Where does this formula come from? We *could* use the formula for expected value and compute the sum

$$E(X) = 0C(n, 0)p^0q^n + 1C(n, 1)p^1q^{n-1} + 2C(n, 2)p^2q^{n-2} + \cdots + nC(n, n)p^nq^0$$

directly (using the binomial theorem), but this is one of the many places in mathematics where a less direct approach is much easier. X is the number of successes in a sequence of n Bernoulli trials, each with probability p of success. Thus, p is the fraction of time we expect a success, so out of n trials we expect np successes. Because X counts successes, we expect the value of X to be np. (With a little more effort, this can be made into a formal proof that the sum above equals np.)

EXAMPLE 5 Guessing on an Exam

An exam has 50 multiple-choice questions, each having four choices. If a student randomly guesses on each question, how many correct answers can he or she expect to get?

Solution Each guess is a Bernoulli trial with probability of success 1 in 4, so $p = .25$. Thus, for a sequence of $n = 50$ trials,

$$\mu = E(X) = np = (50)(.25) = 12.5.$$

Thus, the student can expect to get about 12.5 correct answers.

Q : *Wait a minute. How can a student get a fraction of a correct answer?*

A : Remember that the expected value is the average number of correct answers a student will get if he or she guesses on a large number of such tests. Or, we can say that if many students use this strategy of guessing, they will average about 12.5 correct answers each.

Estimating the Expected Value from a Sample

It is not always possible to know the probability distribution of a random variable. For instance, if we take X to be the income of a randomly selected lawyer, one could not be expected to know the probability distribution of X. However, we can still obtain a good *estimate* of the expected value of X (the average income of all lawyers) by using the relative frequency distribution based on a large random sample.

EXAMPLE 6 Estimating an Expected Value

The following table shows the (fictitious) incomes of a random sample of 1,000 lawyers in the United States in their first year out of law school.

Income Bracket	$20,000–$29,999	$30,000–$39,999	$40,000–$49,999	$50,000–$59,999	$60,000–$69,999	$70,000–$79,999	$80,000–$89,999
Number	20	80	230	400	170	70	30

Estimate the average of the incomes of all lawyers in their first year out of law school.

Solution We first interpret the question in terms of a random variable. Let X be the income of a lawyer selected at random from among all currently practicing first-year lawyers in the United States. We are given a sample of 1,000 values of X, and we are asked to find the expected value of X. First, we use the midpoints of the income brackets to set up a relative frequency distribution for X:

x	25,000	35,000	45,000	55,000	65,000	75,000	85,000
$P(X = x)$	.02	.08	.23	.40	.17	.07	.03

Our estimate for $E(X)$ is then

$$E(X) = \sum_i x_i \cdot P(X = x_i)$$

$$= (25,000)(.02) + (35,000)(.08) + (45,000)(.23) + (55,000)(.40)$$
$$+ (65,000)(.17) + (75,000)(.07) + (85,000)(.03) = \$54,500.$$

Thus, $E(X)$ is approximately \$54,500. That is, the average income of all currently practicing first-year lawyers in the United States is approximately \$54,500.

FAQ

Recognizing When to Compute the Mean and When to Compute the Expected Value

Q : When am I supposed to compute the mean (add the values of X and divide by n) and when am I supposed to use the expected value formula?

A : The formula for the mean (adding and dividing by the number of observations) is used to compute the mean of a sequence of random scores, or sampled values of X. If, on the other hand, you are given the probability distribution for X (even if it is only an estimated probability distribution) then you need to use the expected value formula.

8.3 EXERCISES

▼ more advanced   ◆ challenging
Ⓣ indicates exercises that should be solved using technology

Compute the mean, median, and mode of the data samples in Exercises 1–8. HINT [See Quick Examples on pages 568 and 569.]

1. −1, 5, 5, 7, 14   **2.** 2, 6, 6, 7, −1

3. 2, 5, 6, 7, −1, −1   **4.** 3, 1, 6, −3, 0, 5

5. $\frac{1}{2}, \frac{3}{2}, -4, \frac{5}{4}$ **6.** $-\frac{3}{2}, \frac{3}{8}, -1, \frac{5}{2}$

7. 2.5, −5.4, 4.1, −0.1, −0.1   **8.** 4.2, −3.2, 0, 1.7, 0

9. ▼ Give a sample of six scores with mean 1 and with median ≠ mean. (Arrange the scores in ascending order.)

10. ▼ Give a sample of five scores with mean 100 and median 1. (Arrange the scores in ascending order.)

In Exercises 11–16, calculate the expected value of X for the given probability distribution. HINT [See Quick Example on page 572.]

11.

x	0	1	2	3
$P(X=x)$	.5	.2	.2	.1

12.

x	1	2	3	4
$P(X=x)$	.1	.2	.5	.2

13.

x	10	20	30	40
$P(X=x)$	$\frac{15}{50}$	$\frac{20}{50}$	$\frac{10}{50}$	$\frac{5}{50}$

14.

x	2	4	6	8
$P(X=x)$	$\frac{1}{20}$	$\frac{15}{20}$	$\frac{2}{20}$	$\frac{2}{20}$

15.

x	−5	−1	0	2	5	10
$P(X=x)$	.2	.3	.2	.1	.2	0

16.

x	−20	−10	0	10	20	30
$P(X=x)$	.2	.4	.2	.1	0	.1

In Exercises 17–28, calculate the expected value of the given random variable X. [Exercises 23, 24, 27, and 28 assume familiarity with counting arguments and probability (Section 7.4).] HINT [See Quick Example page 572.]

17. X is the number that faces up when a fair die is rolled.

18. X is a number selected at random from the set {1, 2, 3, 4}.

19. X is the number of tails that come up when a coin is tossed twice.

20. X is the number of tails that come up when a coin is tossed three times.

21. ▼ X is the higher number when two dice are rolled.

22. ▼ X is the lower number when two dice are rolled.

23. ▼ X is the number of red marbles that Suzan has in her hand after she selects four marbles from a bag containing four red marbles and two green ones.

24. ▼ X is the number of green marbles that Suzan has in her hand after she selects four marbles from a bag containing three red marbles and two green ones.

25. ▼ 20 darts are thrown at a dartboard. The probability of hitting a bull's-eye is .1. Let X be the number of bull's-eyes hit.

26. ▼ 30 darts are thrown at a dartboard. The probability of hitting a bull's-eye is $\frac{1}{5}$. Let X be the number of bull's-eyes hit.

27. Ⓣ ▼ Select five cards without replacement from a standard deck of 52, and let X be the number of queens you draw.

28. Ⓣ ▼ Select five cards without replacement from a standard deck of 52, and let X be the number of red cards you draw.

APPLICATIONS

29. *Stock Market Gyrations* Following is a sample of the day-by-day change, rounded to the nearest 100 points, in the Dow Jones Industrial Average during 10 successive business days around the start of the financial crisis in October 2008:[19]

−400, −500, −200, −700, −100, 900, −100, −700, 400, −100

Compute the mean and median of the given sample. Fill in the blank: There were as many days with a change in the Dow above _____ points as there were with changes below that. HINT [See Quick Examples on pages 568 and 569.]

30. *Stock Market Gyrations* Following is a sample of the day-by-day change, rounded to the nearest 100 points, in the Dow Jones Industrial Average during 10 successive business days around the start of the financial crisis in October 2008:[20]

−100, 400, −200, −500, 200, −300, −200, 900, −100, 200

Compute the mean and median of the given sample. Fill in the blank: There were as many days with a change in the Dow above _____ points as there were with changes below that. HINT [See Quick Examples on pages 568 and 569.]

31. *Gold* The following figures show the price of gold per ounce, in dollars, for the 10-business day period Feb. 2–Feb. 13, 2009:[21]

918, 905, 905, 920, 913, 895, 910, 938, 943, 936

---

[19] Source: http://finance.google.com.

[20] Ibid.

[21] Prices rounded to the nearest $1. Source: www.kitco.com/gold.londonfix.html.

Find the sample mean, median, and mode(s). What do your answers tell you about the price of gold?

32. Silver The following figures show the price of silver per ounce, in dollars, for the 10-business day period Feb. 2–Feb. 13, 2009:[22]

12.4, 12.4, 12.4, 12.8, 12.9, 13.0, 13.0, 13.4, 13.3, 13.4

Find the sample mean, median, and mode(s). What do your answers tell you about the price of silver?

33. Supermarkets A survey of 52 U.S. supermarkets yielded the following relative frequency table, where X is the number of checkout lanes at a randomly chosen supermarket.[23]

x	1	2	3	4	5	6	7	8	9	10
$P(X = x)$	.01	.04	.04	.08	.10	.15	.25	.20	.08	.05

a. Compute $\mu = E(X)$ and interpret the result. HINT [See Example 3.]

b. Which is larger, $P(X < \mu)$ or $P(X > \mu)$? Interpret the result.

34. Video Arcades Your company, Sonic Video, Inc., has conducted research that shows the following probability distribution, where X is the number of video arcades in a randomly chosen city with more than 500,000 inhabitants.

x	0	1	2	3	4	5	6	7	8	9
$P(X = x)$	.07	.09	.35	.25	.15	.03	.02	.02	.01	.01

a. Compute $\mu = E(X)$ and interpret the result. HINT [See Example 3.]

b. Which is larger, $P(X < \mu)$ or $P(X > \mu)$? Interpret the result.

35. School Enrollment The following table shows the approximate numbers of school goers in the United States (residents who attended some educational institution) in 1998, broken down by age group.[24]

Age	3–6.9	7–12.9	13–16.9	17–22.9	23–26.9	27–42.9
Population (millions)	12	24	15	14	2	5

Use the rounded midpoints of the given measurement classes to compute the probability distribution of the age X of a school goer. (Round probabilities to two decimal places.) Hence compute the expected value of X. What information does the expected value give about residents enrolled in schools?

36. School Enrollment Repeat Exercise 35, using the following data from 1980.[25]

Age	3–6.9	7–12.9	13–16.9	17–22.9	23–26.9	27–42.9
Population (millions)	8	20	11	13	1	3

37. Employment in Mexico by Age The following chart shows the ages of a survey of 250 working adults in Mexico:[26]

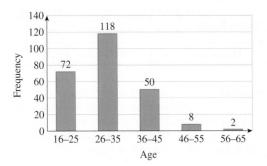

Use the estimated probability distribution based on the (rounded) midpoints of the given measurement classes to obtain an estimate of the expected age of a working adult in Mexico. HINT [See Example 6.]

38. Unemployment in Mexico by Age Repeat the preceding exercise, using the following chart, which shows the ages of a survey of 250 unemployed adults in Mexico:[27]

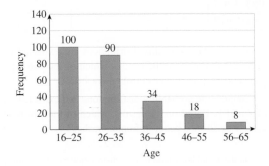

[22] Prices rounded to the nearest $1. Source: www.kitco.com/ gold.londonfix.html.

[23] Sources: J.T. McClave, P.G. Benson, T. Sincich, Statistics for Business and Economics, 7th Ed. (Prentice Hall, 1998) p. 177, W. Chow *et al.* "A model for predicting a supermarket's annual sales per square foot," Graduate School of Management, Rutgers University.

[24] Data are approximate, Source: Statistical Abstract of the United States: 2000.

[25] Ibid.

[26] Based on data from through January 2007. Source for data: Instituto Nacional de Estadística y Geografía (INEGI) (www.inegi.org.mx).

[27] Ibid.

39. ▣ *Income Distribution up to $100,000* The following table shows the distribution of household incomes for a sample of 1,000 households in the United States with incomes up to $100,000.[28]

Income Bracket	0–19,999	20,000–39,999	40,000–59,999	60,000–79,999	80,000–99,999
Households	270	280	200	150	100

Use this information to estimate, to the nearest $1,000, the average household income for such households. HINT [See Example 6.]

40. ▣ *Income Distribution up to $100,000* Repeat Exercise 39, using the following data for a sample of 1,000 Hispanic households in the United States.[29]

Income Bracket	0–19,999	20,000–39,999	40,000–59,999	60,000–79,999	80,000–99,999
Households	300	340	190	110	60

Highway Safety *Exercises 41–44 are based on the following table, which shows crashworthiness ratings for several categories of motor vehicles.[30] In all of these exercises, take X as the crash-test rating of a small car, Y as the crash-test rating for a small SUV, and so on as shown in the table.*

	Number Tested	Overall Frontal Crash-Test Rating			
		3 (Good)	2 (Acceptable)	1 (Marginal)	0 (Poor)
Small Cars X	16	1	11	2	2
Small SUVs Y	10	1	4	4	1
Medium SUVs Z	15	3	5	3	4
Passenger Vans U	13	3	0	3	7
Midsize Cars V	15	3	5	0	7
Large Cars W	19	9	5	3	2

41. ▼ Compute the probability distributions and expected values of X and Y. Based on the results, which of the two types of vehicle performed better in frontal crashes?

42. ▼ Compute the probability distributions and expected values of Z and V. Based on the results, which of the two types of vehicle performed better in frontal crashes?

---

[28] Based on the actual household income distribution in 2003. Source: U.S. Census Bureau, Current Population Survey, 2004 Annual Social and Economic Supplement (http://pubdb3.census.gov/macro/032004/hhinc/new06_000.htm).

[29] Ibid.

[30] Ratings are by the Insurance Institute for Highway Safety. Sources: Oak Ridge National Laboratory: "An Analysis of the Impact of Sport Utility Vehicles in the United States" Stacy C. Davis, Lorena F. Truett, August 2000, Insurance Institute for Highway Safety (www-cta.ornl.gov/Publications/Final SUV report.pdf, www.highwaysafety.org/vehicle_ratings).

43. ▣ ▼ Based on expected values, which of the following categories performed best in crash tests: small cars, midsize cars, or large cars?

44. ▣ ▼ Based on expected values, which of the following categories performed best in crash tests: small SUVs, medium SUVs, or passenger vans?

45. ▼ *Roulette* A roulette wheel has the numbers 1 through 36, 0, and 00. Half of the numbers from 1 through 36 are red, and a bet on red pays even money (that is, if you win, you will get back your $1 plus another $1). How much do you expect to win with a $1 bet on red? HINT [See Example 4.]

46. ▼ *Roulette* A roulette wheel has the numbers 1 through 36, 0, and 00. A bet on two numbers pays 17 to 1 (that is, if one of the two numbers you bet comes up, you get back your $1 plus another $17). How much do you expect to win with a $1 bet on two numbers? HINT [See Example 4.]

47. *Teenage Pastimes* According to a study,[31] the probability that a randomly selected teenager shopped at a mall at least once during a week was .63. How many teenagers in a randomly selected group of 40 would you expect to shop at a mall during the next week? HINT [See Example 5.]

48. *Other Teenage Pastimes* According to the study referred to in the preceding exercise, the probability that a randomly selected teenager played a computer game at least once during a week was .48. How many teenagers in a randomly selected group of 30 would you expect to play a computer game during the next seven days? HINT [See Example 5.]

49. ▼ *Manufacturing* Your manufacturing plant produces air bags, and it is known that 10% of them are defective. A random collection of 20 air bags is tested.

   a. How many of them would you expect to be defective?
   b. In how large a sample would you expect to find 12 defective airbags?

50. ▼ *Spiders* Your pet tarantula, Spider, has a .12 probability of biting an acquaintance who comes into contact with him. Next week, you will be entertaining 20 friends (all of whom will come into contact with Spider).

   a. How many guests should you expect Spider to bite?
   b. At your last party, Spider bit 6 of your guests. Assuming that Spider bit the expected number of guests, how many guests did you have?

Exercises 51 and 52 assume familiarity with counting arguments and probability (Section 7.4).

51. ▼ *Camping* Kent's Tents has four red tents and three green tents in stock. Karin selects four of them at random. Let X be the number of red tents she selects. Give the probability distribution of X and find the expected number of red tents selected.

52. ▼ *Camping* Kent's Tents has five green knapsacks and four yellow ones in stock. Curt selects four of them at random. Let X be the number of green knapsacks he selects. Give the

---

[31] Source: Rand Youth Poll/Teen-age Research Unlimited/*The New York Times*, March 14, 1998, p. D1.

probability distribution of X, and find the expected number of green knapsacks selected.

53. **1** ▼ *Stock Portfolios* You are required to choose between two stock portfolios, FastForward Funds and SolidState Securities. Stock analysts have constructed the following probability distributions for next year's rate of return for the two funds.

FastForward Funds

Rate of Return	−.4	−.3	−.2	−.1	0	.1	.2	.3	.4
Probability	.015	.025	.043	.132	.289	.323	.111	.043	.019

SolidState Securities

Rate of Return	−.4	−.3	−.2	−.1	0	.1	.2	.3	.4
Probability	.012	.023	.050	.131	.207	.330	.188	.043	.016

Which of the two funds gives the higher expected rate of return?

54. **1** ▼ *Risk Management* Before making your final decision whether to invest in FastForward Funds or SolidState Securities (see Exercise 53), you consult your colleague in the risk management department of your company. She informs you that, in the event of a stock market crash, the following probability distributions for next year's rate of return would apply:

FastForward Funds

Rate of Return	−.8	−.7	−.6	−.5	−.4	−.2	−.1	0	.1
Probability	.028	.033	.043	.233	.176	.230	.111	.044	.102

SolidState Securities

Rate of Return	−.8	−.7	−.6	−.5	−.4	−.2	−.1	0	.1
Probability	.033	.036	.038	.167	.176	.230	.211	.074	.035

Which of the two funds offers the lowest risk in case of a market crash?

55. ◆ *Insurance Schemes* The Acme Insurance Company is launching a drive to generate greater profits, and it decides to insure racetrack drivers against wrecking their cars. The company's research shows that, on average, a racetrack driver races four times a year and has a 1 in 10 chance of wrecking a vehicle, worth an average of $100,000, in every race. The annual premium is $5,000, and Acme automatically drops any driver who is involved in an accident (after paying for a new car), but does not refund the premium. How much profit (or loss) can the company expect to earn from a typical driver in a year? HINT [Use a tree diagram to compute the probabilities of the various outcomes.]

56. ◆ *Insurance* The Blue Sky Flight Insurance Company insures passengers against air disasters, charging a prospective passenger $20 for coverage on a single plane ride. In the event of a fatal air disaster, it pays out $100,000 to the named beneficiary. In the event of a nonfatal disaster, it pays out an average of $25,000 for hospital expenses. Given that the probability of a plane's crashing on a single trip is .00000087,[32] and that a passenger involved in a plane crash has a .9 chance of being killed, determine the profit (or loss) per passenger that the insurance company expects to make on each trip. HINT [Use a tree to compute the probabilities of the various outcomes.]

COMMUNICATION AND REASONING EXERCISES

57. In a certain set of scores, there are as many values above the mean as below it. It follows that

(A) The median and mean are equal.
(B) The mean and mode are equal.
(C) The mode and median are equal.
(D) The mean, mode, and median are all equal.

58. In a certain set of scores, the median occurs more often than any other score. It follows that

(A) The median and mean are equal.
(B) The mean and mode are equal.
(C) The mode and median are equal.
(D) The mean, mode, and median are all equal.

59. Your friend Charlesworth claims that the median of a collection of data is always close to the mean. Is he correct? If so, say why; if not, give an example to prove him wrong.

60. Your other friend Imogen asserts that Charlesworth is wrong and that it is the mode and the median that are always close to each other. Is she correct? If so, say why; if not, give an example to prove her wrong.

61. Must the expected number of times you hit a bull's-eye after 50 attempts always be a whole number? Explain.

62. Your statistics instructor tells you that the expected score of the upcoming midterm test is 75%. That means that 75% is the most likely score to occur, right?

63. ▼ Your grade in a recent midterm was 80%, but the class average was 83%. Most people in the class scored better than you, right?

64. ▼ Your grade in a recent midterm was 80%, but the class median was 100%. Your score was lower than the average score, right?

65. ▼ Slim tells you that the population mean is just the mean of a suitably large sample. Is he correct? Explain.

66. ▼ Explain how you can use a sample to estimate an expected value.

67. ▼ Following is an excerpt from a full-page ad by **MoveOn.org** in the *New York Times* criticizing President G.W. Bush:[33]

On Tax Cuts:

George Bush: ". . . Americans will keep, this year, an average of almost $1,000 more of their own money."

The Truth: Nearly half of all taxpayers get less than $100. And 31% of all taxpayers get nothing at all.

The statements referred to as "The Truth" contradict the statement attributed to President Bush, right? Explain.

---

[32] This was the probability of a passenger plane crashing per departure in 1990. (Source: National Transportation Safety Board.)

[33] Source: Full-page ad in the *New York Times*, September 17, 2003, p. A25.

68. ▼ Following is an excerpt from a five-page ad by WeissneggerForGov.org in *The Martian Enquirer* criticizing Supreme Martian Administrator, Gov. Red Davis:

On Worker Accommodation:

Gov. Red Davis: "The median size of Government worker habitats in Valles Marineris is at least 400 square feet."

Weissnegger: "The average size of a Government worker habitat in Valles Marineris is a mere 150 square feet."

The statements attributed to Weissnegger do not contradict the statement attributed to Gov. Davis, right? Explain.

69. ▼ Sonia has just told you that the expected household income in the United States is the same as the population mean of all U.S. household incomes. Clarify her statement by describing an experiment and an associated random variable X so that the expected household income is the expected value of X.

70. ▼ If X is a random variable, what is the difference between a sample mean of measurements of X and the expected value of X? Illustrate by means of an example.

8.4 Measures of Dispersion

Variance and Standard Deviation of a Set of Scores

Figure 5(a)

Figure 5(b)

Your grade on a recent midterm was 68%; the class average was 72%. How do you stand in comparison with the rest of the class? If the grades were widely scattered, then your grade may be close to the mean and a fair number of people may have done a lot worse than you (Figure 5a). If, on the other hand, almost all the grades were within a few points of the average, then your grade may not be much higher than the lowest grade in the class (Figure 5b).

This scenario suggests that it would be useful to have a way of measuring not only the central tendency of a set of scores (mean, median or mode) but also the amount of "scatter" or "dispersion" of the data.

If the scores in our set are $x_1, x_2, \ldots, x_n$ and their mean is $\bar{x}$ (or μ in the case of a population mean), we are really interested in the distribution of the differences $x_i - \bar{x}$. We could compute the *average* of these differences, but this average will always be 0. (Why?) It is really the *sizes* of these differences that interest us, so we might try computing the average of the absolute values of the differences. This idea is reasonable, but it leads to technical difficulties that are avoided by a slightly different approach: The statistic we use is based on the average of the *squares* of the differences, as explained in the following definitions.

Population Variance and Standard Deviation

If the values $x_1, x_2, \ldots, x_n$ are all the measurements of X in the entire population, then the **population variance** is given by

$$\sigma^2 = \frac{(x_1 - \mu)^2 + (x_2 - \mu)^2 + \cdots + (x_n - \mu)^2}{n} = \frac{\sum_{i=1}^{n}(x_i - \mu)^2}{n}.$$

(Remember that μ is the symbol we use for the *population* mean.) The **population standard deviation** is the square root of the population variance:

$$\sigma = \sqrt{\sigma^2}.$$

Sample Variance and Standard Deviation

The **sample variance** of a sample $x_1, x_2, \ldots, x_n$ of n values of X is given by

$$s^2 = \frac{(x_1 - \bar{x})^2 + (x_2 - \bar{x})^2 + \cdots + (x_n - \bar{x})^2}{n-1} = \frac{\sum_{i=1}^{n}(x_i - \bar{x})^2}{n-1}.$$

The **sample standard deviation** is the square-root of the sample variance:

$$s = \sqrt{s^2}.$$

Visualizing Small and Large Variance

Small Variance

Large Variance

Quick Examples

1. The sample variance of the scores 1, 2, 3, 4, 5 is the sum of the squares of the differences between the scores and the mean $\bar{x} = 3$, divided by $n - 1 = 4$:

$$s^2 = \frac{(1-3)^2 + (2-3)^2 + (3-3)^2 + (4-3)^2 + (5-3)^2}{4} = \frac{10}{4} = 2.5$$

so

$$s = \sqrt{2.5} \approx 1.58.$$

2. The population variance of the scores 1, 2, 3, 4, 5 is the sum of the squares of the differences between the scores and the mean $\mu = 3$, divided by $n = 5$:

$$\sigma^2 = \frac{(1-3)^2 + (2-3)^2 + (3-3)^2 + (4-3)^2 + (5-3)^2}{5} = \frac{10}{5} = 2$$

so

$$\sigma = \sqrt{2} \approx 1.41.$$

Q: *The population variance is the average of the squares of the differences between the values and the mean. But why do we divide by $n - 1$ instead of n when calculating the sample variance?*

A: In real-life applications, we would like the variance we calculate from a sample to approximate the variance of the whole population. In statistical terms, we would like the expected value of the sample variance s^2 to be the same as the population variance σ^2. The sample variance s^2 as we have defined it is the "unbiased estimator" of the population variance σ^2 that accomplishes this task; if, instead, we divided by n in the formula for s^2, we would, on average, tend to underestimate the population variance. (See the online text on Sampling Distributions at the Web site for further discussion of unbiased estimators.) Note that as the sample size gets larger and larger, the discrepancy between the formulas for s^2 and σ^2 becomes negligible; dividing by n gives almost the same answer as dividing by $n - 1$. It is traditional, nonetheless, to use the sample variance in preference to the population variance when working with samples, and we do that here. In practice we should not try to draw conclusions about the entire population from samples so small that the difference between the two formulas matters. As one book puts it, "If the difference between n and $n - 1$ ever matters to you, then you are probably up to no good anyway—e.g., trying to substantiate a questionable hypothesis with marginal data."[34]

---

[34] Press, W.H., Teukolsky, S.A., Vetterling, W.T, and Flannery, B.P., *Numerical Recipes: The Art of Scientific Computing*, Cambridge University Press, 2007.

using Technology

Technology can be used to compute the mean and standard deviation in Example 1.

TI-83/84 Plus

STAT EDIT values of x in L_1.
STAT CALC 1-Var Stats
ENTER.
[More details on page 613.]

Excel

x-values in A1–A7
=AVERAGE(A1:A7) in A8
=STDEV(A1:A7) in A9
[More details on page 616.]

Here's a simple example of calculating standard deviation.

EXAMPLE 1 Unemployment

The unemployment rates (in percentage points) in the United States for the months April–October 2008 were:*

$$5, 6, 6, 6, 6, 6, 7.$$

Compute the sample mean and standard deviation, rounded to one decimal place. What percentage of the scores fall within one standard deviation of the mean? What percentage fall within two standard deviations of the mean?

Solution   The sample mean is

$$\bar{x} = \frac{\sum_i x_i}{n} = \frac{5+6+6+6+6+6+7}{7} = \frac{42}{7} = 6.$$

The sample variance is

$$
\begin{aligned}
s^2 &= \frac{\sum_{i=1}^{n}(x_i - \bar{x})^2}{n-1} \\
&= \frac{(5-6)^2 + (6-6)^2 + (6-6)^2 + (6-6)^2 + (6-6)^2 + (6-6)^2 + (7-6)^2}{6} \\
&= \frac{1+0+0+0+0+0+1}{6} = \frac{1}{3}.
\end{aligned}
$$

Thus, the sample standard deviation is

$$s = \sqrt{\frac{1}{3}} \approx 0.6. \qquad \text{Rounded to one decimal place}$$

To ask which scores fall "within one standard deviation of the mean" is to ask which scores fall in the interval $[\bar{x} - s, \bar{x} + s]$, or $[6 - 0.6, 6 + 0.6] = [5.4, 6.6]$. Five out of the seven scores (the five 6s) fall in this interval, so the percentage of scores that fall within one standard deviation of the mean is $5/7 \approx 71\%$.

For two standard deviations, the interval in question is $[\bar{x} - 2s, \bar{x} + 2s] \approx [6 - 1.2, 6 + 1.2] = [4.8, 7.2]$, which includes all of the scores. In other words, 100% of the scores fall within two standard deviations of the mean.

---

* Figures are rounded. Source: Bureau of Labor Statistics (www.bls.gov).

Q : *In Example 1, 71% of the scores fell within one standard deviation of the mean and all of them fell within two standard deviations of the mean. Is this typical?*

A : Actually, the percentage of scores within a number of standard deviations of the mean depends a great deal on the way the scores are distributed. There are two useful methods for *estimating* the percentage of scores that fall within any number of standard deviations of the mean. The first method applies to any set of data, and is due to P.L. Chebyshev (1821–1894), while the second applies to "nice" sets of data, and is based on the "normal distribution," which we shall discuss in Section 5.

Chebyshev's Rule

For any set of data, the following statements are true:

At least 3/4 of the scores fall within two standard deviations of the mean (within the interval $[\bar{x} - 2s, \bar{x} + 2s]$ for samples or $[\mu - 2\sigma, \mu + 2\sigma]$ for populations).

At least 8/9 of the scores fall within three standard deviations of the mean (within the interval $[\bar{x} - 3s, \bar{x} + 3s]$ for samples or $[\mu - 3\sigma, \mu + 3\sigma]$ for populations).

At least 15/16 of the scores fall within four standard deviations of the mean (within the interval $[\bar{x} - 4s, \bar{x} + 4s]$ for samples or $[\mu - 4\sigma, \mu + 4\sigma]$ for populations).

. . .

At least $1 - 1/k^2$ of the scores fall within k standard deviations of the mean (within the interval $[\bar{x} - ks, \bar{x} + ks]$ for samples or $[\mu - k\sigma, \mu + k\sigma]$ for populations).

Visualizing Chebyshev's Rule

Empirical Rule*

For a set of data whose frequency distribution is "bell-shaped" and symmetric (see Figure 6), the following is true:

Bell-Shaped Symmetric Distribution   Not Symmetric   Not Bell-Shaped

Figure 6(a)   **Figure 6(b)**   **Figure 6(c)**

✱ NOTE Unlike Chebyshev's rule, which is a precise theorem, the empirical rule is a "rule of thumb" that is intentionally vague about what exactly is meant by a "bell-shaped distribution" and "approximately such-and-such %." (As a result, the rule is often stated differently in different textbooks.) We will see in Section 8.5 that if the distribution is a *normal* one, the empirical rule translates to a precise statement.

Approximately 68% of the scores fall within one standard deviation of the mean (within the interval $[\bar{x} - s, \bar{x} + s]$ for samples or $[\mu - \sigma, \mu + \sigma]$ for populations).

Approximately 95% of the scores fall within two standard deviations of the mean (within the interval $[\bar{x} - 2s, \bar{x} + 2s]$ for samples or $[\mu - 2\sigma, \mu + 2\sigma]$ for populations).

Approximately 99.7% of the scores fall within three standard deviations of the mean (within the interval $[\bar{x} - 3s, \bar{x} + 3s]$ for samples or $[\mu - 3\sigma, \mu + 3\sigma]$ for populations).

Visualizing the Empirical Rule

Quick Examples

1. If the mean of a sample is 20 with standard deviation $s = 2$, then at least $15/16 = 93.75\%$ of the scores lie within four standard deviations of the mean—that is, in the interval $[12, 28]$.

2. If the mean of a sample with a bell-shaped symmetric distribution is 20 with standard deviation $s = 2$, then approximately 95% of the scores lie in the interval $[16, 24]$.

The empirical rule could not be applied in Example 1. The distribution was not bell-shaped (sketch it to see for yourself) and the fact that there were only six scores limits the accuracy further. The empirical rule is, however, accurate in distributions that are bell-shaped and symmetric, even if not perfectly so. Chebyshev's rule, on the other hand, is always valid (and applies in Example 1 in particular) but tends to be "overcautious" and in practice underestimates how much of a distribution lies in a given interval.

EXAMPLE 2 Automobile Life

The average life span of a Batmobile is 9 years, with a standard deviation of 2 years. My own Batmobile lasted less than 3 years before being condemned to the bat-junkyard.

a. Without any further knowledge about the distribution of Batmobile life spans, what can one say about the percentage of Batmobiles that last less than 3 years?

b. Refine the answer in part (a), assuming that the distribution of Batmobile life spans is bell-shaped and symmetric.

Solution

a. If we are given no further information about the distribution of Batmobile life spans, we need to use Chebyshev's rule. Because the life span of my Batmobile was more than 6 years (or three standard deviations) shorter than the mean, it lies outside the range $[\mu - 3\sigma, \mu + 3\sigma] = [3, 15]$. Because *at least* 8/9 of the life spans of all Batmobiles lie in this range, *at most* 1/9, or 11%, of the life spans lie outside this range (see Figure 7). Some of these, like the life span of my own Batmobile, are less than 3 years, while the rest are more than $\mu + 3\sigma = 15$ years.

b. Because we know more about the distribution now than we did in part (a), we can use the empirical rule and obtain sharper results. The empirical rule predicts that approximately 99.7% of the life spans of Batmobiles lie in the range $[\mu - 3\sigma, \mu + 3\sigma] = [3, 15]$. Thus, approximately $1 - 99.7\% = 0.3\%$ of them lie outside that range. Because the distribution is symmetric, however, more can be said: half of that 0.3%, or 0.15% of Batmobiles will last longer than 15 years, while the other 0.15% are, like my own ill-fated Batmobile, doomed to a life span of less than 3 years (see Figure 8).

Figure 7

Figure 8

Variance and Standard Deviation of a Finite Random Variable

Recall that the expected value of a random variable X is a prediction of the average of a large sample of values of X. Can we similarly predict the variance of a large sample? Suppose we have a sample $x_1, x_2, \ldots, x_n$. If n is large, the sample and population variances are essentially the same, so we concentrate on the population variance, which is the average of the numbers $(x_i - \bar{x})^2$. This average can be predicted using $E([X - \mu]^2)$ the expected value of $(X - \mu)^2$. In general, we make the following definition.

Variance and Standard Deviation of a Finite Random Variable

If X is a finite random variable taking on values $x_1, x_2, \ldots, x_n$, then the **variance** of X is

$$\sigma^2 = E([X - \mu]^2)$$
$$= (x_1 - \mu)^2 P(X = x_1) + (x_2 - \mu)^2 P(X = x_2) + \cdots + (x_n - \mu)^2 P(X = x_n)$$
$$= \sum_i (x_i - \mu)^2 P(X = x_i).$$

The **standard deviation** of X is then the square root of the variance:

$$\sigma = \sqrt{\sigma^2}.$$

To compute the variance from the probability distribution of X, first compute the expected value μ and then compute the expected value of $(X - \mu)^2$.

Quick Example

The following distribution has expected value $\mu = E(X) = 2$:

x	-1	2	3	10
$P(X = x)$	.3	.5	.1	.1

The variance of X is

$$\sigma^2 = (x_1 - \mu)^2 P(X = x_1) + (x_2 - \mu)^2 P(X = x_2) + \cdots + (x_n - \mu)^2 P(X = x_n)$$
$$= (-1 - 2)^2(.3) + (2 - 2)^2(.5) + (3 - 2)^2(.1) + (10 - 2)^2(.1) = 9.2.$$

The standard deviation of X is

$$\sigma = \sqrt{9.2} \approx 3.03.$$

Note We can interpret the variance of X as the number we expect to get for the variance of a large sample of values of X, and similarly for the standard deviation. ■

We can calculate the variance and standard deviation of a random variable using a tabular approach just as when we calculated the expected value in Example 3 in the preceding section.

using Technology

Technology can be used to
automate the calculations of
Example 3.

TI-83/84 Plus
STAT EDIT values of x in L_1,
probabilities in L_2.
Home screen: sum($L_1 * L_2$)
→ M
Then sum($(L_1-M)\wedge 2 * L_2$)
[More details on page 613.]

Excel
x-values in A2–A7, probabilities
in B2–B7
=A2*B2 in C2; copy down
to C7.
=SUM(C2:C7) in C8
=(A2-$C$8)^2*B2 in D2;
copy down to D7.
=SUM(D2:D7) in D8
[More details on page 616.]

Web Site
www.FiniteandCalc.org
  Student Home
    → Online Utilities
    → Histogram Utility
Enter the x-values and
probabilities as shown:

```
10, .2
20, .2
30, .3
40, .1
50, .1
60, .1
```

Make sure "Show expected
value and standard deviation" is
checked, and press "Results."

EXAMPLE 3 **Variance of a Random Variable**

Compute the variance and standard deviation for the following probability distribution.

x	10	20	30	40	50	60
$P(X=x)$	.2	.2	.3	.1	.1	.1

Solution We first compute the expected value, μ, in the usual way:

x	10	20	30	40	50	60	
$P(X=x)$	.2	.2	.3	.1	.1	.1	
$xP(X=x)$	2	4	9	4	5	6	$\mu = 30$

Next, we add an extra three rows:

- a row for the differences $(x - \mu)$, which we get by subtracting μ from the values of X
- a row for the squares $(x - \mu)^2$, which we obtain by squaring the values immediately above
- a row for the products $(x - \mu)^2 P(X = x)$, which we obtain by multiplying the values in the second and the fifth rows.

x	10	20	30	40	50	60	
$P(X=x)$	.2	.2	.3	.1	.1	.1	
$xP(X=x)$	2	4	9	4	5	6	$\mu = 30$
$x - \mu$	-20	-10	0	10	20	30	
$(x - \mu)^2$	400	100	0	100	400	900	
$(x - \mu)^2 P(X=x)$	80	20	0	10	40	90	$\sigma^2 = 240$

The sum of the values in the last row is the variance. The standard deviation is then the square root of the variance:

$$\sigma = \sqrt{240} \approx 15.49.$$

Note Chebyshev's rule and the empirical rule apply to random variables just as they apply to samples and populations, as we illustrate in the following example. ■

EXAMPLE 4 **Internet Commerce**

Your newly launched company, CyberPromo, Inc., sells computer games on the Internet.

a. Statistical research indicates that the lifespan of an Internet marketing company such as yours is symmetrically distributed with an expected value of 30 months and standard deviation of 4 months. Complete the following sentence:

There is (at least/at most/approximately)_____ a _____ percent chance that CyberPromo will still be around for more than 3 years.

b. How would the answer to part (a) be affected if the distribution of lifespans was not known to be symmetric?

Solution

a. Do we use Chebyshev's rule or the empirical rule? Because the empirical rule requires that the distribution be both symmetric and bell-shaped—not just symmetric—we cannot conclude that it applies here, so we are forced to use Chebyshev's rule instead.

Let X be the lifespan of an Internet commerce site. The expected value of X is 30 months, and the hoped-for lifespan of CyberPromo, Inc., is 36 months, which is 6 months, or $6/4 = 1.5$ standard deviations, above the mean. Chebyshev's rule tells us that X is within $k = 1.5$ standard deviations of the mean at least $1 - 1/k^2$ of the time; that is,

$$P(24 \leq X \leq 36) \geq 1 - \frac{1}{k^2} = 1 - \frac{1}{1.5^2} \approx .56.$$

In other words, at least 56% of all Internet marketing companies have life spans in the range of 24 to 36 months. Thus, *at most* 44 % have life spans outside this range. Because the distribution is symmetric, at most 22% have life spans longer than 36 months. Thus we can complete the sentence as follows:

There is <u>at most</u> a <u>22</u>% chance that CyberPromo will still be around for more than 3 years.

b. If the given distribution was not known to be symmetric, how would this affect the answer? We saw above that regardless of whether the distribution is symmetric or not, at most 44% have lifespans outside the range 24 to 36 months. Because the distribution is not symmetric, we cannot conclude that at most half of the 44% have lifespans longer than 36 months, and all we can say is that *no more than 44% can possibly have life spans longer than 36 years.* In other words:

There is <u>at most</u> a <u>44</u>% chance that CyberPromo will still be around for more than 3 years.

Variance and Standard Deviation of a Binomial Random Variable

We saw that there is an easy formula for the expected value of a binomial random variable: $\mu = np$, where n is the number of trials and p is the probability of success. Similarly, there is a simple formula for the variance and standard deviation.

Variance and Standard Deviation of a Binomial Random Variable

If X is a binomial random variable associated with n independent Bernoulli trials, each with probability p of success, then the variance and standard deviation of X are given by

$$\sigma^2 = npq \quad \text{and} \quad \sigma = \sqrt{npq}$$

where $q = 1 - p$ is the probability of failure.

Quick Example

If X is the number of successes in 20 Bernoulli trials with $p = .7$, then the standard deviation is $\sigma = \sqrt{npq} = \sqrt{(20)(.7)(.3)} \approx 2.05$.

> For values of p near $1/2$ and large values of n, a binomial distribution is bell-shaped and (nearly) symmetric, hence the empirical rule applies. One rule of thumb is that we can use the empirical rule when both $np \geq 10$ and $nq \geq 10$.*

* **NOTE** Remember that the empirical rule only gives an *estimate* of probabilities. In Section 8.5 we give a more accurate approximation that takes into account the fact that the binomial distribution is not continuous.

EXAMPLE 5 Internet Commerce

You have calculated that there is a 40% chance that a hit on your Web page results in a fee paid to your company CyberPromo, Inc. Your Web page receives 25 hits per day. Let X be the number of hits that result in payment of the fee ("successful hits").

a. What are the expected value and standard deviation of X?

b. Complete the following: On approximately 95 out of 100 days, I will get between ____ and ____ successful hits.

Solution

a. The random variable X is binomial with $n = 25$ and $p = .4$. To compute μ and σ, we use the formulas

$$\mu = np = (25)(.4) = 10 \text{ successful hits}$$

$$\sigma = \sqrt{npq} = \sqrt{(25)(.4)(.6)} \approx 2.45 \text{ hits}.$$

b. Because $np = 10 \geq 10$ and $nq = (25)(.6) = 15 \geq 10$, we can use the empirical rule, which tells us that there is an approximately 95% probability that the number of successful hits is within two standard deviations of the mean—that is, in the interval

$$[\mu - 2\sigma, \mu + 2\sigma] = [10 - 2(2.45), 10 + 2(2.45)] = [5.1, 14.9].$$

Thus, on approximately 95 out of 100 days, I will get between <u>5.1</u> and <u>14.9</u> successful hits.

FAQ

Recognizing When to Use the Empirical Rule or Chebyshev's Rule

Q : *How do I decide whether to use Chebyshev's rule or the empirical rule?*

A : Check to see whether the probability distribution you are considering is both symmetric and bell-shaped. If so, you can use the empirical rule. If not, then you must use Chebyshev's rule. Thus, for instance, if the distribution is symmetric but not known to be bell-shaped, you must use Chebyshev's rule.

8.4 EXERCISES

▼ more advanced   ◆ challenging

 indicates exercises that should be solved using technology

Compute the (sample) variance and standard deviation of the data samples given in Exercises 1–8. (You calculated the means in the last exercise set. Round all answers to two decimal places.) HINT [See Quick Examples on page 581.]

1. $-1, 5, 5, 7, 14$

2. $2, 6, 6, 7, -1$

3. $2, 5, 6, 7, -1, -1$

4. $3, 1, 6, -3, 0, 5$

5. $\dfrac{1}{2}, \dfrac{3}{2}, -4, \dfrac{5}{4}$

6. $-\dfrac{3}{2}, \dfrac{3}{8}, -1, \dfrac{5}{2}$

7. $2.5, -5.4, 4.1, -0.1, -0.1$

8. $4.2, -3.2, 0, 1.7, 0$

In Exercises 9–14, calculate the standard deviation of X for each probability distribution. (You calculated the expected values in the last exercise set. Round all answers to two decimal places.) HINT [See Quick Examples on page 585.]

9.

x	0	1	2	3
$P(X = x)$	.5	.2	.2	.1

10.

x	1	2	3	4
$P(X = x)$	.1	.2	.5	.2

11.

x	10	20	30	40
$P(X = x)$	$\frac{3}{10}$	$\frac{2}{5}$	$\frac{1}{5}$	$\frac{1}{10}$

12.

x	2	4	6	8
$P(X = x)$	$\frac{1}{20}$	$\frac{15}{20}$	$\frac{2}{20}$	$\frac{2}{20}$

13.

x	−5	−1	0	2	5	10
$P(X = x)$	.2	.3	.2	.1	.2	0

14.

x	−20	−10	0	10	20	30
$P(X = x)$	.2	.4	.2	.1	0	.1

In Exercises 15–24, calculate the expected value, the variance, and the standard deviation of the given random variable X. (You calculated the expected values in the last exercise set. Round all answers to two decimal places.)

15. X is the number that faces up when a fair die is rolled.

16. X is the number selected at random from the set $\{1, 2, 3, 4\}$.

17. X is the number of tails that come up when a coin is tossed twice.

18. X is the number of tails that come up when a coin is tossed three times.

19. ▼ X is the higher number when two dice are rolled.

20. ▼ X is the lower number when two dice are rolled.

21. ▼ X is the number of red marbles that Suzan has in her hand after she selects four marbles from a bag containing four red marbles and two green ones.

22. ▼ X is the number of green marbles that Suzan has in her hand after she selects four marbles from a bag containing three red marbles and two green ones.

23. ▼ Twenty darts are thrown at a dartboard. The probability of hitting a bull's-eye is .1. Let X be the number of bull's-eyes hit.

24. ▼ Thirty darts are thrown at a dartboard. The probability of hitting a bull's-eye is $\frac{1}{5}$. Let X be the number of bull's-eyes hit.

APPLICATIONS

25. *Popularity Ratings* In your bid to be elected class representative, you have your election committee survey five randomly chosen students in your class and ask them to rank you on a scale of 0–10. Your rankings are 3, 2, 0, 9, 1.

   a. Find the sample mean and standard deviation. (Round your answers to two decimal places.) HINT [See Example 1 and Quick Examples on page 581.]

   b. Assuming the sample mean and standard deviation are indicative of the class as a whole, in what range does the empirical rule predict that approximately 68% of the class

will rank you? What other assumptions must we make to use the rule?

26. *Popularity Ratings* Your candidacy for elected class representative is being opposed by Slick Sally. Your election committee has surveyed six of the students in your class and had them rank Sally on a scale of 0–10. The rankings were 2, 8, 7, 10, 5, 8.

   a. Find the sample mean and standard deviation. (Round your answers to two decimal places.) HINT [See Example 1 and Quick Examples on page 581.]

   b. Assuming the sample mean and standard deviation are indicative of the class as a whole, in what range does the empirical rule predict that approximately 95% of the class will rank Sally? What other assumptions must we make to use the rule?

27. *Unemployment* Following is a sample of unemployment rates (in percentage points) in the United States sampled from the period 1990–2004:[35]

$$4.2, 4.7, 5.4, 5.8, 4.9.$$

   a. Compute the mean and standard deviation of the given sample. (Round your answers to one decimal place.)

   b. Assuming the distribution of unemployment rates in the population is symmetric and bell-shaped, 95% of the time, the unemployment rate is between ____ and ____ percent.

28. *Unemployment* Following is a sample of unemployment rates among Hispanics (in percentage points) in the US sampled from the period 1990–2004:[36]

$$7.7, 7.5, 9.3, 6.9, 8.6.$$

   a. Compute the mean and standard deviation of the given sample. (Round your answers to one decimal place.)

   b. Assuming the distribution of unemployment rates in the population of interest is symmetric and bell-shaped, 68% of the time, the unemployment rate is between ____ and ____ percent.

29. *Stock Market Gyrations* Following is a sample of the day-by-day change, rounded to the nearest 100 points, in the Dow Jones Industrial Average during 10 successive business days around the start of the financial crisis in October 2008:[37]

$$-400, -500, -200, -700, -100, 900, -100, -700, 400, -100$$

   a. Compute the mean and standard deviation of the given sample. (Round your answers to the nearest whole number.)

   b. Assuming the distribution of day-by-day changes of the Dow during financial crises is symmetric and bell-shaped, then the Dow falls by more than ____ points 16% of the time. What is the percentage of times in the sample that the Dow actually fell by more than that amount? HINT [See Example 2(b).]

[35] Sources for data: Bureau of Labor Statistics (BLS) (www.bls.gov).

[36] Ibid.

[37] Source: http://finance.google.com.

30. *Stock Market Gyrations* Following is a sample of the day-by-day change, rounded to the nearest 100 points, in the Dow Jones Industrial Average during 10 successive business days around the start of the financial crisis in October 2008:[38]

$$-100, 400, -200, -500, 200, -300, -200, 900, -100, 200.$$

a. Compute the mean and standard deviation of the given sample. (Round your answers to the nearest whole number.)

b. Assuming the distribution of day-by-day changes of the Dow during financial crises is symmetric and bell-shaped, then the Dow rises by more than ___ points 2.5% of the time. What is the percentage of times in the sample that the Dow actually rose by more than that amount? HINT [See Example 2(b).]

31. ▯ *Sport Utility Vehicles* Following are highway driving gas mileages of a selection of medium-sized sport utility vehicles (SUVs):[39]

17, 18, 17, 18, 21, 16, 21, 18, 16, 14, 15, 22, 17, 19, 17, 18.

a. Find the sample standard deviation (rounded to two decimal places).

b. In what gas mileage range does Chebyshev's inequality predict that at least 8/9 (approximately 89%) of the selection will fall?

c. What is the actual percentage of SUV models of the sample that fall in the range predicted in part (b)? Which gives the more accurate prediction of this percentage: Chebyshev's rule or the empirical rule?

32. ▯ *Sport Utility Vehicles* Following are the city driving gas mileages of a selection of sport utility vehicles (SUVs):[40]

14, 15, 14, 15, 13, 16, 12, 14, 19, 18, 16, 16, 12, 15, 15, 13.

a. Find the sample standard deviation (rounded to two decimal places).

b. In what gas mileage range does Chebyshev's inequality predict that at least 75% of the selection will fall?

c. What is the actual percentage of SUV models of the sample that fall in the range predicted in part (b)? Which gives the more accurate prediction of this percentage: Chebyshev's rule or the empirical rule?

33. *Shopping Malls* A survey of all the shopping malls in your region yields the following probability distribution, where X is the number of movie theater screens in a selected mall:

Number of Movie Screens	0	1	2	3	4
Probability	.4	.1	.2	.2	.1

Compute the expected value μ and the standard deviation σ of X. (Round answers to two decimal places.) What percentage of malls have a number of movie theater screens within two standard deviations of μ?

34. *Pastimes* A survey of all the students in your school yields the following probability distribution, where X is the number of movies that a selected student has seen in the past week:

Number of Movies	0	1	2	3	4
Probability	.5	.1	.2	.1	.1

Compute the expected value μ and the standard deviation σ of X. (Round answers to two decimal places.) For what percentage of students is X within two standard deviations of μ?

35. ▯ *Income Distribution up to $100,000* The following table shows the distribution of household incomes for a sample of 1,000 households in the United States with incomes up to $100,000.[41]

2000 Income (thousands)	$10	$30	$50	$70	$90
Households	270	280	200	150	100

Compute the expected value μ and the standard deviation σ of the associated random variable X. If we define a "lower income" family as one whose income is more than one standard deviation below the mean, and a "higher income" family as one whose income is at least one standard deviation above the mean, what is the income gap between higher- and lower-income families in the United States? (Round your answers to the nearest $1,000.)

36. ▯ *Income Distribution up to $100,000* Repeat Exercise 35, using the following data for a sample of 1,000 Hispanic households in the United States.[42]

2000 Income (thousands)	$10	$30	$50	$70	$90
Households	300	340	190	110	60

37. *Hispanic Employment: Male* The following table shows the approximate number of males of Hispanic origin employed in the United States in 2005, broken down by age group.[43]

Age	15–24.9	25–54.9	55–64.9
Employment (thousands)	16,000	13,000	1,600

---

[38] Source: http://finance.google.com.

[39] Figures are the low-end of ranges for 1999 models tested. Source: Oak Ridge National Laboratory: "An Analysis of the Impact of Sport Utility Vehicles in the United States" Stacy C. Davis, Lorena F. Truett (August 2000)/Insurance Institute for Highway Safety (http://cta.ornl.gov/cta/Publications/pdf/ORNL_TM_2000_147.pdf).

[40] Ibid.

[41] Based on the actual household income distribution in 2003. Source: U.S. Census Bureau, Current Population Survey, 2004 Annual Social and Economic Supplement (http://pubdb3.census.gov/macro/032004/hhinc/new06_000.htm).

[42] Ibid.

[43] Figures are rounded. Bounds for the age groups for the first and third categories were adjusted for computational convenience. Source: Bureau of Labor Statistics (ftp://ftp.bls.gov/pub/suppl/empsit.cpseed15.txt).

a. Use the rounded midpoints of the given measurement classes to compute the expected value and the standard deviation of the age X of a male Hispanic worker in the United States. (Round all probabilities and intermediate calculations to two decimal places.)

b. In what age interval does the empirical rule predict that 68% of all male Hispanic workers will fall? (Round answers to the nearest year.)

38. *Hispanic Employment: Female* Repeat Exercise 37, using the corresponding data for females of Hispanic origin.[44]

Age	15–24.9	25–54.9	55–64.9
Employment (thousands)	1,200	5,000	600

a. Use the rounded midpoints of the given measurement classes to compute the expected value and the standard deviation of the age X of a female Hispanic worker in the United States. (Round all probabilities and intermediate calculations to two decimal places.)

b. In what age interval does the empirical rule predict that 68% of all female Hispanic workers will fall? (Round answers to the nearest year.)

39. *Commerce* You have been told that the average life span of an Internet-based company is 2 years, with a standard deviation of 0.15 years. Further, the associated distribution is highly skewed (not symmetric). Your Internet company is now 2.6 years old. What percentage of all Internet-based companies have enjoyed a life span at least as long as yours? Your answer should contain one of the following phrases: *At least; At most; Approximately.* HINT [See Example 2.]

40. *Commerce* You have been told that the average life span of a car-compounding service is 3 years, with a standard deviation of 0.2 years. Further, the associated distribution is symmetric but not bell-shaped. Your car-compounding service is exactly 2.6 years old. What fraction of car-compounding services last at most as long as yours? Your answer should contain one of the following phrases: *At least; At most; Approximately.* HINT [See Example 2.]

41. *Batmobiles* The average life span of a Batmobile is 9 years, with a standard deviation of 2 years.[45] Further, the probability distribution of the life spans of Batmobiles is symmetric, but not known to be bell-shaped.

Because my old Batmobile has been sold as bat-scrap, I have decided to purchase a new one. According to the above information, there is

(A) At least   **(B)** At most   **(C)** Approximately

a ____ percent chance that my new Batmobile will last 13 years or more.

42. *Spiderman Coupés* The average life span of a Spiderman Coupé is 8 years, with a standard deviation of 2 years. Further, the probability distribution of the life spans of Spiderman Coupés is not known to be bell-shaped or symmetric. I have just purchased a brand-new Spiderman Coupé. According to the above information, there is

(A) At least   **(B)** At most   **(C)** Approximately

a ____ percent chance that my new Spiderman Coupé will last for less than 4 years.

43. *Teenage Pastimes* According to a study,[46] the probability that a randomly selected teenager shopped at a mall at least once during a week was .63. Let X be the number of students in a randomly selected group of 40 that will shop at a mall during the next week.

a. Compute the expected value and standard deviation of X. (Round answers to two decimal places.) HINT [See Example 5.]

b. Fill in the missing quantity: There is an approximately 2.5% chance that ____ or more teenagers in the group will shop at a mall during the next week.

44. *Other Teenage Pastimes* According to the study referred to in the preceding exercise, the probability that a randomly selected teenager played a computer game at least once during a week was .48. Let X be the number of teenagers in a randomly selected group of 30 who will play a computer game during the next 7 days.

a. Compute the expected value and standard deviation of X. (Round answers to two decimal places.) HINT [See Example 5.]

b. Fill in the missing quantity: There is an approximately 16% chance that ____ or more teenagers in the group will play a computer game during the next 7 days.

45. ▼ *Teenage Marketing* In 2000, 22% of all teenagers in the United States had checking accounts.[47] Your bank, TeenChex Inc., is interested in targeting teenagers who do not already have a checking account.

a. If TeenChex selects a random sample of 1,000 teenagers, what number of teenagers *without* checking accounts can it expect to find? What is the standard deviation of this number? (Round the standard deviation to one decimal place.)

b. Fill in the missing quantities: There is an approximately 95% chance that between ____ and ____ teenagers in the sample will not have checking accounts. (Round answers to the nearest whole number.)

[44] Figures are rounded. Bounds for the age groups for the first and third categories were adjusted for computational convenience. Source: Bureau of Labor Statistics (ftp://ftp.bls.gov/pub/suppl/empsit.cpseed15.txt).

[45] See Example 2.

[46] Source: Rand Youth Poll/Teenage Research Unlimited/*The New York Times*, March 14, 1998, p. D1.

[47] Source: Teenage Research Unlimited, January 25, 2001 (www.teenresearch.com).

46. ▼ *Teenage Marketing* In 2000, 18% of all teenagers in the United States owned stocks or bonds.[48] Your brokerage company, TeenStox Inc., is interested in targeting teenagers who do not already own stocks or bonds.

a. If TeenStox selects a random sample of 2,000 teenagers, what number of teenagers who *do not* own stocks or bonds can it expect to find? What is the standard deviation of this number? (Round the standard deviation to one decimal place.)

b. Fill in the missing quantities: There is an approximately 99.7% chance that between ___ and ___ teenagers in the sample will not own stocks or bonds. (Round answers to the nearest whole number.)

47. ▣ ▼ ***Supermarkets*** A survey of supermarkets in the United States yielded the following relative frequency table, where X is the number of checkout lanes at a randomly chosen super-market:[49]

x	1	2	3	4	5	6	7	8	9	10
$P(X = x)$	.01	.04	.04	.08	.10	.15	.25	.20	.08	.05

a. Compute the mean, variance, and standard deviation (accurate to one decimal place).

b. As financial planning manager at Express Lane Mart, you wish to install a number of checkout lanes that is in the range of at least 75% of all supermarkets. What is this range according to Chebyshev's inequality? What is the *least* number of checkout lanes you should install so as to fall within this range?

48. ▣ ▼ ***Video Arcades*** Your company, Sonic Video, Inc., has conducted research that shows the following probability distribution, where X is the number of video arcades in a randomly chosen city with more than 500,000 inhabitants:

x	0	1	2	3	4	5	6	7	8	9
$P(X = x)$	.07	.09	.35	.25	.15	.03	.02	.02	.01	.01

a. Compute the mean, variance, and standard deviation (accurate to one decimal place).

b. As CEO of Startrooper Video Unlimited, you wish to install a chain of video arcades in Sleepy City, U.S.A. The city council regulations require that the number of arcades be within the range shared by at least 75% of all cities. What is this range? What is the *largest* number of video arcades you should install so as to comply with this regulation?

Distribution of Wealth *If we model after-tax household income by a normal distribution, then the figures of a 1995 study imply the information in the following table, which should be used for Exercises 49–60.*[50] *Assume that the distribution of incomes in each country is bell-shaped and symmetric.*

Country	United States	Canada	Switzerland	Germany	Sweden
Mean Household Income	$38,000	$35,000	$39,000	$34,000	$32,000
Standard Deviation	$21,000	$17,000	$16,000	$14,000	$11,000

49. If we define a "poor" household as one whose after-tax income is at least 1.3 standard deviations below the mean, what is the household income of a poor family in the United States?

50. If we define a "poor" household as one whose after-tax income is at least 1.3 standard deviations below the mean, what is the household income of a poor family in Switzerland?

51. If we define a "rich" household as one whose after-tax income is at least 1.3 standard deviations above the mean, what is the household income of a rich family in the United States?

52. If we define a "rich" household as one whose after-tax income is at least 1.3 standard deviations above the mean, what is the household income of a rich family in Sweden?

53. ▼ Refer to Exercise 49. Which of the five countries listed has the poorest households (i.e., the lowest cutoff for considering a household poor)?

54. ▼ Refer to Exercise 52. Which of the five countries listed has the wealthiest households (i.e., the highest cutoff for considering a household rich)?

55. ▼ Which of the five countries listed has the largest gap between rich and poor?

56. ▼ Which of the five countries listed has the smallest gap between rich and poor?

57. What percentage of U.S. families earned an after-tax income of $17,000 or less?

58. What percentage of U.S. families earned an after-tax income of $80,000 or more?

59. What is the after-tax income range of approximately 99.7% of all Germans?

60. What is the after-tax income range of approximately 99.7% of all Swedes?

---

[48] Source: Teenage Research Unlimited, January 25, 2001 (www.teenresearch.com).

[49] Source: J.T. McClave, P.G. Benson, T. Sincich, *Statistics for Business and Economics*, 7th Ed. (Prentice Hall, 1998) p. 177, W. Chow *et al.* "A model for predicting a supermarket's annual sales per square foot," Graduate School of Management, Rutgers University.

[50] The data are rounded to the nearest $1,000 and based on a report published by the Luxembourg Income Study. The report shows after-tax income, including government benefits (such as food stamps) of households with children. Our figures were obtained from the published data by assuming a normal distribution of incomes. All data were based on constant 1991 U.S. dollars and converted foreign currencies (adjusted for differences in buying power). Source: Luxembourg Income Study/*The New York Times*, August 14, 1995, p. A9.

⊤ *Aging* Exercises 61–66 are based on the following list, which shows the percentage of aging population (residents of age 65 and older) in each of the 50 states in 1990 and 2000:[51]

2000

6, 9, 10, 10, 10, 11, 11, 11, 11, 11,
11, 11, 12, 12, 12, 12, 12, 12, 12, 12,
12, 12, 12, 13, 13, 13, 13, 13, 13, 13,
13, 13, 13, 13, 13, 13, 14, 14, 14,
14, 14, 14, 14, 15, 15, 15, 15, 16, 18

1990

4, 9, 10, 10, 10, 10, 10, 11, 11, 11,
11, 11, 11, 11, 11, 12, 12, 12, 12, 12,
12, 13, 13, 13, 13, 13, 13, 13, 13, 13,
13, 13, 13, 13, 14, 14, 14, 14, 14,
14, 14, 14, 15, 15, 15, 15, 15, 15, 18.

61. ⊤ Compute the population mean and standard deviation for the 2000 data.

62. ⊤ Compute the population mean and standard deviation for the 1990 data.

63. ⊤ Compare the actual percentage of states whose aging population in 2000 was within one standard deviation of the mean to the percentage predicted by the empirical rule. Comment on your answer.

64. ⊤ Compare the actual percentage of states whose aging population in 1990 was within one standard deviation of the mean to the percentage predicted by the empirical rule. Comment on your answer.

65. ⊤ What was the actual percentage of states whose aging population in 1990 was within two standard deviations of the mean? Is Chebyshev's rule valid? Explain.

66. ⊤ What was the actual percentage of states whose aging population in 2000 was within two standard deviations of the mean? Is Chebyshev's rule valid? Explain.

67. ▼ *Electric Grid Stress* The following chart shows the approximate standard deviation of the power grid frequency, in 1/1,000 cycles per second, taken over six-month periods. (0.9 is the average standard deviation.)[52]

---

[51] Percentages are rounded and listed in ascending order. Source: U.S. Census Bureau, Census 2000 Summary File 1 (www.census.gov/prod/2001pubs/c2kbr01-10.pdf).

[52] Source Robert Blohm, energy consultant and adviser to the North American Electric Reliability Council/*The New York Times*, August 20, 2003, p. A16.

Which of the following statements are true? (More than one may be true.)

(A) The power grid frequency was at or below the mean until late 1999.

(B) The power grid frequency was more stable in mid-1999 than in 1995.

(C) The power grid frequency was more stable in mid-2002 than in mid-1999.

(D) The greatest fluctuations in the power grid frequency occurred in 2000–2001.

(E) The power grid frequency was more stable around January 1995 than around January 1999.

68. ▼ *Electric Grid Stress* The following chart shows the approximate monthly means of the power grid frequency, in 1/1,000 cycles per second. 0.0 represents the desired frequency of exactly 60 cycles per second.[53]

Which of the following statements are true? (More than one may be true.)

(A) Both the mean and the standard deviation show an upward trend from 2000 on.

(B) The mean, but not the standard deviation, shows an upward trend from 2000 on.

(C) The demand for electric power peaked in the second half of 2001.

(D) The standard deviation was larger in the second half of 2002 than in the second half of 1999.

(E) The mean of the monthly means in 2000 was lower than that for 2002, but the standard deviation of the monthly means was higher.

COMMUNICATION AND REASONING EXERCISES

69. Which is greater: the sample standard deviation or the population standard deviation? Explain.

70. Suppose you take larger and larger samples of a given population. Would you expect the sample and population standard deviations to get closer or further apart? Explain.

71. In one Finite Math class, the average grade was 75 and the standard deviation of the grades was 5. In another Finite Math class, the average grade was 65 and the standard deviation of the grades was 20. What conclusions can you draw about the distributions of the grades in each class?

---

[53] Ibid.

72. You are a manager in a precision manufacturing firm and you must evaluate the performance of two employees. You do so by examining the quality of the parts they produce. One particular item should be 50.0 ± 0.3 mm long to be usable. The first employee produces parts that are an average of 50.1 mm long with a standard deviation of 0.15 mm. The second employee produces parts that are an average of 50.0 mm long with a standard deviation of 0.4 mm. Which employee do you rate higher? Why? (Assume that the empirical rule applies.)

73. ▼ If a finite random variable has an expected value of 10 and a standard deviation of 0, what must its probability distribution be?

74. ▼ If the values of X in a population consist of an equal number of 1s and −1s, what is its standard deviation?

75. ◆ Find an algebraic formula for the population standard deviation of a sample $\{x, y\}$ of two scores ($x \leq y$).

76. ◆ Find an algebraic formula for the sample standard deviation of a sample $\{x, y\}$ of two scores ($x \leq y$).

8.5 Normal Distributions

Continuous Random Variables

Figure 9 shows the probability distributions for the number of successes in sequences of 10 and 15 independent Bernoulli trials, each with probability of success $p = .5$.

Figure 9(a)

Figure 9(b)

Figure 10

Because each column is 1 unit wide, its area is numerically equal to its height. Thus, the area of each rectangle can be interpreted as a probability. For example, in Figure 9(a) the area of the rectangle over $X = 3$ represents $P(X = 3)$. If we want to find $P(3 \leq X \leq 5)$, we can add up the areas of the three rectangles over 3, 4, and 5, shown shaded in Figure 10. Notice that if we add up the areas of *all* the rectangles in Figure 9(a), the total is 1 because $P(0 \leq X \leq 10) = 1$. We can summarize these observations.

Properties of the Probability Distribution Histogram

In a probability distribution histogram where each column is 1 unit wide:

- The total area enclosed by the histogram is 1 square unit.
- $P(a \leq X \leq b)$ is the area enclosed by the rectangles lying between and including $X = a$ and $X = b$.

This discussion is motivation for considering another kind of random variable, one whose probability distribution is specified not by a bar graph, as above, but by the graph of a function.

Continuous Random Variable; Probability Density Function

A **continuous random variable** X may take on any real value whatsoever. The probabilities $P(a \leq X \leq b)$ are defined by means of a **probability density function**, a function whose graph lies above the x-axis with the total area between the graph and the x-axis being 1. The probability $P(a \leq X \leq b)$ is defined to be the area enclosed by the curve, the x-axis, and the lines $x = a$ and $x = b$ (see Figure 11).

Figure 11(a)   **Figure 11(b)**

Notes

1. In Chapter 7, we defined probability distributions only for *finite* sample spaces. Because continuous random variables have infinite sample spaces, we need the definition above to give meaning to $P(a \leq X \leq b)$ if X is a continuous random variable.

2. If $a = b$, then $P(X = a) = P(a \leq X \leq a)$ is the area under the curve between the lines $x = a$ and $x = a$—no area at all! Thus, when X is a continuous random variable, $P(X = a) = 0$ for every value of a.

3. Whether we take the region in Figure 11(b) to include the boundary or not does not affect the area. The probability $P(a < X < b)$ is defined as the area strictly between the vertical lines $x = a$ and $x = b$, but is, of course, the same as $P(a \leq X \leq b)$, because the boundary contributes nothing to the area. When we are calculating probabilities associated with a continuous random variable,

$$P(a \leq X \leq b) = P(a < X \leq b) = P(a \leq X < b) = P(a < X < b). \qquad \blacksquare$$

Normal Density Functions

Among all the possible probability density functions, there is an important class of functions called **normal density functions**, or **normal distributions**. The graph of a normal density function is bell-shaped and symmetric, as the following figure shows. The formula for a normal density function is rather complicated looking:

$$f(x) = \frac{1}{\sigma\sqrt{2\pi}} e^{-\frac{(x-\mu)^2}{2\sigma^2}}.$$

The quantity μ is called the **mean** and can be any real number. The quantity σ is called the **standard deviation** and can be any positive real number. The number $e = 2.7182\ldots$ is a useful constant that shows up many places in mathematics, much as the constant π does. Finally, the constant $1/(\sigma\sqrt{2\pi})$ that appears in front is there to make the total area come out to be 1. We rarely use the actual formula in computations; instead, we use tables or technology.

Normal Density Function; Normal Distribution

A **normal density function**, or **normal distribution**, is a function of the form

$$f(x) = \frac{1}{\sigma\sqrt{2\pi}}e^{-\frac{(x-\mu)^2}{2\sigma^2}}$$

where μ is the mean and σ is the standard deviation. The "inflection points" are the points where the curve changes from bending in one direction to bending in another.*

✳ NOTE Pretend you were driving along the curve in a car. Then the points of inflection are the points where you would change the direction in which you are steering (from left to right or right to left).

 using Technology

The graphs in Figure 12 can be drawn on a TI-83/84 Plus or the Web site grapher.

TI-83/84 Plus
Figure 12(a):
Y₁=normalpdf(x,2,1)
Figure 12(b):
Y₁=normalpdf(x,0,2)
Figure 12(c):
Y₁=normalpdf(x)

Web Site
www.FiniteandCalc.org
  Student Home
    → Online Utilities
    → Function Evaluator and
      Grapher
Figure 12(a):
normalpdf(x,2,1)
Figure 12(b):
normalpdf(x,0,2)
Figure 12(c):
normalpdf(x)

Figure 12 shows the graph of several normal density functions. The third of these has mean 0 and standard deviation 1, and is called the **standard normal distribution**. We use Z rather than X to refer to the standard normal variable.

Figure 12(a)

Figure 12(b)

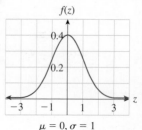

Standard Normal Distribution

Figure 12(c)

Calculating Probabilities Using the Standard Normal Distribution

The standard normal distribution has $\mu = 0$ and $\sigma = 1$. The corresponding variable is called the **standard normal variable**, which we always denote by Z. Recall that to calculate the probability $P(a \leq Z \leq b)$, we need to find the area under the distribution curve between the vertical lines $z = a$ and $z = b$. We can use the table in the Appendix to look up these areas, or we can use technology. Here is an example.

EXAMPLE 1 Standard Normal Distribution

Let Z be the standard normal variable. Calculate the following probabilities:

a. $P(0 \leq Z \leq 2.4)$

b. $P(0 \leq Z \leq 2.43)$

c. $P(-1.37 \leq Z \leq 2.43)$

d. $P(1.37 \leq Z \leq 2.43)$

Solution

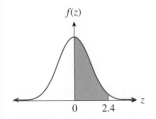

Figure 13

a. We are asking for the shaded area under the standard normal curve shown in Figure 13. We can find this area, correct to four decimal places, by looking at the table in the Appendix, which lists the area under the standard normal curve from $Z = 0$ to $Z = b$ for any value of b between 0 and 3.09. To use the table, write 2.4 as 2.40, and read the entry in the row labeled 2.4 and the column labeled .00 ($2.4 + .00 = 2.40$). Here is the relevant portion of the table:

Z	.00	.01	.02	.03
2.3	.4893	.4896	.4898	.4901
2.4	.4918	.4920	.4922	.4925
2.5	.4938	.4940	.4941	.4943

Thus, $P(0 \leq Z \leq 2.40) = .4918$.

b. The area we require can be read from the same portion of the table shown above. Write 2.43 as $2.4 + .03$, and read the entry in the row labeled 2.4 and the column labeled .03:

Z	.00	.01	.02	.03
2.3	.4893	.4896	.4898	.4901
2.4	.4918	.4920	.4922	.4925
2.5	.4938	.4940	.4941	.4943

Thus, $P(0 \leq Z \leq 2.43) = .4925$.

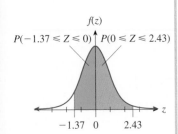

Figure 14

c. Here we cannot use the table directly because the range $-1.37 \leq Z \leq 2.43$ does not start at 0. But we can break the area up into two smaller areas that start or end at 0:

$$P(-1.37 \leq Z \leq 2.43) = P(-1.37 \leq Z \leq 0) + P(0 \leq Z \leq 2.43).$$

In terms of the graph, we are splitting the desired area into two smaller areas (Figure 14).

We already calculated the area of the right-hand piece in part (b):

$$P(0 \leq Z \leq 2.43) = .4925.$$

For the left-hand piece, the symmetry of the normal curve tells us that

$$P(-1.37 \leq Z \leq 0) = P(0 \leq Z \leq 1.37).$$

This we can find on the table. Look at the row labeled 1.3 and the column labeled .07, and read

$$P(-1.37 \leq Z \leq 0) = P(0 \leq Z \leq 1.37) = .4147.$$

Thus,

$$P(-1.37 \leq Z \leq 2.43) = P(-1.37 \leq Z \leq 0) + P(0 \leq Z \leq 2.43)$$
$$= .4147 + .4925$$
$$= .9072.$$

 using Technology

Technology can be used to calculate the probabilities in Example 1. For instance, the calculation for part (c) is as follows:

TI-83/84 Plus
Home Screen:
normalcdf(-1.37, 2.43)
(normalcdf is in 2ND VARS.)
[More details on page 614.]

Excel
=NORMSDIST(2.43)
-NORMSDIST(-1.37)
[More details on page 616.]

d. The range $1.37 \leq Z \leq 2.43$ does not contain 0, so we cannot use the technique of part (c). Instead, the corresponding area can be computed as the *difference* of two areas:

$$P(1.37 \leq Z \leq 2.43) = P(0 \leq Z \leq 2.43) - P(0 \leq Z \leq 1.37)$$
$$= .4925 - .4147$$
$$= .0778.$$

Calculating Probabilities for Any Normal Distribution

Although we have tables to compute the area under the *standard* normal curve, there are no readily available tables for nonstandard distributions. For example, If $\mu = 2$ and $\sigma = 3$, then how would we calculate $P(0.5 \leq X \leq 3.2)$? The following conversion formula provides a method for doing so:

Standardizing a Normal Distribution

If X has a normal distribution with mean μ and standard deviation σ, and if Z is the standard normal variable, then

$$P(a \leq X \leq b) = P\left(\frac{a - \mu}{\sigma} \leq Z \leq \frac{b - \mu}{\sigma}\right).$$

Quick Example

If $\mu = 2$ and $\sigma = 3$, then

$$P(0.5 \leq X \leq 3.2) = P\left(\frac{0.5 - 2}{3} \leq Z \leq \frac{3.2 - 2}{3}\right)$$
$$= P(-0.5 \leq Z \leq 0.4) = .1915 + .1554 = .3469.$$

To completely justify the above formula requires more mathematics than we shall discuss here. However, here is the main idea: if X is normal with mean μ and standard deviation σ, then $X - \mu$ is normal with mean 0 and standard deviation still σ, while $(X - \mu)/\sigma$ is normal with mean 0 and standard deviation 1. In other words, $(X - \mu)/\sigma = Z$. Therefore,

$$P(a \leq X \leq b) = P\left(\frac{a - \mu}{\sigma} \leq \frac{X - \mu}{\sigma} \leq \frac{b - \mu}{\sigma}\right) = P\left(\frac{a - \mu}{\sigma} \leq Z \leq \frac{b - \mu}{\sigma}\right).$$

EXAMPLE 2 Quality Control

Pressure gauges manufactured by Precision Corp. must be checked for accuracy before being placed on the market. To test a pressure gauge, a worker uses it to measure the pressure of a sample of compressed air known to be at a pressure of exactly 50 pounds per square inch. If the gauge reading is off by more than 1% (0.5 pounds), it is rejected. Assuming that the reading of a pressure gauge under these circumstances is a normal random variable with mean 50 and standard deviation 0.4, find the percentage of gauges rejected.

using Technology

Technology can be used to calculate the probability $P(49.5 \leq X \leq 50.5)$ in Example 2:

TI-83/84 Plus

Home Screen:
`normalcdf(49.5, 50.5, 50, 0.4)`
(`normalcdf` is in 2ND VARS .)
[More details on page 614.]

Excel

`=NORMDIST(50.5,50, 0.4,1)`
`-NORMDIST(49.5, 50,0.4,1)`
[More details on page 617.]

Web Site

www.FiniteandCalc.org

Student Home

→ Online Utilities

→ Normal Distribution Utility

Set up as shown and press "Calculate Probability."

Solution If X is the reading of the gauge, then X has a normal distribution with $\mu = 50$ and $\sigma = 0.4$. We are asking for $P(X < 49.5 \text{ or } X > 50.5) = 1 - P(49.5 \leq X \leq 50.5)$. We calculate

$$P(49.5 \leq X \leq 50.5) = P\left(\frac{49.5 - 50}{0.4} \leq Z \leq \frac{50.5 - 50}{0.4}\right) \quad \text{Standardize}$$

$$= P(-1.25 \leq Z \leq 1.25)$$
$$= 2 \cdot P(0 \leq Z \leq 1.25)$$
$$= 2(.3944) = .7888.$$

So, $\quad P(X < 49.5 \text{ or } X > 50.5) = 1 - P(49.5 \leq X \leq 50.5)$
$$= 1 - .7888 = .2112.$$

In other words, about 21% of the gauges will be rejected.

In many applications, we need to know the probability that a value of a normal random variable will lie within one standard deviation of the mean, or within two standard deviations, or within some number of standard deviations. To compute these probabilities, we first notice that, if X has a normal distribution with mean μ and standard deviation σ, then

$$P(\mu - k\sigma \leq X \leq \mu + k\sigma) = P(-k \leq Z \leq k)$$

by the standardizing formula. We can compute these probabilities for various values of k using the table in the Appendix, and we obtain the following results.

Probability of a Normal Distribution Being within k Standard Deviations of Its Mean

$P(\mu - \sigma \leq X \leq \mu + \sigma) =$
$P(-1 \leq Z \leq 1) = .6826$

$P(\mu - 2\sigma \leq X \leq \mu + 2\sigma) =$
$P(-2 \leq Z \leq 2) = .9544$

$P(\mu - 3\sigma \leq X \leq \mu + 3\sigma) =$
$P(-3 \leq Z \leq 3) = .9974$

Now you can see where the empirical rule comes from! Notice also that the probabilities above are a good deal larger than the lower bounds given by Chebyshev's rule. Chebyshev's rule must work for distributions that are skew or any shape whatsoever.

EXAMPLE 3 Loans

The values of mortgage loans made by a certain bank one year were normally distributed with a mean of $120,000 and a standard deviation of $40,000.

a. What is the probability that a randomly selected mortgage loan was in the range of $40,000–$200,000?

b. You would like to state in your annual report that 50% of all mortgage loans were in a certain range with the mean in the center. What is that range?

Solution

a. We are asking for the probability that a loan was within two standard deviations ($80,000) of the mean. By the calculation done previously, this probability is .9544.

b. We look for the k such that

$$P(120{,}000 - k \cdot 40{,}000 \le X \le 120{,}000 + k \cdot 40{,}000) = .5.$$

Because

$$P(120{,}000 - k \cdot 40{,}000 \le X \le 120{,}000 + k \cdot 40{,}000) = P(-k \le Z \le k)$$

we look in the Appendix to see for which k we have

$$P(0 \le Z \le k) = .25$$

so that $P(-k \le Z \le k) = .5$. That is, we look *inside* the table to see where 0.25 is, and find the corresponding k. We find

$$P(0 \le Z \le 0.67) = .2486$$
$$\text{and} \quad P(0 \le Z \le 0.68) = .2517.$$

Therefore, the k we want is about half-way between 0.67 and 0.68, call it 0.675. This tells us that 50% of all mortgage loans were in the range

$$120{,}000 - 0.675 \cdot 40{,}000 = \$93{,}000$$
$$\text{to} \quad 120{,}000 + 0.675 \cdot 40{,}000 = \$147{,}000.$$

Normal Approximation to a Binomial Distribution

You might have noticed that the histograms of some of the binomial distributions we have drawn (for example, those in Figure 1) have a very rough bell shape. In fact, in many cases it is possible to draw a normal curve that closely approximates a given binomial distribution.

Normal Approximation to a Binomial Distribution

If X is the number of successes in a sequence of n independent Bernoulli trials, with probability p of success in each trial, and if the range of values of X within three standard deviations of the mean lies entirely within the range 0 to n (the possible values of X), then

$$P(a \le X \le b) \approx P(a - 0.5 \le Y \le b + 0.5)$$

where Y has a normal distribution with the same mean and standard deviation as X; that is, $\mu = np$ and $\sigma = \sqrt{npq}$, where $q = 1 - p$.

Notes

1. The condition that $0 \le \mu - 3\sigma < \mu + 3\sigma \le n$ is satisfied if n is sufficiently large and p is not too close to 0 or 1; it ensures that most of the normal curve lies in the range 0 to n.

2. In the formula $P(a \leq X \leq b) \approx P(a - 0.5 \leq Y \leq b + 0.5)$, we assume that a and b are integers. The use of $a - 0.5$ and $b + 0.5$ is called the **continuity correction**. To see that it is necessary, think about what would happen if you wanted to approximate, say, $P(X = 2) = P(2 \leq X \leq 2)$. Should the answer be 0? ∎

Figures 15 and 16 show two binomial distributions with their normal approximations superimposed, and illustrate how closely the normal approximation fits the binomial distribution.

Figure 15

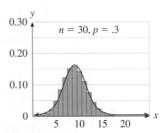

Figure 16

EXAMPLE 4 Coin Tosses

a. If you flip a fair coin 100 times, what is the probability of getting more than 55 heads or fewer than 45 heads?

b. What number of heads (out of 100) would make you suspect that the coin is not fair?

Solution

a. We are asking for

$$P(X < 45 \text{ or } X > 55) = 1 - P(45 \leq X \leq 55).$$

We *could* compute this by calculating

$$1 - [C(100, 45)(.5)^{45}(.5)^{55} + C(100, 46)(.5)^{46}(.5)^{54} + \cdots + C(100, 55)(.5)^{55}(.5)^{45}]$$

but we can much more easily *approximate* it by looking at a normal distribution with mean $\mu = 50$ and standard deviation $\sigma = \sqrt{(100)(.5)(.5)} = 5$. (Notice that three standard deviations above and below the mean is the range 35 to 65, which is well within the range of possible values for X, which is 0 to 100, so the approximation should be a good one.) Let Y have this normal distribution. Then

$$P(45 \leq X \leq 55) \approx P(44.5 \leq Y \leq 55.5)$$
$$= P(-1.1 \leq Z \leq 1.1)$$
$$= .7286.$$

Therefore,

$$P(X < 45 \text{ or } X > 55) \approx 1 - .7286 = .2714.$$

b. This is a deep question that touches on the concept of **statistical significance**: What evidence is strong enough to overturn a reasonable assumption (the assumption that the coin is fair)? Statisticians have developed sophisticated ways of answering this question, but we can look at one simple test now. Suppose we tossed a coin 100 times and got 66 heads. If the coin were fair, then $P(X > 65) \approx P(Y > 65.5) = P(Z > 3.1) \approx .001$. This is small enough to raise a reasonable doubt that the coin is fair. However, we should not be too surprised if we threw 56 heads because we can calculate $P(X > 55) \approx .1357$, which is not such a small probability. As we said, the actual tests of statistical significance are more sophisticated than this, but we shall not go into them.

FAQ

When to Subtract from .5 and When Not To

Q: *When computing probabilities like, say $P(Z \leq 1.2)$, $P(Z \geq 1.2)$, or $P(1.2 \leq Z \leq 2.1)$ using a table, just looking up the given values (1.2, 2.1, or whatever) is not enough. Sometimes you have to subtract from .5, sometimes not. Is there a simple rule telling me what to do when?*

A: The simplest—and also most instructive—way of knowing what to do is to draw a picture of the standard normal curve, and shade in the area you are looking for. Drawing pictures also helps one come up with the following mechanical rules:

1. To compute $P(a \leq Z \leq b)$, look up the areas corresponding to $|a|$ and $|b|$ in the table. If a and b have opposite signs, add these areas. Otherwise, subtract the smaller area from the larger.

2. To compute $P(Z \leq a)$, look up the area corresponding to $|a|$. If a is positive, add .5. Otherwise, subtract from .5.

3. To compute $P(Z \geq a)$, look up the area corresponding to $|a|$. If a is positive, subtract from .5. Otherwise, add .5.

8.5 EXERCISES

▼ more advanced   ◆ challenging
T indicates exercises that should be solved using technology

Note: Answers for Section 8.5 were computed using the 4-digit table in the Appendix, and may differ slightly from the more accurate answers generated using technology.

In Exercises 1–8, Z is the standard normal distribution. Find the indicated probabilities. HINT [See Example 1.]

1. $P(0 \leq Z \leq 0.5)$ **2.** $P(0 \leq Z \leq 1.5)$

3. $P(-0.71 \leq Z \leq 0.71)$ **4.** $P(-1.71 \leq Z \leq 1.71)$

5. $P(-0.71 \leq Z \leq 1.34)$ **6.** $P(-1.71 \leq Z \leq 0.23)$

7. $P(0.5 \leq Z \leq 1.5)$ **8.** $P(0.71 \leq Z \leq 1.82)$

In Exercises 9–14, X has a normal distribution with the given mean and standard deviation. Find the indicated probabilities. HINT [See Quick Example on page 598.]

9. $\mu = 50$, $\sigma = 10$, find $P(35 \leq X \leq 65)$

10. $\mu = 40$, $\sigma = 20$, find $P(35 \leq X \leq 45)$

11. $\mu = 50$, $\sigma = 10$, find $P(30 \leq X \leq 62)$

12. $\mu = 40$, $\sigma = 20$, find $P(30 \leq X \leq 53)$

13. $\mu = 100$, $\sigma = 15$, find $P(110 \leq X \leq 130)$

14. $\mu = 100$, $\sigma = 15$, find $P(70 \leq X \leq 80)$

15. ▼ Find the probability that a normal variable takes on values within 0.5 standard deviations of its mean.

16. ▼ Find the probability that a normal variable takes on values within 1.5 standard deviations of its mean.

17. ▼ Find the probability that a normal variable takes on values more than $\frac{2}{3}$ standard deviations away from its mean.

18. ▼ Find the probability that a normal variable takes on values more than $\frac{5}{3}$ standard deviations away from its mean.

19. If you roll a die 100 times, what is the approximate probability that you will roll between 10 and 15 ones, inclusive? (Round your answer to two decimal places.) HINT [See Example 4.]

20. If you roll a die 100 times, what is the approximate probability that you will roll between 15 and 20 ones, inclusive? (Round your answer to two decimal places.) HINT [See Example 4.]

21. If you roll a die 200 times, what is the approximate probability that you will roll fewer than 25 ones, inclusive? (Round your answer to two decimal places.)

22. If you roll a die 200 times, what is the approximate probability that you will roll more than 40 ones? (Round your answer to two decimal places.)

APPLICATIONS

23. *SAT Scores* SAT test scores are normally distributed with a mean of 500 and a standard deviation of 100. Find the probability that a randomly chosen test-taker will score between 450 and 550. HINT [See Example 3.]

24. *SAT Scores* SAT test scores are normally distributed with a mean of 500 and a standard deviation of 100. Find the probability that a randomly chosen test-taker will score 650 or higher. HINT [See Example 3.]

25. *LSAT Scores* LSAT test scores are normally distributed with a mean of 500 and a standard deviation of 100. Find the probability that a randomly chosen test-taker will score between 300 and 550.

26. *LSAT Scores* LSAT test scores are normally distributed with a mean of 500 and a standard deviation of 100. Find the probability that a randomly chosen test-taker will score 250 or lower.

27. *IQ Scores* IQ scores (as measured by the Stanford-Binet intelligence test) are normally distributed with a mean of 100 and a standard deviation of 16. What percentage of the population has an IQ score between 110 and 140? (Round your answer to the nearest percentage point.)

28. *IQ Scores* Refer to Exercise 27. What percentage of the population has an IQ score between 80 and 90? (Round your answer to the nearest percentage point.)

29. *IQ Scores* Refer to Exercise 27. Find the approximate number of people in the United States (assuming a total population of 280,000,000) with an IQ higher than 120.

30. *IQ Scores* Refer to Exercise 27. Find the approximate number of people in the United States (assuming a total population of 280,000,000) with an IQ higher than 140.

31. *Baseball* The mean batting average in major league baseball is about 0.250. Supposing that batting averages are normally distributed, that the standard deviation in the averages is 0.03, and that there are 250 batters, what is the expected number of batters with an average of at least 0.400?

32. *Baseball* The mean batting average in major league baseball is about 0.250. Supposing that batting averages are normally distributed, that the standard deviation in the averages is 0.05, and that there are 250 batters, what is the expected number of batters with an average of at least 0.400?[54]

33. *Marketing* Your pickle company rates its pickles on a scale of spiciness from 1 to 10. Market research shows that customer preferences for spiciness are normally distributed, with a mean of 7.5 and a standard deviation of 1. Assuming that you sell 100,000 jars of pickles, how many jars with a spiciness of 9 or above do you expect to sell?

34. *Marketing* Your hot sauce company rates its sauce on a scale of spiciness of 1 to 20. Market research shows that customer preferences for spiciness are normally distributed, with a mean of 12 and a standard deviation of 2.5. Assuming that you sell 300,000 bottles of sauce, how many bottles with a spiciness below 9 do you expect to sell?

Distribution of Wealth *If we model after-tax household income with a normal distribution, then the figures of a 1995 study imply the information in the following table, which should be used for Exercises 35–40.[55] Assume that the distribution of incomes in each country is normal, and round all percentages to the nearest whole number.*

Country	United States	Canada	Switzerland	Germany	Sweden
Mean Household Income	$38,000	$35,000	$39,000	$34,000	$32,000
Standard Deviation	$21,000	$17,000	$16,000	$14,000	$11,000

35. What percentage of U.S. households had an income of $50,000 or more?

36. What percentage of German households had an income of $50,000 or more?

37. What percentage of Swiss households are either very wealthy (income at least $100,000) or very poor (income at most $12,000)?

38. What percentage of Swedish households are either very wealthy (income at least $100,000) or very poor (income at most $12,000)?

39. Which country has a higher proportion of very poor families (income $12,000 or less): the United States or Canada?

40. Which country has a higher proportion of very poor families (income $12,000 or less): Canada or Switzerland?

41. ▼ *Comparing IQ Tests* IQ scores as measured by both the Stanford-Binet intelligence test and the Wechsler intelligence test have a mean of 100. The standard deviation for the Stanford-Binet test is 16, while that for the Wechsler test is

---

[54] The last time that a batter ended the year with an average above 0.400 was in 1941. The batter was Ted Williams of the Boston Red Sox, and his average was 0.406. Over the years, as pitching and batting have improved, the standard deviation in batting averages has declined from around 0.05 when professional baseball began to around 0.03 by the end of the twentieth century. For a very interesting discussion of statistics in baseball and in evolution, see Stephen Jay Gould, *Full House: The Spread of Excellence from Plato to Darwin*, Random House, 1997.

[55] The data are rounded to the nearest $1,000 and is based on a report published by the Luxembourg Income Study. The report shows after-tax income, including government benefits (such as food stamps) of households with children. Our figures were obtained from the published data by assuming a normal distribution of incomes. All data were based on constant 1991 U.S. dollars and converted foreign currencies (adjusted for differences in buying power). Source: Luxembourg Income Study/ *The New York Times*, August 14, 1995, p. A9.

15. For which test do a smaller percentage of test-takers score less than 80? Why?

42. ▼ *Comparing IQ Tests* Referring to Exercise 41, for which test do a larger percentage of test-takers score more than 120?

43. ▼ *Product Repairs* The new copier your business bought lists a mean time between failures of 6 months, with a standard deviation of 1 month. One month after a repair, it breaks down again. Is this surprising? (Assume that the times between failures are normally distributed.)

44. ▼ *Product Repairs* The new computer your business bought lists a mean time between failures of 1 year, with a standard deviation of 2 months. Ten months after a repair, it breaks down again. Is this surprising? (Assume that the times between failures are normally distributed.)

Software Testing Exercises 45–50 are based on the following information, gathered from student testing of a statistical software package called MODSTAT.[56] *Students were asked to complete certain tasks using the software, without any instructions. The results were as follows. (Assume that the time for each task is normally distributed.)*

Task	Mean Time (minutes)	Standard Deviation
Task 1: Descriptive Analysis of Data	11.4	5.0
Task 2: Standardizing Scores	11.9	9.0
Task 3: Poisson Probability Table	7.3	3.9
Task 4: Areas under Normal Curve	9.1	5.5

45. Find the probability that a student will take at least 10 minutes to complete Task 1.

46. Find the probability that a student will take at least 10 minutes to complete Task 3.

47. ▼ Assuming that the time it takes a student to complete each task is independent of the others, find the probability that a student will take at least 10 minutes to complete each of Tasks 1 and 2.

48. ▼ Assuming that the time it takes a student to complete each task is independent of the others, find the probability that a student will take at least 10 minutes to complete each of Tasks 3 and 4.

49. ◆ It can be shown that if X and Y are independent normal random variables with means μ_X and μ_Y and standard deviations σ_X and σ_Y respectively, then their sum $X + Y$ is also normally distributed and has mean $\mu = \mu_X + \mu_Y$ and standard deviation $\sigma = \sqrt{\sigma_X^2 + \sigma_Y^2}$. Assuming that the time it takes a student to complete each task is independent of the others, find the

probability that a student will take at least 20 minutes to complete both Tasks 1 and 2.

50. ◆ Referring to Exercise 49, compute the probability that a student will take at least 20 minutes to complete both Tasks 3 and 4.

51. *Computers* In 2001, 51% of all households in the United States had a computer.[57] Find the probability that in a small town with 800 households, at least 400 had a computer in 2001. HINT [See Example 4.]

52. *Television Ratings* Based on data from **Nielsen Research**, there is a 15% chance that any television that is turned on during the time of the evening newscasts will be tuned to **ABC**'s evening news show.[58] Your company wishes to advertise on a small local station carrying **ABC** that serves a community with 2,500 households that regularly tune in during this time slot. Find the approximate probability that at least 400 households will be tuned in to the show. HINT [See Example 4.]

53. *Aviation* The probability of a plane crashing on a single trip in 1989 was .00000165.[59] Find the approximate probability that in 100,000,000 flights, there will be fewer than 180 crashes.

54. *Aviation* The probability of a plane crashing on a single trip in 1990 was .00000087. Find the approximate probability that in 100,000,000 flights, there will be more than 110 crashes.

55. ▼ *Insurance* Your company issues flight insurance. You charge $2 and in the event of a plane crash, you will pay out $1 million to the victim or his or her family. In 1989, the probability of a plane crashing on a single trip was .00000165. If ten people per flight buy insurance from you, what was your approximate probability of losing money over the course of 100 million flights in 1989? HINT [First determine how many crashes there must be for you to lose money.]

56. ▼ *Insurance* Refer back to the preceding exercise. What is your approximate probability of losing money over the course of 10 million flights?

57. ◆ *Polls* In a certain political poll, each person polled has a 90% probability of telling his or her real preference. Suppose that 55% of the population really prefer candidate Goode, and 45% prefer candidate Slick. First find the probability that a person polled will say that he or she prefers Goode. Then find the approximate probability that, if 1,000 people are polled, more than 52% will say they prefer Goode.

58. ◆ *Polls* In a certain political poll, each person polled has a 90% probability of telling his or her real preference. Suppose that 1,000 people are polled and 51% say that they prefer candidate Goode, while 49% say that they prefer candidate

---

[56] Data are rounded to one decimal place. Source: *Student Evaluations of MODSTAT*, by Joseph M. Nowakowski, Muskingum College, New Concord, OH, 1997 (http://members.aol.com/rcknodt/pubpage.htm).

[57] Source: NTIA and ESA, U.S. Department of Commerce, using U.S. Bureau of the Census Current Population Survey supplements.

[58] Source: Nielsen Media Research/ABC Network/*New York Times*, March 18, 2002, p. C1.

[59] Source for this exercise and the following three: National Transportation Safety Board.

Slick. Find the approximate probability that Goode could do at least this well if, in fact, only 49% prefer Goode.

59. ◆ *IQ Scores* Mensa is a club for people with high IQs. To qualify, you must be in the top 2% of the population. One way of qualifying is by having an IQ of at least 148, as measured by the Cattell intelligence test. Assuming that scores on this test are normally distributed with a mean of 100, what is the standard deviation? HINT [Use the table in the Appendix "backwards."]

60. ◆ *SAT Scores* Another way to qualify for Mensa (see the previous exercise) is to score at least 1,250 on the SAT [combined Critical Reading (Verbal, before March 2005) and Math scores], which puts you in the top 2%. Assuming that SAT scores are normally distributed with a mean of 1,000, what is the standard deviation? [See the hint for the previous exercise.]

COMMUNICATION AND REASONING EXERCISES

61. Under what assumptions are the estimates in the empirical rule exact?

62. If X is a continuous random variable, what values can the quantity $P(X = a)$ have?

63. Which is larger for a continuous random variable, $P(X \le a)$ or $P(X < a)$?

64. Which of the following is greater: $P(X \le b)$ or $P(a \le X \le b)$?

65. ▼ A uniform continuous distribution is one with a probability density curve that is a horizontal line. If X takes on values between the numbers a and b with a uniform distribution, find the height of its probability density curve.

66. ▼ Which would you expect to have the greater variance: the standard normal distribution or the uniform distribution taking values between -1 and 1? Explain.

67. ◆ Which would you expect to have a density curve that is higher at the mean: the standard normal distribution, or a normal distribution with standard deviation 0.5? Explain.

68. ◆ Suppose students must perform two tasks: Task 1 and Task 2. Which of the following would you expect to have a smaller standard deviation?

(A) The time it takes a student to perform both tasks if the time it takes to complete Task 2 is independent of the time it takes to complete Task 1.

(B) The time it takes a student to perform both tasks if students will perform similarly in both tasks.

Explain.

KEY CONCEPTS

Web Site www.FiniteandCalc.org
Go to the student Web site at
  www.FiniteandCalc.org to find a
  comprehensive and interactive
  Web-based summary of Chapter 8.

8.1 Random Variables and Distributions

Random variable; discrete vs continuous
  random variable p. 549
Probability distribution of a finite
  random variable p. 551
Using measurement classes p. 552

8.2 Bernoulli Trials and Binomial Random Variables

Bernoulli trial; binomial random variable
  pp. 559, 560
Probability distribution of binomial
  random variable:
$P(X = x) = C(n, x)p^x q^{n-x}$
  p. 562

8.3 Measures of Central Tendency

Sample, sample mean; population, population mean p. 567
Sample median, sample mode p. 569
Expected value of a random variable:
$\mu = E(X) = \sum_i x_i \cdot P(X = x_i)$
  p. 571
Expected value of a binomial random
  variable: $\mu = E(X) = np$ p. 573

8.4 Measures of Dispersion

Population variance:
$$\sigma^2 = \frac{\sum_{i=1}^{n}(x_i - \mu)^2}{n}$$
Population standard deviation:
$\sigma = \sqrt{\sigma^2}$ p. 580
Sample variance:
$$s^2 = \frac{\sum_{i=1}^{n}(x_i - \bar{x})^2}{n - 1}$$
Sample standard deviation:
$s = \sqrt{s^2}$ p. 580

Chebyshev's Rule p. 583
Empirical Rule p. 583
Variance of a random variable:
$\sigma^2 = \sum_i (x_i - \mu)^2 P(X = x_i)$ p. 585
Standard deviation of X: $\sigma = \sqrt{\sigma^2}$ p. 585
Variance and standard deviation of a
  binomial random variable:
$\sigma^2 = npq, \sigma = \sqrt{npq}$ p. 587

8.5 Normal Distributions

Probability density function p. 595
Normal density function; normal
  distribution; standard normal
  distribution p. 595
Calculating probabilities based on the
  standard normal distribution p. 596
Standardizing a normal distribution
  p. 596
Calculating probabilities based on nonstandard normal distributions p. 598
Normal approximation to a binomial
  distribution p. 600

REVIEW EXERCISES

In Exercises 1–6, find the probability distribution for the given random variable and draw a histogram.

1. A couple has two children; $X =$ the number of boys. (Assume an equal likelihood of a child being a boy or a girl.)

2. A couple has three children; $X =$ the number of girls. (Assume an equal likelihood of a child being a boy or a girl.)

3. A four-sided die (with sides numbered 1 through 4) is rolled twice in succession; $X =$ the sum of the two numbers.

4. 48.2% of *Xbox* players are in their teens, 38.6% are in their twenties, 11.6% are in their thirties, and the rest are in their forties; $X =$ age of an *Xbox* player. (Use the midpoints of the measurement classes.)

5. From a bin that contains 20 defective joysticks and 30 good ones, 3 are chosen at random; $X =$ the number of defective joysticks chosen. (Round all probabilities to four decimal places.)

6. Two dice are weighted so that each number 2, 3, 4, and 5 is half as likely to face up as each 1 and 6; $X =$ the number of 1s that face up when both are thrown.

7. Use any method to calculate the sample mean, median, and standard deviation of the following sample of scores: $-1, 2, 0, 3, 6$.

8. Use any method to calculate the sample mean, median, and standard deviation of the following sample of scores: 4, 4, 5, 6, 6.

9. Give an example of a sample of four scores with mean 1, and median 0. (Arrange them in ascending order.)

10. Give an example of a sample of six scores with sample standard deviation 0 and mean 2.

11. Give an example of a population of six scores with mean 0 and population standard deviation 1.

12. Give an example of a sample of five scores with mean 0 and sample standard deviation 1.

A die is constructed in such a way that rolling a 6 is twice as likely as rolling each other number. That die is rolled four times. Let X be the number of times a 6 is rolled. Evaluate the probabilities in Exercises 13–20.

13. $P(X = 1)$

14. $P(X = 3)$

15. The probability that 6 comes up at most twice

16. The probability that 6 comes up at most once

17. The probability that X is more than 3

18. The probability that X is at least 2

19. $P(1 \leq X \leq 3)$

20. $P(X \leq 3)$

21. A couple has three children; $X =$ the number of girls. (Assume an equal likelihood of a child being a boy or a girl.) Find the expected value and standard deviation of X, and complete the following sentence with the smallest possible whole number: All values of X lie within ___ standard deviations of the expected value.

22. A couple has four children; $X =$ the number of boys. (Assume only a 25% chance of a child being a boy.) Find the standard deviation of X, and complete the following sentence with the smallest possible whole number: All values of X lie within ___ standard deviations of the expected value.

23. A random variable X has the following frequency distribution.

x	-3	-2	-1	0	1	2	3
$fr(X = x)$	1	2	3	4	3	2	1

Find the probability distribution, expected value, and standard deviation of X, and complete the following sentence: 87.5% (or 14/16) of the time, X is within ___ (round to one decimal place) standard deviations of the expected value.

24. A random variable X has the following frequency distribution.

x	-4	-2	0	2	4	6
$fr(X = x)$	3	3	4	5	3	2

Find the probability distribution, expected value, and standard deviation of X, and complete the following sentence: ___ percent of the values of X lie within one standard deviation of the expected value.

25. A random variable X has expected value $\mu = 100$ and standard deviation $\sigma = 16$. Use Chebyshev's rule to find an interval in which X is guaranteed to lie with a probability of at least 90%.

26. A random variable X has a symmetric distribution and an expected value $\mu = 200$ and standard deviation $\sigma = 5$. Use Chebyshev's rule to find a value that X is guaranteed to exceed with a probability of at most 10%.

27. A random variable X has a bell-shaped, symmetric distribution, with expected value $\mu = 200$ and standard deviation $\sigma = 20$. The empirical rule tells us that X has a value greater than ___ approximately 0.15% of the time.

28. A random variable X has a bell-shaped, symmetric distribution, with expected value $\mu = 100$ and standard deviation $\sigma = 30$. Use the empirical rule to give an interval in which X lies approximately 95% of the time.

In Exercises 29–34 the mean and standard deviation of a normal variable X are given. Find the indicated probability.

29. X is the standard normal variable Z; $P(0 \leq X \leq 1.5)$.

30. X is the standard normal variable Z; $P(X \leq -1.5)$.

31. X is the standard normal variable Z; $P(|X| \geq 2.1)$.

32. $\mu = 100, \sigma = 16$; $P(80 \leq X \leq 120)$

33. $\mu = 0, \sigma = 2$; $P(X \leq -1)$

34. $\mu = -1, \sigma = 0.5$; $P(X \geq 1)$

APPLICATIONS

Marketing As a promotional gimmick, OHaganBooks.com has been selling copies of the Encyclopædia Galactica at an extremely low price that is changed each week at random in a nationally televised drawing. Exercises 35–40 are based on the following table, which summarizes the anticipated sales.

Price	$5.50	$10	$12	$15
Frequency (weeks)	1	2	3	4
Weekly sales	6,200	3,500	3,000	1,000

35. What is the expected value of the price of *Encyclopædia Galactica*?

36. What are the expected weekly sales of *Encyclopædia Galactica*?

37. What is the expected weekly revenue from sales of *Encyclopædia Galactica*? (Revenue = Price per copy sold × Number of copies sold.)

38. OHaganBooks.com originally paid Duffin Press $20 per copy for the *Encyclopædia Galactica*. What is the expected weekly loss from sales of the encyclopædia? (Loss = Loss per copy sold × Number of copies sold.)

39. True or false? If X and Y are two random variables, then $E(XY) = E(X)E(Y)$ (the expected value of the product of two random variables is the product of the expected values). Support your claim by referring to the answers of Exercises 35, 36, and 37.

40. True or false? If X and Y are two random variables, then $E(X/Y) = E(X)/E(Y)$ (the expected value of the ratio of two random variables is the ratio of the expected values). Support your claim by referring to the answers of Exercises 36 and 38.

41. *Online Sales* The following table shows the number of online orders at OHaganBooks.com per million residents in 100 U.S. cities during one month:

Orders (per million residents)	1–2.9	3–4.9	5–6.9	7–8.9	9–10.9
Number of Cities	25	35	15	15	10

a. Let X be the number of orders per million residents in a randomly chosen U.S. city (use rounded midpoints of the given measurement classes). Construct the probability distribution for X and hence compute the expected value μ of X and standard deviation σ. (Round answers to four decimal places.)

b. What range of orders per million residents does the empirical rule predict from approximately 68% of all cities? Would you judge that the empirical rule applies? Why?

c. The actual percentage of cities from which you obtain between 3 and 8 orders per million residents is (choose the correct answer that gives the most specific information):
(A) Between 50% and 65%   (B) At least 65%
(C) At least 50%   (D) 57.5%

42. *Pollen* Marjory Duffin is planning a joint sales meeting with OHaganBooks.com in Atlanta at the end of March, but is extremely allergic to pollen, so she went online to find pollen counts for the period. The following table shows the results of her search:

Pollen Count	0–1.9	2–3.9	4–5.9	6–7.9	8–9.9	10–11.9
Number of Days	3	5	7	2	1	2

  a. Let X be the pollen count on a given day (use rounded midpoints of the given measurement classes). Construct the probability distribution for X and hence compute the expected value μ of X and standard deviation σ. (Round answers to four decimal places.)

  b. What range of pollen counts does the empirical rule predict on approximately 95% of the days? Would you judge that the empirical rule applies? Why?

  c. The actual percentage of days on which the pollen count is between 2 and 7 is (choose the correct answer that gives the most specific information):

    (A) Between 50% and 60%   **(B)** At least 60%

    (C) At most 70%   **(D)** Between 60% and 70%

Mac vs. Windows *On average, 5% of all hits by Mac OS users and 10% of all hits by Windows users result in orders for books at OHaganBooks.com. Due to online promotional efforts, the site traffic is approximately 10 hits per hour by Mac OS users, and 20 hits per hour by Windows users. Compute the probabilities in Exercises 43–48. (Round all answers to three decimal places.)*

43. What is the probability that exactly three Windows users will order books in the next hour?

44. What is the probability that at most three Windows users will order books in the next hour?

45. What is the probability that exactly one Mac OS user and three Windows users will order books in the next hour?

46. What assumption must you make to justify your calculation in Exercise 45?

47. How many orders for books can OHaganBooks.com expect in the next hour from Mac OS users?

48. How many orders for books can OHaganBooks.com expect in the next hour from Windows users?

Online Cosmetics *OHaganBooks.com has launched a subsidiary, GnuYou.com, which sells beauty products online. Most products sold by GnuYou.com are skin creams and hair products. Exercises 49–52 are based on the following table, which shows monthly revenues earned through sales of these products. (Assume a normal distribution. Round all answers to three decimal places.)*

Product	Skin Creams	Hair Products
Mean Monthly Revenue	$38,000	$34,000
Standard Deviation	$21,000	$14,000

49. What is the probability that GnuYou.com will sell *at least* $50,000 worth of skin cream next month?

50. What is the probability that GnuYou.com will sell *at most* $50,000 worth of hair products next month?

51. What is the probability that GnuYou.com will sell less than $12,000 of skin creams next month?

52. What is the probability that GnuYou.com will sell less than $12,000 of hair products next month?

53. *Intelligence* Billy-Sean O'Hagan, now a senior at Suburban State University, has done exceptionally well and has just joined Mensa, a club for people with high IQs. Within Mensa is a group called the Three Sigma Club because their IQ scores are at least three standard deviations higher than the United States mean. Assuming a U.S. population of 280,000,000, how many people in the United States are qualified for the Three Sigma Club? (Round your answer to the nearest 1,000 people.)

54. *Intelligence* To join Mensa (not necessarily the Three Sigma Club), one needs an IQ of at least 132, corresponding to the top 2% of the population. Assuming that scores on this test are normally distributed with a mean of 100, what is the standard deviation? (Round your answer to the nearest whole number.)

55. *Intelligence* Based on the information given in Exercises 53 and 54, what score must Billy-Sean have to get into the Three Sigma Club? (Assume that IQ scores are normally distributed with a mean of 100, and use the rounded standard deviation.)

Case Study   Spotting Tax Fraud with Benford's Law[60]

You are a tax fraud specialist working for the Internal Revenue Service (IRS), and you have just been handed a portion of the tax return from Colossal Conglomerate. The IRS suspects that the portion you were handed may be fraudulent, and would like your opinion. Is there any mathematical test, you wonder, that can point to a suspicious tax return based on nothing more than the numbers entered?

[60] The discussion is based on the article "Following Benford's Law, or Looking Out for No. 1" by Malcolm W. Browne, *The New York Times*, August 4, 1998, p. F4. The use of Benford's Law in detecting tax evasion is discussed in a Ph.D. dissertation by Dr. Mark J. Nigrini (Southern Methodist University, Dallas).

You decide, on an impulse, to make a list of the first digits of all the numbers entered in the portion of the Colossal Conglomerate tax return (there are 625 of them). You reason that, if the tax return is an honest one, the first digits of the numbers should be uniformly distributed. More precisely, if the experiment consists of selecting a number at random from the tax return, and the random variable X is defined to be the first digit of the selected number, then X should have the following probability distribution:

x	1	2	3	4	5	6	7	8	9
$P(X = x)$	$\frac{1}{9}$	$\frac{1}{9}$	$\frac{1}{9}$	$\frac{1}{9}$	$\frac{1}{9}$	$\frac{1}{9}$	$\frac{1}{9}$	$\frac{1}{9}$	$\frac{1}{9}$

You then do a quick calculation based on this probability distribution, and find an expected value of $E(X) = 5$. Next, you turn to the Colossal Conglomerate tax return data and calculate the relative frequency (estimated probability) of the actual numbers in the tax return. You find the following results.

Colossal Conglomerate Return

y	1	2	3	4	5	6	7	8	9
$P(Y = y)$	.29	.1	.04	.15	.31	.08	.01	.01	.01

It certainly does look suspicious! For one thing, the digits 1 and 5 seem to occur a lot more often than any of the other digits, and roughly three times what you predicted. Moreover, when you compute the expected value, you obtain $E(Y) = 3.48$, considerably lower than the value of 5 you predicted. Gotcha! you exclaim.

You are about to file a report recommending a detailed audit of Colossal Conglomerate when you recall an article you once read about first digits in lists of numbers. The article dealt with a remarkable discovery in 1938 by Dr. Frank Benford, a physicist at General Electric. What Dr. Benford noticed was that the pages of logarithm tables that listed numbers starting with the digits 1 and 2 tended to be more soiled and dog-eared than the pages that listed numbers starting with higher digits—say, 8. For some reason, numbers that start with low digits seemed more prevalent than numbers that start with high digits. He subsequently analyzed more than 20,000 sets of numbers, such as tables of baseball statistics, listings of widths of rivers, half-lives of radioactive elements, street addresses, and numbers in magazine articles. The result was always the same: Inexplicably, numbers that start with low digits tended to appear more frequently than those that start with high ones, with numbers beginning with the digit 1 most prevalent of all.[61] Moreover, the expected value of the first digit was not the expected 5, but 3.44.

Because the first digits in Colossal Conglomerate's return have an expected value of 3.48, very close to Benford's value, it might appear that your suspicion was groundless after all. (Back to the drawing board . . .)

Out of curiosity, you decide to investigate Benford's discovery more carefully. What you find is that Benford did more than simply observe a strange phenomenon in lists of numbers. He went further and derived the following formula for the probability distribution of first digits in lists of numbers:

$$P(X = x) = \log(1 + 1/x) \qquad (x = 1, 2, \ldots, 9).$$

---

[61] This does not apply to all lists of numbers. For instance, a list of randomly chosen numbers between 100 and 999 will have first digits uniformly distributed between 1 and 9.

Benford

Colossal Conglomerate

Figure 17

You compute these probabilities, and find the following distribution (the probabilities are all rounded, and thus do not add to exactly 1).

x	1	2	3	4	5	6	7	8	9
$P(X = x)$	.30	.18	.12	.10	.08	.07	.06	.05	.05

You then enter these data along with the Colossal Conglomerate tax return data in your spreadsheet program and obtain the graph shown in Figure 17.

The graph shows something awfully suspicious happening with the digit 5. The percentage of numbers in the Colossal Conglomerate return that begin with 5 far exceeds Benford's prediction that approximately 8% of all numbers should begin with 5.

Now it seems fairly clear that you are justified in recommending Colossal Conglomerate for an audit, after all.

Q: *Because no given set of data can reasonably be expected to satisfy Benford's Law exactly, how can I be certain that the Colossal Conglomerate data is not simply due to chance?*

A: You can never be 100% certain. It is certainly conceivable that the tax figures just happen to result in the "abnormal" distribution in the Colossal Conglomerate tax return. However—and this is the subject of "inferential statistics"—there is a method for deciding whether you can be, say "95% certain" that the anomaly reflected in the data is not due to chance. To check, you must first compute a statistic that determines how far a given set of data deviates from satisfying a theoretical prediction (Benford's Law, in this case). This statistic is called a **sum-of-squares error**, and given by the following formula (reminiscent of the variance):

$$\text{SSE} = n \left[\frac{[P(y_1) - P(x_1)]^2}{P(x_1)} + \frac{[P(y_2) - P(x_2)]^2}{P(x_2)} + \cdots + \frac{[P(y_9) - P(x_9)]^2}{P(x_9)} \right].$$

Here, n is the sample size: 625 in the case of Colossal Conglomerate. The quantities $P(x_i)$ are the theoretically predicted probabilities according to Benford's Law, and the $P(y_i)$ are the probabilities in the Colossal Conglomerate return. Notice that if the Colossal Conglomerate return probabilities had exactly matched the theoretically predicted probabilities, then SSE would have been zero. Notice also the effect of multiplying by the sample size n: The larger the sample, the more likely that the discrepancy between the $P(x_i)$ and the $P(y_i)$ is not due to chance. Substituting the numbers gives

$$\text{SSE} \approx 625 \left[\frac{[.29 - .30]^2}{.30} + \frac{[.1 - .18]^2}{.18} + \cdots + \frac{[.01 - .05]^2}{.05} \right]$$

$$\approx 552.^{62}$$

Q: *The value of SSE does seem quite large. But how can I use this figure in my report? I would like to say something impressive, such as "Based on the portion of the Colossal Conglomerate tax return analyzed, one can be 95% certain that the figures are anomalous."*

A: The error SSE is used by statisticians to answer exactly such a question. What they would do is compare this figure to the largest SSE we would have expected to get by

---

[62] If you use more accurate values for the probabilities in Benford's distribution, the value is approximately 560.

chance in 95 out of 100 selections of data that *do* satisfy Benford's law. This "biggest error" is computed using a "Chi-Squared" distribution and can be found in Excel by entering

`=CHIINV(0.05, 8)`.

Here, the 0.05 is $1 - 0.95$, encoding the "95% certainty," and the 8 is called the "number of degrees of freedom" = number of outcomes (9) minus 1.

You now find, using Excel, that the chi-squared figure is 15.5, meaning that the largest SSE that you could have expected purely by chance is 15.5. Because Colossal Conglomerate's error is much larger at 552, you can now justifiably say in your report that there is a 95% certainty that the figures are anomalous.[63]

EXERCISES

Which of the following lists of data would you expect to follow Benford's law? If the answer is "no," give a reason.

1. Distances between cities in France, measured in kilometers.

2. Distances between cities in France, measured in miles.

3. The grades (0–100) in your math instructor's grade book.

4. The Dow Jones averages for the past 100 years.

5. Verbal SAT scores of college-bound high school seniors.

6. Life spans of companies.

⊤ *Use technology to determine whether the given distribution of first digits fails, with 95% certainty, to follow Benford's law.*

7. Good Neighbor Inc.'s tax return ($n = 1,000$)

y	1	2	3	4	5	6	7	8	9
$P(Y = y)$	.31	.16	.13	.11	.07	.07	.05	.06	.04

8. Honest Growth Funds Stockholder Report ($n = 400$)

y	1	2	3	4	5	6	7	8	9
$P(Y = y)$	.28	.16	.1	.11	.07	.09	.05	.07	.07

---

[63] What this actually means is that, if you were to do a similar analysis on a large number of tax returns, and you designated as "not conforming to Benford's Law" all of those whose value of SSE was larger than 15.5, you would be justified in 95% of the cases.

TI-83/84 Plus Technology Guide

Section 8.1

Example 3 (page 552) Let X be the number of heads that face up in three tosses of a coin. We obtained the following probability distribution of X in the text:

x	0	1	2	3
$P(X = x)$	$\frac{1}{8}$	$\frac{3}{8}$	$\frac{3}{8}$	$\frac{1}{8}$

Use technology to obtain the corresponding histogram.

Solution with Technology

1. In the TI-83/84 Plus, you can enter a list of probabilities as follows: press STAT, choose EDIT, and then press ENTER. Clear columns L_1 and L_2 if they are not already cleared. (Select the heading of a column and press CLEAR ENTER to clear it.) Enter the values of X in the column under L_1 (pressing ENTER after each entry) and enter the frequencies in the column under L_2.

2. To graph the data as in Figure 1, first set the WINDOW to $0 \le X \le 4$, $0 \le Y \le 0.5$, and Xscl $= 1$ (the width of the bars). Then turn STAT PLOT on ([2nd] Y=), and configure it by selecting the histogram icon, setting Xlist $= L_1$ and Freq $= L_2$. Then hit GRAPH.

Example 4 (page 552) We obtained the following frequency table in the text:

x	25,000	35,000	45,000	55,000	65,000	75,000	85,000
Frequency	20	80	230	400	170	70	30

Find the probability distribution of X.

Solution with Technology

We need to divide each frequency by the sum. Although the computations in this example (dividing the seven frequencies by 1,000) are simple to do by hand, they could become tedious in general, so technology is helpful.

1. On the TI-83/84 Plus, press STAT, select EDIT, enter the values of X in the L_1 list, and enter the frequencies in the L_2 list as in Example 3.

2. Then, on the home screen, enter

$$L_2/1{,}000 \to L_3 \qquad L_2 \text{ is } \boxed{2nd} \ \boxed{2}, L_3 \text{ is } \boxed{2nd} \ \boxed{3}.$$

or, better yet,

$$L_2/\text{sum}(L_2) \to L_3 \qquad \text{Sum is found in } \boxed{2nd} \ \boxed{STAT},$$
$$\text{under MATH.}$$

3. After pressing ENTER you can now go back to the STAT EDIT screen, and you will find the probabilities displayed in L_3 as shown.

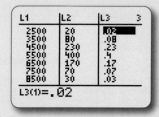

Section 8.2

Example 2(b) (page 562) By 2030, the probability that a randomly chosen resident in the United States will be 65 years old or older is projected to be .2. If X is the number of people aged 65 or older in a sample of 6, construct the probability distribution of X.

Solution with Technology

In the "Y=" screen, you can enter the binomial distribution formula

$$Y_1 = 6 \text{ nCr } X*0.2\char`^X*0.8\char`^(6-X)$$

directly (to get nCr, press MATH and select PRB), and hit TABLE. You can then replicate the table in the text by choosing $X = 0, 1, \ldots, 6$ (use the TBLSET screen to set "Indpnt" to "Ask" if you have not already done so).

The TI-83/84 Plus also has a built-in binomial distribution function that you can use in place of the explicit formula:

$Y_1 =$ binompdf(6, 0.2, X)   Press 2nd VARS 0.

The TI-83/84 Plus function binompcf (directly following binompdf) gives the value of the *cumulative* distribution function, $P(0 \le X \le x)$.

To graph the resulting probability distribution on your calculator, follow the instructions for graphing a histogram in Section 8.1.

Section 8.3

Example 3 (page 572) According to historical data, the number of injuries that a member of the Enormous State University women's soccer team will sustain during a typical season is given by the following probability distribution table:

Injuries	0	1	2	3	4	5	6
Probability	.2	.2	.22	.2	.15	.01	.02

If X denotes the number of injuries sustained by a player during one season, compute $E(X)$.

Solution with Technology

To obtain the expected value of a probability distribution on the TI-83/84 Plus, press STAT, select EDIT, and then press ENTER, and enter the values of X in the L_1 list and the probabilities in the column in the L_2 list. Then, on the home screen, you can obtain the expected value as

sum $(L_1 * L_2)$ L_1 is 2nd 1 L_2 is 2nd 2
                      Sum is found in 2nd STAT, under MATH

Section 8.4

Example 1 (page 582) The unemployment rates (in percentage points) in the U.S. for the months April–October 2008 were[64]

$$5, 6, 6, 6, 6, 6, 7.$$

Compute the sample mean and standard deviation.

Solution with Technology

On the TI-83/84 Plus, enter the sample scores in list L_1 on the STAT/EDIT screen, then go to STAT/CALC, select 1-Var Stats, and hit ENTER. The resulting display shows, among other statistics, the sample standard deviation s as "Sx" as well as the population standard deviation σ as "σx."

Example 3 (page 586) Compute the variance and standard deviation for the following probability distribution.

x	10	20	30	40	50	60
$P(X = x)$	.2	.2	.3	.1	.1	.1

Solution with Technology

1. As in Example 3 in the preceding section, begin by entering the probability distribution of X into columns

---

[64] Figures are rounded. Sources: Bureau of Labor Statistics (BLS) (www.bls.gov).

L_1 and L_2 in the LIST screen (press STAT and select EDIT).

2. Then, on the home screen, enter

$$\text{sum}(L_1*L_2) \rightarrow M$$ Stores the value of μ as M

Sum is found in 2nd STAT, under MATH.

3. To obtain the variance, enter the following.

$$\text{sum}((L_1-M)\char94 2*L_2)$$ Computation of $\sum(x-\mu)^2 P(X=x)$

Section 8.5

Example 1(b), (c) (page 596)   Let Z be the standard normal variable. Calculate the following probabilities.
b. $P(0 \le Z \le 2.43)$
c. $P(-1.37 \le Z \le 2.43)$

Solution with Technology

On the TI-83/84 Plus, press 2nd VARS to obtain the selection of distribution functions. The first function, normalpdf, gives the values of the normal density function (whose graph is the normal curve). The second, normalcdf, gives $P(a \le Z \le b)$. For example, to compute $P(0 \le Z \le 2.43)$, enter

normalcdf(0, 2.43)

To compute $P(-1.37 \le Z \le 2.43)$, enter

normalcdf(-1.37, 2.43)

Example 2 (page 598)   Pressure gauges manufactured by Precision Corp. must be checked for accuracy before being placed on the market. To test a pressure gauge, a worker uses it to measure the pressure of a sample of compressed air known to be at a pressure of exactly 50 pounds per square inch. If the gauge reading is off by more than 1% (0.5 pounds), it is rejected. Assuming that the reading of a pressure gauge under these circumstances is a normal random variable with mean 50 and standard deviation 0.4, find the percentage of gauges rejected.

Solution with Technology

As seen in the text, we need to compute $1 - P(49.5 \le X \le 50.5)$ with $\mu = 50$ and $\sigma = 0.4$. On the TI-83/84 Plus, the built-in normalcdf function permits us to compute $P(a \le X \le b)$ for nonstandard normal distributions as well. The format is

$$\text{normalcdf}(a,\ b,\ \mu,\ \sigma)$$ $P(a \le X \le b)$

For example, we can compute $P(49.5 \le X \le 50.5)$ by entering

normalcdf(49.5, 50.5, 50, 0.4)

Then subtract it from 1 to obtain the answer:

EXCEL Technology Guide

Section 8.1

Example 3 (page 552)   Let X be the number of heads that face up in three tosses of a coin. We obtained the following probability distribution of X in the text:

x	0	1	2	3
$P(X = x)$	$\frac{1}{8}$	$\frac{3}{8}$	$\frac{3}{8}$	$\frac{1}{8}$

Use technology to obtain the corresponding histogram.

Solution with Technology

1. In Excel, enter the values of X in one column and the probabilities in another.

	A	B
1	x	P(X=x)
2	0	0.125
3	1	0.375
4	2	0.375
5	3	0.125

2. Next, select *only* the column of probabilities (B2–B5) and then choose Insert → Column Chart. (Select the first type of column chart that appears.) Right-click on the resulting chart and choose "Select Data." In the resulting dialog box, click on "Edit" under "Horizontal (Category) Axis Labels," highlight the values of x (A2–A8 in Example 4), then click OK. To adjust the width of the bars, right-click on a bar, select "Format Data Series," and adjust the gap width to your liking. Here is a possible result (gap width zero):

Example 4 (page 552)   We obtained the following frequency table in the text:

x	25,000	35,000	45,000	55,000	65,000	75,000	85,000
Frequency	20	80	230	400	170	70	30

Find the probability distribution of X.

Solution with Technology

We need to divide each frequency by the sum. Although the computations in this example (dividing the seven frequencies by 1,000) are simple to do by hand, they could become tedious in general, so technology is helpful. Excel manipulates lists with ease. Set up your spreadsheet as shown.

	A	B	C
1	x	Fr	P(X=x)
2	25000	20	=B2/SUM(B:B)
3	35000	80	
4	45000	230	
5	55000	400	
6	65000	170	
7	75000	70	
8	85000	30	

↓

	A	B	C
1	x	Fr	P(X=x)
2	25000	20	0.02
3	35000	80	0.08
4	45000	230	0.23
5	55000	400	0.4
6	65000	170	0.17
7	75000	70	0.07
8	85000	30	0.03

The formula SUM(B:B) gives the sum of all the numerical entries in Column B. You can now change the frequencies to see the effect on the probabilities. You can also add new values and frequencies to the list if you copy the formula in column C further down the column.

Section 8.2

Example 2(b) (page 562)   By 2030, the probability that a randomly chosen resident in the United States will be 65 years old or older is projected to be .2. If X is the number of people aged 65 or older in a sample of 6, construct the probability distribution of X.

Solution with Technology

You can generate the binomial distribution as follows in Excel:

	A	B
1	x	P(X=x)
2	0	=BINOMDIST(A2,6,0.2,0)
3	1	
4	2	
5	3	
6	4	
7	5	
8	6	

↓

	A	B
1	x	P(X=x)
2	0	0.262144
3	1	0.393216
4	2	0.24576
5	3	0.08192
6	4	0.01536
7	5	0.001536
8	6	6.4E-05

The values of X are shown in column A, and the probabilities are computed in column B. The arguments of the BINOMDIST function are as follows:

BINOMDIST(x, n, p, Cumulative (0 = no, 1 = yes)).

Setting the last argument to 0 (as shown) gives $P(X = x)$. Setting it to 1 gives $P(X \le x)$.

To graph the resulting probability distribution using Excel, follow the instructions for graphing a histogram in Section 8.1.

Section 8.3

Example 3 (page 572) According to historical data, the number of injuries that a member of the Enormous State University women's soccer team will sustain during a typical season is given by the following probability distribution table:

Injuries	0	1	2	3	4	5	6
Probability	.2	.2	.22	.2	.15	.01	.02

If X denotes the number of injuries sustained by a player during one season, compute $E(X)$.

Solution with Technology

As the method we used suggests, the calculation of the expected value from the probability distribution is particularly easy to do using a spreadsheet program such as Excel. The following worksheet shows one way to do it. (The first two columns contain the probability distribution of X; the quantities $xP(X=x)$ are summed in cell C9.)

	A	B	C
1	x	P(X=x)	x*P(X=x)
2	0	0.2	=A2*B2
3	1	0.2	
4	2	0.22	
5	3	0.2	
6	4	0.15	
7	5	0.01	
8	6	0.02	
9			=SUM(C2:C8)

↓

	A	B	C
1	x	P(X=x)	x*P(X=x)
2	0	0.2	0
3	1	0.2	0.2
4	2	0.22	0.44
5	3	0.2	0.6
6	4	0.15	0.6
7	5	0.01	0.05
8	6	0.02	0.12
9			2.01

An alternative is to use the SUMPRODUCT function in Excel: Once we enter the first two columns above, the formula

=SUMPRODUCT(A2:A8,B2:B8)

computes the sum of the products of corresponding entries in the columns, giving us the expected value.

Section 8.4

Example 1 (page 582) The unemployment rates (in percentage points) in the U.S. for the months April–October 2008 were[65]

5, 6, 6, 6, 6, 6, 7.

Compute the sample mean and standard deviation.

---

[65] Figures are rounded. Sources: Bureau of Labor Statistics (BLS) (www.bls.gov).

Solution with Technology

To compute the sample mean and standard deviation of a collection of scores in Excel, set up your spreadsheet as follows:

	A
1	5
2	6
3	6
4	6
5	6
6	6
7	7
8	=AVERAGE(A1:A7)
9	=STDEV(A1:A7)

→

	A
1	5
2	6
3	6
4	6
5	6
6	6
7	7
8	6
9	0.57735027

For the population standard deviation, use

$$=STDEVP(A1:A6)$$

Example 3 (page 586)
Compute the variance and standard deviation for the following probability distribution.

x	10	20	30	40	50	60
$P(X = x)$	.2	.2	.3	.1	.1	.1

Solution with Technology

As in Example 3 in the preceding section, begin by entering the probability distribution into columns A and B, and then proceed as shown:

The variance then appears in cell D8:

Section 8.5

Example 1(b), (c) (page 596)
Let Z be the standard normal variable. Calculate the following probabilities.
b. $P(0 \le Z \le 2.43)$
c. $P(-1.37 \le Z \le 2.43)$

Solution with Technology

In Excel, the function NORMSDIST (Normal Standard Distribution) gives the area shown on the left in Figure 18. (Tables such as the one in the Appendix give the area shown on the right.)

Figure 18

To compute a general area, $P(a \le Z \le b)$ in Excel, subtract the cumulative area to a from that to b:

$$=NORMSDIST(b)-NORMSDIST(a) \quad P(a \le Z \le b)$$

In particular, to compute $P(0 \le Z \le 2.43)$, use

$$=NORMSDIST(2.43)-NORMSDIST(0)$$

and to compute $P(-1.37 \le Z \le 2.43)$, use

$$=NORMSDIST(2.43)-NORMSDIST(-1.37)$$

Example 2 (page 598)
Pressure gauges manufactured by Precision Corp. must be checked for accuracy before being placed on the market. To test a pressure gauge, a worker uses it to measure the pressure of a sample of compressed air known to be at a pressure of exactly 50 pounds

per square inch. If the gauge reading is off by more than 1% (0.5 pounds), it is rejected. Assuming that the reading of a pressure gauge under these circumstances is a normal random variable with mean 50 and standard deviation 0.4, find the percentage of gauges rejected.

Solution with Technology

In Excel, we use the function NORMDIST instead of NORMSDIST. Its format is similar to NORMSDIST, but includes extra arguments as shown.

=NORMDIST(a, μ, σ, 1) $P(X \le a)$

(The last argument, set to 1, tells Excel that you want the cumulative distribution.) To compute $P(a \le X \le b)$ we

enter the following in any vacant cell:

=NORMDIST(b, μ, σ, 1)
  -NORMDIST(a, μ, σ, 1) $P(a \le X \le b)$

For example, we can compute $P(49.5 \le X \le 50.5)$ by entering

=NORMDIST(50.5,50,0.4,1)
  -NORMDIST(49.5,50,0.4,1)

We then subtract it from 1 to obtain the answer:

10

Introduction to the Derivative

Case Study Reducing Sulfur Emissions

The Environmental Protection Agency (EPA) wants to formulate a policy that will encourage utilities to reduce sulfur emissions. Its goal is to reduce annual emissions of sulfur dioxide by a total of 10 million tons from the current level of 25 million tons by imposing a fixed charge for every ton of sulfur released into the environment per year. The EPA has some data showing the marginal cost to utilities of reducing sulfur emissions. As a consultant to the EPA, you must determine the amount to be charged per ton of sulfur emissions in light of these data.

Web Site

At the Web site you will find:

- Section by section tutorials, including game tutorials with randomized quizzes

- A detailed chapter summary

- A true/false quiz

- Additional review exercises

- Graphers, Excel tutorials, and other resources

- The following extra topics:

    Sketching the graph of the derivative

    Continuity and differentiability

Norbert Schaefer/CORBIS

Introduction

In the world around us, everything is changing. The mathematics of change is largely about the rate of change: how fast and in which direction the change is occurring. Is the Dow Jones average going up, and if so, how fast? If I raise my prices, how many customers will I lose? If I launch this missile, how fast will it be traveling after two seconds, how high will it go, and where will it come down?

We have already discussed the concept of rate of change for linear functions (straight lines), where the slope measures the rate of change. But this works only because a straight line maintains a constant rate of change along its whole length. Other functions rise faster here than there—or rise in one place and fall in another—so that the rate of change varies along the graph. The first achievement of calculus is to provide a systematic and straight-forward way of calculating (hence the name) these rates of change. To describe a changing world, we need a language of change, and that is what calculus is.

The history of calculus is an interesting story of personalities, intellectual movements, and controversy. Credit for its invention is given to two mathematicians: Isaac Newton (1642–1727) and Gottfried Leibniz (1646–1716). Newton, an English mathematician and scientist, developed calculus first, probably in the 1660s. We say "probably" because, for various reasons, he did not publish his ideas until much later. This allowed Leibniz, a German mathematician and philosopher, to publish his own version of calculus first, in 1684. Fifteen years later, stirred up by nationalist fervor in England and on the continent, controversy erupted over who should get the credit for the invention of calculus. The debate got so heated that the Royal Society (of which Newton and Leibniz were both members) set up a commission to investigate the question. The commission decided in favor of Newton, who happened to be president of the society at the time. The consensus today is that both mathematicians deserve credit because they came to the same conclusions working independently. This is not really surprising: Both built on well-known work of other people, and it was almost inevitable that someone would put it all together at about that time.

algebra Review

For this chapter, you should be familiar with the algebra reviewed in **Chapter 0, Section 2.**

10.1 Limits: Numerical and Graphical Approaches

Rates of change are calculated by derivatives, but an important part of the definition of the derivative is something called a **limit**. Arguably, much of mathematics since the 18th century has revolved around understanding, refining, and exploiting the idea of the limit. The basic idea is easy, but getting the technicalities right is not.

Evaluating Limits Numerically

Start with a very simple example: Look at the function $f(x) = 2 + x$ and ask: What happens to $f(x)$ as x approaches 3? The following table shows the value of $f(x)$ for values of x close to and on either side of 3:

	x approaching 3 from the left →					← x approaching 3 from the right			
x	2.9	2.99	2.999	2.9999	3	3.0001	3.001	3.01	3.1
$f(x) = 2 + x$	4.9	4.99	4.999	4.9999		5.0001	5.001	5.01	5.1

We have left the entry under 3 blank to emphasize that when calculating the limit of $f(x)$ as x *approaches* 3, we are not interested in its value when x *equals* 3.

Notice from the table that the closer x gets to 3 from either side, the closer $f(x)$ gets to 5. We write this as

$$\lim_{x \to 3} f(x) = 5. \qquad \text{The limit of } f(x), \text{ as } x \text{ approaches 3, equals 5.}$$

Q: *Why all the fuss? Can't we simply substitute $x = 3$ and avoid having to use a table?*

A: This happens to work for *some* functions, but not for *all* functions. The following example illustrates this point.

EXAMPLE 1 **Estimating a Limit Numerically**

Use a table to estimate the following limits:

a. $\lim\limits_{x \to 2} \dfrac{x^3 - 8}{x - 2}$ **b.** $\lim\limits_{x \to 0} \dfrac{e^{2x} - 1}{x}$

Solution

a. We cannot simply substitute $x = 2$, because the function $f(x) = \dfrac{x^3 - 8}{x - 2}$ is not defined at $x = 2$. (Why?)* Instead, we use a table of values as we did above, with x approaching 2 from both sides.

x approaching 2 from the left → *← x approaching 2 from the right*

x	1.9	1.99	1.999	1.9999	2	2.0001	2.001	2.01	2.1
$f(x) = \dfrac{x^3 - 8}{x - 2}$	11.41	11.9401	11.9940	11.9994		12.0006	12.0060	12.0601	12.61

✳ NOTE However, if you factor $x^3 - 8$, you will find that $f(x)$ can be simplified to a function which *is* defined at $x = 2$. This point will be discussed (and this example redone) in Section 10.3. The function in part (b) cannot be simplified by factoring.

We notice that as x approaches 2 from either side, $f(x)$ appears to be approaching 12. This suggests that the limit is 12, and we write

$$\lim_{x \to 2} \frac{x^3 - 8}{x - 2} = 12.$$

b. The function $g(x) = \dfrac{e^{2x} - 1}{x}$ is not defined at $x = 0$ (nor can it even be simplified to one which *is* defined at $x = 0$). In the following table, we allow x to approach 0 from both sides:

x approaching 0 from the left → *← x approaching 0 from the right*

x	−0.1	−0.01	−0.001	−0.0001	0	0.0001	0.001	0.01	0.1
$g(x) = \dfrac{e^{2x} - 1}{x}$	1.8127	1.9801	1.9980	1.9998		2.0002	2.0020	2.0201	2.2140

The table suggests that $\lim\limits_{x \to 0} \dfrac{e^{2x} - 1}{x} = 2$.

⬛ using Technology

We can automate the computations in Example 1 using a graphing calculator or Excel. See the Technology Guides at the end of the section to find out how to create tables like these using a TI-83/84 Plus or Excel. Here is an outline for part (a):

TI-83/84 Plus
Home screen: Y₁= (X^3-8) / (X-2)
2ND TBLSET Indpnt set to Ask
2ND TABLE Enter some values of x from the example: 1.9, 1.99, 1.999 . . .
[More details on page 776.]

Excel
Enter the headings *x*, *f*(*x*) in
A1–B1 and again in C1–D1.
In A2–A5 enter 1.9, 1.99,
1.999, 1.9999.
In C1–C5 enter 2.1, 2.01,
2.001, 2.0001. Enter

`=(A2^3-8)/(A2-2)`

in B2 and copy down to B5.
Copy and paste the same
formula in D2–D5.
[More details on page 778.]

Web Site
www.FiniteandCalc.org
Student Home → Online
Utilities → Function Evaluator
and Grapher Enter `(x^3-8)/`
`(x-2)` for y_1. To obtain a table
of values, enter the various
x-values in the Evaluator box,
and press "Evaluate."

➡ **Before we go on...** Although the table *suggests* that the limit in Example 1 part (b) is 2, it by no means establishes that fact conclusively. It is *conceivable* (though not in fact the case here) that putting $x = 0.000000087$ could result in $g(x) = 426$. Using a table can only suggest a value for the limit. In the next two sections we shall discuss algebraic techniques for finding limits. ■

Before we continue, let us make a more formal definition.

Definition of a Limit

If $f(x)$ approaches the number L as x approaches (but is not equal to) a from both sides, then we say that $f(x)$ **approaches L as $x \to a$** ("x approaches a") or that the **limit** of $f(x)$ as $x \to a$ is L. More precisely, *we can make $f(x)$ be as close to L as we like by choosing any x sufficiently close to (but not equal to) a on either side*. We write

$$\lim_{x \to a} f(x) = L$$

or

$$f(x) \to L \text{ as } x \to a.$$

If $f(x)$ *fails* to approach *a single fixed number* as x approaches a from both sides, then we say that $f(x)$ **has no limit** as $x \to a$, or

$$\lim_{x \to a} f(x) \textbf{ does not exist.}$$

Quick Examples

1. $\lim_{x \to 3}(2 + x) = 5$ See discussion before Example 1.

2. $\lim_{x \to -2}(3x) = -6$ As x approaches -2, $3x$ approaches -6.

3. $\lim_{x \to 0}(x^2 - 2x + 1)$ exists.   In fact, the limit is 1.

4. $\lim_{x \to 5}\dfrac{1}{x} = \dfrac{1}{5}$ As x approaches 5, $\dfrac{1}{x}$ approaches $\dfrac{1}{5}$.

5. $\lim_{x \to 2}\dfrac{x^3 - 8}{x - 2} = 12$ See Example 1. (We cannot just put $x = 2$ here.)

(For examples where the limit does not exist, see Example 2.)

Notes

1. It is important that $f(x)$ approach the same number as x approaches a from either side. For instance, if $f(x)$ approaches 5 for $x = 1.9, 1.99, 1.999, \ldots$, but approaches 4 for $x = 2.1, 2.01, 2.001, \ldots$, then the limit as $x \to 2$ does not exist. (See Example 2 for such a situation.)

2. It may happen that $f(x)$ does not approach any fixed number at all as $x \to a$ from either side. In this case, we also say that the limit does not exist.

3. If a happens to be an endpoint of the domain of f, then x can only approach a from one side. In this case, we relax the definition of the limit and require only that x approach a from the side it can. For example, $f(x) = \sqrt{x-1}$ has natural domain $[1, +\infty)$, and we say that

$$\lim_{x \to 1} \sqrt{x - 1} = 0$$

even though x can only approach 1 from the right. ■

The following example gives instances in which a stated limit does not exist.

EXAMPLE 2 Limits Do Not Always Exist

Do the following limits exist?

a. $\lim\limits_{x \to 0} \dfrac{1}{x^2}$ **b.** $\lim\limits_{x \to 0} \dfrac{|x|}{x}$ **c.** $\lim\limits_{x \to 2} \dfrac{1}{x - 2}$

Solution

a. Here is a table of values for $f(x) = \dfrac{1}{x^2}$, with x approaching 0 from both sides.

x approaching 0 from the left $\to$ $\leftarrow$ x approaching 0 from the right

x	-0.1	-0.01	-0.001	-0.0001	0	0.0001	0.001	0.01	0.1
$f(x) = \dfrac{1}{x^2}$	100	10,000	1,000,000	100,000,000		100,000,000	1,000,000	10,000	100

The table shows that as x gets closer to zero on either side, $f(x)$ gets larger and larger **without bound**—that is, if you name any number, no matter how large, $f(x)$ will be even larger than that if x is sufficiently close to 0. Because $f(x)$ is not approaching any real number, we conclude that $\lim\limits_{x \to 0} \dfrac{1}{x^2}$ does not exist. Because $f(x)$ is becoming arbitrarily large, we also say that $\lim\limits_{x \to 0} \dfrac{1}{x^2}$ **diverges to** $+\infty$, or just

$$\lim\limits_{x \to 0} \dfrac{1}{x^2} = +\infty$$

Note This is not meant to imply that the limit exists; the symbol $+\infty$ does not represent any real number. We write $\lim\limits_{x \to a} f(x) = +\infty$ to indicate two things: (1) the limit does not exist and (2) the function gets large without bound as x approaches a. ∎

b. Here is a table of values for $f(x) = \dfrac{|x|}{x}$, with x approaching 0 from both sides.

x approaching 0 from the left $\to$ · $\leftarrow$ x approaching 0 from the right

x	-0.1	-0.01	-0.001	-0.0001	0	0.0001	0.001	0.01	0.1
$f(x) = \dfrac{|x|}{x}$	-1	-1	-1	-1		1	1	1	1

The table shows that $f(x)$ does not approach the same limit as x approaches 0 from both sides. There appear to be two *different* limits: the limit as we approach 0 from the left and the limit as we approach from the right. We write

$$\lim\limits_{x \to 0^-} f(x) = -1$$

read as "the limit as x approaches 0 from the left (or from below) is -1" and

$$\lim\limits_{x \to 0^+} f(x) = 1$$

read as "the limit as x approaches 0 from the right (or from above) is 1." These are called the **one-sided limits** of $f(x)$. In order for f to have a **two-sided limit**, the two one-sided limits must be equal. Because they are not, we conclude that $\lim\limits_{x \to 0} f(x)$ does not exist.

c. Near $x = 2$, we have the following table of values for $f(x) = \dfrac{1}{x - 2}$:

	x approaching 2 from the left $\rightarrow$					$\leftarrow x$ approaching 2 from the right			
x	1.9	1.99	1.999	1.9999	2	2.0001	2.001	2.01	2.1
$f(x) = \dfrac{1}{x - 2}$	-10	-100	-1000	$-10{,}000$		$10{,}000$	1000	100	10

Because $\dfrac{1}{x - 2}$ is approaching no (single) real number as $x \to 2$, we see that $\displaystyle\lim_{x \to 2} \dfrac{1}{x - 2}$ does not exist. Notice also that $\dfrac{1}{x - 2}$ diverges to $+\infty$ as $x \to 2$ from the positive side (right half of the table) and to $-\infty$ as $x \to 2$ from the left (left half of the table). In other words,

$$\lim_{x \to 2^-} \frac{1}{x - 2} = -\infty$$

$$\lim_{x \to 2^+} \frac{1}{x - 2} = +\infty$$

$$\lim_{x \to 2} \frac{1}{x - 2} \text{ does not exist.}$$

In another useful kind of limit, we let x approach either $+\infty$ or $-\infty$, by which we mean that we let x get arbitrarily large or let x become an arbitrarily large negative number. The next example illustrates this.

EXAMPLE 3 Limits at Infinity

Use a table to estimate: **a.** $\displaystyle\lim_{x \to +\infty} \dfrac{2x^2 - 4x}{x^2 - 1}$ and **b.** $\displaystyle\lim_{x \to -\infty} \dfrac{2x^2 - 4x}{x^2 - 1}$.

Solution

a. By saying that x is "approaching $+\infty$," we mean that x is getting larger and larger without bound, so we make the following table:

				x approaching $+\infty \rightarrow$	
x	10	100	1,000	10,000	100,000
$f(x) = \dfrac{2x^2 - 4x}{x^2 - 1}$	1.6162	1.9602	1.9960	1.9996	2.0000

(Note that we are only approaching $+\infty$ from the left because we can hardly approach it from the right!) What seems to be happening is that $f(x)$ is approaching 2. Thus we write

$$\lim_{x \to +\infty} f(x) = 2$$

b. Here, x is approaching $-\infty$, so we make a similar table, this time with x assuming negative values of greater and greater magnitude (read this table from right to left):

$\leftarrow x$ approaching $-\infty$

x	$-100,000$	$-10,000$	$-1,000$	-100	-10
$f(x) = \dfrac{2x^2 - 4x}{x^2 - 1}$	2.0000	2.0004	2.0040	2.0402	2.4242

Once again, $f(x)$ is approaching 2. Thus, $\lim_{x \to -\infty} f(x) = 2$.

Estimating Limits Graphically

We can often estimate a limit from a graph, as the next example shows.

EXAMPLE 4 Estimating Limits Graphically

The graph of a function f is shown in Figure 1. (Recall that the solid dots indicate points on the graph, and the hollow dots indicate points not on the graph.)

Figure 1

From the graph, analyze the following limits.

a. $\lim_{x \to -2} f(x)$ **b.** $\lim_{x \to 0} f(x)$ **c.** $\lim_{x \to 1} f(x)$ **d.** $\lim_{x \to +\infty} f(x)$

Solution Since we are given only a graph of f, we must analyze these limits graphically.

a. Imagine that Figure 1 was drawn on a graphing calculator equipped with a trace feature that allows us to move a cursor along the graph and see the coordinates as we go. To simulate this, place a pencil point on the graph to the left of $x = -2$, and move it along the curve so that the x-coordinate approaches -2. (See Figure 2.) We evaluate the limit numerically by noting the behavior of the y-coordinates.*

However, we can see directly from the graph that the y-coordinate approaches 2. Similarly, if we place our pencil point to the right of $x = -2$ and move it to the left, the y coordinate will approach 2 from that side as well (Figure 3). Therefore, as x approaches -2 from either side, $f(x)$ approaches 2, so

$$\lim_{x \to -2} f(x) = 2.$$

✳ NOTE For a visual animation of this process, look at the online tutorial for this section at the Web site.

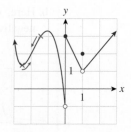

Figure 2   **Figure 3**

b. This time we move our pencil point toward $x = 0$. Referring to Figure 4, if we start from the left of $x = 0$ and approach 0 (by moving right), the y-coordinate approaches -1. However, if we start from the right of $x = 0$ and approach 0 (by moving left), the y-coordinate approaches 3. Thus (see Example 2),

$$\lim_{x \to 0^-} f(x) = -1$$

and

$$\lim_{x \to 0^+} f(x) = 3.$$

Because these limits are not equal, we conclude that

$$\lim_{x \to 0} f(x) \text{ does not exist.}$$

In this case there is a "break" in the graph at $x = 0$, and we say that the function is **discontinuous** at $x = 0$. (See Section 10.2.)

Figure 4   **Figure 5**   **Figure 6**

c. Once more we think about a pencil point moving along the graph with the x-coordinate this time approaching $x = 1$ from the left and from the right (Figure 5). As the x-coordinate of the point approaches 1 from either side, the y-coordinate approaches 1 also. Therefore,

$$\lim_{x \to 1} f(x) = 1.$$

d. For this limit, x is supposed to approach infinity. We think about a pencil point moving along the graph further and further to the right as shown in Figure 6.

As the x-coordinate gets larger, the y-coordinate also gets larger and larger without bound. Thus, $f(x)$ diverges to $+\infty$:

$$\lim_{x \to +\infty} f(x) = +\infty.$$

Similarly,

$$\lim_{x \to -\infty} f(x) = +\infty.$$

➡ **Before we go on...** In Example 4(c) $\lim_{x \to 1} f(x) = 1$ but $f(1) = 2$ (why?). Thus, $\lim_{x \to 1} f(x) \neq f(1)$. In other words, the limit of $f(x)$ as x *approaches* 1 is not the same as the value of f *at* $x = 1$. Always keep in mind that when we evaluate a limit as $x \to a$, *we do not care about the value of the function at* $x = a$. We only care about the value of $f(x)$ as x *approaches* a. In other words, $f(a)$ may or may not equal $\lim_{x \to a} f(x)$. ■

Here is a summary of the graphical method we used in Example 4, together with some additional information:

Evaluating Limits Graphically

To decide whether $\lim_{x \to a} f(x)$ exists and to find its value if it does:

1. Draw the graph of $f(x)$ by hand or with graphing technology.
2. Position your pencil point (or the Trace cursor) on a point of the graph to the right of $x = a$.
3. Move the point *along the graph* toward $x = a$ from the right and read the y-coordinate as you go. The value the y-coordinate approaches (if any) is the limit $\lim_{x \to a^+} f(x)$.
4. Repeat Steps 2 and 3, this time starting from a point on the graph to the left of $x = a$, and approaching $x = a$ along the graph from the left. The value the y-coordinate approaches (if any) is $\lim_{x \to a^-} f(x)$.
5. If the left and right limits both exist and have the same value L, then $\lim_{x \to a} f(x) = L$. Otherwise, the limit does not exist. The value $f(a)$ has no relevance whatsoever.
6. To evaluate $\lim_{x \to +\infty} f(x)$, move the pencil point toward the far right of the graph and estimate the value the y-coordinate approaches (if any). For $\lim_{x \to -\infty} f(x)$, move the pencil point toward the far left.
7. If $x = a$ happens to be an endpoint of the domain of f, then only a one-sided limit is possible at $x = a$. For instance, if the domain is $(-\infty, 4]$, then $\lim_{x \to 4^-} f(x)$ can be computed, but not $\lim_{x \to 4^+} f(x)$. In this case, we have said that $\lim_{x \to 4} f(x)$ is just the one-sided limit $\lim_{x \to 4^-} f(x)$.

In the next example we use both the numerical and graphical approaches.

EXAMPLE 5 Infinite Limit

Does $\lim_{x \to 0^+} \dfrac{1}{x}$ exist?

Solution

Numerical Method Because we are asked for only the right-hand limit, we need only list values of x approaching 0 from the right.

← *x* approaching 0 from the right

x	0	0.0001	0.001	0.01	0.1
$f(x) = \dfrac{1}{x}$		10,000	1,000	100	10

What seems to be happening as x approaches 0 from the right is that $f(x)$ is increasing without bound, as in Example 4(d). That is, if you name any number, no matter how large, $f(x)$ will be even larger than that if x is sufficiently close to zero. Thus, the limit diverges to $+\infty$, so

$$\lim_{x \to 0^+} \frac{1}{x} = +\infty$$

Graphical Method Recall that the graph of $f(x) = \dfrac{1}{x}$ is the standard hyperbola shown in Figure 7. The figure also shows the pencil point moving so that its x-coordinate approaches 0 from the right. Because the point moves along the graph, it is forced to go higher and higher. In other words, its y-coordinate becomes larger and larger, approaching $+\infty$. Thus, we conclude that

$$\lim_{x \to 0^+} \frac{1}{x} = +\infty$$

Figure 7

➡ **Before we go on...** In Example 5(a) you should also check that

$$\lim_{x \to 0^-} \frac{1}{x} = -\infty.$$

We say that as x approaches 0 from the left, $\dfrac{1}{x}$ diverges to $-\infty$. Also, check that

$$\lim_{x \to +\infty} \frac{1}{x} = \lim_{x \to -\infty} \frac{1}{x} = 0. \quad \blacksquare$$

APPLICATION

EXAMPLE 6 Broadband

The percentage of U.S. Internet-connected households that have broadband connections can be modeled by

$$P(t) = \frac{100}{1 + 10.8(1.7)^{-t}} \quad (t \geq 0)$$

where t is time in years since 2000.*

a. Estimate $\lim_{t \to +\infty} P(t)$ and interpret the answer.

b. Estimate $\lim_{t \to 0^+} P(t)$ and interpret the answer.

Solution

a. Figure 8 shows a plot of $P(t)$ for $0 \leq t \leq 20$.

Using either the numerical or the graphical approach, we find

$$\lim_{t \to +\infty} P(t) = \lim_{t \to +\infty} \frac{100}{1 + 10.8(1.7)^{-t}} = 100.$$

Thus, in the long term (as t gets larger and larger), the percentage of U.S. Internet-connected households that have broadband is expected to approach 100%.

P(t) graph

Tech Formula:
`100/(1+10.8*1.7^(-x))`

Figure 8

---
*See Example 2 in Section 9.4. Source for data: www.Nielsen.com.

b. The limit here is

$$\lim_{t \to 0^+} P(t) = \lim_{t \to 0^+} \frac{100}{1 + 10.8(1.7)^{-t}} \approx 8.475.$$

(Notice that in this case, we can simply put $t = 0$ to evaluate this limit.) Thus, the closer t gets to 0 (representing 2000) the closer $P(t)$ gets to 8.475%, meaning that, in 2000, about 8.5% of Internet-connected households had broadband.

FAQs

Determining When a Limit Does or Does Not Exist

Q : *If I substitute $x = a$ in the formula for a function and find that the function is not defined there, it means that $\lim_{x \to a} f(x)$ does not exist, right?*

A : Wrong. The limit may still exist, as in Example 1, or may not exist, as in Example 2. In general, whether or not $\lim_{x \to a} f(x)$ exists has nothing to do with $f(a)$, but rather the value of f when x is *very close to, but not equal to a.*

Q : *Is there a quick and easy way of telling from a graph whether $\lim_{x \to a} f(x)$ exists?*

A : Yes. If you cover up the portion of the graph corresponding to $x = a$, and it appears as though the visible part of the graph could be made into a continuous curve by filling in a suitable point at $x = a$, then the limit exists. (The "suitable point" need not be $(a, f(a)$.) Otherwise, it does not. Try this method with the curves in Example 4.

10.1 EXERCISES

▼ more advanced   ◆ challenging
T indicates exercises that should be solved using technology

Estimate the limits in Exercises 1–18 numerically.
HINT [See Example 1.]

1. $\lim_{x \to 0} \dfrac{x^2}{x + 1}$

2. $\lim_{x \to 0} \dfrac{x - 3}{x - 1}$

3. $\lim_{x \to 2} \dfrac{x^2 - 4}{x - 2}$

4. $\lim_{x \to 2} \dfrac{x^2 - 1}{x - 2}$

5. $\lim_{x \to -1} \dfrac{x^2 + 1}{x + 1}$

6. $\lim_{x \to -1} \dfrac{x^2 + 2x + 1}{x + 1}$

7. $\lim_{x \to +\infty} \dfrac{3x^2 + 10x - 1}{2x^2 - 5x}$ HINT [See Example 3.]

8. $\lim_{x \to +\infty} \dfrac{6x^2 + 5x + 100}{3x^2 - 9}$ HINT [See Example 3.]

9. $\lim_{x \to -\infty} \dfrac{x^5 - 1,000x^4}{2x^5 + 10,000}$

10. $\lim_{x \to -\infty} \dfrac{x^6 + 3,000x^3 + 1,000,000}{2x^6 + 1,000x^3}$

11. $\lim_{x \to +\infty} \dfrac{10x^2 + 300x + 1}{5x + 2}$

12. $\lim_{x \to +\infty} \dfrac{2x^4 + 20x^3}{1,000x^6 + 6}$

13. $\lim_{x \to +\infty} \dfrac{10x^2 + 300x + 1}{5x^3 + 2}$

14. $\lim_{x \to +\infty} \dfrac{2x^4 + 20x^3}{1,000x^3 + 6}$

15. $\lim_{x \to 2} e^{x-2}$

16. $\lim_{x \to +\infty} e^{-x}$

17. $\lim_{x \to +\infty} xe^{-x}$

18. $\lim_{x \to -\infty} xe^x$

In each of Exercises 19–30, the graph of f is given. Use the graph to compute the quantities asked for. HINT [See Example 4.]

19. a. $\lim_{x \to 1} f(x)$ **b.** $\lim_{x \to -1} f(x)$

20. a. $\lim_{x \to -1} f(x)$ **b.** $\lim_{x \to 1} f(x)$

21. a. $\lim_{x \to 0^-} f(x)$ **b.** $\lim_{x \to 2} f(x)$ **22. a.** $\lim_{x \to -1} f(x)$ **b.** $\lim_{x \to 1} f(x)$

c. $\lim_{x \to -\infty} f(x)$ **d.** $\lim_{x \to +\infty} f(x)$ **c.** $\lim_{x \to +\infty} f(x)$ **d.** $\lim_{x \to -\infty} f(x)$

23. a. $\lim_{x \to 2^-} f(x)$ **b.** $\lim_{x \to 0^+} f(x)$ **24. a.** $\lim_{x \to 3^-} f(x)$ **b.** $\lim_{x \to 1^+} f(x)$

c. $\lim_{x \to 0^-} f(x)$ **d.** $\lim_{x \to 0^-} f(x)$ **c.** $\lim_{x \to 1^-} f(x)$ **d.** $\lim_{x \to 1^+} f(x)$

e. $f(0)$ **f.** $\lim_{x \to -\infty} f(x)$ **e.** $f(1)$ **f.** $\lim_{x \to +\infty} f(x)$

25. a. $\lim_{x \to -2} f(x)$ **b.** $\lim_{x \to -1^+} f(x)$ **26. a.** $\lim_{x \to -1} f(x)$ **b.** $\lim_{x \to 0^+} f(x)$

c. $\lim_{x \to -1^-} f(x)$ **d.** $\lim_{x \to -1} f(x)$ **c.** $\lim_{x \to 0^-} f(x)$ **d.** $\lim_{x \to 0} f(x)$

e. $f(-1)$ **f.** $\lim_{x \to +\infty} f(x)$ **e.** $f(0)$ **f.** $\lim_{x \to -\infty} f(x)$

27. a. $\lim_{x \to -1} f(x)$ **b.** $\lim_{x \to 0^+} f(x)$ **28. a.** $\lim_{x \to 1} f(x)$ **b.** $\lim_{x \to 0^+} f(x)$

c. $\lim_{x \to 0^-} f(x)$ **d.** $\lim_{x \to 0} f(x)$ **c.** $\lim_{x \to 0^-} f(x)$ **d.** $\lim_{x \to 0} f(x)$

e. $f(0)$ **f.** $\lim_{x \to +\infty} f(x)$ **e.** $f(0)$ **f.** $\lim_{x \to -\infty} f(x)$

29. a. $\lim_{x \to -1} f(x)$ **b.** $\lim_{x \to 0^+} f(x)$ **30. a.** $\lim_{x \to 0^-} f(x)$ **b.** $\lim_{x \to 1^+} f(x)$

c. $\lim_{x \to 0^-} f(x)$ **d.** $\lim_{x \to 0} f(x)$ **c.** $\lim_{x \to 0} f(x)$ **d.** $\lim_{x \to 1} f(x)$

e. $f(0)$ **f.** $f(-1)$ **e.** $f(0)$ **f.** $f(1)$

APPLICATIONS

31. *Economic Growth* The value of sold goods in Mexico can be approximated by

$$v(t) = 210 - 62e^{-0.05t} \text{ trillion pesos per month} \quad (t \ge 0)$$

where t is time in months since January 2005.[1] Numerically estimate $\lim_{t \to +\infty} v(t)$ and interpret the answer. HINT [See Example 6.]

32. *Housing Starts* Housing starts in the United States can be approximated by

$$n(t) = \frac{1}{12}(1.1 + 1.2e^{-0.08t}) \text{ million homes per month} \quad (t \ge 0)$$

where t is time in months since January 2006.[2] Numerically estimate $\lim_{t \to +\infty} n(t)$ and interpret the answer. HINT [See Example 6.]

33. *Scientific Research* The number of research articles per year, in thousands, in the prominent journal *Physical Review* written by researchers in Europe can be modeled by

$$A(t) = \frac{7.0}{1 + 5.4(1.2)^{-t}}$$

where t is time in years ($t = 0$ represents 1983).[3] Numerically estimate $\lim_{t \to +\infty} A(t)$ and interpret the answer. HINT [See Example 6.]

34. *Scientific Research* The percentage of research articles in the prominent journal *Physical Review* written by researchers in the United States can be modeled by

$$A(t) = 25 + \frac{36}{1 + 0.6(0.7)^{-t}},$$

where t is time in years ($t = 0$ represents 1983).[4] Numerically estimate $\lim_{t \to -\infty} A(t)$ and interpret the answer. HINT [See Example 6.]

---

[1] Source: Instituto Nacional de Estadística y Geografía (INEGI), www.inegi.org.mx.

[2] Source for data: *New York Times*, February 17, 2007, p. C3.

[3] Based on data from 1983 to 2003. Source: The American Physical Society/*New York Times*, May 3, 2003, p. A1.

[4] Ibid.

35. *SAT Scores by Income* The following bar graph shows U.S. verbal SAT scores as a function of parents' income level:[5]

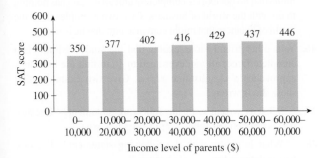

These data can be modeled by

$$S(x) = 470 - 136(0.974)^x.$$

where $S(x)$ is the average SAT verbal score of a student whose parents' income is x thousand dollars per year. Numerically estimate $\lim_{x \to +\infty} S(x)$ and interpret the result.

36. *SAT Scores by Income* The following bar graph shows U.S. math SAT scores as a function of parents' income level:[6]

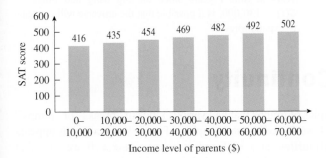

These data can be modeled by

$$S(x) = 535 - 136(0.979)^x,$$

where $S(x)$ is the average math SAT score of a student whose parents' income is x thousand dollars per year. Numerically estimate $\lim_{x \to +\infty} S(x)$ and interpret the result.

37. *Home Prices* The following graph shows the approximate value of the home price index as a percentage change from 2003.[7]

Home price index

Estimate $\lim_{t \to +\infty} p(t)$ and interpret your answer.

38. *Existing Home Sales* The following graph shows the approximate value of existing home sales as a percentage change from 2003.[8]

Existing home sales

Estimate $\lim_{t \to +\infty} s(t)$ and interpret your answer.

39. *Electric Rates* The cost of electricity in Portland, Oregon, for residential customers increased suddenly on October 1, 2001, from around $0.06 to around $0.08 per kilowatt hour.[9] Let $C(t)$ be this cost at time t, and take $t = 1$ to represent October 1, 2001. What does the given information tell you about $\lim_{t \to 1} C(t)$? HINT [See Example 4(b).]

40. *Airline Stocks* Prior to the September 11, 2001 attacks, **United Airlines** stock was trading at around $35 per share. Immediately following the attacks, the share price dropped by $15.[10] Let $U(t)$ be this cost at time t, and take $t = 11$ to represent September 11, 2001. What does the given information tell you about $\lim_{t \to 11} U(t)$? HINT [See Example 4(b).]

[5] Based on 1994 data. Source: The College Board/*New York Times*, March 5, 1995, p. E16.

[6] Ibid.

[7] S&P/Case-Shiller Home Price Index. Source: Standard & Poors/*New York Times*, September 29, 2007, p. C3. Projection is the authors'.

[8] Source: Bloomberg Finiancial Markets/*New York Times*, September 29, 2007, p. C3. Projection is the authors'.

[9] Source: Portland General Electric/*New York Times*, February 2, 2002, p. C1.

[10] Stock prices are approximate.

Foreign Trade Annual U.S. imports from China in the years 1996 through 2003 can be approximated by

$$I(t) = t^2 + 3.5t + 50 \qquad (1 \le t \le 9)$$

billion dollars, where t represents time in years since 1995. Annual U.S. exports to China in the same years can be approximated by

$$E(t) = 0.4t^2 - 1.6t + 14$$

billion dollars.[11] *Exercises 41 and 42 are based on these models.*

41. ▼ Assuming the trends shown in the above models continued indefinitely, numerically estimate

$$\lim_{t \to +\infty} I(t) \text{ and } \lim_{t \to +\infty} \frac{I(t)}{E(t)},$$

interpret your answers, and comment on the results.

42. ▼ Repeat Exercise 41, this time calculating

$$\lim_{t \to +\infty} E(t) \text{ and } \lim_{t \to +\infty} \frac{E(t)}{I(t)}.$$

COMMUNICATION AND REASONING EXERCISES

43. Describe the method of evaluating limits numerically. Give at least one disadvantage of this method.

---

[11] Based on quadratic regression using data from the U.S. Census Bureau Foreign Trade Division Web site www.census.gov/foreign-trade/sitc1/ as of December 2004.

44. Describe the method of evaluating limits graphically. Give at least one disadvantage of this method.

45. Your friend Dion, a business student, claims that the study of limits that do not exist is completely unrealistic and has nothing to do with the world of business. Give two examples from the world of business that might convince him that he is wrong.

46. Your other friend Fiona claims that the study of limits is a complete farce; all you ever need to do to find the limit as x approaches a is substitute $x = a$. Give two examples that show she is wrong.

47. ▼ What is wrong with the following statement? "Because $f(a)$ is not defined, $\lim_{x \to a} f(x)$ does not exist."

48. ▼ What is wrong with the following statement? "Because $f(a)$ is defined, $\lim_{x \to a} f(x)$ exists."

49. ▼ What is wrong with the following statement? "If $f(a)$ is defined, then $\lim_{x \to a} f(x)$ exists and equals $f(a)$."

50. ▼ If $D(t)$ is the Dow Jones Average at time t and $\lim_{t \to +\infty} D(t) = +\infty$, is it possible that the Dow will fluctuate indefinitely into the future?

51. ◆ Give an example of a function f with $\lim_{x \to 1} f(x) = f(2)$.

52. ◆ If $S(t)$ represents the size of the universe in billions of light years at time t years since the big bang and $\lim_{t \to +\infty} S(t) = 130,000$, is it possible that the universe will continue to expand forever?

10.2 Limits and Continuity

Figure 9

In Section 9.1 we saw examples of graphs that had various kinds of "breaks" or "jumps." For instance, in Example 4 we looked at the graph in Figure 9. This graph appears to have breaks, or **discontinuities**, at $x = 0$ and at $x = 1$. At $x = 0$ we saw that $\lim_{x \to 0} f(x)$ does not exist because the left- and right-hand limits are not the same. Thus, the discontinuity at $x = 0$ seems to be due to the fact that the limit does not exist there. On the other hand, at $x = 1$, $\lim_{x \to 1} f(x)$ *does* exist (it is equal to 1), but is not equal to $f(1) = 2$.

Thus, we have identified two kinds of discontinuity:

1. Points where the limit of the function does not exist. $x = 0$ in Figure 9 because $\lim_{x \to 0} f(x)$ does not exist.

2. Points where the limit exists but does not equal the value of the function. $x = 1$ in Figure 9 because $\lim_{x \to 1} f(x) = 1 \ne f(1)$

On the other hand, there is no discontinuity at, say, $x = -2$, where we find that $\lim_{x \to -2} f(x)$ exists and equals 2 and $f(-2)$ is also equal to 2. In other words,

$$\lim_{x \to -2} f(x) = 2 = f(-2).$$

The point $x = -2$ is an example of a point where f is **continuous**. (Notice that you can draw the portion of the graph near $x = -2$ without lifting your pencil from the paper.) Similarly, f is continuous at *every* point other than $x = 0$ and $x = 1$. Here is the mathematical definition.

Continuous Function

Let f be a function and let a be a number in the domain of f. Then f is **continuous at a** if

    a. $\lim_{x \to a} f(x)$ exists, and

    b. $\lim_{x \to a} f(x) = f(a)$.

The function f is said to be **continuous on its domain** if it is continuous at each point in its domain.

    If f is not continuous at a particular a in its domain, we say that f is **discontinuous** at a or that f has a **discontinuity** at a. Thus, a discontinuity can occur at $x = a$ if either

    a. $\lim_{x \to a} f(x)$ does not exist, or

    b. $\lim_{x \to a} f(x)$ exists but is not equal to $f(a)$.

Quick Examples

1. The function shown in Figure 9 is continuous at $x = -1$ and $x = 2$. It is discontinuous at $x = 0$ and $x = 1$, and so is not continuous on its domain.

2. The function $f(x) = x^2$ is continuous on its domain. (Think of its graph, which contains no breaks).

3. The function f whose graph is shown on the left in the following figure is continuous on its domain. (Although the graph breaks at $x = 2$, that is not a point of its domain.) The function g whose graph is shown on the right is not continuous on its domain because it has a discontinuity at $x = 2$. (Here, $x = 2$ is a point of the domain of g.)

$y = f(x)$: Continuous on
its domain

$y = g(x)$:0 Not continuous on
its domain

Note If the number a is not in the domain of f—that is, if $f(a)$ is not defined—we will not consider the question of continuity at a. A function cannot be continuous at a point not in its domain, and it cannot be discontinuous there either. ∎

EXAMPLE 1 Continuous and Discontinuous Functions

Which of the following functions are continuous on their domains?

a. $h(x) = \begin{cases} x + 3 & \text{if } x \leq 1 \\ 5 - x & \text{if } x > 1 \end{cases}$ **b.** $k(x) = \begin{cases} x + 3 & \text{if } x \leq 1 \\ 1 - x & \text{if } x > 1 \end{cases}$

c. $f(x) = \dfrac{1}{x}$ **d.** $g(x) = \begin{cases} \dfrac{1}{x} & \text{if } x \neq 0 \\ 0 & \text{if } x = 0 \end{cases}$

Solution

a and **b.** The graphs of h and k are shown in Figure 10.

$y = h(x)$ $y = k(x)$

Figure 10

Even though the graph of h is made up of two different line segments, it is continuous at every point of its domain, including $x = 1$ because

$$\lim_{x \to 1} h(x) = 4 = h(1).$$

On the other hand, $x = 1$ is also in the domain of k, but $\lim_{x \to 1} k(x)$ does not exist. Thus, k is discontinuous at $x = 1$ and thus not continuous on its domain.

c and **d.** The graphs of f and g are shown in Figure 11.

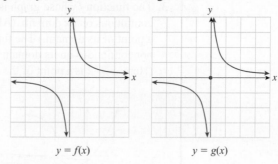

$y = f(x)$ $y = g(x)$

Figure 11

The domain of f consists of all real numbers except 0 and f is continuous at all such numbers. (Notice that 0 is not in the domain of f, so the question of continuity at 0 does not arise.) Thus, f is continuous on its domain.

The function g, on the other hand, has its domain expanded to include 0, so we now need to check whether g is continuous at 0. From the graph, it is easy to see that g is discontinuous there because $\lim_{x \to 0} g(x)$ does not exist. Thus, g is not continuous on its domain because it is discontinuous at 0.

➡ **Before we go on...**

Q: *Wait a minute! How can a function like $f(x) = 1/x$ be continuous when its graph has a break in it?*

A: We are not claiming that f is continuous *at every real number*. What we are saying is that f is continuous *on its domain;* the break in the graph occurs at a point not in the domain of f. In other words, f is continuous on the set of all nonzero real numbers; it is not continuous on the set of *all* real numbers because it is not even defined on that set.

■

Figure 12

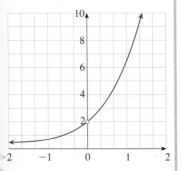

Figure 13

![using Technology icon] **using** Technology

It is instructive to see how technology handles the functions in Example 2. Here are the technology formulas that will work for the TI-83/84 Plus, Excel, and Web site function evaluator and grapher. (In Excel, replace x by a cell reference and insert an equal sign in front of the formula.)

a. `(x^3-8)/(x-2)`

b. `(e^(2x)-1)/x`

Excel:
`=(exp(2*A2)-1)/A2`

c. `abs(x)/x`

In each case, compare the graph rendered by technology with the corresponding figure in Example 2.

EXAMPLE 2 Continuous Except at a Point

In each case, say what, if any, value of $f(a)$ would make f continuous at a.

a. $f(x) = \dfrac{x^3 - 8}{x - 2}$; $a = 2$ **b.** $f(x) = \dfrac{e^{2x} - 1}{x}$; $a = 0$ **c.** $f(x) = \dfrac{|x|}{x}$; $a = 0$

Solution

a. In Figure 12 we see the graph of $f(x) = \dfrac{x^3 - 8}{x - 2}$. The point corresponding to $x = 2$ is missing because f is not (yet) defined there. (Your graphing utility will probably miss this subtlety and render a continuous curve. See the technology note in the margin.) To turn f into a function that is continuous at $x = 2$, we need to "fill in the gap" so as to obtain a continuous curve. Since the graph suggests that the missing point is $(2, 12)$, let us define $f(2) = 12$.

Does f now become continuous if we take $f(2) = 12$? From the graph, or Example 1(a) of Section 10.1,

$$\lim_{x \to 2} f(x) = \lim_{x \to 2} \frac{x^3 - 8}{x - 2} = 12,$$

which is now equal to $f(2)$. Thus, $\lim_{x \to 2} f(x) = f(2)$, showing that f is now continuous at $x = 2$.

b. In Example 1(b) of the preceding section, we saw that

$$\lim_{x \to 0} f(x) = \lim_{x \to 0} \frac{e^{2x} - 1}{x} = 2$$

and so, as in part (a), we must define $f(0) = 2$. This is confirmed by the graph, shown in Figure 13.

c. We considered the function $f(x) = |x|/x$ in Example 2 in Section 10.1. Its graph is shown in Figure 14.

Figure 14

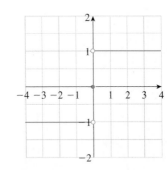

Figure 15

Now we encounter a problem: No matter how we try to fill in the gap at $x = 0$, the result will be a discontinuous function. For example, setting $f(0) = 0$ will result in the discontinuous function shown in Figure 15. We conclude that it is impossible to assign any value to $f(0)$ to turn f into a function that is continuous at $x = 0$.

We can also see this result algebraically: In Example 2 of Section 10.1, we saw that $\lim_{x \to 0} \dfrac{|x|}{x}$ does not exist. Thus, the resulting function will fail to be continuous at 0, no matter how we define $f(0)$.

A function not defined at an isolated point is said to have a **singularity** at that point. The function in part (a) of Example 2 has a singularity at $x = 2$, and the functions in parts (b) and (c) have singularities at $x = 0$. The functions in parts (a) and (b) have *removable* singularities because we can make these functions continuous at $x = a$ by properly defining $f(a)$. The function in part (c) has an **essential singularity** because we cannot make f continuous at $x = a$ just by defining $f(a)$ properly.

10.2 EXERCISES

▼ more advanced   ◆ challenging

T indicates exercises that should be solved using technology

In Exercises 1–12, the graph of a function f is given. Determine whether f is continuous on its domain. If it is not continuous on its domain, say why. HINT [See Quick Examples page 701.]

1.

2.

3.

4.

5.

6.

7.

8.

9.

10.

11.

12.

In Exercises 13 and 14, identify which (if any) of the given graphs represent functions continuous on their domains. HINT [See Quick Examples page 701.]

13. (A)

(B)

(C)

(D)

(E)

14. (A)

(B)

(C)

(D)

(E)

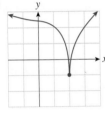

In Exercises 23–32, use a graph to determine whether the given function is continuous on its domain. If it is not continuous on its domain, list the points of discontinuity. HINT [See Example 1.]

23. $f(x) = |x|$

24. $f(x) = \dfrac{|x|}{x}$

25. $g(x) = \dfrac{1}{x^2 - 1}$

26. $g(x) = \dfrac{x - 1}{x + 2}$

27. $f(x) = \begin{cases} x + 2 & \text{if } x < 0 \\ 2x - 1 & \text{if } x \ge 0 \end{cases}$

28. $f(x) = \begin{cases} 1 - x & \text{if } x \le 1 \\ x - 1 & \text{if } x > 1 \end{cases}$

29. $h(x) = \begin{cases} \dfrac{|x|}{x} & \text{if } x \ne 0 \\ 0 & \text{if } x = 0 \end{cases}$

30. $h(x) = \begin{cases} \dfrac{1}{x^2} & \text{if } x \ne 0 \\ 2 & \text{if } x = 0 \end{cases}$

31. $g(x) = \begin{cases} x + 2 & \text{if } x < 0 \\ 2x + 2 & \text{if } x \ge 0 \end{cases}$

32. $g(x) = \begin{cases} 1 - x & \text{if } x \le 1 \\ x + 1 & \text{if } x > 1 \end{cases}$

In Exercises 15–22, use a graph of f or some other method to determine what, if any, value to assign to f(a) to make f continuous at x = a. HINT [See Example 2.]

15. $f(x) = \dfrac{x^2 - 2x + 1}{x - 1}; \; a = 1$

16. $f(x) = \dfrac{x^2 + 3x + 2}{x + 1}; \; a = -1$

17. $f(x) = \dfrac{x}{3x^2 - x}; \; a = 0$

18. $f(x) = \dfrac{x^2 - 3x}{x + 4}; \; a = -4$

19. $f(x) = \dfrac{3}{3x^2 - x}; \; a = 0$

20. $f(x) = \dfrac{x - 1}{x^3 - 1}; \; a = 1$

21. $f(x) = \dfrac{1 - e^x}{x}; \; a = 0$

22. $f(x) = \dfrac{1 + e^x}{1 - e^x}; \; a = 0$

COMMUNICATION AND REASONING EXERCISES

33. If a function is continuous on its domain, is it continuous at every real number? Explain.

34. True or false? The graph of a function that is continuous on its domain is a continuous curve with no breaks in it. Explain your answer.

35. True or false? The graph of a function that is continuous at every real number is a continuous curve with no breaks in it. Explain your answer.

36. True or false? If the graph of a function is a continuous curve with no breaks in it, then the function is continuous on its domain. Explain your answer.

37. ▼ Give a formula for a function that is continuous on its domain but whose graph consists of three distinct curves.

38. ▼ Give a formula for a function that is not continuous at $x = -1$ but is not discontinuous there either.

39. ▼ Draw the graph of a function that is discontinuous at every integer.

40. ▼ Draw the graph of a function that is continuous on its domain but whose graph has a break at every integer.

41. ▼ Describe a real-life scenario in the stock market that can be modeled by a discontinuous function.

42. ▼ Describe a real-life scenario in your room that can be modeled by a discontinuous function.

10.3 Limits and Continuity: Algebraic Approach

Although numerical and graphical estimation of limits is effective, the estimates these methods yield may not be perfectly accurate. The algebraic method, when it can be used, will always yield an exact answer. Moreover, algebraic analysis of a function often enables us to take a function apart and see "what makes it tick."

Let's start with the function $f(x) = 2 + x$ and ask: What happens to $f(x)$ as x approaches 3? To answer this algebraically, notice that as x gets closer and closer to 3, the quantity $2 + x$ must get closer and closer to $2 + 3 = 5$. Hence,

$$\lim_{x \to 3} f(x) = \lim_{x \to 3} (2 + x) = 2 + 3 = 5$$

Q : *Is that all there is to the algebraic method? Just substitute $x = a$?*

A : Under certain circumstances: Notice that by substituting $x = 3$ we *evaluated the function at $x = 3$*. In other words, we relied on the fact that

$$\lim_{x \to 3} f(x) = f(3).$$

In Section 10.2 we said that a function satisfying this equation is *continuous* at $x = 3$.

Thus,

If we know that the function f is continuous at a point a, we can compute $\lim_{x \to a} f(x)$ by simply substituting $x = a$ into $f(x)$.

To use this fact, we need to know how to recognize continuous functions when we see them. Geometrically, they are easy to spot: A function is continuous at $x = a$ if its graph has no break at $x = a$. Algebraically, a large class of functions are known to be continuous on their domains—those, roughly speaking, that are *specified by a single formula*.

We can be more precise: A **closed-form function** is any function that can be obtained by combining constants, powers of x, exponential functions, radicals, logarithms, absolute values, trigonometric functions (and some other functions we do not encounter in this text) into a *single* mathematical formula by means of the usual arithmetic operations and composition of functions. (They can be as complicated as we like.)

Closed-Form Functions

A function is **written in closed form** if it is specified by combining constants, powers of x, exponential functions, radicals, logarithms, absolute values, trigonometric functions (and some other functions we do not encounter in this text) into a *single* mathematical formula by means of the usual arithmetic operations and composition of functions. A **closed-form function** is any function that can be written in closed form.

Quick Examples

1. $3x^2 - |x| + 1$, $\dfrac{\sqrt{x^2 - 1}}{6x - 1}$, $e^{-\frac{4x^2-1}{x}}$, and $\sqrt{\log_3(x^2 - 1)}$ are written in closed form, so they are all closed-form functions.

2. $f(x) = \begin{cases} -1 & \text{if } x \le -1 \\ x^2 + x & \text{if } -1 < x \le 1 \\ 2 - x & \text{if } 1 < x \le 2 \end{cases}$ is not written in closed-form because $f(x)$ is not expressed by a *single* mathematical formula.*

✱ NOTE It is possible to rewrite some piecewise defined functions in closed form (using a single formula), but not this particular function, so $f(x)$ is not a closed-form function.

What is so special about closed-form functions is the following theorem.

Theorem 10.1 Continuity of Closed-Form Functions

Every closed-form function is continuous on its domain. Thus, if f is a closed-form function and $f(a)$ is defined, we have $\lim_{x \to a} f(x) = f(a)$.

Quick Example

$f(x) = 1/x$ is a closed-form function, and its natural domain consists of all real numbers except 0. Thus, f is continuous at every nonzero real number. That is,

$$\lim_{x \to a} \frac{1}{x} = \frac{1}{a}$$

provided $a \neq 0$.

Mathematics majors spend a great deal of time studying the proof of this theorem. We ask you to accept it without proof.

EXAMPLE 1 Limit of a Closed-Form Function at a Point in Its Domain

Evaluate $\lim_{x \to 1} \dfrac{x^3 - 8}{x - 2}$ algebraically.

Solution First, notice that $(x^3 - 8)/(x - 2)$ is a closed-form function because it is specified by a single algebraic formula. Also, $x = 1$ is in the domain of this function. Therefore,

$$\lim_{x \to 1} \frac{x^3 - 8}{x - 2} = \frac{1^3 - 8}{1 - 2} = 7.$$

➡ **Before we go on...** In Example 1, the point $x = 2$ is not in the domain of the function $(x^3 - 8)/(x - 2)$, so we cannot evaluate $\lim_{x \to 2} \dfrac{x^3 - 8}{x - 2}$ by substituting $x = 2$. However— and this is the key to finding such limits—some preliminary algebraic simplification will allow us to obtain a closed-form function with $x = 2$ in its domain, as we shall see in Example 2. ∎

EXAMPLE 2 Limit of a Closed-Form Function at a Point Not in Its Domain: Simplifying to Obtain the Limit

Evaluate $\lim_{x \to 2} \dfrac{x^3 - 8}{x - 2}$ algebraically.

Solution Again, although $(x^3 - 8)/(x - 2)$ is a closed-form function, $x = 2$ is not in its domain. Thus, we cannot obtain the limit by substitution. Instead, we first simplify $f(x)$ to obtain a new function with $x = 2$ in its domain. To do this, notice first that the numerator can be factored as

$$x^3 - 8 = (x - 2)(x^2 + 2x + 4).$$

Thus,

$$\frac{x^3 - 8}{x - 2} = \frac{(x - 2)(x^2 + 2x + 4)}{x - 2} = x^2 + 2x + 4.$$

Once we have canceled the offending $(x - 2)$ in the denominator, we are left with a closed-form function *with 2 in its domain*. Thus,

$$\lim_{x \to 2} \frac{x^3 - 8}{x - 2} = \lim_{x \to 2}(x^2 + 2x + 4)$$

$$= 2^2 + 2(2) + 4 = 12. \quad \text{Substitute } x = 2.$$

This confirms the answer we found numerically in Example 1 in Section 10.1.

➡ **Before we go on...** Notice that in Example 2, before simplification, the substitution $x = 2$ yields

$$\frac{x^3 - 8}{x - 2} = \frac{8 - 8}{2 - 2} = \frac{0}{0}.$$

Worse than the fact that 0/0 is undefined, it also conveys absolutely no information as to what the limit might be. (The limit turned out to be 12!) We therefore call the expression 0/0 an **indeterminate form**. Once simplified, the function became $x^2 + 2x + 4$, which, upon the substitution $x = 2$, yielded 12—no longer an indeterminate form. In general, we have the following rule of thumb:

If the substitution $x = a$ yields the indeterminate form 0/0, try simplifying by the method in Example 2.

We will say more about indeterminate forms in Example 3. ∎

Q : *There is something suspicious about Example 2. If 2 was not in the domain before simplifying but was in the domain after simplifying, we must have changed the function, right?*

A : Correct. In fact, when we said that

$$\frac{x^3 - 8}{x - 2} = x^2 + 2x + 4$$

Domain excludes 2   Domain includes 2

we were lying a little bit. What we really meant is that these two expressions are equal *where both are defined*. The functions $(x^3 - 8)/(x - 2)$ and $x^2 + 2x + 4$ are different functions. The difference is that $x = 2$ is not in the domain of $(x^3 - 8)/(x - 2)$ and is in the domain of $x^2 + 2x + 4$. Since $\lim_{x \to 2} f(x)$ explicitly *ignores* any value that f may have at 2, this does not affect the limit. From the point of view of the limit at 2, these functions *are* equal. In general we have the following rule.

Functions with Equal Limits

If $f(x) = g(x)$ for all x except possibly $x = a$, then

$$\lim_{x \to a} f(x) = \lim_{x \to a} g(x).$$

Quick Example

$$\frac{x^2 - 1}{x - 1} = x + 1 \text{ for all } x \text{ except } x = 1. \quad \text{Write } \frac{x^2 - 1}{x - 1} \text{ as } \frac{(x + 1)(x - 1)}{x - 1}$$
$$\text{and cancel the } (x - 1)$$

Therefore,

$$\lim_{x \to 1} \frac{x^2 - 1}{x - 1} = \lim_{x \to 1} (x + 1) = 1 + 1 = 2.$$

Q: *How do we find* $\lim_{x \to a} f(x)$ *when* $x = a$ *is not in the domain of the function f, and we cannot simplify the given function to make a a point of the domain?*

A: In such a case, it might be necessary to analyze the function by some other method, such as numerically or graphically. However, if we do not obtain the indeterminate form 0/0 upon substitution, we can often say what the limit is, as the following example shows.

EXAMPLE 3 Limit of a Closed-Form Function at a Point Not in Its Domain: The Determinate Form *k*/0

Evaluate the following limits, if they exist:

a. $\lim\limits_{x \to 1^+} \dfrac{x^2 - 4x + 1}{x - 1}$ **b.** $\lim\limits_{x \to 1} \dfrac{x^2 - 4x + 1}{x - 1}$ **c.** $\lim\limits_{x \to 1} \dfrac{x^2 - 4x + 1}{x^2 - 2x + 1}$

Solution

a. Although the function $f(x) = \dfrac{x^2 - 4x + 1}{x - 1}$ is a closed-form function, $x = 1$ is not in its domain. Notice that substituting $x = 1$ gives

$$\frac{x^2 - 4x + 1}{x - 1} = \frac{1^2 - 4 + 1}{1 - 1} = \frac{-2}{0} \qquad \text{The } \textbf{determinate} \text{ form } \frac{k}{0}$$

which, although not defined, conveys important information to us: As x gets closer and closer to 1, the numerator approaches -2 and the denominator gets closer and closer to 0. Now, if we divide a number close to -2 by a number close to zero, we get a number of large absolute value; for instance

$$\frac{-2.1}{0.0001} = -21,000 \qquad \text{and} \qquad \frac{-2.1}{-0.0001} = 21,000$$

$$\frac{-2.01}{0.00001} = -201,000 \qquad \text{and} \qquad \frac{-2.01}{-0.00001} = 201,000.$$

(Compare Example 5 in Section 10.1.) In our limit for part (a), x is approaching 1 from the right, so the denominator $x - 1$ is positive (as x is to the right of 1). Thus we have the scenario illustrated previously on the left, and we can conclude that

$$\lim_{x \to 1^+} \frac{x^2 - 4x + 1}{x - 1} = -\infty. \qquad \text{Think of this as } \frac{-2}{0^+} = -\infty.$$

b. This time, x could be approaching 1 from either side. We already have, from part (a)

$$\lim_{x \to 1^+} \frac{x^2 - 4x + 1}{x - 1} = -\infty.$$

The same reasoning we used in part (a) gives

$$\lim_{x \to 1^-} \frac{x^2 - 4x + 1}{x - 1} = +\infty \qquad \text{Think of this as } \frac{-2}{0^-} = +\infty.$$

because now the denominator is negative and still approaching zero while the numerator still approaches -2 and therefore is also negative. (See the numerical calculations above on the right.) Because the left and right limits do not agree, we conclude that

$$\lim_{x \to 1} \frac{x^2 - 4x + 1}{x - 1} \text{ does not exist.}$$

c. First notice that the denominator factors:

$$\lim_{x \to 1} \frac{x^2 - 4x + 1}{x^2 - 2x + 1} = \lim_{x \to 1} \frac{x^2 - 4x + 1}{(x - 1)^2}$$

As x approaches 1, the numerator approaches -2 as before, and the denominator approaches 0. However, this time, the denominator $(x - 1)^2$, being a square, is ≥ 0, regardless of from which side x is approaching 1. Thus, the entire function is negative as x approaches 1, and

$$\lim_{x \to 1} \frac{x^2 - 4x + 1}{(x - 1)^2} = -\infty. \qquad \frac{-2}{0^+} = -\infty$$

➡ **Before we go on...** In general, the determinate forms $\dfrac{k}{0^+}$ and $\dfrac{k}{0^-}$ will always yield $\pm\infty$, with the sign depending on the sign of the overall expression as $x \to a$. (When we write the form $\dfrac{k}{0}$ we always mean $k \neq 0$.) This and other determinate forms are discussed further after Example 5.

Figure 16 shows the graphs of $\dfrac{x^2 - 4x + 1}{x - 1}$ and $\dfrac{x^2 - 4x + 1}{(x - 1)^2}$ from Example 3. You should check that results we obtained above agree with a geometric analysis of these graphs near $x = 1$.

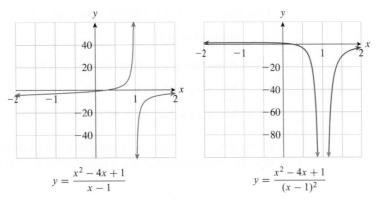

$$y = \frac{x^2 - 4x + 1}{x - 1}$$

$$y = \frac{x^2 - 4x + 1}{(x - 1)^2}$$

Figure 16

■

We can also use algebraic techniques to analyze functions that are not given in closed form.

EXAMPLE 4 Functions Not Written in Closed Form

For which values of x are the following piecewise defined functions continuous?

a. $f(x) = \begin{cases} x^2 + 2 & \text{if } x < 1 \\ 2x - 1 & \text{if } x \geq 1 \end{cases}$ **b.** $g(x) = \begin{cases} x^2 - x + 1 & \text{if } x \leq 0 \\ 1 - x & \text{if } 0 < x \leq 1 \\ x - 3 & \text{if } x > 1 \end{cases}$

Solution

a. The function $f(x)$ is given in closed form over the intervals $(-\infty, 1)$ and $[1, +\infty)$. At $x = 1$, $f(x)$ suddenly switches from one closed-form formula to another, so $x = 1$ is the only place where there is a potential problem with continuity. To investigate the continuity of $f(x)$ at $x = 1$, let's calculate the limit there:

$$\lim_{x \to 1^-} f(x) = \lim_{x \to 1^-} (x^2 + 2) \qquad f(x) = x^2 + 2 \text{ for } x < 1.$$
$$= (1)^2 + 2 = 3 \qquad x^2 + 2 \text{ is closed-form.}$$

$$\lim_{x \to 1^+} f(x) = \lim_{x \to 1^+} (2x - 1) \qquad f(x) = 2x - 1 \text{ for } x > 1.$$
$$= 2(1) - 1 = 1. \qquad 2x - 1 \text{ is closed-form.}$$

Because the left and right limits are different, $\lim_{x \to 1} f(x)$ does not exist, and so $f(x)$ is discontinuous at $x = 1$.

b. The only potential points of discontinuity for $g(x)$ occur at $x = 0$ and $x = 1$:

$$\lim_{x \to 0^-} g(x) = \lim_{x \to 0^-} (x^2 - x + 1) = 1$$

$$\lim_{x \to 0^+} g(x) = \lim_{x \to 0^+} (1 - x) = 1.$$

Thus, $\lim_{x \to 0} g(x) = 1$. Further, $g(0) = 0^2 - 0 + 1 = 1$ from the formula, and so

$$\lim_{x \to 0} g(x) = g(0),$$

which shows that $g(x)$ is continuous at $x = 0$. At $x = 1$ we have

$$\lim_{x \to 1^-} g(x) = \lim_{x \to 1^-} (1 - x) = 0$$

$$\lim_{x \to 1^+} g(x) = \lim_{x \to 1^+} (x - 3) = -2$$

so that $\lim_{x \to 1} g(x)$ does not exist. Thus, $g(x)$ is discontinuous at $x = 1$. We conclude that $g(x)$ is continuous at every real number x except $x = 1$.

➡ **Before we go on...** Figure 17 shows the graph of g from Example 4(b). Notice how the discontinuity at $x = 1$ shows up as a break in the graph, whereas at $x = 0$ the two pieces "fit together" at the point $(0, 1)$. ■

$y = g(x)$

Figure 17

Limits at Infinity

Let's look once again at some limits similar to those in Examples 3 and 6 in Section 10.1.

EXAMPLE 5   Limits at Infinity

Compute the following limits, if they exist:

a. $\lim_{x \to +\infty} \dfrac{2x^2 - 4x}{x^2 - 1}$ **b.** $\lim_{x \to -\infty} \dfrac{2x^2 - 4x}{x^2 - 1}$

c. $\lim_{x \to +\infty} \dfrac{-x^3 - 4x}{2x^2 - 1}$ **d.** $\lim_{x \to +\infty} \dfrac{2x^2 - 4x}{5x^3 - 3x + 5}$

e. $\lim_{t \to +\infty} e^{0.1t} - 20$ **f.** $\lim_{t \to +\infty} \dfrac{80}{1 + 2.2(3.68)^{-t}}$

Solution   a and **b.** While calculating the values for the tables used in Example 3 in Section 10.1, you might have noticed that the highest power of x in both the numerator and denominator dominated the calculations. For instance, when $x = 100,000$, the term $2x^2$ in the numerator has the value of 20,000,000,000, whereas the term $4x$ has the comparatively insignificant value of 400,000. Similarly, the term x^2 in the denominator overwhelms the term -1. In other words, for large values of x (or negative values with large magnitude),

$$\frac{2x^2 - 4x}{x^2 - 1} \approx \frac{2x^2}{x^2} \qquad \text{Use only the highest powers top and bottom.}$$

$$= 2.$$

Therefore,

$$\lim_{x \to \pm\infty} \frac{2x^2 - 4x}{x^2 - 1} = \lim_{x \to \pm\infty} \frac{2x^2}{x^2}$$

$$= \lim_{x \to \pm\infty} 2 = 2.$$

The procedure of using only the highest powers of x to compute the limit is stated formally and justified after this example.

c. Applying the previous technique of looking only at highest powers gives

$$\lim_{x \to +\infty} \frac{-x^3 - 4x}{2x^2 - 1} = \lim_{x \to +\infty} \frac{-x^3}{2x^2}$$ Use only the highest powers top and bottom.

$$= \lim_{x \to +\infty} \frac{-x}{2}.$$ Simplify.

As x gets large, $-x/2$ gets large in magnitude but negative, so the limit is

$$\lim_{x \to +\infty} \frac{-x}{2} = -\infty.$$ $\frac{-\infty}{2} = -\infty$ (See below.)

d. $\lim\limits_{x \to +\infty} \dfrac{2x^2 - 4x}{5x^3 - 3x + 5} = \lim\limits_{x \to +\infty} \dfrac{2x^2}{5x^3}$ Use only the highest powers top and bottom.

$$= \lim_{x \to +\infty} \frac{2}{5x}.$$

As x gets large, $2/(5x)$ gets close to zero, so the limit is

$$\lim_{x \to +\infty} \frac{2}{5x} = 0.$$ $\frac{2}{\infty} = 0$ (See below.)

e. Here we do not have a ratio of polynomials. However, we know that, as t becomes large and positive, so does $e^{0.1t}$, and hence also $e^{0.1t} - 20$. Thus,

$$\lim_{t \to +\infty} e^{0.1t} - 20 = +\infty$$ $e^{+\infty} = +\infty$ (See below.)

f. As $t \to +\infty$, the term $(3.68)^{-t} = \dfrac{1}{3.68^t}$ in the denominator, being 1 divided by a very large number, approaches zero. Hence the denominator $1 + 2.2(3.68)^{-t}$ approaches $1 + 2.2(0) = 1$ as $t \to +\infty$. Thus,

$$\lim_{t \to +\infty} \frac{80}{1 + 2.2(3.68)^{-t}} = \frac{80}{1 + 2.2(0)} = 80$$ $(3.68)^{-\infty} = 0$ (See below.)

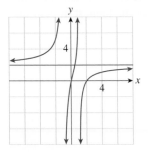

Figure 18

➡ **Before we go on...** Let's now look at the graph of the function $\dfrac{2x^2 - 4x}{x^2 - 1}$ in parts (a) and (b) of Example 5. We say that the graph of f has a **horizontal asymptote** at $y = 2$ because of the limits we have just calculated. This means that the graph approaches the horizontal line $y = 2$ far to the right or left (in this case, to both the right and left). Figure 18 shows the graph of f together with the line $y = 2$.

The graph reveals some additional interesting information: as $x \to 1^+$, $f(x) \to -\infty$, and as $x \to 1^-$, $f(x) \to +\infty$. Thus,

$$\lim_{x \to 1} f(x) \text{ does not exist.}$$

See if you can determine what happens as $x \to -1$.

If you graph the functions in parts (d) and (f) of Example 5, you will again see a horizontal asymptote. Do the limits in parts (c) and (e) show horizontal asymptotes? ∎

It is worthwhile looking again at what we did in each of the limits in Example 5:

a and **b.** We saw that $\dfrac{2x^2 - 4x}{x^2 - 1} \approx \dfrac{2x^2}{x^2}$, and then we canceled the x^2. Notice that, before we cancel, letting x approach $\pm\infty$ in the numerator and denominator yields the ratio $\dfrac{\infty}{\infty}$ which, like $\dfrac{0}{0}$, is another *indeterminate form*, and indicates to us that further work is needed—in this case cancellation—before we can write down the limit.

c. We obtained $\dfrac{-x^3 - 4x}{2x^2 - 1} \approx \dfrac{-x^3}{2x^2}$ which results in another indeterminate form, $\dfrac{-\infty}{\infty}$, as $x \to +\infty$. Cancellation of the x^2 gave us $\dfrac{-x}{2}$, resulting in the *determinate* form

$\dfrac{-\infty}{2} = -\infty$ (a very large number divided by 2 is again a very large number).

d. Here, $\dfrac{2x^2 - 4x}{5x^3 - 3x + 5} \approx \dfrac{2x^2}{5x^3} = \dfrac{2}{5x}$, and the cancellation step turns the indeterminate

form $\dfrac{\infty}{\infty}$ into the determinate form $\dfrac{2}{\infty} = 0$ (dividing 2 by a very large number yields a very small number).

e. We reasoned that e raised to a large positive number is large and positive. Putting $t = +\infty$ gives us the determinate form $e^{+\infty} = +\infty$.

f. Here we reasoned that 3.68 raised to a large *negative* number is close to zero. Putting $t = +\infty$ gives us the determinate form $3.68^{-\infty} = 1/3.68^{+\infty} = 1/\infty = 0$ (see (d)).

In parts (a)–(d) of Example 5, $f(x)$ was a **rational function**: a quotient of polynomial functions. We calculated the limit of $f(x)$ at $\pm\infty$ by ignoring all powers of x in both the numerator and denominator except for the largest. Following is a theorem that justifies this procedure.

Theorem 10.2 Evaluating the Limit of a Rational Function at $\pm\infty$

If $f(x)$ has the form

$$f(x) = \frac{c_n x^n + c_{n-1} x^{n-1} + \cdots + c_1 x + c_0}{d_m x^m + d_{m-1} x^{m-1} + \cdots + d_1 x + d_0}$$

with the c_i and d_i constants ($c_n \neq 0$ and $d_m \neq 0$), then we can calculate the limit of $f(x)$ as $x \to \pm\infty$ by ignoring all powers of x except the highest in both the numerator and denominator. Thus,

$$\lim_{x \to \pm\infty} f(x) = \lim_{x \to \pm\infty} \frac{c_n x^n}{d_m x^m}.$$

Quick Examples

(See Example 5.)

1. $\displaystyle\lim_{x \to +\infty} \frac{2x^2 - 4x}{x^2 - 1} = \lim_{x \to +\infty} \frac{2x^2}{x^2} = \lim_{x \to +\infty} 2 = 2$

2. $\displaystyle\lim_{x \to +\infty} \frac{-x^3 - 4x}{2x^2 - 1} = \lim_{x \to +\infty} \frac{-x^3}{2x^2} = \lim_{x \to +\infty} \frac{-x}{2} = -\infty$

3. $\displaystyle\lim_{x \to +\infty} \frac{2x^2 - 4x}{5x^3 - 3x + 5} = \lim_{x \to +\infty} \frac{2x^2}{5x^3} = \lim_{x \to +\infty} \frac{2}{5x} = 0$

Proof Our function $f(x)$ is a polynomial of degree n divided by a polynomial of degree m. If n happens to be larger than m, then dividing the top and bottom by the largest power x^n of x gives

$$f(x) = \frac{c_n x^n + c_{n-1} x^{n-1} + \cdots + c_1 x + c_0}{d_m x^m + d_{m-1} x^{m-1} + \cdots + d_1 x + d_0}$$

$$= \frac{c_n x^n / x^n + c_{n-1} x^{n-1} / x^n + \cdots + c_1 x / x^n + c_0 / x^n}{d_m x^m / x^n + d_{m-1} x^{m-1} / x^n + \cdots + d_1 x / x^n + d_0 / x^n}.$$

Canceling powers of x in each term and remembering that $n > m$ leaves us with

$$f(x) = \frac{c_n + c_{n-1}/x + \cdots + c_1/x^{n-1} + c_0/x^n}{d_m/x^{n-m} + d_{m-1}/x^{n-m+1} + \cdots + d_1/x^{n-1} + d_0/x^n}.$$

As $x \to \pm\infty$, all the terms shown in red approach 0, so we can ignore them in taking the limit. (The first term in the denominator happens to approach 0 as well, but we retain it for convenience.) Thus,

$$\lim_{x \to \pm\infty} f(x) = \lim_{x \to \pm\infty} \frac{c_n}{d_m/x^{n-m}} = \lim_{x \to \pm\infty} \frac{c_n x^n}{d_m x^m},$$

as required. The cases when n is smaller than m and $m = n$ are proved similarly by dividing top and bottom by the largest power of x in each case.

Some Determinate and Indeterminate Forms

The following table brings these ideas together with our observations in Example 3.

Some Determinate and Indeterminate Forms

$\dfrac{0}{0}$ and $\pm\dfrac{\infty}{\infty}$ are **indeterminate**; evaluating limits in which these arise requires simplification or further analysis.

The following are **determinate** forms for any nonzero number k:

* **NOTE** The sign gets switched in these forms if k is negative.

$$\frac{k}{0^{\pm}} = \pm\infty \qquad\qquad \frac{k}{\text{Small}} = \text{Big*} \ (\text{See Example 3.})$$

$$k(\pm\infty) = \pm\infty \qquad\qquad k \times \text{Big} = \text{Big*}$$

$$k \pm \infty = \pm\infty \qquad\qquad k \pm \text{Big} = \pm\text{Big*}$$

$$\pm\frac{\infty}{k} = \pm\infty \qquad\qquad \frac{\text{Big}}{k} = \text{Big*}$$

$$\pm\frac{k}{\infty} = 0 \qquad\qquad \frac{k}{\text{Big}} = \text{Small}$$

and, if k is positive, then

$$k^{+\infty} = +\infty \qquad\qquad k^{\text{Big positive}} = \text{Big}$$

$$k^{-\infty} = 0 \qquad\qquad k^{\text{Big negative}} = \text{Small}$$

Quick Examples

1. $\displaystyle\lim_{x \to 0} \frac{60}{2x^2} = +\infty$ $\dfrac{k}{0^+} = +\infty$

2. $\displaystyle\lim_{x \to -1^-} \frac{2x - 6}{x + 1} = +\infty$ $\dfrac{-4}{0^-} = +\infty$

3. $\displaystyle\lim_{x \to -\infty} 3x - 5 = -\infty$ $3(-\infty) - 5 = -\infty - 5 = -\infty$

4. $\displaystyle\lim_{x \to +\infty} \frac{2x}{60} = +\infty$ $\dfrac{2(\infty)}{60} = \infty$

5. $\displaystyle\lim_{x \to -\infty} \frac{60}{2x} = 0$ $\dfrac{60}{2(-\infty)} = 0$

6. $\displaystyle\lim_{x \to +\infty} \frac{60x}{2x} = 30$ $\dfrac{\infty}{\infty}$ is indeterminate but we can cancel.

7. $\displaystyle\lim_{x \to -\infty} \frac{60}{e^x - 1} = \frac{60}{0 - 1} = -60$ $e^{-\infty} = 0$

FAQs

Strategy for Evaluating Limits Algebraically

Q: *Is there a systematic way to evaluate a limit* $\lim_{x \to a} f(x)$ *algebraically?*

A: The following approach is often successful:

Case 1: *a* Is a Finite Number (Not $\pm\infty$)

1. Decide whether *f* is a closed-form function. If it is not, then find the left and right limits at the values of *x* where the function changes from one formula to another.

2. If *f* is a closed-form function, try substituting $x = a$ in the formula for $f(x)$. Then one of the following three things may happen:

   $f(a)$ is defined. Then $\lim_{x \to a} f(x) = f(a)$.

   $f(a)$ is not defined and has the indeterminate form 0/0. Try to simplify the expression for *f* to cancel one of the terms that gives 0.

   $f(a)$ is not defined and has one of the determinate forms listed above in the above table. Use the table to determine the limit as in the Quick Examples

Case 2: $a = \pm\infty$

Remember that we can use the determinate forms $k^{+\infty} = \infty$ and $k^{-\infty} = 0$ if *k* is positive. Further, if the given function is a polynomial or ratio of polynomials, use the technique of Example 5: Focus only on the highest powers of *x* and then simplify to obtain either a number *L*, in which case the limit exists and equals *L*, or one of the determinate forms $\pm\infty/k = \pm\infty$ or $\pm k/\infty = 0$.

There is another technique for evaluating certain difficult limits, called *l'Hospital's Rule*, but this uses derivatives, so we'll have to wait to discuss it until Section 11.1.

10.3 EXERCISES

▼ more advanced   ◆ challenging
Ⓣ indicates exercises that should be solved using technology

In Exercises 1–4 complete the given sentence.

1. The closed-form function $f(x) = \dfrac{1}{x-1}$ is continuous for all x except _____. HINT [See Quick Example on page 707.]

2. The closed-form function $f(x) = \dfrac{1}{x^2-1}$ is continuous for all x except _____. HINT [See Quick Example on page 707.]

3. The closed-form function $f(x) = \sqrt{x+1}$ has $x = 3$ in its domain. Therefore, $\lim_{x \to 3} \sqrt{x+1} =$ ___. HINT [See Example 1.]

4. The closed-form function $f(x) = \sqrt{x-1}$ has $x = 10$ in its domain. Therefore, $\lim_{x \to 10} \sqrt{x-1} =$ ___. HINT [See Example 1.]

In Exercises 5–20 determine if the given limit leads to a determinate or indeterminate form. Evaluate the limit if it exists, or say why if not. HINT [See Example 3 and Quick Examples on page 716.]

5. $\lim_{x \to 0} \dfrac{60}{x^4}$

6. $\lim_{x \to 0} \dfrac{2x^2}{x^2}$

7. $\lim_{x \to 0} \dfrac{x^3 - 1}{x^3}$

8. $\lim_{x \to 0} \dfrac{-2}{x^2}$

9. $\lim_{x \to -\infty} (-x^2 + 5)$

10. $\lim_{x \to 0} \dfrac{2x^2 + 4}{x}$

11. $\lim_{x \to +\infty} 4^{-x}$

12. $\lim_{x \to +\infty} \dfrac{60 + e^{-x}}{2 - e^{-x}}$

13. $\lim_{x \to 0} \dfrac{-x^3}{3x^3}$

14. $\lim_{x \to -\infty} 3x^2 + 6$

15. $\lim_{x \to -\infty} \dfrac{-x^3}{3x^6}$

16. $\lim_{x \to +\infty} \dfrac{-x^6}{3x^3}$

17. $\lim_{x \to -\infty} \dfrac{4}{-x + 2}$

18. $\lim_{x \to -\infty} e^x$

19. $\lim_{x \to -\infty} \dfrac{60}{e^x - 1}$

20. $\lim_{x \to -\infty} \dfrac{2}{2x^2 + 3}$

Calculate the limits in Exercises 21–72 algebraically. If a limit does not exist, say why.

21. $\lim_{x \to 0} (x + 1)$
HINT [See Example 1.]

22. $\lim_{x \to 0} (2x - 4)$
HINT [See Example 1.]

23. $\lim_{x \to 2} \dfrac{2 + x}{x}$

24. $\lim_{x \to -1} \dfrac{4x^2 + 1}{x}$

25. $\lim_{x \to -1} \dfrac{x + 1}{x}$

26. $\lim_{x \to 4} (x + \sqrt{x})$

27. $\lim_{x \to 8} (x - \sqrt[3]{x})$

28. $\lim_{x \to 1} \dfrac{x - 2}{x + 1}$

29. $\lim_{h \to 1} (h^2 + 2h + 1)$

30. $\lim_{h \to 0} (h^3 - 4)$

31. $\lim_{h \to 3} 2$

32. $\lim_{h \to 0} -5$

33. $\lim_{h \to 0} \dfrac{h^2}{h + h^2}$
HINT [See Example 2.]

34. $\lim_{h \to 0} \dfrac{h^2 + h}{h^2 + 2h}$
HINT [See Example 2.]

35. $\lim_{x \to 1} \dfrac{x^2 - 2x + 1}{x^2 - x}$

36. $\lim_{x \to -1} \dfrac{x^2 + 3x + 2}{x^2 + x}$

37. $\lim_{x \to 2} \dfrac{x^3 - 8}{x - 2}$

38. $\lim_{x \to -2} \dfrac{x^3 + 8}{x^2 + 3x + 2}$

39. $\lim_{x \to 0+} \dfrac{1}{x^2}$ HINT [See Example 3.]

40. $\lim_{x \to 0+} \dfrac{1}{x^2 - x}$ HINT [See Example 3.]

41. $\lim_{x \to -1} \dfrac{x^2 + 1}{x + 1}$

42. $\lim_{x \to -1^-} \dfrac{x^2 + 1}{x + 1}$

43. $\lim_{x \to -2+} \dfrac{x^2 + 8}{x^2 + 3x + 2}$

44. $\lim_{x \to -1} \dfrac{x^2 + 3x}{x^2 + x}$

45. $\lim_{x \to -2} \dfrac{x^2 + 8}{x^2 + 3x + 2}$

46. $\lim_{x \to -1} \dfrac{x^2 + 3x}{x^2 + 2x + 1}$

47. $\lim_{x \to 2} \dfrac{x^2 + 8}{x^2 - 4x + 4}$

48. $\lim_{x \to -1} \dfrac{x^2 + 3x}{x^2 + 3x + 2}$

49. $\lim_{x \to +\infty} \dfrac{3x^2 + 10x - 1}{2x^2 - 5x}$ HINT [See Example 5.]

50. $\lim_{x \to +\infty} \dfrac{6x^2 + 5x + 100}{3x^2 - 9}$ HINT [See Example 5.]

51. $\lim_{x \to +\infty} \dfrac{x^5 - 1{,}000x^4}{2x^5 + 10{,}000}$

52. $\lim_{x \to +\infty} \dfrac{x^6 + 3{,}000x^3 + 1{,}000{,}000}{2x^6 + 1{,}000x^3}$

53. $\lim_{x \to +\infty} \dfrac{10x^2 + 300x + 1}{5x + 2}$

54. $\lim_{x \to +\infty} \dfrac{2x^4 + 20x^3}{1{,}000x^3 + 6}$

55. $\lim_{x \to +\infty} \dfrac{10x^2 + 300x + 1}{5x^3 + 2}$

56. $\lim_{x \to +\infty} \dfrac{2x^4 + 20x^3}{1{,}000x^6 + 6}$

57. $\lim_{x \to -\infty} \dfrac{3x^2 + 10x - 1}{2x^2 - 5x}$

58. $\lim_{x \to -\infty} \dfrac{6x^2 + 5x + 100}{3x^2 - 9}$

59. $\lim_{x \to -\infty} \dfrac{x^5 - 1{,}000x^4}{2x^5 + 10{,}000}$

60. $\lim_{x \to -\infty} \dfrac{x^6 + 3000x^3 + 1{,}000{,}000}{2x^6 + 1{,}000x^3}$

61. $\lim_{x \to -\infty} \dfrac{10x^2 + 300x + 1}{5x + 2}$

62. $\lim_{x \to -\infty} \dfrac{2x^4 + 20x^3}{1{,}000x^3 + 6}$

63. $\lim_{x \to -\infty} \dfrac{10x^2 + 300x + 1}{5x^3 + 2}$

64. $\lim_{x \to -\infty} \dfrac{2x^4 + 20x^3}{1{,}000x^6 + 6}$

65. $\lim_{x \to +\infty} (4e^{-3x} + 12)$

66. $\lim_{x \to +\infty} \dfrac{2}{5 - 5.3e^{-3x}}$

67. $\lim_{t \to +\infty} \dfrac{2}{5 - 5.3(3^{3t})}$

68. $\lim_{t \to +\infty} (4.1 - 2e^{3t})$

69. $\lim\limits_{t \to +\infty} \dfrac{2^{3t}}{1 + 5.3e^{-t}}$

70. $\lim\limits_{x \to -\infty} \dfrac{4.2}{2 - 3^{2x}}$

71. $\lim\limits_{x \to -\infty} \dfrac{-3^{2x}}{2 + e^x}$

72. $\lim\limits_{x \to +\infty} \dfrac{2^{-3x}}{1 + 5.3e^{-x}}$

In each of Exercises 73–80, find all points of discontinuity of the given function. HINT [See Example 4.]

73. $f(x) = \begin{cases} x + 2 & \text{if } x < 0 \\ 2x - 1 & \text{if } x \geq 0 \end{cases}$

74. $g(x) = \begin{cases} 1 - x & \text{if } x \leq 1 \\ x - 1 & \text{if } x > 1 \end{cases}$

75. $g(x) = \begin{cases} x + 2 & \text{if } x < 0 \\ 2x + 2 & \text{if } 0 \leq x < 2 \\ x^2 + 2 & \text{if } x \geq 2 \end{cases}$

76. $f(x) = \begin{cases} 1 - x & \text{if } x \leq 1 \\ x + 2 & \text{if } 1 < x < 3 \\ x^2 - 4 & \text{if } x \geq 3 \end{cases}$

77. ▼ $h(x) = \begin{cases} x + 2 & \text{if } x < 0 \\ 0 & \text{if } x = 0 \\ 2x + 2 & \text{if } x > 0 \end{cases}$

78. ▼ $h(x) = \begin{cases} 1 - x & \text{if } x < 1 \\ 1 & \text{if } x = 1 \\ x + 2 & \text{if } x > 1 \end{cases}$

79. ▼ $f(x) = \begin{cases} 1/x & \text{if } x < 0 \\ x & \text{if } 0 \leq x \leq 2 \\ 2^{x-1} & \text{if } x > 2 \end{cases}$

80. ▼ $f(x) = \begin{cases} x^3 + 2 & \text{if } x \leq -1 \\ x^2 & \text{if } -1 < x < 0 \\ x & \text{if } x \geq 0 \end{cases}$

APPLICATIONS

81. *Employment in Mexico* The number N of workers employed in manufacturing jobs in Mexico between 1995 and 2004 can be modeled by

$$N(t) = \begin{cases} 0.22t + 3 & \text{if } 0 \leq t \leq 5 \\ -0.15t + 4.85 & \text{if } 5 < t \leq 9 \end{cases} \text{ million jobs}$$

where t is time in years since 1995.[12]

a. Compute $\lim\limits_{t \to 5^-} N(t)$ and $\lim\limits_{t \to 5^+} N(t)$, and interpret each answer. HINT [See Example 4.]

b. Is the function N continuous at $t = 5$? Did the number of workers employed in manufacturing jobs in Mexico experience any abrupt changes during the period 1995–2004?

82. *Mortgage Delinquencies* The percentage P of borrowers in the highest risk category who were delinquent on their payments between 2001 and 2007 can be approximated by

$$P = \begin{cases} -1.8t + 9.7 & \text{if } 0 \leq t \leq 3 \\ 2t - 1.7 & \text{if } 3 < t \leq 6 \end{cases} \text{ percent}$$

where t is time in years since 2001.[13]

a. Compute $\lim\limits_{t \to 3^-} P(t)$ and $\lim\limits_{t \to 3^+} P(t)$, and interpret each answer.

b. Is the function P continuous at $t = 3$? Did the percentage of borrowers who were delinquent on their payments experience any abrupt changes during the period 2001–2007?

83. *Movie Advertising* Movie expenditures, in billions of dollars, on advertising in newspapers from 1995 to 2004 can be approximated by

$$f(t) = \begin{cases} 0.04t + 0.33 & \text{if } t \leq 4 \\ -0.01t + 1.2 & \text{if } t > 4 \end{cases}$$

where t is time in years since 1995.[14]

a. Compute $\lim\limits_{t \to 4^-} f(t)$ and $\lim\limits_{t \to 4^+} f(t)$, and interpret each answer. HINT [See Example 4.]

b. Is the function f continuous at $t = 4$? What does the answer tell you about movie advertising expenditures?

84. *Movie Advertising* The percentage of movie advertising as a share of newspapers' total advertising revenue from 1995 to 2004 can be approximated by

$$p(t) = \begin{cases} -0.07t + 6.0 & \text{if } t \leq 4 \\ 0.3t + 17.0 & \text{if } t > 4 \end{cases}$$

where t is time in years since 1995.[15]

a. Compute $\lim\limits_{t \to 4^-} p(t)$ and $\lim\limits_{t \to 4^+} p(t)$, and interpret each answer. HINT [See Example 4.]

b. Is the function p continuous at $t = 4$? What does the answer tell you about newspaper revenues?

85. *Law Enforcement* The cost of fighting crime in the United States increased steadily in the period 1982–1999. Total spending on police and courts can be approximated, respectively, by[16]

$$\begin{aligned} P(t) &= 1.745t + 29.84 \text{ billion dollars} & (2 \leq t \leq 19) \\ C(t) &= 1.097t + 10.65 \text{ billion dollars} & (2 \leq t \leq 19) \end{aligned}$$

where t is time in years since 1980. Compute $\lim\limits_{t \to +\infty} \dfrac{P(t)}{C(t)}$ to two decimal places and interpret the result. HINT [See Example 5.]

86. *Law Enforcement* Refer to Exercise 85. Total spending on police, courts, and prisons can be approximated, respectively, by[17]

$$\begin{aligned} P(t) &= 1.745t + 29.84 \text{ billion dollars} & (2 \leq t \leq 19) \\ C(t) &= 1.097t + 10.65 \text{ billion dollars} & (2 \leq t \leq 19) \\ J(t) &= 1.919t + 12.36 \text{ billion dollars} & (2 \leq t \leq 19) \end{aligned}$$

where t is time in years since 2001.[13]

[13] Ibid.

[14] Model by the authors. Source for data: Newspaper Association of America Business Analysis and Research/*New York Times*, May 16, 2005.

[15] Ibid.

[16] Spending is adjusted for inflation and shown in 1999 dollars. Models are based on a linear regression. Source for data: Bureau of Justice Statistics/*New York Times*, February 11, 2002, p. A14.

[17] Ibid.

where t is time in years since 1980. Compute $\lim_{t \to +\infty} \dfrac{P(t)}{P(t) + C(t) + J(t)}$ to two decimal places and interpret the result.

87. Casino Revenues Annual revenues in 1996–2006 from slot machines and video poker machines at **Foxwoods** casino in Connecticut can be modeled by

$$R(t) = 825 - 240e^{-0.4t} \text{ million dollars} \quad (0 \le t \le 10)$$

where t is time in years since 1996.[18] If we extrapolate this model into the indefinite future, compute and interpret $\lim_{t \to +\infty} R(t)$. HINT [See Quick Example on page 716.]

88. Casino Revenues Annual revenues in 1996–2006 from slot machines and video poker machines at the **Mohegan Sun** casino in Connecticut can be modeled by

$$R(t) = 1,260 - 1,030e^{-0.1t} \text{ million dollars} \quad (0 \le t \le 10)$$

where t is time in years since 1996.[19] If we extrapolate this model into the indefinite future, compute and interpret $\lim_{t \to +\infty} R(t)$. HINT [See Quick Example on page 716.]

Foreign Trade Annual U.S. imports from China in the years 1996 through 2003 can be approximated by

$$I(t) = t^2 + 3.5t + 50 \quad (1 \le t \le 8)$$

billion dollars, where t represents time in years since 1995. Annual U.S. exports to China in the same years can be approximated by

$$E(t) = 0.4t^2 + 1.6t + 14 \quad (0 \le t \le 10)$$

billion dollars.[20] *Exercises 89 and 90 are based on these models.*

89. Assuming that the trends shown in the above models continue indefinitely, calculate the limits

$$\lim_{t \to +\infty} I(t) \text{ and } \lim_{t \to +\infty} \dfrac{I(t)}{E(t)}$$

algebraically, interpret your answers, and comment on the results. HINT [See Example 5.]

90. Repeat Exercise 89, this time calculating

$$\lim_{t \to +\infty} E(t) \text{ and } \lim_{t \to +\infty} \dfrac{E(t)}{I(t)} \quad \text{HINT [See Example 5.]}$$

91. ▼ **Acquisition of Language** The percentage $p(t)$ of children who can speak in at least single words by the age of t months can be approximated by the equation[21]

$$p(t) = 100\left(\dfrac{1 - 12,200}{t^{4.48}}\right). \quad (t \ge 8.5)$$

Calculate $\lim_{t \to +\infty} p(t)$ and interpret the results. HINT [See Example 5(e), (f).]

92. ▼ **Acquisition of Language** The percentage $q(t)$ of children who can speak in sentences of five or more words by the age of t months can be approximated by the equation[22]

$$q(t) = 100\left(1 - \dfrac{5.27 \times 10^{17}}{t^{12}}\right). \quad (t \ge 30)$$

If p is the function referred to in the preceding exercise, calculate $\lim_{t \to +\infty}[p(t) - q(t)]$ and interpret the result. HINT [See Example 5(e), (f).]

COMMUNICATION AND REASONING EXERCISES

93. Describe the algebraic method of evaluating limits as discussed in this section and give at least one disadvantage of this method.

94. What is a closed-form function? What can we say about such functions?

95. ▼ Your friend Karin tells you that $f(x) = 1/(x - 2)^2$ cannot be a closed-form function because it is not continuous at $x = 2$. Comment on her assertion.

96. ▼ Give an example of a function f specified by means of algebraic formulas such that the domain of f consists of all real numbers and f is not continuous at $x = 2$. Is f a closed-form function?

97. Give examples of two limits that lead to two different indeterminate forms, but where both limits exist.

98. Give examples of two limits; one that leads to a determinate form and another that leads to an indeterminate form, but where neither limit exists.

99. ▼ What is wrong with the following statement? If $f(x)$ is specified algebraically and $f(a)$ is defined, then $\lim_{x \to a} f(x)$ exists and equals $f(a)$.

100. ▼ What is wrong with the following statement? $\lim_{x \to -2} \dfrac{x^2 - 4}{x + 2}$ does not exist because substituting $x = -2$ yields $0/0$, which is undefined.

101. ▼ Give the formula for a function that is continuous everywhere except at two points.

102. ▼ Give the formula for a function that is continuous everywhere except at three points.

103. ◆ **The Indeterminate Form** $\infty - \infty$ An indeterminate form not mentioned in Section 10.3 is $\infty - \infty$. Give examples of three limits that lead to this indeterminate form, and where the first limit exists and equals 5, where the second limit diverges to $+\infty$, and where the third exists and equals -5.

104. ◆ **The Indeterminate Form** 1^∞ An indeterminate form not mentioned in Section 10.3 is 1^∞. Give examples of three limits that lead to this indeterminate form, and where the first limit exists and equals 1, where the second limit exists and equals e, and where the third diverges to $+\infty$. HINT [For the third, consider modifying the second.]

---

[18] Source for data: Connecticut Division of Special Revenue/*New York Times*, Sept. 23, 2007, p. C1.

[19] Ibid.

[20] Based on quadratic regression using data from the U.S. Census Bureau Foreign Trade Division Web site www.census.gov/foreign-trade/sitc1/ as of December 2004.

[21] The model is the authors' and is based on data presented in the article *The Emergence of Intelligence* by William H. Calvin, *Scientific American*, October, 1994, pp. 101–107.

[22] Ibid.

10.4 Average Rate of Change

Calculus is the mathematics of change, inspired largely by observation of continuously changing quantities around us in the real world. As an example, the New York metro area consumer confidence index C decreased from 100 points in January 2000 to 80 points in January 2002.[23] As we saw in Chapter 1, the **change** in this index can be measured as the difference:

$$\Delta C = \text{Second value} - \text{First value} = 80 - 100 = -20 \text{ points}$$

(The fact that the confidence index decreased is reflected in the negative sign of the change.) The kind of question we will concentrate on is *how fast* the confidence index was dropping. Because C decreased by 20 points in 2 years, we say it averaged a $20/2 = 10$ point drop each year. (It actually dropped less than 10 points the first year and more the second, giving an average drop of 10 points each year.)

Alternatively, we might want to measure this rate in points per month rather than points per year. Because C decreased by 20 points in 24 months, it went down at an average rate of $20/24 \approx 0.833$ points per month.

In both cases, we obtained the average rate of change by dividing the change by the corresponding length of time:

$$\text{Average rate of change} = \frac{\text{Change in } C}{\text{Change in time}} = \frac{-20}{2} = -10 \text{ points per year}$$

$$\text{Average rate of change} = \frac{\text{Change in } C}{\text{Change in time}} = \frac{-20}{24} \approx -0.833 \text{ points per month}$$

Average Rate of Change of a Function Numerically and Graphically

LWA-Dann Tardif/CORBIS

EXAMPLE 1 Standard and Poor's 500

The following table lists the approximate value of Standard and Poor's 500 stock market index (S&P) during the period 2000–2008* ($t = 0$ represents 2000):

t (year)	0	1	2	3	4	5	6	7	8
$S(t)$ S&P 500 Index (points)	1,450	1,200	950	1,000	1,100	1,200	1,250	1,500	1,300

a. What was the average rate of change in the S&P over the 2-year period 2005–2007 (the period $5 \le t \le 7$ or [5, 7] in interval notation); over the 4-year period 2000–2004 (the period $0 \le t \le 4$ or [0, 4]); and over the period [1, 5]?

b. Graph the values shown in the table. How are the rates of change reflected in the graph?

---

*The values are approximate values midway through the given year. Source: www.finance.google.com.

---

[23] Figures are approximate. Source: Siena College Research Institute/*New York Times*, February 10, 2002, p. LI.

Solution

a. During the 2-year period [5, 7], the S&P changed as follows:

Start of the period ($t = 5$):	$S(5) = 1{,}200$
End of the period ($t = 7$):	$S(7) = 1{,}500$

Change during the period [5, 7]: $S(7) - S(5) = 300$

Thus, the S&P increased by 300 points in 2 years, giving an average rate of change of $300/2 = 150$ points per year. We can write the calculation this way:

$$\text{Average rate of change of } S = \frac{\text{Change in } S}{\text{Change in } t}$$

$$= \frac{\Delta S}{\Delta t}$$

$$= \frac{S(7) - S(5)}{7 - 5}$$

$$= \frac{1{,}500 - 1{,}200}{7 - 5} = \frac{300}{2} = 150 \text{ points per year}$$

Interpreting the result: During the period [5, 7] (that is, 2005–2007), the S&P increased at an average rate of 150 points per year.

Similarly, the average rate of change during the period [0, 4] was

$$\text{Average rate of change of } S = \frac{\Delta S}{\Delta t} = \frac{S(4) - S(0)}{4 - 0} = \frac{1{,}100 - 1{,}450}{4 - 0}$$

$$= -\frac{350}{4} = -87.5 \text{ points per year.}$$

Interpreting the result: During the period [0, 4] the S&P *decreased* at an average rate of 87.5 points per year.

Finally, during the period [1, 5], the average rate of change was

$$\text{Average rate of change of } S = \frac{\Delta S}{\Delta t} = \frac{S(5) - S(1)}{5 - 1} = \frac{1{,}200 - 1{,}200}{5 - 1}$$

$$= \frac{0}{4} = 0 \text{ points per year.}$$

Interpreting the result: During the period [1, 5] the average rate of change of the S&P was zero points per year (even though its value did fluctuate during that period).

b. In Chapter 1, we saw that the rate of change of a quantity that changes linearly with time is measured by the slope of its graph. However, the S&P index does not change linearly with time. Figure 19 shows the data plotted two different ways: (a) as a bar chart and (b) as a piecewise linear graph. Bar charts are more commonly used in the media, but Figure 19(b) illustrates the changing index more clearly.

Figure 19(a)

Figure 19(b)

We saw in part (a) that the average rate of change of S over the interval $[5, 7]$ is the ratio

$$\text{Rate of change of } S = \frac{\Delta S}{\Delta t} = \frac{\text{Change in } S}{\text{Change in } t} = \frac{S(7) - S(5)}{7 - 5}.$$

Notice that this rate of change is also the slope of the line through P and Q shown in Figure 20, and we can estimate this slope directly from the graph as shown.

Figure 20

Average Rate of Change as Slope: The average rate of change of the S&P over the interval $[5, 7]$ is the slope of the line passing through the points on the graph where $t = 5$ and $t = 7$.

Similarly, the average rates of change of the S&P over the intervals $[0, 4]$ and $[1, 5]$ are the slopes of the lines through pairs of corresponding points.

Here is the formal definition of the average rate of change of a function over an interval.

Change and Average Rate of Change of *f* over [*a, b*]: Difference Quotient

The **change** in $f(x)$ over the interval $[a, b]$ is

Change in $f = \Delta f$

$\qquad\quad = $ Second value $-$ First value

$\qquad\quad = f(b) - f(a).$

The **average rate of change** of $f(x)$ over the interval $[a, b]$ is

$$\text{Average rate of change of } f = \frac{\text{Change in } f}{\text{Change in } x}$$

$$= \frac{\Delta f}{\Delta x} = \frac{f(b) - f(a)}{b - a}$$

$$= \text{Slope of line through points } P \text{ and } Q$$
$$\text{(see figure).}$$

Average rate of change $=$ Slope of PQ

We also call this average rate of change the **difference quotient** of f over the interval $[a, b]$. (It is the *quotient* of the *differences* $f(b) - f(a)$ and $b - a$.) A line through two points of a graph like P and Q is called a **secant line** of the graph.

Units

The units of the change in f are the units of $f(x)$.
The units of the average rate of change of f are units of $f(x)$ per unit of x.

Quick Example

If $f(3) = -1$ billion dollars, $f(5) = 0.5$ billion dollars, and x is measured in years, then the change and average rate of change of f over the interval $[3, 5]$ are given by

Change in $f = f(5) - f(3) = 0.5 - (-1) = 1.5$ billion dollars

$$\text{Average rate of change} = \frac{f(5) - f(3)}{5 - 3} = \frac{0.5 - (-1)}{2}$$

$$= 0.75 \text{ billion dollars/year.}$$

Alternative Formula: Average Rate of Change of *f* over [*a, a + h*]

(Replace b above by $a + h$.) The average rate of change of f over the interval $[a, a + h]$ is

$$\text{Average rate of change of } f = \frac{f(a + h) - f(a)}{h}.$$

In Example 1 we saw that the average rate of change of a quantity can be estimated directly from a graph. Here is an example that further illustrates the graphical approach.

EXAMPLE 2 **Freon Production**

Figure 21 shows a function we looked at in Section 1.1: Let $f(t)$ be the number of tons of ozone-layer damaging Freon 22 (chlorodifluoromethane) produced in year t in developing countries, where $t = 0$ represents the year 2000.*

Figure 21

a. Use the graph to estimate the average rate of change of $f(t)$ with respect to t over the interval [4, 8] and interpret the result.

b. Over which 2-year period(s) was the average rate of change of Freon production the greatest?

c. Multiple choice: For the period of time under consideration, Freon production was

(**A**) increasing at a faster and faster rate.
(**B**) increasing at a slower and slower rate.
(**C**) decreasing at a faster and faster rate.
(**D**) decreasing at a slower and slower rate.

Solution

a. The average rate of change of f over the interval [4, 8] is given by the slope of the line through the points P and Q shown in Figure 22.

Figure 22

---

*Source: *New York Times*, February 23, 2007, p. C1.

From the figure,

$$\text{Average rate of change of } f = \frac{\Delta f}{\Delta t} = \text{slope } PQ \approx \frac{400 - 200}{8 - 4} = \frac{200}{4} = 50.$$

Thus, the rate of change of f over the interval $[4, 8]$ is approximately 50.

Q : *How do we interpret the result?*

A : A clue is given by the units of the average rate of change: units of f per unit of t. The units of f are tons of Freon and the units of t are years. Thus, the average rate of change of f is measured in tons of Freon per year, and we can now interpret the result as follows:

Interpreting the average rate of change: Annual production of Freon was increasing at an average rate of 50 tons of Freon per year from 2004 to 2008.

---

b. The rates of change of Freon production over successive 2-year periods are given by the slopes of the individual line segments that make up the graph in Figure 21. Thus, the greatest average rate of change in a single two-year period corresponds to the segment(s) with the largest slope. If you look at the figure, you will notice that the segment corresponding to $[8, 10]$ is the steepest. Thus, the average rate of change of Freon production was largest over the 2-year period from 2008 to 2010.

c. Looking again at the figure, notice that the graph rises as we go from left to right; that is, the value of the function (Freon production) is increasing with increasing t. At the same time, the fact that the curve bends up (is concave up) with increasing t tells us that the successive slopes get steeper, and so the average rates of change increase as well (Choice (A)).

➡ **Before we go on...** Notice in Example 2 that we do not get exact answers from a graph; the best we can do is *estimate* the rates of change: Was the exact answer to part (a) closer to 49 or 51? Two people can reasonably disagree about results read from a graph, and you should bear this in mind when you check the answers to the exercises. ■

Perhaps the most sophisticated way to compute the average rate of change of a quantity is through the use of a mathematical formula or model for the quantity in question.

Average Rate of Change of a Function Using Algebraic Data

EXAMPLE 3 Average Rate of Change from a Formula

You are a commodities trader and you monitor the price of gold on the New York Spot Market very closely during an active morning. Suppose you find that the price of an ounce of gold can be approximated by the function

$$G(t) = -8t^2 + 144t + 150 \text{ dollars} \qquad (7.5 \le t \le 10.5)$$

where t is time in hours. (See Figure 23. $t = 8$ represents 8:00 AM.)

Source: www.kitco.com August 15, 2008

$$G(t) = -8t^2 + 144t + 150$$

Figure 23

using Technology

See the Technology Guides at the end of the chapter for detailed instructions on how to calculate the average rate of change of the function in Example 3 using a TI-83/84 Plus or Excel. Here is an outline:

TI-83/84 Plus
$Y_1 = -8X^2 + 144X + 150$
Home screen: $(Y_1(9.5) - Y_1(8))/(9.5 - 8)$
[More details on page 776.]

Excel
Enter the headings t, $G(t)$, Rate of Change in A1–C1
t-values 8, 9.5 in A2–A3
$= -8*A2^2 + 144*A2 + 150$
in B2 and copy down to B3
$= (B3-B2)/(A3-A2)$ in C2.
[More details on page 778.]

Looking at the graph on the right, we can see that the price of gold rose rather rapidly at the beginning of the time period, but by $t = 8.5$ the rise had slowed, until the market faltered and the price began to fall more and more rapidly toward the end of the period. What was the average rate of change of the price of gold over the $1\frac{1}{2}$-hour period starting at 8:00 AM (the interval [8, 9.5] on the t-axis)?

Solution We have

$$\text{Average rate of change of } G \text{ over } [8, 9.5] = \frac{\Delta G}{\Delta t} = \frac{G(9.5) - G(8)}{9.5 - 8}.$$

From the formula for $G(t)$, we find

$$G(9.5) = -8(9.5)^2 + 144(9.5) + 150 = 796$$
$$G(8) = -8(8)^2 + 144(8) + 150 = 790.$$

Thus, the average rate of change of G is given by

$$\frac{G(9.5) - G(8)}{9.5 - 8} = \frac{796 - 790}{1.5} = \frac{6}{1.5} = \$4 \text{ per hour.}$$

In other words, the price of gold was increasing at an average rate of $4 per hour over the given $1\frac{1}{2}$-hour period.

EXAMPLE 4 Rates of Change over Shorter Intervals

Continuing with Example 3, use technology to compute the average rate of change of

$$G(t) = -8t^2 + 144t + 150 \qquad (7.5 \le t \le 10.5)$$

over the intervals [8, 8 + h], where $h = 1, 0.1, 0.01, 0.001$, and 0.0001. What do the answers tell you about the price of gold?

Solution

We use the alternative formula

$$\text{Average rate of change of } G \text{ over } [a, a+h] = \frac{G(a+h) - G(a)}{h},$$

so

$$\text{Average rate of change of } G \text{ over } [8, 8+h] = \frac{G(8+h) - G(8)}{h}.$$

Let us calculate this average rate of change for some of the values of h listed:

$h = 1$: $G(8+h) = G(8+1) = G(9) = -8(9)^2 + 144(9) + 150 = 798$
$G(8) = -8(8)^2 + 144(8) + 150 = 790$

$$\text{Average rate of change of } G = \frac{G(9) - G(8)}{1} = \frac{798 - 790}{1} = 8$$

$h = 0.1$: $G(8+h) = G(8+0.1) = G(8.1) = -8(8.1)^2 + 144(8.1) + 150 = 791.52$
$G(8) = -8(8)^2 + 144(8) + 150 = 790$

$$\text{Average rate of change of } G = \frac{G(8.1) - G(8)}{0.1} = \frac{791.52 - 790}{0.1} = 15.2$$

$h = 0.01$: $G(8+h) = G(8+0.01) = G(8.01) = -8(8.01)^2 + 144(8.01) + 150$
$= 790.1592$
$G(8) = -8(8)^2 + 144(8) + 150 = 790$

$$\text{Average rate of change of } G = \frac{G(8.01) - G(8)}{0.01} = \frac{790.1592 - 790}{0.01}$$
$$= 15.92$$

Continuing in this way, we get the values in the following table:

h	1	0.1	0.01	0.001	0.0001
Ave. Rate of Change $\dfrac{G(8+h) - G(8)}{h}$	8	15.2	15.92	15.992	15.9992

Each value is an average rate of change of G. For example, the value corresponding to $h = 0.01$ is 15.92, which tells us:

Over the interval $[8, 8.01]$ *the price of gold was increasing at an average rate of* $15.92 *per hour.*

In other words, during the first one-hundredth of an hour (or 36 seconds) starting at $t = 8:00$ AM, the price of gold was increasing at an average rate of $15.92 per hour. Put another way, in those 36 seconds, the price of gold increased at a rate that, if continued, would have produced an increase of $15.92 in the price of gold during the next hour. We will return to this example at the beginning of Section 10.5.

using Technology

Example 4 is the kind of example where the use of technology can make a huge difference. See the Technology Guides at the end of the chapter to find out how to do these computations almost effortlessly using a TI-83/84 Plus or Excel. Here is an outline:

TI-83/84 Plus
$Y_1 = -8X^2 + 144X + 150$
Home screen:
$(Y_1(8+1) - Y_1(8))/1$
$(Y_1(8+0.1) - Y_1(8))/0.1$
$(Y_1(8+0.01) -$
$Y_1(8))/0.01$ etc.
[More details on page 776.]

Excel
Headings a, h, t, G(t), Rate of Change in A1–E1
8 in A2, 1 in B2,
=A2 in C2, =A2+B2 in C3
=-8*C2^2+144*C2+150 in D2; copy down to D3
= (D3-D2)/(C3-C2) in E2
[More details on page 778.]

Recognizing When and How to Compute the Average Rate of Change and How to Interpret the Answer

Q: *How do I know, by looking at the wording of a problem, that it is asking for an average rate of change?*

A: If a problem does not ask for an average rate of change directly, it might do so indirectly, as in "On average, how fast is quantity q increasing?"

Q: *If I know that a problem calls for computing an average rate of change, how should I compute it? By hand or using technology?*

A: All the computations can be done by hand, but when hand calculations are not called for, using technology might save time.

Q: *Lots of problems ask us to "interpret" the answer. How do I do that for questions involving average rates of change?*

A: The *units* of the average rate of change are often the key to interpreting the results:

The units of the average rate of change of f(x) are units of f(x) per unit of x.

Thus, for instance, if $f(x)$ is the cost, in dollars, of a trip of x miles in length, and the average rate of change of f is calculated to be 10, then the units of the average rate of change are dollars per mile, and so we can interpret the answer by saying that the cost of a trip rises an average of $10 for each additional mile.

10.4 **EXERCISES**

▼ more advanced   ◆ challenging
T indicates exercises that should be solved using technology

In Exercises 1–18, calculate the average rate of change of the given function over the given interval. Where appropriate, specify the units of measurement. HINT [See Example 1.]

1.

x	0	1	2	3
f(x)	3	5	2	−1

Interval: [1, 3]

2.

x	0	1	2	3
f(x)	−1	3	2	1

Interval: [0, 2]

3.

x	−3	−2	−1	0
f(x)	−2.1	0	−1.5	0

Interval: [−3, −1]

4.

x	−2	−1	0	1
f(x)	−1.5	−0.5	4	6.5

Interval: [−1, 1]

5.

t (months)	2	4	6
R(t) ($ millions)	20.2	24.3	20.1

Interval: [2, 6]

6.

x (kilos)	1	2	3
C(x) (£)	2.20	3.30	4.00

Interval: [1, 3]

7.

p ($)	5.00	5.50	6.00
q(p) (items)	400	300	150

Interval: [5, 5.5]

8.

t (hours)	0	0.1	0.2
D(t) (miles)	0	3	6

Interval: [0.1, 0.2]

9.

Apple Computer Stock Price ($)

Dec Jan Feb Mar Apr May
2003   2004

Interval: [2, 5]
HINT [See Example 2.]

10.

Cisco Systems Stock Price ($)

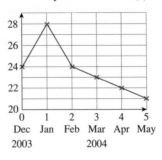

Dec Jan Feb Mar Apr May
2003   2004

Interval: [1, 5]
HINT [See Example 2.]

11.

Unemployment (%)

Budget deficit (% of GNP)

Interval: [0, 4]

12.

Inflation (%)

Budget deficit (% of GNP)

Interval: [0, 4]

13. $f(x) = x^2 - 3$; $[1, 3]$ HINT [See Example 3.]

14. $f(x) = 2x^2 + 4$; $[-1, 2]$ HINT [See Example 3.]

15. $f(x) = 2x + 4$; $[-2, 0]$

16. $f(x) = \dfrac{1}{x}$; $[1, 4]$

17. $f(x) = \dfrac{x^2}{2} + \dfrac{1}{x}$; $[2, 3]$ **18.** $f(x) = 3x^2 - \dfrac{x}{2}$; $[3, 4]$

In Exercises 19–24, calculate the average rate of change of the given function f over the intervals [a, a + h] where h = 1, 0.1, 0.01, 0.001, and 0.0001. (Technology is recommended for the cases h = 0.01, 0.001, and 0.0001.) HINT [See Example 4.]

19. $f(x) = 2x^2$; $a = 0$ **20.** $f(x) = \dfrac{x^2}{2}$; $a = 1$

21. $f(x) = \dfrac{1}{x}$; $a = 2$ **22.** $f(x) = \dfrac{2}{x}$; $a = 1$

23. $f(x) = x^2 + 2x$; $a = 3$ **24.** $f(x) = 3x^2 - 2x$; $a = 0$

APPLICATIONS

25. World Military Expenditure The following table shows total military and arms trade expenditure in 1994, 1998, and 2006 ($t = 0$ represents 2000).[24]

---

[24] Source: www.globalissues.org/Geopolitics/ArmsTrade/Spending.asp.

Year t	−6	−2	6
Military Expenditure $C(t)$ ($ billion)	900	800	1,200

Compute and interpret the average rate of change of $C(t)$ **(a)** over the period 1994–2006 (that is, $[-6, 6]$), and **(b)** over the period $[-2, 6]$. Be sure to state the units of measurement. HINT [See Example 1.]

26. Education Expenditure The following table shows the percentage of the U.S. Discretionary Budget allocated to education in 2003, 2005, and 2009 ($t = 0$ represents 2000).[25]

Year t	3	5	9
Percentage $P(t)$	6.8	7	6.2

Compute and interpret the average rate of change of $P(t)$ **(a)** over the period 2003–2009 (that is, $[3, 9]$), and **(b)** over the period $[5, 9]$. Be sure to state the units of measurement. HINT [See Example 1.]

27. Oil Production in Mexico The following table shows approximate daily oil production by **Pemex**, Mexico's national oil company, for 2001–2009 ($t = 1$ represents the start of 2001):[26]

t (year since 2000)	1	2	3	4	5	6	7	8	9
$P(t)$ (million barrels)	3.1	3.3	3.4	3.4	3.4	3.3	3.2	3.1	3.0

a. Compute the average rate of change of $P(t)$ over the period 2002–2007. Interpret the result. HINT [See Example 1.]
b. Which of the following is true? From 2001 to 2008, the one-year average rates of change of oil production by **Pemex**

(A) increased in value
(B) decreased in value
(C) never increased in value
(D) never decreased in value
HINT [See Example 2.]

28. Oil Imports from Mexico The following table shows U.S. daily oil imports from Mexico, for 2000–2008 ($t = 0$ represents the start of 2000):[27]

t (year since 2000)	0	1	2	3	4	5	6	7	8
$I(t)$ (million barrels)	1.4	1.35	1.5	1.55	1.6	1.5	1.5	1.5	1.2

---

[25] Ibid.

[26] Figures are approximate, and 2008–2009 figures are projections by the Department of Energy. Source: Energy Information Administration/Pemex (http://www.eia.doe.gov).

[27] Ibid.

a. Use the data in the table to compute the average rate of change of $I(t)$ over the period 2001–2006. Interpret the result.

b. Which of the following is true? From 2000 to 2003, the one-year rate of change of oil imports from Mexico

   (A) increased in value

   (B) decreased in value

   (C) never increased in value

   (D) never decreased in value

29. Subprime Mortgages The following graph shows the approximate percentage $P(t)$ of mortgages issued in the U.S. that are subprime (normally classified as risky):[28]

Subprime mortgages

a. Use the graph to estimate, to one decimal place, the average rate of change of $P(t)$ with respect to t over the interval [0, 6] and interpret the result.

b. Over which 2-year period(s) was the average rate of change of $P(t)$ the greatest? HINT [See Example 2.]

30. Subprime Mortgage Debt The following graph shows the approximate value $V(t)$ of subprime (normally classified as risky) mortgage debt outstanding in the United States:[29]

Subprime debt outstanding

a. Use the graph to estimate, to one decimal place, the average rate of change of $V(t)$ with respect to t over the interval [2, 6] and interpret the result.

b. Over which 2-year period(s) was the average rate of change of $V(t)$ the least? HINT [See Example 2.]

---

[28] Sources: Mortgage Bankers Association, UBS.

[29] 2008 figure is an estimate. Source: www.data360.org/dataset .aspx?Data_Set_Id=9549.

31. iPhone Sales The following graph shows approximate **Apple** iPhone sales from the 2nd quarter in 2007 through the second quarter in 2008 ($t = 2$ represents the start of the second quarter of 2007):[30]

iPhone sales (thousands)

During which 2-quarter interval(s) was the average rate of change of $S(t)$ **(a)** greatest **(b)** least? Interpret your answers by referring to the rates of change. HINT [See Example 2.]

32. Facebook Membership The following graph gives the approximate number of **Facebook** users at various times since its establishment ($t = 0$ represents the start of 2004).[31]

Facebook membership (millions)

During which 1-year interval(s) was the average rate of change of $N(t)$ **(a)** greatest **(b)** least? Interpret your answers by referring to the rates of change. HINT [See Example 2.]

33. ▼ Physics Research in the U.S. The following table shows the number of research articles in the journal *Physical Review* authored by U.S researchers during the period 1993–2003 ($t = 3$ represents 1993):[32]

t (year since 1990)	3	5	7	9	11	13
N(t) (articles, thousands)	5.1	4.6	4.3	4.3	4.5	4.2

---

[30] Source: Apple financial statements (www.apple.com).

[31] Sources: Some data are interpolated. (www.facebook.com/, www.insidehighered.com).

[32] Source: The Americal Physical Society/*New York Times*, May 3, 2003, p. A1.

a. Find the interval(s) over which the average rate of change of N was the most negative. What was that rate of change? Interpret your answer.

b. The **percentage change of N over the interval $[a, b]$** is defined to be

$$\text{Percentage change of } N = \frac{\text{Change in } N}{\text{First value}} = \frac{N(b) - N(a)}{N(a)}.$$

Compute the percentage change of N over the interval $[3, 13]$ and also the average rate of change. Interpret the answers.

34. ▼ **Physics Research in Europe** The following table shows the number of research articles in the journal *Physical Review* authored by researchers in Europe during the period 1993–2003 ($t = 3$ represents 1993):[33]

t (year since 1990)	3	5	7	9	11	13
$N(t)$ (articles, thousands)	3.8	4.6	5.0	5.0	6.0	5.7

a. Find the interval(s) over which the average rate of change of N was the most positive. What was that rate of change? Interpret your answer.

b. The **percentage change of N over the interval $[a, b]$** is defined to be

$$\text{Percentage change of } N = \frac{\text{Change in } N}{\text{First value}} = \frac{N(b) - N(a)}{N(a)}.$$

Compute the percentage change of N over the interval $[7, 13]$ and also the average rate of change. Interpret the answers.

35. **College Basketball: Men** The following chart shows the number of NCAA men's college basketball teams in the United States for various years since 2000.[34]

Men's basketball teams

a. On average, how fast was the number of men's college basketball teams growing over the four-year period beginning in 2002?

b. By inspecting the graph, determine whether the four-year average rates of change increased or decreased beginning in 2002. HINT [See Example 2.]

36. **College Basketball: Women** The following chart shows the number of NCAA women's college basketball teams in the United States for various years since 2000.[35]

Women's basketball teams

a. On average, how fast was the number of women's college basketball teams growing over the three-year period beginning in 2004?

b. By inspecting the graph, find the three-year period over which the average rate of change was largest. HINT [See Example 2.]

37. ▼ **Funding for the Arts** The following chart shows the total annual support for the arts in the U.S. by federal, state, and local government in 1995–2003 as a function of time in years ($t = 0$ represents 1995) together with the regression line:[36]

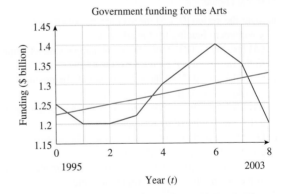

Government funding for the Arts

Multiple choice:

a. Over the period $[0, 4]$ the average rate of change of government funding for the arts was
(A) less than (B) greater than (C) approximately equal to the rate predicted by the regression line.

b. Over the period $[4, 8]$ the average rate of change of government funding for the arts was
(A) less than (B) greater than (C) approximately equal to the rate predicted by the regression line.

[33]Source: The Americal Physical Society/*New York Times*, May, 3, 2003, p. A1.

[34]2007 and 2008 figures are estimates. Source: The 2008 Statistical Abstract www.census.gov/.

[35]Ibid.

[36]Figures are adjusted for inflation. Sources: Giving USA, The Foundation Center, Americans for the Arts/*New York Times*, June 19, 2004, p. B7.

c. Over the period [3, 6] the average rate of change of government funding for the arts was
(A) less than   **(B)** greater than   **(C)** approximately equal to the rate predicted by the regression line.

d. Estimate, to two significant digits, the average rate of change of government funding for the arts over the period [0, 8]. (Be careful to state the units of measurement.) How does it compare to the slope of the regression line?

38. ▼ *Funding for the Arts* The following chart shows the total annual support for the arts in the U.S. by foundation endowments in 1995–2002 as a function of time in years ($t = 0$ represents 1995) together with the regression line:[37]

Foundation funding for the Arts

Multiple choice:

a. Over the period [0, 2.5] the average rate of change of government funding for the arts was
(A) less than   **(B)** greater than   **(C)** approximately equal to the rate predicted by the regression line.

b. Over the period [2, 6] the average rate of change of government funding for the arts was
(A) less than   **(B)** greater than   **(C)** approximately equal to the rate predicted by the regression line.

c. Over the period [3, 7] the average rate of change of government funding for the arts was
(A) less than   **(B)** greater than   **(C)** approximately equal to the rate predicted by the regression line.

d. Estimate, to two significant digits, the average rate of change of foundation funding for the arts over the period [0, 7]. (Be careful to state the units of measurement.) How does it compare to the slope of the regression line?

39. ▼ *Market Volatility During the Dot-com Boom* A volatility index generally measures the extent to which a market undergoes sudden changes in value. The volatility of the S&P 500 (as measured by one such index) was decreasing at an average rate of 0.2 points per year during 1991–1995, and was increasing at an average rate of about 0.3 points per year during

1995–1999. In 1995, the volatility of the S&P was 1.1.[38] Use this information to give a rough sketch of the volatility of the S&P 500 as a function of time, showing its values in 1991 and 1999.

40. ▼ *Market Volatility During the Dot-com Boom* The volatility (see the preceding exercise) of the NASDAQ had an average rate of change of 0 points per year during 1992–1995, and increased at an average rate of 0.2 points per year during 1995–1998. In 1995, the volatility of the NASDAQ was 1.1.[39] Use this information to give a rough sketch of the volatility of the NASDAQ as a function of time.

41. *Market Index* Joe Downs runs a small investment company from his basement. Every week he publishes a report on the success of his investments, including the progress of the "Joe Downs Index." At the end of one particularly memorable week, he reported that the index for that week had the value $I(t) = 1,000 + 1,500t - 800t^2 + 100t^3$ points, where t represents the number of business days into the week; t ranges from 0 at the beginning of the week to 5 at the end of the week. The graph of I is shown below.

On average, how fast, and in what direction, was the index changing over the first two business days (the interval [0, 2])? HINT [See Example 3.]

42. *Market Index* Refer to the Joe Downs Index in the preceding exercise. On average, how fast, and in which direction, was the index changing over the last three business days (the interval [2, 5])? HINT [See Example 3.]

43. *Crude Oil Prices* The price per barrel of crude oil in constant 2008 dollars can be approximated by
$$P(t) = 0.45t^2 - 12t + 105 \text{ dollars} \quad (0 \le t \le 28)$$
where t is time in years since the start of 1980.[40]

a. What, in constant 2008 dollars, was the average rate of change of the price of oil from the start of 1981 ($t = 1$) to the start of 2006 ($t = 26$)? HINT [See Example 3.]

b. Your answer to part (a) is quite small. Can you conclude that the price of oil hardly changed at all over the 25-year period 1981 to 2006? Explain.

---

[37] Figures are adjusted for inflation. Sources: Giving USA, The Foundation Center, Americans for the Arts/*New York Times*, June 19, 2004, p. B7.

[38] Source for data: Sanford C. Bernstein Company/*New York Times*, March 24, 2000, p. C1.

[39] Ibid.

[40] Source for data: www.inflationdata.com

44. *Median Home Price* The median home price in the U.S. over the period 2004–2009 can be approximated by

$$P(t) = -5t^2 + 75t - 30 \text{ thousand dollars} \quad (4 \le t \le 9)$$

where t is time in years since the start of 2000.[41]

a. What was the average rate of change of the median home price from the start of 2007 to the start of 2009? HINT [See Example 3.]

b. What, if anything, does your answer to part (a) say about the median home price in 2008? Explain.

45. *SARS* In the early stages of the deadly SARS (Severe Acute Respiratory Syndrome) epidemic in 2003, the number of reported cases can be approximated by

$$A(t) = 167(1.18)^t \quad (0 \le t \le 20)$$

t days after March 17, 2003 (the first day for which statistics were reported by the World Health Organization).

a. What was the average rate of change of $A(t)$ from March 17 to March 23? Interpret the result.

b. Which of the following is true? For the first 20 days of the epidemic, the number of reported cases

(A) increased at a faster and faster rate

(B) increased at a slower and slower rate

(C) decreased at a faster and faster rate

(D) decreased at a slower and slower rate HINT [See Example 2.]

46. *SARS* A few weeks into the deadly SARS (Severe Acute Respiratory Syndrome) epidemic in 2003, the number of reported cases can be approximated by

$$A(t) = 1,804(1.04)^t \quad (0 \le t \le 30)$$

t days after April 1, 2003.

a. What was the average rate of change of $A(t)$ from April 19 ($t = 18$) to April 29? Interpret the result.

b. Which of the following is true? During the 30-day period beginning April 1, the number of reported cases

(A) increased at a faster and faster rate

(B) increased at a slower and slower rate

(C) decreased at a faster and faster rate

(D) decreased at a slower and slower rate
HINT [See Example 2.]

47. ▼ *Ecology* Increasing numbers of manatees ("sea sirens") have been killed by boats off the Florida coast. The following graph shows the relationship between the number of boats registered in Florida and the number of manatees killed each year:

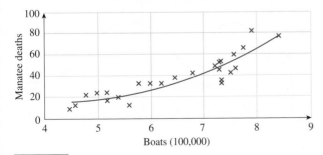

Boats (100,000)

The regression curve shown is given by

$$f(x) = 3.55x^2 - 30.2x + 81 \text{ manatees} \quad (4.5 \le x \le 8.5)$$

where x is the number of boats (in hundreds of thousands) registered in Florida in a particular year, and $f(x)$ is the number of manatees killed by boats in Florida that year.[42]

a. Compute the average rate of change of f over the intervals [5, 6] and [7, 8].

b. What does the answer to part (a) tell you about the manatee deaths per boat?

48. ▼ *Ecology* Refer to Exercise 47.

a. Compute the average rate of change of f over the intervals [5, 7] and [6, 8].

b. Had we used a linear model instead of a quadratic one, how would the two answers in part (a) be related to each other?

49. ⬛▼ *Poverty vs. Income* Based on data from 1988 through 2003, the poverty rate (percentage of households with incomes below the poverty threshold) in the U.S. can be approximated by

$$p(x) = 0.092x^2 - 8.1x + 190 \text{ percentage points} \quad (38 \le x \le 44)$$

where x is the U.S. median household income in thousands of dollars.[43]

a. Use technology to complete the following table which shows the average rate of change of p over successive intervals of length $\frac{1}{2}$. (Round all answers to two decimal places.) HINT [See Example 4.]

Interval	[39, 39.5]	[39.5, 40]	[40, 40.5]	[40.5, 41]	[41, 41.5]	[41.5, 42]
Average Rate of Change of p						

b. Interpret your answer for the interval [40, 40.5], being sure to indicate the direction of change and the units of measurement.

c. Multiple choice: As the median household income rises, the poverty rate

(A) increases

(B) decreases

(C) increases, then decreases

(D) decreases, then increases

d. Multiple choice: As the median income increases, the effect on the poverty rate is

(A) more pronounced

(B) less pronounced

---

[41]Source for data: www.investmenttools.com.

[42]Regression model is based on data from 1976 to 2000. Sources for data: Florida Department of Highway Safety & Motor Vehicles, Florida Marine Institute/*New York Times*, February 12, 2002, p. F4.

[43]The model is based on a quadratic regression. Household incomes are in constant 2002 dollars. The poverty threshold is approximately $18,000 for a family of four and $9,200 for an individual. Sources: Census Bureau Current Population Survey/*New York Times*, Sept 27, 2003, p. A10/ U.S. Department of Labor Bureau of Labor Statistics www.stats.bls.gov June 17, 2004.

50. ▣ ▼ *Poverty vs. Unemployment* Based on data from 1988 through 2003, the poverty rate (percentage of households with incomes below the poverty threshold) in the U.S. can be approximated by

$$p(x) = -0.12x^2 + 2.4x + 3.2 \text{ percentage points} \quad (4 \le x \le 8)$$

where x is the unemployment rate in percentage points.[44]

a. Use technology to complete the following table which shows the average rate of change of p over successive intervals of length $\frac{1}{2}$. (Round all answers to two decimal places.)

Interval	[5.0, 5.5]	[5.5, 6.0]	[6.0, 6.5]	[6.5, 7.0]	[7.0, 7.5]	[7.5, 8.0]
Average Rate of Change of p						

b. Interpret your answer for the interval [5.0, 5.5], being sure to indicate the direction of change and the units of measurement. HINT [See Example 4.]

c. Multiple choice: As the median household income rises, the poverty rate
(A) increases
(B) decreases
(C) increases, then decreases
(D) decreases, then increases

d. Multiple choice: As the unemployment rate increases, the effect on the poverty rate is
(A) more pronounced
(B) less pronounced

COMMUNICATION AND REASONING EXERCISES

51. Describe three ways we have used to determine the average rate of change of f over an interval $[a, b]$. Which of the three ways is *least* precise? Explain.

52. If f is a linear function of x with slope m, what is its average rate of change over any interval $[a, b]$?

53. Is the average rate of change of a function over $[a, b]$ affected by the values of the function between a and b? Explain.

54. If the average rate of change of a function over $[a, b]$ is zero, this means that the function has not changed over $[a, b]$, right?

55. Sketch the graph of a function whose average rate of change over [0, 3] is negative but whose average rate of change over [1, 3] is positive.

56. Sketch the graph of a function whose average rate of change over [0, 2] is positive but whose average rate of change over [0, 1] is negative.

[44] The model is based on a quadratic regression. Household incomes are in constant 2002 dollars. The poverty threshold is approximately $18,000 for a family of four and $9,200 for an individual. Sources: Census Bureau Current Population Survey/*New York Times*, Sept 27, 2003, p. A10; U.S. Department of Labor Bureau of Labor Statistics www.stats.bls.gov June 17, 2004.

57. ▼ If the rate of change of quantity A is 2 units of quantity A per unit of quantity B, and the rate of change of quantity B is 3 units of quantity B per unit of quantity C, what is the rate of change of quantity A with respect to quantity C?

58. ▼ If the rate of change of quantity A is 2 units of quantity A per unit of quantity B, what is the rate of change of quantity B with respect to quantity A?

59. ▼ A certain function has the property that its average rate of change over the interval $[1, 1+h]$ (for positive h) increases as h decreases. Which of the following graphs could be the graph of f?

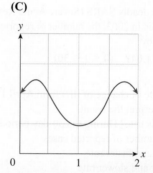

60. ▼ A certain function has the property that its average rate of change over the interval $[1, 1 + h]$ (for positive h) decreases as h decreases. Which of the following graphs could be the graph of f?

(C)

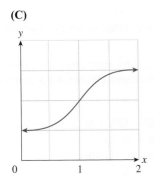

61. ▼ Is it possible for a company's revenue to have a negative 3-year average rate of growth, but a positive average rate of growth in 2 of the 3 years? (If not, explain; if so, illustrate with an example.)

62. ▼ Is it possible for a company's revenue to have a larger 2-year average rate of change than either of the 1-year average rates of change? (If not, explain why with the aid of a graph; if so, illustrate with an example.)

63. ◆ The average rate of change of f over $[1, 3]$ is

(A) always equal to
(B) never equal to
(C) sometimes equal to

the average of its average rates of change over $[1, 2]$ and $[2, 3]$.

64. ◆ The average rate of change of f over $[1, 4]$ is

(A) always equal to
(B) never equal to
(C) sometimes equal to

the average of its average rates of change over $[1, 2]$, $[2, 3]$, and $[3, 4]$.

10.5 Derivatives: Numerical and Graphical Viewpoints

In Example 4 of Section 10.4, we looked at the average rate of change of the function $G(t) = -8t^2 + 144t + 150$, approximating the price of gold on the New York Spot Market, over the intervals $[8, 8 + h]$ for successively smaller values of h. Here are some values we got:

h getting smaller; interval $[8, 8 + h]$ getting smaller →

h	1	0.1	0.01	0.001
Average Rate of Change Over $[8, 8 + h]$	8	15.2	15.92	15.992

Rate of change approaching $16 per hour →

The average rates of change of the price of gold over smaller and smaller periods of time, starting at the instant $t = 8$ (8:00 AM), appear to be getting closer and closer to $16 per hour. As we look at these shrinking periods of time, we are getting closer to looking at what happens at the *instant* $t = 8$. So it seems reasonable to say that the average rates of change are approaching the **instantaneous rate of change** at $t = 8$, which the table suggests is $16 per hour. This is how fast the price of gold was changing *exactly* at 8:00 AM.

> At $t = 8$, *the instantaneous rate of change of $G(t)$ is* 16.

We express this fact mathematically by writing $G'(8) = 16$ (which we read as "G prime of 8 equals 16"). Thus,

> $G'(8) = 16$ *means that, at $t = 8$, the instantaneous rate of change of $G(t)$ is* 16.

The process of letting h get smaller and smaller is called taking the **limit** as h approaches 0 (as you recognize if you've done the sections on limits). We write $h \to 0$ as shorthand for "h approaches 0." Thus, taking the limit of the average rates of change as $h \to 0$ gives us the instantaneous rate of change.

Q :*All these intervals [8, 8 + h] are intervals to the right of 8. What about small intervals to the left of 8, such as [7.9, 8]?*

A :We can compute the average rate of change of our function for such intervals by choosing h to be negative (h = −0.1, −0.01, etc.) and using the same difference quotient formula we used for positive h:

$$\text{Average rate of change of } G \text{ over } [8 + h, 8] = \frac{G(8) - G(8 + h)}{8 - (8 + h)}$$

$$= \frac{G(8 + h) - G(8)}{h}.$$

Here are the results we get using negative h:

h getting closer to 0; interval [8 + h, 8] getting smaller →

h	−0.1	−0.01	−0.001	−0.0001
Average Rate of Change Over [8 + h, 8]	16.8	16.08	16.008	16.0008

Rate of change approaching $16 per hour →

Notice that the average rates of change are again getting closer and closer to 16 as h approaches 0, suggesting once again that the instantaneous rate of change is $16 per hour.

Instantaneous Rate of Change of f(x) at x = a: Derivative

The **instantaneous rate of change** of $f(x)$ at $x = a$ is defined as

$$f'(a) = \lim_{h \to 0} \frac{f(a + h) - f(a)}{h}.$$

f prime of a equals the limit as h approaches 0, of the ratio $\dfrac{f(a + h) - f(a)}{h}$

The quantity $f'(a)$ is also called the **derivative of f(x) at x = a**. Finding the derivative of f is called **differentiating f**.

Units

The units of $f'(a)$ are the same as the units of the average rate of change: units of f per unit of x.

Quick Examples

1. If $f(x) = -8x^2 + 144x + 150$, then the two previous tables suggest that

$$f'(8) = \lim_{h \to 0} \frac{f(8 + h) - f(8)}{h} = 16.$$

2. If $f(t)$ is the number of insects in your room at time t hours, and we know that $f(3) = 5$ and $f'(3) = 8$, this means that, at time $t = 3$ hours, there are 5 insects in your room, and this number is growing at an instantaneous rate of 8 insects per hour.

IMPORTANT NOTES

1. Sections 10.1–10.3 discuss limits in some detail. If you have not (yet) covered those sections, you can trust to your intuition.

2. The formula for the derivative tells us that the instantaneous rate of change is the limit of the average rates of change $[f(a + h) - f(a)]/h$ over smaller and smaller intervals. Thus, the value of $f'(a)$ can be approximated by computing the average rate of change for smaller and smaller values of h, both positive and negative.*

3. In this section we will only *approximate* derivatives. In Section 10.6 we will begin to see how we find the *exact* values of derivatives.

4. $f'(a)$ is a number we can calculate, or at least approximate, for various values of a, as we have done in the earlier example. Since $f'(a)$ depends on the value of a, we can think of f' as *a function of a*. (We return to this idea at the end of this section.) An old name for f' is "the function *derived from f*," which has been shortened to the *derivative* of f.

5. It is because f' is a function that we sometimes refer to $f'(a)$ as "the derivative of f evaluated at a," or the "derivative of $f(x)$ evaluated at $x = a$."

> **✳ NOTE** If a happens to be an endpoint of the domain of f, then $f'(a)$ can still exist, as the defining limit becomes a one-sided limit; for instance, if f has domain $[2, +\infty)$ then $f'(2)$ would be defined as
>
> $$f'(2) = \lim_{h \to 0^+} \frac{f(2 + h) - f(2)}{h}.$$

It may happen that the average rates of change $[f(a + h) - f(a)]/h$ do not approach any fixed number at all as h approaches zero, or that they approach one number on the intervals using positive h, and another on those using negative h. If this happens, $\lim_{h \to 0}[f(a + h) - f(a)]/h$ does not exist, and we say that f is **not differentiable** at $x = a$, or $f'(a)$ **does not exist**. When the limit *does* exist, we say that f is **differentiable** at the point $x = a$, or $f'(a)$ **exists**. It is comforting to know that all polynomials and exponential functions are differentiable at *every* point. On the other hand, certain functions are not differentiable. Examples are $f(x) = |x|$ and $f(x) = x^{1/3}$, neither of which is differentiable at $x = 0$. (See Section 11.1.)

EXAMPLE 1 Instantaneous Rate of Change: Numerically and Graphically

The air temperature one spring morning, t hours after 7:00 AM, was given by the function $f(t) = 50 + 0.1t^4$ degrees Fahrenheit $(0 \le t \le 4)$.

a. How fast was the temperature rising at 9:00 AM?

b. How is the instantaneous rate of change of temperature at 9:00 AM reflected in the graph of temperature vs. time?

Solution

a. We are being asked to find the instantaneous rate of change of the temperature at $t = 2$, so we need to find $f'(2)$. To do this we examine the average rates of change

$$\frac{f(2 + h) - f(2)}{h} \qquad \text{Average rate of change} = \text{difference quotient}$$

for values of h approaching 0. Calculating the average rate of change over $[2, 2 + h]$ for $h = 1, 0.1, 0.01, 0.001,$ and 0.0001 we get the following values (rounded to four decimal places):*

> **✳ NOTE** We can quickly compute these values using technology as in Example 4 in Section 10.4. (See the Technology Guides at the end of the chapter.)

h	1	0.1	0.01	0.001	0.0001
Average Rate of Change Over $[2, 2 + h]$	6.5	3.4481	3.2241	3.2024	3.2002

Here are the values we get using negative values of h:

h	-1	-0.1	-0.01	-0.001	-0.0001
Average Rate of Change Over $[2 + h, 2]$	1.5	2.9679	3.1761	3.1976	3.1998

The average rates of change are clearly approaching the number 3.2, so we can say that $f'(2) = 3.2$. Thus, at 9:00 in the morning, the temperature was rising at the rate of 3.2 degrees per hour.

b. We saw in Section 10.4 that the average rate of change of f over an interval is the slope of the secant line through the corresponding points on the graph of f. Figure 24 illustrates this for the intervals $[2, 2 + h]$ with $h = 1, 0.5,$ and 0.1.

Figure 24

All three secant lines pass though the point $(2, f(2)) = (2, 51.6)$ on the graph of f. Each of them passes through a second point on the curve (the second point is different for each secant line) and this second point gets closer and closer to $(2, 51.6)$ as h gets closer to 0. What seems to be happening is that the secant lines are getting closer and closer to a line that just touches the curve at $(2, 51.6)$: the **tangent line** at $(2, 51.6)$, shown in Figure 25.

Figure 25

Q:What is the slope of this tangent line?

A:Because the slopes of the secant lines are getting closer and closer to 3.2, and because the secant lines are approaching the tangent line, the tangent line must have slope 3.2. In other words,

At the point on the graph where $x = 2$, the slope of the tangent line is $f'(2)$.

Be sure you understand the difference between $f(2)$ and $f'(2)$: Briefly, $f(2)$ is the *value of f* when $t = 2$, while $f'(2)$ is the *rate at which f is changing* when $t = 2$. Here,

$$f(2) = 50 + 0.1(2)^4 = 51.6 \text{ degrees.}$$

Thus, at 9:00 AM ($t = 2$), the temperature was 51.6 degrees. On the other hand,

$$f'(2) = 3.2 \text{ degrees per hour.} \qquad \text{\small Units of slope are units of } f \text{ per unit of } t.$$

This means that, at 9:00 AM ($t = 2$), the temperature was increasing at a rate of 3.2 degrees per hour.

Because we have been talking about tangent lines, we should say more about what they *are*. A tangent line to a *circle* is a line that touches the circle in just one point. A tangent line gives the circle "a glancing blow," as shown in Figure 26.

For a smooth curve other than a circle, a tangent line may touch the curve at more than one point, or pass through it (Figure 27).

Figure 26

Tangent line to the circle at P

Tangent line at P intersects graph at Q

Tangent line at P passes through curve at P

Figure 27

However, all tangent lines have the following interesting property in common: If we focus on a small portion of the curve very close to the point P—in other words, if we "zoom in" to the graph near the point P—the curve will appear almost straight, and almost indistinguishable from the tangent line (Figure 28).

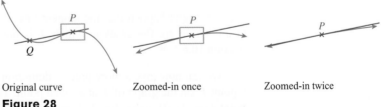

Original curve

Zoomed-in once

Zoomed-in twice

Figure 28

You can check this property by zooming in on the curve shown in Figures 24 and 25 in the previous example near the point where $x = 2$.

Secant and Tangent Lines

The *slope of the secant line* through the points on the graph of f where $x = a$ and $x = a + h$ is given by the average rate of change, or difference quotient,

$$m_{\text{sec}} = \text{slope of secant} = \text{average rate of change} = \frac{f(a + h) - f(a)}{h}.$$

The *slope of the tangent line* through the point on the graph of f where $x = a$ is given by the instantaneous rate of change, or derivative

$$m_{\text{tan}} = \text{slope of tangent} = \text{derivative} = f'(a) = \lim_{h \to 0} \frac{f(a + h) - f(a)}{h}.$$

Quick Example

In the following graph, the tangent line at the point where $x = 2$ has slope 3. Therefore, the derivative at $x = 2$ is 3. That is, $f'(2) = 3$.

Note It might happen that the tangent line is vertical at some point or does not exist at all. These are the cases in which f is not differentiable at the given point. (See Section 10.6.) ∎

We can now give a more precise definition of what we mean by the tangent line to a point P on the graph of f at a given point: The **tangent line** to the graph of f at the point $P(a, f(a))$ is the straight line passing through P with slope $f'(a)$.

Quick Approximation of the Derivative

Q : *Do we always need to make tables of difference quotients as above in order to calculate an approximate value for the derivative?*

A : We can usually *approximate* the value of the derivative by using a single, small value of h. In the example above, the value $h = 0.0001$ would have given a pretty good approximation. The problems with using a fixed value of h are that (1) we do not get an *exact* answer, only an *approximation* of the derivative, and (2) how good an approximation it is depends on the function we're differentiating.[*] However, with most of the functions we'll be considering, setting $h = 0.0001$ does give us a good approximation.

✶ NOTE In fact, no matter how small the value we decide to use for h, it is possible to craft a function f for which the difference quotient at a is not even close to $f'(a)$.

Calculating a Quick Approximation of the Derivative

We can calculate an approximate value of $f'(a)$ by using the formula

$$f'(a) \approx \frac{f(a+h) - f(a)}{h}$$
     Rate of change over $[a, a+h]$

with a small value of h. The value $h = 0.0001$ often works (but see the next example for a graphical way of determining a good value to use).

Alternative Formula: The Balanced Difference Quotient

The following alternative formula, which measures the rate of change of f over the interval $[a - h, a + h]$, often gives a more accurate result, and is the one used in many calculators:

$$f'(a) \approx \frac{f(a+h) - f(a-h)}{2h}.$$
     Rate of change over $[a - h, a + h]$

Note For the quick approximations to be valid, the function f must be differentiable; that is, $f'(a)$ must exist. ∎

EXAMPLE 2 Quick Approximation of the Derivative

a. Calculate an approximate value of $f'(1.5)$ if $f(x) = x^2 - 4x$.

b. Find the equation of the tangent line at the point on the graph where $x = 1.5$.

Solution

a. We shall compute both the ordinary difference quotient and the balanced difference quotient.

Ordinary Difference Quotient: Using $h = 0.0001$, the ordinary difference quotient is:

$$f'(1.5) \approx \frac{f(1.5 + 0.0001) - f(1.5)}{0.0001}$$
     Usual difference quotient

$$= \frac{f(1.5001) - f(1.5)}{0.0001}$$

$$= \frac{(1.5001^2 - 4 \times 1.5001) - (1.5^2 - 4 \times 1.5)}{0.0001} = -0.9999$$

This answer is accurate to 0.0001; in fact, $f'(1.5) = -1$.

     Graphically, we can picture this approximation as follows: Zoom in on the curve using the window $1.5 \le x \le 1.5001$ and measure the slope of the secant line joining both ends of the curve segment. Figure 29 shows close-up views of the curve and tangent line near the point P in which we are interested, the third view being the zoomed-in view used for this approximation.

Figure 29

Notice that in the third window the tangent line and curve are indistinguishable. Also, the point P in which we are interested is on the left edge of the window.

Balanced Difference Quotient: For the balanced difference quotient, we get

$$f'(1.5) \approx \frac{f(1.5+0.0001) - f(1.5-0.0001)}{2(0.0001)} \quad \text{Balanced difference quotient}$$

$$= \frac{f(1.5001) - f(1.4999)}{0.0002}$$

$$= \frac{(1.5001^2 - 4 \times 1.5001) - (1.4999^2 - 4 \times 1.4999)}{0.0002} = -1.$$

This balanced difference quotient gives the exact answer in this case!* Graphically, it is as though we have zoomed in using a window that puts the point P in the *center* of the screen (Figure 30) rather than at the left edge.

Slope $RQ = -1$

Figure 30

b. We find the equation of the tangent line from a point on the line and its slope, as we did in Chapter 1:

- **Point** $(1.5, f(1.5)) = (1.5, -3.75)$.
- **Slope** $m = f'(1.5) = -1$.   Slope of the tangent line = derivative.

The equation is

$$y = mx + b$$

where $m = -1$ and $b = y_1 - mx_1 = -3.75 - (-1)(1.5) = -2.25$. Thus, the equation of the tangent line is

$$y = -x - 2.25.$$

✱ **NOTE** The balanced difference quotient always gives the exact derivative for a quadratic function.

 using Technology

See the Technology Guides at the end of the chapter to find out how to calculate the quick approximations to the derivative in Example 2 using a TI-83/84 Plus or Excel. Here is an outline:

TI-83/84 Plus
$Y_1=X^2-4*X$
Home screen:
   $(Y_1(1.5001)-$
   $Y_1(1.5))/0.0001$
   $(Y_1(1.5001)-$
   $Y_1(1.4999))/0.0002$
[More details on page 777.]

Excel
Headings a, h, x, f(x), Diff
Quotient, Balanced Diff
Quotient in A1–F1
   1.5 in A2, 0.0001 in B2,
   =A2-B2 in C2, =A2 in C3,
   =A2+B2 in C4
   =C2^2-4*C2 in D2; copy
   down to D4
   =(D3-D2)/(C3-C2) in E2
   =(D4-D2)/(C4-C2) in E3
[More details on page 779.]

Q : *Why can't we simply put* $h = 0.000\,000\,000\,000\,000\,000\,000\,01$ *for an incredibly accurate approximation to the instantaneous rate of change and be done with it?*

A : This approach would certainly work if you were patient enough to do the (thankless) calculation by hand! However, doing it with the help of technology–even an ordinary calculator–will cause problems: The issue is that calculators and spreadsheets represent numbers with a maximum number of significant digits (15 in the case of Excel). As the value of h gets smaller, the value of $f(a + h)$ gets closer and closer to the value of $f(a)$. For example, if $f(x) = 50 + 0.1x^4$, Excel might compute

$$f(2 + 0.000\,000\,000\,000\,1) - f(2)$$
$$= 51.600\,000\,000\,000\,3 - 51.6 \qquad \text{Rounded to 15 digits}$$
$$= 0.000\,000\,000\,000\,3$$

and the corresponding difference quotient would be 3, not 3.2 as it should be. If h gets even smaller, Excel will not be able to distinguish between $f(a + h)$ and $f(a)$ at all, in which case it will compute 0 for the rate of change. This loss in accuracy when subtracting two very close numbers is called **subtractive error**.

Thus, there is a trade-off in lowering the value of h: smaller values of h yield *mathematically* more accurate approximations of the derivative, but if h gets too small, subtractive error becomes a problem and decreases the accuracy of computations that use technology.

Leibniz *d* Notation

We introduced the notation $f'(x)$ for the derivative of f at x, but there is another interesting notation. We have written the average rate of change as

$$\text{Average rate of change} = \frac{\Delta f}{\Delta x}. \qquad \frac{\text{Change in } f}{\text{Change in } x}$$

As we use smaller and smaller values for Δx, we approach the instantaneous rate of change, or derivative, for which we also have the notation df/dx, due to Leibniz:

$$\text{Instantaneous rate of change} = \lim_{\Delta x \to 0} \frac{\Delta f}{\Delta x} = \frac{df}{dx}.$$

That is, df/dx is just another notation for $f'(x)$. Do not think of df/dx as an actual quotient of two numbers: remember that we only use an actual quotient $\Delta f/\Delta x$ to *approximate* the value of df/dx.

In Example 3, we apply the quick approximation method of estimating the derivative.

EXAMPLE 3 **Velocity**

* NOTE Eric's claim is difficult to believe; 100 ft/s corresponds to around 68 mph, and professional pitchers can throw *forward* at about 100 mph.

My friend Eric, an enthusiastic baseball player, claims he can "probably" throw a ball upward at a speed of 100 feet per second (ft/s).* Our physicist friends tell us that its height s (in feet) t seconds later would be $s = 100t - 16t^2$. Find its average velocity over the interval [2, 3] and its instantaneous velocity exactly 2 seconds after Eric throws it.

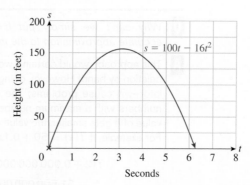

Figure 31

Solution The graph of the ball's height as a function of time is shown in Figure 31. Asking for the velocity is really asking for the rate of change of height with respect to time. (Why?) Consider average velocity first. To compute the **average velocity** of the ball from time 2 to time 3, we first compute the change in height:

$$\Delta s = s(3) - s(2) = 156 - 136 = 20 \text{ ft}$$

Since it rises 20 feet in $\Delta t = 1$ second, we use the defining formula *speed = distance/ time* to get the average velocity:

$$\text{Average velocity} = \frac{\Delta s}{\Delta t} = \frac{20}{1} = 20 \text{ ft/s}$$

from time $t = 2$ to $t = 3$. This is just the difference quotient, so

The average velocity is the average rate of change of height.

To get the **instantaneous velocity** at $t = 2$, we find the instantaneous rate of change of height. In other words, we need to calculate the derivative ds/dt at $t = 2$. Using the balanced quick approximation described earlier, we get

$$\frac{ds}{dt} \approx \frac{s(2 + 0.0001) - s(2 - 0.0001)}{2(0.0001)}$$

$$= \frac{s(2.0001) - s(1.9999)}{0.0002}$$

$$= \frac{100(2.0001) - 16(2.0001)^2 - (100(1.9999) - 16(1.9999)^2)}{0.0002}$$

$$= 36 \text{ ft/s}.$$

In fact, this happens to be the exact answer; the instantaneous velocity at $t = 2$ is exactly 36 ft/s. (Try an even smaller value of h to persuade yourself.)

➡ **Before we go on...** If we repeat the calculation in Example 3 at time $t = 5$, we get

$$\frac{ds}{dt} = -60 \text{ ft/s}$$

The negative sign tells us that the ball is *falling* at a rate of 60 feet per second at time $t = 5$. (How does the fact that it is falling at $t = 5$ show up on the graph?) ■

The preceding example gives another interpretation of the derivative.

Average and Instantaneous Velocity

For an object moving in a straight line with position $s(t)$ at time t, the **average velocity** from time t to time $t + h$ is the average rate of change of position with respect to time:

$$v_{ave} = \frac{s(t + h) - s(t)}{h} = \frac{\Delta s}{\Delta t}$$

Average velocity =
Average rate of change of position

The **instantaneous velocity** at time t is

$$v = \lim_{h \to 0} \frac{s(t + h) - s(t)}{h} = \frac{ds}{dt}$$

Instantaneous velocity =
Instantaneous rate of change of position

In other words, *instantaneous velocity is the derivative of position with respect to time.*

Here is one last comment on Leibniz notation. In Example 3, we could have written the velocity either as s' or as ds/dt, as we chose to do. To write the answer to the question, that the velocity at $t = 2$ sec was 36 ft/s, we can write either

$$s'(2) = 36$$

or

$$\left. \frac{ds}{dt} \right|_{t=2} = 36.$$

The notation "$|_{t=2}$" is read "evaluated at $t = 2$." Similarly, if $y = f(x)$, we can write the instantaneous rate of change of f at $x = 5$ in either functional notation as

$$f'(5) \qquad \text{The derivative of } f, \text{ evaluated at } x = 5$$

or in Leibniz notation as

$$\left. \frac{dy}{dx} \right|_{x=5}. \qquad \text{The derivative of } y, \text{ evaluated at } x = 5$$

The latter notation is obviously more cumbersome than the functional notation $f'(5)$, but the notation dy/dx has compensating advantages. You should practice using both notations.

The Derivative Function

The derivative $f'(x)$ is a number we can calculate, or at least approximate, for various values of x. Because $f'(x)$ depends on the value of x, we may think of f' as a function of x. This function is the **derivative function**.

Derivative Function

If f is a function, its **derivative function** f' is the function whose value $f'(x)$ is the derivative of f at x. Its domain is the set of all x at which f is differentiable. Equivalently, f' associates to each x the slope of the tangent to the graph of the function f at x, or the rate of change of f at x. The formula for the derivative function is

$$f'(x) = \lim_{h \to 0} \frac{f(x+h) - f(x)}{h}.$$ Derivative function

Quick Examples

1. Let $f(x) = 3x - 1$. The graph of f is a straight line that has slope 3 everywhere. In other words, $f'(x) = 3$ for every choice of x; that is, f' is a constant function.

Original Function f **Derivative Function** f'

$f(x) = 3x - 1$ $f'(x) = 3$

2. Given the graph of a function f, we can get a rough sketch of the graph of f' by estimating the slope of the tangent to the graph of f at several points, as illustrated below.*

✳ **NOTE** This method is discussed in detail on the Web site at Web site → Online Text → Sketching the Graph of the Derivative.

Original Function f **Derivative Function** f'

$y = f(x)$ $y = f'(x)$

For x between -2 and 0, the graph of f is linear with slope -2. As x increases from 0 to 2, the slope increases from -2 to 2. For x larger than 2, the graph of f is linear with slope 2. (Notice that, when $x = 1$, the graph of f has a horizontal tangent, so $f'(1) = 0$.)

3. Look again at the graph on the left in Quick Example 2. When $x < 1$ the derivative $f'(x)$ is negative, so the graph has negative slope and f is **decreasing**; its values are going down as x increases. When $x > 1$ the derivative $f'(x)$ is positive, so the graph has positive slope and f is **increasing**; its values are going up as x increases.

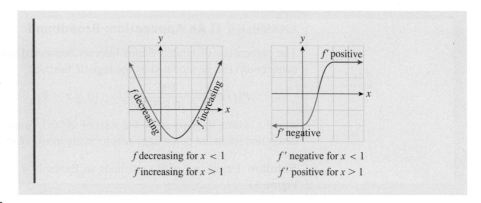

f decreasing for $x < 1$ f' negative for $x < 1$
f increasing for $x > 1$ f' positive for $x > 1$

using Technology

See the Technology Guides at the end of the chapter to find out how to obtain a table of values of and graph the derivative in Example 4 using a TI-83/84 Plus or Excel. Here is an outline:

TI-83/84 Plus
Y₁=-2X^2+6X+5
Y₂=nDeriv(Y₁,X,X)
[More details on page 777.]

Excel
Value of h in E2
Values of x from A2 down increasing by h
-2*A2^2+6*A2+5 from B2 down = (B3-B2)/$E$2 from C2 down
Insert scatter chart using columns A and C [More details on page 779.]

Web Site
www.FiniteandCalc.org
Web grapher:
Student Home→Online Utilities→ Function Evaluator and Grapher
Enter
deriv(-2*x^2+6*x+5) for y_1. Alternatively, enter
-2*x^2+6*x+5 for y_1 and deriv(y1) for y_2.
Excel grapher:
Student Home→Online Utilities→Excel First and Second Derivative Graphing Utility
Function: -2*x^2+6*x+5

The following example shows how we can use technology to graph the (approximate) derivative of a function, where it exists.

EXAMPLE 4 ⓘ Graphing the Derivative with Technology

Use technology to graph of the derivative of $f(x) = -2x^2 + 6x + 5$ for values of x starting at -5.

Solution The TI-83/84 Plus has a built-in function that approximates the derivative, and we can use it to graph the derivative of a function. In Excel, we need to create the approximation using one of the quick approximation formulas and we can then graph a table of its values. See the Technology Guides at the end of the chapter to find out how to graph the derivative (Figure 32) using the TI-83/84 Plus and Excel.

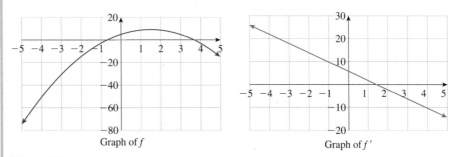

Graph of f Graph of f'

Figure 32

We said that f' records the slope of (the tangent line to) the function f at each point. Notice that the graph of f' confirms that the slope of the graph of f is decreasing as x increases from -5 to 5. Note also that the graph of f reaches a high point at $x = 1.5$ (the vertex of the parabola). At that point, the slope of the tangent is zero; that is, $f'(1.5) = 0$ as we see in the graph of f'.

EXAMPLE 5 🔢 An Application: Broadband

The percentage of United States Internet-connected households that have broadband connections can be modeled by the logistic function

$$P(t) = \frac{100}{1 + 10.8(1.7)^{-t}} \qquad (0 \le t \le 9)$$

where t is time in years since the start of 2000.* Graph both P and its derivative, and determine when the percentage was growing most rapidly.

Solution Using one of the methods in Example 4, we obtain the graphs shown in Figure 33.

Figure 33
Technology formula: `100/(1+10.8*1.7^(-x))`

From the graph on the right, we see that P' reaches a peak somewhere between $t = 4$ and $t = 5$ (sometime during 2004). Recalling that P' measures the *slope* of the graph of P, we can conclude that the graph of P is steepest between $t = 4$ and $t = 5$, indicating that, according to the model, the percentage of Internet-connected households with broadband was growing most rapidly during 2004. Notice that this is not so easy to see directly on the graph of P.

To determine the point of maximum growth more accurately, we can zoom in on the graph of P' using the range $4 \le t \le 5$ (Figure 34).

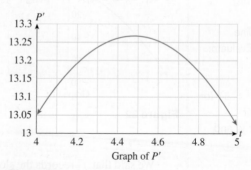

Graph of P'

Figure 34

We can now see that P' reaches its highest point around $t = 4.5$, so we conclude that the percentage of Internet-connected households with broadband was growing most rapidly midway through 2004.

---

*See Example 2 in Section 9.4. Source for data: www.Nielsen.com.

➡ **Before we go on...** Besides helping us to determine the point of maximum growth, the graph of P' in Example 5 gives us a great deal of additional information. As just one example, in Figure 34 we can see that the maximum value of P' is just under 13.3, indicating that the percentage of Internet-connected households that have broadband never grew at a fastest rate of about 13.3 percentage points per quarter. ■

FAQs

Recognizing When and How to Compute the Instantaneous Rate of Change

Q : *How do I know, by looking at the wording of a problem, that it is asking for an instantaneous rate of change?*

A : If a problem does not ask for an instantaneous rate of change directly, it might do so indirectly, as in "How fast is quantity q increasing?" or "Find the rate of increase of q."

Q : *If I know that a problem calls for estimating an instantaneous rate of change, how should I estimate it: with a table showing smaller and smaller values of h, or by using a quick approximation?*

A : For most practical purposes, a quick approximation is accurate enough. Use a table showing smaller and smaller values of h when you would like to check the accuracy.

Q : *Which should I use in computing a quick approximation: the balanced difference quotient or the ordinary difference quotient?*

A : In general, the balanced difference quotient gives a more accurate answer.

Web Site

At the student Web site at www.FiniteandCalc.org you can find the following optional interactive online sections:

- **Continuity and Differentiability**
- **Sketching the Graph of the Derivative**

You can find these sections by following

   Chapter 9 → Online Text

10.5 EXERCISES

▼ more advanced   ◆ challenging
🅣 indicates exercises that should be solved using technology

In Exercises 1–4, estimate the derivative from the table of average rates of change. HINT *[See discussion at the beginning of the section.]*

1.

h	1	0.1	0.01	0.001	0.0001
Average Rate of Change of f Over $[5, 5 + h]$	12	6.4	6.04	6.004	6.0004

h	−1	−0.1	−0.01	−0.001	−0.0001
Average Rate of Change of f Over $[5 + h, 5]$	3	5.6	5.96	5.996	5.9996

Estimate $f'(5)$.

2.

h	1	0.1	0.01	0.001	0.0001
Average Rate of Change of g Over $[7, 7 + h]$	4	4.8	4.98	4.998	4.9998

h	−1	−0.1	−0.01	−0.001	−0.0001
Average Rate of Change of g Over $[7 + h, 7]$	5	5.3	5.03	5.003	5.0003

Estimate $g'(7)$.

3.

h	1	0.1	0.01	0.001	0.0001
Average Rate of Change of r Over $[-6, -6 + h]$	−5.4	−5.498	−5.4998	−5.499982	−5.49999822

h	−1	−0.1	−0.01	−0.001	−0.0001
Average Rate of Change of r Over $[-6 + h, -6]$	−7.52	−6.13	−5.5014	−5.5000144	−5.500001444

Estimate $r'(-6)$.

4.

h	1	0.1	0.01	0.001	0.0001
Average Rate of Change of s Over $[0, h]$	−2.52	−1.13	−0.6014	−0.6000144	−0.600001444

h	−1	−0.1	−0.01	−0.001	−0.0001
Average Rate of Change of s Over $[h, 0]$	−0.4	−0.598	−0.5998	−0.599982	−0.59999822

Estimate $s'(0)$.

Consider the functions in Exercises 5–8 as representing the value of an ounce of palladium in U.S. dollars as a function of the time t in days.[45] Find the average rates of change of R(t) over the time intervals [t, t + h], where t is as indicated and h = 1, 0.1, and 0.01 days. Hence, estimate the instantaneous rate of change of R at time t, specifying the units of measurement. (Use smaller values of h to check your estimates.) HINT [See Example 1.]

5. $R(t) = 60 + 50t - t^2; t = 5$

6. $R(t) = 60t - 2t^2; t = 3$

7. $R(t) = 270 + 20t^3; t = 1$

8. $R(t) = 200 + 50t - t^3; t = 2$

Each of the functions in Exercises 9–12 gives the cost to manufacture x items. Find the average cost per unit of manufacturing h more items (i.e., the average rate of change of the total cost) at a production level of x, where x is as indicated and h = 10 and 1. Hence, estimate the instantaneous rate of change of the total cost at the given production level x, specifying the units of measurement. (Use smaller values of h to check your estimates.) HINT [See Example 1.]

9. $C(x) = 10,000 + 5x - \dfrac{x^2}{10,000}; x = 1,000$

10. $C(x) = 20,000 + 7x - \dfrac{x^2}{20,000}; x = 10,000$

11. $C(x) = 15,000 + 100x + \dfrac{1,000}{x}; x = 100$

12. $C(x) = 20,000 + 50x + \dfrac{10,000}{x}; x = 100$

In Exercises 13–16, the graph of a function is shown together with the tangent line at a point P. Estimate the derivative of f at the corresponding x value. HINT [See Quick Example page 740.]

13.

14.

15.

16.

In each of the graphs given in Exercises 17–22, say at which labeled point the slope of the tangent is **(a)** greatest and **(b)** least (in the sense that −7 is less than 1). HINT [See Quick Example page 740.]

17.

18.

19.

20.

21.

22.

In each of Exercises 23–26, three slopes are given. For each slope, determine at which of the labeled points on the graph the tangent line has that slope.

23. a. 0 **b.** 4 **c.** −1

24. a. 0 **b.** 1 **c.** −1

25. a. 0 **b.** 3 **c.** −3

26. a. 0 **b.** 3 **c.** 1

---

[45] Palladium was trading at around $290 in August 2008.

*In each of Exercises 27–30, find the approximate coordinates of all points (if any) where the slope of the tangent is: **(a)** 0, **(b)** 1, **(c)** −1.* HINT [See Quick Example page 740.]

27.

28.

29.

30.

31. Complete the following: The tangent to the graph of the function f at the point where $x = a$ is the line passing through the point _____ with slope _____ .

32. Complete the following: The difference quotient for f at the point where $x = a$ gives the slope of the _____ line that passes through _____ .

33. Which is correct? The derivative function assigns to each value x

(A) the average rate of change of f at x
(B) the slope of the tangent to the graph of f at $(x, f(x))$
(C) the rate at which f is changing over the interval $[x, x + h]$ for $h = 0.0001$
(D) the balanced difference quotient $[f(x + h) - f(x - h)]/(2h)$ for $h \approx 0.0001$

34. Which is correct? The derivative function $f'(x)$ tells us

(A) the slope of the tangent line at each of the points $(x, f(x))$
(B) the approximate slope of the tangent line at each of the points $(x, f(x))$
(C) the slope of the secant line through $(x, f(x))$ and $(x + h, f(x + h))$ for $h = 0.0001$
(D) the slope of a certain secant line through each of the points $(x, f(x))$

35. ▼ Let f have the graph shown.

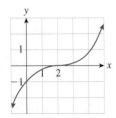

a. The average rate of change of f over the interval $[2, 4]$ is
(A) greater than $f'(2)$ (B) less than $f'(2)$
(C) approximately equal to $f'(2)$

b. The average rate of change of f over the interval $[-1, 1]$ is
(A) greater than $f'(0)$ (B) less than $f'(0)$
(C) approximately equal to $f'(0)$

c. Over the interval $[0, 2]$, the instantaneous rate of change of f is
(A) increasing   (B) decreasing   (C) neither

d. Over the interval $[0, 4]$, the instantaneous rate of change of f is
(A) increasing, then decreasing
(B) decreasing, then increasing
(C) always increasing
(D) always decreasing

e. When $x = 4$, $f(x)$ is
(A) approximately 0, and increasing at a rate of about 0.7 units per unit of x
(B) approximately 0, and decreasing at a rate of about 0.7 units per unit of x
(C) approximately 0.7, and increasing at a rate of about 1 unit per unit of x
(D) approximately 0.7, and increasing at a rate of about 3 units per unit of x

36. ▼ A function f has the following graph.

a. The average rate of change of f over $[0, 200]$ is
(A) greater than
(B) less than
(C) approximately equal to
the instantaneous rate of change at $x = 100$.

b. The average rate of change of f over $[0, 200]$ is
(A) greater than
(B) less than
(C) approximately equal to
the instantaneous rate of change at $x = 150$.

c. Over the interval $[0, 50]$ the instantaneous rate of change of f is
(A) increasing, then decreasing
(B) decreasing, then increasing
(C) always increasing
(D) always decreasing

d. On the interval $[0, 200]$, the instantaneous rate of change of f is
(A) always positive   (B) always negative
(C) negative, positive, and then negative

e. $f'(100)$ is

    (A) greater than $f'(25)$ **(B)** less than $f'(25)$

    (C) approximately equal to $f'(25)$

In Exercises 37–40, use a quick approximation to estimate the derivative of the given function at the indicated point. HINT [See Example 2(a).]

37. $f(x) = 1 - 2x$; $x = 2$ **38.** $f(x) = \dfrac{x}{3} - 1$; $x = -3$

39. $f(x) = \dfrac{x^2}{4} - \dfrac{x^3}{3}$; $x = -1$ **40.** $f(x) = \dfrac{x^2}{2} + \dfrac{x}{4}$; $x = 2$

In Exercises 41–48, estimate the indicated derivative by any method. HINT [See Example 2.]

41. $g(t) = \dfrac{1}{t^5}$; estimate $g'(1)$

42. $s(t) = \dfrac{1}{t^3}$; estimate $s'(-2)$

43. $y = 4x^2$; estimate $\left.\dfrac{dy}{dx}\right|_{x=2}$

44. $y = 1 - x^2$; estimate $\left.\dfrac{dy}{dx}\right|_{x=-1}$

45. $s = 4t + t^2$; estimate $\left.\dfrac{ds}{dt}\right|_{t=-2}$

46. $s = t - t^2$; estimate $\left.\dfrac{ds}{dt}\right|_{t=2}$

47. $R = \dfrac{1}{p}$; estimate $\left.\dfrac{dR}{dp}\right|_{p=20}$

48. $R = \sqrt{p}$; estimate $\left.\dfrac{dR}{dp}\right|_{p=400}$

*In Exercises 49–54, **(a)** use any method to estimate the slope of the tangent to the graph of the given function at the point with the given x-coordinate and **(b)** find an equation of the tangent line in part (a). In each case, sketch the curve together with the appropriate tangent line.* HINT [See Example 2(b).]

49. $f(x) = x^3$; $x = -1$ **50.** $f(x) = x^2$; $x = 0$

51. $f(x) = x + \dfrac{1}{x}$; $x = 2$ **52.** $f(x) = \dfrac{1}{x^2}$; $x = 1$

53. $f(x) = \sqrt{x}$; $x = 4$ **54.** $f(x) = 2x + 4$; $x = -1$

In each of Exercises 55–58, estimate the given quantity.

55. $f(x) = e^x$; estimate $f'(0)$

56. $f(x) = 2e^x$; estimate $f'(1)$

57. $f(x) = \ln x$; estimate $f'(1)$

58. $f(x) = \ln x$; estimate $f'(2)$

In Exercises 59–64, match the graph of f to the graph of f' (the graphs of f' are shown after Exercise 64).

59. ▼

60. ▼

61. ▼

62. ▼

63. ▼

64. ▼

Graphs of derivatives for Exercises 59–64:

(A)

(B)

(C)

(D)

(E)

(F)

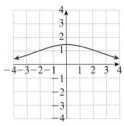

In Exercises 65–68 the graph of a function is given. For which x in the range shown is the function increasing? For which x is the function decreasing? HINT [See Quick Example 3 page 746.]

65.

66.

67.

68.

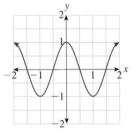

In Exercises 69–72 the graph of the derivative of a function is given. For which x is the (original) function increasing? For which x is the (original) function decreasing? HINT [See Quick Example 3 page 746.]

69.

70.

71.

72.

 In Exercises 73 and 74, use technology to graph the derivative of the given function for the given range of values of x. Then use your graph to estimate all values of x (if any) where the tangent line to the graph of the given function is horizontal. Round answers to one decimal place. HINT [See Example 4.]

73. $f(x) = x^4 + 2x^3 - 1$; $-2 \le x \le 1$

74. $f(x) = -x^3 - 3x^2 - 1$; $-3 \le x \le 1$

 In Exercises 75 and 76, use the method of Example 4 to list approximate values of f'(x) for x in the given range. Graph f(x) together with f'(x) for x in the given range.

75. $f(x) = \dfrac{x+2}{x-3}$; $4 \le x \le 5$

76. $f(x) = \dfrac{10x}{x-2}$; $2.5 \le x \le 3$

APPLICATIONS

77. *Demand* Suppose the demand for a new brand of sneakers is given by

$$q = \frac{5,000,000}{p}$$

where p is the price per pair of sneakers, in dollars, and q is the number of pairs of sneakers that can be sold at price p. Find $q(100)$ and estimate $q'(100)$. Interpret your answers. HINT [See Example 1.]

78. *Demand* Suppose the demand for an old brand of TV is given by

$$q = \frac{100,000}{p+10}$$

where p is the price per TV set, in dollars, and q is the number of TV sets that can be sold at price p. Find $q(190)$ and estimate $q'(190)$. Interpret your answers. HINT [See Example 1.]

79. *Oil Imports from Mexico* The following graph shows approximate daily oil imports to the U.S. from Mexico.[46] Also shown is the tangent line (and its slope) at the point corresponding to year 2005.

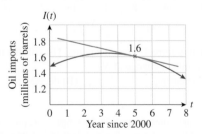

[46] Figures are approximate, and 2008–2009 figures are projections by the Department of Energy. Source: Energy Information Administration/Pemex (http://www.eia.doe.gov).

a. Estimate the slope of the tangent line shown on the graph. What does the graph tell you about oil imports from Mexico in 2005? **HINT** [Identify two points on the tangent line. Then see Quick Example page 740.]

b. According to the graph, is the rate of change of oil imports from Mexico increasing, decreasing, or increasing then decreasing? Why?

80. *Oil Production in Mexico* The following graph shows approximate daily oil production by **Pemex**, Mexico's national oil company.[47] Also shown is the tangent line (and its slope) at the point corresponding to year 2003.

P(t)

Oil production (millions of barrels)

Year since 2000

a. Estimate the slope of the tangent line shown on the graph. What does the graph tell you about oil production by **Pemex** in 2003? **HINT** [Identify two points on the tangent line. Then see Quick Example page 740.]

b. According to the graph, is the rate of change of oil production by **Pemex** increasing or decreasing over the range [0, 4]? Why?

81. ▼ *Prison Population* The following curve is a model of the total population in state prisons as a function of time in years ($t = 0$ represents 1980).[48]

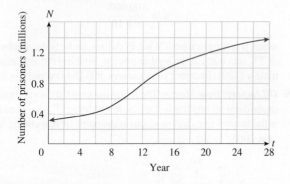

N

Number of prisoners (millions)

Year

a. Which is correct? Over the period [16, 20] the instantaneous rate of change of *N* is
(A) increasing   **(B)** decreasing

b. Which is correct? The instantaneous rate of change of prison population at $t = 12$ was
(A) less than   **(B)** greater than
(C) approximately equal to
the average rate of change over the interval [0, 24].

c. Which is correct? Over the period [0, 28] the instantaneous rate of change of *N* is
(A) increasing, then decreasing
(B) decreasing, then increasing
(C) always increasing
(D) always decreasing

d. According to the model, the total state prison population was increasing fastest around what year?

e. Roughly estimate the instantaneous rate of change of *N* at $t = 16$ by using a balanced difference quotient with $h = 4$. Interpret the result.

82. ▼ *Demand for Freon* The demand for chlorofluorocarbon-12 (CFC-12)—the ozone-depleting refrigerant commonly known as Freon[49]—has been declining significantly in response to regulation and concern about the ozone layer. The graph below represents a model for the projected demand for CFC-12 as a function of time in years ($t = 0$ represents 1990).[50]

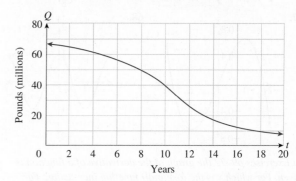

Q

Pounds (millions)

Years

a. Which is correct? Over the period [12, 20] the instantaneous rate of change of *Q* is
(A) increasing   **(B)** decreasing

b. Which is correct? The instantaneous rate of change of demand for Freon at $t = 10$ was
(A) less than   **(B)** greater than
(C) approximately equal to
the average rate of change over the interval [0, 20].

c. Which is correct? Over the period [0, 20] the instantaneous rate of change of *Q* is
(A) increasing, then decreasing
(B) decreasing, then increasing
(C) always increasing
(D) always decreasing

d. According to the model, the demand for Freon was decreasing most rapidly around what year?

---

[47] Figures are approximate, and 2008–2009 figures are projections by the Department of Energy. Source: Energy Information Administration/ Pemex (http://www.eia.doe.gov).

[48] The prison population represented excludes federal prisons. Source for 1980–2000 data: Bureau of Justice Statistics/*New York Times*, June 9, 2001, p. A10.

[49] The name given to it by DuPont.

[50] Source for data: The Automobile Consulting Group (*New York Times*, December 26, 1993, p. F23). The exact figures were not given, and the chart is a reasonable facsimile of the chart that appeared in *New York Times*.

e. Roughly estimate the instantaneous rate of change of Q at $t = 13$ by using a balanced difference quotient with $h = 5$. Interpret the result.

83. Velocity If a stone is dropped from a height of 400 feet, its height after t seconds is given by $s = 400 - 16t^2$.

a. Find its average velocity over the period $[2, 4]$.

b. Estimate its instantaneous velocity at time $t = 4$. HINT [See Example 3.]

84. Velocity If a stone is thrown down at 120 ft/s from a height of 1,000 feet, its height after t seconds is given by $s = 1,000 - 120t - 16t^2$.

a. Find its average velocity over the period $[1, 3]$.

b. Estimate its instantaneous velocity at time $t = 3$. HINT [See Example 3.]

85. Crude Oil Prices The price per barrel of crude oil in constant 2008 dollars can be approximated by

$$P(t) = 0.45t^2 - 12t + 105 \text{ dollars} \quad (0 \le t \le 28)$$

where t is time in years since the start of 1980.[51]

a. Compute the average rate of change of $P(t)$ over the interval $[0, 28]$, and interpret your answer. HINT [See Section 10.4 Example 3.]

b. Estimate the instantaneous rate of change of $P(t)$ at $t = 0$, and interpret your answer. HINT [See Example 2(a).]

c. The answers to part (a) and part (b) have opposite signs. What does this indicate about the price of oil?

86. Median Home Price The median home price in the U.S. over the period 2004–2009 can be approximated by

$$P(t) = -5t^2 + 75t - 30 \text{ thousand dollars} \quad (4 \le t \le 9)$$

where t is time in years since the start of 2000.[52]

a. Compute the average rate of change of $P(t)$ over the interval $[5, 9]$, and interpret your answer. HINT [See Section 10.4 Example 3.]

b. Estimate the instantaneous rate of change of $P(t)$ at $t = 5$, and interpret your answer. HINT [See Example 2(a).]

c. The answer to part (b) has larger absolute value than the answer to part (a). What does this indicate about the median home price?

87. SARS In the early stages of the deadly SARS (Severe Acute Respiratory Syndrome) epidemic in 2003, the number of reported cases can be approximated by

$$A(t) = 167(1.18)^t \quad (0 \le t \le 20)$$

t days after March 17, 2003 (the first day in which statistics were reported by the World Health Organization).

a. What, approximately, was the instantaneous rate of change of $A(t)$ on March 27 ($t = 10$)? Interpret the result.

b. Which of the following is true? For the first 20 days of the epidemic, the instantaneous rate of change of the number of cases

(A) increased   **(B)** decreased
(C) increased and then decreased
(D) decreased and then increased

88. SARS A few weeks into the deadly SARS (Severe Acute Respiratory Syndrome) epidemic in 2003, the number of reported cases can be approximated by

$$A(t) = 1,804(1.04)^t \quad (0 \le t \le 30)$$

t days after April 1, 2003.

a. What, approximately, was the instantaneous rate of change of $A(t)$ on April 21 ($t = 20$)? Interpret the result.

b. Which of the following is true? During April, the instantaneous rate of change of the number of cases

(A) increased   **(B)** decreased
(C) increased and then decreased
(D) decreased and then increased

89. Sales Weekly sales of a new brand of sneakers are given by

$$S(t) = 200 - 150e^{-t/10}$$

pairs sold per week, where t is the number of weeks since the introduction of the brand. Estimate $S(5)$ and $\left.\dfrac{dS}{dt}\right|_{t=5}$ and interpret your answers.

90. Sales Weekly sales of an old brand of TV are given by

$$S(t) = 100e^{-t/5}$$

sets per week, where t is the number of weeks after the introduction of a competing brand. Estimate $S(5)$ and $\left.\dfrac{dS}{dt}\right|_{t=5}$ and interpret your answers.

91. Early Internet Online Services On January 1, 1996, **America Online** was the biggest online service provider, with 4.5 million subscribers, and was adding new subscribers at a rate of 60,000 per week.[53] If $A(t)$ is the number of **America Online** subscribers t weeks after January 1, 1996, what do the given data tell you about values of the function A and its derivative? HINT [See Quick Example 2 on page 736.]

92. Early Internet Online Services On January 1, 1996, **Prodigy** was the third-biggest online service provider, with 1.6 million subscribers, but was losing subscribers.[54] If $P(t)$ is the number of **Prodigy** subscribers t weeks after January 1, 1996, what do the given data tell you about values of the function P and its derivative? HINT [See Quick Example 2 on page 736.]

93. ▼ **Learning to Speak** Let $p(t)$ represent the percentage of children who are able to speak at the age of t months.

a. It is found that $p(10) = 60$ and $\left.\dfrac{dp}{dt}\right|_{t=10} = 18.2$. What does this mean?[55] HINT [See Quick Example 2 on page 736.]

b. As t increases, what happens to p and $\dfrac{dp}{dt}$?

---

[53] Source: Information and Interactive Services Report/*New York Times*, January 2, 1996, p. C14.

[54] Ibid.

[55] Based on data presented in the article *The Emergence of Intelligence* by William H. Calvin, *Scientific American*, October, 1994, pp. 101–107.

---

[51] Source for data: www.inflationdata.com.
[52] Source for data: www.investmenttools.com.

94. ▼ *Learning to Read* Let $p(t)$ represent the number of children in your class who learned to read at the age of t years.

   a. Assuming that everyone in your class could read by the age of 7, what does this tell you about $p(7)$ and $\left.\dfrac{dp}{dt}\right|_{t=7}$?
   HINT [See Quick Example 2 on page 736.]

   b. Assuming that 25.0% of the people in your class could read by the age of 5, and that 25.3% of them could read by the age of 5 years and one month, estimate $\left.\dfrac{dp}{dt}\right|_{t=5}$.
   Remember to give its units.

95. *Subprime Mortgages* (Compare Exercise 29 of Section 10.4.) The percentage of mortgages issued in the United States that are subprime (normally classified as risky) can be approximated by

$$A(t) = \frac{15}{1 + 8.6(1.8)^{-t}} \quad (0 \le t \le 9)$$

where t is the number of years since the start of 2000.

   a. Estimate $A(6)$ and $A'(6)$. (Round answers to two significant digits.) What do the answers tell you about subprime mortgages?

   b. ▐ Graph the extrapolated function and its derivative for $0 \le t \le 16$ and use your graphs to describe how the derivative behaves as t becomes large. (Express this behavior in terms of limits if you have studied the sections on limits.) What does this tell you about subprime mortgages? HINT [See Example 5.]

96. *Subprime Mortgage Debt* (Compare Exercise 30 of Section 10.4.) The value of subprime (normally classified as risky) mortgage debt outstanding in the U.S. can be approximated by

$$A(t) = \frac{1,350}{1 + 4.2(1.7)^{-t}} \text{ billion dollars} \quad (0 \le t \le 9)$$

where t is the number of years since the start of 2000.

   a. Estimate $A(7)$ and $A'(7)$. (Round answers to three significant digits.) What do the answers tell you about subprime mortgages?

   b. ▐ Graph the function and its derivative and use your graphs to estimate when, to the nearest year, $A'(t)$ is greatest. What does this tell you about subprime mortgages? HINT [See Example 5.]

97. ▐ ▼ *Embryo Development* The oxygen consumption of a turkey embryo increases from the time the egg is laid through the time the turkey chick hatches. In a brush turkey, the oxygen consumption (in milliliters per hour) can be approximated by
$$c(t) = -0.0012t^3 + 0.12t^2 - 1.83t + 3.97 \quad (20 \le t \le 50)$$
where t is the time (in days) since the egg was laid.[56] (An egg will typically hatch at around $t = 50$.) Use technology to graph $c'(t)$ and use your graph to answer the following questions. HINT [See Example 5.]

   a. Over the interval [20, 32] the derivative c' is
   (A) increasing, then decreasing
   (B) decreasing, then increasing
   (C) decreasing   (D) increasing

   b. When, to the nearest day, is the oxygen consumption increasing at the fastest rate?

   c. When, to the nearest day, is the oxygen consumption increasing at the slowest rate?

98. ▐ ▼ *Embryo Development* The oxygen consumption of a bird embryo increases from the time the egg is laid through the time the chick hatches. In a typical galliform bird, the oxygen consumption (in milliliters per hour) can be approximated by

$$c(t) = -0.0027t^3 + 0.14t^2 - 0.89t + 0.15 \quad (8 \le t \le 30)$$

where t is the time (in days) since the egg was laid.[57] (An egg will typically hatch at around $t = 28$.) Use technology to graph $c'(t)$ and use your graph to answer the following questions. HINT [See Example 5.]

   a. Over the interval [8, 30] the derivative c' is
   (A) increasing, then decreasing
   (B) decreasing, then increasing
   (C) decreasing   (D) increasing

   b. When, to the nearest day, is the oxygen consumption increasing the fastest?

   c. When, to the nearest day, is the oxygen consumption increasing at the slowest rate?

The next two exercises are applications of Einstein's Special Theory of Relativity and relate to objects that are moving extremely fast. In science fiction terminology, a speed of warp 1 is the speed of light—about 3×10^8 meters per second. (Thus, for instance, a speed of warp 0.8 corresponds to 80% of the speed of light—about 2.4×10^8 meters per second.)

99. ◆ *Lorentz Contraction* According to Einstein's Special Theory of Relativity, a moving object appears to get shorter to a stationary observer as its speed approaches the speed of light. If a spaceship that has a length of 100 meters at rest travels at a speed of warp p, its length in meters, as measured by a stationary observer, is given by

$$L(p) = 100\sqrt{1 - p^2}$$

with domain [0, 1). Estimate $L(0.95)$ and $L'(0.95)$. What do these figures tell you?

100. ◆ *Time Dilation* Another prediction of Einstein's Special Theory of Relativity is that, to a stationary observer, clocks (as well as all biological processes) in a moving object appear to go more and more slowly as the speed of the object approaches that of light. If a spaceship travels at a speed of warp p, the time it takes for an onboard clock to register

---

[56] The model approximates graphical data published in the article *The Brush Turkey* by Roger S. *Seymour, Scientific American*, December, 1991, pp. 108–114.

[57] Ibid.

one second, as measured by a stationary observer, will be given by

$$T(p) = \frac{1}{\sqrt{1 - p^2}} \text{ seconds}$$

with domain $[0, 1)$. Estimate $T(0.95)$ and $T'(0.95)$. What do these figures tell you?

COMMUNICATION AND REASONING EXERCISES

101. Explain why we cannot put $h = 0$ in the approximation

$$f'(x) \approx \frac{f(x + h) - f(x)}{h}$$

for the derivative of f.

102. The balanced difference quotient

$$f'(a) \approx \frac{f(a + 0.0001) - f(a - 0.0001)}{0.0002}$$

is the average rate of change of f on what interval?

103. Let $H(t)$ represent the number of Handbook members in millions t years after its inception in 2020. It is found that $H(10) = 50$ and $H'(10) = -6$. This means that, in 2030 (Multiple Choice):

  (A) There were 6 million members and this number was decreasing at a rate of 50 million per year

  (B) There were –6 million members and this number was increasing at a rate of 50 million per year.

  (C) Membership had dropped by 6 million since the previous year, but was now increasing at a rate of 50 million per year

  (D) There were 50 million members and this number was decreasing at a rate of 6 million per year.

  (E) There were 50 million members and membership had dropped by 6 million since the previous year.

104. Let $F(t)$ represent the net earnings of Footbook Inc. in millions of dollars t years after its inception in 3020. It is found that $F(100) = -10$ and $F'(100) = 60$. This means that, in 3120 (Multiple Choice):

  (A) Footbook lost $10 million but its net earnings were increasing at a rate of $60 million per year.

  (B) Footbook earned $60 million but its earnings were decreasing at a rate of $10 million per year.

  (C) Footbook's net earnings had increased by $60 million since the year before, but it still lost $10 million.

  (D) Footbook earned $10 million but its net earnings were decreasing at a rate of $60 million per year.

  (E) Footbook's net earnings had decreased by $10 million since the year before, but it still earned $60 million.

105. It is now eight months since the Garden City lacrosse team won the national championship, and sales of team paraphernalia, while still increasing, have been leveling off. What does this tell you about the derivative of the sales curve?

106. Having been soundly defeated in the national lacrosse championships, Brakpan High has been faced with decreasing sales of its team paraphernalia. However, sales, while still decreasing, appear to be bottoming out. What does this tell you about the derivative of the sales curve?

107. ▼ Company A's profits are given by $P(0) = \$1$ million and $P'(0) = -\$1$ million/month. Company B's profits are given by $P(0) = -\$1$ million and $P'(0) = \$1$ million/month. In which company would you rather invest? Why?

108. ▼ Company C's profits are given by $P(0) = \$1$ million and $P'(0) = \$0.5$ million/month. Company D's profits are given by $P(0) = \$0.5$ million and $P'(0) = \$1$ million/month. In which company would you rather invest? Why?

109. ▼ During the one-month period starting last January 1, your company's profits increased at an average rate of change of $4 million per month. On January 1, profits were increasing at an instantaneous rate of $5 million per month. Which of the following graphs could represent your company's profits? Why?

(A)

(B)

(C)

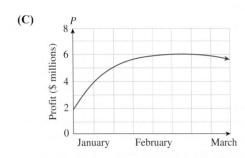

110. ▼ During the one-month period starting last January 1, your company's sales increased at an average rate of change of $3,000 per month. On January 1, sales were changing at an instantaneous rate of –$1,000 per month. Which of the following graphs could represent your company's sales? Why?

(A)

(B)

(C)

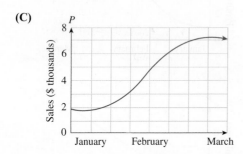

111. ▼ If the derivative of f is zero at a point, what do you know about the graph of f near that point?

112. ▼ Sketch the graph of a function whose derivative never exceeds 1.

113. ▼ Sketch the graph of a function whose derivative exceeds 1 at every point.

114. ▼ Sketch the graph of a function whose derivative is exactly 1 at every point.

115. ▼ Use the difference quotient to explain the fact that if f is a linear function, then the average rate of change over any interval equals the instantaneous rate of change at any point.

116. ▼ Give a numerical explanation of the fact that if f is a linear function, then the average rate of change over any interval equals the instantaneous rate of change at any point.

117. ◆ Consider the following values of the function f from Exercise 1.

h	0.1	0.01	0.001	0.0001
Average Rate of Change of f over [5, 5+h]	6.4	6.04	6.004	6.0004
h	−0.1	−0.01	−0.001	−0.0001
Average Rate of Change of f over [5+h, 5]	5.6	5.96	5.996	5.9996

Does the table suggests that the instantaneous rate of change of f is

(A) increasing   **(B)** decreasing

as x increases toward 5?

118. ◆ Consider the following values of the function g from Exercise 2.

h	0.1	0.01	0.001	0.0001
Average Rate of Change of g over [7, 7+h]	4.8	4.98	4.998	4.9998
h	−0.1	−0.01	−0.001	−0.0001
Average Rate of Change of g over [7+h, 7]	5.3	5.03	5.003	5.0003

Does the table suggest that the instantaneous rate of change of g is

(A) increasing   **(B)** decreasing

as x increases toward 7?

119. ▼ Sketch the graph of a function whose derivative is never zero but decreases as x increases.

120. ▼ Sketch the graph of a function whose derivative is never negative but is zero at exactly two points.

121. ◆ Here is the graph of the derivative f' of a function f. Give a rough sketch of the graph of f, given that $f(0) = 0$.

122. ◆ Here is the graph of the derivative f' of a function f. Give a rough sketch of the graph of f, given that $f(0) = 0$.

123. ◆ Professor Talker of the physics department drove a 60-mile stretch of road in exactly one hour. The speed limit along that stretch was 55 miles per hour. Which of the following must be correct:

(A) He exceeded the speed limit at no point of the journey.

(B) He exceeded the speed limit at some point of the journey.

(C) He exceeded the speed limit throughout the journey.
(D) He traveled slower than the speed limit at some point of the journey.

124. ◆ Professor Silent, another physics professor, drove a 50-mile stretch of road in exactly one hour. The speed limit along that stretch was 55 miles per hour. Which of the following must be correct:

(A) She exceeded the speed limit at no point of the journey.
(B) She exceeded the speed limit at some point of the journey.

(C) She traveled slower than the speed limit throughout the journey.
(D) She traveled slower than the speed limit at some point of the journey.

125. ◆ Draw the graph of a function f with the property that the balanced difference quotient gives a more accurate approximation of $f'(1)$ than the ordinary difference quotient.

126. ◆ Draw the graph of a function f with the property that the balanced difference quotient gives a less accurate approximation of $f'(1)$ than the ordinary difference quotient.

10.6 The Derivative: Algebraic Viewpoint

In Section 10.5 we saw how to estimate the derivative of a function using numerical and graphical approaches. In this section we use an algebraic approach that will give us the *exact value* of the derivative, rather than just an approximation, when the function is specified algebraically.

This algebraic approach is quite straightforward: Instead of subtracting numbers to estimate the average rate of change over smaller and smaller intervals, we subtract algebraic expressions. Our starting point is the definition of the derivative in terms of the difference quotient:

$$f'(a) = \lim_{h \to 0} \frac{f(a+h) - f(a)}{h}.$$

EXAMPLE 1 Calculating the Derivative at a Point Algebraically

Let $f(x) = x^2$. Use the definition of the derivative to compute $f'(3)$ algebraically.

Solution Substituting $a = 3$ into the definition of the derivative, we get:

$$f'(3) = \lim_{h \to 0} \frac{f(3+h) - f(3)}{h} \qquad \text{Formula for the derivative}$$

$$= \lim_{h \to 0} \frac{\overbrace{(3+h)^2}^{f(3+h)} - \overbrace{3^2}^{f(3)}}{h} \qquad \text{Substitute for } f(3) \text{ and } f(3+h).$$

$$= \lim_{h \to 0} \frac{(9 + 6h + h^2) - 9}{h} \qquad \text{Expand } (3+h)^2.$$

$$= \lim_{h \to 0} \frac{6h + h^2}{h} \qquad \text{Cancel the 9.}$$

$$= \lim_{h \to 0} \frac{h(6+h)}{h} \qquad \text{Factor out } h.$$

$$= \lim_{h \to 0} (6+h) \qquad \text{Cancel the } h.$$

Now we let h approach 0. As h gets closer and closer to 0, the sum $6 + h$ clearly gets closer and closer to $6 + 0 = 6$. Thus,

$$f'(3) = \lim_{h \to 0} (6+h) = 6. \qquad \text{As } h \to 0, (6+h) \to 6$$

(Calculations of limits like this are discussed and justified more fully in Sections 10.2 and 10.3.)

Figure 35

➡ **Before we go on...** We did the following calculation in Example 1: If $f(x) = x^2$, then $f'(3) = 6$. In other words, the tangent to the graph of $y = x^2$ at the point $(3, 9)$ has slope 6 (Figure 35). ∎

There is nothing very special about $a = 3$ in Example 1. Let's try to compute $f'(x)$ for general x.

EXAMPLE 2 Calculating the Derivative Function Algebraically

Let $f(x) = x^2$.

a. Use the definition of the derivative to compute $f'(x)$ algebraically.
b. Use the answer to evaluate $f'(3)$.

Solution

a. Once again, our starting point is the definition of the derivative in terms of the difference quotient:

$$f'(x) = \lim_{h \to 0} \frac{f(x+h) - f(x)}{h} \qquad \text{Formula for the derivative}$$

$$= \lim_{h \to 0} \frac{\overbrace{(x+h)^2}^{f(x+h)} - \overbrace{x^2}^{f(x)}}{h} \qquad \text{Substitute for } f(x) \text{ and } f(x+h).$$

$$= \lim_{h \to 0} \frac{(x^2 + 2xh + h^2) - x^2}{h} \qquad \text{Expand } (x+h)^2.$$

$$= \lim_{h \to 0} \frac{2xh + h^2}{h} \qquad \text{Cancel the } x^2.$$

$$= \lim_{h \to 0} \frac{h(2x + h)}{h} \qquad \text{Factor out } h.$$

$$= \lim_{h \to 0} (2x + h) \qquad \text{Cancel the } h.$$

Now we let h approach 0. As h gets closer and closer to 0, the sum $2x + h$ clearly gets closer and closer to $2x + 0 = 2x$. Thus,

$$f'(x) = \lim_{h \to 0} (2x + h) = 2x.$$

This is the derivative function.

b. Now that we have a *formula* for the derivative of f, we can obtain $f'(a)$ for any value of a we choose by simply evaluating f' there. For instance,

$$f'(3) = 2(3) = 6$$

as we saw in Example 1.

Figure 36

➡ **Before we go on...** The graphs of $f(x) = x^2$ and $f'(x) = 2x$ from Example 2 are familiar. Their graphs are shown in Figure 36.

When $x < 0$, the parabola slopes downward, which is reflected in the fact that the derivative $2x$ is negative there. When $x > 0$, the parabola slopes upward, which is reflected in the fact that the derivative is positive there. The parabola has a horizontal tangent line at $x = 0$, reflected in the fact that $2x = 0$ there. ∎

EXAMPLE 3 More Computations of Derivative Functions

Compute the derivative $f'(x)$ for each of the following functions:

a. $f(x) = x^3$ **b.** $f(x) = 2x^2 - x$ **c.** $f(x) = \dfrac{1}{x}$

Solution

a. $f'(x) = \lim\limits_{h \to 0} \dfrac{f(x+h) - f(x)}{h}$ Derivative formula

$= \lim\limits_{h \to 0} \dfrac{\overbrace{(x+h)^3}^{f(x+h)} - \overbrace{x^3}^{f(x)}}{h}$ Substitute for $f(x)$ and $f(x+h)$.

$= \lim\limits_{h \to 0} \dfrac{(x^3 + 3x^2h + 3xh^2 + h^3) - x^3}{h}$ Expand $(x+h)^3$.

$= \lim\limits_{h \to 0} \dfrac{3x^2h + 3xh^2 + h^3}{h}$ Cancel the x^3.

$= \lim\limits_{h \to 0} \dfrac{h(3x^2 + 3xh + h^2)}{h}$ Factor out h.

$= \lim\limits_{h \to 0} (3x^2 + 3xh + h^2)$ Cancel the h.

$= 3x^2.$ Let h approach 0.

b. $f'(x) = \lim\limits_{h \to 0} \dfrac{f(x+h) - f(x)}{h}$ Derivative formula

$= \lim\limits_{h \to 0} \dfrac{\overbrace{(2(x+h)^2 - (x+h))}^{f(x+h)} - \overbrace{(2x^2 - x)}^{f(x)}}{h}$ Substitute for $f(x)$ and $f(x+h)$.

$= \lim\limits_{h \to 0} \dfrac{(2x^2 + 4xh + 2h^2 - x - h) - (2x^2 - x)}{h}$ Expand.

$= \lim\limits_{h \to 0} \dfrac{4xh + 2h^2 - h}{h}$ Cancel the $2x^2$ and x.

$= \lim\limits_{h \to 0} \dfrac{h(4x + 2h - 1)}{h}$ Factor out h.

$= \lim\limits_{h \to 0} (4x + 2h - 1)$ Cancel the h.

$= 4x - 1.$ Let h approach 0.

c. $f'(x) = \lim\limits_{h \to 0} \dfrac{f(x+h) - f(x)}{h}$ Derivative formula

$= \lim\limits_{h \to 0} \dfrac{\left[\overbrace{\dfrac{1}{x+h}}^{f(x+h)} - \overbrace{\dfrac{1}{x}}^{f(x)} \right]}{h}$ Substitute for $f(x)$ and $f(x+h)$.

$= \lim\limits_{h \to 0} \dfrac{\left[\dfrac{x - (x+h)}{(x+h)x} \right]}{h}$ Subtract the fractions.

$$= \lim_{h \to 0} \frac{1}{h} \left[\frac{x - (x+h)}{(x+h)x} \right]$$ Dividing by h = Multiplying by $1/h$.

$$= \lim_{h \to 0} \left[\frac{-h}{h(x+h)x} \right]$$ Simplify.

$$= \lim_{h \to 0} \left[\frac{-1}{(x+h)x} \right]$$ Cancel the h.

$$= \frac{-1}{x^2}$$ Let h approach 0.

In Example 4, we redo Example 3 of Section 10.5, this time getting an exact, rather than approximate, answer.

Joseph Gareri/istockphoto.com

EXAMPLE 4 **Velocity**

My friend Eric, an enthusiastic baseball player, claims he can "probably" throw a ball upward at a speed of 100 feet per second (ft/s). Our physicist friends tell us that its height s (in feet) t seconds later would be $s(t) = 100t - 16t^2$. Find the ball's instantaneous velocity function and its velocity exactly 2 seconds after Eric throws it.

Solution The instantaneous velocity function is the derivative ds/dt, which we calculate as follow:

$$\frac{ds}{dt} = \lim_{h \to 0} \frac{s(t+h) - s(t)}{h}$$

Let us compute $s(t+h)$ and $s(t)$ separately:

$$s(t) = 100t - 16t^2$$
$$s(t+h) = 100(t+h) - 16(t+h)^2$$
$$= 100t + 100h - 16(t^2 + 2th + h^2)$$
$$= 100t + 100h - 16t^2 - 32th - 16h^2.$$

Therefore,

$$\frac{ds}{dt} = \lim_{h \to 0} \frac{s(t+h) - s(t)}{h}$$

$$= \lim_{h \to 0} \frac{100t + 100h - 16t^2 - 32th - 16h^2 - (100t - 16t^2)}{h}$$

$$= \lim_{h \to 0} \frac{100h - 32th - 16h^2}{h}$$

$$= \lim_{h \to 0} \frac{h(100 - 32t - 16h)}{h}$$

$$= \lim_{h \to 0} (100 - 32t - 16h)$$

$$= 100 - 32t \text{ ft/s.}$$

Thus, the velocity exactly 2 seconds after Eric throws it is

$$\left. \frac{ds}{dt} \right|_{t=2} = 100 - 32(2) = 36 \text{ ft/s.}$$

This verifies the accuracy of the approximation we made in Section 10.5.

➡️ **Before we go on...** From the derivative function in Example 4, we can now describe the behavior of the velocity of the ball: Immediately on release ($t = 0$) the ball is traveling at 100 feet per second upward. The ball then slows down; precisely, it loses 32 feet per second of speed every second. When, exactly, does the velocity become zero and what happens after that? ■

Q : *Do we always have to calculate the limit of the difference quotient to find a formula for the derivative function?*

A : As it turns out, no. In Section 11.1 we will start to look at shortcuts for finding derivatives that allow us to bypass the definition of the derivative in many cases.

A Function Not Differentiable at a Point

Recall from Section 10.5 that a function is **differentiable** at a point a if $f'(a)$ exists; that is, if the difference quotient $[f(a + h) - f(a)]/h$ approaches a fixed value as h approaches 0. In Section 10.5, we mentioned that the function $f(x) = |x|$ is not differentiable at $x = 0$. In Example 5, we find out why.

EXAMPLE 5 A Function Not Differentiable at 0

Numerically, graphically, and algebraically investigate the differentiability of the function $f(x) = |x|$ at the points **(a)** $x = 1$ and **(b)** $x = 0$.

Solution

a. We compute

$$f'(1) = \lim_{h \to 0} \frac{f(1 + h) - f(1)}{h}$$

$$= \lim_{h \to 0} \frac{|1 + h| - 1}{h}.$$

Numerically, we can make tables of the values of the average rate of change $(|1 + h| - 1)/h$ for h positive or negative and approaching 0:

h	1	0.1	0.01	0.001	0.0001
Average Rate of Change Over $[1, 1 + h]$	1	1	1	1	1

h	-1	-0.1	-0.01	-0.001	-0.0001
Average Rate of Change Over $[1 + h, 1]$	1	1	1	1	1

From these tables it appears that $f'(1)$ is equal to 1. We can verify that algebraically: For h that is sufficiently small, $1 + h$ is positive (even if h is negative) and so

$$f'(1) = \lim_{h \to 0} \frac{1 + h - 1}{h}$$

$$= \lim_{h \to 0} \frac{h}{h} \qquad \text{Cancel the 1s.}$$

$$= \lim_{h \to 0} 1 \qquad \text{Cancel the } h.$$

$$= 1$$

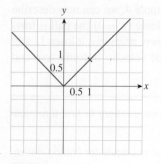

Figure 37

Graphically, we are seeing the fact that the tangent line at the point $(1, 1)$ has slope 1 because the graph is a straight line with slope 1 near that point (Figure 37).

b. $f'(0) = \lim\limits_{h \to 0} \dfrac{f(0 + h) - f(0)}{h}$

$= \lim\limits_{h \to 0} \dfrac{|0 + h| - 0}{h}$

$= \lim\limits_{h \to 0} \dfrac{|h|}{h}$

If we make tables of values in this case we get the following:

h	1	0.1	0.01	0.001	0.0001
Average Rate of Change over $[0, 0 + h]$	1	1	1	1	1

h	-1	-0.1	-0.01	-0.001	-0.0001
Average Rate of Change over $[0 + h, 0]$	-1	-1	-1	-1	-1

For the limit and hence the derivative $f'(0)$ to exist, the average rates of change should approach the same number for both positive and negative h. Because they do not, f is not differentiable at $x = 0$. We can verify this conclusion algebraically: If h is positive, then $|h| = h$, and so the ratio $|h|/h$ is 1, regardless of how small h is. Thus, according to the values of the difference quotients with $h > 0$, the limit should be 1. On the other hand if h is negative, then $|h| = -h$ (positive) and so $|h|/h = -1$, meaning that the limit should be -1. Because the limit cannot be both -1 and 1 (it must be a single number for the derivative to exist), we conclude that $f'(0)$ does not exist.

To see what is happening graphically, take a look at Figure 38, which shows zoomed-in views of the graph of f near $x = 0$.

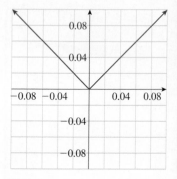

Figure 38

No matter what scale we use to view the graph, it has a sharp corner at $x = 0$ and hence has no tangent line there. Since there is no tangent line at $x = 0$, the function is not differentiable there.

➡ **Before we go on...** Notice that $|x| = \begin{cases} -x & \text{if } x < 0 \\ x & \text{if } x \geq 0 \end{cases}$ is an example of a piecewise-

linear function whose graph comes to a point at $x = 0$. In general, if $f(x)$ is any piecewise linear function whose graph comes to a point at $x = a$, it will be non-differentiable at $x = a$ for the same reason that $|x|$ fails to be differentiable at $x = 0$.

If we repeat the computation in Example 5(a) using any nonzero value for a in place of 1, we see that f is differentiable there as well. If a is positive, we find that $f'(a) = 1$ and, if a is negative, $f'(a) = -1$. In other words, the derivative function is

$$f'(x) = \begin{cases} -1 & \text{if } x < 0 \\ 1 & \text{if } x > 0 \end{cases}.$$

Immediately to the left of $x = 0$, we see that $f'(x) = -1$, immediately to the right, $f'(x) = 1$, and when $x = 0$, $f'(x)$ is not defined. ■

FAQ

Computing Derivatives Algebraically

Q: The algebraic computation of $f'(x)$ seems to require a number of steps. How do I remember what to do, and when?

A: If you examine the computations in the previous examples, you will find the following pattern:

1. Write out the formula for $f'(x)$, as the limit of the difference quotient, then substitute $f(x + h)$ and $f(x)$.
2. Expand and simplify the *numerator* of the expression, but not the denominator.
3. After simplifying the numerator, factor out an h to cancel with the h in the denominator. If h does not factor out of the numerator, you might have made an error. (A frequent error is a wrong sign.)
4. After canceling the h, you should be able to see what the limit is by letting $h \to 0$.

10.6 EXERCISES

▼ more advanced ◆ challenging
T indicates exercises that should be solved using technology

In Exercises 1–14, compute $f'(a)$ algebraically for the given value of a. HINT [See Example 1.]

1. $f(x) = x^2 + 1; a = 2$

2. $f(x) = x^2 - 3; a = 1$

3. $f(x) = 3x - 4; a = -1$

4. $f(x) = -2x + 4; a = -1$

5. $f(x) = 3x^2 + x; a = 1$

6. $f(x) = 2x^2 + x; a = -2$

7. $f(x) = 2x - x^2; a = -1$

8. $f(x) = -x - x^2; a = 0$

9. $f(x) = x^3 + 2x; a = 2$

10. $f(x) = x - 2x^3; a = 1$

11. $f(x) = \dfrac{-1}{x}; a = 1$ HINT [See Example 3.]

12. $f(x) = \dfrac{2}{x}; a = 5$ HINT [See Example 3.]

13. ▼ $f(x) = mx + b; a = 43$

14. ▼ $f(x) = \dfrac{x}{k} - b \ (k \neq 0); a = 12$

In Exercises 15–28, compute the derivative function $f'(x)$ algebraically. (Notice that the functions are the same as those in Exercises 1–14.) HINT [See Examples 2 and 3.]

15. $f(x) = x^2 + 1$ 16. $f(x) = x^2 - 3$

17. $f(x) = 3x - 4$ 18. $f(x) = -2x + 4$

19. $f(x) = 3x^2 + x$ 20. $f(x) = 2x^2 + x$

21. $f(x) = 2x - x^2$ 22. $f(x) = -x - x^2$

23. $f(x) = x^3 + 2x$ 24. $f(x) = x - 2x^3$

25. ▼ $f(x) = \dfrac{-1}{x}$ 26. ▼ $f(x) = \dfrac{2}{x}$

27. ▼ $f(x) = mx + b$ 28. ▼ $f(x) = \dfrac{x}{k} - b \ (k \neq 0)$

In Exercises 29–38, compute the indicated derivative.

29. $R(t) = -0.3t^2; R'(2)$

30. $S(t) = 1.4t^2$; $S'(-1)$

31. $U(t) = 5.1t^2 + 5.1$; $U'(3)$

32. $U(t) = -1.3t^2 + 1.1$; $U'(4)$

33. $U(t) = -1.3t^2 - 4.5t$; $U'(1)$

34. $U(t) = 5.1t^2 - 1.1t$; $U'(1)$

35. $L(r) = 4.25r - 5.01$; $L'(1.2)$

36. $L(r) = -1.02r + 5.7$; $L'(3.1)$

37. ▼ $q(p) = \dfrac{2.4}{p} + 3.1$; $q'(2)$

38. ▼ $q(p) = \dfrac{1}{0.5p} - 3.1$; $q'(2)$

In Exercises 39–44, find the equation of the tangent to the graph at the indicated point. HINT [Compute the derivative algebraically; then see Example 2(b) in Section 10.5.]

39. ▼ $f(x) = x^2 - 3$; $a = 2$ 40. ▼ $f(x) = x^2 + 1$; $a = 2$

41. ▼ $f(x) = -2x - 4$; $a = 3$ 42. ▼ $f(x) = 3x + 1$; $a = 1$

43. ▼ $f(x) = x^2 - x$; $a = -1$ 44. ▼ $f(x) = x^2 + x$; $a = -1$

APPLICATIONS

45. **Velocity** If a stone is dropped from a height of 400 feet, its height after t seconds is given by $s = 400 - 16t^2$. Find its instantaneous velocity function and its velocity at time $t = 4$. HINT [See Example 4.]

46. **Velocity** If a stone is thrown down at 120 feet per second from a height of 1,000 feet, its height after t seconds is given by $s = 1,000 - 120t - 16t^2$. Find its instantaneous velocity function and its velocity at time $t = 3$. HINT [See Example 4.]

47. **Oil Imports from Mexico** Daily oil imports to the United States from Mexico can be approximated by

$I(t) = -0.015t^2 + 0.1t + 1.4$ million barrels $(0 \le t \le 8)$

where t is time in years since the start of 2000.[58] Find the derivative function $\dfrac{dI}{dt}$. At what rate were oil imports changing at the start of 2007 ($t = 7$)? HINT [See Example 4.]

48. **Oil Production in Mexico** Daily oil production by **Pemex**, Mexico's national oil company, can be approximated by

$P(t) = -0.022t^2 + 0.2t + 2.9$ million barrels $(1 \le t \le 9)$

where t is time in years since the start of 2000.[59] Find the derivative function $\dfrac{dP}{dt}$. At what rate was oil production changing at the start of 2004 ($t = 4$)? HINT [See Example 4.]

49. **Bottled Water Sales** Annual U.S. sales of bottled water rose through the period 2000–2008 as shown in the following chart.[60]

---

58 Source for data: Energy Information Administration/Pemex (http://www.eia.doe.gov).

59 Ibid.

60 The 2008 figure is an estimate. Source: Beverage Marketing Corporation, www.bottledwater.org.

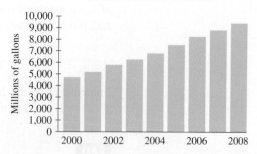

Bottled water sales in the U.S.

The function

$R(t) = 12t^2 + 500t + 4,700$ million gallons $(0 \le t \le 8)$

gives a good approximation, where t is time in years since 2000. Find the derivative function $R'(t)$. According to the model, how fast were annual sales of bottled water increasing in 2005?

50. **Bottled Water Sales** Annual U.S. per capita sales of bottled water rose through the period 2000–2008 as shown in the following chart.[61]

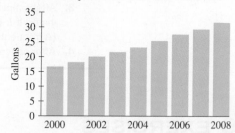

Per capita bottled water sales in the U.S.

The function

$$Q(t) = 0.04t^2 + 1.5t + 17 \text{ gallons} \qquad (0 \le t \le 8)$$

gives a good approximation, where t is the time in years since 2000. Find the derivative function $Q'(t)$. According to the model, how fast were annual per capita sales of bottled water increasing in 2008?

51. ▼ **Ecology** Increasing numbers of manatees ("sea sirens") have been killed by boats off the Florida coast. The following graph shows the relationship between the number of boats registered in Florida and the number of manatees killed each year.

---

61 Ibid.

The regression curve shown is given by

$$f(x) = 3.55x^2 - 30.2x + 81 \text{ manatee deaths}$$
$$(4.5 \leq x \leq 8.5)$$

where x is the number of boats (hundreds of thousands) registered in Florida in a particular year and $f(x)$ is the number of manatees killed by boats in Florida that year.[62] Compute and interpret $f'(8)$.

52. ▼ **SAT Scores by Income** The following graph shows U.S. verbal SAT scores as a function of parents' income level.[63]

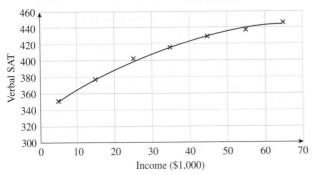

The regression curve shown is given by

$$f(x) = -0.021x^2 + 3.0x + 336 \quad (5 \leq x \leq 65)$$

where $f(x)$ is the average SAT verbal score of a student whose parents earn x thousand dollars per year. Compute and interpret $f'(30)$.

53. ▼ **Television Advertising** The cost, in millions of dollars, of a 30-second television ad during the Super Bowl in the years 1990 to 2007 can be approximated by the following piecewise linear function ($t = 0$ represents 1990):[64]

$$C(t) = \begin{cases} 0.08t + 0.6 & \text{if } 0 \leq t < 8 \\ 0.13t + 0.20 & \text{if } 8 \leq t \leq 17 \end{cases}$$

a. Is C a continuous function of t? Why? HINT [See Example 4 of Section 10.3.]

b. Is C a differentiable function of t? Compute $\lim_{t \to 8^-} C'(t)$ and $\lim_{t \to 8^+} C'(t)$ and interpret the results. HINT [See *Before we go on...* after Example 5.]

54. ▼ **Processor Speeds** The processor speed, in megahertz (MHz), of **Intel** processors can be approximated by the following function of time t in years since the start of 1995:[65]

$$P(t) = \begin{cases} 180t + 200 & \text{if } 0 \leq t \leq 5 \\ 3,000t - 13,900 & \text{if } 5 < t \leq 12 \end{cases}$$

---

[62] Regression model is based on data from 1976 to 2000. Sources for data: Florida Department of Highway Safety & Motor Vehicles, Florida Marine Institute/*New York Times*, February 12, 2002, p. F4.

[63] Based on 1994 data. Source: The College Board/*New York Times*, March 5, 1995, p. E16.

[64] Sources for data: *New York Times*, January 26, 2001, p. C1., www.money.cnn.com.

[65] Sources for data: Sandpile.org/*New York Times*, May 17, 2004, p. C1 and www.Intel.com.

a. Is P a continuous function of t? Why? HINT [See Example 4 of Section 10.3.]

b. Is P a differentiable function of t? Compute $\lim_{t \to 5^-} P'(t)$ and $\lim_{t \to 5^+} P'(t)$ and interpret the results. HINT [See *Before we go on...* after Example 5.]

COMMUNICATION AND REASONING EXERCISES

55. Of the three methods (numerical, graphical, algebraic) we can use to estimate the derivative of a function at a given value of x, which is always the most accurate? Explain.

56. Explain why we cannot put $h = 0$ in the formula

$$f'(a) = \lim_{h \to 0} \frac{f(a + h) - f(a)}{h}$$

for the derivative of f.

57. You just got your derivatives test back and you can't understand why that teacher of yours deducted so many points for what you thought was your best work:

$$\lim_{h \to 0} \frac{f(x + h) - f(x)}{h}$$
$$= \lim_{h \to 0} \frac{f(x) + h - f(x)}{h}$$
$$= \lim_{h \to 0} \frac{h}{h} \qquad \text{Canceled the } f(x)$$
$$= 1 \qquad \qquad ✗ \text{ WRONG } -10$$

What was wrong with your answer?

58. Your friend just got his derivatives test back and can't understand why that teacher of his deducted so many points for the following:

$$\lim_{h \to 0} \frac{f(x + h) - f(x)}{h}$$
$$= \lim_{h \to 0} \frac{f(x) + f(h) - f(x)}{h}$$
$$= \lim_{h \to 0} \frac{f(h)}{h} \qquad \text{Canceled the } f(x)$$
$$= \lim_{h \to 0} \frac{f(h)}{h} \qquad \text{Now cancel the } h.$$
$$= f() \qquad \qquad ✗ \text{ WRONG } -50$$

What was wrong with his answer?

59. Your other friend just got her derivatives test back and can't understand why that teacher of hers took off so many points for the following:

$$\lim_{h \to 0} \frac{f(x + h) - f(x)}{h}$$
$$= \lim_{h \to 0} \frac{f(x + h) - f(x)}{h} \qquad \text{Now cancel the } h.$$
$$= \lim_{h \to 0} f(x) - f(x) \qquad \text{Canceled the } f(x)$$
$$= 0 \qquad \qquad ✗ \text{ WRONG } -15$$

What was wrong with his answer?

60. Your third friend just got her derivatives test back and can't understand why that teacher of hers took off so many points for the following:

$$\lim_{h\to 0} \frac{f(x+h) - f(x)}{h}$$

$$= \lim_{h\to 0} \frac{f(x) + h - f(x)}{h}$$

$$= \lim_{h\to 0} \frac{f(x) + h - f(x)}{h} \qquad \text{Now cancel the } h.$$

$$= \lim_{h\to 0} f(x) - f(x) \qquad \text{Canceled the } f(x)$$

$$= 0 \qquad\qquad\qquad\qquad \text{✗ } WRONG \quad -25$$

What was wrong with her answer?

61. Your friend Muffy claims that, because the balanced difference quotient is more accurate, it would be better to use that instead of the usual difference quotient when computing the derivative algebraically. Comment on this advice.

62. Use the balanced difference quotient formula,

$$f'(a) = \lim_{h\to 0} \frac{f(a+h) - f(a-h)}{2h}$$

to compute $f'(3)$ when $f(x) = x^2$. What do you find?

63. ▼ A certain function f has the property that $f'(a)$ does not exist. How is that reflected in the attempt to compute $f'(a)$ algebraically?

64. ▼ One cannot put $h = 0$ in the formula

$$f'(a) = \lim_{h\to 0} \frac{f(a+h) - f(a)}{h}$$

for the derivative of f. (See Exercise 56.) However, in the last step of each of the computations in the text, we are effectively setting $h = 0$ when taking the limit. What is going on here?

KEY CONCEPTS

Web Site www.FiniteandCalc.org
Go to the student Web site at
www.FiniteandCalc.org to find a
comprehensive and interactive
Web-based summary of Chapter 10.

10.1 Limits: Numerical and Graphical Approaches

$\lim_{x \to a} f(x) = L$ means that $f(x)$
approaches L as x approaches a *p. 690*

What it means for a limit to exist *p. 690*

Limits at infinity *p. 692*

Estimating limits graphically *p. 695*

Interpreting limits in real-world
situations *p. 696*

10.2 Limits and Continuity

f is continuous at a if $\lim_{x \to a} f(x)$ exists
and $\lim_{x \to a} f(x) = f(a)$ *p. 701*

Discontinuous, continuous on domain *p. 701*

Determining whether a given function is
continuous *p. 701*

10.3 Limits and Continuity: Algebraic Approach

Closed-form function *p. 706*

Limits of closed form functions *p. 707*

Simplifying to obtain limits *p. 707*

The indeterminate form 0/0 *p. 708*

The determinate form $k/0$ *p. 709*

Limits of piecewise defined
functions *p. 711*

Limits at infinity *p. 712*

Determinate and indeterminate
forms *p. 715*

10.4 Average Rate of Change

Average rate of change of $f(x)$ over

$[a, b]$: $\dfrac{\Delta f}{\Delta x} = \dfrac{f(b) - f(a)}{b - a}$ *p. 723*

Average rate of change as slope of the
secant line *p. 723*

Computing the average rate of change
from a graph *p. 724*

Computing the average rate of change
from a formula *p. 725*

Computing the average rate of change
over short intervals $[a, a + h]$ *p. 726*

10.5 The Derivative: Numerical and Graphical Viewpoints

Instantaneous rate of change of $f(x)$
(derivative of f at a);

$f'(a) = \lim_{h \to 0} \dfrac{f(a + h) - f(a)}{h}$ *p. 736*

The derivative as slope of the tangent
line *p. 739*

Quick approximation of the derivative
p. 741

$\dfrac{d}{dx}$ Notation *p. 743*

The derivative as velocity *p. 743*

Average and instantaneous velocity *p. 745*

The derivative function *p. 746*

Graphing the derivative function with
technology *p. 747*

10.6 The Derivative: Algebraic Viewpoint

Derivative at the point $x = a$:

$f'(a) = \lim_{h \to 0} \dfrac{f(a + h) - f(a)}{h}$ *p. 759*

Derivative function:

$f'(x) = \lim_{h \to 0} \dfrac{f(x + h) - f(x)}{h}$ *p. 760*

Examples of the computation of $f'(x)$
p. 761

$f(x) = |x|$ is not differentiable at $x = 0$
p. 763

REVIEW EXERCISES

 indicates exercises that must be solved using technology

Numerically *estimate whether the limits in Exercises 1–4 exist.
If a limit does exist, give its approximate value.*

1. $\lim_{x \to 3} \dfrac{x^2 - x - 6}{x - 3}$

2. $\lim_{x \to 3} \dfrac{x^2 - 2x - 6}{x - 3}$

3. $\lim_{x \to -1} \dfrac{|x + 1|}{x^2 - x - 2}$

4. $\lim_{x \to -1} \dfrac{|x + 1|}{x^2 + x - 2}$

*In Exercises 5 and 6, the graph of a function f is shown.
Graphically determine whether the given limits exist. If a limit
does exist, give its approximate value.*

5.

6.

a. $\lim_{x \to 0} f(x)$ **b.** $\lim_{x \to 1} f(x)$

c. $\lim_{x \to 2} f(x)$

a. $\lim_{x \to 0} f(x)$ **b.** $\lim_{x \to -2} f(x)$

c. $\lim_{x \to 2} f(x)$

*Calculate the limits in Exercises 7–24 algebraically. If a limit
does not exist, say why.*

7. $\lim_{x \to -2} \dfrac{x^2}{x - 3}$

8. $\lim_{x \to 3} \dfrac{x^2 - 9}{2x - 6}$

9. $\lim_{x \to 0} \dfrac{x}{2x^2 - x}$

10. $\lim_{x \to 1} \dfrac{x^2 - 9}{x - 1}$

11. $\lim_{x \to -1} \dfrac{x^2 + 3x}{x^2 - x - 2}$

12. $\lim_{x \to -1^+} \dfrac{x^2 + 1}{x^2 + 3x + 2}$

13. $\lim_{x \to 4} \dfrac{x^2 + 8}{x^2 - 2x - 8}$

14. $\lim_{x \to 4} \dfrac{x^2 + 3x}{x^2 - 8x + 16}$

15. $\lim_{x \to 1/2} \dfrac{x^2 + 8}{4x^2 - 4x + 1}$

16. $\lim_{x \to 1/2} \dfrac{x^2 + 3x}{2x^2 + 3x - 1}$

17. $\lim_{x \to -\infty} \dfrac{x^2 - x - 6}{x - 3}$

18. $\lim_{x \to \infty} \dfrac{x^2 - x - 6}{4x^2 - 3}$

19. $\lim_{t \to +\infty} \dfrac{-5}{5 + 5.3(3^{2t})}$

20. $\lim_{t \to +\infty} \left(3 + \dfrac{2}{e^{4t}}\right)$

21. $\lim_{x \to +\infty} \dfrac{2}{5 + 4e^{-3x}}$

22. $\lim_{x \to +\infty} (4e^{3x} + 12)$

23. $\lim_{t \to +\infty} \dfrac{1 + 2^{-3t}}{1 + 5.3e^{-t}}$

24. $\lim_{x \to -\infty} \dfrac{8 + 0.5^x}{2 - 3^{2x}}$

In Exercises 25–28, find the average rate of change of the given function over the interval $[a, a+h]$ *for* $h = 1, 0.01,$ *and* 0.001. *(Round answers to four decimal places.) Then estimate the slope of the tangent line to the graph of the function at a.*

25. $f(x) = \frac{1}{x+1}$; $a = 0$ **26.** $f(x) = x^x$; $a = 2$

27. $f(x) = e^{2x}$; $a = 0$ **28.** $f(x) = \ln(2x)$; $a = 1$

In Exercises 29–32 you are given the graph of a function with four points marked. Determine at which (if any) of these points the derivative of the function is: (i) −1 (ii) 0 (iii) 1, and (iv) 2.

29.

30.

31.

32.

33. Let f have the graph shown.

Select the correct answer.

a. The average rate of change of f over the interval $[0, 2]$ is
  (A) greater than $f'(0)$ **(B)** less than $f'(0)$
  (C) approximately equal to $f'(0)$

b. The average rate of change of f over the interval $[-1, 1]$ is
  (A) greater than $f'(0)$ **(B)** less than $f'(0)$
  (C) approximately equal to $f'(0)$

c. Over the interval $[0, 2]$, the instantaneous rate of change of f is
  (A) increasing   **(B)** decreasing
  (C) neither increasing nor decreasing

d. Over the interval $[-2, 2]$, the instantaneous rate of change of f is
  (A) increasing, then decreasing
  (B) decreasing, then increasing
  (C) approximately constant

e. When $x = 2$, $f(x)$ is
  (A) approximately 1 and increasing at a rate of about 2.5 units per unit of x
  (B) approximately 1.2 and increasing at a rate of about 1 unit per unit of x

(C) approximately 2.5 and increasing at a rate of about 0.5 units per unit of x
(D) approximately 2.5 and increasing at a rate of about 2.5 units per unit of x

34. Let f have the graph shown.

Select the correct answer.

a. The average rate of change of f over the interval $[0, 1]$ is
  (A) greater than $f'(0)$ **(B)** less than $f'(0)$
  (C) approximately equal to $f'(0)$

b. The average rate of change of f over the interval $[0, 2]$ is
  (A) greater than $f'(1)$ **(B)** less than $f'(1)$
  (C) approximately equal to $f'(1)$

c. Over the interval $[-2, 0]$, the instantaneous rate of change of f is
  (A) increasing   **(B)** decreasing
  (C) neither increasing nor decreasing

d. Over the interval $[-2, 2]$, the instantaneous rate of change of f is
  (A) increasing, then decreasing
  (B) decreasing, then increasing
  (C) approximately constant

e. When $x = 0$, $f(x)$ is
  (A) approximately 0 and increasing at a rate of about 1.5 units per unit of x
  (B) approximately 0 and decreasing at a rate of about 1.5 units per unit of x
  (C) approximately 1.5 and neither increasing nor decreasing
  (D) approximately 0 and neither increasing nor decreasing

In Exercises 35–38, use the definition of the derivative to calculate the derivative of each of the given functions algebraically.

35. $f(x) = x^2 + x$ **36.** $f(x) = 3x^2 - x + 1$

37. $f(x) = 1 - \frac{2}{x}$ **38.** $f(x) = \frac{1}{x} + 1$

T *In Exercises 39–42, use technology to graph the derivative of the given function. In each case, choose a range of x-values and y-values that shows the interesting features of the graph.*

39. $f(x) = 10x^5 + \frac{1}{2}x^4 - x + 2$

40. $f(x) = \frac{10}{x^5} + \frac{1}{2x^4} - \frac{1}{x} + 2$

41. $f(x) = 3x^3 + 3\sqrt[3]{x}$

42. $f(x) = \frac{2}{x^{2.1}} - \frac{x^{0.1}}{2}$

APPLICATIONS

43. *Stock Investments* OHaganBooks.com CEO John O'Hagan has terrible luck with stocks. The following graph shows the value of Fly-By-Night Airlines stock that he bought acting on a "hot tip" from Marjory Duffin (CEO of Duffin Press and a close business associate):

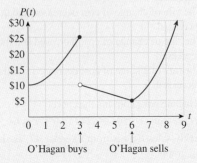

Fly-by-night stock

a. Compute $P(3)$, $\lim_{t\to 3^-} P(t)$ and $\lim_{t\to 3^+} P(t)$. Does $\lim_{t\to 3} P(t)$ exist? Interpret your answers in terms of Fly-By-Night stock.

b. Is P continuous at $t = 6$? Is P differentiable at $t = 6$? Interpret your answers in terms of Fly-By-Night stock.

44. *Stock Investments* John O'Hagan's golf partner Juan Robles seems to have had better luck with his investment in Gapple Gomputer Inc. stocks as shown in the following graph:

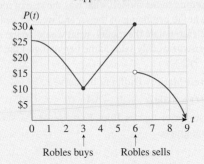

Gapple Inc. Stock

a. Compute $P(6)$, $\lim_{t\to 6^-} P(t)$ and $\lim_{t\to 6^+} P(t)$. Does $\lim_{t\to 6} P(t)$ exist? Interpret your answers in terms of Gapple stock.

b. Is P continuous at $t = 3$? Is P differentiable at $t = 3$? Interpret your answers in terms of Gapple stock.

45. *Real Estate* Marjory Duffin has persuaded John O'Hagan to consider investing a portion of OHaganBooks.com profits in real estate, now that the real estate market seems to have bottomed out. A real estate broker friend of hers e-mailed her the following (somewhat optimistic) graph from brokersadvocacy.com:[66]

---

[66] Authors' note: As of August 2008, brokersadvocacy.com is unregistered.

Home price index

Here, $p(t)$ is the home price percentage over the 2003 level.

a. Assuming the trend shown in the graph were to continue indefinitely, estimate $\lim_{t\to 3} p(t)$ and $\lim_{t\to +\infty} p(t)$ and interpret the results.

b. Estimate $\lim_{t\to +\infty} p'(t)$ and interpret the result.

46. *Advertising Costs* OHaganBooks.com has (on further advice from Marjory Duffin) mounted an aggressive online marketing strategy. The following graph shows the weekly cost of this campaign for the six-week period since the start of July (t is time in weeks):

a. Assuming the trend shown in the graph were to continue indefinitely, estimate $\lim_{t\to 2} C(t)$ and $\lim_{t\to +\infty} C(t)$ and interpret the results.

b. Estimate $\lim_{t\to +\infty} C'(t)$ and interpret the result.

47. *Sales* Since the start of July, OHaganBooks.com has seen its weekly sales increase, as shown in the following table:

Week	1	2	3	4	5	6
Sales (books)	6,500	7,000	7,200	7,800	8,500	9,000

a. What was the average rate of increase of weekly sales over this entire period?

b. During which 1-week interval(s) did the rate of increase of sales exceed the average rate?

c. During which 2-week interval(s) did the weekly sales rise at the highest average rate, and what was that average rate?

48. *Rising Sea Level* Marjory Duffin recently purchased a beachfront condominium in New York and is now in a panic, having just seen some disturbing figures about rising sea levels (sea levels as measured in New York relative to the 1900 level).[67]

Year since 1900	0	25	50	75	100	125
Sea Level (mm)	0	60	140	240	310	390

a. What was the average rate of increase of the sea level over this entire period?

b. During which 25-year interval(s) did the rate of increase of the sea level exceed the average rate?

c. Marjory Duffin's condominium is about 2 meters above sea level. Using the average rate of change from part (a), estimate how long she has before the sea rises to her condominium.

49. *Real Estate* The following graph (see Exercise 45) shows the home price index chart e-mailed to Marjory Duffin by a real estate broker:

Home price index

Use the graph to answer the following questions:

a. What was the average rate of change of the index over the 10-year period beginning 2004?

b. What was the average rate of change of the index over the period [3, 10]?

c. Which of the following is correct? Over the period [4, 6],

(A) The rate of change of the index increased.

(B) The rate of change of the index increased and then decreased.

(C) The rate of change of the index decreased.

(D) The rate of change of the index decreased and then increased.

50. *Advertising Costs* The following graph (see Exercise 46) shows the weekly cost of OHaganBooks.com's online ad campaign for the six-week period since the start of July (t is time in weeks).

Use the graph to answer the following questions:

a. What was the average rate of change of cost over the entire six-week period?

b. What was the average rate of change of cost over the period [2, 6]?

c. Which of the following is correct? Over the period [2, 6],

(A) The rate of change of cost increased and the cost increased.

(B) The rate of change of cost decreased and the cost increased.

(C) The rate of change of cost increased and the cost decreased.

(D) The rate of change of cost decreased and the cost decreased.

51. *Sales* OHaganBooks.com fits the curve
$$w(t) = 36t^2 + 250t + 6240 \quad (0 \le t \le 6)$$
to its weekly sales figures from Exercise 47, as shown in the following graph:

a. Compute the derivative function $w'(t)$.

b. According to the model, what was the rate of increase of sales at the beginning of the second week ($t = 1$)?

c. If we extrapolate the model, what would be the rate of increase of weekly sales at the beginning of the 8th week ($t = 7$)?

52. *Sea Levels* Marjory Duffin fit the curve
$$s(t) = 0.002t^2 + 3t - 6.4 \quad (0 \le t \le 125)$$
to her sea level figures from Exercise 48, as shown in the following graph:

a. Compute the derivative function $s'(t)$.

b. According to the model, what was the rate of increase of the sea level in 2000 ($t = 100$)?

c. If we extrapolate the model, what would be the rate of increase of the sea level in 2100 ($t = 200$)?

Case Study   Reducing Sulfur Emissions

The Environmental Protection Agency (EPA) wishes to formulate a policy that will encourage utilities to reduce sulfur emissions. Its goal is to reduce annual emissions of sulfur dioxide by a total of 10 million tons from the current level of 25 million tons by imposing a fixed charge for every ton of sulfur released into the environment per year. As a consultant to the EPA, you must determine the amount to be charged per ton of sulfur emissions.

You would like first to know the cost to the utility industry of reducing sulfur emissions. In other words, you would like to have a cost function of the form

$$C(q) = \text{Cost of removing } q \text{ tons of sulfur dioxide.}$$

Unfortunately, you do not have such a function handy. You do, however, have the following data, which show the *marginal* cost (that is, the *rate of change* of cost) to the utility industry of reducing sulfur emissions at several levels of reduction.[68]

Reduction (tons) q	8,000,000	10,000,000	12,000,000
Marginal Cost ($ per ton) $C'(q)$	270	360	779

C

Cost of reducing sulfur emissions by q tons

0   5   10   15 q

Million tons of sulfur reduction

Figure 39

The table tells you that $C'(8,000,000) = \$270$ per ton, $C'(10,000,000) = \$360$ per ton, and $C'(12,000,000) = \$779$ per ton. Recalling that $C'(q)$ is the slope of the tangent to the graph of the cost function, you can see from the table that this slope is positive and increasing as q increases, so the graph of the cost function has the general shape shown in Figure 39.

Notice that the slope (additional cost) is increasing as you move to the right, so the utility industry has no cost incentive to reduce emissions further, as it costs the industry significantly more per ton for each additional ton of sulfur it removes. What you would like—if the goal of reducing total emissions by 10 million tons is to be reached—is that, somehow, the imposition of a fixed charge for every ton of sulfur dioxide released will *alter* the form of the cost curve so that it has the general shape shown in Figure 40. In this ideal curve, the cost D to utilities is lowest at a reduction level of 10 million tons, so if the utilities act to minimize cost, they can be expected to reduce emissions by 10 million tons, which is exactly the EPA goal! From the graph, you can see that the tangent line to the curve at the point where $q = 10$ million tons is horizontal, and thus has zero slope: $D'(10,000,000) = \$0$ per ton. Further, the slope $D'(q)$ is negative for values of q to the left of 10 million tons and positive for values to the right.

D

Cost of reducing sulfur emissions by q tons

0   5   10   15 q

Million tons of sulfur reduction

Figure 40

So, how much should the EPA charge per ton of sulfur released into the environment? Suppose the EPA charges $\$k$ per ton, so that

$$\text{Emission charge to utilities} = k \times \text{Sulfur emission}$$

It is your job to calculate k. Because you are working with q as the independent variable, you decide that it would be best to formulate the emission charge as a function of q. However, q represents the amount by which sulfur emissions have been reduced from the original 25 million tons; that is, the amount by which sulfur emissions are *lower than* the original 25 million tons:

$$q = 25,000,000 - \text{Sulfur emissions}$$

---

[68] These figures were produced in a computerized study of reducing sulfur emissions from the 1980 level by the given amounts. Source: Congress of the United States, Congressional Budget Office, *Curbing Acid Rain: Cost, Budget and Coal Market Effects* (Washington, DC: Government Printing Office, 1986): xx, xxii, 23, 80.

Thus, the total annual emission charge to the utilities is

$$k \times \text{Sulfur emission} = k(25,000,000 - q) = 25,000,000k - kq$$

This results in a total cost to the utilities of

$$\text{Total cost} = \text{Cost of reducing emissions} + \text{Emission charge}$$
$$D(q) = C(q) + 25,000,000k - kq$$

You now recall from calculus that the derivative of a sum of two functions is the sum of their derivatives (you will see why in Section 11.1*), so the derivative of D is given by

$$D'(q) = \text{Derivative of } C + \text{Derivative of } (25,000,000k - kq)$$

The function $y = 25,000,000k - kq$ is a linear function of q with slope $-k$ and intercept $25,000,000k$. Thus its derivative is just its slope: $-k$. Therefore:

$$D'(q) = C'(q) - k$$

Remember that you want

$$D'(10,000,000) = 0.$$

Thus,

$$C'(10,000,000) - k = 0$$

Referring to the table, you see that

$$360 - k = 0$$

or

$$k = \$360 \text{ per ton.}$$

In other words, all you need to do is set the emission charge at $k = \$360$ per ton of sulfur emitted. Further, to ensure that the resulting curve will have the general shape shown in Figure 40, you would like to have $D'(q)$ negative for $q < 10,000,000$ and positive for $q > 10,000,000$. To check this, write

$$D'(q) = C'(q) - k$$
$$= C'(q) - 360$$

and refer to the table to obtain

$$D'(8,000,000) = 270 - 360 = -90 < 0 \checkmark$$

and

$$D'(12,000,000) = 779 - 360 = 419 > 0 \checkmark$$

Thus, based on the given data, the resulting curve will have the shape you require. You therefore inform the EPA that an annual emissions charge of \$360 per ton of sulfur released into the environment will create the desired incentive: to reduce sulfur emissions by 10 million tons per year.

One week later, you are informed that this charge would be unrealistic because the utilities cannot possibly afford such a cost. You are asked whether there is an alternative plan that accomplishes the 10-million-ton reduction goal and yet is cheaper to the utilities by \$5 billion per year. You then look at your expression for the emission charge

$$25,000,000k - kq$$

∗ NOTE This statement makes intuitive sense: For instance, if C is changing at a rate of 3 units per second and D is changing at a rate of 2 units per second, then their sum is changing at a rate of $3 + 2 = 5$ units per second.

and notice that, if you decrease this amount by \$5 billion, the derivative will not change at all because it will still have the same slope (only the intercept is affected). Thus, you propose the following revised formula for the emission charge:

$$25,000,000k - kq - 5,000,000,000$$
$$= 25,000,000(360) - 360q - 5,000,000,000$$
$$= 4,000,000,000 - 360q$$

At the expected reduction level of 10 million tons, the total amount paid by the utilities will then be

$$4,000,000,000 - 360(10,000,000) = \$400,000,000$$

Thus, your revised proposal is the following: Impose an annual emissions charge of \$360 per ton of sulfur released into the environment and hand back \$5 billion in the form of subsidies. The effect of this policy will be to cause the utilities industry to reduce sulfur emissions by 10 million tons per year and will result in \$400 million in annual revenues to the government.

Notice that this policy also provides an incentive for the utilities to search for cheaper ways to reduce emissions. For instance, if they lowered costs to the point where they could achieve a reduction level of 12 million tons, they would have a total emission charge of

$$4,000,000,000 - 360(12,000,000) = -\$320,000,000.$$

The fact that this is negative means that the government would be paying the utilities industry \$320 million more in annual subsidies than the industry is paying in per ton emission charges.

EXERCISES

1. Excluding subsidies, what should the annual emission charge be if the goal is to reduce sulfur emissions by 8 million tons?
2. Excluding subsidies, what should the annual emission charge be if the goal is to reduce sulfur emissions by 12 million tons?
3. What is the *marginal emission charge* (derivative of emission charge) in your revised proposal (as stated before the exercise set)? What is the relationship between the marginal cost of reducing sulfur emissions before emissions charges are implemented and the marginal emission charge, at the optimal reduction under your revised proposal?
4. We said that the revised policy provided an incentive for utilities to find cheaper ways to reduce emissions. How would $C(q)$ have to change to make 12 million tons the optimum reduction?
5. What change in $C(q)$ would make 8 million tons the optimum reduction?
6. If the scenario in Exercise 5 took place, what would the EPA have to do in order to make 10 million tons the optimal reduction once again?
7. Due to intense lobbying by the utility industry, you are asked to revise the proposed policy so that the utility industry will pay no charge if sulfur emissions are reduced by the desired 10 million tons. How can you accomplish this?
8. Suppose that instead of imposing a fixed charge per ton of emission, you decide to use a sliding scale, so that the total charge to the industry for annual emissions of x tons will be $\$kx^2$ for some k. What must k be to again make 10 million tons the optimum reduction? HINT [The derivative of kx^2 is $2kx$.]

TI-83/84 Plus Technology Guide

Section 10.1

Example 1 (page 689) Use a table to estimate the following limits.

a. $\lim_{x \to 2} \dfrac{x^3 - 8}{x - 2}$

b. $\lim_{x \to 0} \dfrac{e^{2x} - 1}{x}$

Solution with Technology

On the TI-83/84 Plus, use the table feature to automate these computations as follows:

1. Define $Y_1=(X^3-8)/(X-2)$ for part (a) or $Y_1=(e^(2X)-1)/X$ for part (b).

2. Press 2ND TABLE to list its values for the given values of x. (If the calculator does not allow you to enter values of x, press 2ND TBLSET and set Indpnt to Ask).

   Here is the table showing some of the values for part (a):

3. For part (b) use $Y_1=(e^(2X)-1)/X$ and use values of x approaching 0 from either side.

Section 10.4

Example 3 (page 725) The price of an ounce of gold can be approximated by the function

$G(t) = -8t^2 + 144t + 150$ dollars $(7.5 \le t \le 10.5)$

where t is time in hours. What was the average rate of change of the price of gold over the $1\frac{1}{2}$-hour period starting at 8:00 AM (the interval [8, 9.5] on the t-axis)?

Solution with Technology

On the TI-83/84 Plus:

1. Enter the function G as Y_1 (using X for t):
   $Y_1=-8X^2+144X+150$

2. Now find the average rate of change over [8, 9.5] by evaluating the following on the home screen:
   $(Y_1(9.5)-Y_1(8))/(9.5-8)$

As shown on the screen, the average rate is of change is 4.

Example 4 (page 726) Continuing with Example 3, use technology to compute the average rate of change of

$$G(t) = -8t^2 + 144t + 150 \qquad (7.5 \le t \le 10.5)$$

over the intervals [8, 8 + h], where $h = 1, 0.1, 0.01, 0.001$, and 0.0001.

Solution with Technology

1. As in Example 3, enter the function G as Y_1 (using X for t):

   $$Y_1=-8X^2+144X+150$$

2. Now find the average rate of change for $h = 1$ by evaluating, on the home screen,

   $$(Y_1(8+1)-Y_1(8))/1$$

   which gives 8.

3. To evaluate for $h = 0.1$, recall the expression using 2ND ENTER and then change the 1, both places it occurs, to 0.1, getting

   $$(Y_1(8+0.1)-Y_1(8))/0.1$$

   which gives 15.2.

4. Continuing, we can evaluate the average rate of change for all the desired values of h:

We get the values in the following table:

h	1	0.1	0.01	0.001	0.0001
Ave. Rate of Change $\dfrac{G(8+h) - G(8)}{h}$	8	15.2	15.92	15.992	15.9992

Section 10.5

Example 2 (page 741) Calculate an approximate value of $f'(1.5)$ if $f(x) = x^2 - 4x$, and then find the equation of the tangent line at the point on the graph where $x = 1.5$.

Solution with Technology

1. In the TI-83/84 Plus, enter the function f as Y_1

$$Y_1 = X^2 - 4*X$$

2. Go to the home screen to compute the approximations:

$$(Y_1(1.5001) - Y_1(1.5))/0.0001$$

Usual difference quotient

$$(Y_1(1.5001) - Y_1(1.4999))/0.0002$$

Balanced difference quotient

From the display on the right, we find that the difference quotient quick approximation is -0.9999 and the balanced difference quotient quick approximation is -1, which is in fact the exact value of $f'(1.5)$. See the discussion in the text for the calculation of the equation of the tangent line.

Example 4 (page 747) Use technology to graph of the derivative of $f(x) = -2x^2 + 6x + 5$ for values of x in starting at -5.

Solution with Technology

On the TI-83/84 Plus, the easiest way to obtain quick approximations of the derivative of a given function is to use the built-in `nDeriv` function, which calculates balanced difference quotients.

1. On the $Y=$ screen, first enter the function:

$$Y_1 = -2X^2 + 6X + 5$$

2. Then set

$$Y_2 = nDeriv(Y_1, X, X) \quad \text{For nDeriv press [MATH] [8]}$$

which is the TI-83's approximation of $f'(x)$.

Alternatively, we can enter the balanced difference quotient directly:

$$Y_2 = (Y_1(X+0.001) - Y_1(X-0.001))/0.002$$

(The TI-83 uses $h = 0.001$ by default in the balanced difference quotient when calculating `nDeriv`, but this can be changed by giving a value of h as a fourth argument, like `nDeriv(Y_1,X,X,0.0001)`.) To see a table of approximate values of the derivative, we press $\boxed{2\text{ND}}$ $\boxed{\text{TABLE}}$ and choose a collection of values for x:

Here, Y_1 shows the value of f and Y_2 shows the values of f'.

To graph the function or its derivative, we can graph Y_1 or Y_2 in a window showing the given domain $[-5, 5]$:

Graph of f Graph of f'

EXCEL Technology Guide

Section 10.1

Example 1 (page 689)   Use a table to estimate the following limits.

a. $\lim\limits_{x \to 2} \dfrac{x^3 - 8}{x - 2}$ **b.** $\lim\limits_{x \to 0} \dfrac{e^{2x} - 1}{x}$

Solution with Technology

1. Set up your spreadsheet to duplicate the table in part (a) as follows:

	A	B	C	D
1	x	f(x)	x	f(x)
2	1.9	=(A2^3-8)/(A2-2)	2.1	
3	1.99		2.01	
4	1.999		2.001	
5	1.9999		2.0001	

	A	B	C	D
1	x	f(x)	x	f(x)
2	1.9	11.41	2.1	12.61
3	1.99	11.9401	2.01	12.0601
4	1.999	11.994001	2.001	12.006001
5	1.9999	11.99940001	2.0001	12.00060001

(The formula in cell B2 is copied to columns B and D as indicated by the shading.) The values of $f(x)$ will be calculated in columns B and D.

2. For part (b), use the formula = (EXP(2*A2)-1)/A2 in cell B2 and, in columns A and C, use values of x approaching 0 from either side.

Section 10.4

Example 3 (page 725)   The price of an ounce of gold can be approximated by the function

$$G(t) = -8t^2 + 144t + 150 \text{ dollars}   (7.5 \le t \le 10.5)$$

where t is time in hours. What was the average rate of change of the price of gold over the $1\frac{1}{2}$-hour period starting at 8:00 AM (the interval [8, 9.5] on the t-axis)?

Solution with Technology

To use Excel to compute the average rate of change of G:

1. Start with two columns, one for values of t and one for values of $G(t)$, which you enter using the formula for G:

	A	B
1	t	G(t)
2	8	=-8*A2^2+144*A2+150
3	9.5	

2. Next, calculate the average rate of change as shown here:

	A	B	C
1	t	G(t)	
2	8	790	Rate of change over [8, 9.5]:
3	9.5	796	=(B3-B2)/(A3-A2)

	A	B	C	D
1	t	G(t)		
2	8	790	Rate of change over [8, 9.5]:	
3	9.5	796		4

In Example 4, we describe another, more versatile Excel template for computing rates of change. ■

Example 4 (page 726)   Continuing with Example 3, use technology to compute the average rate of change of

$$G(t) = -8t^2 + 144t + 150   (7.5 \le t \le 10.5)$$

over the intervals [8, 8 + h], where $h = 1, 0.1, 0.01, 0.001,$ and 0.0001.

Solution with Technology

The template we can use to compute the rates of change is an extension of what we used in Example 3:

1. Column C contains the values $t = a$ and $t = a + h$ we are using for the independent variable.

2. The formula in cell E2 is the average rate of change formula $\Delta G / \Delta t$. Entering the different values $h = 1, 0.1, 0.01, 0.001,$ and 0.0001 in cell B2 gives the results shown in the following table:

h	1	0.1	0.01	0.001	0.0001
Ave. Rate of Change $\dfrac{G(8 + h) - G(8)}{h}$	8	15.2	15.92	15.992	15.9992

Section 10.5

Example 2 (page 741) Calculate an approximate value of $f'(1.5)$ if $f(x) = x^2 - 4x$, and then find the equation of the tangent line at the point on the graph where $x = 1.5$.

Solution with Technology

You can compute both the difference quotient and the balanced difference quotient approximations in Excel using the following extension of the worksheet in Example 4 in Section 10.4.

Notice that we get two difference quotients in column E. The first uses $h = -0.0001$ while the second uses $h = 0.0001$ and is the one we use for our quick approximation. The balanced quotient is their average (column F). The results are as follows.

	A	B	C	D	E	F
1	a	h	x	f(x)	Diff Quotients	Balanced Diff Quotient
2	1.5	0.0001	1.4999	-3.7499	-1.0001	-1
3			1.5	-3.75	-0.9999	
4			1.5001	-3.7501		

From the results shown above, we find that the difference quotient quick approximation is -0.9999 and that the balanced difference quotient quick approximation is -1, which is in fact the exact value of $f'(1.5)$. See the discussion in the text for the calculation of the equation of the tangent line.

Example 4 (page 747) Use technology to graph of the derivative of $f(x) = -2x^2 + 6x + 5$ for values of x in starting at -5.

Solution with Technology

1. Start with a table of values for the function f:

2. Next, compute approximate derivatives in Column C:

	A	B	C	D	E
1	x	f(x)	f'(x)	Xmin	-5
2		-5	-75	25.8 h	0.1
3	-4.9	-72.42	25.4		
4	-4.8	-69.88	25		
5	-4.7	-67.38	24.6		
101	4.9	-13.62	-13.8		
102	5	-15			

You cannot paste the difference quotient formula into cell C102. (Why?) Notice that this worksheet uses the ordinary difference quotients, $[f(x + h) - f(x)]/h$. If you prefer, you can use balanced difference quotients $[f(x + h) - f(x - h)]/(2h)$, in which case cells C2 and C102 would both have to be left blank.

We then graph the function and the derivative on different graphs as follows:

1. First, graph the function f in the usual way, using Columns A and B.

2. Make a copy of this graph and click on it once. Columns A and B should be outlined, indicating that these are the columns used in the graph.

TECHNOLOGY GUIDE

3. By dragging from the center of the bottom edge of the box, move the Column B box over to Column C as shown:

	A	B	C
96	4.4	-7.32	-11.8
97	4.5	-8.5	-12.2
98	4.6	-9.72	-12.6
99	4.7	-10.98	-13
100	4.8	-12.28	-13.4
101	4.9	-13.62	-13.8
102	5	-15	

→

	A	B	C
96	4.4	-7.32	-11.8
97	4.5	-8.5	-12.2
98	4.6	-9.72	-12.6
99	4.7	-10.98	-13
100	4.8	-12.28	-13.4
101	4.9	-13.62	-13.8
102	5	-15	

The graph will then show the derivative (Columns A and C):

Graph of f

Graph of f'

11

Techniques of Differentiation with Applications

Case Study Projecting Market Growth

You are on the board of directors at Fullcourt Academic Press. The sales director of the high school division has just burst into your office with a proposal for an expansion strategy based on the assumption that the number of high school seniors in the United States will be growing at a rate of at least 5,600 per year through the year 2015. Because the figures actually appear to be leveling off, you are suspicious about this estimate. You would like to devise a model that predicts this trend before tomorrow's scheduled board meeting. **How do you go about doing this?**

Yuri Arcurs, 2009/Used under license from Shutterstock.com

Web Site

At the Web site you will find:

- Section by section tutorials, including game tutorials with randomized quizzes

- A detailed chapter summary

- A true/false quiz

- Additional review exercises

- Graphers, Excel tutorials, and other resources

- The following extra topic:

    Linear Approximation and Error Estimation

Introduction

In Chapter 10 we studied the concept of the derivative of a function, and we saw some of the applications for which derivatives are useful. However, computing the derivative of a function algebraically seemed to be a time-consuming process, forcing us to restrict attention to fairly simply functions.

In this chapter we develop shortcut techniques that will allow us to write down the derivative of a function directly without having to calculate any limit. These techniques will also enable us to differentiate any closed-form function—that is, any function, no matter how complicated, that can be specified by a formula involving powers, radicals, absolute values, exponents, and logarithms. (In a later chapter, we will discuss how to add trigonometric functions to this list.) We also show how to find the derivatives of functions that are only specified *implicitly*—that is, functions for which we are not given an explicit formula for y in terms of x but only an equation relating x and y.

algebra Review

For this chapter, you should be familiar with the algebra reviewed in **Chapter 0, Sections 3 and 4.**

11.1 Derivatives of Powers, Sums, and Constant Multiples

Up to this point we have approximated derivatives using difference quotients, and we have done exact calculations using the definition of the derivative as the limit of a difference quotient. In general, we would prefer to have an exact calculation, and it is also very useful to have a formula for the derivative function when we can find one. However, the calculation of a derivative as a limit is often tedious, so it would be nice to have a quicker method. We discuss the first of the shortcut rules in this section. By the end of this chapter, we will be able to find fairly quickly the derivative of almost any function we can write.

Shortcut Formula: The Power Rule

If you look at Examples 2 and 3 in Section 10.6, you may notice a pattern:

$$f(x) = x^2 \implies f'(x) = 2x$$
$$f(x) = x^3 \implies f'(x) = 3x^2$$

This pattern generalizes to any power of x:

Theorem 11.1 The Power Rule

If n is any constant and $f(x) = x^n$, then

$$f'(x) = nx^{n-1}.$$

Quick Examples

1. If $f(x) = x^2$, then $f'(x) = 2x^1 = 2x$.
2. If $f(x) = x^3$, then $f'(x) = 3x^2$.
3. If $f(x) = x$, rewrite as $f(x) = x^1$, so $f'(x) = 1x^0 = 1$.
4. If $f(x) = 1$, rewrite as $f(x) = x^0$, so $f'(x) = 0x^{-1} = 0$.

Web Site

www.FiniteandCalc.org

At the Web site you can find a proof of the power rule by following:

Everything for Calculus

→ Chapter 11

→ Proof of the Power Rule

The proof of the power rule involves first studying the case when n is a positive integer, and then studying the cases of other types of exponents (negative integer, rational number, irrational number). You can find a proof at the Web site.

EXAMPLE 1 Using the Power Rule for Negative and Fractional Exponents

Calculate the derivatives of the following:

a. $f(x) = \dfrac{1}{x}$ **b.** $f(x) = \dfrac{1}{x^2}$ **c.** $f(x) = \sqrt{x}$

Solution

* NOTE See the section on exponents in the algebra review to brush up on negative and fractional exponents.

a. Rewrite* as $f(x) = x^{-1}$. Then $f'(x) = (-1)x^{-2} = -\dfrac{1}{x^2}$.

b. Rewrite as $f(x) = x^{-2}$. Then $f'(x) = (-2)x^{-3} = -\dfrac{2}{x^3}$.

c. Rewrite as $f(x) = x^{0.5}$. Then $f'(x) = 0.5x^{-0.5} = \dfrac{0.5}{x^{0.5}}$. Alternatively, rewrite $f(x)$ as $x^{1/2}$, so that $f'(x) = \dfrac{1}{2}x^{-1/2} = \dfrac{1}{2x^{1/2}} = \dfrac{1}{2\sqrt{x}}$.

By rewriting the given functions in Example 1 before taking derivatives, we converted them from **rational** or **radical form** (as in, say, $\dfrac{1}{x^2}$ and $\sqrt{x}$) to **exponent form** (as in x^{-2} and $x^{0.5}$; see the Algebra Review, Section 0.2) to enable us to use the power rule. (See the Caution below.)

Caution

We cannot apply the power rule to terms in the denominators or under square roots. For example:

1. The derivative of $\dfrac{1}{x^2}$ is **NOT** $\dfrac{1}{2x}$; it is $-\dfrac{2}{x^3}$.   See Example 1(b).

2. The derivative of $\sqrt{x^3}$ is **NOT** $\sqrt{3x^2}$; it is $1.5x^{0.5}$.   Rewrite $\sqrt{x^3}$ as $x^{3/2}$ or $x^{1.5}$ and apply the power rule.

Table 1 Table of Derivative Formulas

$f(x)$	$f'(x)$
1	0
x	1
x^2	$2x$
x^3	$3x^2$
x^n	nx^{n-1}
$\dfrac{1}{x}$	$-\dfrac{1}{x^2}$
$\dfrac{1}{x^2}$	$-\dfrac{2}{x^3}$
$\sqrt{x}$	$\dfrac{1}{2\sqrt{x}}$

Some of the derivatives in Example 1 are very useful to remember, so we summarize them in Table 1. We suggest that you add to this table as you learn more derivatives. It is *extremely* helpful to remember the derivatives of common functions such as $1/x$ and $\sqrt{x}$, even though they can be obtained by using the power rule as in the above example.

Another Notation: Differential Notation

Here is a useful notation based on the "*d*-notation" we discussed in Section 10.5. **Differential notation** is based on an abbreviation for the phrase "the derivative with respect to *x*." For example, we learned that if $f(x) = x^3$, then $f'(x) = 3x^2$. When we say "$f'(x) = 3x^2$," we mean the following:

The derivative of x^3 with respect to x equals $3x^2$.

✳ NOTE This may seem odd in the case of $f(x) = x^3$ because there are no other variables to worry about. But in expressions like st^3 that involve variables other than x, it is necessary to specify just what the variable of the function is. This is the same reason that we write "$f(x) = x^3$" rather than just "$f = x^3$."

You may wonder why we sneaked in the words "with respect to x." All this means is that the variable of the function is x, and not any other variable.✳ Because we use the phrase "the derivative with respect to x" often, we use the following abbreviation.

Differential Notation; Differentiation

$\dfrac{d}{dx}$ means "the derivative with respect to x."

Thus, $\dfrac{d}{dx}[f(x)]$ is the same thing as $f'(x)$, the derivative of $f(x)$ with respect to x. If y is a function of x, then the derivative of y with respect to x is

$$\frac{d}{dx}(y) \qquad \text{or, more compactly,} \qquad \frac{dy}{dx}$$

To **differentiate** a function $f(x)$ with respect to x means to take its derivative with respect to x.

Quick Examples

In Words	Formula
1. The derivative with respect to x of x^3 is $3x^2$.	$\dfrac{d}{dx}(x^3) = 3x^2$
2. The derivative with respect to t of $\dfrac{1}{t}$ is $-\dfrac{1}{t^2}$.	$\dfrac{d}{dt}\left(\dfrac{1}{t}\right) = -\dfrac{1}{t^2}$
3. If $y = x^4$, then $\dfrac{dy}{dx} = 4x^3$.	
4. If $u = \dfrac{1}{t^2}$, then $\dfrac{du}{dt} = -\dfrac{2}{t^3}$.	

Notes

1. $\dfrac{dy}{dx}$ is Leibniz' notation for the derivative we discussed in Section 10.5. (See the discussion before Example 3 there.)

2. Leibniz notation illustrates units nicely: units of $\dfrac{dy}{dx}$ are units of y per unit of x. ■

The Rules for Sums and Constant Multiples

We can now find the derivatives of more complicated functions, such as polynomials, using the following rules:

Theorem 11.2 Derivatives of Sums, Differences, and Constant Multiples

If $f(x)$ and $g(x)$ are any two differentiable functions, and if c is any constant, then the functions $f(x) + g(x)$ and $cf(x)$ are differentiable, and

$$[f(x) \pm g(x)]' = f'(x) \pm g'(x) \qquad \text{Sum Rule}$$

$$[cf(x)]' = cf'(x). \qquad \text{Constant Multiple Rule}$$

In Words:

- The derivative of a sum is the sum of the derivatives, and the derivative of a difference is the difference of the derivatives.
- The derivative of c times a function is c times the derivative of the function.

Differential Notation:

$$\frac{d}{dx}[f(x) \pm g(x)] = \frac{d}{dx}f(x) \pm \frac{d}{dx}g(x)$$

$$\frac{d}{dx}[cf(x)] = c\frac{d}{dx}f(x)$$

Quick Examples

1. $\dfrac{d}{dx}[x^2 - x^4] = \dfrac{d}{dx}[x^2] - \dfrac{d}{dx}[x^4] = 2x - 4x^3$

2. $\dfrac{d}{dx}[7x^3] = 7\dfrac{d}{dx}[x^3] = 7(3x^2) = 21x^3$

   In other words, we multiply the coefficient (7) by the exponent (3), and then decrease the exponent by 1.

3. $\dfrac{d}{dx}[12x] = 12\dfrac{d}{dx}[x] = 12(1) = 12$

   In other words, the derivative of a constant times x is that constant.

4. $\dfrac{d}{dx}[-x^{0.5}] = \dfrac{d}{dx}[(-1)x^{0.5}] = (-1)\dfrac{d}{dx}[x^{0.5}] = (-1)(0.5)x^{-0.5}$

   $= -0.5x^{-0.5}$

5. $\dfrac{d}{dx}[12] = \dfrac{d}{dx}[12(1)] = 12\dfrac{d}{dx}[1] = 12(0) = 0.$

   In other words, the derivative of a constant is zero.

6. If my company earns twice as much (annual) revenue as yours and the derivative of your revenue function is the curve on the left, then the derivative of my revenue function is the curve on the right.

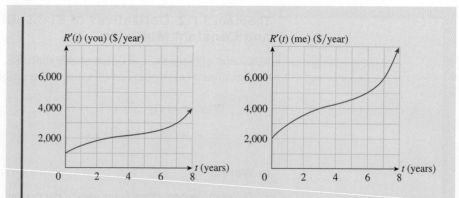

7. Suppose that a company's revenue R and cost C are changing with time. Then so is the profit, $P(t) = R(t) - C(t)$, and the rate of change of the profit is

$$P'(t) = R'(t) - C'(t).$$

In words: *The derivative of the profit is the derivative of revenue minus the derivative of cost.*

Proof of the Sum Rule

By the definition of the derivative of a function,

$$\frac{d}{dx}[f(x) + g(x)] = \lim_{h \to 0} \frac{[f(x + h) + g(x + h)] - [f(x) + g(x)]}{h}$$

$$= \lim_{h \to 0} \frac{[f(x + h) - f(x)] + [g(x + h) - g(x)]}{h}$$

$$= \lim_{h \to 0} \left[\frac{f(x + h) - f(x)}{h} + \frac{g(x + h) - g(x)}{h} \right]$$

$$= \lim_{h \to 0} \frac{f(x + h) - f(x)}{h} + \lim_{h \to 0} \frac{g(x + h) - g(x)}{h}$$

$$= \frac{d}{dx}[f(x)] + \frac{d}{dx}[g(x)].$$

The next-to-last step uses a property of limits: the limit of a sum is the sum of the limits. Think about why this should be true. The last step uses the definition of the derivative again (and the fact that the functions are differentiable).

The proof of the rule for constant multiples is similar.

EXAMPLE 2 Combining the Sum and Constant Multiple Rules, and Dealing with x in the Denominator

Find the derivatives of the following:

a. $f(x) = 3x^2 + 2x - 4$

b. $f(x) = \dfrac{2x}{3} - \dfrac{6}{x} + \dfrac{2}{3x^{0.2}} - \dfrac{x^4}{2}$

Solution

a. $\dfrac{d}{dx}(3x^2 + 2x - 4) = \dfrac{d}{dx}(3x^2) + \dfrac{d}{dx}(2x - 4)$ ⟶ Rule for sums

$\qquad\qquad\qquad = \dfrac{d}{dx}(3x^2) + \dfrac{d}{dx}(2x) - \dfrac{d}{dx}(4)$ ⟶ Rule for differences

$\qquad\qquad\qquad = 3(2x) + 2(1) - 0$ ⟶ See Quick Example 2.

$\qquad\qquad\qquad = 6x + 2$

b. Notice that f has x and powers of x in the denominator. We deal with these terms the same way we did in Example 1, by rewriting them in exponent form (that is, in the form constant × power of x):

$$f(x) = \frac{2x}{3} - \frac{6}{x} + \frac{2}{3x^{0.2}} - \frac{x^4}{2}$$ ⟶ Rational form

$$= \frac{2}{3}x - 6x^{-1} + \frac{2}{3}x^{-0.2} - \frac{1}{2}x^4$$ ⟶ Exponent form

We are now ready to take the derivative:

$$f'(x) = \frac{2}{3}(1) - 6(-1)x^{-2} + \frac{2}{3}(-0.2)x^{-1.2} - \frac{1}{2}(4x^3)$$

$$= \frac{2}{3} + 6x^{-2} - \frac{0.4}{3}x^{-1.2} - 2x^3$$ ⟶ Exponent form

$$= \frac{2}{3} + \frac{6}{x^2} - \frac{0.4}{3x^{1.2}} - 2x^3$$ ⟶ Rational form

Notice that in Example 2(a) we had three terms in the expression for $f(x)$, not just two. By applying the rule for sums and differences twice, we saw that the derivative of a sum or difference of three terms is the sum or difference of the derivatives of the terms. (One of those terms had zero derivative, so the final answer had only two terms.) In fact, the derivative of a sum or difference of any number of terms is the sum or difference of the derivatives of the terms. Put another way, to take the derivative of a sum or difference of any number of terms, we take derivatives term by term.

Note Nothing forces us to use only x as the independent variable when taking derivatives (although it is traditional to give x preference). For instance, part (a) in Example 2 can be rewritten as

$$\frac{d}{dt}(3t^2 + 2t - 4) = 6t + 2$$ ⟶ $\dfrac{d}{dt}$ means "derivative with respect to t."

or

$$\frac{d}{du}(3u^2 + 2u - 4) = 6u + 2.$$ ⟶ $\dfrac{d}{du}$ means "derivative with respect to u." ∎

In the previous examples, we saw instances of the following important facts. (Think about these graphically to see why they must be true.)

The Derivative of a Constant Times *x* and the Derivative of a Constant

If c is any constant, then:

Rule	Quick Examples	
$\dfrac{d}{dx}(cx) = c$	$\dfrac{d}{dx}(6x) = 6$	$\dfrac{d}{dx}(-x) = -1$
$\dfrac{d}{dx}(c) = 0$	$\dfrac{d}{dx}(5) = 0$	$\dfrac{d}{dx}(\pi) = 0$

In Example 5 of Section 10.6 we saw that $f(x) = |x|$ fails to be differentiable at $x = 0$. In the next example we use the power rule and find more functions not differentiable at a point.

$f(x) = x^{1/3}$

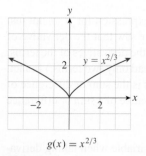

$g(x) = x^{2/3}$

Figure 1

EXAMPLE 3 Functions Not Differentiable at a Point

Find the natural domains of the derivatives of $f(x) = x^{1/3}$ and $g(x) = x^{2/3}$, and $h(x) = |x|$.

Solution Let's first look at the functions f and g. By the power rule,

$$f'(x) = \frac{1}{3}x^{-2/3} = \frac{1}{3x^{2/3}}$$

and

$$g'(x) = \frac{2}{3}x^{-1/3} = \frac{2}{3x^{1/3}}.$$

$f'(x)$ and $g'(x)$ are defined only for nonzero values of x, and their natural domains consist of all real numbers except 0. Thus, the derivatives f' and g' do not exist at $x = 0$. In other words, f and g are not differentiable at $x = 0$. If we look at Figure 1, we notice why these functions fail to be differentiable at $x = 0$: The graph of f has a vertical tangent line at 0. Because a vertical line has undefined slope, the derivative is undefined at that point. The graph of g comes to a sharp point (called a **cusp**) at 0, so it is not meaningful to speak about a tangent line at that point; therefore, the derivative of g is not defined there. (Actually, there is a reasonable candidate for the tangent line at $x = 0$, but it is the vertical line again.)

We can also detect this nondifferentiability by computing some difference quotients numerically. In the case of $f(x) = x^{1/3}$, we get the following table:

h	± 1	± 0.1	± 0.01	± 0.001	± 0.0001
$\dfrac{f(0+h) - f(0)}{h}$	1	4.6416	21.544	100	464.16

suggesting that the difference quotients $[f(0+h) - f(0)]/h$ grow large without bound rather than approach any fixed number as h approaches 0. (Can you see how the behavior of the difference quotients in the table is reflected in the graph?)

using Technology

If you try to graph the function $f(x) = x^{2/3}$ using the format

$$X^{\wedge}(2/3)$$

you may get only the right-hand portion of Figure 1 because graphing utilities are (often) not programmed to raise negative numbers to fractional exponents. (However, many will handle $X^{\wedge}(1/3)$ correctly, as a special case they recognize.) To avoid this difficulty, you can take advantage of the identity

$$x^{2/3} = (x^2)^{1/3}$$

so that it is always a nonnegative number that is being raised to a fractional exponent. Thus, use the format

$$(X^{\wedge}2)^{\wedge}(1/3)$$

to obtain both portions of the graph.

Now we return to the function $h(x) = |x|$ discussed in Example 5 of Section 10.6. We saw there that $|x|$ is not differentiable at $x = 0$. What about values of x *other than* 0? For such values, we can write:

$$|x| = \begin{cases} -x & \text{if } x < 0 \\ x & \text{if } x > 0 \end{cases}$$

Hence, by the power rule (think of x as x^1):

$$f'(x) = \begin{cases} -1 & \text{if } x < 0 \\ 1 & \text{if } x > 0 \end{cases}$$

Q : *So does that mean there is no single formula for the derivative of $|x|$?*

A : Actually, there *is* a convenient formula. Consider the ratio

$$\frac{|x|}{x}.$$

If x is positive, then $|x| = x$, so $|x|/x = x/x = 1$. On the other hand, if x is negative then $|x| = -x$, so $|x|/x = -x/x = -1$. In other words,

$$\frac{|x|}{x} = \begin{cases} -1 & \text{if } x < 0 \\ 1 & \text{if } x > 0 \end{cases},$$

which is exactly the formula we obtained for $f'(x)$. In other words:

Derivative of $|x|$

$$\frac{d}{dx}|x| = \frac{|x|}{x}$$

Note that the derivative does not exist when $x = 0$.

Quick Example

$$\frac{d}{dx}[3|x| + x] = 3\frac{|x|}{x} + 1$$

APPLICATION

The next Example is similar to Example 3 in Section 10.4, but this time we analyze the curve using the derivative.

EXAMPLE 4 Gold Price

You are a commodities trader and you monitor the price of gold on the New York Spot Market very closely during an active morning. Suppose you find that the price of an ounce of gold can be approximated by the function

$$G(t) = -8t^2 + 144t + 150 \text{ dollars} \quad (7.5 \le t \le 10.5)$$

where t is time in hours. (See Figure 2. $t = 8$ represents 8:00 AM.)

Source: www.kitco.com (August 15, 2008) $G(t) = -8t^2 + 144t + 150$

Figure 2

a. According to the model, how fast was the price of gold changing at 10:00 AM?

b. According to the model, the price of gold

 (A) increased at a faster and faster rate
 (B) increased at a slower and slower rate
 (C) decreased at a faster and faster rate
 (D) decreased at a slower and slower rate

between 9:30 and 10:30 AM.

Solution

a. Differentiating the given function with respect to t gives

$$G'(t) = -16t + 144.$$

Because 10:00 AM corresponds to $t = 10$, we obtain

$$G'(10) = -16(10) + 144 = -16.$$

The units of the derivative are dollars per hour, so we conclude that, at 10:00 AM, the price of gold was dropping at a rate of $16 per hour.

b. From the graph, we can see that, between 9:30 and 10:30 AM (the interval [9.5, 10.5]), the price of gold was decreasing. Also from the graph, we see that the slope of the tangent becomes more and more negative as t increases, so the price of gold is decreasing at a faster and faster rate (choice (C)).

We can also see this algebraically from the derivative, $G'(t) = -16t + 144$: For values of t larger than 9, $G'(t)$ is negative; that is, the rate of change of G is negative, so the price of gold is decreasing. Further, as t increases, $G'(t)$ becomes more and more negative, so the price of gold is decreasing at a faster and faster rate, confirming that choice (C) is the correct one.

An Application to Limits: L'Hospital's Rule

The limits that caused us some trouble in Sections 10.1–10.3 are those of the form $\lim_{x \to a} f(x)$ in which substituting $x = a$ gave us an indeterminate form, such as

$$\lim_{x \to 2} \frac{x^3 - 8}{x - 2} \qquad \text{Substituting } x = 2 \text{ yields } \frac{0}{0}.$$

$$\lim_{x \to +\infty} \frac{2x - 4}{x - 1} \qquad \text{Substituting } x = +\infty \text{ yields } \frac{\infty}{\infty}.$$

L'Hospital's rule gives us an alternate way of computing limits such as these without the need to do any preliminary simplification. It also allows us to compute some limits for which algebraic simplification does not work.*

✳ **NOTE** Guillaume François Antoine, Marquis de l'Hospital (1661–1704) wrote the first textbook on calculus, *Analyse des infiniment petits pour l'intelligence des lignes courbes,* in 1692. The rule now known as l'Hospital's Rule appeared first in this book.

> ### Theorem 11.3 L'Hospital's Rule
>
> If f and g are two differentiable functions such that substituting $x = a$ in the expression $\dfrac{f(x)}{g(x)}$ gives the indeterminate form $\dfrac{0}{0}$ or $\dfrac{\infty}{\infty}$, then
>
> $$\lim_{x \to a} \frac{f(x)}{g(x)} = \lim_{x \to a} \frac{f'(x)}{g'(x)}$$
>
> That is, we can replace $f(x)$ and $g(x)$ with their *derivatives* and try again to take the limit.
>
> **Quick Examples**
>
> 1. Substituting $x = 2$ in $\dfrac{x^3 - 8}{x - 2}$ yields $\dfrac{0}{0}$. Therefore, l'Hospital's rule applies and
>
> $$\lim_{x \to 2} \frac{x^3 - 8}{x - 2} = \lim_{x \to 2} \frac{3x^2}{1} = \frac{3(2)^2}{1} = 12.$$
>
> 2. Substituting $x = +\infty$ in $\dfrac{2x - 4}{x - 1}$ yields $\dfrac{\infty}{\infty}$. Therefore, l'Hospital's rule applies and
>
> $$\lim_{x \to +\infty} \frac{2x - 4}{x - 1} = \lim_{x \to +\infty} \frac{2}{1} = 2.$$

✳ **NOTE** A proof of l'Hospital's rule can be found in most advanced calculus textbooks.

The proof of l'Hospital's rule is beyond the scope of this text.*

EXAMPLE 5 Applying L'Hospital's Rule

Check whether l'Hospital's rule applies to each of the following limits. If it does, use it to evaluate the limit. Otherwise, use some other method to evaluate the limit.

a. $\lim_{x \to 1} \dfrac{x^2 - 2x + 1}{4x^3 - 3x^2 - 6x + 5}$ **b.** $\lim_{x \to +\infty} \dfrac{2x^2 - 4x}{5x^3 - 3x + 5}$

c. $\lim\limits_{x \to 1} \dfrac{x - 1}{x^3 - 3x^2 + 3x - 1}$

d. $\lim\limits_{x \to 1} \dfrac{x}{x^3 - 3x^2 + 3x - 1}$

Solution

a. Setting $x = 1$ yields

$$\frac{1 - 2 + 1}{4 - 3 - 6 + 5} = \frac{0}{0}.$$

Therefore, l'Hospital's rule applies and

$$\lim_{x \to 1} \frac{x^2 - 2x + 1}{4x^3 - 3x^2 - 6x + 5} = \lim_{x \to 1} \frac{2x - 2}{12x^2 - 6x - 6}.$$

We are left with a closed-form function. However, we cannot substitute $x = 1$ to find the limit because the function $(2x - 2)/(12x^2 - 6x - 6)$ is still not defined at $x = 1$. In fact, if we set $x = 1$, we again get $0/0$. Thus, l'Hospital's rule applies again, and

$$\lim_{x \to 1} \frac{2x - 2}{12x^2 - 6x - 6} = \lim_{x \to 1} \frac{2}{24x - 6}.$$

Once again we have a closed-form function, but this time it is defined when $x = 1$, giving

$$\frac{2}{24 - 6} = \frac{1}{9}.$$

Thus,

$$\lim_{x \to 1} \frac{x^2 - 2x + 1}{4x^3 - 3x^2 - 6x + 5} = \frac{1}{9}.$$

b. Setting $x = +\infty$ yields $\dfrac{\infty}{\infty}$, so

$$\lim_{x \to +\infty} \frac{2x^2 - 4x}{5x^3 - 3x + 5} = \lim_{x \to +\infty} \frac{4x - 4}{15x^2 - 3}.$$

Setting $x = +\infty$ again yields $\dfrac{\infty}{\infty}$, so we can apply the rule again to obtain

$$\lim_{x \to +\infty} \frac{4x - 4}{15x^2 - 3} = \lim_{x \to +\infty} \frac{4}{30x}.$$

Note that we cannot apply l'Hospital's rule a third time because setting $x = +\infty$ yields the *determinate* form $4/\infty = 0$ (see the discussion at the end of Section 10.3). Thus, the limit is 0.

c. Setting $x = 1$ yields $0/0$ so, by l'Hospital's rule,

$$\lim_{x \to 1} \frac{x - 1}{x^3 - 3x^2 + 3x - 1} = \lim_{x \to 1} \frac{1}{3x^2 - 6x + 3}.$$

We are left with a closed-form function that is still not defined at $x = 1$. Further, l'Hospital's rule no longer applies because putting $x = 1$ yields the determinate form $1/0$. To investigate this limit, we refer to the discussion at the end of Section 10.3 and find

$$\lim_{x \to 1} \frac{1}{3x^2 - 6x + 3} = \lim_{x \to 1} \frac{1}{3(x - 1)^2} = +\infty. \qquad \frac{1}{0^+} = +\infty$$

d. Setting $x = 1$ in the expression yields the determinate form $1/0$, so l'Hospital's rule does not apply here. Using the methods of Section 10.3 again, we find that the limit does not exist.

FAQs

Using the Rules and Recognizing When a Function is Not Differentiable

Q: I would *like* to say that the derivative of $5x^2 - 8x + 4$ is just $10x - 8$ without having to go through all that stuff about derivatives of sums and constant multiples. Can I simply forget about all the rules and write down the answer?

A: We developed the rules for sums and constant multiples precisely for that reason: so that we could simply write down a derivative without having to think about it too hard. So, you are perfectly justified in simply writing down the derivative without going through the rules, but bear in mind that what you are really doing is applying the power rule, the rule for sums, and the rule for multiples over and over.

Q: Is there a way of telling from its formula whether a function f is not differentiable at a point?

A: Here are some indicators to look for in the formula for f:

- The absolute value of some expression; f may not be differentiable at points where that expression is zero.

  Example: $f(x) = 3x^2 - |x - 4|$ is not differentiable at $x = 4$.

- A fractional power smaller than 1 of some expression; f may not be differentiable at points where that expression is zero.

  Example: $f(x) = (x^2 - 16)^{2/3}$ is not differentiable at $x = \pm 4$.

11.1 EXERCISES

▼ more advanced   ◆ challenging
T indicates exercises that should be solved using technology

*In Exercises 1–10, use the shortcut rules to **mentally** calculate the derivative of the given function. HINT [See Examples 1 and 2.]*

1. $f(x) = x^5$ **2.** $f(x) = x^4$

3. $f(x) = 2x^{-2}$ **4.** $f(x) = 3x^{-1}$

5. $f(x) = -x^{0.25}$ **6.** $f(x) = -x^{-0.5}$

7. $f(x) = 2x^4 + 3x^3 - 1$ **8.** $f(x) = -x^3 - 3x^2 - 1$

9. $f(x) = -x + \dfrac{1}{x} + 1$ **10.** $f(x) = \dfrac{1}{x} + \dfrac{1}{x^2}$

In Exercises 11–16, obtain the derivative dy/dx and state the rules that you use. HINT [See Example 2.]

11. $y = 10$ **12.** $y = x^3$

13. $y = x^2 + x$ **14.** $y = x - 5$

15. $y = 4x^3 + 2x - 1$ **16.** $y = 4x^{-1} - 2x - 10$

In Exercises 17–40, find the derivative of each function. HINT [See Examples 1 and 2.]

17. $f(x) = x^2 - 3x + 5$ **18.** $f(x) = 3x^3 - 2x^2 + x$

19. $f(x) = x + x^{0.5}$ **20.** $f(x) = x^{0.5} + 2x^{-0.5}$

21. $g(x) = x^{-2} - 3x^{-1} - 2$ **22.** $g(x) = 2x^{-1} + 4x^{-2}$

23. $g(x) = \dfrac{1}{x} - \dfrac{1}{x^2}$ **24.** $g(x) = \dfrac{1}{x^2} + \dfrac{1}{x^3}$

25. $h(x) = \dfrac{2}{x^{0.4}}$ **26.** $h(x) = -\dfrac{1}{2x^{0.2}}$

27. $h(x) = \dfrac{1}{x^2} + \dfrac{2}{x^3}$ **28.** $h(x) = \dfrac{2}{x} - \dfrac{2}{x^3} + \dfrac{1}{x^4}$

29. $r(x) = \dfrac{2}{3x} - \dfrac{1}{2x^{0.1}}$ **30.** $r(x) = \dfrac{4}{3x^2} + \dfrac{1}{x^{3.2}}$

31. $r(x) = \dfrac{2x}{3} - \dfrac{x^{0.1}}{2} + \dfrac{4}{3x^{1.1}} - 2$

32. $r(x) = \dfrac{4x^2}{3} + \dfrac{x^{3.2}}{6} - \dfrac{2}{3x^2} + 4$

33. $t(x) = |x| + \dfrac{1}{x}$ **34.** $t(x) = 3|x| - \sqrt{x}$

35. $s(x) = \sqrt{x} + \dfrac{1}{\sqrt{x}}$ **36.** $s(x) = x + \dfrac{7}{\sqrt{x}}$

HINT [For Exercises 37–40, first expand the given function.]

37. ▼ $s(x) = x\left(x^2 - \dfrac{1}{x}\right)$

38. ▼ $s(x) = x^{-1}\left(x - \dfrac{2}{x}\right)$

39. ▼ $t(x) = \dfrac{x^2 - 2x^3}{x}$

40. ▼ $t(x) = \dfrac{2x + x^2}{x}$

In Exercises 41–46, evaluate the given expression.

41. $\dfrac{d}{dx}(2x^{1.3} - x^{-1.2})$

42. $\dfrac{d}{dx}(2x^{4.3} + x^{0.6})$

43. ▼ $\dfrac{d}{dx}[1.2(x - |x|)]$

44. ▼ $\dfrac{d}{dx}[4(x^2 + 3|x|)]$

45. ▼ $\dfrac{d}{dt}(at^3 - 4at)$;   (*a* constant)

46. ▼ $\dfrac{d}{dt}(at^2 + bt + c)$;   (*a, b, c* constant)

In Exercises 47–52, find the indicated derivative.

47. $y = \dfrac{x^{10.3}}{2} + 99x^{-1}$; $\dfrac{dy}{dx}$

48. $y = \dfrac{x^{1.2}}{3} - \dfrac{x^{0.9}}{2}$; $\dfrac{dy}{dx}$

49. $s = 2.3 + \dfrac{2.1}{t^{1.1}} - \dfrac{t^{0.6}}{2}$; $\dfrac{ds}{dt}$

50. $s = \dfrac{2}{t^{1.1}} + t^{-1.2}$; $\dfrac{ds}{dt}$

51. ▼ $V = \dfrac{4}{3}\pi r^3$; $\dfrac{dV}{dr}$

52. ▼ $A = 4\pi r^2$; $\dfrac{dA}{dr}$

In Exercises 53–58, find the slope of the tangent to the graph of the given function at the indicated point. HINT [Recall that the slope of the tangent to the graph of f at x = a is f′(a).]

53. $f(x) = x^3$; $(-1, -1)$

54. $g(x) = x^4$; $(-2, 16)$

55. $f(x) = 1 - 2x$; $(2, -3)$

56. $f(x) = \dfrac{x}{3} - 1$; $(-3, -2)$

57. $g(t) = \dfrac{1}{t^5}$; $(1, 1)$

58. $s(t) = \dfrac{1}{t^3}$; $\left(-2, -\dfrac{1}{8}\right)$

In Exercises 59–64, find the equation of the tangent line to the graph of the given function at the point with the indicated x-coordinate. In each case, sketch the curve together with the appropriate tangent line.

59. ▼ $f(x) = x^3$; $x = -1$

60. ▼ $f(x) = x^2$; $x = 0$

61. ▼ $f(x) = x + \dfrac{1}{x}$; $x = 2$

62. ▼ $f(x) = \dfrac{1}{x^2}$; $x = 1$

63. ▼ $f(x) = \sqrt{x}$; $x = 4$

64. ▼ $f(x) = 2x + 4$; $x = -1$

In Exercises 65–70, find all values of x (if any) where the tangent line to the graph of the given equation is horizontal. HINT [The tangent line is horizontal when its slope is zero.]

65. ▼ $y = 2x^2 + 3x - 1$

66. ▼ $y = -3x^2 - x$

67. ▼ $y = 2x + 8$

68. ▼ $y = -x + 1$

69. ▼ $y = x + \dfrac{1}{x}$

70. ▼ $y = x - \sqrt{x}$

71. ◆ Write out the proof that $\dfrac{d}{dx}(x^4) = 4x^3$.

72. ◆ Write out the proof that $\dfrac{d}{dx}(x^5) = 5x^4$.

▉ *In Exercises 73–76, use technology to graph the derivative of the given function for the given range of values of x. Then use your graph to estimate all values of x (if any) where (a) the given function is not differentiable, and (b) the tangent line to the graph of the given function is horizontal. Round answers to one decimal place.*

73. ▼ $h(x) = |x - 3|$; $-5 \le x \le 5$

74. ▼ $h(x) = 2x + (x - 3)^{1/3}$; $-5 \le x \le 5$

75. ▼ $f(x) = x - 5(x - 1)^{2/5}$; $-4 \le x \le 6$

76. ▼ $f(x) = |2x + 5| - x^2$; $-4 \le x \le 4$

▉ *In Exercises 77–80, investigate the differentiability of the given function at the given points numerically (that is, use a table of values). If f′(a) exists, give its approximate value.* HINT [See Example 3.]

77. $f(x) = x^{1/3}$ **a.** $a = 1$ **b.** $a = 0$

78. $f(x) = x + |1 - x|$ **a.** $a = 1$ **b.** $a = 0$

79. ▼ $f(x) = [x(1 - x)]^{1/3}$ **a.** $a = 1$ **b.** $a = 0$

80. ▼ $f(x) = (1 - x)^{2/3}$ **a.** $a = -1$ **b.** $a = 1$

In Exercises 81–92 say whether l'Hospital's rule applies. If is does, use it to evaluate the given limit. If not, use some other method.

81. $\lim\limits_{x \to 1} \dfrac{x^2 - 2x + 1}{x^2 - x}$

82. $\lim\limits_{x \to -1} \dfrac{x^2 + 3x + 2}{x^2 + x}$

83. $\lim\limits_{x \to 2} \dfrac{x^3 - 8}{x - 2}$

84. $\lim\limits_{x \to 0} \dfrac{x^3 + 8}{x^2 + 3x + 2}$

85. $\lim\limits_{x \to 1} \dfrac{x^2 + 3x + 2}{x^2 + x}$

86. $\lim\limits_{x \to -2} \dfrac{x^3 + 8}{x^2 + 3x + 2}$

87. $\lim\limits_{x \to -\infty} \dfrac{3x^2 + 10x - 1}{2x^2 - 5x}$

88. $\lim\limits_{x \to -\infty} \dfrac{6x^2 + 5x + 100}{3x^2 - 9}$

89. $\lim\limits_{x \to -\infty} \dfrac{10x^2 + 300x + 1}{5x + 2}$

90. $\lim\limits_{x \to -\infty} \dfrac{2x^4 + 20x^3}{1000x^3 + 6}$

91. $\lim\limits_{x \to -\infty} \dfrac{x^3 - 100}{2x^2 + 500}$

92. $\lim\limits_{x \to -\infty} \dfrac{x^2 + 30x}{2x^6 + 10x}$

APPLICATIONS

93. *Crude Oil Prices* The price per barrel of crude oil in constant 2008 dollars can be approximated by

$$P(t) = 0.45t^2 - 12t + 105 \text{ dollars}   (0 \le t \le 28)$$

where t is time in years since the start of 1980.[1] Find $P'(t)$ and $P'(20)$. What does the answer tell you about the price of crude oil? HINT [See Example 2.]

94. Median Home Price The median home price in the United States over the period 2004–2009 can be approximated by

$$P(t) = -5t^2 + 75t - 30 \text{ thousand dollars} \quad (4 \le t \le 9)$$

where t is time in years since the start of 2000.[2] Find $P'(t)$ and $P'(6)$. What does the answer tell you about home prices? HINT [See Example 2.]

95. College Basketball: Men The number of NCAA men's college basketball teams in the United States can be modeled by:

$$n(t) = -0.56t^2 + 14t + 930 \quad (0 \le t \le 8)$$

where t is time in years since 2000.[3]

Men's Basketball Teams

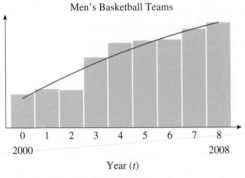

Year (t)

a. Find $n'(t)$. HINT [See Example 2.]

b. How fast (to the nearest whole number) was the number of men's college basketball teams increasing in 2006?

c. According to the model, did the rate of increase of the number of teams increase or decrease with time? Explain. HINT [See Example 4.]

96. College Basketball: Women The number of NCAA women's college basketball teams in the United States can be modeled by:

$$n(t) = -0.98t^2 + 32t + 1,850 \quad (0 \le t \le 8)$$

where t is time in years since 2000.[4]

Women's basketball teams

Year (t)

a. Find $n'(t)$. HINT [See Example 2.]

b. How fast (to the nearest whole number) was the number of women's college basketball teams increasing in 2005?

c. According to the model, did the rate of increase of the number of teams increase or decrease with time? Explain. HINT [See Example 4.]

97. Food Versus Education The following equation shows the approximate relationship between the percentage y of total personal consumption spent on food and the corresponding percentage x spent on education.[5]

$$y = \frac{35}{x^{0.35}} \text{ percentage points} \quad (6.5 \le x \le 17.5)$$

According to the model, spending on food is decreasing at a rate of _____ percentage points per one percentage point increase in spending on education when 10% of total consumption is spent on education. (Answer should be rounded to two significant digits.) HINT [See Example 2(b).]

98. Food Versus Recreation The following equation shows the approximate relationship between the percentage y of total personal consumption spent on food and the corresponding percentage x spent on recreation.[6]

$$y = \frac{33}{x^{0.63}} \text{ percentage points} \quad (2.5 \le x \le 4.5)$$

According to the model, spending on food is decreasing at a rate of _____ percentage points per one percentage point increase in spending on recreation when 3% of total consumption is spent on recreation. (Answer should be rounded to two significant digits.) HINT [See Example 2(b).]

99. Velocity If a stone is dropped from a height of 400 feet, its height s after t seconds is given by $s(t) = 400 - 16t^2$, with s in feet.

a. Compute $s'(t)$ and hence find its velocity at times $t = 0$, 1, 2, 3, and 4 seconds.

b. When does it reach the ground, and how fast is it traveling when it hits the ground? HINT [It reaches the ground when $s(t) = 0$.]

100. Velocity If a stone is thrown down at 120 ft/s from a height of 1,000 feet, its height s after t seconds is given by $s(t) = 1,000 - 120t - 16t^2$, with s in feet.

a. Compute $s'(t)$ and hence find its velocity at times $t = 0$, 1, 2, 3, and 4 seconds.

b. When does it reach the ground, and how fast is it traveling when it hits the ground? HINT [It reaches the ground when $s(t) = 0$.]

---

[1] Source for data: www.inflationdata.com.

[2] Source for data: www.investmenttools.com.

[3] 2007 and 2008 figures are estimates. Source: The 2008 Statistical Abstract, www.census.gov/.

[4] Ibid.

---

[5] Model based on historical and projected data from 1908–2010. Sources: Historical data, Bureau of Economic Analysis; projected data, Bureau of Labor Statistics/*New York Times*, December 1, 2003, p. C2.

[6] Ibid.

101. *iPhone Sales* iPhone sales from the 2nd quarter in 2007 through the 2nd quarter in 2008 can be approximated by

$$S(t) = -390t^2 + 3,300t - 4,800 \text{ thousand phones}$$
$$(2 \le t \le 6)$$

in quarter t. ($t = 1$ represents the start of the first quarter of 2007.)[7]

iPhone sales (thousands)

2007 Q2   2008 Q2

a. Compute $S'(t)$. How fast were iPhone sales changing in the first quarter of 2008 ($t = 5$)? (Be careful to give correct units of measurement.)

b. According to the model, iPhone sales

(A) increased at a faster and faster rate
(B) increased at a slower and slower rate
(C) decreased at a faster and faster rate
(D) decreased at a slower and slower rate

during the first two quarters shown (the interval $[2, 4]$). Justify your answer in two ways: geometrically, reasoning entirely from the graph; and algebraically, reasoning from the derivative of S. **HINT [See Example 4.]**

102. *Facebook Membership* The number of **Facebook** members from the start of 2006 to mid-2008 can be approximated by

$$S(t) = 15t^2 - 76t + 101 \text{ million members} (2 \le t \le 4.5)$$

in year t ($t = 0$ represents the start of 2004).[8]

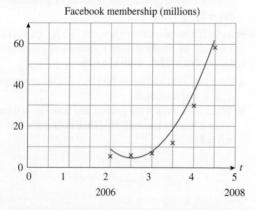

Facebook membership (millions)

2006   2008

a. Compute $S'(t)$. According to the model, how fast was **Facebook** membership changing at the start of 2008 ($t = 4$)? (Be careful to give correct units of measurement.)

b. According to the model, **Facebook** membership

(A) increased at a faster and faster rate
(B) increased at a slower and slower rate
(C) decreased at a faster and faster rate
(D) decreased at a slower and slower rate

during 2007 (the interval $[3, 4]$). Justify your answer in two ways: geometrically, reasoning entirely from the graph; and algebraically, reasoning from the derivative of S. **HINT [See Example 4.]**

103. *Ecology* Increasing numbers of manatees ("sea sirens") have been killed by boats off the Florida coast. The following graph shows the relationship between the number of boats registered in Florida and the number of manatees killed each year.

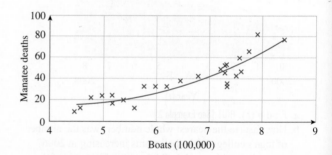

Boats (100,000)

The regression curve shown is given by

$$f(x) = 3.55x^2 - 30.2x + 81   (4.5 \le x \le 8.5)$$

where x is the number of boats (hundreds of thousands) registered in Florida in a particular year and $f(x)$ is the number of manatees killed by boats in Florida that year.[9]

a. Compute $f'(x)$. What are the units of measurement of $f'(x)$?

b. Is $f'(x)$ increasing or decreasing with increasing x? Interpret the answer. **HINT [See Example 4.]**

c. Compute and interpret $f'(8)$.

104. *SAT Scores by Income* The graph on the next page shows U.S. verbal SAT scores as a function of parents' income level.[10]

---

[7] The model is the authors'. Source for data: Apple financial statements, www.apple.com.

[8] The model is the authors'. Sources for data: www.facebook.com/, http://insidehighered.com (Some data are interpolated.)

[9] Regression model is based on data from 1976 to 2000. Sources for data: Florida Department of Highway Safety & Motor Vehicles, Florida Marine Institute/*New York Times*, February 12, 2002, p. F4.

[10] Based on 1994 data. Source: The College Board/*New York Times*, March 5, 1995, p. E16.

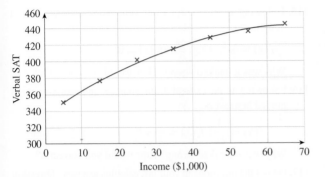

The regression curve shown is given by

$$f(x) = -0.021x^2 + 3.0x + 336 \quad (5 \le x \le 65)$$

where $f(x)$ is the average SAT verbal score of a student whose parents earn x thousand dollars per year.[11]

a. Compute $f'(x)$. What are the units of measurement of $f'(x)$?
b. Is $f'(x)$ increasing or decreasing with increasing x? Interpret the answer. HINT [See Example 4.]
c. Compute and interpret $f'(30)$.

105. *ISP Market Share* The following graph shows approximate market shares, in percentage points, of **Microsoft's MSN** Internet service provider, and the combined shares of **MSN**, **Comcast**, **Earthlink**, and **AOL** for the period 1999–2004.[12]

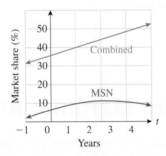

Here, t is time in years since June 2000. Let $c(t)$ be the combined market share at time t, and let $m(t)$ be MSN's share at time t.

a. What does the function $c(t) - m(t)$ measure? What does $c'(t) - m'(t)$ measure?
b. Based on the graphs shown, $c(t) - m(t)$ is

(A) increasing
(B) decreasing
(C) increasing, then decreasing
(D) decreasing, then increasing

on the interval $[3, 4]$.

c. Based on the graphs shown, $c'(t) - m'(t)$ is

(A) positive
(B) negative
(C) positive, then negative
(D) negative, then positive

on the interval $[3, 4]$.

d. The two market shares are approximated by

MSN: $m(t) = -0.83t^2 + 3.8t + 6.8 \quad (-1 \le t \le 4)$
Combined: $c(t) = 4.2t + 36 \quad (-1 \le t \le 4)$

Compute $c'(2) - m'(2)$. Interpret your answer.

106. ▼ *ISP Revenue* The following graph shows the approximate total revenue, in millions of dollars, of **Microsoft's MSN** Internet service provider, as well as the portion of the revenue due to advertising for the period June 2001–January 2004.[13]

Here, t is time in years since January 2000. Let $s(t)$ be the total revenue at time t, and let $a(t)$ be revenue due to advertising at time t.

a. What does the function $s(t) - a(t)$ measure? What does $s'(t) - a'(t)$ measure?
b. Based on the graphs shown, $s(t) - a(t)$ is

(A) increasing
(B) decreasing
(C) increasing, then decreasing
(D) decreasing, then increasing

on the interval $[2, 4]$.

c. Based on the graphs shown, $s'(t) - a'(t)$ is

(A) positive
(B) negative
(C) positive, then negative
(D) negative, then positive

on the interval $[2, 4]$.

d. The two revenue curves are approximated by

Advertising: $a(t) = 20t^2 - 27t + 120 \quad (1.5 \le t \le 4)$
Total: $s(t) = 96t + 190 \quad (1.5 \le t \le 4)$

Compute $a'(2)$, $s'(2)$, and hence $s'(2) - a'(2)$. Interpret your answer.

---

[11] Regression model is based on 1994 data. Source: The College Board/ *New York Times*, March 5, 1995, p. E16.

[12] The curves are regression models. Source for data: Solomon Research, Morgan Stanley/*New York Times*, July 19, 2004.

[13] Ibid.

COMMUNICATION AND REASONING EXERCISES

107. What instructions would you give to a fellow student who wanted to accurately graph the tangent line to the curve $y = 3x^2$ at the point $(-1, 3)$?

108. What instructions would you give to a fellow student who wanted to accurately graph a line at right angles to the curve $y = 4/x$ at the point where $x = 0.5$?

109. Consider $f(x) = x^2$ and $g(x) = 2x^2$. How do the slopes of the tangent lines of f and g at the same x compare?

110. Consider $f(x) = x^3$ and $g(x) = x^3 + 3$. How do the slopes of the tangent lines of f and g compare?

111. Suppose $g(x) = -f(x)$. How do the derivatives of f and g compare?

112. Suppose $g(x) = f(x) - 50$. How do the derivatives of f and g compare?

113. Following is an excerpt from your best friend's graded homework:

$$3x^4 + 11x^5 = 12x^3 + 55x^4 \quad \textbf{✗ WRONG} \quad -8$$

Why was it marked wrong? How would you correct it?

114. Following is an excerpt from your second best friend's graded homework:

$$f(x) = \frac{3}{4x^2}; f'(x) = \frac{3}{8x} \quad \textbf{✗ WRONG} \quad -10$$

Why was it marked wrong? How would you correct it?

115. Following is an excerpt from your worst enemy's graded homework:

$$f(x) = 4x^2; f'(x) = (0)(2x) = 0 \quad \textbf{✗ WRONG} \quad -6$$

Why was it marked wrong? How would you correct it?

116. Following is an excerpt from your second worst enemy's graded homework:

$$f(x) = \frac{3}{4x}; f'(x) = \frac{0}{4} = 0 \quad \textbf{✗ WRONG} \quad -10$$

Why was it marked wrong? How would you correct it?

117. One of the questions in your last calculus test was "**Question 1(a)** Give the definition of the derivative of a function f." Following is your answer and the grade you received:

$$nx^{n-1} \quad \textbf{✗ WRONG} \quad -10$$

Why was it marked wrong? What is the correct answer?

118. ▼ How would you respond to an acquaintance who says, "I finally understand what the derivative is: It is nx^{n-1}! Why weren't we taught that in the first place instead of the difficult way using limits?"

119. ▼ Sketch the graph of a function whose derivative is undefined at exactly two points but which has a tangent line at all but one point.

120. ▼ Sketch the graph of a function that has a tangent line at each of its points, but whose derivative is undefined at exactly two points.

11.2 A First Application: Marginal Analysis

In Chapter 1, we considered linear *cost functions* of the form $C(x) = mx + b$, where C is the total cost, x is the number of items, and m and b are constants. The slope m is the *marginal cost*. It measures the *cost of one more item*. Notice that the derivative of $C(x) = mx + b$ is $C'(x) = m$. In other words, for a linear cost function, *the marginal cost is the derivative of the cost function*.

In general, we make the following definition.

Marginal Cost

A **cost function** specifies the total cost C as a function of the number of items x. In other words, $C(x)$ is the total cost of x items. The **marginal cost function** is the derivative $C'(x)$ of the cost function $C(x)$. It measures the rate of change of cost with respect to x.

Units

The units of marginal cost are units of cost (dollars, say) per item.

✳ **NOTE** See Example 1.

Interpretation
We interpret $C'(x)$ as the approximate cost of one more item.✳

Quick Example

If $C(x) = 400x + 1,000$ dollars, then the marginal cost function is $C'(x) = \$400$ per item (a constant).

EXAMPLE 1 Marginal Cost

Suppose that the cost in dollars to manufacture portable CD players is given by

$$C(x) = 150,000 + 20x - 0.0001x^2$$

where x is the number of CD players manufactured.✳ Find the marginal cost function $C'(x)$ and use it to estimate the cost of manufacturing the 50,001st CD player.

Solution Since

$$C(x) = 150,000 + 20x - 0.0001x^2$$

the marginal cost function is

$$C'(x) = 20 - 0.0002x.$$

The units of $C'(x)$ are units of C (dollars) per unit of x (CD players). Thus, $C'(x)$ is measured in dollars per CD player.

The cost of the 50,001st CD player is the amount by which the total cost would rise if we increased production from 50,000 CD players to 50,001. Thus, we need to know the rate at which the total cost rises as we increase production. This rate of change is measured by the derivative, or marginal cost, which we just computed. At $x = 50,000$, we get

$$C'(50,000) = 20 - 0.0002(50,000) = \$10 \text{ per CD player.}$$

In other words, we estimate that the 50,001st CD player will cost approximately $10.

✳ **NOTE** You might well ask where on Earth this formula came from. There are two approaches to obtaining cost functions in real life: analytical and empirical. The analytical approach is to calculate the cost function from scratch. For example, in the above situation, we might have fixed costs of $150,000, plus a production cost of $20 per CD player. The term $0.0001x^2$ may reflect a cost saving for high levels of production, such as a bulk discount in the cost of electronic components. In the empirical approach, we first obtain the cost at several different production levels by direct observation. This gives several points on the (as yet unknown) cost versus production level graph. Then find the equation of the curve that best fits these points, usually using regression.

➡ **Before we go on...** In Example 1, the marginal cost is really only an *approximation* to the cost of the 50,001st CD player:

$$C'(50,000) \approx \frac{C(50,001) - C(50,000)}{1} \qquad \text{Set } h = 1 \text{ in the definition of the derivative.}$$

$$= C(50,001) - C(50,000)$$

$$= \text{cost of the 50,001st CD player}$$

The exact cost of the 50,001st CD player is

$$C(50,001) - C(50,000) = [150,000 + 20(50,001) - 0.0001(50,001)^2]$$
$$- [150,000 + 20(50,000) - 0.0001(50,000)^2]$$
$$= \$9.9999$$

So, the marginal cost is a good approximation to the actual cost.

Graphically, we are using the tangent line to approximate the cost function near a production level of 50,000. Figure 3 shows the graph of the cost function together with the tangent line at $x = 50,000$. Notice that the tangent line is essentially indistinguishable from the graph of the function for some distance on either side of 50,000.

Figure 3

Notes
1. In general, the difference quotient $[C(x + h) - C(x)]/h$ gives the **average cost per item** to produce h more items at a current production level of x items. (Why?)
2. Notice that $C'(x)$ is much easier to calculate than $[C(x + h) - C(x)]/h$. (Try it.)

We can extend the idea of marginal cost to include other functions, like revenue and profit:

Marginal Revenue and Profit

A **revenue** or **profit function** specifies the total revenue R or profit P as a function of the number of items x. The derivatives, $R'(x)$ and $P'(x)$ of these functions are called the **marginal revenue** and **marginal profit** functions. They measure the rate of change of revenue and profit with respect to x.

Units
The units of marginal revenue and profit are the same as those of marginal cost: dollars (or euros, pesos, etc.) per item.

Interpretation
We interpret $R'(x)$ and $P'(x)$ as the approximate revenue and profit from the sale of one more item.

EXAMPLE 2 Marginal Revenue and Profit

You operate an *iPod* customizing service (a typical customized iPod might have a custom color case with blinking lights and a personalized logo). The cost to refurbish x iPods in a month is calculated to be

$$C(x) = 0.25x^2 + 40x + 1,000 \text{ dollars.}$$

You charge customers $80 per iPod for the work.

a. Calculate the marginal revenue and profit functions. Interpret the results.

b. Compute the revenue and profit, and also the marginal revenue and profit, if you have refurbished 20 units this month. Interpret the results.

c. For which value of x is the marginal profit zero? Interpret your answer.

Solution

a. We first calculate the revenue and profit functions:

$$R(x) = 80x \qquad\qquad \text{Revenue = Price} \times \text{Quantity}$$

$$P(x) = R(x) - C(x) \qquad \text{Profit = Revenue} - \text{Cost}$$

$$= 80x - (0.25x^2 + 40x + 1,000)$$

$$P(x) = -0.25x^2 + 40x - 1,000.$$

The marginal revenue and profit functions are then the derivatives:

Marginal revenue $= R'(x) = 80$

Marginal profit $= P'(x) = -0.5x + 40.$

Interpretation: $R'(x)$ gives the approximate revenue from the refurbishing of one more item, and $P'(x)$ gives the approximate profit from the refurbishing of one more item. Thus, if x iPods have been refurbished in a month, you will earn a revenue of $80 and make a profit of approximately $(-0.5x + 40)$ if you refurbish one more that month.

    Notice that the marginal revenue is a constant, so you earn the same revenue ($80) for each iPod you refurbish. However, the marginal profit, $(-0.5x + 40)$, decreases as x increases, so your additional profit is about 50¢ less for each additional iPod you refurbish.

b. From part (a), the revenue, profit, marginal revenue, and marginal profit functions are

$$R(x) = 80x$$

$$P(x) = -0.25x^2 + 40x - 1,000$$

$$R'(x) = 80$$

$$P'(x) = -0.5x + 40$$

Because you have refurbished $x = 20$ iPods this month, $x = 20$, so

$R(20) = 80(20) = \$1,600$	Total revenue from 20 iPods
$P(20) = -0.25(20)^2 + 40(20) - 1,000 = -\$300$	Total profit from 20 iPods
$R'(20) = \$80$ per unit	Approximate revenue from the 21st iPod
$P'(20) = -0.5(20) + 40 = \$30$ per unit	Approximate profit from the 21st iPod

Interpretation: If you refurbish 20 iPods in a month, you will earn a total revenue of $160 and a profit of –$300 (indicating a loss of $300). Refurbishing one more iPod that month will earn you an additional revenue of $80 and an additional profit of about $30.

$P(x) = -0.25x^2 + 40x - 1,000$

Figure 4

c. The marginal profit is zero when $P'(x) = 0$:

$$-0.5x + 40 = 0$$

$$x = \frac{40}{0.5} = 80 \text{ iPods}$$

Thus, if you refurbish 80 iPods in a month, refurbishing one more will get you (approximately) zero additional profit. To understand this further, let us take a look at the graph of the profit function, shown in Figure 4. Notice that the graph is a parabola (the profit function is quadratic) with vertex at the point $x = 80$, where $P'(x) = 0$, so the profit is a maximum at this value of x.

➡ **Before we go on...** In general, setting $P'(x) = 0$ and solving for x will always give the exact values of x for which the profit peaks as in Figure 4, assuming there is such a value. We recommend that you graph the profit function to check whether the profit is indeed a maximum at such a point. ∎

EXAMPLE 3 Marginal Product

A consultant determines that Precision Manufacturers' annual profit (in dollars) is given by

$$P(n) = -200,000 + 400,000n - 4,600n^2 - 10n^3 \qquad (10 \le n \le 50)$$

where n is the number of assembly-line workers it employs.

a. Compute $P'(n)$. $P'(n)$ is called the **marginal product** at the employment level of n assembly-line workers. What are its units?

b. Calculate $P(20)$ and $P'(20)$, and interpret the results.

c. Precision Manufacturers currently employs 20 assembly-line workers and is considering laying off some of them. What advice would you give the company's management?

Solution

a. Taking the derivative gives

$$P'(n) = 400,000 - 9,200n - 30n^2.$$

The units of $P'(n)$ are profit (in dollars) per worker.

b. Substituting into the formula for $P(n)$, we get

$$P(20) = -200,000 + 400,000(20) - 4,600(20)^2 - 10(20)^3 = \$5,880,000.$$

Thus, Precision Manufacturer will make an annual profit of $5,880,000 if it employs 20 assembly-line workers. On the other hand,

$$P'(20) = 400,000 - 9,200(20) - 30(20)^2 = \$204,000/\text{worker}.$$

Thus, at an employment level of 20 assembly-line workers, annual profit is increasing at a rate of $204,000 per additional worker. In other words, if the company were to employ one more assembly-line worker, its annual profit would increase by approximately $204,000.

c. Because the marginal product is positive, profits will increase if the company increases the number of workers and will decrease if it decreases the number of workers, so your advice would be to hire additional assembly-line workers. Downsizing their assembly-line workforce would reduce their annual profits.

Figure 5

➡ **Before we go on...** In Example 3, it would be interesting for Precision Manufacturers to ascertain how many additional assembly-line workers they should hire to obtain the *maximum* annual profit. Taking our cue from Example 2, we suspect that such a value of n would correspond to a point where $P'(n) = 0$. Figure 5 shows the graph of P, and on it we see that the highest point of the graph is indeed a point where the tangent line is horizontal; that is, $P'(n) = 0$, and occurs somewhere between $n = 35$ and 40. To compute this value of n more accurately, set $P'(n) = 0$ and solve for n:

$$P'(n) = 400,000 - 9,200n - 30n^2 = 0 \quad \text{or} \quad 40,000 - 920n - 3n^2 = 0.$$

We can now obtain n using the quadratic formula:

$$n = \frac{-b \pm \sqrt{b^2 - 4ac}}{2a} = \frac{920 \pm \sqrt{920^2 - 4(-3)(40,000)}}{2(-3)}$$

$$= \frac{920 \pm \sqrt{1,326,400}}{-6} \approx -345.3 \text{ or } 38.6.$$

The only meaningful solution is the positive one, $n \approx 38.6$ workers, and we conclude that the company should employ between 38 and 39 assembly-line workers for a maximum profit. To see which gives the larger profit, 38 or 39, we check:

$$P(38) = \$7,808,880$$

while

$$P(39) = \$7,810,210.$$

This tells us that the company should employ 39 assembly-line workers for a maximum profit. Thus, instead of laying off any of its 20 assembly-line workers, the company should hire 19 additional assembly line workers for a total of 39. ∎

Average Cost

EXAMPLE 4 **Average Cost**

Suppose the cost in dollars to manufacture portable CD players is given by

$$C(x) = 150,000 + 20x - 0.0001x^2$$

where x is the number of CD players manufactured. (This is the cost equation we saw in Example 1.)

a. Find the average cost per CD player if 50,000 CD players are manufactured.

b. Find a formula for the average cost per CD player if x CD players are manufactured. This function of x is called the **average cost function, $\bar{C}(x)$**.

Solution

a. The total cost of manufacturing 50,000 CD players is given by

$$C(50,000) = 150,000 + 20(50,000) - 0.0001(50,000)^2$$
$$= \$900,000.$$

Because 50,000 CD players cost a total of \$900,000 to manufacture, the average cost of manufacturing one CD player is this total cost divided by 50,000:

$$\bar{C}(50,000) = \frac{900,000}{50,000} = \$18.00 \text{ per CD player.}$$

Thus, if 50,000 CD players are manufactured, each CD player costs the manufacturer an average of \$18.00 to manufacture.

b. If we replace 50,000 by x, we get the general formula for the average cost of manufacturing x CD players:

$$\bar{C}(x) = \frac{C(x)}{x}$$

$$= \frac{1}{x}(150,000 + 20x - 0.0001x^2)$$

$$= \frac{150,000}{x} + 20 - 0.0001x. \qquad \text{Average cost function}$$

Figure 6

➡ **Before we go on...** Average cost and marginal cost convey different but related information. The average cost $\bar{C}(50,000) = \$18$ that we calculated in Example 4 is the cost per item of manufacturing the first 50,000 CD players, whereas the marginal cost $C'(50,000) = \$10$ that we calculated in Example 1 gives the (approximate) cost of manufacturing the *next* CD player. Thus, according to our calculations, the first 50,000 CD players cost an average of \$18 to manufacture, but it costs only about \$10 to manufacture the next one. Note that the marginal cost at a production level of 50,000 CD players is lower than the average cost. This means that the average cost to manufacture CDs is going down with increasing volume. (Think about why.)

Figure 6 shows the graphs of average and marginal cost. Notice how the decreasing marginal cost seems to pull the average cost down with it. ■

To summarize:

Average Cost

Given a cost function C, the **average cost** of the first x items is given by

$$\bar{C}(x) = \frac{C(x)}{x}.$$

The average cost is distinct from the **marginal cost** $C'(x)$, which tells us the approximate cost of the *next* item.

Quick Example

For the cost function $C(x) = 20x + 100$ dollars

Marginal Cost $= C'(x) = \$20$ per additional item.

Average Cost $= \bar{C}(x) = \dfrac{C(x)}{x} = \dfrac{20x + 100}{x} = \$(20 + 100/x)$ per item.

11.2 EXERCISES

In Exercises 1–4, for each cost function, find the marginal cost at the given production level x, and state the units of measurement. (All costs are in dollars.) HINT [See Example 1.]

1. $C(x) = 10,000 + 5x - 0.0001x^2$; $x = 1,000$

2. $C(x) = 20,000 + 7x - 0.00005x^2$; $x = 10,000$

3. $C(x) = 15,000 + 100x + \dfrac{1,000}{x}$; $x = 100$

4. $C(x) = 20,000 + 50x + \dfrac{10,000}{x}$; $x = 100$

In Exercises 5 and 6, find the marginal cost, marginal revenue, and marginal profit functions, and find all values of x for which the marginal profit is zero. Interpret your answer. HINT [See Example 2.]

5. $C(x) = 4x$; $R(x) = 8x - 0.001x^2$

6. $C(x) = 5x^2$; $R(x) = x^3 + 7x + 10$

7. ▼ A certain cost function has the following graph:

a. The associated marginal cost is

   (A) increasing, then decreasing
   (B) decreasing, then increasing
   (C) always increasing
   (D) always decreasing

b. The marginal cost is least at approximately

   (A) $x = 0$ **(B)** $x = 50$ **(C)** $x = 100$ **(D)** $x = 150$

c. The cost of 50 items is

   (A) approximately $20, and increasing at a rate of about $3,000 per item
   (B) approximately $0.50, and increasing at a rate of about $3,000 per item
   (C) approximately $3,000, and increasing at a rate of about $20 per item
   (D) approximately $3,000, and increasing at a rate of about $0.50 per item

8. ▼ A certain cost function has the following graph:

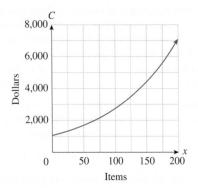

a. The associated marginal cost is

   (A) increasing, then decreasing
   (B) decreasing, then increasing
   (C) always increasing
   (D) always decreasing

b. When $x = 100$, the marginal cost is

   (A) greater than the average cost
   (B) less than the average cost
   (C) approximately equal to the average cost

c. The cost of 150 items is

   (A) approximately $4,400, and increasing at a rate of about $40 per item
   (B) approximately $40, and increasing at a rate of about $4,400 per item
   (C) approximately $4,400, and increasing at a rate of about $1 per item
   (D) approximately $1, and increasing at a rate of about $4,400 per item

APPLICATIONS

9. *Advertising Costs* The cost, in thousands of dollars, of airing x television commercials during a Super Bowl game is given by[14]

$$C(x) = 150 + 2,250x - 0.02x^2.$$

a. Find the marginal cost function and use it to estimate how fast the cost is increasing when $x = 4$. Compare this with the exact cost of airing the fifth commercial. HINT [See Example 1.]

b. Find the average cost function $\bar{C}$, and evaluate $\bar{C}(4)$. What does the answer tell you? HINT [See Example 4.]

---

[14] CBS charged an average of $2.25 million per 30-second television spot during the 2004 Super Bowl game. This explains the coefficient of x in the cost function. Source: Advertising Age Research, www.AdAge.com/.

10. *Marginal Cost and Average Cost* The cost of producing x teddy bears per day at the Cuddly Companion Co. is calculated by their marketing staff to be given by the formula

$$C(x) = 100 + 40x - 0.001x^2.$$

a. Find the marginal cost function and use it to estimate how fast the cost is going up at a production level of 100 teddy bears. Compare this with the exact cost of producing the 101st teddy bear. HINT [See Example 1.]

b. Find the average cost function $\bar{C}$, and evaluate $\bar{C}(100)$. What does the answer tell you? HINT [See Example 4.]

11. *Marginal Revenue and Profit* Your college newspaper, *The Collegiate Investigator*, sells for 90¢ per copy. The cost of producing x copies of an edition is given by

$$C(x) = 70 + 0.10x + 0.001x^2 \text{ dollars}.$$

a. Calculate the marginal revenue and profit functions. HINT [See Example 2.]

b. Compute the revenue and profit, and also the marginal revenue and profit, if you have produced and sold 500 copies of the latest edition. Interpret the results.

c. For which value of x is the marginal profit zero? Interpret your answer.

12. *Marginal Revenue and Profit* The Audubon Society at Enormous State University (ESU) is planning its annual fundraising "Eatathon." The society will charge students $1.10 per serving of pasta. The society estimates that the total cost of producing x servings of pasta at the event will be

$$C(x) = 350 + 0.10x + 0.002x^2 \text{ dollars}.$$

a. Calculate the marginal revenue and profit functions. HINT [See Example 2.]

b. Compute the revenue and profit, and also the marginal revenue and profit, if you have produced and sold 200 servings of pasta. Interpret the results.

c. For which value of x is the marginal profit zero? Interpret your answer.

13. *Marginal Profit* Suppose $P(x)$ represents the profit on the sale of x DVDs. If $P(1,000) = 3,000$ and $P'(1,000) = -3$, what do these values tell you about the profit?

14. *Marginal Loss* An automobile retailer calculates that its loss on the sale of type M cars is given by $L(50) = 5,000$ and $L'(50) = -200$, where $L(x)$ represents the loss on the sale of x type M cars. What do these values tell you about losses?

15. *Marginal Profit* Your monthly profit (in dollars) from selling magazines is given by

$$P = 5x + \sqrt{x}$$

where x is the number of magazines you sell in a month. If you are currently selling $x = 50$ magazines per month, find your profit and your marginal profit. Interpret your answers.

16. *Marginal Profit* Your monthly profit (in dollars) from your newspaper route is given by

$$P = 2n - \sqrt{n}$$

where n is the number of subscribers on your route. If you currently have 100 subscribers, find your profit and your marginal profit. Interpret your answers.

17. ▼ *Marginal Revenue: Pricing Tuna* Assume that the demand function for tuna in a small coastal town is given by

$$p = \frac{20,000}{q^{1.5}} \qquad (200 \le q \le 800)$$

where p is the price (in dollars) per pound of tuna, and q is the number of pounds of tuna that can be sold at the price p in one month.

a. Calculate the price that the town's fishery should charge for tuna in order to produce a demand of 400 pounds of tuna per month.

b. Calculate the monthly revenue R as a function of the number of pounds of tuna q.

c. Calculate the revenue and marginal revenue (derivative of the revenue with respect to q) at a demand level of 400 pounds per month, and interpret the results.

d. If the town fishery's monthly tuna catch amounted to 400 pounds of tuna, and the price is at the level in part (a), would you recommend that the fishery raise or lower the price of tuna in order to increase its revenue?

18. ▼ *Marginal Revenue: Pricing Tuna* Repeat Exercise 17, assuming a demand equation of

$$p = \frac{60}{q^{0.5}} \qquad (200 \le q \le 800).$$

19. *Marginal Product* A car wash firm calculates that its daily profit (in dollars) depends on the number n of workers it employs according to the formula

$$P = 400n - 0.5n^2.$$

Calculate the marginal product at an employment level of 50 workers, and interpret the result. HINT [See Example 3.]

20. *Marginal Product* Repeat the preceding exercise using the formula

$$P = -100n + 25n^2 - 0.005n^4.$$

HINT [See Example 3.]

21. *Average and Marginal Cost* The daily cost to manufacture generic trinkets for gullible tourists is given by the cost function

$$C(x) = -0.001x^2 + 0.3x + 500 \text{ dollars}$$

where x is the number of trinkets.

a. As x increases, the marginal cost

(A) increases   (B) decreases   (C) increases, then decreases   (D) decreases, then increases

b. As x increases, the average cost
   (A) increases   **(B)** decreases   **(C)** increases, then decreases   **(D)** decreases, then increases
c. The marginal cost is
   (A) greater than   **(B)** equal to   **(C)** less than the average cost when $x = 100$. HINT [See Example 4.]

22. *Average and Marginal Cost* Repeat Exercise 21, using the following cost function for imitation oil paintings (x is the number of "oil paintings" manufactured):

$$C(x) = 0.1x^2 - 3.5x + 500 \text{ dollars.}$$

HINT [See Example 4.]

23. *Advertising Cost* Your company is planning to air a number of television commercials during the ABC Television Network's presentation of the Academy Awards. ABC is charging your company $1.6 million per 30-second spot.[15] Additional fixed costs (development and personnel costs) amount to $500,000, and the network has agreed to provide a discount of $10,000\sqrt{x}$ for x television spots.

a. Write down the cost function C, marginal cost function C', and average cost function $\bar{C}$.
b. Compute $C'(3)$ and $\bar{C}(3)$. (Round all answers to three significant digits.) Use these two answers to say whether the average cost is increasing or decreasing as x increases.

24. *Housing Costs* The cost C of building a house is related to the number k of carpenters used and the number x of electricians used by the formula[16]

$$C = 15,000 + 50k^2 + 60x^2.$$

a. Assuming that 10 carpenters are currently being used, find the cost function C, marginal cost function C', and average cost function $\bar{C}$, all as functions of x.
b. Use the functions you obtained in part (a) to compute $C'(15)$ and $\bar{C}(15)$. Use these two answers to say whether the average cost is increasing or decreasing as the number of electricians increases.

25. ▼ *Emission Control* The cost of controlling emissions at a firm rises rapidly as the amount of emissions reduced increases. Here is a possible model:

$$C(q) = 4,000 + 100q^2$$

where q is the reduction in emissions (in pounds of pollutant per day) and C is the daily cost (in dollars) of this reduction.

a. If a firm is currently reducing its emissions by 10 pounds each day, what is the marginal cost of reducing emissions further?
b. Government clean-air subsidies to the firm are based on the formula

$$S(q) = 500q$$

where q is again the reduction in emissions (in pounds per day) and S is the subsidy (in dollars). At what reduction level does the marginal cost surpass the marginal subsidy?
c. Calculate the net cost function, $N(q) = C(q) - S(q)$, given the cost function and subsidy above, and find the value of q that gives the lowest net cost. What is this lowest net cost? Compare your answer to that for part (b) and comment on what you find.

26. ▼ *Taxation Schemes* Here is a curious proposal for taxation rates based on income:

$$T(i) = 0.001i^{0.5}$$

where i represents total annual income in dollars and $T(i)$ is the income tax rate as a percentage of total annual income. (Thus, for example, an income of $50,000 per year would be taxed at about 22%, while an income of double that amount would be taxed at about 32%.)[17]

a. Calculate the after-tax (net) income $N(i)$ an individual can expect to earn as a function of income i.
b. Calculate an individual's marginal after-tax income at income levels of $100,000 and $500,000.
c. At what income does an individual's marginal after-tax income become negative? What is the after-tax income at that level, and what happens at higher income levels?
d. What do you suspect is the most anyone can earn after taxes? (See NOTE at the bottom of this page.)

27. ▼ *Fuel Economy* Your Porsche's gas mileage (in miles per gallon) is given as a function $M(x)$ of speed x in miles per hour. It is found that

$$M'(x) = \frac{3,600x^{-2} - 1}{(3,600x^{-1} + x)^2}.$$

Estimate $M'(10)$, $M'(60)$, and $M'(70)$. What do the answers tell you about your car?

28. ▼ *Marginal Revenue* The estimated marginal revenue for sales of ESU soccer team T-shirts is given by

$$R'(p) = \frac{(8 - 2p)e^{-p^2 + 8p}}{10,000,000}$$

---

[15] ABC charged an average of $1.6 million for a 30-second spot during the 2005 Academy Awards presentation. Source: CNN/Reuters, www.cnn.com, February 9, 2005.

[16] Based on an exercise in *Introduction to Mathematical Economics* by A. L. Ostrosky, Jr., and J. V. Koch (Waveland Press, Prospect Heights, Illinois, 1979).

[17] This model has the following interesting feature: An income of $1 million per year would be taxed at 100%, leaving the individual penniless!

where p is the price (in dollars) that the soccer players charge for each shirt. Estimate $R'(3)$, $R'(4)$, and $R'(5)$. What do the answers tell you?

29. ◆ **Marginal Cost** *(from the GRE Economics Test)* In a multi-plant firm in which the different plants have different and continuous cost schedules, if costs of production for a given output level are to be minimized, which of the following is essential?

(A) Marginal costs must equal marginal revenue.
(B) Average variable costs must be the same in all plants.
(C) Marginal costs must be the same in all plants.
(D) Total costs must be the same in all plants.
(E) Output per worker per hour must be the same in all plants.

30. ◆ **Study Time** *(from the GRE economics test)* A student has a fixed number of hours to devote to study and is certain of the relationship between hours of study and the final grade for each course. Grades are given on a numerical scale (0 to 100), and each course is counted equally in computing the grade average. In order to maximize his or her grade average, the student should allocate these hours to different courses so that

(A) the grade in each course is the same.
(B) the marginal product of an hour's study (in terms of final grade) in each course is zero.
(C) the marginal product of an hour's study (in terms of final grade) in each course is equal, although not necessarily equal to zero.
(D) the average product of an hour's study (in terms of final grade) in each course is equal.
(E) the number of hours spent in study for each course is equal.

31. ◆ **Marginal Product** *(from the GRE Economics Test)* Assume that the marginal product of an additional senior professor is 50% higher than the marginal product of an additional junior professor and that junior professors are paid one-half the amount that senior professors receive. With a fixed overall budget, a university that wishes to maximize its quantity of output from professors should do which of the following?

(A) Hire equal numbers of senior professors and junior professors.
(B) Hire more senior professors and junior professors.
(C) Hire more senior professors and discharge junior professors.
(D) Discharge senior professors and hire more junior professors.
(E) Discharge all senior professors and half of the junior professors.

32. ◆ **Marginal Product** *(based on a question from the GRE Economics Test)* Assume that the marginal product of an additional senior professor is twice the marginal product of an additional junior professor and that junior professors are paid two-thirds the amount that senior professors receive. With a fixed overall budget, a university that wishes to maximize its quantity of output from professors should do which of the following?

(A) Hire equal numbers of senior professors and junior professors.
(B) Hire more senior professors and junior professors.
(C) Hire more senior professors and discharge junior professors.
(D) Discharge senior professors and hire more junior professors.
(E) Discharge all senior professors and half of the junior professors.

COMMUNICATION AND REASONING EXERCISES

33. The marginal cost of producing the 1,001st item is

(A) equal to
(B) approximately equal to
(C) always slightly greater than

the actual cost of producing the 1,001st item.

34. For the cost function $C(x) = mx + b$, the marginal cost of producing the 1,001st item is,

(A) equal to
(B) approximately equal to
(C) always slightly greater than

the actual cost of producing the 1,001st item.

35. What is a cost function? Carefully explain the difference between *average cost* and *marginal cost* in terms of (a) their mathematical definition, (b) graphs, and (c) interpretation.

36. The cost function for your grand piano manufacturing plant has the property that $\bar{C}(1,000) = \$3,000$ per unit and $C'(1,000) = \$2,500$ per unit. Will the average cost increase or decrease if your company manufactures a slightly larger number of pianos? Explain your reasoning.

37. If the average cost to manufacture one grand piano increases as the production level increases, which is greater, the marginal cost or the average cost?

38. If your analysis of a manufacturing company yielded positive marginal profit but negative profit at the company's current production levels, what would you advise the company to do?

39. ▼ If the marginal cost is decreasing, is the average cost necessarily decreasing? Explain.

40. ▼ If the average cost is decreasing, is the marginal cost necessarily decreasing? Explain.

41. ◆ If a company's marginal average cost is zero at the current production level, positive for a slightly higher production level, and negative for a slightly lower production level, what should you advise the company to do?

42. ◆ The **acceleration** of cost is defined as the derivative of the marginal cost function: that is, the derivative of the derivative—or *second derivative*—of the cost function. What are the units of acceleration of cost, and how does one interpret this measure?

11.3 The Product and Quotient Rules

We know how to find the derivatives of functions that are sums of powers, such as polynomials. In general, if a function is a sum or difference of functions whose derivatives we know, then we know how to find its derivative. But what about *products and quotients* of functions whose derivatives we know? For instance, how do we calculate the derivative of something like $x^2/(x+1)$? The derivative of $x^2/(x+1)$ is not, as one might suspect, $2x/1 = 2x$. That calculation is based on an assumption that the derivative of a quotient is the quotient of the derivatives. But it is easy to see that this assumption is false: For instance, the derivative of $1/x$ is not $0/1 = 0$, but $-1/x^2$. Similarly, the derivative of a product is not the product of the derivatives: For instance, the derivative of $x = 1 \cdot x$ is not $0 \cdot 1 = 0$, but 1.

To identify the correct method of computing the derivatives of products and quotients, let's look at a simple example. We know that the daily revenue resulting from the sale of q items per day at a price of p dollars per item is given by the product, $R = pq$ dollars. Suppose you are currently selling wall posters on campus. At this time your daily sales are 50 posters, and sales are increasing at a rate of 4 per day. Furthermore, you are currently charging $10 per poster, and you are also raising the price at a rate of $2 per day. Let's use this information to estimate how fast your daily revenue is increasing. In other words, let us estimate the rate of change, dR/dt, of the revenue R.

There are two contributions to the rate of change of daily revenue: the increase in daily sales and the increase in the unit price. We have

$\dfrac{dR}{dt}$ due to increasing price: $2 per day $\times$ 50 posters = $100 per day

$\dfrac{dR}{dt}$ due to increasing sales: $10 per poster $\times$ 4 posters per day = $40 per day

Thus, we estimate the daily revenue to be increasing at a rate of $100 + $40 = $140 per day. Let us translate what we have said into symbols:

$\dfrac{dR}{dt}$ due to increasing price: $\dfrac{dp}{dt} \times q$

$\dfrac{dR}{dt}$ due to increasing sales: $p \times \dfrac{dq}{dt}$

Thus, the rate of change of revenue is given by

$$\frac{dR}{dt} = \frac{dp}{dt}q + p\frac{dq}{dt}.$$

Because $R = pq$, we have discovered the following rule for differentiating a product:

$$\frac{d}{dt}(pq) = \frac{dp}{dt}q + p\frac{dq}{dt}$$ The derivative of a product is the derivative of the first times the second, plus the first times the derivative of the second.

This rule and a similar rule for differentiating quotients are given next, and also a discussion of how these results are proved rigorously.

Product Rule

If $f(x)$ and $g(x)$ are differentiable functions of x, then so is their product $f(x)g(x)$, and

$$\frac{d}{dx}[f(x)g(x)] = f'(x)g(x) + f(x)g'(x).$$

Product Rule in Words

The derivative of a product is the derivative of the first times the second, plus the first times the derivative of the second.

Quick Example

$f(x) = x^2$ and $g(x) = 3x - 1$ are both differentiable functions of x, and so their product $x^2(3x - 1)$ is differentiable, and

$$\frac{d}{dx}[x^2(3x - 1)] = 2x \cdot (3x - 1) + x^2 \cdot (3).$$

Derivative of first   Second   First   Derivative of second

Quotient Rule

If $f(x)$ and $g(x)$ are differentiable functions of x, then so is their quotient $f(x)/g(x)$ (provided $g(x) \neq 0$), and

$$\frac{d}{dx}\left(\frac{f(x)}{g(x)}\right) = \frac{f'(x)g(x) - f(x)g'(x)}{[g(x)]^2}.$$

Quotient Rule in Words

The derivative of a quotient is the derivative of the top times the bottom, minus the top times the derivative of the bottom, all over the bottom squared.

Quick Example

$f(x) = x^3$ and $g(x) = x^2 + 1$ are both differentiable functions of x, and so their quotient $x^3/(x^2 + 1)$ is differentiable, and

Derivative of top   Bottom   Top   Derivative of bottom

$$\frac{d}{dx}\left(\frac{x^3}{x^2 + 1}\right) = \frac{3x^2(x^2 + 1) - x^3 \cdot 2x}{(x^2 + 1)^2}$$

Bottom squared

Notes

1. Don't try to remember the rules by the symbols we have used, but remember them in words. (The slogans are easy to remember, even if the terms are not precise.)

2. One more time: *The derivative of a product is* NOT *the product of the derivatives, and the derivative of a quotient is* NOT *the quotient of the derivatives.* To find the derivative of a product, you must use the product rule, and to find the derivative of a quotient, you must use the quotient rule.*

✱ **NOTE** Leibniz made this mistake at first, too, so you would be in good company if you forgot to use the product or quotient rule.

Q: *Wait a minute! The expression $2x^3$ is a product, and we already know that its derivative is $6x^2$. Where did we use the product rule?*

A: To differentiate functions such as $2x^3$, we have used the rule from Section 10.4:

The derivative of c times a function is c times the derivative of the function.

However, the product rule gives us the same result:

Derivative of first Second   First   Derivative of second
         ↓   ↓   ↓   ↓

$$\frac{d}{dx}(2x^3) = (0)(x^3) \quad + \quad (2)(3x^2) = 6x^2 \qquad \text{Product rule}$$

$$\frac{d}{dx}(2x^3) = (2)(3x^2) = 6x^2 \qquad \begin{array}{l}\text{Derivative of a constant}\\ \text{times a function}\end{array}$$

We do not recommend that you use the product rule to differentiate functions such as $2x^3$; continue to use the simpler rule when one of the factors is a constant.

Derivation of the Product Rule

Before we look at more examples of using the product and quotient rules, let's see why the product rule is true. To calculate the derivative of the product $f(x)g(x)$ of two differentiable functions, we go back to the definition of the derivative:

$$\frac{d}{dx}[f(x)g(x)] = \lim_{h \to 0} \frac{f(x+h)g(x+h) - f(x)g(x)}{h}.$$

* NOTE Adding an appropriate form of zero is an age-old mathematical ploy.

We now rewrite this expression so that we can evaluate the limit: Notice that the numerator reflects a simultaneous change in f [from $f(x)$ to $f(x+h)$] and g [from $g(x)$ to $g(x+h)$]. To separate the two effects, we add and subtract a quantity in the numerator that reflects a change in only one of the functions:

$$\frac{d}{dx}[f(x)g(x)] = \lim_{h \to 0} \frac{f(x+h)g(x+h) - f(x)g(x)}{h}$$

$$= \lim_{h \to 0} \frac{f(x+h)g(x+h) - f(x)g(x+h) + f(x)g(x+h) - f(x)g(x)}{h} \qquad \begin{array}{l}\text{We subtracted and added}\\ \text{the quantity}^* f(x)g(x+h).\end{array}$$

$$= \lim_{h \to 0} \frac{[f(x+h) - f(x)]g(x+h) + f(x)[g(x+h) - g(x)]}{h} \qquad \text{Common factors}$$

$$= \lim_{h \to 0} \left(\frac{f(x+h) - f(x)}{h} \right) g(x+h) + \lim_{h \to 0} f(x) \left(\frac{g(x+h) - g(x)}{h} \right) \qquad \text{Limit of sum}$$

$$= \lim_{h \to 0} \left(\frac{f(x+h) - f(x)}{h} \right) \lim_{h \to 0} g(x+h) + \lim_{h \to 0} f(x) \lim_{h \to 0} \left(\frac{g(x+h) - g(x)}{h} \right) \qquad \text{Limit of product}$$

Web Site
www.FiniteandCalc.org
For a proof of the fact that, if g is differentiable, it must be continuous, go to the Web site and follow the path

Everything for Calculus
→ Chapter 11
→ Continuity and
   Differentiability

Now we already know the following four limits:

$$\lim_{h \to 0} \frac{f(x+h) - f(x)}{h} = f'(x) \qquad \text{Definition of derivative of } f; f \text{ is differentiable.}$$

$$\lim_{h \to 0} \frac{g(x+h) - g(x)}{h} = g'(x) \qquad \text{Definition of derivative of } g; g \text{ is differentiable.}$$

$$\lim_{h \to 0} g(x+h) = g(x) \qquad \text{If } g \text{ is differentiable, it must be continuous.}$$

$$\lim_{h \to 0} f(x) = f(x) \qquad \text{Limit of a constant}$$

Web Site

www.FiniteandCalc.org

The quotient rule can be proved in a very similar way. Go to the Web site and follow the path

Everything for Calculus

→ Chapter 11

→ Proof of Quotient Rule

Putting these limits into the one we're calculating, we get

$$\frac{d}{dx}[f(x)g(x)] = f'(x)g(x) + f(x)g'(x)$$

which is the product rule.

EXAMPLE 5 Using the Product Rule

Compute the following derivatives.

a. $\dfrac{d}{dx}[(x^{3.2} + 1)(1 - x)]$ Simplify the answer.

b. $\dfrac{d}{dx}[(x + 1)(x^2 + 1)(x^3 + 1)]$ Do not expand the answer.

Solution

a. We can do the calculation in two ways.

Derivative of first   Second   First   Derivative of second

Using the Product Rule: $\dfrac{d}{dx}[(x^{3.2} + 1)(1 - x)] = (3.2x^{2.2})(1 - x) + (x^{3.2} + 1)(-1)$

$$= 3.2x^{2.2} - 3.2x^{3.2} - x^{3.2} - 1 \quad \text{Expand the}$$
$$= -4.2x^{3.2} + 3.2x^{2.2} - 1 \quad \text{answer.}$$

Not Using the Product Rule: First, expand the given expression.

$$(x^{3.2} + 1)(1 - x) = -x^{4.2} + x^{3.2} - x + 1$$

Thus,

$$\frac{d}{dx}[(x^{3.2} + 1)(1 - x)] = \frac{d}{dx}(-x^{4.2} + x^{3.2} - x + 1)$$
$$= -4.2x^{3.2} + 3.2x^{2.2} - 1$$

In this example the product rule saves us little or no work, but in later sections we shall see examples that can be done in no other way. Learn how to use the product rule now!

b. Here we have a product of *three* functions, not just two. We can find the derivative by using the product rule twice:

$$\frac{d}{dx}[(x + 1)(x^2 + 1)(x^3 + 1)]$$

$$= \frac{d}{dx}(x + 1) \cdot [(x^2 + 1)(x^3 + 1)] + (x + 1) \cdot \frac{d}{dx}[(x^2 + 1)(x^3 + 1)]$$

$$= (1)(x^2 + 1)(x^3 + 1) + (x + 1)[(2x)(x^3 + 1) + (x^2 + 1)(3x^2)]$$

$$= (1)(x^2 + 1)(x^3 + 1) + (x + 1)(2x)(x^3 + 1) + (x + 1)(x^2 + 1)(3x^2)$$

We can see here a more general product rule:

$$(fgh)' = f'gh + fg'h + fgh'$$

Notice that every factor has a chance to contribute to the rate of change of the product. There are similar formulas for products of four or more functions.

EXAMPLE 6 Using the Quotient Rule

Compute the derivatives **a.** $\dfrac{d}{dx}\left[\dfrac{1 - 3.2x^{-0.1}}{x + 1}\right]$ **b.** $\dfrac{d}{dx}\left[\dfrac{(x + 1)(x + 2)}{x - 1}\right]$

Solution

$$\text{Derivative of top}\quad\text{Bottom}\qquad\text{Top}\quad\text{Derivative of bottom}$$
$$\downarrow\qquad\qquad\downarrow\qquad\qquad\downarrow\qquad\qquad\downarrow$$

a. $\dfrac{d}{dx}\left[\dfrac{1 - 3.2x^{-0.1}}{x + 1}\right] = \dfrac{(0.32x^{-1.1})(x + 1) - (1 - 3.2x^{-0.1})(1)}{(x + 1)^2}$

$$\uparrow$$
$$\text{Bottom squared}$$

$$= \dfrac{0.32x^{-0.1} + 0.32x^{-1.1} - 1 + 3.2x^{-0.1}}{(x + 1)^2} \qquad \text{Expand the numerator.}$$

$$= \dfrac{3.52x^{-0.1} + 0.32x^{-1.1} - 1}{(x + 1)^2}$$

b. Here we have both a product and a quotient. Which rule do we use, the product or the quotient rule? Here is a way to decide. Think about how we would calculate, step by step, the value of $(x + 1)(x + 2)/(x - 1)$ for a specific value of x—say $x = 11$. Here is how we would probably do it:

1. Calculate $(x + 1)(x + 2) = (11 + 1)(11 + 2) = 156$.

2. Calculate $x - 1 = 11 - 1 = 10$.

3. Divide 156 by 10 to get 15.6.

Now ask: *What was the last operation we performed?* The last operation we performed was division, so we can regard the whole expression as a *quotient*—that is, as $(x + 1)(x + 2)$ *divided by* $(x - 1)$. Therefore, we should use the quotient rule.

The first thing the quotient rule tells us to do is to take the derivative of the numerator. Now, the numerator is a product, so we must use the product rule to take its derivative. Here is the calculation:

$$\qquad\qquad\qquad\qquad\qquad\qquad\qquad\qquad\qquad\qquad\qquad\qquad\text{Derivative}$$
$$\text{Derivative of top}\qquad\qquad\text{Bottom}\quad\text{Top}\quad\text{of bottom}$$
$$\downarrow\qquad\qquad\qquad\qquad\downarrow\qquad\downarrow\qquad\downarrow$$

$$\dfrac{d}{dx}\left[\dfrac{(x + 1)(x + 2)}{x - 1}\right] = \dfrac{[(1)(x + 2) + (x + 1)(1)](x - 1) - [(x + 1)(x + 2)](1)}{(x - 1)^2}$$

$$\uparrow$$
$$\text{Bottom squared}$$

$$= \dfrac{(2x + 3)(x - 1) - (x + 1)(x + 2)}{(x - 1)^2}$$

$$= \dfrac{x^2 - 2x - 5}{(x - 1)^2}$$

What is important is to determine the *order of operations* and, in particular, to determine the last operation to be performed. Pretending to do an actual calculation reminds us of the order of operations; we call this technique the **calculation thought experiment**.

➡ **Before we go on...** We used the quotient rule in Example 6 because the function was a quotient; we used the product rule to calculate the derivative of the numerator because the numerator was a product. Get used to this: Differentiation rules usually must be used in combination.

Here is another way we could have done this problem: Our calculation thought experiment could have taken the following form.

1. Calculate $(x + 1)/(x - 1) = (11 + 1)/(11 - 1) = 1.2$.

2. Calculate $x + 2 = 11 + 2 = 13$.

3. Multiply 1.2 by 13 to get 15.6.

We would have then regarded the expression as a *product*—the product of the factors $(x + 1)/(x - 1)$ and $(x + 2)$—and used the product rule instead. We can't escape the quotient rule, however: We need to use it to take the derivative of the first factor, $(x + 1)/(x - 1)$. Try this approach for practice and check that you get the same answer. ∎

Calculation Thought Experiment

The **calculation thought experiment** is a technique to determine whether to treat an algebraic expression as a product, quotient, sum, or difference. Given an expression, consider the steps you would use in computing its value. If the last operation is multiplication, treat the expression as a product; if the last operation is division, treat the expression as a quotient; and so on.

Quick Examples

1. $(3x^2 - 4)(2x + 1)$ can be computed by first calculating the expressions in parentheses and then multiplying. Because the last step is multiplication, we can treat the expression as a product.

2. $\dfrac{2x - 1}{x}$ can be computed by first calculating the numerator and denominator and then dividing one by the other. Because the last step is division, we can treat the expression as a quotient.

3. $x^2 + (4x - 1)(x + 2)$ can be computed by first calculating x^2, then calculating the product $(4x - 1)(x + 2)$, and finally adding the two answers. Thus, we can treat the expression as a sum.

4. $(3x^2 - 1)^5$ can be computed by first calculating the expression in parentheses and then raising the answer to the fifth power. Thus, we can treat the expression as a power. (We shall see how to differentiate powers of expressions in Section 11.4.)

5. The expression $(x + 1)(x + 2)/(x - 1)$ can be treated as either a quotient or a product: We can write it as a quotient: $\dfrac{(x + 1)(x + 2)}{x - 1}$ or as a product: $(x + 1)\left(\dfrac{x + 2}{x - 1}\right)$. (See Example 6(b).)

EXAMPLE 7 Using the Calculation Thought Experiment

Find $\dfrac{d}{dx}\left[6x^2 + 5\left(\dfrac{x}{x-1}\right)\right]$.

Solution The calculation thought experiment tells us that the expression we are asked to differentiate can be treated as a *sum*. Because the derivative of a sum is the sum of the derivatives, we get

$$\frac{d}{dx}\left[6x^2 + 5\left(\frac{x}{x-1}\right)\right] = \frac{d}{dx}(6x^2) + \frac{d}{dx}\left[5\left(\frac{x}{x-1}\right)\right].$$

In other words, we must take the derivatives of $6x^2$ and $5\left(\dfrac{x}{x-1}\right)$ separately and then add the answers. The derivative of $6x^2$ is $12x$. There are two ways of taking the derivative of $5\left(\dfrac{x}{x-1}\right)$: We could either first multiply the expression $\left(\dfrac{x}{x-1}\right)$ by 5 to get $\left(\dfrac{5x}{x-1}\right)$ and then take its derivative using the quotient rule, or we could pull the 5 out, as we do next.

$$\frac{d}{dx}\left(6x^2 + 5\left(\frac{x}{x-1}\right)\right) = \frac{d}{dx}(6x^2) + \frac{d}{dx}\left[5\left(\frac{x}{x-1}\right)\right] \qquad \text{Derivative of sum}$$

$$= 12x + 5\frac{d}{dx}\left(\frac{x}{x-1}\right) \qquad \text{Constant} \times \text{Function}$$

$$= 12x + 5\left(\frac{(1)(x-1)-(x)(1)}{(x-1)^2}\right) \qquad \text{Quotient rule}$$

$$= 12x + 5\left(\frac{-1}{(x-1)^2}\right)$$

$$= 12x - \frac{5}{(x-1)^2}$$

APPLICATIONS

In the next example, we return to a scenario similar to the one discussed at the start of this section.

EXAMPLE 8 Applying the Product and Quotient Rules: Revenue and Average Cost

Sales of your newly launched miniature wall posters for college dorms, *iMiniPosters*, are really taking off. (Those old-fashioned large wall posters no longer fit in today's "downsized" college dorm rooms.) Monthly sales to students at the start of this year were 1,500 iMiniPosters, and since that time, sales have been increasing by 300 posters each month, even though the price you charge has also been going up.

a. The price you charge for iMiniPosters is given by:

$$p(t) = 10 + 0.05t^2 \text{ dollars per poster,}$$

where t is time in months since the start of January of this year. Find a formula for the monthly revenue, and then compute its rate of change at the beginning of March.

b. The number of students who purchase iMiniPosters in a month is given by

$$n(t) = 800 + 0.2t,$$

where t is as in part (a). Find a formula for the average number of posters each student buys, and hence estimate the rate at which this number was growing at the beginning of March.

Solution

a. To compute monthly revenue as a function of time t, we use

$$R(t) = p(t)q(t). \qquad \text{Revenue = Price × Quantity}$$

We already have a formula for $p(t)$. The function $q(t)$ measures sales, which were 1,500 posters/month at time $t = 0$, and rising by 300 per month:

$$q(t) = 1,500 + 300t.$$

Therefore, the formula for revenue is

$$R(t) = p(t)q(t)$$

$$R(t) = (10 + 0.05t^2)(1,500 + 300t).$$

Rather than expand this expression, we shall leave it as a product so that we can use the product rule in computing its rate of change:

$$R'(t) = p'(t)q(t) + p(t)q'(t)$$

$$= [0.10t][1,500 + 300t] + [10 + 0.05t^2][300].$$

Because the beginning of March corresponds to $t = 2$, we have

$$R'(2) = [0.10(2)][1,500 + 300(2)] + [10 + 0.05(2)^2][300]$$

$$= (0.2)(2,100) + (10.2)(300) = \$3,480 \text{ per month.}$$

Therefore, your monthly revenue was increasing at a rate of $3,480 per month at the beginning of March.

b. The average number of posters sold to each student is

$$k(t) = \frac{\text{Number of posters}}{\text{Number of students}}$$

$$k(t) = \frac{q(t)}{n(t)} = \frac{1,500 + 300t}{800 + 0.2t}.$$

The rate of change of $k(t)$ is computed with the quotient rule:

$$k'(t) = \frac{q'(t)n(t) - q(t)n'(t)}{n(t)^2}$$

$$= \frac{(300)(800 + 0.2t) - (1,500 + 300t)(0.2)}{(800 + 0.2t)^2}$$

so that

$$k'(2) = \frac{(300)[800 + 0.2(2)] - [1,500 + 300(2)](0.2)}{[800 + 0.2(2)]^2}$$

$$= \frac{(300)(800.4) - (2,100)(0.2)}{800.4^2} \approx 0.37 \text{ posters/student per month.}$$

Therefore, the average number of posters sold to each student was increasing at a rate of about 0.37 posters/student per month.

11.3 EXERCISES

▼ more advanced   ◆ challenging
T indicates exercises that should be solved using technology

In Exercises 1–12:

a. Calculate the derivative of the given function without using either the product or quotient rule.
b. Use the product or quotient rule to find the derivative. Check that you obtain the same answer. HINT [See Quick Examples on page 810.]

1. $f(x) = 3x$ 2. $f(x) = 2x^2$
3. $g(x) = x \cdot x^2$ 4. $g(x) = x \cdot x$
5. $h(x) = x(x + 3)$ 6. $h(x) = x(1 + 2x)$

7. $r(x) = 100x^{2.1}$ 8. $r(x) = 0.2x^{-1}$ 9. $s(x) = \dfrac{2}{x}$

10. $t(x) = \dfrac{x}{3}$ 11. $u(x) = \dfrac{x^2}{3}$ 12. $s(x) = \dfrac{3}{x^2}$

Calculate $\dfrac{dy}{dx}$ *in Exercises 13–20. Simplify your answer.*
HINT [See Example 5.]

13. $y = 3x(4x^2 - 1)$ 14. $y = 3x^2(2x + 1)$
15. $y = x^3(1 - x^2)$ 16. $y = x^5(1 - x)$
17. $y = (2x + 3)^2$ 18. $y = (4x - 1)^2$
19. $x\sqrt{x}$ 20. $x^2\sqrt{x}$

Calculate $\dfrac{dy}{dx}$ *in Exercises 21–50. You need not expand your answers.*

21. $y = (x + 1)(x^2 - 1)$
22. $y = (4x^2 + x)(x - x^2)$
23. $y = (2x^{0.5} + 4x - 5)(x - x^{-1})$
24. $y = (x^{0.7} - 4x - 5)(x^{-1} + x^{-2})$
25. $y = (2x^2 - 4x + 1)^2$
26. $y = (2x^{0.5} - x^2)^2$
27. $y = \left(\dfrac{x}{3.2} + \dfrac{3.2}{x}\right)(x^2 + 1)$
28. $y = \left(\dfrac{x^{2.1}}{7} + \dfrac{2}{x^{2.1}}\right)(7x - 1)$
29. $x^2(2x + 3)(7x + 2)$ HINT [See Example 5b.]
30. $x(x^2 - 3)(2x^2 + 1)$ HINT [See Example 5b.]
31. $(5.3x - 1)(1 - x^{2.1})(x^{-2.3} - 3.4)$
32. $(1.1x + 4)(x^{2.1} - x)(3.4 - x^{-2.1})$
33. ▼ $y = (\sqrt{x} + 1)\left(\sqrt{x} + \dfrac{1}{x^2}\right)$

34. ▼ $y = \left(4x^2 - \sqrt{x}\right)\left(\sqrt{x} - \dfrac{2}{x^2}\right)$
35. $y = \dfrac{2x + 4}{3x - 1}$ HINT [See Example 6.]
36. $y = \dfrac{3x - 9}{2x + 4}$ HINT [See Example 6.]
37. $y = \dfrac{2x^2 + 4x + 1}{3x - 1}$ 38. $y = \dfrac{3x^2 - 9x + 11}{2x + 4}$
39. $y = \dfrac{x^2 - 4x + 1}{x^2 + x + 1}$ 40. $y = \dfrac{x^2 + 9x - 1}{x^2 + 2x - 1}$
41. $y = \dfrac{x^{0.23} - 5.7x}{1 - x^{-2.9}}$ 42. $y = \dfrac{8.43x^{-0.1} - 0.5x^{-1}}{3.2 + x^{2.9}}$
43. ▼ $y = \dfrac{\sqrt{x} + 1}{\sqrt{x} - 1}$ 44. ▼ $y = \dfrac{\sqrt{x} - 1}{\sqrt{x} + 1}$
45. ▼ $y = \dfrac{\left(\dfrac{1}{x} + \dfrac{1}{x^2}\right)}{x + x^2}$ 46. ▼ $y = \dfrac{\left(1 - \dfrac{1}{x^2}\right)}{x^2 - 1}$
47. $y = \dfrac{(x + 3)(x + 1)}{3x - 1}$ HINT [See Example 6b.]
48. $y = \dfrac{x}{(x - 5)(x - 4)}$ HINT [See Example 6b.]
49. $y = \dfrac{(x + 3)(x + 1)(x + 2)}{3x - 1}$
50. $y = \dfrac{3x - 1}{(x - 5)(x - 4)(x - 1)}$

In Exercises 51–56, compute the derivatives.

51. $\dfrac{d}{dx}[(x^2 + x)(x^2 - x)]$
52. $\dfrac{d}{dx}[(x^2 + x^3)(x + 1)]$
53. $\dfrac{d}{dx}[(x^3 + 2x)(x^2 - x)]\Big|_{x=2}$
54. $\dfrac{d}{dx}[(x^2 + x)(x^2 - x)]\Big|_{x=1}$
55. $\dfrac{d}{dt}[(t^2 - t^{0.5})(t^{0.5} + t^{-0.5})]\Big|_{t=1}$
56. $\dfrac{d}{dt}[(t^2 + t^{0.5})(t^{0.5} - t^{-0.5})]\Big|_{t=1}$

In Exercises 57–64 use the calculation thought experiment to say whether the expression is written as a sum, difference, scalar multiple, product, or quotient. Then use the appropriate rules to find its derivative. HINT [See Quick Examples on page 814 and Example 7.]

57. $y = x^4 - (x^2 + 120)(4x - 1)$

58. $y = x^4 - \dfrac{x^2 + 120}{4x - 1}$

59. $y = x + 1 + 2\left(\dfrac{x}{x + 1}\right)$

60. $y = (x + 2) - 4(x^2 - x)\left(x + \dfrac{1}{x}\right)$

(Do not simplify the answer.)

61. $y = (x + 2)\left(\dfrac{x}{x + 1}\right)$

(Do not simplify the answer.)

62. $y = \dfrac{(x + 2)x}{x + 1}$

(Do not simplify the answer.)

63. $y = (x + 1)(x - 2) - 2\left(\dfrac{x}{x + 1}\right)$

64. $y = \dfrac{x + 2}{x + 1} + (x + 1)(x - 2)$

In Exercises 65–70, find the equation of the line tangent to the graph of the given function at the point with the indicated x-coordinate.

65. $f(x) = (x^2 + 1)(x^3 + x);\ x = 1$

66. $f(x) = (x^{0.5} + 1)(x^2 + x);\ x = 1$

67. $f(x) = \dfrac{x + 1}{x + 2};\ x = 0$ **68.** $f(x) = \dfrac{\sqrt{x} + 1}{\sqrt{x} + 2};\ x = 4$

69. $f(x) = \dfrac{x^2 + 1}{x};\ x = -1$ **70.** $f(x) = \dfrac{x}{x^2 + 1};\ x = 1$

APPLICATIONS

71. *Revenue* The monthly sales of **Sunny Electronics**' new sound system are given by $q(t) = 2,000t - 100t^2$ units per month, t months after its introduction. The price Sunny charges is $p(t) = 1,000 - t^2$ dollars per sound system, t months after introduction. Find the rate of change of monthly sales, the rate of change of the price, and the rate of change of monthly revenue five months after the introduction of the sound system. Interpret your answers. HINT [See Example 8(a).]

72. *Revenue* The monthly sales of **Sunny Electronics**' new *iSun* walkman is given by $q(t) = 2,000t - 100t^2$ units per month, t months after its introduction. The price Sunny charges is $p(t) = 100 - t^2$ dollars per *iSun*, t months after introduction. Find the rate of change of monthly sales, the rate of change of the price, and the rate of change of monthly revenue six months after the introduction of the *iSun*. Interpret your answers. HINT [See Example 8(a).]

73. *Saudi Oil Revenues* The spot price of crude oil during the period 2000–2005 can be approximated by

$$P(t) = 5t + 25 \text{ dollars per barrel} \quad (0 \le t \le 5)$$

in year t, where $t = 0$ represents 2000. Saudi Arabia's crude oil production over the same period can be approximated by

$$Q(t) = 0.082t^2 - 0.22t + 8.2 \text{ million barrels per day.}[18]$$

$$(0 \le t \le 5)$$

Use these models to estimate Saudi Arabia's daily oil revenue and also its rate of change in 2001. (Round your answers to the nearest $1 million.)

74. *Russian Oil Revenues* Russia's crude oil production during the period 2000–2005 can be approximated by

$$Q(t) = -0.066t^2 + 0.96t + 6.1 \text{ million barrels per day}[19]$$

$$(0 \le t \le 5)$$

in year t, where $t = 0$ represents 2000. Use the model for the spot price in Exercise 73 to estimate Russia's daily oil revenue and also its rate of change in 2001.

75. *Revenue* Dorothy Wagner is currently selling 20 "I ♥ Calculus" T-shirts per day, but sales are dropping at a rate of 3 per day. She is currently charging $7 per T-shirt, but to compensate for dwindling sales, she is increasing the unit price by $1 per day. How fast, and in what direction is her daily revenue currently changing?

76. *Pricing Policy* Let us turn Exercise 75 around a little: Dorothy Wagner is currently selling 20 "I ♥ Calculus" T-shirts per day, but sales are dropping at a rate of 3 per day. She is currently charging $7 per T-shirt, and she wishes to increase her daily revenue by $10 per day. At what rate should she increase the unit price to accomplish this (assuming that the price increase does not affect sales)?

77. *Bus Travel* Thoroughbred Bus Company finds that its monthly costs for one particular year were given by $C(t) = 10,000 + t^2$ dollars after t months. After t months the company had $P(t) = 1,000 + t^2$ passengers per month. How fast is its cost per passenger changing after 6 months? HINT [See Example 8(b).]

78. *Bus Travel* Thoroughbred Bus Company finds that its monthly costs for one particular year were given by $C(t) = 100 + t^2$ dollars after t months. After t months, the company had $P(t) = 1,000 + t^2$ passengers per month. How fast is its cost per passenger changing after 6 months? HINT [See Example 8(b).]

79. *Fuel Economy* Your muscle car's gas mileage (in miles per gallon) is given as a function $M(x)$ of speed x in mph, where

$$M(x) = \frac{3,000}{x + 3,600x^{-1}}.$$

Calculate $M'(x)$, and then $M'(10)$, $M'(60)$, and $M'(70)$. What do the answers tell you about your car?

---

[18] Source for data: EIA/Saudi British Bank (www.sabb.com). 2004 figures are based on mid-year data, and 2005 data are estimates.

[19] Source for data: Energy Information Administration (www.eia.doe.gov), Pravda (http://english.pravda.ru). 2004 figures are based on mid-year data, and 2005 data are estimates.

80. *Fuel Economy* Your used Chevy's gas mileage (in miles per gallon) is given as a function $M(x)$ of speed x in mph, where

$$M(x) = \frac{4{,}000}{x + 3{,}025x^{-1}}.$$

Calculate $M'(x)$ and hence determine *the sign* of each of the following: $M'(40)$, $M'(55)$, and $M'(60)$. Interpret your results.

81. ▼*Oil Imports from Mexico* Daily oil production in Mexico and daily U.S. oil imports from Mexico during 2005–2009 can be approximated by

$$P(t) = 3.9 - 0.10t \text{ million barrels} \quad (5 \le t \le 9)$$

$$I(t) = 2.1 - 0.11t \text{ million barrels} \quad (5 \le t \le 9)$$

where t is time in years since the start of 2000.[20]

a. What are represented by the functions $P(t) - I(t)$ and $I(t)/P(t)$?

b. Compute $\left. \dfrac{d}{dt} \left[\dfrac{I(t)}{P(t)} \right] \right|_{t=8}$ to two significant digits. What does the answer tell you about oil imports from Mexico?

82. ▼*Oil Imports from Mexico* Daily oil production in Mexico and daily U.S. oil imports from Mexico during 2000–2004 can be approximated by

$$P(t) = 3.0 + 0.13t \text{ million barrels} \quad (0 \le t \le 4)$$

$$I(t) = 1.4 + 0.06t \text{ million barrels} \quad (0 \le t \le 4)$$

where t is time in years since the start of 2000.[21]

a. What are represented by the functions $P(t) - I(t)$ and $I(t)/P(t)$?

b. Compute $\left. \dfrac{d}{dt} \left[\dfrac{I(t)}{P(t)} \right] \right|_{t=3}$ to two significant digits. What does the answer tell you about oil imports from Mexico?

83. ▼*Military Spending* The annual cost per active-duty armed service member in the United States increased from $80,000 in 1995 to a projected $120,000 in 2007. In 1995, there were 1.5 million armed service personnel, and this number was projected to decrease to 1.4 million in 2003.[22] Use linear models for annual cost and personnel to estimate, to the nearest $10 million, the rate of change of total military personnel costs in 2002.

84. ▼*Military Spending in the 1990s* The annual cost per active-duty armed service member in the United States increased from $80,000 in 1995 to $90,000 in 2000. In 1990, there were 2 million armed service personnel and this number decreased to 1.5 million in 2000.[23] Use linear models for annual cost and personnel to estimate, to the nearest $10 million, the rate of change of total military personnel costs in 1995.

85. ▼*Biology—Reproduction* The Verhulst model for population growth specifies the reproductive rate of an organism as a function of the total population according to the following formula:

$$R(p) = \frac{r}{1 + kp}$$

where p is the total population in thousands of organisms, r and k are constants that depend on the particular circumstances and the organism being studied, and $R(p)$ is the reproduction rate in thousands of organisms per hour.[24] If $k = 0.125$ and $r = 45$, find $R'(p)$ and then $R'(4)$. Interpret the result.

86. ▼*Biology—Reproduction* Another model, the predator satiation model for population growth, specifies that the reproductive rate of an organism as a function of the total population varies according to the following formula:

$$R(p) = \frac{rp}{1 + kp}$$

where p is the total population in thousands of organisms, r and k are constants that depend on the particular circumstances and the organism being studied, and $R(p)$ is the reproduction rate in new organisms per hour.[25] Given that $k = 0.2$ and $r = 0.08$, find $R'(p)$ and $R'(2)$. Interpret the result.

[20] Source for data: Energy Information Administration (www.eia.doe.gov)/Pemex.

[21] Ibid.

[22] Annual costs are adjusted for inflation. Sources: Department of Defense, Stephen Daggett, military analyst, Congressional Research Service/*New York Times*, April 19, 2002, p. A21.

[23] Ibid.

[24] Source: *Mathematics in Medicine and the Life Sciences* by F. C. Hoppensteadt and C. S. Peskin (Springer-Verlag, New York, 1992) pp. 20–22.

[25] Ibid.

87. ▼*Embryo Development* Bird embryos consume oxygen from the time the egg is laid through the time the chick hatches. For a typical galliform bird egg, the oxygen consumption (in milliliters) t days after the egg was laid can be approximated by[26]

$$C(t) = -0.016t^4 + 1.1t^3 - 11t^2 + 3.6t. \quad (15 \le t \le 30)$$

(An egg will usually hatch at around $t = 28$.) Suppose that at time $t = 0$ you have a collection of 30 newly laid eggs and that the number of eggs decreases linearly to zero at time $t = 30$ days. How fast is the total oxygen consumption of your collection of embryos changing after 25 days? (Round your answers to two significant digits.) Comment on the result. HINT [Total oxygen consumption = Oxygen consumption per egg × Number of eggs.]

88. ▼*Embryo Development* Turkey embryos consume oxygen from the time the egg is laid through the time the chick hatches. For a brush turkey, the oxygen consumption (in milliliters) t days after the egg was laid can be approximated by[27]

$$C(t) = -0.0071t^4 + 0.95t^3 - 22t^2 + 95t. \quad (25 \le t \le 50)$$

(An egg will typically hatch at around $t = 50$.) Suppose that at time $t = 0$ you have a collection of 100 newly laid eggs and that the number of eggs decreases linearly to zero at time $t = 50$ days. How fast is the total oxygen consumption of your collection of embryos changing after 40 days? (Round your answer to two significant digits.) Interpret the result. HINT [Total oxygen consumption = Oxygen consumption per egg × Number of eggs.]

COMMUNICATION AND REASONING EXERCISES

89. If f and g are functions of time, and at time $t = 3$, f equals 5 and is rising at a rate of 2 units per second, and g equals 4 and is rising at a rate of 5 units per second, then the product fg equals _____ and is rising at a rate of _____ units per second.

90. If f and g are functions of time, and at time $t = 2$, f equals 3 and is rising at a rate of 4 units per second, and g equals 5 and is rising at a rate of 6 units per second, then fg equals _____ and is rising at a rate of _____ units per second.

91. If f and g are functions of time, and at time $t = 3$, f equals 5 and is rising at a rate of 2 units per second, and g equals 4 and is rising at a rate of 5 units per second, then f/g equals _____ and is changing at a rate of _____ units per second.

92. If f and g are functions of time, and at time $t = 2$, f equals 3 and is rising at a rate of 4 units per second, and g equals 5 and is rising at a rate of 6 units per second, then f/g equals _____ and is changing at a rate of _____ units per second.

---

[26] The model is derived from graphical data published in the article "The Brush Turkey" by Roger S. Seymour, *Scientific American,* December, 1991, pp. 108–114.

[27] Ibid.

93. You have come across the following in a newspaper article: "Revenues of HAL Home Heating Oil Inc. are rising by \$4.2 million per year. This is due to an annual increase of 70¢ per gallon in the price HAL charges for heating oil and an increase in sales of 6 million gallons of oil per year." Comment on this analysis.

94. Your friend says that because average cost is obtained by dividing the cost function by the number of units x, it follows that the derivative of average cost is the same as marginal cost because the derivative of x is 1. Comment on this analysis.

95. ▼Find a demand function $q(p)$ such that, at a price per item of $p = \$100$, revenue will rise if the price per item is increased.

96. ▼What must be true about a demand function $q(p)$ so that, at a price per item of $p = \$100$, revenue will decrease if the price per item is increased?

97. ▼You and I are both selling a steady 20 T-shirts per day. The price I am getting for my T-shirts is increasing twice as fast as yours, but your T-shirts are currently selling for twice the price of mine. Whose revenue is increasing faster: yours, mine, or neither? Explain.

98. ▼You and I are both selling T-shirts for a steady \$20 per shirt. Sales of my T-shirts are increasing at twice the rate of yours, but you are currently selling twice as many as I am. Whose revenue is increasing faster: yours, mine, or neither? Explain.

99. ◆*Marginal Product (from the GRE Economics Test)* Which of the following statements about average product and marginal product is correct?

(A) If average product is decreasing, marginal product must be less than average product.

(B) If average product is increasing, marginal product must be increasing.

(C) If marginal product is decreasing, average product must be less than marginal product.

(D) If marginal product is increasing, average product must be decreasing.

(E) If marginal product is constant over some range, average product must be constant over that range.

100. ◆*Marginal Cost (based on a question from the GRE Economics Test)* Which of the following statements about average cost and marginal cost is correct?

(A) If average cost is increasing, marginal cost must be increasing.

(B) If average cost is increasing, marginal cost must be decreasing.

(C) If average cost is increasing, marginal cost must be more than average cost.

(D) If marginal cost is increasing, average cost must be increasing.

(E) If marginal cost is increasing, average cost must be larger than marginal cost.

11.4 The Chain Rule

We can now find the derivatives of expressions involving powers of x combined using addition, subtraction, multiplication, and division, but we still cannot take the derivative of an expression like $(3x + 1)^{0.5}$. For this we need one more rule. The function $h(x) = (3x + 1)^{0.5}$ is not a sum, difference, product, or quotient. To find out what it is, we can use the calculation thought experiment and think about the last operation we would perform in calculating $h(x)$.

1. Calculate $3x + 1$.

2. Take the 0.5 power (square root) of the answer.

The last operation is "take the 0.5 power." We do not yet have a rule for finding the derivative of the 0.5 power of a quantity other than x.

There is a way to build $h(x) = (3x + 1)^{0.5}$ out of two simpler functions: $u(x) = 3x + 1$ (the function that corresponds to the first step in the calculation above) and $f(x) = x^{0.5}$ (the function that corresponds to the second step):

$$h(x) = (3x + 1)^{0.5}$$
$$= [u(x)]^{0.5} \qquad u(x) = 3x + 1$$
$$= f(u(x)) \qquad f(x) = x^{0.5}$$

We say that h is the **composite** of f and u. We read $f(u(x))$ as "f of u of x."

To compute $h(1)$, say, we first compute $3 \cdot 1 + 1 = 4$ and then take the square root of 4, giving $h(1) = 2$. To compute $f(u(1))$ we follow exactly the same steps: First compute $u(1) = 4$ and then $f(u(1)) = f(4) = 2$. We always compute $f(u(x))$ numerically from the inside out: Given x, first compute $u(x)$ and then $f(u(x))$.

Now, f and u are functions *whose derivatives we know.* The *chain rule* allows us to use our knowledge of the derivatives of f and u to find the derivative of $f(u(x))$. For the purposes of stating the rule, let us avoid some of the nested parentheses by abbreviating $u(x)$ as u. Thus, we write $f(u)$ instead of $f(u(x))$ and remember that u is a function of x.

Chain Rule

If f is a differentiable function of u and u is a differentiable function of x, then the composite $f(u)$ is a differentiable function of x, and

$$\frac{d}{dx}[f(u)] = f'(u)\frac{du}{dx} \qquad \text{Chain Rule}$$

In words *The derivative of f(quantity) is the derivative of f, evaluated at that quantity, times the derivative of the quantity.*

Quick Examples

1. Take $f(u) = u^2$. Then

$$\frac{d}{dx}[u^2] = 2u\frac{du}{dx} \qquad \text{Because } f'(u) = 2u$$

The derivative of a quantity squared is two times the quantity, times the derivative of the quantity.

2. Take $f(u) = u^{0.5}$. Then

$$\frac{d}{dx}[u^{0.5}] = 0.5u^{-0.5}\frac{du}{dx} \qquad \text{Because } f'(u) = 0.5u^{-0.5}$$

The derivative of a quantity raised to the 0.5 is 0.5 times the quantity raised to the −0.5, times the derivative of the quantity.

As the quick examples illustrate, for every power of a function u whose derivative we know, we now get a "generalized" differentiation rule. The following table gives more examples.

Original Rule	*Generalized Rule*	*In Words*
$\dfrac{d}{dx}[x^2] = 2x$	$\dfrac{d}{dx}[u^2] = 2u\dfrac{du}{dx}$	The derivative of a quantity squared is twice the quantity, times the derivative of the quantity.
$\dfrac{d}{dx}[x^3] = 3x^2$	$\dfrac{d}{dx}[u^3] = 3u^2\dfrac{du}{dx}$	The derivative of a quantity cubed is 3 times the quantity squared, times the derivative of the quantity.
$\dfrac{d}{dx}\left(\dfrac{1}{x}\right) = -\dfrac{1}{x^2}$	$\dfrac{d}{dx}\left(\dfrac{1}{u}\right) = -\dfrac{1}{u^2}\dfrac{du}{dx}$	The derivative of 1 over a quantity is negative 1 over the quantity squared, times the derivative of the quantity.
Power Rule	*Generalized Power Rule*	*In Words*
$\dfrac{d}{dx}[x^n] = nx^{n-1}$	$\dfrac{d}{dx}[u^n] = nu^{n-1}\dfrac{du}{dx}$	The derivative of a quantity raised to the n is n times the quantity raised to the $n-1$, times the derivative of the quantity.

To motivate the chain rule, let us see why it is true in the special case when $f(u) = u^3$, where the chain rule tells us that

$$\frac{d}{dx}[u^3] = 3u^2\frac{du}{dx} \qquad \text{Generalized Power Rule with } n = 3$$

But we could have done this using the product rule instead:

$$\frac{d}{dx}[u^3] = \frac{d}{dx}[u \cdot u \cdot u] = \frac{du}{dx}u \cdot u + u\frac{du}{dx}u + u \cdot u\frac{du}{dx} = 3u^2\frac{du}{dx}$$

Web Site

www.FiniteandCalc.org

Everything for Calculus

→ Chapter 11

  → Proof of Chain Rule

which gives us the same result. A similar argument works for $f(u) = u^n$ where $n = 2, 3, 4, \ldots$ We can then use the quotient rule and the chain rule for positive powers to verify the generalized power rule for *negative* powers as well. For the case of a general differentiable function f, the proof of the chain rule is beyond the scope of this book, but you can find one on the Web site by the path shown in the margin.

EXAMPLE 1 Using the Chain Rule

Compute the following derivatives.

a. $\dfrac{d}{dx}[(2x^2 + x)^3]$ **b.** $\dfrac{d}{dx}[(x^3 + x)^{100}]$ **c.** $\dfrac{d}{dx}\sqrt{3x + 1}$

Solution

a. Using the calculation thought experiment, we see that the last operation we would perform in calculating $(2x^2 + x)^3$ is that of *cubing*. Thus we think of $(2x^2 + x)^3$ as *a quantity cubed*. There are two similar methods we can use to calculate its derivative.

Method 1: Using the formula We think of $(2x^2 + x)^3$ as u^3, where $u = 2x^2 + x$. By the formula,

$$\frac{d}{dx}[u^3] = 3u^2 \frac{du}{dx} \qquad \text{Generalized Power Rule}$$

Now substitute for u:

$$\frac{d}{dx}[(2x^2 + x)^3] = 3(2x^2 + x)^2 \frac{d}{dx}(2x^2 + x)$$
$$= 3(2x^2 + x)^2(4x + 1)$$

Method 2: Using the verbal form If we prefer to use the verbal form, we get:

The derivative of $(2x^2 + x)$ cubed is three times $(2x^2 + x)$ squared, times the derivative of $(2x^2 + x)$.

In symbols,

$$\frac{d}{dx}[(2x^2 + x)^3] = 3(2x^2 + x)^2(4x + 1),$$

as we obtained above.

b. First, the calculation thought experiment: If we were computing $(x^3 + x)^{100}$, the last operation we would perform is *raising a quantity to the power* 100. Thus we are dealing with *a quantity raised to the power* 100, and so we must again use the generalized power rule. According to the verbal form of the generalized power rule, the derivative of a quantity raised to the power 100 is 100 times that quantity to the power 99, times the derivative of that quantity. In symbols,

$$\frac{d}{dx}[(x^3 + x)^{100}] = 100(x^3 + x)^{99}(3x^2 + 1).$$

c. We first rewrite the expression $\sqrt{3x + 1}$ as $(3x + 1)^{0.5}$ and then use the generalized power rule as in parts (a) and (b):

The derivative of a quantity raised to the 0.5 is 0.5 times the quantity raised to the -0.5, times the derivative of the quantity.

Thus,

$$\frac{d}{dx}[(3x + 1)^{0.5}] = 0.5(3x + 1)^{-0.5} \cdot 3 = 1.5(3x + 1)^{-0.5}.$$

➡ **Before we go on...** The following are examples of common errors in solving Example 1(b):

$$\text{``} \frac{d}{dx}[(x^3 + x)^{100}] = 100(3x^2 + 1)^{99} \text{''} \qquad ✗ \quad \textit{WRONG!}$$

$$\text{``} \frac{d}{dx}[(x^3 + x)^{100}] = 100(x^3 + x)^{99} \text{''} \qquad ✗ \quad \textit{WRONG!}$$

Remember that the generalized power rule says that the derivative of a quantity to the power 100 is 100 times *that same quantity* raised to the power 99, *times the derivative of that quantity.* ∎

Q: *It seems that there are now two formulas for the derivative of an nth power:*

1. $\dfrac{d}{dx}[x^n] = nx^{n-1}$

2. $\dfrac{d}{dx}[u^n] = nu^{n-1}\dfrac{du}{dx}$

Which one do I use?

A: Formula 1 is the original power rule, which applies only to a power of *x*. For instance, it applies to x^{10}, but it does not apply to $(2x + 1)^{10}$ because the quantity that is being raised to a power is not *x*. Formula 2 applies to a power of any *function of x*, such as $(2x + 1)^{10}$. It can even be used in place of the original power rule. For example, if we take $u = x$ in Formula 2, we obtain

$$\frac{d}{dx}[x^n] = nx^{n-1}\frac{dx}{dx}$$

$$= nx^{n-1} \qquad \text{The derivative of } x \text{ with respect to } x \text{ is 1.}$$

Thus, the generalized power rule really *is* a generalization of the original power rule, as its name suggests.

EXAMPLE 2 More Examples Using the Chain Rule

Find: **a.** $\dfrac{d}{dx}[(2x^5 + x^2 - 20)^{-2/3}]$ **b.** $\dfrac{d}{dx}\left[\dfrac{1}{\sqrt{x+2}}\right]$ **c.** $\dfrac{d}{dx}\left[\dfrac{1}{x^2+x}\right]$

Solution Each of the given functions is, or can be rewritten as, a power of a function whose derivative we know. Thus, we can use the method of Example 1.

a. $\dfrac{d}{dx}[(2x^5 + x^2 - 20)^{-2/3}] = -\dfrac{2}{3}(2x^5 + x^2 - 20)^{-5/3}(10x^4 + 2x)$

b. $\dfrac{d}{dx}\left[\dfrac{1}{\sqrt{x+2}}\right] = \dfrac{d}{dx}(x+2)^{-1/2} = -\dfrac{1}{2}(x+2)^{-3/2} \cdot 1 = -\dfrac{1}{2(x+2)^{3/2}}$

c. $\dfrac{d}{dx}\left[\dfrac{1}{x^2+x}\right] = \dfrac{d}{dx}(x^2+x)^{-1} = -(x^2+x)^{-2}(2x+1) = -\dfrac{2x+1}{(x^2+x)^2}$

➡ **Before we go on...** In Example 2(c), we could have used the quotient rule instead of the generalized power rule. We can think of the quantity $1/(x^2 + x)$ in two different ways using the calculation thought experiment:

1. As 1 divided by something—in other words, as a quotient

2. As something raised to the −1 power

Of course, we get the same derivative using either approach. ∎

We now look at some more complicated examples.

EXAMPLE 3 Harder Examples Using the Chain Rule

Find $\dfrac{dy}{dx}$ in each case.   **a.** $y = [(x + 1)^{-2.5} + 3x]^{-3}$ **b.** $y = (x + 10)^3 \sqrt{1 - x^2}$

Solution

a. The calculation thought experiment tells us that the last operation we would perform in calculating y is raising the quantity $[(x + 1)^{-2.5} + 3x]$ to the power -3. Thus, we use the generalized power rule.

$$\frac{dy}{dx} = -3[(x + 1)^{-2.5} + 3x]^{-4} \frac{d}{dx}[(x + 1)^{-2.5} + 3x]$$

We are not yet done; we must still find the derivative of $(x + 1)^{-2.5} + 3x$. Finding the derivative of a complicated function in several steps helps to keep the problem manageable. Continuing, we have

$$\frac{dy}{dx} = -3[(x + 1)^{-2.5} + 3x]^{-4} \frac{d}{dx}[(x + 1)^{-2.5} + 3x]$$

$$= -3[(x + 1)^{-2.5} + 3x]^{-4} \left[\frac{d}{dx}[(x + 1)^{-2.5}] + \frac{d}{dx}(3x) \right] \quad \text{Derivative of a sum}$$

Now we have two derivatives left to calculate. The second of these we know to be 3, and the first is the derivative of a quantity raised to the -2.5 power. Thus

$$\frac{dy}{dx} = -3[(x + 1)^{-2.5} + 3x]^{-4}[-2.5(x + 1)^{-3.5} \cdot 1 + 3].$$

b. The expression $(x + 10)^3 \sqrt{1 - x^2}$ is a product, so we use the product rule:

$$\frac{d}{dx}[(x + 10)^3 \sqrt{1 - x^2}] = \left(\frac{d}{dx}[(x + 10)^3] \right) \sqrt{1 - x^2} + (x + 10)^3 \left(\frac{d}{dx} \sqrt{1 - x^2} \right)$$

$$= 3(x + 10)^2 \sqrt{1 - x^2} + (x + 10)^3 \frac{1}{2\sqrt{1 - x^2}}(-2x)$$

$$= 3(x + 10)^2 \sqrt{1 - x^2} - \frac{x(x + 10)^3}{\sqrt{1 - x^2}}$$

APPLICATIONS

The next example is a new treatment of Example 3 from Section 11.2.

EXAMPLE 4 Marginal Product

Precision Manufacturers is informed by a consultant that its annual profit is given by

$$P = -200,000 + 4,000q - 0.46q^2 - 0.00001q^3$$

where q is the number of surgical lasers it sells each year. The consultant also informs Precision that the number of surgical lasers it can manufacture each year depends on the number n of assembly line workers it employs according to the equation

$$q = 100n \qquad \text{Each worker contributes 100 lasers per year.}$$

Use the chain rule to find the marginal product $\dfrac{dP}{dn}$.

Solution We could calculate the marginal product by substituting the expression for q in the expression for P to obtain P as a function of n (as given in Example 3 from Section 11.2) and then finding dP/dn. Alternatively—and this will simplify the calculation—we can use the chain rule. To see how the chain rule applies, notice that P is a function of q, where q in turn is given as a function of n. By the chain rule,

$$\frac{dP}{dn} = P'(q)\frac{dq}{dn} \qquad \text{Chain Rule}$$

$$= \frac{dP}{dq}\frac{dq}{dn} \qquad \text{Notice how the "quantities" } dq \text{ appear to cancel.}$$

Now we compute

$$\frac{dP}{dq} = 4{,}000 - 0.92q - 0.00003q^2$$

and $\qquad \dfrac{dq}{dn} = 100.$

Substituting into the equation for $\dfrac{dP}{dn}$ gives

$$\frac{dP}{dn} = (4{,}000 - 0.92q - 0.00003q^2)(100)$$

$$= 400{,}000 - 92q - 0.003q^2$$

Notice that the answer has q as a variable. We can express dP/dn as a function of n by substituting $100n$ for q:

$$\frac{dP}{dn} = 400{,}000 - 92(100n) - 0.003(100n)^2$$

$$= 400{,}000 - 9{,}200n - 30n^2$$

The equation

$$\frac{dP}{dn} = \frac{dP}{dq}\frac{dq}{dn}$$

in the example above is an appealing way of writing the chain rule because it suggests that the "quantities" dq cancel. In general, we can write the chain rule as follows.

Chain Rule in Differential Notation

If y is a differentiable function of u, and u is a differentiable function of x, then

$$\frac{dy}{dx} = \frac{dy}{du}\frac{du}{dx}$$

Notice how the units cancel:

$$\frac{\text{Units of } y}{\text{Units of } x} = \frac{\text{Units of } y}{\text{Units of } u}\frac{\text{Units of } u}{\text{Units of } x}$$

Quick Examples

1. If $y = u^3$, where $u = 4x + 1$, then

$$\frac{dy}{dx} = \frac{dy}{du}\frac{du}{dx} = 3u^2 \cdot 4 = 12u^2 = 12(4x + 1)^2.$$

2. If $q = 43p^2$ where p (and hence q also) is a differentiable function of t, then

$$\frac{dq}{dt} = \frac{dq}{dp}\frac{dp}{dt}$$

$$= 86p\frac{dp}{dt}. \qquad p \text{ is not specified, so we leave } dp/dt \text{ as is.}$$

You can see one of the reasons we still use Leibniz differential notation: The chain rule looks like a simple "cancellation" of du terms.

EXAMPLE 5   Marginal Revenue

Suppose a company's weekly revenue R is given as a function of the unit price p, and p in turn is given as a function of weekly sales q (by means of a demand equation). If

$$\frac{dR}{dp}\bigg|_{q=1,000} = \$40 \text{ per } \$1 \text{ increase in price}$$

and

$$\frac{dp}{dq}\bigg|_{q=1,000} = -\$20 \text{ per additional item sold per week}$$

find the marginal revenue when sales are 1,000 items per week.

Solution   The marginal revenue is $\dfrac{dR}{dq}$. By the chain rule, we have

$$\frac{dR}{dq} = \frac{dR}{dp}\frac{dp}{dq} \qquad \begin{array}{l}\text{Units: Revenue per item}\\ = \text{Revenue per } \$1 \text{ price increase} \times \text{price increase per additional item}\end{array}$$

Because we are interested in the marginal revenue at a demand level of 1,000 items per week, we have

$$\frac{dR}{dq}\bigg|_{q=1,000} = (40)(-20) = -\$800 \text{ per additional item sold.}$$

Thus, if the price is lowered to increase the demand from 1,000 to 1,001 items per week, the weekly revenue will drop by approximately $800.

Look again at the way the terms "du" appeared to cancel in the differential formula $\dfrac{dy}{dx} = \dfrac{dy}{du}\dfrac{du}{dx}$. In fact, the chain rule tells us more:

✳ NOTE The notion of "thinking of x as a function of y" will be made more precise in Section 11.4.

Manipulating Derivatives in Differential Notation

1. Suppose y is a function of x. Then, thinking of x as a function of y (as, for instance, when we can solve for x)* one has

$$\frac{dx}{dy} = \frac{1}{\left(\dfrac{dy}{dx}\right)}, \text{ provided } \frac{dy}{dx} \neq 0.$$ Notice again how $\frac{dy}{dx}$ behaves like a fraction.

Quick Example

In the demand equation $q = -0.2p - 8$, we have $\dfrac{dq}{dp} = -0.2$. Therefore,

$$\frac{dp}{dq} = \frac{1}{\left(\dfrac{dq}{dp}\right)} = \frac{1}{-0.2} = -5.$$

2. Suppose x and y are functions of t. Then, thinking of y as a function of x (as, for instance, when we can solve for t as a function of x, and hence obtain y as a function of x) one has

$$\frac{dy}{dx} = \frac{dy/dt}{dx/dt}.$$ The terms dt appear to cancel.

Quick Example

If $x = 3 - 0.2t$ and $y = 6 + 6t$, then

$$\frac{dy}{dx} = \frac{dy/dt}{dx/dt} = \frac{6}{-0.2} = -30.$$

To see why the above formulas work, notice that the second formula,

$$\frac{dy}{dx} = \frac{\left(\dfrac{dy}{dt}\right)}{\left(\dfrac{dx}{dt}\right)}$$

can be written as

$$\frac{dy}{dx}\frac{dx}{dt} = \frac{dy}{dt},$$ Multiply both sides by $\frac{dx}{dt}$.

which is just the differential form of the chain rule. For the first formula, use the second formula with y playing the role of t:

$$\frac{dy}{dx} = \frac{dy/dy}{dx/dy}$$

$$= \frac{1}{dx/dy}.$$ $\dfrac{dy}{dy} = \dfrac{d}{dy}[y] = 1$

FAQs

Using the Chain Rule

Q : *How do I decide whether or not to use the chain rule when taking a derivative?*

A : Use the calculation thought experiment (Section 11.3): Given an expression, consider the steps you would use in computing its value.

- If the last step is *raising a quantity to a power*, as in $\left(\dfrac{x^2 - 1}{x + 4}\right)^4$, then the first

  step to use is the chain rule (in the form of the generalized power rule):

$$\frac{d}{dx}\left(\frac{x^2 - 1}{x + 4}\right)^4 = 4\left(\frac{x^2 - 1}{x + 4}\right)^3 \frac{d}{dx}\left(\frac{x^2 - 1}{x + 4}\right).$$

  Then use the appropriate rules to finish the computation. You may need to again use the calculation thought experiment to decide on the next step (here the quotient rule):

$$= 4\left(\frac{x^2 - 1}{x + 4}\right)^3 \frac{(2x)(x + 4) - (x^2 - 1)(1)}{(x + 4)^2}.$$

- If the last step is *division*, as in $\dfrac{(x^2 - 1)}{(3x + 4)^4}$, then the first step to use is the quotient

  rule:

$$\frac{d}{dx}\frac{(x^2 - 1)}{(3x + 4)^4} = \frac{(2x)(3x + 4)^4 - (x^2 - 1)\dfrac{d}{dx}(3x + 4)^4}{(3x + 4)^8}.$$

  Then use the appropriate rules to finish the computation (here the chain rule):

$$= \frac{(2x)(3x + 4)^4 - (x^2 - 1)4(3x + 4)^3(3)}{(3x + 4)^8}.$$

- If the last step is *multiplication, addition, subtraction, or multiplication by a constant,* then the first rule to use is the product rule, or the rule for sums, differences, or constant multiples as appropriate.

Q : *Every time I compute a derivative, I leave something out. How do I make sure I am really done when taking the derivative of a complicated-looking expression?*

A : Until you are an expert at taking derivatives, the key is to use one rule at a time and write out each step, rather than trying to compute the derivative in a single step.

To illustrate this, try computing the derivative of $(x + 10)^3\sqrt{1 - x^2}$ in Example 3(b) in two ways: First try to compute it in a single step, and then compute it by writing out each step as shown in the example. How do your results compare? For more practice, try Exercises 83 and 84 following.

11.4 EXERCISES

▼ more advanced   ◆ challenging
⊞ indicates exercises that should be solved using technology

Calculate the derivatives of the functions in Exercises 1–46.
HINT [See Example 1.]

1. $f(x) = (2x + 1)^2$

2. $f(x) = (3x - 1)^2$

3. $f(x) = (x - 1)^{-1}$

4. $f(x) = (2x - 1)^{-2}$

5. $f(x) = (2 - x)^{-2}$

6. $f(x) = (1 - x)^{-1}$

7. $f(x) = (2x + 1)^{0.5}$

8. $f(x) = (-x + 2)^{1.5}$

9. $f(x) = (4x - 1)^{-1}$

10. $f(x) = (x + 7)^{-2}$

11. $f(x) = \dfrac{1}{3x - 1}$

12. $f(x) = \dfrac{1}{(x + 1)^2}$

13. $f(x) = (x^2 + 2x)^4$

14. $f(x) = (x^3 - x)^3$

15. $f(x) = (2x^2 - 2)^{-1}$

16. $f(x) = (2x^3 + x)^{-2}$

17. $g(x) = (x^2 - 3x - 1)^{-5}$

18. $g(x) = (2x^2 + x + 1)^{-3}$

19. $h(x) = \dfrac{1}{(x^2 + 1)^3}$

20. $h(x) = \dfrac{1}{(x^2 + x + 1)^2}$

HINT [See Example 2.]   HINT [See Example 2.]

21. $r(x) = (0.1x^2 - 4.2x + 9.5)^{1.5}$

22. $r(x) = (0.1x - 4.2x^{-1})^{0.5}$

23. $r(s) = (s^2 - s^{0.5})^4$

24. $r(s) = (2s + s^{0.5})^{-1}$

25. $f(x) = \sqrt{1 - x^2}$

26. $f(x) = \sqrt{x + x^2}$

27. $h(x) = 2[(x + 1)(x^2 - 1)]^{-1/2}$ HINT [See Example 3.]

28. $h(x) = 3[(2x - 1)(x - 1)]^{-1/3}$ HINT [See Example 3.]

29. $h(x) = (3.1x - 2)^2 - \dfrac{1}{(3.1x - 2)^2}$

30. $h(x) = \left[3.1x^2 - 2 - \dfrac{1}{3.1x - 2} \right]^2$

31. $f(x) = [(6.4x - 1)^2 + (5.4x - 2)^3]^2$

32. $f(x) = (6.4x - 3)^{-2} + (4.3x - 1)^{-2}$

33. $f(x) = (x^2 - 3x)^{-2}(1 - x^2)^{0.5}$

34. $f(x) = (3x^2 + x)(1 - x^2)^{0.5}$

35. $s(x) = \left(\dfrac{2x + 4}{3x - 1} \right)^2$

36. $s(x) = \left(\dfrac{3x - 9}{2x + 4} \right)^3$

37. $g(z) = \left(\dfrac{z}{1 + z^2} \right)^3$

38. $g(z) = \left(\dfrac{z^2}{1 + z} \right)^2$

39. $f(x) = [(1 + 2x)^4 - (1 - x)^2]^3$

40. $f(x) = [(3x - 1)^2 + (1 - x)^5]^2$

41. $t(x) = [2 + (x + 1)^{-0.1}]^{4.3}$

42. $t(x) = [(x + 1)^{0.1} - 4x]^{-5.1}$

43. ▼ $r(x) = \left(\sqrt{2x + 1} - x^2 \right)^{-1}$

44. ▼ $r(x) = \left(\sqrt{x + 1} + \sqrt{x} \right)^3$

45. ▼ $f(x) = (1 + (1 + (1 + 2x)^3)^3)^3$

46. ▼ $f(x) = 2x + (2x + (2x + 1)^3)^3$

Find the indicated derivatives in Exercises 47–54. In each case, the independent variable is a (unspecified) function of t.
HINT [See Quick Example 2 on page 827.]

47. $y = x^{100} + 99x^{-1}$. Find $\dfrac{dy}{dt}$.

48. $y = x^{0.5}(1 + x)$. Find $\dfrac{dy}{dt}$.

49. $s = \dfrac{1}{r^3} + r^{0.5}$. Find $\dfrac{ds}{dt}$.

50. $s = r + r^{-1}$. Find $\dfrac{ds}{dt}$.

51. $V = \dfrac{4}{3}\pi r^3$. Find $\dfrac{dV}{dt}$.

52. $A = 4\pi r^2$. Find $\dfrac{dA}{dt}$.

53. ▼ $y = x^3 + \dfrac{1}{x}$, $x = 2$ when $t = 1$, $\left. \dfrac{dx}{dt} \right|_{t=1} = -1$

Find $\left. \dfrac{dy}{dt} \right|_{t=1}$.

54. ▼ $y = \sqrt{x} + \dfrac{1}{\sqrt{x}}$, $x = 9$ when $t = 1$, $\left. \dfrac{dx}{dt} \right|_{t=1} = -1$

Find $\left. \dfrac{dy}{dt} \right|_{t=1}$.

In Exercises 55–60, compute the indicated derivative using the chain rule. HINT [See Quick Examples on page 828.]

55. $y = 3x - 2$; $\dfrac{dx}{dy}$

56. $y = 8x + 4$; $\dfrac{dx}{dy}$

57. $x = 2 + 3t$, $y = -5t$; $\dfrac{dy}{dx}$

58. $x = 1 - t/2$, $y = 4t - 1$; $\dfrac{dy}{dx}$

59. $y = 3x^2 - 2x$; $\left. \dfrac{dx}{dy} \right|_{x=1}$

60. $y = 3x - \dfrac{2}{x}$; $\left. \dfrac{dx}{dy} \right|_{x=2}$

APPLICATIONS

61. *Marginal Product* Paramount Electronics has an annual profit given by

$$P = -100,000 + 5,000q - 0.25q^2$$

where q is the number of laptop computers it sells each year. The number of laptop computers it can make and sell each year depends on the number n of electrical engineers Paramount employs, according to the equation

$$q = 30n + 0.01n^2.$$

Use the chain rule to find $\dfrac{dP}{dn}\Big|_{n=10}$ and interpret the result.
HINT [See Example 3.]

62. Marginal Product Refer back to Exercise 61. The average profit $\bar{P}$ per computer is given by dividing the total profit P by q:

$$\bar{P} = -\frac{100{,}000}{q} + 5{,}000 - 0.25q.$$

Determine the **marginal average product**, $d\bar{P}/dn$ at an employee level of 10 engineers. Interpret the result. HINT [See Example 3.]

63. Food Versus Education The percentage y (of total personal consumption) an individual spends on food is approximately

$$y = 35x^{-0.25} \text{ percentage points} \quad (6.5 \le x \le 17.5)$$

where x is the percentage the individual spends on education.[28] An individual finds that she is spending

$$x = 7 + 0.2t$$

percent of her personal consumption on education, where t is time in months since January 1. Use direct substitution to express the percentage y as a function of time t (do not simplify the expression) and then use the chain rule to estimate how fast the percentage she spends on food is changing on November 1. Be sure to specify the units.

64. Food Versus Recreation The percentage y (of total personal consumption) an individual spends on food is approximately

$$y = 33x^{-0.63} \text{ percentage points} \quad (2.5 \le x \le 4.5)$$

where x is the percentage the individual spends on recreation.[29] A college student finds that he is spending

$$x = 3.5 + 0.1t$$

percent of his personal consumption on recreation, where t is time in months since January 1. Use direct substitution to express the percentage y as a function of time t (do not simplify the expression) and then use the chain rule to estimate how fast the percentage he spends on food is changing on November 1. Be sure to specify the units.

65. Marginal Revenue The weekly revenue from the sale of rubies at **Royal Ruby Retailers (RRR)** is increasing at a rate of $40 per $1 increase in price, and the price is decreasing at a rate of $0.75 per additional ruby sold. What is the marginal revenue? (Be sure to state the units of measurement.) Interpret the result. HINT [See Example 5.]

66. Marginal Revenue The weekly revenue from the sale of emeralds at **Eduardo's Emerald Emporium (EEE)** is decreasing at a rate of €500 per €1 increase in price, and the price is decreasing at a rate of €0.45 per additional emerald sold.

What is the marginal revenue? (Be sure to state the units of measurement.) Interpret the result. HINT [See Example 5.]

67. Crime Statistics The murder rate in large cities (over 1 million residents) can be related to that in smaller cities (500,000–1,000,000 residents) by the following linear model:[30]

$$y = 1.5x - 1.9 \quad (15 \le x \le 25)$$

where y is the murder rate (in murders per 100,000 residents each year) in large cities and x is the murder rate in smaller cities. During the period 1991–1998, the murder rate in small cities was decreasing at an average rate of 2 murders per 100,000 residents each year. Use the chain rule to estimate how fast the murder rate was changing in larger cities during that period. (Show how you used the chain rule in your answer.)

68. Crime Statistics Following is a quadratic model relating the murder rates described in the preceding exercise:

$$y = 0.1x^2 - 3x + 39 \quad (15 \le x \le 25)$$

In 1996, the murder rate in smaller cities was approximately 22 murders per 100,000 residents each year and was decreasing at a rate of approximately 2.5 murders per 100,000 residents each year. Use the chain rule to estimate how fast the murder rate was changing for large cities. (Show how you used the chain rule in your answer.)

69. Existing Home Sales The following graph shows the approximate value of home prices and existing home sales in 2006–2010 as a percentage change from 2003, together with quadratic approximations.[31]

Home prices and sales of existing homes

The quadratic approximations are given by

Home Prices: $\quad P(t) = t^2 - 10t + 41 \quad (0 \le t \le 4)$

Existing Home Sales: $\quad S(t) = 1.5t^2 - 11t \quad (0 \le t \le 4)$

where t is time in years since the start of 2006. Use the chain rule to estimate $\dfrac{dS}{dP}\Big|_{t=2}$. What does the answer tell you about home sales and prices? HINT [See Quick Example 2 on page 828.]

---

[28] Model based on historical and projected data from 1908–2010. Sources: Historical data, Bureau of Economic Analysis; projected data, Bureau of Labor Statistics/*New York Times*, December 1, 2003, p. C2.
[29] Ibid.

[30] The model is a linear regression model. Source for data: Federal Bureau of Investigation, Supplementary Homicide Reports/*New York Times*, May 29, 2000, p. A12.
[31] Sources: Standard & Poors/Bloomberg Financial Markets/*New York Times*, September 29, 2007, p. C3. Projection is the authors'.

70. *Existing Home Sales* The following graph shows the approximate value of home prices and existing home sales in 2004–2007 as a percentage change from 2003, together with quadratic approximations.[32]

Home prices and sales of existing homes

The quadratic approximations are given by

Home Prices: $P(t) = -6t^2 + 27t + 10 \quad (0 \le t \le 3)$

Existing Home Sales: $S(t) = -4t^2 + 4t + 11 \quad (0 \le t \le 3)$

where *t* is time in years since the start of 2004. Use the chain rule to estimate $\dfrac{dS}{dP}\Big|_{t=2}$. What does the answer tell you about home sales and prices? HINT [See Quick Example 2 on page 828.]

71. ▼ *Pollution* An offshore oil well is leaking oil and creating a circular oil slick. If the radius of the slick is growing at a rate of 2 miles/hour, find the rate at which the area is increasing when the radius is 3 miles. (The area of a disc of radius *r* is $A = \pi r^2$.) HINT [See Quick Example 2 on page 828.]

72. ▼ *Mold* A mold culture in a dorm refrigerator is circular and growing. The radius is growing at a rate of 0.3 cm/day. How fast is the area growing when the culture is 4 centimeters in radius? (The area of a disc of radius *r* is $A = \pi r^2$.) HINT [See Quick Example 2 on page 828.]

73. ▼ *Budget Overruns* The Pentagon is planning to build a new, spherical satellite. As is typical in these cases, the specifications keep changing, so that the size of the satellite keeps growing. In fact, the radius of the planned satellite is growing 0.5 feet per week. Its cost will be $1,000 per cubic foot. At the point when the plans call for a satellite 10 feet in radius, how fast is the cost growing? (The volume of a solid sphere of radius *r* is $V = \frac{4}{3}\pi r^3$.)

74. ▼ *Soap Bubbles* The soap bubble I am blowing has a radius that is growing at a rate of 4 cm/s. How fast is the surface area growing when the radius is 10 cm? (The surface area of a sphere of radius *r* is $S = 4\pi r^2$.)

75. ▯ ▼ *Revenue Growth* The demand for the Cyberpunk II arcade video game is modeled by the logistic curve

$$q(t) = \frac{10,000}{1 + 0.5e^{-0.4t}}$$

where $q(t)$ is the total number of units sold *t* months after its introduction.

a. Use technology to estimate $q'(4)$.
b. Assume that the manufacturers of Cyberpunk II sell each unit for $800. What is the company's marginal revenue dR/dq?
c. Use the chain rule to estimate the rate at which revenue is growing 4 months after the introduction of the video game.

76. ▯ ▼ *Information Highway* The amount of information transmitted each month in the early years of the Internet (1988 to 1994) can be modeled by the equation

$$q(t) = \frac{2e^{0.69t}}{3 + 1.5e^{-0.4t}} \qquad (0 \le t \le 6)$$

where *q* is the amount of information transmitted each month in billions of data packets and *t* is the number of years since the start of 1988.[33]

a. Use technology to estimate $q'(2)$.
b. Assume that it costs $5 to transmit a million packets of data. What is the marginal cost $C'(q)$?
c. How fast was the cost increasing at the start of 1990?

Money Stock *Exercises 77–80 are based on the following demand function for money (taken from a question on the GRE Economics Test):*

$$M_d = 2 \times y^{0.6} \times r^{-0.3} \times p$$

where
  M_d = *demand for nominal money balances (money stock)*
  y = *real income*
  r = *an index of interest rates*
  p = *an index of prices*

*These exercises also use the idea of **percentage rate of growth**:*

Percentage Rate of Growth of $M = \dfrac{\text{Rate of Growth of } M}{M}$

$$= \frac{dM/dt}{M}$$

77. ◆ (from the GRE Economics Test) If the interest rate and price level are to remain constant while real income grows at 5 percent per year, the money stock must grow at what percent per year?

78. ◆ (from the GRE Economics Test) If real income and price level are to remain constant while the interest rate grows at 5 percent per year, the money stock must change by what percent per year?

79. ◆ (from the GRE Economics Test) If the interest rate is to remain constant while real income grows at 5 percent per year

[32] Sources: Standard & Poors /Bloomberg Financial Markets/*New York Times*, September 29, 2007, p. C3. Projection is the authors'.

[33] This is the authors' model, based on figures published in *New York Times*, Nov. 3, 1993.

and the price level rises at 5 percent per year, the money stock must grow at what percent per year?

80. ◆ (from the GRE Economics Test) If real income grows by 5 percent per year, the interest rate grows by 2 percent per year, and the price level drops by 3 percent per year, the money stock must change by what percent per year?

COMMUNICATION AND REASONING EXERCISES

81. Complete the following: The derivative of 1 over a glob is -1 over . . . .

82. Complete the following: The derivative of the square root of a glob is 1 over . . . .

83. Say why the following was marked wrong and give the correct answer.

$$\frac{d}{dx}[(3x^3 - x)^3] = 3(9x^2 - 1)^2 \qquad ✗ \quad \textit{WRONG!}$$

84. Say why the following was marked wrong and give the correct answer.

$$\frac{d}{dx}\left[\left(\frac{3x^2 - 1}{2x - 2}\right)^3\right] = 3\left(\frac{3x^2 - 1}{2x - 2}\right)^2\left(\frac{6x}{2}\right) \qquad ✗ \quad \textit{WRONG!}$$

85. Name two major errors in the following graded test question and give the correct answer.

$$\frac{d}{dx}\left[\left(\frac{3x^2 - 1}{2x - 2}\right)^3\right] = 3\left(\frac{6x}{2}\right)^2 \qquad ✗ \quad \textit{WRONG! SEE ME!}$$

86. Name two major errors in the following graded test question and give the correct answer.

$$\frac{d}{dx}[(3x^3 - x)(2x + 1)]^4 = 4[(9x^2 - 1)(2)]^3 \qquad ✗ \quad \textit{WRONG! SEE ME!}$$

87. ▼ Formulate a simple procedure for deciding whether to apply first the chain rule, the product rule, or the quotient rule when finding the derivative of a function.

88. ▼ Give an example of a function f with the property that calculating $f'(x)$ requires use of the following rules in the given order: (1) the chain rule, (2) the quotient rule, and (3) the chain rule.

89. ◆ Give an example of a function f with the property that calculating $f'(x)$ requires use of the chain rule five times in succession.

90. ◆ What can you say about composites of linear functions?

11.5 Derivatives of Logarithmic and Exponential Functions

At this point, we know how to take the derivative of any algebraic expression in x (involving powers, radicals, and so on). We now turn to the derivatives of logarithmic and exponential functions.

Derivative of the Natural Logarithm

$$\frac{d}{dx}[\ln x] = \frac{1}{x} \qquad \text{Recall that } \ln x = \log_e x.$$

Quick Examples

1. $\dfrac{d}{dx}[3 \ln x] = 3 \cdot \dfrac{1}{x} = \dfrac{3}{x}$ Derivative of a constant times a function

2. $\dfrac{d}{dx}[x \ln x] = 1 \cdot \ln x + x \cdot \dfrac{1}{x}$ Product rule, because $x \ln x$ is a product

   $= \ln x + 1.$

The above simple formula works only for the natural logarithm (the logarithm with base e). For logarithms with bases other than e, we have the following:

Derivative of the Logarithm with Base b

$$\frac{d}{dx}[\log_b x] = \frac{1}{x \ln b}$$

Notice that, if $b = e$, we get the same formula as previously.

Quick Examples

1. $\dfrac{d}{dx}[\log_3 x] = \dfrac{1}{x \ln 3} \approx \dfrac{1}{1.0986x}$

2. $\dfrac{d}{dx}[\log_2(x^4)] = \dfrac{d}{dx}(4 \log_2 x)$ We used the logarithm identity $\log_b(x^r) = r \log_b x$.

   $= 4 \cdot \dfrac{1}{x \ln 2} \approx \dfrac{4}{0.6931x}$

Derivation of the formulas $\dfrac{d}{dx}[\ln x] = \dfrac{1}{x}$ and $\dfrac{d}{dx}[\log_b x] = \dfrac{1}{x \ln b}$

To compute $\dfrac{d}{dx}[\ln x]$, we need to use the definition of the derivative. We also use properties of the logarithm to help evaluate the limit.

$$\frac{d}{dx}[\ln x] = \lim_{h \to 0} \frac{\ln(x + h) - \ln x}{h}$$ Definition of the derivative

$$= \lim_{h \to 0} \frac{1}{h}[\ln(x + h) - \ln x]$$ Algebra

$$= \lim_{h \to 0} \frac{1}{h} \ln\left(\frac{x + h}{x}\right)$$ Properties of the logarithm

$$= \lim_{h \to 0} \frac{1}{h} \ln\left(1 + \frac{h}{x}\right)$$ Algebra

$$= \lim_{h \to 0} \ln\left(1 + \frac{h}{x}\right)^{1/h}$$ Properties of the logarithm

which we rewrite as

$$\lim_{h \to 0} \ln\left[\left(1 + \frac{1}{(x/h)}\right)^{x/h}\right]^{1/x}.$$

As $h \to 0^+$, the quantity x/h is getting large and positive, and so the quantity in brackets is approaching e (see the definition of e in Section 9.2), which leaves us with

$$\ln[e]^{1/x} = \frac{1}{x} \ln e = \frac{1}{x}$$

which is the derivative we are after.* What about the limit as $h \to 0^-$? We will glide over that case and leave it for the interested reader to pursue.†

The rule for the derivative of $\log_b x$ follows from the fact that $\log_b x = \ln x / \ln b$.

If we were to take the derivative of the natural logarithm of a *quantity* (a function of x), rather than just x, we would need to use the chain rule:

Derivatives of Logarithms of Functions

Original Rule	*Generalized Rule*	*In Words*
$\dfrac{d}{dx}[\ln x] = \dfrac{1}{x}$	$\dfrac{d}{dx}[\ln u] = \dfrac{1}{u}\dfrac{du}{dx}$	*The derivative of the natural logarithm of a quantity is 1 over that quantity, times the derivative of that quantity.*
$\dfrac{d}{dx}[\log_b x] = \dfrac{1}{x \ln b}$	$\dfrac{d}{dx}[\log_b u] = \dfrac{1}{u \ln b}\dfrac{du}{dx}$	*The derivative of the log to base b of a quantity is 1 over the product of ln b and that quantity, times the derivative of that quantity.*

Quick Examples

1. $\dfrac{d}{dx}\ln[x^2 + 1] = \dfrac{1}{x^2 + 1}\dfrac{d}{dx}(x^2 + 1)$ $u = x^2 + 1$ (See the margin note.§)

   $= \dfrac{1}{x^2 + 1}(2x) = \dfrac{2x}{x^2 + 1}$

2. $\dfrac{d}{dx}\log_2[x^3 + x] = \dfrac{1}{(x^3 + x)\ln 2}\dfrac{d}{dx}(x^3 + x)$ $u = x^3 + x$

   $= \dfrac{1}{(x^3 + x)\ln 2}(3x^2 + 1) = \dfrac{3x^2 + 1}{(x^3 + x)\ln 2}$

EXAMPLE 1 Derivative of Logarithmic Function

Find $\dfrac{d}{dx}[\ln\sqrt{x + 1}]$.

Solution The calculation thought experiment tells us that we have the natural logarithm of a quantity, so

$$\frac{d}{dx}[\ln\sqrt{x+1}] = \frac{1}{\sqrt{x+1}}\frac{d}{dx}\sqrt{x+1} \qquad \frac{d}{dx}\ln u = \frac{1}{u}\frac{du}{dx}$$

$$= \frac{1}{\sqrt{x+1}} \cdot \frac{1}{2\sqrt{x+1}} \qquad \frac{d}{dx}\sqrt{u} = \frac{1}{2\sqrt{u}}\frac{du}{dx}$$

$$= \frac{1}{2(x+1)}.$$

➡ **Before we go on...** What happened to the square root in Example 1? As with many problems involving logarithms, we could have done this one differently and with less bother if we had simplified the expression $\ln\sqrt{x+1}$ using the properties of logarithms *before* differentiating. Doing this, we get

$$\ln\sqrt{x+1} = \ln(x+1)^{1/2} = \frac{1}{2}\ln(x+1). \qquad \text{Simplify the logarithm first.}$$

Thus,

$$\frac{d}{dx}[\ln\sqrt{x+1}] = \frac{d}{dx}\left[\frac{1}{2}\ln(x+1)\right]$$

$$= \frac{1}{2}\left(\frac{1}{x+1}\right) \cdot 1 = \frac{1}{2(x+1)},$$

the same answer as above. ■

EXAMPLE 2 **Derivative of a Logarithmic Function**

Find $\dfrac{d}{dx}[\ln[(1+x)(2-x)]]$.

Solution This time, we simplify the expression $\ln[(1+x)(2-x)]$ before taking the derivative.

$$\ln[(1+x)(2-x)] = \ln(1+x) + \ln(2-x) \qquad \text{Simplify the logarithm first.}$$

Thus,

$$\frac{d}{dx}[\ln[(1+x)(2-x)]] = \frac{d}{dx}[\ln(1+x)] + \frac{d}{dx}\ln(2-x)]$$

$$= \frac{1}{1+x} - \frac{1}{2-x} \qquad \text{Because } \frac{d}{dx}\ln(2-x) = -\frac{1}{2-x}$$

$$= \frac{1-2x}{(1+x)(2-x)}.$$

➡ **Before we go on...** For practice, try doing Example 2 without simplifying first. What other differentiation rule do you need to use? ∎

EXAMPLE 3 Logarithm of an Absolute Value

Find $\dfrac{d}{dx}[\ln|x|]$.

Solution Before we start, we note that $\ln x$ is defined only for positive values of x, so its domain is the set of positive real numbers. The domain of $\ln|x|$, on the other hand, is the set of *all* nonzero real numbers. For example, $\ln|-2| = \ln 2 \approx 0.6931$. For this reason, $\ln|x|$ often turns out to be more useful than the ordinary logarithm function.

Now we'll get to work. The calculation thought experiment tells us that $\ln|x|$ is the natural logarithm of a quantity, so we use the chain rule:

$$\frac{d}{dx}[\ln|x|] = \frac{1}{|x|}\frac{d}{dx}|x| \qquad u = |x|$$

$$= \frac{1}{|x|}\frac{|x|}{x} \qquad \text{Recall that } \frac{d}{dx}|x| = \frac{|x|}{x}.$$

$$= \frac{1}{x}.$$

➡ **Before we go on...** Figure 7(a) shows the graphs of $y = \ln|x|$ and $y = 1/x$. Figure 7(b) shows the graphs of $y = \ln|x|$ and $y = 1/|x|$. You should be able to see from these graphs why the derivative of $\ln|x|$ is $1/x$ and not $1/|x|$.

Figure 7(a)

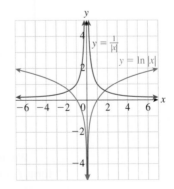

Figure 7(b) ∎

This last example, in conjunction with the chain rule, gives us the following formulas.

Derivative of Logarithms of Absolute Values

Original Rule	*Generalized Rule*	*In Words*
$\dfrac{d}{dx}[\ln |x|] = \dfrac{1}{x}$	$\dfrac{d}{dx}[\ln |u|] = \dfrac{1}{u}\dfrac{du}{dx}$	*The derivative of the natural logarithm of the absolute value of a quantity is 1 over that quantity, times the derivative of that quantity.*
$\dfrac{d}{dx}[\log_b |x|] = \dfrac{1}{x \ln b}$	$\dfrac{d}{dx}[\log_b |u|] = \dfrac{1}{u \ln b}\dfrac{du}{dx}$	*The derivative of the log to base b of the absolute value of a quantity is 1 over the product of $\ln b$ and that quantity, times the derivative of that quantity.*

Note: Compare the above formulas with those on page 835. They tell us that we can simply ignore the absolute values in $\ln |u|$ or $\log_b |u|$ when taking the derivative.

Quick Examples

1. $\dfrac{d}{dx}[\ln|x^2 + 1|] = \dfrac{1}{x^2+1}\dfrac{d}{dx}(x^2+1)$ $u = x^2 + 1$

   $= \dfrac{1}{x^2+1}(2x) = \dfrac{2x}{x^2+1}$

2. $\dfrac{d}{dx}[\log_2|x^3 + x|] = \dfrac{1}{(x^3+x)\ln 2}\dfrac{d}{dx}(x^3+x)$ $u = x^3 + x$

   $= \dfrac{1}{(x^3+x)\ln 2}(3x^2+1) = \dfrac{3x^2+1}{(x^3+x)\ln 2}$

We now turn to the derivatives of *exponential* functions—that is, functions of the form $f(x) = b^x$. We begin by showing how *not* to differentiate them.

Caution The derivative of b^x is *not* xb^{x-1}. The power rule applies only to *constant* exponents. In this case the exponent is decidedly *not* constant, and so the power rule does not apply.

The following shows the correct way of differentiating b^x, beginning with a special case.

Derivative of e^x

$$\frac{d}{dx}[e^x] = e^x$$

Quick Examples

1. $\dfrac{d}{dx}[3e^x] = 3\dfrac{d}{dx}[e^x] = 3e^x$

2. $\dfrac{d}{dx}\left[\dfrac{e^x}{x}\right] = \dfrac{e^x x - e^x(1)}{x^2}$ Quotient rule

   $\qquad\qquad = \dfrac{e^x(x-1)}{x^2}$

✱ NOTE There is another—very simple—function that is its own derivative. What is it?

Thus, e^x has the amazing property that its derivative is itself!✱ For bases other than e, we have the following generalization:

Derivative of b^x

If b is any positive number, then

$$\frac{d}{dx}[b^x] = b^x \ln b.$$

Note that if $b = e$, we obtain the previous formula.

Quick Example

$$\frac{d}{dx}[3^x] = 3^x \ln 3$$

Derivation of the formula $\dfrac{d}{dx}[e^x] = e^x$

✱ NOTE This shortcut is an example of a technique called *logarithmic differentiation*, which is occasionally useful. We will see it again in the next section.

To find the derivative of e^x we use a shortcut.✱ Write $g(x) = e^x$. Then
$$\ln g(x) = x.$$
Take the derivative of both sides of this equation to get
$$\frac{g'(x)}{g(x)} = 1$$
or
$$g'(x) = g(x) = e^x.$$

In other words, the exponential function with base e is its own derivative. The rule for exponential functions with other bases follows from the equality $b^x = e^{x \ln b}$ (why?) and the chain rule. (Try it.)

If we were to take the derivative of e raised to a *quantity*, not just x, we would need to use the chain rule, as follows.

Derivatives of Exponentials of Functions

Original Rule	*Generalized Rule*	*In Words*
$\dfrac{d}{dx}[e^x] = e^x$	$\dfrac{d}{dx}[e^u] = e^u \dfrac{du}{dx}$	*The derivative of e raised to a quantity is e raised to that quantity, times the derivative of that quantity.*
$\dfrac{d}{dx}[b^x] = b^x \ln b$	$\dfrac{d}{dx}[b^u] = b^u \ln b \dfrac{du}{dx}$	*The derivative of b raised to a quantity is b raised to that quantity, times ln b, times the derivative of that quantity.*

Quick Examples

* **NOTE** The calculation thought experiment tells us that we have e raised to a quantity.

1. $\dfrac{d}{dx}\left[e^{x^2+1}\right] = e^{x^2+1}\dfrac{d}{dx}[x^2+1]$ $u = x^2 + 1$ (See margin note.*)

$\quad = e^{x^2+1}(2x) = 2x\, e^{x^2+1}$

2. $\dfrac{d}{dx}[2^{3x}] = 2^{3x}\ln 2\dfrac{d}{dx}[3x]$ $u = 3x$

$\quad = 2^{3x}(\ln 2)(3) = (3\ln 2)2^{3x}$

3. $\dfrac{d}{dt}[30e^{1.02t}] = 30e^{1.02t}(1.02) = 30.6e^{1.02t}$ $u = 1.02t$

4. If \$1,000 is invested in an account earning 5% per year compounded continuously, then the rate of change of the account balance after t years is

$$\dfrac{d}{dt}[1,000e^{0.05t}] = 1,000(0.05)e^{0.05t} = 50e^{0.05t} \text{ dollars/year.}$$

APPLICATIONS

EXAMPLE 4 Epidemics

In the early stages of the AIDS epidemic during the 1980s, the number of cases in the United States was increasing by about 50% every 6 months. By the start of 1983, there were approximately 1,600 AIDS cases in the United States.* Had this trend continued, how many new cases per year would have been occurring by the start of 1993?

---

* Data based on regression of 1982–1986 figures. Source for data: Centers for Disease Control and Prevention. HIV/AIDS Surveillance Report, 2000;12 (No. 2).

Solution To find the answer, we must first model this exponential growth using the methods of Chapter 9. Referring to Example 4 in Section 9.2, we find that t years after the start of 1983 the number of cases is

$$A = 1,600(2.25^t).$$

We are asking for the number of new cases each year. In other words, we want the rate of change, dA/dt:

$$\frac{dA}{dt} = 1,600(2.25)^t \ln 2.25 \text{ cases per year.}$$

At the start of 1993, $t = 10$, so the number of new cases per year is

$$\left.\frac{dA}{dt}\right|_{t=10} = 1,600(2.25)^{10} \ln 2.25 \approx 4,300,000 \text{ cases per year.}$$

➡ **Before we go on...** In Example 4, the figure for the number of new cases per year is so large because we assumed that exponential growth—the 50% increase every six months—would continue. A more realistic model for the spread of a disease is the logistic model. (See Section 9.4, as well as the next example.) ∎

EXAMPLE 5 Sales Growth

The sales of the Cyberpunk II video game can be modeled by the logistic curve

$$q(t) = \frac{10,000}{1 + 0.5e^{-0.4t}}$$

where $q(t)$ is the total number of units sold t months after its introduction. How fast is the game selling 2 years after its introduction?

Solution We are asked for $q'(24)$. We can find the derivative of $q(t)$ using the quotient rule, or we can first write

$$q(t) = 10,000(1 + 0.5e^{-0.4t})^{-1}$$

and then use the generalized power rule:

$$q'(t) = -10,000(1 + 0.5e^{-0.4t})^{-2}(0.5e^{-0.4t})(-0.4)$$

$$= \frac{2,000e^{-0.4t}}{(1 + 0.5e^{-0.4t})^2}.$$

Thus,

$$q'(24) = \frac{2,000e^{-0.4(24)}}{(1 + 0.5e^{-0.4(24)})^2} \approx 0.135 \text{ units per month.}$$

So, after 2 years, sales are quite slow.

Figure 8

➡ **Before we go on...** We can check the answer in Example 5 graphically. If we plot the total sales curve for $0 \le t \le 30$ and $6,000 \le q \le 10,000$, on a TI-83/84 Plus, for example, we get the graph shown in Figure 8. Notice that total sales level off at about

* NOTE We can also say this using limits:
$$\lim_{t \to +\infty} q(t) = 10,000.$$

Figure 9

10,000 units.* We computed $q'(24)$, which is the slope of the curve at the point with t-coordinate 24. If we zoom in to the portion of the curve near $t = 24$, we obtain the graph shown in Figure 9, with $23 \le t \le 25$ and $9,999 \le q \le 10,000$. The curve is almost linear in this range. If we use the two endpoints of this segment of the curve, $(23, 9,999.4948)$ and $(25, 9,999.7730)$, we can approximate the derivative as

$$\frac{9,999.7730 - 9,999.4948}{25 - 23} = 0.1391$$

which is accurate to two decimal places. ∎

11.5 EXERCISES

▼ more advanced   ◆ challenging
$\boxed{\text{T}}$ indicates exercises that should be solved using technology

Find the derivatives of the functions in Exercises 1–76. HINT [See Quick Examples on page 835.]

1. $f(x) = \ln(x - 1)$

2. $f(x) = \ln(x + 3)$

3. $f(x) = \log_2 x$

4. $f(x) = \log_3 x$

5. $g(x) = \ln|x^2 + 3|$

6. $g(x) = \ln|2x - 4|$

7. $h(x) = e^{x+3}$
   HINT [See Quick Examples on page 840.]

8. $h(x) = e^{x^2}$
   HINT [See Quick Examples on page 840.]

9. $f(x) = e^{-x}$

10. $f(x) = e^{1-x}$

11. $g(x) = 4^x$

12. $g(x) = 5^x$

13. $h(x) = 2^{x^2-1}$

14. $h(x) = 3^{x^2-x}$

15. $f(x) = x \ln x$

16. $f(x) = 3 \ln x$

17. $f(x) = (x^2 + 1) \ln x$

18. $f(x) = (4x^2 - x) \ln x$

19. $f(x) = (x^2 + 1)^5 \ln x$

20. $f(x) = (x + 1)^{0.5} \ln x$

21. $g(x) = \ln|3x - 1|$

22. $g(x) = \ln|5 - 9x|$

23. $g(x) = \ln|2x^2 + 1|$

24. $g(x) = \ln|x^2 - x|$

25. $g(x) = \ln(x^2 - 2.1x^{0.3})$

26. $g(x) = \ln(x - 3.1x^{-1})$

27. $h(x) = \ln[(-2x + 1)(x + 1)]$

28. $h(x) = \ln[(3x + 1)(-x + 1)]$

29. $h(x) = \ln\left(\dfrac{3x + 1}{4x - 2}\right)$

30. $h(x) = \ln\left(\dfrac{9x}{4x - 2}\right)$

31. $r(x) = \ln\left|\dfrac{(x + 1)(x - 3)}{-2x - 9}\right|$

32. $r(x) = \ln\left|\dfrac{-x + 1}{(3x - 4)(x - 9)}\right|$

33. $s(x) = \ln(4x - 2)^{1.3}$

34. $s(x) = \ln(x - 8)^{-2}$

35. $s(x) = \ln\left|\dfrac{(x + 1)^2}{(3x - 4)^3(x - 9)}\right|$

36. $s(x) = \ln\left|\dfrac{(x + 1)^2(x - 3)^4}{2x + 9}\right|$

37. $h(x) = \log_2(x + 1)$

38. $h(x) = \log_3(x^2 + x)$

39. $r(t) = \log_3(t + 1/t)$

40. $r(t) = \log_3\left(t + \sqrt{t}\right)$

41. $f(x) = (\ln|x|)^2$

42. $f(x) = \dfrac{1}{\ln|x|}$

43. $r(x) = \ln(x^2) - [\ln(x - 1)]^2$

44. $r(x) = (\ln(x^2))^2$

45. $f(x) = xe^x$

46. $f(x) = 2e^x - x^2 e^x$

47. $r(x) = \ln(x + 1) + 3x^3 e^x$

48. $r(x) = \ln|x + e^x|$

49. $f(x) = e^x \ln|x|$

50. $f(x) = e^x \log_2|x|$

51. $f(x) = e^{2x+1}$

52. $f(x) = e^{4x-5}$

53. $h(x) = e^{x^2-x+1}$

54. $h(x) = e^{2x^2-x+1/x}$

55. $s(x) = x^2 e^{2x-1}$

56. $s(x) = \dfrac{e^{4x-1}}{x^3 - 1}$

57. $r(x) = (e^{2x-1})^2$

58. $r(x) = (e^{2x^2})^3$

59. $t(x) = 3^{2x-4}$

60. $t(x) = 4^{-x+5}$

61. $v(x) = 3^{2x+1} + e^{3x+1}$

62. $v(x) = e^{2x} 4^{2x}$

63. $u(x) = \dfrac{3^{x^2}}{x^2 + 1}$

64. $u(x) = (x^2 + 1)4^{x^2-1}$

65. $g(x) = \dfrac{e^x + e^{-x}}{e^x - e^{-x}}$

66. $g(x) = \dfrac{1}{e^x + e^{-x}}$

67. ▼$g(x) = e^{3x-1}e^{x-2}e^x$

68. ▼$g(x) = e^{-x+3}e^{2x-1}e^{-x+11}$

69. ▼$f(x) = \dfrac{1}{x \ln x}$

70. ▼$f(x) = \dfrac{e^{-x}}{xe^x}$

71. ▼$f(x) = [\ln(e^x)]^2 - \ln[(e^x)^2]$

72. ▼$f(x) = e^{\ln x} - e^{2\ln(x^2)}$

73. ▼$f(x) = \ln|\ln x|$

74. ▼$f(x) = \ln|\ln|\ln x||$

75. ▼$s(x) = \ln\sqrt{\ln x}$

76. ▼$s(x) = \sqrt{\ln(\ln x)}$

Find the equations of the straight lines described in Exercises 77–82. Use graphing technology to check your answers by plotting the given curve together with the tangent line.

77. Tangent to $y = e^x \log_2 x$ at the point $(1, 0)$

78. Tangent to $y = e^x + e^{-x}$ at the point $(0, 2)$

79. Tangent to $y = \ln\sqrt{2x + 1}$ at the point where $x = 0$

80. Tangent to $y = \ln\sqrt{2x^2 + 1}$ at the point where $x = 1$

81. At right angles to $y = e^{x^2}$ at the point where $x = 1$

82. At right angles to $y = \log_2(3x + 1)$ at the point where $x = 1$

APPLICATIONS

83. *Research and Development: Industry* The total spent on research and development by industry in the United States during 1995–2007 can be approximated by

$$S(t) = 57.5 \ln t + 31 \text{ billion dollars} \quad (5 \le t \le 19)$$

where t is the year since 1990.[34] What was the total spent in 2000 ($t = 10$) and how fast was it increasing? HINT [See Quick Examples on page 833.]

84. *Research and Development: Federal* The total spent on research and development by the federal government in the United States during 1995–2007 can be approximated by

$$S(t) = 7.4 \ln t + 3 \text{ billion dollars} \quad (5 \le t \le 19)$$

where t is the year since 1990.[35] What was the total spent in 2005 ($t = 15$) and how fast was it increasing? HINT [See Quick Examples on page 833.]

85. *Research and Development: Industry* The function $S(t)$ in Exercise 83 can also be written (approximately) as

$$S(t) = 57.5 \ln (1.71t + 17.1) \text{ billion dollars}$$
$$(-5 \le t \le 9)$$

where this time t is the year since 2000. Use this alternative formula to estimate the amount spent in 2000 and its rate of change, and check your answers by comparing it with those in Exercise 83.

86. *Research and Development: Federal* The function $S(t)$ in Exercise 84 can also be written (approximately) as

$$S(t) = 7.4 \ln (1.5t + 15) \text{ billion dollars}$$
$$(-5 \le t \le 9)$$

where this time t is the year since 2000. Use this alternative formula to estimate the amount spent in 2005 and its rate of change, and check your answers by comparing it with those in Exercise 84.

87. ▼ *Carbon Dating* The age in years of a specimen that originally contained 10g of carbon 14 is given by

$$y = \log_{0.999879}(0.1x)$$

where x is the amount of carbon 14 it currently contains. Compute $\dfrac{dy}{dx}\bigg|_{x=5}$ and interpret your answer. HINT [For the calculation, see Quick Examples on page 835.]

88. ▼ *Iodine Dating* The age in years of a specimen that originally contained 10g of iodine 131 is given by

$$y = \log_{0.999567}(0.1x)$$

where x is the amount of iodine 131 it currently contains. Compute $\dfrac{dy}{dx}\bigg|_{x=8}$ and interpret your answer. HINT [For the calculation, see Quick Examples on page 835.]

89. *New York City Housing Costs: Downtown* The average price of a two-bedroom apartment in downtown New York City during the real estate boom from 1994 to 2004 can be approximated by

$$p(t) = 0.33e^{0.16t} \text{ million dollars} \quad (0 \le t \le 10)$$

where t is time in years ($t = 0$ represents 1994).[36] What was the average price of a two-bedroom apartment in downtown New York City in 2003, and how fast was it increasing? (Round your answers to two significant digits.) HINT [See Quick Example 3 on page 840.]

90. *New York City Housing Costs: Uptown* The average price of a two-bedroom apartment in uptown New York City during the real estate boom from 1994 to 2004 can be approximated by

$$p(t) = 0.14e^{0.10t} \text{ million dollars} \quad (0 \le t \le 10)$$

where t is time in years ($t = 0$ represents 1994).[37] What was the average price of a two-bedroom apartment in uptown New York City in 2002, and how fast was it increasing? (Round your answers to two significant digits.) HINT [See Quick Example 3 on page 840.]

91. *Big Brother* The following chart shows the total number of wiretaps authorized each year by U.S. state and federal courts from 1990 to 2007 ($t = 0$ represents 1990):[38]

These data can be approximated with the model (shown on the graph)

$$N(t) = 820e^{0.051t}. \quad (0 \le t \le 17)$$

---

[34] Spending is in constant 2000 dollars. Source for data through 2006: National Science Foundation, Division of Science Resources Statistics, National Patterns of R&D Resources (www.nsf.gov/statistics) August 2008.

[35] Federal funding excluding grants to industry and nonprofit organizations. Spending is in constant 2000 dollars. Source for data through 2006: National Science Foundation, Division of Science Resources Statistics, National Patterns of R&D Resources (www.nsf.gov/statistics) August 2008.

[36] Model is based on a exponential regression. Source for data: Miller Samuel/*New York Times*, March 28, 2004, p. RE 11.

[37] Ibid.

[38] Source for data: 2007 Wiretap Report, Administrative Office of the United States Courts (www.uscourts.gov/wiretap07/2007WTText.pdf).

a. Find $N(15)$ and $N'(15)$. Be sure to state the units of measurement. To how many significant digits should we round the answers? Why?

b. The number of people whose communications are intercepted averages around 100 per wiretap order.[39] What does the answer to part (a) tell you about the number of people whose communications were intercepted?[40]

c. According to the model, the number of wiretaps orders each year (choose one):

   (A) increased at a linear rate
   (B) decreased at a quadratic rate
   (C) increased at an exponential rate
   (D) increased at a logarithmic rate

   over the period shown.

92. *Big Brother* The following chart shows the number of wiretaps authorized each year by U.S. state courts from 1990 to 2007 ($t = 0$ represents 1990):[41]

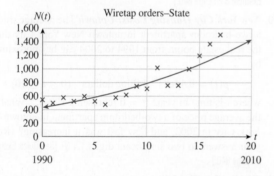

Wiretap orders–State

These data can be approximated with the model (shown on the graph)

$$N(t) = 440e^{0.06t}. \quad (0 \le t \le 17)$$

a. Find $N(10)$ and $N'(10)$. Be sure to state the units of measurement. To how many significant digits should we round the answers? Why?

b. The number of people whose communications are intercepted averages around 100 per wiretap order.[42] What does the answer to part (a) tell you about the number of people whose communications were intercepted?[43]

c. According to the model, the number of wiretaps orders each year (choose one)

   (A) increased at a linear rate
   (B) decreased at a quadratic rate

   (C) increased at an exponential rate
   (D) increased at a logarithmic rate

   over the period shown.

93. *Investments* If \$10,000 is invested in a savings account offering 4% per year, compounded continuously, how fast is the balance growing after 3 years?

94. *Investments* If \$20,000 is invested in a savings account offering 3.5% per year, compounded continuously, how fast is the balance growing after 3 years?

95. *Investments* If \$10,000 is invested in a savings account offering 4% per year, compounded semiannually, how fast is the balance growing after 3 years?

96. *Investments* If \$20,000 is invested in a savings account offering 3.5% per year, compounded semiannually, how fast is the balance growing after 3 years?

97. *SARS* In the early stages of the deadly SARS (Severe Acute Respiratory Syndrome) epidemic in 2003, the number of cases was increasing by about 18% each day.[44] On March 17, 2003 (the first day for which statistics were reported by the World Health Organization) there were 167 cases. Find an exponential model that predicts the number of people infected t days after March 17, 2003, and use it to estimate how fast the epidemic was spreading on March 31, 2003. (Round your answer to the nearest whole number of new cases per day.) HINT [See Example 4.]

98. *SARS* A few weeks into the deadly SARS (Severe Acute Respiratory Syndrome) epidemic in 2003, the number of cases was increasing by about 4% each day.[45] On April 1, 2003 there were 1,804 cases. Find an exponential model that predicts the number $A(t)$ of people infected t days after April 1, 2003, and use it to estimate how fast the epidemic was spreading on April 30, 2003. (Round your answer to the nearest whole number of new cases per day.) HINT [See Example 4.]

99. ▼ *SAT Scores by Income* The following chart shows United State verbal SAT scores as a function of parents' income level:[46]

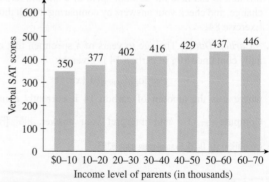

a. The data can best be modeled by which of the following?

   (A) $S(x) = 470 - 136e^{-0.0000264x}$
   (B) $S(x) = 136e^{-0.0000264x}$

---

[39] Source for data: 2007 Wiretap Report, Administrative Office of the United States Courts (www.uscourts.gov/wiretap07/2007WTText.pdf).

[40] Assume there is no significant overlap between the people whose communications are intercepted in different wiretap orders.

[41] Source for data: 2007 Wiretap Report, Administrative Office of the United States Courts (www.uscourts.gov/wiretap07/2007WTText.pdf).

[42] Ibid.

[43] Assume there is no significant overlap between the people whose communications are intercepted in different wiretap orders.

[44] World Health Organization (www.who.int).

[45] Ibid.

[46] Source: The College Board/*New York Times*, March 5, 1995, p. E16.

(C) $S(x) = 355(1.000004^x)$

(D) $S(x) = 470 - 355(1.000004^x)$

($S(x)$ is the average verbal SAT score of students whose parents earn $x per year.)

b. Use $S'(x)$ to predict how a student's verbal SAT score is affected by a $1,000 increase in parents' income for a student whose parents earn $45,000.

c. Does $S'(x)$ increase or decrease as x increases? Interpret your answer.

100. ▼ *SAT Scores by Income* The following chart shows U.S. average math SAT scores as a function of parents' income level:[47]

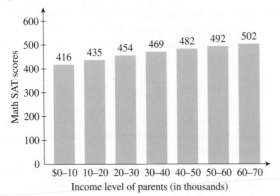

Income level of parents (in thousands)

a. The data can best be modeled by which of the following?

(A) $S(x) = 535 - 415(1.000003^x)$

(B) $S(x) = 535 - 136e^{0.0000213x}$

(C) $S(x) = 535 - 136e^{-0.0000213x}$

(D) $S(x) = 415(1.000003^x)$

($S(x)$ is the average math SAT score of students whose parents earn $x per year.)

b. Use $S'(x)$ to predict how a student's math SAT score is affected by a $1,000 increase in parents' income for a student whose parents earn $45,000.

c. Does $S'(x)$ increase or decrease as x increases? Interpret your answer.

101. ▼ *Demographics: Average Age and Fertility* The following graph shows a plot of average age of a population versus fertility rate (the average number of children each woman has in her lifetime) in the United States and Europe over the period 1950–2005.[48]

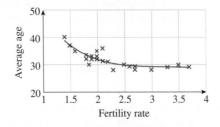

Fertility rate

The equation of the accompanying curve is

$$a = 28.5 + 120(0.172)^x \quad (1.4 \le x \le 3.7)$$

where a is the average age (in years) of the population and x is the fertility rate.

a. Compute $a'(2)$. What does the answer tell you about average age and fertility rates?

b. Use the answer to part (a) to estimate how much the fertility rate would need to increase from a level of 2 children per woman to lower the average age of a population by about 1 year.

102. ▼ *Demographics: Average Age and Fertility* The following graph shows a plot of average age of a population versus fertility rate (the average number of children each woman has in her lifetime) in Europe over the period 1950–2005.[49]

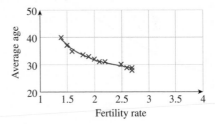

Fertility rate

The equation of the accompanying curve is

$$g = 27.6 + 128(0.181)^x \quad (1.4 \le x \le 3.7)$$

where g is the average age (in years) of the population and x is the fertility rate.

a. Compute $g'(2.5)$. What does the answer tell you about average age and fertility rates?

b. Referring to the model that combines the data for Europe and the United States in Exercise 101, which population's average age is affected more by a changing fertility rate at the level of 2.5 children per woman?

103. *Epidemics* A flu epidemic described in Example 1 in Section 9.4 approximately followed the curve

$$P = \frac{150}{1 + 15,000e^{-0.35t}} \text{ million people}$$

where P is the number of people infected and t is the number of weeks after the start of the epidemic. How fast is the epidemic growing (that is, how many new cases are there each week) after 20 weeks? After 30 weeks? After 40 weeks? (Round your answers to two significant digits.) HINT [See Example 5.]

104. *Epidemics* Another epidemic follows the curve

$$P = \frac{200}{1 + 20,000e^{-0.549t}} \text{ million people}$$

[47] Source: The College Board/*New York Times*, March 5, 1995, p. E16.

[48] The separate data for Europe and the United States are collected in the same graph. 2005 figures are estimates. Source: United Nations World Population Division/*New York Times*, June 29, 2003, p. 3.

[49] All European countries including the Russian Federation. 2005 figures are estimates. Source: United Nations World Population Division/*New York Times*, June 29, 2003, p. 3.

where t is in years. How fast is the epidemic growing after 10 years? After 20 years? After 30 years? (Round your answers to two significant digits.) HINT [See Example 5.]

105. Subprime Mortgages The percentage of mortgages issued in the United States that are subprime (normally classified as risky) can be approximated by

$$A(t) = \frac{15.0}{1 + 8.6e^{-0.59t}} \text{ percent} \quad (0 \le t \le 8)$$

t years after the start of 2000.[50]

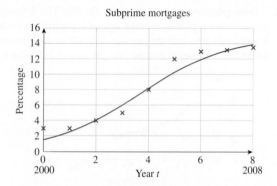

Subprime mortgages

How fast, to the nearest 0.1 percent, was the percentage increasing at the start of 2003? How would you check that the answer is approximately correct by looking at the graph?

106. Subprime Mortgage Debt The approximate value of subprime (normally classified as risky) mortgage debt outstanding in the United States can be approximated by

$$A(t) = \frac{1,350}{1 + 4.2e^{-0.53t}} \text{ \$ billion} \quad (0 \le t \le 8)$$

t years after the start of 2000.[51]

Subprime debt outstanding

How fast, to the nearest \$1 billion, was the subprime mortgage debt increasing at the start of 2005? How would you

check that the answer is approximately correct by looking at the graph?

107. Subprime Mortgages (Compare Exercise 105.) The percentage of mortgages issued in the United States that are subprime (normally classified as risky) can be approximated by

$$A(t) = \frac{15.0}{1 + 8.6(1.8)^{-t}} \text{ percent} \quad (0 \le t \le 8)$$

t years after the start of 2000.[52] How fast, to the nearest 0.1 percent, was the percentage increasing at the start of 2003?

108. Subprime Mortgage Debt (Compare Exercise 106.) The approximate value of subprime (normally classified as risky) mortgage debt outstanding in the United States can be approximated by

$$A(t) = \frac{1,350}{1 + 4.2(1.7)^{-t}} \text{ \$ billion} \quad (0 \le t \le 8)$$

t years after the start of 2000.[53] How fast, to the nearest \$1 billion, was the subprime mortgage debt increasing at the start of 2005?

109. ▼ Population Growth The population of Lower Anchovia was 4,000,000 at the start of 2010 and was doubling every 10 years. How fast was it growing per year at the start of 2010? (Round your answer to three significant digits.) HINT [Use the method of Example 2 in Section 9.2 to obtain an exponential model for the population.]

110. ▼ Population Growth The population of Upper Anchovia was 3,000,000 at the start of 2011 and doubling every 7 years. How fast was it growing per year at the start of 2011? (Round your answer to three significant digits.) HINT [Use the method of Example 2 in Section 9.2 to obtain an exponential model for the population.]

111. ▼ Radioactive Decay Plutonium 239 has a half-life of 24,400 years. How fast is a lump of 10 grams decaying after 100 years?

112. ▼ Radioactive Decay Carbon 14 has a half-life of 5,730 years. How fast is a lump of 20 grams decaying after 100 years?

113. ▣ ▼ Diffusion of New Technology Numeric control is a technology whereby the operation of machines is controlled by numerical instructions on disks, tapes, or cards. In a study, E. Mansfield and associates[54] modeled the growth of this technology using the equation

$$p(t) = \frac{0.80}{1 + e^{4.46 - 0.477t}}$$

[50] 2009 figure is an estimate. Sources: Mortgage Bankers Association, UBS.

[51] 2008–2009 figures are estimates. Source: www.data360.org/dataset.aspx? Data_Set_Id=9549.

[52] 2009 figure is an estimate. Sources: Mortgage Bankers Association, UBS.

[53] 2008–2009 figures are estimates. Source: www.data360.org/dataset.aspx? Data_Set_Id=9549.

[54] Source: "The Diffusion of a Major Manufacturing Innovation," in *Research and Innovation in the Modern Corporation* (W.W. Norton and Company, Inc., New York, 1971, pp. 186–205).

where $p(t)$ is the fraction of firms using numeric control in year t.

a. Graph this function for $0 \le t \le 20$ and estimate $p'(10)$ graphically. Interpret the result.

b. Use your graph to estimate $\lim_{t \to +\infty} p(t)$ and interpret the result.

c. Compute $p'(t)$, graph it, and again find $p'(10)$.

d. Use your graph to estimate $\lim_{t \to +\infty} p'(t)$ and interpret the result.

114. ▣ ▼ *Diffusion of New Technology* Repeat Exercise 113 using the revised formula

$$p(t) = \frac{0.90e^{-0.1t}}{1 + e^{4.50 - 0.477t}}$$

which takes into account that in the long run this new technology will eventually become outmoded and will be replaced by a newer technology. Draw your graphs using the range $0 \le t \le 40$.

115. ◆ *Cell Phone Revenues* The number of cell phone subscribers in China for the period 2000–2005 was projected to follow the equation[55]

$$N(t) = 39t + 68 \text{ million subscribers}$$

in year t ($t = 0$ represents 2000). The average annual revenue per cell phone user was $350 in 2000. Assuming that, due to competition, the revenue per cell phone user decreases continuously at an annual rate of 10%, give a formula for the annual revenue in year t. Hence, project the annual revenue and its rate of change in 2002. Round all answers to the nearest billion dollars or billion dollars per year.

116. ◆ *Cell Phone Revenues* The annual revenue for cell phone use in China for the period 2000–2005 was projected to follow the equation[56]

$$R(t) = 14t + 24 \text{ billion dollars}$$

in year t ($t = 0$ represents 2000). At the same time, there were approximately 68 million subscribers in 2000. Assuming that the number of subscribers increases continuously at an annual rate of 10%, give a formula for the annual revenue per subscriber in year t. Hence, project to the nearest dollar the annual revenue per subscriber and its rate of change in 2002. (Be careful with units!)

---

[55] Based on a regression of projected figures (coefficients are rounded). Source: Intrinsic Technology/*New York Times*, Nov. 24, 2000, p. C1.

[56] Not allowing for discounting due to increased competition. Source: Ibid.

COMMUNICATION AND REASONING EXERCISES

117. Complete the following: The derivative of e raised to a glob is . . . .

118. Complete the following: The derivative of the natural logarithm of a glob is . . . .

119. Complete the following: The derivative of 2 raised to a glob is . . . .

120. Complete the following: The derivative of the base 2 logarithm of a glob is . . . .

121. What is wrong with the following?

$$\frac{d}{dx} \ln|3x + 1| = \frac{3}{|3x + 1|} \qquad ✗ \quad WRONG!$$

122. What is wrong with the following?

$$\frac{d}{dx} 2^{2x} = (2)2^{2x} \qquad ✗ \quad WRONG!$$

123. What is wrong with the following?

$$\frac{d}{dx} 3^{2x} = (2x)3^{2x-1} \qquad ✗ \quad WRONG!$$

124. What is wrong with the following?

$$\frac{d}{dx} \ln(3x^2 - 1) = \frac{1}{6x} \qquad ✗ \quad WRONG!$$

125. ▼ The number N of music downloads on campus is growing exponentially with time. Can $N'(t)$ grow linearly with time? Explain.

126. ▼ The number N of graphing calculators sold on campus is decaying exponentially with time. Can $N'(t)$ grow with time? Explain.

*The **percentage rate of change** or **fractional rate of change** of a function is defined to be the ratio $f'(x)/f(x)$. (It is customary to express this as a percentage when speaking about percentage rate of change.)*

127. ◆ Show that the fractional rate of change of the exponential function e^{kx} is equal to k, which is often called its **fractional growth rate**.

128. ◆ Show that the fractional rate of change of $f(x)$ is the rate of change of $\ln(f(x))$.

129. ◆ Let $A(t)$ represent a quantity growing exponentially. Show that the percentage rate of change, $A'(t)/A(t)$, is constant.

130. ◆ Let $A(t)$ be the amount of money in an account that pays interest which is compounded some number of times per year. Show that the percentage rate of growth, $A'(t)/A(t)$, is constant. What might this constant represent?

11.6 Implicit Differentiation

Consider the equation $y^5 + y + x = 0$, whose graph is shown in Figure 10.

How did we obtain this graph? We did not solve for y as a function of x; that is impossible. In fact, we solved for x in terms of y to find points to plot. Nonetheless, the graph in Figure 10 is the graph of a function because it passes the vertical line test: Every vertical line crosses the graph no more than once, so for each value of x there is no more than one corresponding value of y. Because we cannot solve for y explicitly in terms of x, we say that the equation $y^5 + y + x = 0$ determines y as an **implicit function** of x.

Now, suppose we want to find the slope of the tangent line to this curve at, say, the point $(2, -1)$ (which, you should check, is a point on the curve). In the following example we find, surprisingly, that it is possible to obtain a formula for dy/dx without having to first solve the equation for y.

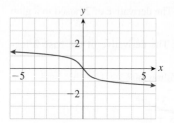

Figure 10

EXAMPLE 1 Implicit Differentiation

Find $\dfrac{dy}{dx}$, given that $y^5 + y + x = 0$.

Solution We use the chain rule and a little cleverness. Think of y as a function of x and take the derivative with respect to x of both sides of the equation:

$$y^5 + y + x = 0 \qquad \text{Original equation}$$

$$\frac{d}{dx}[y^5 + y + x] = \frac{d}{dx}[0] \qquad \text{Derivative with respect to } x \text{ of both sides}$$

$$\frac{d}{dx}[y^5] + \frac{d}{dx}[y] + \frac{d}{dx}[x] = 0 \qquad \text{Derivative rules}$$

Now we must be careful. The derivative *with respect to x* of y^5 is *not* $5y^4$. Rather, because y is a function of x, we must use the chain rule, which tells us that

$$\frac{d}{dx}[y^5] = 5y^4 \frac{dy}{dx}.$$

Thus, we get

$$5y^4 \frac{dy}{dx} + \frac{dy}{dx} + 1 = 0.$$

We want to find dy/dx, so we *solve for it*:

$$(5y^4 + 1)\frac{dy}{dx} = -1 \qquad \text{Isolate } dy/dx \text{ on one side.}$$

$$\frac{dy}{dx} = -\frac{1}{5y^4 + 1} \qquad \text{Divide both sides by } 5y^4 + 1.$$

➡ **Before we go on...** Note that we should not expect to obtain dy/dx as an explicit function of x if y was not an explicit function of x to begin with. For example, the formula we found in Example 1 for dy/dx is not a function of x because there is a y in it. However, the result is still useful because we can evaluate the derivative at any point on the graph. For instance, at the point $(2, -1)$ on the graph, we get

$$\frac{dy}{dx} = -\frac{1}{5y^4 + 1} = -\frac{1}{5(-1)^4 + 1} = -\frac{1}{6}.$$

Figure 11

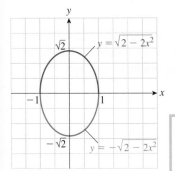

Figure 12

Thus, the slope of the tangent line to the curve $y^5 + y + x = 0$ at the point $(2, -1)$ is $-1/6$. Figure 11 shows the graph and this tangent line. ∎

This procedure we just used—differentiating an equation to find dy/dx without first solving the equation for y—is called **implicit differentiation.**

In Example 1 we were given an equation in x and y that determined y as an (implicit) function of x, even though we could not solve for y. But an equation in x and y need not always determine y as a function of x. Consider, for example, the equation

$$2x^2 + y^2 = 2.$$

Solving for y yields $y = \pm\sqrt{2 - 2x^2}$. The $\pm$ sign reminds us that for some values of x there are two corresponding values for y. We can graph this equation by superimposing the graphs of

$$y = \sqrt{2 - 2x^2} \quad \text{and} \quad y = -\sqrt{2 - 2x^2}.$$

The graph, an *ellipse*, is shown in Figure 12.

The graph of $y = \sqrt{2 - 2x^2}$ constitutes the top half of the ellipse, and the graph of $y = -\sqrt{2 - 2x^2}$ constitutes the bottom half.

EXAMPLE 2 Slope of Tangent Line

Refer to Figure 12. Find the slope of the tangent line to the ellipse $2x^2 + y^2 = 2$ at the point $(1/\sqrt{2}, 1)$.

Solution Because $(1/\sqrt{2}, 1)$ is on the top half of the ellipse in Figure 12, we *could* differentiate the function $y = \sqrt{2 - 2x^2}$, to obtain the result, but it is actually easier to apply implicit differentiation to the original equation.

$$2x^2 + y^2 = 2 \qquad \text{Original equation}$$

$$\frac{d}{dx}[2x^2 + y^2] = \frac{d}{dx}[2] \qquad \text{Derivative with respect to } x \text{ of both sides}$$

$$4x + 2y\frac{dy}{dx} = 0$$

$$2y\frac{dy}{dx} = -4x \qquad \text{Solve for } dy/dx.$$

$$\frac{dy}{dx} = -\frac{4x}{2y} = -\frac{2x}{y}$$

To find the slope at $(1/\sqrt{2}, 1)$ we now substitute for x and y:

$$\frac{dy}{dx}\bigg|_{(1/\sqrt{2}, 1)} - \frac{2/\sqrt{2}}{1} = -\sqrt{2}.$$

Thus, the slope of the tangent to the ellipse at the point $(1/\sqrt{2}, 1)$ is $-\sqrt{2} \approx -1.414$.

EXAMPLE 3 Tangent Line for an Implicit Function

Find the equation of the tangent line to the curve $\ln y = xy$ at the point where $y = 1$.

Solution First, we use implicit differentiation to find dy/dx:

$$\frac{d}{dx}[\ln y] = \frac{d}{dx}[xy] \qquad \text{Take } d/dx \text{ of both sides.}$$

$$\frac{1}{y}\frac{dy}{dx} = (1)y + x\frac{dy}{dx}. \qquad \text{Chain rule on left, product rule on right}$$

To solve for dy/dx, we bring all the terms containing dy/dx to the left-hand side and all terms not containing it to the right-hand side:

$$\frac{1}{y}\frac{dy}{dx} - x\frac{dy}{dx} = y \qquad \text{Bring the terms with } dy/dx \text{ to the left.}$$

$$\frac{dy}{dx}\left(\frac{1}{y} - x\right) = y \qquad \text{Factor out } dy/dx.$$

$$\frac{dy}{dx}\left(\frac{1 - xy}{y}\right) = y$$

$$\frac{dy}{dx} = y\left(\frac{y}{1 - xy}\right) = \frac{y^2}{1 - xy}. \qquad \text{Solve for } dy/dx.$$

The derivative gives the slope of the tangent line, so we want to evaluate the derivative at the point where $y = 1$. However, the formula for dy/dx requires values for both x and y. We get the value of x by substituting $y = 1$ in the original equation:

$$\ln y = xy$$

$$\ln(1) = x \cdot 1$$

But $\ln(1) = 0$, and so $x = 0$ for this point. Thus,

$$\frac{dy}{dx}\Bigg|_{(0,1)} = \frac{1^2}{1 - (0)(1)} = 1.$$

Therefore, the tangent line is the line through $(x, y) = (0, 1)$ with slope 1, which is

$$y = x + 1.$$

➡ **Before we go on...** Example 3 presents an instance of an implicit function in which it is simply not possible to solve for y. Try it. ∎

Sometimes, it is easiest to differentiate a complicated function of x by first taking the logarithm and then using implicit differentiation—a technique called **logarithmic differentiation**.

EXAMPLE 4 **Logarithmic Differentiation**

Find $\dfrac{d}{dx}\left[\dfrac{(x + 1)^{10}(x^2 + 1)^{11}}{(x^3 + 1)^{12}}\right]$ without using the product or quotient rules.

Solution Write

$$y = \frac{(x + 1)^{10}(x^2 + 1)^{11}}{(x^3 + 1)^{12}}$$

and then take the natural logarithm of both sides:

$$\ln y = \ln\left[\frac{(x + 1)^{10}(x^2 + 1)^{11}}{(x^3 + 1)^{12}}\right].$$

We can use properties of the logarithm to simplify the right-hand side:

$$\ln y = \ln(x + 1)^{10} + \ln(x^2 + 1)^{11} - \ln(x^3 + 1)^{12}$$

$$= 10\ln(x + 1) + 11\ln(x^2 + 1) - 12\ln(x^3 + 1).$$

Now we can find $\dfrac{dy}{dx}$ using implicit differentiation:

$$\frac{1}{y}\frac{dy}{dx} = \frac{10}{x+1} + \frac{22x}{x^2+1} - \frac{36x^2}{x^3+1} \qquad \text{Take } d/dx \text{ of both sides.}$$

$$\frac{dy}{dx} = y\left(\frac{10}{x+1} + \frac{22x}{x^2+1} - \frac{36x^2}{x^3+1}\right) \qquad \text{Solve for } dy/dx.$$

$$= \frac{(x+1)^{10}(x^2+1)^{11}}{(x^3+1)^{12}}\left(\frac{10}{x+1} + \frac{22x}{x^2+1} - \frac{36x^2}{x^3+1}\right). \qquad \text{Substitute for } y.$$

➡ **Before we go on...** Redo Example 4 using the product and quotient rules (and the chain rule) instead of logarithmic differentiation and compare the answers. Compare also the amount of work involved in both methods. ∎

APPLICATION

Productivity usually depends on both labor and capital. Suppose, for example, you are managing a surfboard manufacturing company. You can measure its productivity by counting the number of surfboards the company makes each year. As a measure of labor, you can use the number of employees, and as a measure of capital you can use its operating budget. The so-called *Cobb-Douglas* model uses a function of the form:

$$P = Kx^a y^{1-a} \qquad \text{Cobb-Douglas model for productivity}$$

where P stands for the number of surfboards made each year, x is the number of employees, and y is the operating budget. The numbers K and a are constants that depend on the particular situation studied, with a between 0 and 1.

David Samuel Robbins/CORBIS

EXAMPLE 5 **Cobb-Douglas Production Function**

The surfboard company you own has the Cobb-Douglas production function

$$P = x^{0.3}y^{0.7}$$

where P is the number of surfboards it produces per year, x is the number of employees, and y is the daily operating budget (in dollars). Assume that the production level P is constant.

a. Find $\dfrac{dy}{dx}$.

b. Evaluate this derivative at $x = 30$ and $y = 10{,}000$, and interpret the answer.

Solution

a. We are given the equation $P = x^{0.3}y^{0.7}$, in which P is constant. We find $\dfrac{dy}{dx}$ by implicit differentiation

$$0 = \frac{d}{dx}[x^{0.3}y^{0.7}] \qquad d/dx \text{ of both sides}$$

$$0 = 0.3x^{-0.7}y^{0.7} + x^{0.3}(0.7)y^{-0.3}\frac{dy}{dx} \qquad \text{Product and chain rules}$$

$$-0.7x^{0.3}y^{-0.3}\frac{dy}{dx} = 0.3x^{-0.7}y^{0.7} \qquad \text{Bring term with } dy/dx \text{ to left.}$$

$$\frac{dy}{dx} = -\frac{0.3x^{-0.7}y^{0.7}}{0.7x^{0.3}y^{-0.3}} \qquad \text{Solve for } dy/dx.$$

$$= -\frac{3y}{7x}. \qquad \text{Simplify.}$$

b. Evaluating this derivative at $x = 30$ and $y = 10,000$ gives

$$\left.\frac{dy}{dx}\right|_{x=30,\ y=10,000} = -\frac{3(10,000)}{7(30)} \approx -143.$$

To interpret this result, first look at the units of the derivative: We recall that the units of dy/dx are units of y per unit of x. Because y is the daily budget, its units are dollars; because x is the number of employees, its units are employees. Thus,

$$\left.\frac{dy}{dx}\right|_{x=30,\ y=10,000} \approx -\$143 \text{ per employee.}$$

Next, recall that dy/dx measures the rate of change of y as x changes. Because the answer is negative, the daily budget to maintain production at the fixed level is decreasing by approximately \$143 per additional employee at an employment level of 30 employees and a daily operating budget of \$10,000. In other words, increasing the workforce by one worker will result in a savings of approximately \$143 per day. Roughly speaking, *a new employee is worth \$143 per day* at the current levels of employment and production.

11.6 EXERCISES

▼ more advanced   ◆ challenging
🔢 indicates exercises that should be solved using technology

In Exercises 1–10, find dy/dx, using implicit differentiation. In each case, compare your answer with the result obtained by first solving for y as a function of x and then taking the derivative. HINT [See Example 1.]

1. $2x + 3y = 7$

2. $4x - 5y = 9$

3. $x^2 - 2y = 6$

4. $3y + x^2 = 5$

5. $2x + 3y = xy$

6. $x - y = xy$

7. $e^x y = 1$

8. $e^x y - y = 2$

9. $y \ln x + y = 2$

10. $\dfrac{\ln x}{y} = 2 - x$

In Exercises 11–30, find the indicated derivative using implicit differentiation. HINT [See Example 1.]

11. $x^2 + y^2 = 5;\ \dfrac{dy}{dx}$

12. $2x^2 - y^2 = 4;\ \dfrac{dy}{dx}$

13. $x^2 y - y^2 = 4;\ \dfrac{dy}{dx}$

14. $xy^2 - y = x;\ \dfrac{dy}{dx}$

15. $3xy - \dfrac{y}{3} = \dfrac{2}{x};\ \dfrac{dy}{dx}$

16. $\dfrac{xy}{2} - y^2 = 3;\ \dfrac{dy}{dx}$

17. $x^2 - 3y^2 = 8;\ \dfrac{dx}{dy}$

18. $(xy)^2 + y^2 = 8;\ \dfrac{dx}{dy}$

19. $p^2 - pq = 5p^2 q^2;\ \dfrac{dp}{dq}$

20. $q^2 - pq = 5p^2 q^2;\ \dfrac{dp}{dq}$

21. $xe^y - ye^x = 1;\ \dfrac{dy}{dx}$

22. $x^2 e^y - y^2 = e^x;\ \dfrac{dy}{dx}$

23. ▼ $e^{st} = s^2;\ \dfrac{ds}{dt}$

24. ▼ $e^{s^2 t} - st = 1;\ \dfrac{ds}{dt}$

25. ▼ $\dfrac{e^x}{y^2} = 1 + e^y;\ \dfrac{dy}{dx}$

26. ▼ $\dfrac{x}{e^y} + xy = 9y;\ \dfrac{dy}{dx}$

27. ▼ $\ln(y^2 - y) + x = y;\ \dfrac{dy}{dx}$

28. ▼ $\ln(xy) - x \ln y = y;\ \dfrac{dy}{dx}$

29. ▼ $\ln(xy + y^2) = e^y;\ \dfrac{dy}{dx}$

30. ▼ $\ln(1 + e^{xy}) = y;\ \dfrac{dy}{dx}$

In Exercises 31–42, use implicit differentiation to find (a) the slope of the tangent line, and (b) the equation of the tangent line at the indicated point on the graph. (Round answers to four decimal places as needed.) If only the x-coordinate is given, you must also find the y-coordinate.) HINT [See Examples 2, 3.]

31. $4x^2 + 2y^2 = 12, (1, -2)$ **32.** $3x^2 - y^2 = 11, (-2, 1)$

33. $2x^2 - y^2 = xy, (-1, 2)$ **34.** $2x^2 + xy = 3y^2, (-1, -1)$

35. $x^2y - y^2 + x = 1, (1, 0)$

36. $(xy)^2 + xy - x = 8, (-8, 0)$

37. $xy - 2000 = y, x = 2$

38. $x^2 - 10xy = 200, x = 10$

39. ▼ $\ln(x + y) - x = 3x^2, x = 0$

40. ▼ $\ln(x - y) + 1 = 3x^2, x = 0$

41. ▼ $e^{xy} - x = 4x, x = 3$

42. ▼ $e^{-xy} + 2x = 1, x = -1$

In Exercises 43–52, use logarithmic differentiation to find dy/dx. Do not simplify the result. HINT [See Example 4.]

43. $y = \dfrac{2x + 1}{4x - 2}$

44. $y = (3x + 2)(8x - 5)$

45. $y = \dfrac{(3x + 1)^2}{4x(2x - 1)^3}$

46. $y = \dfrac{x^2(3x + 1)^2}{(2x - 1)^3}$

47. $y = (8x - 1)^{1/3}(x - 1)$

48. $y = \dfrac{(3x + 2)^{2/3}}{3x - 1}$

49. $y = (x^3 + x)\sqrt{x^3 + 2}$

50. $y = \sqrt{\dfrac{x - 1}{x^2 + 2}}$

51. ▼ $y = x^x$

52. ▼ $y = x^{-x}$

APPLICATIONS

53. Productivity The number of CDs per hour that Snappy Hardware can manufacture at its plant is given by

$$P = x^{0.6}y^{0.4}$$

where x is the number of workers at the plant and y is the monthly budget (in dollars). Assume P is constant, and compute $\dfrac{dy}{dx}$ when $x = 100$ and $y = 200,000$. Interpret the result. HINT [See Example 5.]

54. Productivity The number of cell-phone accessory kits (neon lights, matching covers, and earpods) per day that USA Cellular Makeover Inc. can manufacture at its plant in Cambodia is given by

$$P = x^{0.5}y^{0.5}$$

where x is the number of workers at the plant and y is the monthly budget (in dollars). Assume P is constant, and compute $\dfrac{dy}{dx}$ when $x = 200$ and $y = 100,000$. Interpret the result. HINT [See Example 5.]

55. Demand The demand equation for soccer tournament T-shirts is

$$xy - 2,000 = y$$

where y is the number of T-shirts the Enormous State University soccer team can sell at a price of $x per shirt. Find $\dfrac{dy}{dx}\Big|_{x=5}$, and interpret the result.

56. Cost Equations The cost y (in cents) of producing x gallons of Ectoplasm hair gel is given by the cost equation

$$y^2 - 10xy = 200.$$

Evaluate $\dfrac{dy}{dx}$ at $x = 1$ and interpret the result.

57. Housing Costs[57] The cost C (in dollars) of building a house is related to the number k of carpenters used and the number e of electricians used by the formula

$$C = 15,000 + 50k^2 + 60e^2.$$

If the cost of the house is fixed at $200,000, find $\dfrac{dk}{de}\Big|_{e=15}$ and interpret your result.

58. Employment An employment research company estimates that the value of a recent MBA graduate to an accounting company is

$$V = 3e^2 + 5g^3$$

where V is the value of the graduate, e is the number of years of prior business experience, and g is the graduate school grade-point average. If V is fixed at 200, find $\dfrac{de}{dg}$ when $g = 3.0$ and interpret the result.

59. ▼ **Grades**[58] A productivity formula for a student's performance on a difficult English examination is

$$g = 4tx - 0.2t^2 - 10x^2 \quad (t < 30)$$

where g is the score the student can expect to obtain, t is the number of hours of study for the examination, and x is the student's grade-point average.

a. For how long should a student with a 3.0 grade-point average study in order to score 80 on the examination?

b. Find $\dfrac{dt}{dx}$ for a student who earns a score of 80, evaluate it when $x = 3.0$, and interpret the result.

60. ▼ **Grades** Repeat the preceding exercise using the following productivity formula for a basket-weaving examination:

$$g = 10tx - 0.2t^2 - 10x^2 \quad (t < 10).$$

Comment on the result.

---

[57] Based on an Exercise in *Introduction to Mathematical Economics* by A. L. Ostrosky Jr., and J. V. Koch (Waveland Press, Springfield, Illinois, 1979).

[58] Ibid.

Exercises 61 and 62 are based on the following demand function for money (taken from a question on the GRE Economics Test):

$$M_d = (2) \times (y)^{0.6} \times (r)^{-0.3} \times (p)$$

where

  M_d = *demand for nominal money balances (money stock)*

  y = *real income*

  r = *an index of interest rates*

  p = *an index of prices.*

61. ◆ *Money Stock* If real income grows while the money stock and the price level remain constant, the interest rate must change at what rate? (First find dr/dy, then dr/dt; your answers will be expressed in terms of r, y, and $\dfrac{dy}{dt}$.)

62. ◆ *Money Stock* If real income grows while the money stock and the interest rate remain constant, the price level must change at what rate?

COMMUNICATION AND REASONING EXERCISES

63. Fill in the missing terms: The equation $x = y^3 + y - 3$ specifies ___ as a function of ___, and ___ as an implicit function of ___.

64. Fill in the missing terms: When $x \neq 0$ in the equation $xy = x^3 + 4$, it is possible to specify ___ as a function of ___. However, ___ is only an implicit function of ___.

65. ▼ Use logarithmic differentiation to give another proof of the product rule.

66. ▼ Use logarithmic differentiation to give a proof of the quotient rule.

67. ▼ If y is given explicitly as a function of x by an equation $y = f(x)$, compare finding dy/dx by implicit differentiation to finding it explicitly in the usual way.

68. ▼ Explain why one should not expect dy/dx to be a function of x if y is not a function of x.

69. ◆ If y is a function of x and $dy/dx \neq 0$ at some point, regard x as an implicit function of y and use implicit differentiation to obtain the equation

$$\frac{dx}{dy} = \frac{1}{dy/dx}.$$

70. ◆ If you are given an equation in x and y such that dy/dx is a function of x only, what can you say about the graph of the equation?

KEY CONCEPTS

Web Site www.FiniteandCalc.org
Go to the student Web site at
www.FiniteandCalc.org to find a
comprehensive and interactive
Web-based summary of Chapter 11.

11.1 Derivatives of Powers, Sums, and Constant Multiples

Power Rule: If n is any constant and
$f(x) = x^n$, then $f'(x) = nx^{n-1}$.
p. 782

Using the power rule for negative and
fractional exponents p. 783

Sums, differences, and constant multiples
p. 785

Combining the rules p. 786

$\frac{d}{dx}(cx) = c$, $\frac{d}{dx}(c) = 0$ p. 788

$f(x) = x^{1/3}$ and $g(x) = x^{2/3}$ are not
differentiable at $x = 0$. p. 788

Derivative of $f(x) = |x|$: $\frac{d}{dx}|x| = \frac{|x|}{x}$
p. 789

L'Hospital's Rule p. 791

11.2 A First Application: Marginal Analysis

Marginal cost function $C'(x)$ p. 798

Marginal revenue and profit functions
$R'(x)$ and $P'(x)$ p. 800

What it means when the marginal profit
is zero p. 801

Marginal product p. 802

Average cost of the first x items:

$\bar{C}(x) = \frac{C(x)}{x}$ p. 803

11.3 The Product and Quotient Rules

Product rule: $\frac{d}{dx}[f(x)g(x)] =$

$f'(x)g(x) + f(x)g'(x)$ p. 809

Quotient rule: $\frac{d}{dx}\left[\frac{f(x)}{g(x)}\right] =$

$\frac{f'(x)g(x) - f(x)g'(x)}{[g(x)]^2}$ p. 810

Using the product rule p. 812
Using the quotient rule p. 813
Calculation thought experiment p. 814
Application to revenue and average
cost p. 815

11.4 The Chain Rule

Chain rule: $\frac{d}{dx}[f(u)] = f'(u)\frac{du}{dx}$ p. 821

Generalized power rule:

$\frac{d}{dx}[u^n] = nu^{n-1}\frac{du}{dx}$ p. 822

Using the chain rule p. 822
Application to marginal product p. 825
Chain rule in differential notation:

$\frac{dy}{dx} = \frac{dy}{du}\frac{du}{dx}$ p. 826

Manipulating derivatives in differential
notation p. 828

11.5 Derivatives of Logarithmic and Exponential Functions

Derivative of the natural logarithm:

$\frac{d}{dx}[\ln x] = \frac{1}{x}$ p. 833

Derivative of logarithm with base b:

$\frac{d}{dx}[\log_b x] = \frac{1}{x \ln b}$ p. 834

Derivatives of logarithms of functions:

$\frac{d}{dx}[\ln u] = \frac{1}{u}\frac{du}{dx}$

$\frac{d}{dx}[\log_b u] = \frac{1}{u \ln b}\frac{du}{dx}$ p. 835

Derivatives of logarithms of absolute
values:

$\frac{d}{dx}[\ln |x|] = \frac{1}{x}$ $\frac{d}{dx}[\ln |u|] = \frac{1}{u}\frac{du}{dx}$

$\frac{d}{dx}[\log_b |x|] = \frac{1}{x \ln b}$

$\frac{d}{dx}[\log_b |u|] = \frac{1}{u \ln b}\frac{du}{dx}$ p. 838

Derivative of e^x: $\frac{d}{dx}[e^x] = e^x$ p. 839

Derivative of b^x: $\frac{d}{dx}[b^x] = b^x \ln b$ p. 839

Derivatives of exponential functions
p. 840
Application to epidemics p. 840
Application to sales growth (logistic
function) p. 841

11.6 Implicit Differentiation

Implicit function of x p. 848
Implicit differentiation p. 848
Using implicit differentiation p. 848
Finding a tangent line p. 849
Logarithmic differentiation p. 850

REVIEW EXERCISES

In Exercises 1–20 find the derivative of the given function.

1. $f(x) = 10x^5 + \frac{1}{2}x^4 - x + 2$

2. $f(x) = \frac{10}{x^5} + \frac{1}{2x^4} - \frac{1}{x} + 2$

3. $f(x) = 3x^3 + 3\sqrt[3]{x}$

4. $f(x) = \frac{2}{x^{2.1}} - \frac{x^{0.1}}{2}$

5. $f(x) = x + \frac{1}{x^2}$

6. $f(x) = 2x - \frac{1}{x}$

7. $f(x) = \frac{4}{3x} - \frac{2}{x^{0.1}} + \frac{x^{1.1}}{3.2} - 4$

8. $f(x) = \frac{4}{x} + \frac{x}{4} - |x|$

9. $f(x) = e^x(x^2 - 1)$

10. $f(x) = \frac{x^2 + 1}{x^2 - 1}$

11. $f(x) = (x^2 - 1)^{10}$

12. $f(x) = \frac{1}{(x^2 - 1)^{10}}$

13. $f(x) = e^x(x^2 + 1)^{10}$

14. $f(x) = \left[\frac{x - 1}{3x + 1}\right]^3$

15. $f(x) = \frac{3^x}{x - 1}$

16. $f(x) = 4^{-x}(x + 1)$

17. $f(x) = e^{x^2 - 1}$

18. $f(x) = (x^2 + 1)e^{x^2 - 1}$

19. $f(x) = \ln(x^2 - 1)$

20. $f(x) = \frac{\ln(x^2 - 1)}{x^2 - 1}$

In Exercises 21–28 find all values of x (if any) where the tangent line to the graph of the given equation is horizontal.

21. $y = -3x^2 + 7x - 1$ **22.** $y = 5x^2 - 2x + 1$

23. $y = \dfrac{x}{2} + \dfrac{2}{x}$ **24.** $y = \dfrac{x^2}{2} - \dfrac{8}{x^2}$

25. $y = x - e^{2x-1}$ **26.** $y = e^{x^2}$

27. $y = \dfrac{x}{x+1}$ **28.** $y = \sqrt{x}(x-1)$

In Exercises 29–34, find dy/dx for the given equation.

29. $x^2 - y^2 = x$ **30.** $2xy + y^2 = y$

31. $e^{xy} + xy = 1$ **32.** $\ln\left(\dfrac{y}{x}\right) = y$

33. $y = \dfrac{(2x-1)^4(3x+4)}{(x+1)(3x-1)^3}$ **34.** $y = x^{x-1}3^x$

In Exercises 35–40 find the equation of the tangent line to the graph of the given equation at the specified point.

35. $y = (x^2 - 3x)^{-2}; \ x = 1$ **36.** $y = (2x^2 - 3)^{-3}; \ x = -1$

37. $y = x^2 e^{-x}; \ x = -1$ **38.** $y = \dfrac{x}{1+e^x}; \ x = 0$

39. $xy - y^2 = x^2 - 3; \ (-1, 1)$ **40.** $\ln(xy) + y^2 = 1; \ (-1, -1)$

APPLICATIONS

41. *Sales* OHaganBooks.com fits the cubic curve

$$w(t) = -3.7t^3 + 74.6t^2 + 135.5t + 6{,}300$$

to its weekly sales figures (see Chapter 10 Review Exercise 47), as shown in the following graph:

Week

a. According to the cubic model, what was the rate of increase of sales at the beginning of the second week ($t = 1$)? (Round your answer to the nearest unit.)
b. If we extrapolate the model, what would be the rate of increase of weekly sales at the beginning of the 8th week ($t = 7$)?
c. Graph the function w for $0 \le t \le 20$. Would it be realistic to use the function to predict sales through week 20? Why?

d. By examining the graph, say why the choice of a quadratic model would result in radically different long-term predictions of sales.

42. *Rising Sea Level* Marjory Duffin fit the cubic curve

$$L(t) = -0.0001t^3 + 0.02t^2 + 2.2t \text{ mm}$$

to the New York sea level figures she had seen after purchasing a beachfront condominium in New York (see Chapter 10 Review Exercise 48; t is time in years since 1900). The curve and data are shown in the following graph:

Sea Level Change since 1900

a. According to the cubic model, what was the rate at which the sea level was rising in 2000 ($t = 100$)? (Round your answer to two significant digits.)
b. If we extrapolate the model, what would be the rate at which the sea level is rising in 2025 ($t = 125$)?
c. Graph the function L for $0 \le t \le 200$. Why is it not realistic to use the function to predict the sea level through 2100?
d. James Stewart, a summer intern at Duffin House Publishers, differs. As he puts it, "The cubic curve came from doing regression on the actual data, and thus reflects the actual trend of the data. We can't argue against reality!" Comment on this assertion.

43. *Cost* As OHaganBooks.com's sales increase, so do its costs. If we take into account volume discounts from suppliers and shippers, the weekly cost of selling x books is

$$C(x) = -0.00002x^2 + 3.2x + 5{,}400 \text{ dollars}$$

a. What is the marginal cost at a sales level of 8,000 books per week?
b. What is the average cost per book at a sales level of 8,000 books per week?
c. What is the marginal average cost ($d\bar{C}/dx$) at a sales level of 8,000 books per week?
d. Interpret the results of parts (a)–(c).

44. *Cost* OHaganBooks.com has been experiencing a run of bad luck with its summer college intern program in association with Party Central University (begun as a result of a suggestion by Marjory Duffin over dinner one evening). The frequent errors in filling orders, charges from movie download sites and dating sites, and beverages spilled on computer equipment have resulted in an estimated weekly cost to the company of

$$C(x) = 25x^2 - 5.2x + 4{,}000 \text{ dollars}$$

where x is the number of college interns employed.

a. What is the marginal cost at a level of 10 interns?
b. What is the average cost per intern at a level of 10 interns?
c. What is the marginal average cost at a level of 10 interns?
d. Interpret the results of parts (a)–(c).

45. **Revenue** At the moment, OHaganBooks.com is selling 1,000 books per week and its sales are rising at a rate of 200 books per week. Also, it is now selling all its books for $20 each, but its price is dropping at a rate of $1 per week.

a. At what rate is OHaganBooks.com's weekly revenue rising or falling?
b. John O'Hagan would like to see the company's weekly revenue increase at a rate of $5,000 per week. At what rate would sales have to have been increasing to accomplish that goal, assuming all the other information is as given above?

46. **Revenue** Due to ongoing problems with its large college intern program, OHaganBooks.com has decided to offer to transfer its interns to its competitor JungleBooks.com (whose headquarters happens to be across the road) for a small fee. At the moment, it is transferring 5 students per week, and this number is rising at a rate of 4 students per week. Also, it is now charging JungleBooks $400 per intern, but this amount is decreasing at a rate of $20 per week.

a. At what rate is OHaganBooks.com's weekly revenue from this transaction rising or falling?
b. Flush with success of the transfer program, John O'Hagan would like to see the company's resulting revenue increase at a rate of $3,900 per week. At what rate would the transfer of interns have to increase to accomplish that goal, assuming all the other information is as given above?

47. **Percentage Rate of Change of Revenue** The percentage rate of change of a quantity Q is Q'/Q. Why is the percentage rate of change of revenue always equal to the sum of the percentage rates of change of unit price and weekly sales?

48. **P/E Ratios** At the beginning of last week, OHaganBooks.com stock was selling for $100 per share, rising at a rate of $50 per year. Its earnings amounted to $1 per share, rising at a rate of $0.10 per year. At what rate was its price-to-earnings (P/E) ratio, the ratio of its stock price to its earnings per share, rising or falling?

49. **P/E Ratios** Refer to Exercise 48. Curt Hinrichs, who recently invested in OHaganBooks.com stock, would have liked to see the P/E ratio increase at a rate of 100 points per year. How fast would the stock have to have been rising, assuming all the other information is as given in Exercise 48?

50. **Percentage Rate of Change of P/E Ratios** The percentage rate of change of a quantity Q is Q'/Q. Why is the percentage rate of change of P/E always equal to the percentage rate of change of unit price minus the percentage rate of change of earnings?

51. **Sales** OHaganBooks.com decided that the cubic curve in Exercise 41 was not suitable for extrapolation, so instead it tried

$$s(t) = 6{,}000 + \frac{4{,}500}{1 + e^{-0.55(t-4.8)}}$$

as shown in the following graph:

a. Compute $s'(t)$ and use the answer to estimate the rate of increase of weekly sales at the beginning of the 7th week ($t = 6$). (Round your answer to the nearest unit.)
b. Compute $\lim_{t \to +\infty} s'(t)$ and interpret the answer.

52. **Rising Sea Level** Upon some reflection, Marjory Duffin decided that the curve in Exercise 42 was not suitable for extrapolation, so instead she tried

$$L(t) = \frac{418}{1 + 17.2e^{-0.041t}} \qquad (0 \le t \le 125)$$

(t is time in years since 1900) as shown in the following graph:

a. Compute $L'(t)$ and use the answer to estimate the rate at which the sea level was rising in 2000 ($t = 100$). (Round your answer to two decimal places.)
b. Compute $\lim_{t \to +\infty} L'(t)$ and interpret the answer.

53. **Web Site Activity** The number of "hits" on OHaganBooks.com's Web site was 1,000 per day at the beginning of the year, and was growing at a rate of 5% per week. If this growth rate continued for the whole year (52 weeks), find the rate of increase (in hits per day per week) at the end of the year.

54. *Web Site Activity* The number of "hits" on ShadyDownload
.net during the summer intern program at OHaganBooks.com
was 100 per day at the beginning of the intern program, and
was growing at a rate of 15% per day. If this growth rate continued for the duration of the whole summer intern program
(85 days), find the rate of increase (in hits per day per day) at
the end of the program.

55. *Demand and Revenue* The price *p* that OHaganBooks.com
charges for its latest leather-bound gift edition of *The Complete Harry Potter* is related to the demand *q* in weekly sales
by the equation

$$250pq + q^2 = 13{,}500{,}000$$

Suppose the price is set at $50, which would make the demand
1,000 copies per week.

a. Using implicit differentiation, compute the rate of change
of demand with respect to price, and interpret the result.
(Round the answer to two decimal places.)

b. Use the result of part (a) to compute the rate of change of
revenue with respect to price. Should the price be raised
or lowered to increase revenue?

56. *Demand and Revenue* The price *p* that OHaganBooks.com
charges for its latest leather-bound gift edition of *The Lord of
the Rings* is related to the demand *q* in weekly sales by the
equation

$$100pq + q^2 = 5{,}000{,}000.$$

Suppose the price is set at $40, which would make the demand
1,000 copies per week.

a. Using implicit differentiation, compute the rate of change
of demand with respect to price, and interpret the result.
(Round the answer to two decimal places.)

b. Use the result of part (a) to compute the rate of change of
revenue with respect to price. Should the price be raised
or lowered to increase revenue?

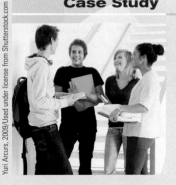

Case Study   Projecting Market Growth

You are on the board of directors at Fullcourt Academic Press, a major textbook supplier
to private schools, and TJM, the sales director of the high school division, has just burst
into your office with data showing the number of private high school graduates each
year over the past 14 years (Figure 13).[59]

Private high school graduates (thousands)

Figure 13

TJM is pleased that the figures appear to support a basic premise of his recent proposal
for an expansion strategy: The number of high school seniors in private schools in the
United States will be growing at a rate of at least 5,600 per year through the year 2015.
TJM points out that the rate of increase predicted by the regression line (see Figure 14)
based on the data since 1994 is around 5.6 thousand students per year, so it would not be
overly optimistic to assume that the trend will continue—at least for the next 7 years.

---

[59] Source: National Center for Educational Statistics (http://nces.ed.gov/).

Figure 14

Although you are tempted to support TJM's proposal at the next board meeting, you would like to estimate first whether the 5,600 figure is a realistic expectation, especially because the graph suggests that the number of graduates began to "level off" (in the language of calculus, the *derivative appears to be decreasing*) toward the end of the period. Moreover, you recall reading somewhere that the numbers of students in the lower grades have also begun to level off, so it is safe to predict that the slowing of growth in the senior class will continue over the next few years. You really need precise data about numbers in the lower grades in order to make a meaningful prediction, but TJM's report is scheduled to be presented tomorrow and you would like a quick and easy way of "extending the curve to the right" by then.

It would certainly be helpful if you had a mathematical model of the data in Figure 13 that you could use to project the current trend. But what kind of model should you use? A linear model would be no good because it would not show any change in the derivative (the derivative of a linear function is constant). In addition, best-fit polynomial and exponential functions do not accurately reflect the leveling off, as you realize after trying to fit a few of them (Figure 15).

Figure 15

You then recall that a logistic curve can model the leveling-off property you desire, and so you try fitting a curve of the form

$$y = \frac{N}{1 + Ab^{-t}}.$$

Figure 16 shows the best-fit logistic curve, which eventually levels off at around $N = 390$.

Figure 16

* NOTE There is another, more mathematical, reason for not using logistic regression to predict long-term leveling off: The regression value of the long-term level N is extremely sensitive to the values of the other coefficients. As a result, there can be good fits to the same set of data with a wide variety of values of N.

Web Site

www.FiniteandCalc.org
Follow the path

  Chapter 1

  → New Functions from Old:
    Scaled and Shifted
    Functions

to find a detailed treatment of scaled and shifted functions.

You are slightly troubled by the shape of the regression curve: It doesn't seem to "follow the s-shape" of the data very convincingly. Moreover, the curve doesn't appear to fit the data significantly more snugly than the quadratic or cubic models.* To reassure yourself, you decide to look for another kind of s-shaped model as a backup.

After flipping through a calculus book, you stumble across a function that is slightly more general than the one you have:

$$y = c + \frac{N}{1 + Ab^{-t}} \qquad \text{Shifted Logistic Curve}$$

The added term c has the effect of shifting the graph up c units. Turning once again to your calculus book (see the discussion of logistic regression in Section 9.4), you see that a best-fit curve is one that minimizes the sum-of-squares error. Here is an Excel spreadsheet showing the errors for $c = 200, N = 100, A = 3$, and $b = 1.2$.

	A	B	C	D	E	F	G	H
1	t (Year)	y (Observed)	y (Predicted)	residual^2	N	A	b	c
2	0	243	225	324	100	3	1.2	200
3	1	246	228.5714286	303.755102				
4	2	245	232.4324324	157.9437546	SSE:	11120.4856		
5	3	254	236.5482234	304.5645082				
6	4	265	240.8703879	582.2381806				
7	5	273	245.3384642	765.1605612				
8	6	279	249.8829265	847.8039683				
9	7	279	254.4293239	603.7181244				
10	8	285	258.9030791	681.0492791				
11	9	296	263.2343045	1073.590803				
12	10	299	267.3619884	1000.963778				
13	11	304	271.2370477	1073.411042				
14	12	309	274.8239786	1168.000439				
15	13	311	278.1011037	1082.337379				
16	14	315	281.0596311	1151.94864				

The formula for the function in cell C2 is

=$H$2+$E$2/(1+$F$2*$G$2^(-A2)) $c + \dfrac{N}{1 + Ab^{-t}}$

Figure 17

Figure 17 shows how to set up Solver to find the best values for N, A, b, and c for the setup used in this spreadsheet. The Target Cell, $F$4, contains the value of SSE, which is to be minimized. The Changing Cells are the cells containing the values of the constants N, A, b, and c that we want to change. That's it.

Now click "Solve." After thinking about it for a few seconds, Excel gives the optimal values of N, A, b, and c in cells E2–H2, and the minimum value of SSE in cell F4.* You find

$$N = 108.248027, \quad A = 3.85006915, \quad b = 1.27688839, \quad c = 218.351709$$

with SSE $\approx$ 101.2, which is a better fit than the unshifted logistic regression curve (SSE $\approx$ 129.8). Figure 18 shows that not only does this choice of model and constants give a good fit, but that the curve seems to follow the "s-shape" more convincingly than the unshifted logistic curve.

✳ **NOTE** Depending on the settings in Solver, you may need to run the utility twice in succession to reach the minimum value of SSE.

Figure 18

The derivative, dy/dt, will represent the rate of increase of high school graduates, which is exactly what you wish to estimate:

$$y = c + \frac{N}{1 + Ab^{-t}}$$

$$\frac{dy}{dt} = -\frac{N}{(1 + Ab^{-t})^2} \frac{d}{dt}\left[1 + Ab^{-t}\right]$$

$$= \frac{NAb^{-t} \ln b}{(1 + Ab^{-t})^2}$$

The rate of increase in the number of high school students in 2015 ($t = 21$) is given by

$$\frac{dy}{dt}\bigg|_{t=21} = \frac{(108.248027)(3.85006915)1.27688839^{-21} \ln 1.27688839}{(1 + (3.85006915)1.27688839^{-21})^2}$$

$$\approx 0.5745 \text{ thousand students per year}$$

or 570 students per year—far less than the optimistic estimate of 5,600 in the proposal!

You now conclude that TJM's prediction is suspect and that further research will have to be done before the board can support the proposal.

Q: *How accurately does the model predict the number of high school graduates?*

A: Using a regression curve-fitting model to make long-term predictions is always risky. A more accurate model would have to take into account such factors as the birth rate and current school populations at all levels.

Q: *Which values of the constants should I use as starting values when using Excel to find the best-fit curve?*

A: If the starting values of the constants are far from the optimal values, Solver may find a nonoptimal solution. Thus, you need to obtain some rough initial estimate of the constants by examining the graph. Figure 19 shows some important features of the curve that you can use to obtain estimates of N, A, b, and c by inspecting the graph.

From the graph, c is the lower asymptote (in a graph showing only the right-hand portion of the curve in Figure 19 we need to mentally extend the curve to the left), and N is the vertical distance between the upper and lower asymptotes. Once we have estimates for c and N, we can estimate A from the y-intercept m using

$$A = 1 - \frac{N}{m - c}. \qquad m = y\text{-intercept}$$

As in the discussion of logistic curves in Chapter 9, b is the base of exponential growth for values of t close to zero.

Figure 19

EXERCISES

1. In 1993 there were 247,000 private high school graduates. What does the regression model "predict" for 1993? (Round answer to the nearest 1,000.) What is the residual ($y_{\text{observed}} - y_{\text{predicted}}$)?

2. What is the long-term prediction of the model? (Round answer to the nearest 1,000.)

3. Find $\lim\limits_{t \to \infty} \dfrac{dy}{dt}$ and interpret the result.

4. ▥ You receive a memo to the effect that the 2007 and 2008 figures are not accurate. Use Excel Solver to re-estimate the best-fit constants N, a, b, and c in the absence of this data and obtain new estimates for the 2007 and 2008 data. What does the new model predict the rate of change in the number of high school seniors will be in 2015?

5. ■ *Another Model* Using the original data, find the best-fit shifted *predator-prey satiation curve* of the form

$$f(t) = y = c + b \frac{a(t - m)}{1 + a|t - m|}. \quad (a, b, c, m \text{ constant})$$

Its graph is shown below:

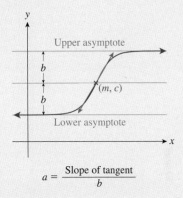

$$a = \frac{\text{Slope of tangent}}{b}$$

(Start with the following values: $a = 0.05$, $b = 160$, $c = 250$, $m = 5$. You might have to run Solver twice in succession to minimize SSE.) Graph the data together with the model. What is SSE? Is the model as accurate a fit as the model used in the text? What does this model predict will be the growth rate of the number of high school graduates in 2015? Comment on the answer. (Round the coefficients in the model and all answers to four decimal places.)

6. ■ *Demand for Freon* The demand for chlorofluorocarbon-12 (CFC-12)—the ozone-depleting refrigerant commonly known as Freon[60]—has been declining significantly in response to regulation and concern about the ozone layer. The chart below shows the projected demand for CFC-12 for the period 1994–2005.[61]

a. Use Excel Solver to obtain the best-fit equation of the form

$$f(t) = c + b \frac{a(t - m)}{1 + a|t - m|}$$

where $t =$ years since 1990. Use your function to estimate the total demand for CFC-12 from the start of the year 2000 to the start of 2010. (Start with the following values: $a = 1$, $b = -25$, $c = 35$, and $m = 10$, and round your answers to four decimal places.)

b. According to your model, how fast is the demand for Freon declining in 2000?

---

[60] The name given to it by Du Pont.

[61] Source: The Automobile Consulting Group (*New York Times*, December 26, 1993, p. F23). The exact figures were not given, and the chart is a reasonable facsimile of the chart that appeared in *New York Times*.

12

Further Applications of the Derivative

Case Study Production Lot Size Management

Your publishing company is planning the production of its latest best seller, which it predicts will sell 100,000 copies each month over the coming year. The book will be printed in several batches of the same number, evenly spaced throughout the year. Each print run has a setup cost of $5,000, a single book costs $1 to produce, and monthly storage costs for books awaiting shipment average 1¢ per book. **To meet the anticipated demand at minimum total cost to your company, how many printing runs should you plan?**

SUNNYphotography.com/Alamy

Web Site

At the Web site you will find:

- Section by section tutorials, including game tutorials with randomized quizzes

- A detailed chapter summary

- A true/false quiz

- Additional review exercises

- Graphers, Excel tutorials, and other resources

- The following extra topic:

    Linear Approximation and Error Estimation

Introduction

In this chapter we begin to see the power of calculus as an optimization tool. In Chapter 9 we saw how to price an item in order to get the largest revenue when the demand function is linear. Using calculus, we can handle nonlinear functions, which are much more general. In Section 12.1 we show how calculus can be used to solve the problem of finding the values of a variable that lead to a maximum or minimum value of a given function. In Section 12.2 we show how this helps us in various real-world applications.

Another theme in this chapter is that calculus can help us to draw and understand the graph of a function. By the time you have completed the material in Section 12.1, you will be able to locate and sketch some of the important features of a graph, such as where it rises and where it falls. In Section 12.3 we look at the *second derivative,* the derivative of the derivative function, and what it tells us about how the graph *curves.* In Section 12.4 we put a number of ideas together that help to explain what you see in a graph (drawn, for example, using graphing technology) and to locate its most important points.

We also include sections on related rates and elasticity of demand. The first of these (Section 12.5) examines further the concept of the derivative as a rate of change. The second (Section 12.6) returns to the problem of optimizing revenue based on the demand equation, looking at it in a new way that leads to an important idea in economics—elasticity.

algebra Review

For this chapter, you should be familiar with the algebra reviewed in **Chapter 0**, **sections 5 and 6**.

12.1 Maxima and Minima

Figure 1

Figure 1 shows the graph of a function f whose domain is the closed interval $[a, b]$. A mathematician sees lots of interesting things going on here. There are hills and valleys, and even a small chasm (called a *cusp*) near the center. For many purposes, the important features of this curve are the highs and lows. Suppose, for example, you know that the price of the stock of a certain company will follow this graph during the course of a week. Although you would certainly make a handsome profit if you bought at time a and sold at time b, your best strategy would be to follow the old adage to "buy low and sell high," buying at all the lows and selling at all the highs.

Figure 2 shows the graph once again with the highs and lows marked. Mathematicians have names for these points: the highs (at the x-values p, r, and b) are referred to as **relative maxima**, and the lows (at the x-values a, q, and s) are referred to as **relative minima**. Collectively, these highs and lows are referred to as **relative extrema**. (A point of language: The singular forms of the plurals *minima, maxima,* and *extrema* are *minimum, maximum,* and *extremum.*)

Figure 2

Why do we refer to these points as relative extrema? Take a look at the point corresponding to $x = r$. It is the highest point of the graph *compared to other points nearby.*

Figure 3

If you were an extremely nearsighted mountaineer standing at the point where $x = r$, you would *think* that you were at the highest point of the graph, not being able to see the distant peaks at $x = p$ and $x = b$.

Let's translate into mathematical terms. We are talking about the heights of various points on the curve. The height of the curve at $x = r$ is $f(r)$, so we are saying that $f(r)$ is greater than or equal to $f(x)$ for every x near r. In other words, $f(r)$ *is the greatest value that $f(x)$ has for all choices of x between $r - h$ and $r + h$* for some (possibly small) h. (See Figure 3.)

We can phrase the formal definition as follows.

Relative Extrema

f has a **relative maximum** at $x = r$ if there is some interval $(r - h, r + h)$ (even a very small one) for which $f(r) \geq f(x)$ for all x in $(r - h, r + h)$ for which $f(x)$ is defined.

f has a **relative minimum** at $x = r$ if there is some interval $(r - h, r + h)$ (even a very small one) for which $f(r) \leq f(x)$ for all x in $(r - h, r + h)$ for which $f(x)$ is defined.

Quick Examples

In Figure 2, f has the following relative extrema:

1. Relative maxima at p and r.

2. A relative maximum at b. (See Figure 4.) Note that $f(x)$ is not defined for $x > b$. However, $f(b) \geq f(x)$ for every x in the interval $(b - h, b + h)$ *for which $f(x)$ is defined*—that is, for every x in $(b - h, b]$.

3. Relative minima at a, q, and s.

Figure 4

Note Our definition of relative extremum allows f to have a relative extremum at an endpoint of its domain; the definitions used in some books do not. In view of examples like the stock-market investing strategy mentioned above, we find it more useful to allow endpoints as relative extrema. ∎

Looking carefully at Figure 2, we can see that the lowest point on the whole graph is where $x = s$ and the highest point is where $x = b$. This means that $f(s)$ is the least value of f on the whole domain of f (the interval $[a, b]$) and $f(b)$ is the greatest value. We call these the *absolute* minimum and maximum.

Absolute Extrema

f has an **absolute maximum** at r if $f(r) \geq f(x)$ for every x in the domain of f.

f has an **absolute minimum** at r if $f(r) \leq f(x)$ for every x in the domain of f.

Quick Examples

1. In Figure 2, f has an absolute maximum at b and an absolute minimum at s.

2. If $f(x) = x^2$ then $f(x) \geq f(0)$ for every real number x. Therefore, $f(x) = x^2$ has an absolute minimum at $x = 0$. (See the figure.)

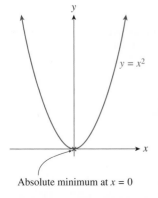

Absolute minimum at $x = 0$

> **3.** Generalizing (2), every quadratic function $f(x) = ax^2 + bx + c$ has an absolute extremum at its vertex $x = -b/(2a)$, an absolute minimum if $a > 0$, and an absolute maximum if $a < 0$.

Absolute maxima at $x = a$ and $x = b$

Figure 5

Some graphs have no absolute extrema at all (think of the graph of $y = x$), while others might have an absolute maximum but no absolute minimum (like $y = x^2$), or vice versa. When f does have an absolute maximum, there is only one absolute maximum *value* of f, but this value may occur at different values of x. (See Figure 5.)

Q: *At how many different values of x can f take on its absolute maximum value?*

A: An extreme case is that of a constant function; because we use $\geq$ in the definition of absolute maximum, a constant function has an absolute maximum (and minimum) at every point in its domain.

Figure 6

Now, how do we go about locating extrema? In many cases we can get a good idea by using graphing technology to zoom in on a maximum or minimum and approximate its coordinates. However, calculus gives us a way to find the exact locations of the extrema and at the same time to understand why the graph of a function behaves the way it does. In fact, it is often best to combine the powers of graphing technology with those of calculus, as we shall see.

In Figure 6 we see the graph from Figure 1 once more, but we have labeled each extreme point as one of three types. At the points labeled "Stationary," the tangent lines to the graph are horizontal, and so have slope 0, so f' (which gives the slope) is 0. Any time $f'(x) = 0$, we say that f has a **stationary point** at x because the rate of change of f is zero there. We call an extremum that occurs at a stationary point a **stationary extremum**. In general, to find the exact location of each stationary point, we need to solve the equation $f'(x) = 0$.

There is a relative minimum in Figure 6 at $x = q$, but there is no horizontal tangent there. In fact, there is no tangent line at all; $f'(q)$ is not defined. (Recall a similar situation with the graph of $f(x) = |x|$ at $x = 0$.) When $f'(x)$ does not exist for some x in the domain of f, we say that f has a **singular point** at x. We shall call an extremum that occurs at a singular point a **singular extremum**. The points that are either stationary or singular we call collectively the **critical points** of f.

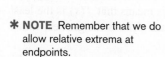

✱ NOTE Remember that we do allow relative extrema at endpoints.

The remaining two extrema are at the **endpoints** of the domain.✱ As we see in the figure, they are (almost) always either relative maxima or relative minima.

We bring all the above information together in Figure 7:

Figure 7

✳ **NOTE** Here is an outline of the argument. Suppose f has a relative maximum, say, at $x = a$, at a point other than an endpoint of the domain. Then either f is differentiable there, or it is not. If it is not, then we have a singular point. If f is differentiable at $x = a$, then consider the slope of the secant line through the points where $x = a$ and $x = a + h$ for small positive h. Because f has a relative maximum at $x = a$, it is falling (or level) to the right of $x = a$, and so the slope of this secant line must be ≤ 0. Thus, we must have $f'(a) \leq 0$ in the limit as $h \to 0$. On the other hand, if h is small and *negative*, then the corresponding secant line must have slope ≥ 0 because f is also falling (or level) as we move left from $x = a$, and so $f'(a) \geq 0$. Because $f'(a)$ is both ≥ 0 and ≤ 0, it must be zero, and so we have a stationary point at $x = a$.

Q : *Are there any other types of relative extrema?*

A : No; relative extrema of a function always occur at critical points or endpoints. (A rigorous proof is beyond the scope of this book.)✳

Locating Candidates for Relative Extrema

If f is a real valued function, then its relative extrema occur among the following types of points:

1. **Stationary Points:** f has a stationary point at x if x is in the domain and $f'(x) = 0$. To locate stationary points, set $f'(x) = 0$ and solve for x.
2. **Singular Points:** f has a singular point at x if x is in the domain and $f'(x)$ is not defined. To locate singular points, find values of x where $f'(x)$ is *not* defined, but $f(x)$ *is* defined.
3. **Endpoints:** The x-coordinates of endpoints are endpoints of the domain, if any. Recall that closed intervals contain endpoints, but open intervals do not.

Once we have the x-coordinates of a candidate for a relative extremum, we find the corresponding y-coordinate using $y = f(x)$.

Quick Examples

1. **Stationary Points:** Let $f(x) = x^3 - 12x$. Then to locate the stationary points, set $f'(x) = 0$ and solve for x. This gives $3x^2 - 12 = 0$, so f has stationary points at $x = \pm 2$. Thus, the stationary points are $(-2, f(-2)) = (-2, 16)$ and $(2, f(2)) = (2, -16)$.
2. **Singular points:** Let $f(x) = 3(x - 1)^{1/3}$. Then $f'(x) = (x - 1)^{-2/3} = 1/(x - 1)^{2/3}$. $f'(1)$ is not defined, although $f(1)$ *is* defined. Thus, the (only) singular point occurs at $x = 1$. Its coordinates are $(1, f(1)) = (1, 0)$.
3. **Endpoints:** Let $f(x) = 1/x$, with domain $(-\infty, 0) \cup [1, +\infty)$. Then the only endpoint in the domain of f occurs when $x = 1$ and has coordinates $(1, 1)$. The natural domain of $1/x$ has no endpoints.

Remember, though, that these are only *candidates* for relative extrema. It is quite possible, as we shall see, to have a stationary point or a singular point that is neither a relative maximum nor a relative minimum. (It is also possible for an endpoint to be neither a maximum nor a minimum, but only in functions whose graphs are rather bizarre—see Exercise 65.)

Now let's look at some examples of finding maxima and minima. In all of these examples, we will use the following procedure: First, we find the derivative, which we examine to find the stationary points and singular points. Next, we make a table listing the x-coordinates of the critical points and endpoints, together with their y-coordinates. We use this table to make a rough sketch of the graph. From the table and rough sketch, we usually have enough data to be able to say where the extreme points are and what kind they are.

EXAMPLE 1 **Maxima and Minima**

Find the relative and absolute maxima and minima of

$$f(x) = x^2 - 2x$$

on the interval $[0, 4]$.

Solution We first calculate $f'(x) = 2x - 2$. We use this derivative to locate the critical points (stationary and singular points).

Stationary Points To locate the stationary points, we solve the equation $f'(x) = 0$, or

$$2x - 2 = 0,$$

getting $x = 1$. The domain of the function is $[0, 4]$, so $x = 1$ is in the domain. Thus, the only candidate for a stationary relative extremum occurs when $x = 1$.

Singular Points We look for points where the derivative is not defined. However, the derivative is $2x - 2$, which is defined for every x. Thus, there are no singular points and hence no candidates for singular relative extrema.

Endpoints The domain is $[0, 4]$, so the endpoints occur when $x = 0$ and $x = 4$.

We record these values of x in a table, together with the corresponding y-coordinates (values of f):

x	0	1	4
$f(x) = x^2 - 2x$	0	-1	8

Figure 8

This gives us three points on the graph, $(0, 0)$, $(1, -1)$, and $(4, 8)$, which we plot in Figure 8. We remind ourselves that the point $(1, -1)$ is a stationary point of the graph by drawing in a part of the horizontal tangent line. Connecting these points must give us a graph something like that in Figure 9. Notice that the graph has a horizontal tangent line at $x = 1$ but not at either of the endpoints because the endpoints are not stationary points.

From Figure 9 we can see that f has the following extrema:

x	$y = x^2 - 2x$	Classification
0	0	Relative maximum (endpoint)
1	-1	Absolute minimum (stationary point)
4	8	Absolute maximum (endpoint)

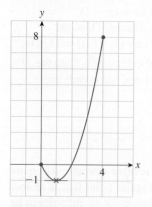

Figure 9

➡ **Before we go on...** A little terminology: If the point (a, b) on the graph of f represents a maximum (or minimum) of f, we sometimes say that f **has a maximum (or minimum) value of b at $x = a$.** Thus, in the above example, we could have said the following:

- f has a relative maximum value of 0 at $x = 0$.
- f has an absolute minimum value of -1 at $x = 1$.
- f has an absolute maximum value of 8 at $x = 4$.

Figure 10

* **NOTE** Why "first" derivative
test? To distinguish it from
a test based on the **second
derivative** of a function,
which we shall discuss in
Section 12.3.

Q : *How can we be sure that the graph in Example 1 doesn't look like Figure 10?*

A : If it did, there would be another critical point somewhere between $x = 1$ and $x = 4$. But
we already know that there aren't any other critical points. The table we made listed all
of the possible extrema; there can be no more.

■

First Derivative Test

The **first derivative test*** gives another, very systematic, way of checking whether a critical point is a relative maximum or minimum. To motivate the first derivative test, consider
again the critical point $x = 1$ in Example 1. If we look at some values of $f'(x)$ to the left
and right of the critical point, we obtain the information shown in the following table:

	Point to the Left	**Critical Point**	**Point to the Right**
x	0	1	2
$f'(x) = 2x - 2$	-2	0	2
Direction of Graph	↘	→	↗

At $x = 0$ (to the left of the critical point) we see that $f'(0) = -2 < 0$, so the graph
has negative slope and f is decreasing. We note this with the downward pointing arrow.
At $x = 2$ (to the right of the critical point), we find $f'(2) = 2 > 0$, so the graph has positive slope and f is increasing. In fact, because $f'(x) = 0$ only at $x = 1$, we know that
$f'(x) < 0$ for all x in $[0, 1)$, and we can say that f is decreasing on the interval $[0, 1]$.
Similarly, f is increasing on $[1, 4]$.

So, starting at $x = 0$, the graph of f goes down until we reach $x = 1$ and then it goes
back up, telling us that $x = 1$ must be a relative minimum. Notice how the relative minimum is suggested by the arrows to the left and right.

First Derivative Test for Relative Extrema

Suppose that c is a critical point of the continuous function f, and that its derivative is defined for x close to, and on both sides of, $x = c$. Then, determine the sign
of the derivative to the left and right of $x = c$.

1. If $f'(x)$ is positive to the left of $x = c$ and negative to the right, then f has a
relative maximum at $x = c$.

2. If $f'(x)$ is negative to the left of $x = c$ and positive to the right, then f has a
relative minimum at $x = c$.

3. If $f'(x)$ has the same sign on both sides of $x = c$, then f has neither a relative
maximum nor a relative minimum at $x = c$.

Quick Examples

1. In Example 1 above, we saw that $f(x) = x^2 - 2x$ has a critical point at
$x = 1$ with $f'(x)$ negative to the left of $x = 1$ and positive to the right (see
the table). Therefore, f has a relative minimum at $x = 1$.

2. Here is a graph showing a function f with a singular point at $x = 1$:

The graph gives us the information shown in the table:

	Point to the Left	Critical Point	Point to the Right
x	0.5	1	1.5
$f'(x)$	+	Undefined	−
Direction of Graph	↗		↘

Since $f'(x)$ is positive to the left of $x = 1$ and negative to the right, we see that f has a relative maximum at $x = 1$. (Notice again how this is suggested by the direction of the arrows.)

EXAMPLE 2 Unbounded Interval

Find all extrema of $f(x) = 3x^4 - 4x^3$ on $[-1, \infty)$.

Solution We first calculate $f'(x) = 12x^3 - 12x^2$.

Stationary points We solve the equation $f'(x) = 0$, which is

$$12x^3 - 12x^2 = 0 \text{ or}$$
$$12x^2(x - 1) = 0.$$

There are two solutions, $x = 0$ and $x = 1$, and both are in the domain. These are our candidates for the x-coordinates of stationary relative extrema.

Singular points There are no points where $f'(x)$ is not defined, so there are no singular points.

Endpoints The domain is $[-1, \infty)$, so there is one endpoint, at $x = -1$.

We record these points in a table with the corresponding y-coordinates:

x	−1	0	1
$f(x) = 3x^4 - 4x^3$	7	0	−1

We will illustrate three methods we can use to determine which are minima, which are maxima, and which are neither:

1. Plot these points and sketch the graph by hand.

2. Use the First Derivative Test.

3. Use technology to help us.

Use the method you find most convenient.

(a)   **(b)**

Figure 11

Figure 12

Figure 13

Using a Hand Plot: If we plot these points by hand, we obtain Figure 11(a), which suggests Figure 11(b).

We can't be sure what happens to the right of $x = 1$. Does the curve go up, or does it go down? To find out, let's plot a "test point" to the right of $x = 1$. Choosing $x = 2$, we obtain $y = 3(2)^4 - 4(2)^3 = 16$, so $(2, 16)$ is another point on the graph. Thus, it must turn upward to the right of $x = 1$, as shown in Figure 12.

From the graph, we find that f has the following extrema:

A relative (endpoint) maximum at $(-1, 7)$

An absolute (stationary) minimum at $(1, -1)$

Using the First Derivative Test: List the critical and endpoints in a table, and add additional points as necessary so that each critical point has a noncritical point on either side. Then compute the derivative at each of these points, and draw an arrow to indicate the direction of the graph.

	End Point	Critical Point		Critical Point	
x	-1	0	0.5	1	2
$f'(x) = 12x^3 - 12x^2$	-24	0	-1.5	0	48
Direction of Graph	↘	→	↘	→	↗

Notice that the arrows now suggest the shape of the curve in Figure 12. The first derivative test tells us that the function has a relative maximum at $x = -1$, neither a maximum nor a minimum at $x = 0$, and a relative minimum at $x = 1$. Deciding which of these extrema are absolute and which are relative requires us to compute y-coordinates and plot the corresponding points on the graph by hand, as we did in the first method.

using Technology

If we use technology to show the graph, we should choose the viewing window so that it contains the three interesting points we found: $x = -1$, $x = 0$, and $x = 1$. Again, we can't be sure yet what happens to the right of $x = 1$; does the graph go up or down from that point? If we set the viewing window to an interval of $[-1, 2]$ for x and $[-2, 8]$ for y, we will leave enough room to the right of $x = 1$ and below $y = -1$ to see what the graph will do. The result will be something like Figure 13.

Now we can tell what happens to the right of $x = 1$: the function increases. We know that it cannot later decrease again because if it did, there would have to be another critical point where it turns around, and we found that there are no other critical points. ∎

➡ **Before we go on...** Notice that the stationary point at $x = 0$ in Example 2 is neither a relative maximum nor a relative minimum. It is simply a place where the graph of f flattens out for a moment before it continues to fall. Notice also that f has no absolute maximum because $f(x)$ increases without bound as x gets large. ∎

EXAMPLE 3 Singular Point

Find all extrema of $f(t) = t^{2/3}$ on $[-1, 1]$.

Solution First, $f'(t) = \dfrac{2}{3}t^{-1/3}$.

Stationary points We need to solve

$$\frac{2}{3}t^{-1/3} = 0.$$

We can rewrite this equation without the negative exponent:

$$\frac{2}{3t^{1/3}} = 0.$$

Now, the only way that a fraction can equal 0 is if the numerator is 0, so this fraction can never equal 0. Thus, there are no stationary points.

Singular points The derivative

$$f'(t) = \frac{2}{3t^{1/3}}$$

is not defined for $t = 0$. However, f itself *is* defined at $t = 0$, so 0 is in the domain. Thus, f has a singular point at $t = 0$.

Endpoints There are two endpoints, -1 and 1.

We now put these three points in a table with the corresponding y-coordinates:

t	-1	0	1
$f(t)$	1	0	1

Using a Hand Plot: The derivative, $f'(t) = 2/(3t^{1/3})$, is not defined at the singular point $t = 0$. To help us sketch the graph, let's use limits to investigate what happens to the derivative as we approach 0 from either side:

$$\lim_{t \to 0^-} f'(t) = \lim_{t \to 0^-} \frac{2}{3t^{1/3}} = -\infty$$

$$\lim_{t \to 0^+} f'(t) = \lim_{t \to 0^+} \frac{2}{3t^{1/3}} = +\infty.$$

Thus, the graph decreases very steeply, approaching $t = 0$ from the left, and then rises very steeply as it leaves to the right. It would make sense to say that the tangent line at $x = 0$ is vertical, as seen in Figure 14.

From this graph, we find the following extrema for f:

An absolute (endpoint) maximum at $(-1, 1)$
An absolute (singular) minimum at $(0, 0)$
An absolute (endpoint) maximum at $(1, 1)$.

Notice that the absolute maximum value of f is achieved at two values of t: $t = -1$ and $t = 1$.

First Derivative Test: Here is the corresponding table for the first derivative test.

Figure 14

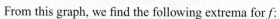

t	-1	0	1
$f'(t) = \dfrac{2}{3t^{1/3}}$	$-\dfrac{2}{3}$	Undefined	$\dfrac{2}{3}$
Direction of Graph	↘	↕	↗

(We drew a vertical arrow at $t = 0$ to indicate a vertical tangent.) Again, notice how the arrows suggest the shape of the curve in Figure 14, and the first derivative test confirms that we have a relative minimum at $x = 0$.

✱ NOTE Many graphing calculators will give you only the right-hand half of the graph shown in Figure 14 because fractional powers of negative numbers are not, in general, real numbers. To obtain the whole curve, enter the formula as `Y=(x^2)^(1/3)`, a fractional power of the non-negative function x^2.

In Examples 1 and 3, we could have found the absolute maxima and minima without doing any graphing. In Example 1, after finding the critical points and endpoints, we created the following table:

x	0	1	4
$f(x)$	0	-1	8

From this table we can see that f must decrease from its value of 0 at $x = 0$ to -1 at $x = 1$, and then increase to 8 at $x = 4$. The value of 8 must be the largest value it takes on, and the value of -1 must be the smallest, on the interval $[0, 4]$. Similarly, in Example 3 we created the following table:

t	-1	0	1
$f(t)$	1	0	1

From this table we can see that the largest value of f on the interval $[-1, 1]$ is 1 and the smallest value is 0. We are taking advantage of the following fact, the proof of which uses some deep and beautiful mathematics (alas, beyond the scope of this book):

Extreme Value Theorem

If f is *continuous* on a *closed interval* $[a, b]$, then it will have an absolute maximum and an absolute minimum value on that interval. Each absolute extremum must occur at either an endpoint or a critical point. Therefore, the absolute maximum is the largest value in a table of the values of f at the endpoints and critical points, and the absolute minimum is the smallest value.

Quick Example

The function $f(x) = 3x - x^3$ on the interval $[0, 2]$ has one critical point at $x = 1$. The values of f at the critical point and the endpoints of the interval are given in the following table:

	Endpoint	Critical point	Endpoint
x	0	1	2
$f(x)$	0	2	-2

From this table we can say that the absolute maximum value of f on $[0, 2]$ is 2, which occurs at $x = 1$, and the absolute minimum value of f is -2, which occurs at $x = 2$.

As we can see in Example 2 and the following examples, if the domain is not a closed interval then f may not have an absolute maximum and minimum, and a table of values as above is of little help in determining whether it does.

EXAMPLE 4 **Domain Not a Closed Interval**

Find all extrema of $f(x) = x + \dfrac{1}{x}$.

Solution Because no domain is specified, we take the domain to be as large as possible. The function is not defined at $x = 0$ but is at all other points, so we take its domain to be $(-\infty, 0) \cup (0, +\infty)$. We calculate

$$f'(x) = 1 - \frac{1}{x^2}.$$

Stationary Points Setting $f'(x) = 0$, we solve

$$1 - \frac{1}{x^2} = 0$$

to find $x = \pm 1$. Calculating the corresponding values of f, we get the two stationary points $(1, 2)$ and $(-1, -2)$.

Singular Points The only value of x for which $f'(x)$ is not defined is $x = 0$, but then f is not defined there either, so there are no singular points in the domain.

Endpoints The domain, $(-\infty, 0) \cup (0, +\infty)$, has no endpoints.

From this scant information, it is hard to tell what f does. If we are sketching the graph by hand, or using the first derivative test, we will need to plot additional "test points" to the left and right of the stationary points $x = \pm 1$.

---

using Technology

For the technology approach, let's choose a viewing window with an interval of $[-3, 3]$ for x and $[-4, 4]$ for y, which should leave plenty of room to see how f behaves near the stationary points. The result is something like Figure 15.

From this graph we can see that f has:

A relative (stationary) maximum at $(-1, -2)$

A relative (stationary) minimum at $(1, 2)$

Curiously, the relative maximum is lower than the relative minimum! Notice also that, because of the break in the graph at $x = 0$, the graph did not need to rise to get from $(-1, -2)$ to $(1, 2)$. ■

Figure 15

So far we have been solving the equation $f'(x) = 0$ to obtain our candidates for stationary extrema. However, it is often not easy—or even possible—to solve equations analytically. In the next example, we show a way around this problem by using graphing technology.

EXAMPLE 5 **Finding Approximate Extrema Using Technology**

Graph the function $f(x) = (x - 1)^{2/3} - \dfrac{x^2}{2}$ with domain $[-2, +\infty)$. Also graph its derivative and hence locate and classify all extrema of f, with coordinates accurate to two decimal places.

Solution In Example 4 of Section 10.5, we saw how to draw the graphs of f and f' using technology. Note that the technology formula to use for the graph of f is

```
((x-1)^2)^(1/3)-0.5*x^2
```

instead of

```
(x-1)^(2/3)-0.5*x^2.
```

(Why?)

Figure 16 shows the resulting graphs of f and f'.

Graph of f	Graph of f'

Figure 16   **(a)**   **(b)**

If we extend Xmax beyond $x = 2$, we find that the graph continues downward, apparently without any further interesting behavior.

Stationary Points The graph of f shows two stationary points, both maxima, at around $x = -0.6$ and $x = 1.2$. Notice that the graph of f' is zero at precisely these points. Moreover, it is easier to locate these values accurately on the graph of f' because it is easier to pinpoint where a graph crosses the x-axis than to locate a stationary point. Zooming in to the stationary point at $x \approx -0.6$ results in Figure 17.

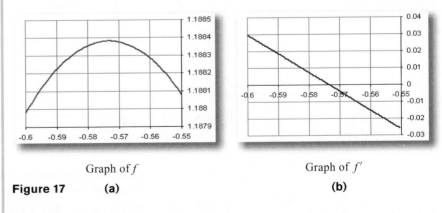

Graph of f	Graph of f'

Figure 17   **(a)**   **(b)**

From the graph of f, we can see that the stationary point is somewhere between -0.58 and -0.57. The graph of f' shows more clearly that the zero of f', hence the stationary point of f lies somewhat closer to -0.57 than to -0.58. Thus, the stationary point occurs at $x \approx -0.57$, rounded to two decimal places.

In a similar way, we find the second stationary point at $x \approx 1.18$.

Singular Points Going back to Figure 16, we notice what appears to be a cusp (singular point) at the relative minimum around $x = 1$, and this is confirmed by a glance at the graph of f', which seems to take a sudden jump at that value. Zooming in closer suggests that the singular point occurs at exactly $x = 1$. In fact, we can calculate

$$f'(x) = \frac{2}{3(x-1)^{1/3}} - x.$$

From this formula we see clearly that $f'(x)$ is defined everywhere except at $x = 1$.

Endpoints The only endpoint in the domain is $x = -2$, which gives a relative minimum.

Thus, we have found the following approximate extrema for f:

A relative (endpoint) minimum at $(-2, 0.08)$

An absolute (stationary) maximum at $(-0.57, 1.19)$

A relative (singular) minimum at $(1, -0.5)$

A relative (stationary) maximum at $(1.18, -0.38)$.

12.1 EXERCISES

▼ more advanced   ◆ challenging

⊺ indicates exercises that should be solved using technology

In Exercises 1–12, locate and classify all extrema in each graph. (By classifying the extrema, we mean listing whether each extremum is a relative or absolute maximum or minimum.) Also, locate any stationary points or singular points that are not relative extrema. HINT [See Figure 7.]

1.

2.

3.

4.

5.

6.

7.

8.

9.

10.

11.

12.

Find the exact location of all the relative and absolute extrema of each function in Exercises 13–44. HINT [See Example 1.]

13. $f(x) = x^2 - 4x + 1$ with domain $[0, 3]$

14. $f(x) = 2x^2 - 2x + 3$ with domain $[0, 3]$

15. $g(x) = x^3 - 12x$ with domain $[-4, 4]$

16. $g(x) = 2x^3 - 6x + 3$ with domain $[-2, 2]$

17. $f(t) = t^3 + t$ with domain $[-2, 2]$

18. $f(t) = -2t^3 - 3t$ with domain $[-1, 1]$

19. $h(t) = 2t^3 + 3t^2$ with domain $[-2, +\infty)$ HINT [See Example 2.]

20. $h(t) = t^3 - 3t^2$ with domain $[-1, +\infty)$ HINT [See Example 2.]

21. $f(x) = x^4 - 4x^3$ with domain $[-1, +\infty)$

22. $f(x) = 3x^4 - 2x^3$ with domain $[-1, +\infty)$

23. $g(t) = \frac{1}{4}t^4 - \frac{2}{3}t^3 + \frac{1}{2}t^2$ with domain $(-\infty, +\infty)$

24. $g(t) = 3t^4 - 16t^3 + 24t^2 + 1$ with domain $(-\infty, +\infty)$

25. $h(x) = (x - 1)^{2/3}$ with domain $[0, 2]$ HINT [See Example 3.]

26. $h(x) = (x + 1)^{2/5}$ with domain $[-2, 0]$ HINT [See Example 3.]

27. $k(x) = \frac{2x}{3} + (x + 1)^{2/3}$ with domain $(-\infty, 0]$

28. $k(x) = \frac{2x}{5} - (x - 1)^{2/5}$ with domain $[0, +\infty)$

29. ▼ $f(t) = \frac{t^2 + 1}{t^2 - 1};\ -2 \le t \le 2, t \ne \pm 1$

30. ▼ $f(t) = \frac{t^2 - 1}{t^2 + 1}$ with domain $[-2, 2]$

31. ▼ $f(x) = \sqrt{x}(x - 1);\ x \ge 0$

32. ▼ $f(x) = \sqrt{x}(x + 1);\ x \ge 0$

33. ▼ $g(x) = x^2 - 4\sqrt{x}$

34. ▼ $g(x) = \frac{1}{x} - \frac{1}{x^2}$

35. ▼ $g(x) = \frac{x^3}{x^2 + 3}$

36. ▼ $g(x) = \frac{x^3}{x^2 - 3}$

37. ▼ $f(x) = x - \ln x$ with domain $(0, +\infty)$

38. ▼ $f(x) = x - \ln x^2$ with domain $(0, +\infty)$

39. ▼ $g(t) = e^t - t$ with domain $[-1, 1]$

40. ▼ $g(t) = e^{-t^2}$ with domain $(-\infty, +\infty)$

41. ▼ $f(x) = \frac{2x^2 - 24}{x + 4}$

42. ▼ $f(x) = \frac{x - 4}{x^2 + 20}$

43. ▼ $f(x) = xe^{1 - x^2}$

44. ▼ $f(x) = x \ln x$ with domain $(0, +\infty)$

In Exercises 45–48, use graphing technology and the method in Example 5 to find the x-coordinates of the critical points, accurate to two decimal places. Find all relative and absolute maxima and minima. HINT [See Example 5.]

45. ⊡ $y = x^2 + \frac{1}{x - 2}$ with domain $(-3, 2) \cup (2, 6)$

46. ⊡ $y = x^2 - 10(x - 1)^{2/3}$ with domain $(-4, 4)$

47. ⊡ $f(x) = (x - 5)^2(x + 4)(x - 2)$ with domain $[-5, 6]$

48. ⊡ $f(x) = (x + 3)^2(x - 2)^2$ with domain $[-5, 5]$

In Exercises 49–56, the graph of the derivative of a function f is shown. Determine the x-coordinates of all stationary and singular points of f, and classify each as a relative maximum, relative minimum, or neither. (Assume that f(x) is defined and continuous everywhere in $[-3, 3]$.) HINT [See Example 5.]

49. ▼

50. ▼

51. ▼

52. ▼

53. ▼

54. ▼

55. ▼

56. ▼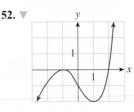

COMMUNICATION AND REASONING EXERCISES

57. Draw the graph of a function f with domain the set of all real numbers, such that f is not linear and has no relative extrema.

58. Draw the graph of a function g with domain the set of all real numbers, such that g has a relative maximum and minimum but no absolute extrema.

59. Draw the graph of a function that has stationary and singular points but no relative extrema.

60. Draw the graph of a function that has relative, not absolute, maxima and minima, but has no stationary or singular points.

61. If a stationary point is not a relative maximum, then must it be a relative minimum? Explain your answer.

62. If one endpoint is a relative maximum, must the other be a relative minimum? Explain your answer.

63. ▼ We said that if f is continuous on a closed interval $[a, b]$, then it will have an absolute maximum and an absolute minimum. Draw the graph of a function with domain $[0, 1]$ having an absolute maximum but no absolute minimum.

64. ▼ Refer to Exercise 63. Draw the graph of a function with domain $[0, 1]$ having no absolute extrema.

65. ▣ ▼ Must endpoints always be extrema? Consider the following function (based on the trigonometric sine function—see Chapter 16 for a discussion of its properties):

$$f(x) = \begin{cases} x \sin\left(\dfrac{1}{x}\right) & \text{if } x > 0 \\ 0 & \text{if } x = 0 \end{cases}.$$

Technology formula: x*sin(1/x)

Graph this function using the technology formula above for $0 \le x \le h$, choosing smaller and smaller values of h, and decide whether f has a either a relative maximum or relative

minimum at the endpoint $x = 0$. Explain your answer. (Note: Very few graphers can draw this curve accurately; the grapher that comes with Mac computers is probably among the best, while the TI-83/84 Plus is probably among the worst.)

66. ▣ ▼ Refer to the preceding exercise, and consider the function

$$f(x) = \begin{cases} x^2 \sin\left(\dfrac{1}{x}\right) & \text{if } x \ne 0 \\ 0 & \text{if } x = 0 \end{cases}.$$

Technology formula: $\text{x\^2*sin(1/x)}$

Graph this function using the technology formula above for $0 \le x \le h$, choosing smaller and smaller values of h, and decide **(a)** whether $x = 0$ is a stationary point, and **(b)** whether f has either a relative maximum or a relative minimum at $x = 0$. [For part (a), use technology to estimate the derivative at $x = 0$.] Explain your answers.

12.2 Applications of Maxima and Minima

In many applications we would like to find the largest or smallest possible value of some quantity—for instance, the greatest possible profit or the lowest cost. We call this the *optimal* (best) value. In this section we consider several such examples and use calculus to find the optimal value in each.

In all applications the first step is to translate a written description into a mathematical problem. In the problems we look at in this section, there are *unknowns* that we are asked to find, there is an expression involving those unknowns that must be made as large or as small as possible—the **objective function**—and there may be **constraints**— equations or inequalities relating the variables.*

✳ NOTE If you have studied linear programming, you will notice a similarity here, but unlike the situation in linear programming, neither the objective function nor the constraints need be linear.

EXAMPLE 1 Minimizing Average Cost

Gymnast Clothing manufactures expensive hockey jerseys for sale to college bookstores in runs of up to 500. Its cost (in dollars) for a run of x hockey jerseys is

$$C(x) = 2,000 + 10x + 0.2x^2.$$

How many jerseys should Gymnast produce per run in order to minimize average cost?*

✳ NOTE Why don't we seek to minimize total cost? The answer would be uninteresting; to minimize total cost, we would make *no* jerseys at all. Minimizing the average cost is a more practical objective.

Solution Here is the procedure we will follow to solve problems like this.

1. *Identify the unknown(s).* There is one unknown: x, the number of hockey jerseys Gymnast should produce per run. (We know this because the question is, How many jerseys . . . ?)

2. *Identify the objective function.* The objective function is the quantity that must be made as small (in this case) as possible. In this example it is the average cost, which is given by

$$\bar{C}(x) = \frac{C(x)}{x} = \frac{2,000 + 10x + 0.2x^2}{x}$$

$$= \frac{2,000}{x} + 10 + 0.2x \text{ dollars/jersey.}$$

3. *Identify the constraints (if any).* At most 500 jerseys can be manufactured in a run. Also, $\bar{C}(0)$ is not defined. Thus, x is constrained by

$$0 < x \le 500.$$

Put another way, the domain of the objective function $\bar{C}(x)$ is (0, 500].

4. *State and solve the resulting optimization problem.* Our optimization problem is:

$$\text{Minimize } \bar{C}(x) = \frac{2{,}000}{x} + 10 + 0.2x \qquad \text{Objective function}$$

$$\text{subject to } 0 < x \le 500. \qquad \text{Constraint}$$

We now solve this problem as in Section 12.1. We first calculate

$$\bar{C}'(x) = -\frac{2{,}000}{x^2} + 0.2.$$

We solve $\bar{C}'(x) = 0$ to find $x = \pm 100$. We reject $x = -100$ because -100 is not in the domain of $\bar{C}$ (and makes no sense), so we have one stationary point, at $x = 100$. There, the average cost is $\bar{C}(100) = \$50$ per jersey.

The only point at which the formula for $\bar{C}'$ is not defined is $x = 0$, but that is not in the domain of $\bar{C}$, so we have no singular points. We have one endpoint in the domain, at $x = 500$. There, the average cost is $\bar{C}(500) = \$114$.

Figure 18

using Technology

Let's plot $\bar{C}$ in a viewing window with the intervals [0, 500] for x and [0, 150] for y, which will show the whole domain and the two interesting points we've found so far. The result is Figure 18.

From the graph of $\bar{C}$, we can see that the stationary point at $x = 100$ gives the absolute minimum. We can therefore say that Gymnast Clothing should produce 100 jerseys per run, for a lowest possible average cost of \$50 per jersey. ■

EXAMPLE 2 **Maximizing Area**

Slim wants to build a rectangular enclosure for his pet rabbit, Killer, against the side of his house, as shown in Figure 19. He has bought 100 feet of fencing. What are the dimensions of the largest area that he can enclose?

Figure 19

Solution

1. *Identify the unknown(s).* To identify the unknown(s), we look at the question: What are the *dimensions* of the largest area he can enclose? Thus, the unknowns are the dimensions of the fence. We call these x and y, as shown in Figure 20.

2. *Identify the objective function.* We look for what it is that we are trying to maximize (or minimize). The phrase "largest area" tells us that our object is to *maximize the area*, which is the product of length and width, so our objective function is

$$A = xy, \text{ where } A \text{ is the area of the enclosure.}$$

Figure 20

3. *Identify the constraints (if any).* What stops Slim from making the area as large as he wants? He has only 100 feet of fencing to work with. Looking again at Figure 20, we see that the sum of the lengths of the three sides must equal 100, so

$$x + 2y = 100.$$

One more point: Because x and y represent the lengths of the sides of the enclosure, neither can be a negative number.

4. *State and solve the resulting optimization problem.* Our mathematical problem is:

Maximize $A = xy$	Objective function
subject to $x + 2y = 100$, $x \geq 0$, and $y \geq 0$.	Constraints

We know how to find maxima and minima of a function of one variable, but A appears to depend on two variables. We can remedy this by using a constraint to express one variable in terms of the other. Let's take the constraint $x + 2y = 100$ and solve for x in terms of y:

$$x = 100 - 2y.$$

Substituting into the objective function gives

$$A = xy = (100 - 2y)y = 100y - 2y^2$$

and we have eliminated x from the objective function. What about the inequalities? One says that $x \geq 0$, but we want to eliminate x from this as well. We substitute for x again, getting

$$100 - 2y \geq 0.$$

Solving this inequality for y gives $y \leq 50$. The second inequality says that $y \geq 0$. Now, we can restate our problem with x eliminated:

Maximize $A(y) = 100y - 2y^2$ subject to $0 \leq y \leq 50$.

We now proceed with our usual method of solving such problems. We calculate $A'(y) = 100 - 4y$. Solving $100 - 4y = 0$, we get one stationary point at $y = 25$. There, $A(25) = 1{,}250$. There are no points at which $A'(y)$ is not defined, so there are no singular points. We have two endpoints, at $y = 0$ and $y = 50$. The corresponding areas are $A(0) = 0$ and $A(50) = 0$. We record the three points we found in a table:

y	0	25	50
$A(y)$	0	1,250	0

It's clear now how A must behave: It increases from 0 at $y = 0$ to 1,250 at $y = 25$ and then decreases back to 0 at $y = 50$. Thus, the largest possible value of A is 1,250 square feet, which occurs when $y = 25$. To completely answer the question that was asked, we need to know the corresponding value of x. We have $x = 100 - 2y$, so $x = 50$ when $y = 25$. Thus, Slim should build his enclosure 50 feet across and 25 feet deep (with the "missing" 50-foot side being formed by part of the house).

➡ **Before we go on...** Notice that the problem in Example 2 came down to finding the absolute maximum value of A on the closed and bounded interval [0, 50]. As we noted in the preceding section, the table of values of A at its critical points and the endpoints of the interval gives us enough information to find the absolute maximum. ■

Let's stop for a moment and summarize the steps we've taken in these two examples.

Solving an Optimization Problem

1. **Identify the unknown(s), possibly with the aid of a diagram.** These are usually the quantities asked for in the problem.

2. **Identify the objective function.** This is the quantity you are asked to maximize or minimize. You should name it explicitly, as in "Let S = surface area."

3. **Identify the constraint(s).** These can be equations relating variables or inequalities expressing limitations on the values of variables.

4. **State the optimization problem.** This will have the form "Maximize [minimize] the objective function subject to the constraint(s)."

5. **Eliminate extra variables.** If the objective function depends on several variables, solve the constraint equations to express all variables in terms of one particular variable. Substitute these expressions into the objective function to rewrite it as a function of a single variable. Substitute the expressions into any inequality constraints to help determine the domain of the objective function.

6. **Find the absolute maximum (or minimum) of the objective function.** Use the techniques of the preceding section.

Now for some further examples.

EXAMPLE 3 Maximizing Revenue

Cozy Carriage Company builds baby strollers. Using market research, the company estimates that if it sets the price of a stroller at p dollars, then it can sell $q = 300{,}000 - 10p^2$ strollers per year. What price will bring in the greatest annual revenue?

Solution The question we are asked identifies our main unknown, the price p. However, there is another quantity that we do not know, q, the number of strollers the company will sell per year. The question also identifies the objective function, revenue, which is

$$R = pq.$$

Including the equality constraint given to us, that $q = 300{,}000 - 10p^2$, and the "reality" inequality constraints $p \geq 0$ and $q \geq 0$, we can write our problem as

Maximize $R = pq$ subject to $q = 300{,}000 - 10p^2$, $p \geq 0$, and $q \geq 0$.

We are given q in terms of p, so let's substitute to eliminate q:

$$R = pq = p(300{,}000 - 10p^2) = 300{,}000p - 10p^3$$

Substituting in the inequality $q \geq 0$, we get

$$300{,}000 - 10p^2 \geq 0.$$

Thus, $p^2 \leq 30{,}000$, which gives $-100\sqrt{3} \leq p \leq 100\sqrt{3}$. When we combine this with $p \geq 0$, we get the following restatement of our problem:

Maximize $R(p) = 300{,}000p - 10p^3$ such that $0 \leq p \leq 100\sqrt{3}$.

We solve this problem in much the same way we did the preceding one. We calculate $R'(p) = 300,000 - 30p^2$. Setting $300,000 - 30p^2 = 0$, we find one stationary point at $p = 100$. There are no singular points and we have the endpoints $p = 0$ and $p = 100\sqrt{3}$. Putting these points in a table and computing the corresponding values of R, we get the following:

p	0	100	$100\sqrt{3}$
$R(p)$	0	20,000,000	0

Thus, Cozy Carriage should price its strollers at $100 each, which will bring in the largest possible revenue of $20,000,000.

EXAMPLE 4 Optimizing Resources

The Metal Can Company has an order to make cylindrical cans with a volume of 250 cubic centimeters. What should be the dimensions of the cans in order to use the least amount of metal in their production?

Figure 21

Solution We are asked to find the dimensions of the cans. It is traditional to take as the dimensions of a cylinder the height h and the radius of the base r, as in Figure 21.

We are also asked to minimize the amount of metal used in the can, which is the area of the surface of the cylinder. We can look up the formula or figure it out ourselves: Imagine removing the circular top and bottom and then cutting vertically and flattening out the hollow cylinder to get a rectangle, as shown in Figure 22.

Figure 22

Our objective function is the (total) surface area S of the can. The area of each disc is πr^2, while the area of the rectangular piece is $2\pi rh$. Thus, our objective function is

$$S = 2\pi r^2 + 2\pi rh.$$

As usual, there is a constraint: The volume must be exactly 250 cubic centimeters. The formula for the volume of a cylinder is $V = \pi r^2 h$, so

$$\pi r^2 h = 250.$$

It is easiest to solve this constraint for h in terms of r:

$$h = \frac{250}{\pi r^2}.$$

Substituting in the objective function, we get

$$S = 2\pi r^2 + 2\pi r \frac{250}{\pi r^2} = 2\pi r^2 + \frac{500}{r}.$$

Now r cannot be negative or 0, but it can become very large (a very wide but very short can could have the right volume). We therefore take the domain of $S(r)$ to be $(0, +\infty)$, so our mathematical problem is as follows:

$$\text{Minimize } S(r) = 2\pi r^2 + \frac{500}{r} \text{ subject to } r > 0.$$

Now we calculate

$$S'(r) = 4\pi r - \frac{500}{r^2}.$$

To find stationary points, we set this equal to 0 and solve:

$$4\pi r - \frac{500}{r^2} = 0$$

$$4\pi r = \frac{500}{r^2}$$

$$4\pi r^3 = 500$$

$$r^3 = \frac{125}{\pi}.$$

So

$$r = \sqrt[3]{\frac{125}{\pi}} = \frac{5}{\sqrt[3]{\pi}} \approx 3.41.$$

The corresponding surface area is approximately $S(3.41) \approx 220$. There are no singular points or endpoints in the domain.

Figure 23

---

using Technology

To see how S behaves near the one stationary point, let's graph it in a viewing window with interval $[0, 5]$ for r and $[0, 300]$ for S. The result is Figure 23.

From the graph we can clearly see that the smallest surface area occurs at the stationary point at $r \approx 3.41$. The height of the can will be

$$h = \frac{250}{\pi r^2} \approx 6.83.$$

Thus, the can that uses the least amount of metal has a height of approximately 6.83 centimeters and a radius of approximately 3.41 centimeters. Such a can will use approximately 220 square centimeters of metal.

➡ **Before we go on...** We obtained the value of r in Example 4 by solving the equation

$$4\pi r = \frac{500}{r^2}.$$

This time, let us do things differently: Divide both sides by 4π to obtain

$$r = \frac{500}{4\pi r^2} = \frac{125}{\pi r^2}$$

and compare what we got with the expression for h:

$$h = \frac{250}{\pi r^2}$$

which we see is exactly twice the expression for r. Put another way, the height is exactly equal to the diameter so that the can looks square when viewed from the side. Have you ever seen cans with that shape? Why do you think most cans do not have this shape? ◼

EXAMPLE 5 Allocation of Labor

∗ **NOTE** Cobb-Douglas production formulas were discussed in Section 11.6.

The Gym Sock Company manufactures cotton athletic socks. Production is partially automated through the use of robots. Daily operating costs amount to $50 per laborer and $30 per robot. The number of pairs of socks the company can manufacture in a day is given by a Cobb-Douglas∗ production formula

$$q = 50n^{0.6}r^{0.4}$$

where q is the number of pairs of socks that can be manufactured by n laborers and r robots. Assuming that the company wishes to produce 1,000 pairs of socks per day at a minimum cost, how many laborers and how many robots should it use?

Solution The unknowns are the number of laborers n and the number of robots r. The objective is to minimize the daily cost:

$$C = 50n + 30r.$$

The constraints are given by the daily quota

$$1{,}000 = 50n^{0.6}r^{0.4}$$

and the fact that n and r are nonnegative. We solve the constraint equation for one of the variables; let's solve for n:

$$n^{0.6} = \frac{1{,}000}{50r^{0.4}} = \frac{20}{r^{0.4}}.$$

Taking the $1/0.6$ power of both sides gives

$$n = \left(\frac{20}{r^{0.4}}\right)^{1/0.6} = \frac{20^{1/0.6}}{r^{0.4/0.6}} = \frac{20^{5/3}}{r^{2/3}} \approx \frac{147.36}{r^{2/3}}.$$

Substituting in the objective equation gives us the cost as a function of r:

$$C(r) \approx 50\left(\frac{147.36}{r^{2/3}}\right) + 30r$$

$$= 7{,}368r^{-2/3} + 30r.$$

The only remaining constraint on r is that $r > 0$. To find the minimum value of $C(r)$, we first take the derivative:

$$C'(r) \approx -4{,}912r^{-5/3} + 30.$$

Setting this equal to zero, we solve for r:

$$r^{-5/3} \approx 0.006107$$

$$r \approx (0.006107)^{-3/5} \approx 21.3.$$

The corresponding cost is $C(21.3) \approx \$1{,}600$. There are no singular points or endpoints in the domain of C.

Figure 24

To see how C behaves near its stationary point, let's draw its graph in a viewing window with an interval of $[0, 40]$ for r and $[0, 2,000]$ for C. The result is Figure 24.

From the graph we can see that C does have its minimum at the stationary point. The corresponding value of n is

$$n \approx \frac{147.36}{r^{2/3}} \approx 19.2.$$

At this point, our solution appears to be this: Use (approximately) 19.2 laborers and (approximately) 21.3 robots to meet the manufacturing quota at a minimum cost. However, we are not interested in fractions of robots or people, so we need to find integer solutions for n and r. If we round these numbers, we get the solution $(n, r) = (19, 21)$. However, a quick calculation shows that

$$q = 50(19)^{0.6}(21)^{0.4} \approx 989 \text{ pairs of socks,}$$

which fails to meet the quota of 1,000. Thus, we need to round at least one of the quantities n and r *upward* in order to meet the quota. The three possibilities, with corresponding values of q and C, are as follows:

$(n, r) = (20, 21)$, with $q \approx 1,020$ and $C = \$1,630$

$(n, r) = (19, 22)$, with $q \approx 1,007$ and $C = \$1,610$

$(n, r) = (20, 22)$, with $q \approx 1,039$ and $C = \$1,660$.

Of these, the solution that meets the quota at a minimum cost is $(n, r) = (19, 22)$. Thus, the Gym Sock Co. should use 19 laborers and 22 robots, at a cost of $50 \times 19 + 30 \times 22 = \$1,610$, to manufacture $50 \times 19^{0.6} \times 22^{0.4} \approx 1,007$ pairs of socks. ∎

12.2 EXERCISES

▼ more advanced   ◆ challenging
⊤ indicates exercises that should be solved using technology

Solve the optimization problems in Exercises 1–8. HINT [See Example 2.]

1. Maximize $P = xy$ with $x + y = 10$.

2. Maximize $P = xy$ with $x + 2y = 40$.

3. Minimize $S = x + y$ with $xy = 9$ and both x and $y > 0$.

4. Minimize $S = x + 2y$ with $xy = 2$ and both x and $y > 0$.

5. Minimize $F = x^2 + y^2$ with $x + 2y = 10$.

6. Minimize $F = x^2 + y^2$ with $xy^2 = 16$.

7. Maximize $P = xyz$ with $x + y = 30$ and $y + z = 30$, and $x, y,$ and $z \geq 0$.

8. Maximize $P = xyz$ with $x + z = 12$ and $y + z = 12$, and $x, y,$ and $z \geq 0$.

9. For a rectangle with perimeter 20 to have the largest area, what dimensions should it have?

10. For a rectangle with area 100 to have the smallest perimeter, what dimensions should it have?

APPLICATIONS

11. *Average Cost: iPods* Assume that it costs **Apple** approximately

$$C(x) = 22,500 + 100x + 0.01x^2$$

dollars to manufacture x 30-gigabyte video iPods in a day.[1] How many iPods should be manufactured in order to minimize average cost? What is the resulting average cost of an iPod? (Give your answer to the nearest dollar.) HINT [See Example 1.]

12. *Average Cost: Xboxes* Assume that it costs **Microsoft** approximately

$$C(x) = 14,400 + 550x + 0.01x^2$$

---

[1] Not the actual cost equation; the authors do not know Apple's actual cost equation. The marginal cost in the model given is in rough agreement with the actual marginal cost for reasonable values of x. Source for cost data: *Manufacturing & Technology News*, July 31, 2007 Volume 14, No. 14 (www.manufacturingnews.com).

dollars to manufacture x Xbox 360s in a day.[2] How many Xboxes should be manufactured in order to minimize average cost? What is the resulting average cost of an Xbox? (Give your answer to the nearest dollar.) HINT [See Example 1.]

13. **Pollution Control** The cost of controlling emissions at a firm rises rapidly as the amount of emissions reduced increases. Here is a possible model:

$$C(q) = 4,000 + 100q^2$$

where q is the reduction in emissions (in pounds of pollutant per day) and C is the daily cost to the firm (in dollars) of this reduction. What level of reduction corresponds to the lowest average cost per pound of pollutant, and what would be the resulting average cost to the nearest dollar?

14. **Pollution Control** Repeat the preceding exercise using the following cost function:

$$C(q) = 2,000 + 200q^2.$$

15. **Pollution Control** (Compare Exercise 13.) The cost of controlling emissions at a firm is given by

$$C(q) = 4,000 + 100q^2$$

where q is the reduction in emissions (in pounds of pollutant per day) and C is the daily cost to the firm (in dollars) of this reduction. Government clean-air subsidies amount to $500 per pound of pollutant removed. How many pounds of pollutant should the firm remove each day in order to minimize *net* cost (cost minus subsidy)?

16. **Pollution Control** (Compare Exercise 14.) Repeat the preceding exercise, using the following cost function:

$$C(q) = 2,000 + 200q^2$$

with government subsidies amounting to $100 per pound of pollutant removed per day.

17. **Fences** I would like to create a rectangular vegetable patch. The fencing for the east and west sides costs $4 per foot, and the fencing for the north and south sides costs only $2 per foot. I have a budget of $80 for the project. What are the dimensions of the vegetable patch with the largest area I can enclose? HINT [See Example 2.]

18. **Fences** I would like to create a rectangular orchid garden that abuts my house so that the house itself forms the northern boundary. The fencing for the southern boundary costs $4 per foot, and the fencing for the east and west sides costs $2 per foot. If I have a budget of $80 for the project, what are the dimensions of the garden with the largest area I can enclose? HINT [See Example 2.]

19. **Fences** You are building a right-angled triangular flower garden along a stream as shown in the figure.

The fencing of the left border costs $5 per foot, while the fencing of the lower border costs $1 per foot. (No fencing is required along the river.) You want to spend $100 and enclose as much area as possible. What are the dimensions of your garden, and what area does it enclose? [The area of a right-triangle is given by $A = xy/2$.]

20. **Fences** Repeat Exercise 19, this time assuming that the fencing of the left border costs $8 per foot, while the fencing of the lower border costs $2 per foot, and that you can spend $400.

21. ▼ **Fences** (Compare Exercise 17.) For tax reasons, I need to create a rectangular vegetable patch with an area of exactly 242 sq. ft. The fencing for the east and west sides costs $4 per foot, and the fencing for the north and south sides costs only $2 per foot. What are the dimensions of the vegetable patch with the least expensive fence? HINT [Compare Exercise 3.]

22. ▼ **Fences** (Compare Exercise 18.) For reasons too complicated to explain, I need to create a rectangular orchid garden with an area of exactly 324 sq. ft. abutting my house so that the house itself forms the northern boundary. The fencing for the southern boundary costs $4 per foot, and the fencing for the east and west sides costs $2 per foot. What are the dimensions of the orchid garden with the least expensive fence? HINT [Compare Exercise 4.]

23. **Revenue** Hercules Films is deciding on the price of the video release of its film *Son of Frankenstein*. Its marketing people estimate that at a price of p dollars, it can sell a total of $q = 200,000 - 10,000p$ copies. What price will bring in the greatest revenue? HINT [See Example 3.]

24. **Profit** Hercules Films is also deciding on the price of the video release of its film *Bride of the Son of Frankenstein*. Again, marketing estimates that at a price of p dollars, it can sell $q = 200,000 - 10,000p$ copies, but each copy costs $4 to make. What price will give the greatest *profit*?

25. **Revenue: Cell Phones** Worldwide quarterly sales of **Nokia** cell phones were approximately $q = -p + 156$ million phones

when the wholesale price was $p. At what wholesale price should **Nokia** have sold its phones to maximize its quarterly revenue? What would have been the resulting revenue?[3]

26. **Revenue: Cell Phones** Worldwide annual sales of all cell phones were approximately $-10p + 1,600$ million phones when the wholesale price was $p. At what wholesale price should cell phones have been sold to maximize annual revenue? What would have been the resulting revenue?[4]

27. **Revenue: Monorail Service** The demand, in rides per day, for monorail service in Las Vegas in 2005 can be approximated by $q = -4,500p + 41,500$ when the fare was $p. What price should have been charged to maximize total revenue?[5]

28. **Demand for Monorail Service, Mars** The demand, in rides per day, for monorail service in the three urbynes (or districts) of Utarek, Mars, can be approximated by $q = -2p + 24$ million riders when the fare is $\overline{Z}p$. What price should be charged to maximize total revenue?[6]

29. ▼ **Revenue** Assume that the demand for tuna in a small coastal town is given by

$$p = \frac{500,000}{q^{1.5}}$$

where q is the number of pounds of tuna that can be sold in a month at p dollars per pound. Assume that the town's fishery wishes to sell at least 5,000 pounds of tuna per month.

  a. How much should the town's fishery charge for tuna in order to maximize monthly revenue? HINT [See Example 3, and don't neglect endpoints.]

  b. How much tuna will it sell per month at that price?

  c. What will be its resulting revenue?

30. ▼ **Revenue** Economist Henry Schultz devised the following demand function for corn:

$$p = \frac{6,570,000}{q^{1.3}}$$

where q is the number of bushels of corn that could be sold at p dollars per bushel in one year.[7] Assume that at least 10,000 bushels of corn per year must be sold.

  a. How much should farmers charge per bushel of corn to maximize annual revenue? HINT [See Example 3, and don't neglect endpoints.]

b. How much corn can farmers sell per year at that price?

c. What will be the farmers' resulting revenue?

31. ▼ **Revenue** The wholesale price for chicken in the United States fell from 25¢ per pound to 14¢ per pound, while per capita chicken consumption rose from 22 pounds per year to 27.5 pounds per year.[8] Assuming that the demand for chicken depends linearly on the price, what wholesale price for chicken maximizes revenues for poultry farmers, and what does that revenue amount to?

32. ▼ **Revenue** Your underground used-book business is booming. Your policy is to sell all used versions of *Calculus and You* at the same price (regardless of condition). When you set the price at $10, sales amounted to 120 volumes during the first week of classes. The following semester, you set the price at $30 and sold not a single book. Assuming that the demand for books depends linearly on the price, what price gives you the maximum revenue, and what does that revenue amount to?

33. **Profit: Cell Phones** (Compare Exercise 25.) Worldwide quarterly sales of **Nokia** cell phones were approximately $q = -p + 156$ million phones when the wholesale price was $p. Assuming that it cost **Nokia** $40 to manufacture each cell phone, at what wholesale price should **Nokia** have sold its phones to maximize its quarterly profit? What would have been the resulting profit?[9] (The actual wholesale price was $105 in the fourth quarter of 2004.) HINT [See Example 3, and recall that Profit = Revenue − Cost.]

34. **Profit: Cell Phones** (Compare Exercise 26.) Worldwide annual sales of all cell phones were approximately $-10p + 1,600$ million phones when the wholesale price was $p. Assuming that it costs $30 to manufacture each cell phone, at what wholesale price should cell phones have been sold to maximize annual profit? What would have been the resulting profit?[10] HINT [See Example 3, and recall that Profit = Revenue − Cost.]

35. ▼ **Profit** The demand equation for your company's virtual reality video headsets is

$$p = \frac{1,000}{q^{0.3}}$$

where q is the total number of headsets that your company can sell in a week at a price of p dollars. The total manufacturing and shipping cost amounts to $100 per headset.

  a. What is the greatest profit your company can make in a week, and how many headsets will your company sell at this level of profit? (Give answers to the nearest whole number.)

  b. How much, to the nearest $1, should your company charge per headset for the maximum profit?

---

[3] Demand equation based on second- and fourth-quarter sales. Source: Embedded.com/Company reports December, 2004.

[4] Demand equation based on estimated 2004 sales and projected 2008 sales. Source: I-Stat/NDR, December 2004.

[5] Source for ridership data: *New York Times*, February 10, 2007, p. A9.

[6] $\overline{Z}$ designates Zonars, the official currency in Mars. See www.marsnext .com for details of the Mars colony, its commerce, and its culture.

[7] Based on data for the period 1915–1929. Source: Henry Schultz, *The Theory and Measurement of Demand*, (as cited in *Introduction to Mathematical Economics* by A. L. Ostrosky, Jr., and J. V. Koch, Waveland Press, Prospect Heights, Illinois, 1979).

[8] Data are provided for the years 1951–1958. Source: U.S. Department of Agriculture, *Agricultural Statistics*.

[9] Source: Embedded.com/Company reports, December 2004.

[10] Wholesale price projections are the authors'. Source for sales prediction: I-Stat/NDR, December 2004.

36. ▼ **Profit** Due to sales by a competing company, your company's sales of virtual reality video headsets have dropped, and your financial consultant revises the demand equation to

$$p = \frac{800}{q^{0.35}}$$

where q is the total number of headsets that your company can sell in a week at a price of p dollars. The total manufacturing and shipping cost still amounts to $100 per headset.

a. What is the greatest profit your company can make in a week, and how many headsets will your company sell at this level of profit? (Give answers to the nearest whole number.)

b. How much, to the nearest $1, should your company charge per headset for the maximum profit?

37. **Paint Cans** A company manufactures cylindrical paint cans with open tops with a volume of 27,000 cubic centimeters. What should be the dimensions of the cans in order to use the least amount of metal in their production? HINT [See Example 4.]

38. **Metal Drums** A company manufactures cylindrical metal drums with open tops with a volume of 1 cubic meter. What should be the dimensions of the drum in order to use the least amount of metal in their production? HINT [See Example 4.]

39. **Tin Cans** A company manufactures cylindrical tin cans with closed tops with a volume of 250 cubic centimeters. The metal used to manufacture the cans costs $0.01 per square cm for the sides and $0.02 per square cm for the (thicker) top and bottom. What should be the dimensions of the cans in order to minimize the cost of metal in their production? What is the ratio height/radius? HINT [See Example 4.]

40. **Metal Drums** A company manufactures cylindrical metal drums with open tops with a volume of 2 cubic meters. The metal used to manufacture the cans costs $2 per square meter for the sides and $3 per square meter for the (thicker) bottom. What should be the dimensions of the drums in order to minimize the cost of metal in their production? What is the ratio height/radius? HINT [See Example 4.]

41. ▼ **Box Design** Chocolate Box Company is going to make open-topped boxes out of 6 × 16-inch rectangles of cardboard by cutting squares out of the corners and folding up the sides. What is the largest volume box it can make this way?

42. ▼ **Box Design** Vanilla Box Company is going to make open-topped boxes out of 12 × 12-inch rectangles of cardboard by cutting squares out of the corners and folding up the sides. What is the largest volume box it can make this way?

43. ▼ **Box Design** A packaging company is going to make closed boxes, with square bases, that hold 125 cubic centimeters. What are the dimensions of the box that can be built with the least material?

44. ▼ **Box Design** A packaging company is going to make open-topped boxes, with square bases, that hold 108 cubic centimeters. What are the dimensions of the box that can be built with the least material?

45. ▼ **Luggage Dimensions** American Airlines requires that the total outside dimensions (length + width + height) of a checked bag not exceed 62 inches.[11] Suppose you want to check a bag whose height equals its width. What is the largest volume bag of this shape that you can check on an American flight?

46. ▼ **Luggage Dimensions** American Airlines requires that the total outside dimensions (length + width + height) of a carry-on bag not exceed 45 inches.[12] Suppose you want to carry on a bag whose length is twice its height. What is the largest volume bag of this shape that you can carry on an American flight?

47. ▼ **Luggage Dimensions** Fly-by-Night Airlines has a peculiar rule about luggage: The length and width of a bag must add up to at most 45 inches, and the width and height must also add up to 45 inches. What are the dimensions of the bag with the largest volume that Fly-by-Night will accept?

48. ▼ **Luggage Dimensions** Fair Weather Airlines has a similar rule. It will accept only bags for which the sum of the length and width is at most 36 inches, while the sum of length, height, and twice the width is at most 72 inches. What are the dimensions of the bag with the largest volume that Fair Weather will accept?

49. ▼ **Package Dimensions** The **U.S. Postal Service (USPS)** will accept packages only if the length plus girth is no more than 108 inches.[13] (See the figure.)

Girth   Length

Assuming that the front face of the package (as shown in the figure) is square, what is the largest volume package that the **USPS** will accept?

50. ▼ **Package Dimensions** United Parcel Service (UPS) will accept only packages with a length of no more than 108 inches and length plus girth of no more than 165 inches.[14] (See figure for the preceding exercise.) Assuming that the front face of the package (as shown in the figure) is square, what is the largest volume package that **UPS** will accept?

51. ▼ **Cell Phone Revenues** The number of cell phone subscribers in China in the years 2000–2005 was projected to follow the equation $N(t) = 39t + 68$ million subscribers in year t ($t = 0$ represents January 2000). The average annual revenue per cell phone user was $350 in 2000.[15] If we assume

---

[11] According to information on its Web site (www.aa.com/).

[12] Ibid.

[13] The requirement for packages sent other than Parcel Post, as of September 2008 (www.usps.com/).

[14] The requirement as of September 2008 (www.ups.com/).

[15] Based on a regression of projected figures (coefficients are rounded). Source: Intrinsic Technology/*New York Times*, Nov. 24, 2000, p. C1.

that due to competition the revenue per cell phone user decreases continuously at an annual rate of 30%, we can model the annual revenue as

$$R(t) = 350(39t + 68)e^{-0.3t} \text{ million dollars.}$$

Determine **a.** when to the nearest 0.1 year the revenue was projected to peak and **b.** the revenue, to the nearest $1 million, at that time.

52. ▼ *Cell Phone Revenues* (Refer to Exercise 51.) If we assume instead that the revenue per cell phone user decreases continuously at an annual rate of 20%, we obtain the revenue model

$$R(t) = 350(39t + 68)e^{-0.2t} \text{ million dollars.}$$

Determine **a.** when to the nearest 0.1 year the revenue was projected to peak and **b.** the revenue, to the nearest $1 million, at that time.

53. ▼ *Research and Development* Spending on research and development by drug companies in the United States t years after 1970 can be modeled by

$$S(t) = 2.5e^{0.08t} \text{ billion dollars.} \quad (0 \le t \le 31)$$

The number of new drugs approved by the Federal Drug Administration (FDA) over the same period can be modeled by

$$D(t) = 10 + t \text{ drugs per year.}^{16} \quad (0 \le t \le 31)$$

When was the function $D(t)/S(t)$ at a maximum? What is the maximum value of $D(t)/S(t)$? What does the answer tell you about the cost of developing new drugs?

54. ▼ *Research and Development* (Refer to Exercise 53.) If the number of new drugs approved by the FDA had been $10 + 2t$ new drugs each year, when would the function $D(t)/S(t)$ have reached a maximum? What does the answer tell you about the cost of developing new drugs?

55. ▼ *Asset Appreciation* As the financial consultant to a classic auto dealership, you estimate that the total value (in dollars) of its collection of 1959 Chevrolets and Fords is given by the formula

$$v = 300{,}000 + 1{,}000t^2 \quad (t \ge 5)$$

where t is the number of years from now. You anticipate a continuous inflation rate of 5% per year, so that the discounted (present) value of an item that will be worth $\$v$ in t years' time is

$$p = ve^{-0.05t}.$$

When would you advise the dealership to sell the vehicles to maximize their discounted value?

56. ▼ *Plantation Management* The value of a fir tree in your plantation increases with the age of the tree according to the formula

$$v = \frac{20t}{1 + 0.05t}$$

where t is the age of the tree in years. Given a continuous inflation rate of 5% per year, the discounted (present) value of a newly planted seedling is

$$p = ve^{-0.05t}.$$

At what age (to the nearest year) should you harvest your trees in order to ensure the greatest possible discounted value?

57. ▼ *Marketing Strategy* FeatureRich Software Company has a dilemma. Its new program, Doors-X 10.27, is almost ready to go on the market. However, the longer the company works on it, the better it can make the program and the more it can charge for it. The company's marketing analysts estimate that if it delays t days, it can set the price at $100 + 2t$ dollars. On the other hand, the longer it delays, the more market share they will lose to their main competitor (see the next exercise) so that if it delays t days it will be able to sell $400{,}000 - 2{,}500t$ copies of the program. How many days should FeatureRich delay the release in order to get the greatest revenue?

58. ▼ *Marketing Strategy* FeatureRich Software's main competitor (see previous exercise) is Moon Systems, and Moon is in a similar predicament. Its product, Walls-Y 11.4, could be sold now for $200, but for each day Moon delays, it could increase the price by $4. On the other hand, it could sell 300,000 copies now, but each day it waits will cut sales by 1,500. How many days should Moon delay the release in order to get the greatest revenue?

59. ▼ *Average Profit* The FeatureRich Software Company sells its graphing program, Dogwood, with a volume discount. If a customer buys x copies, then he or she pays[17] $\$500\sqrt{x}$. It cost the company $10,000 to develop the program and $2 to manufacture each copy. If a single customer were to buy all the copies of Dogwood, how many copies would the customer have to buy for FeatureRich Software's average profit per copy to be maximized? How are average profit and marginal profit related at this number of copies?

60. ▼ *Average Profit* Repeat the preceding exercise with the charge to the customer $\$600\sqrt{x}$ and the cost to develop the program $9,000.

61. *Resource Allocation* Your company manufactures automobile alternators, and production is partially automated through the use of robots. Daily operating costs amount to $100 per laborer and $16 per robot. In order to meet production deadlines, the company calculates that the numbers of laborers and robots must satisfy the constraint

$$xy = 10{,}000$$

---

[16] The exponential model for R&D is based on the 1970 and 2001 spending in constant 2001 dollars, while the linear model for new drugs approved is based on the 6-year moving average from data from 1970–2000. Source for data: Pharmaceutical Research and Manufacturers of America, FDA/*New York Times*, April 19, 2002, p. C1.

---

[17] This is similar to the way site licenses have been structured for the program Maple®.

where x is the number of laborers and y is the number of robots. Assuming that the company wishes to meet production deadlines at a minimum cost, how many laborers and how many robots should it use? HINT [See Example 5.]

62. *Resource Allocation* Your company is the largest sock manufacturer in the solar system, and production is automated through the use of androids and robots. Daily operating costs amount to Ʉ200 per android and Ʉ8 per robot.[18] In order to meet production deadlines, the company calculates that the numbers of androids and robots must satisfy the constraint

$$xy = 1,000,000$$

where x is the number of androids and y is the number of robots. Assuming that the company wishes to meet production deadlines at a minimum cost, how many androids and how many robots should it use? HINT [See Example 5.]

63. ▼ *Resource Allocation* Your automobile assembly plant has a Cobb-Douglas production function given by

$$q = x^{0.4}y^{0.6}$$

where q is the number of automobiles it produces per year, x is the number of employees, and y is the daily operating budget (in dollars). Annual operating costs amount to an average of \$20,000 per employee plus the operating budget of \$365y. Assume that you wish to produce 1,000 automobiles per year at a minimum cost. How many employees should you hire? HINT [See Example 5.]

64. ▼ *Resource Allocation* Repeat the preceding exercise using the production formula

$$q = x^{0.5}y^{0.5}.$$

HINT [See Example 5.]

65. ▼ *Incarceration Rate* The incarceration rate (the number of persons in prison per 100,000 residents) in the United States can be approximated by

$$N(t) = 0.04t^3 - 2t^2 + 40t + 460 \quad (0 \le t \le 18)$$

(t is the year since 1990).[19] When, to the nearest year, was the incarceration rate increasing most rapidly? When was it increasing least rapidly? HINT [You are being asked to find the extreme values of the rate of change of the incarceration rate.]

66. ▼ *Prison Population* The prison population in the United States can be approximated by

$$N(t) = 0.02t^3 - 2t^2 + 100t + 1,100 \text{ thousand people}$$
$$(0 \le t \le 18)$$

(t is the year since 1990).[20] When, to the nearest year, was the prison population increasing most rapidly? When was it increasing least rapidly? HINT [You are being asked to find the extreme values of the rate of change of the prison population.]

67. ▼ *Embryo Development* The oxygen consumption of a bird embryo increases from the time the egg is laid through the time the chick hatches. In a typical galliform bird, the oxygen consumption can be approximated by

$$c(t) = -0.065t^3 + 3.4t^2 - 22t + 3.6 \text{ milliliters per day}$$
$$(8 \le t \le 30)$$

where t is the time (in days) since the egg was laid.[21] (An egg will typically hatch at around $t = 28$.) When, to the nearest day, is $c'(t)$ a maximum? What does the answer tell you?

68. ▼ *Embryo Development* The oxygen consumption of a turkey embryo increases from the time the egg is laid through the time the chick hatches. In a brush turkey, the oxygen consumption can be approximated by

$$c(t) = -0.028t^3 + 2.9t^2 - 44t + 95 \text{ milliliters per day}$$
$$(20 \le t \le 50)$$

where t is the time (in days) since the egg was laid.[22] (An egg will typically hatch at around $t = 50$.) When, to the nearest day, is $c'(t)$ a maximum? What does the answer tell you?

69. 🔲 ▼ *Subprime Mortgages* The percentage of U.S.-issued mortgages that are subprime can be approximated by

$$A(t) = \frac{15.0}{1 + 8.6(1.8)^{-t}} \text{ percent} \quad (0 \le t \le 8)$$

t years after the start of 2000.[23] Graph the *derivative* of $A(t)$ and determine the year during which this derivative had an absolute maximum and also its value at that point. What does the answer tell you?

70. 🔲 ▼ *Subprime Mortgage Debt* The approximate value of subprime (normally classified as risky) mortgage debt outstanding in the United States can be approximated by

$$A(t) = \frac{1,350}{1 + 4.2(1.7)^{-t}} \text{ billion dollars} \quad (0 \le t \le 8)$$

t years after the start of 2000.[24] Graph the *derivative* of $A(t)$ and determine the year during which this derivative had an absolute maximum and also its value at that point. What does the answer tell you?

71. 🔲 ▼ *Asset Appreciation* You manage a small antique company that owns a collection of Louis XVI jewelry boxes. Their value v is increasing according to the formula

$$v = \frac{10,000}{1 + 500e^{-0.5t}}$$

---

[18] Ʉ are Standard Solar Units of currency.

[19] Source for data: Sourcebook of Criminal Justice Statistics Online (www.albany.edu/sourcebook).

[20] Ibid.

[21] The model approximates graphical data published in the article "The Brush Turkey" by Roger S. Seymour, *Scientific American,* December, 1991, pp. 108–114.

[22] Ibid.

[23] Sources: Mortgage Bankers Association, UBS.

[24] Source: www.data360.org/dataset.aspx?Data_Set_Id=9549.

where t is the number of years from now. You anticipate an inflation rate of 5% per year, so that the present value of an item that will be worth v in t years' time is given by

$$p = v(1.05)^{-t}.$$

When (to the nearest year) should you sell the jewelry boxes to maximize their present value? How much (to the nearest constant dollar) will they be worth at that time?

72. ▣ ▼ *Harvesting Forests* The following equation models the approximate volume in cubic feet of a typical Douglas fir tree of age t years.[25]

$$V = \frac{22,514}{1 + 22,514t^{-2.55}}$$

The lumber will be sold at $10 per cubic foot, and you do not expect the price of lumber to appreciate in the foreseeable future. On the other hand, you anticipate a general inflation rate of 5% per year, so that the present value of an item that will be worth v in t years' time is given by

$$p = v(1.05)^{-t}.$$

At what age (to the nearest year) should you harvest a Douglas fir tree in order to maximize its present value? How much (to the nearest constant dollar) will a Douglas fir tree be worth at that time?

73. ◆ *Agriculture* The fruit yield per tree in an orchard containing 50 trees is 100 pounds per tree each year. Due to crowding, the yield decreases by 1 pound per season for every additional tree planted. How may additional trees should be planted for a maximum total annual yield?

74. ◆ *Agriculture* Two years ago your orange orchard contained 50 trees and the total yield was 75 bags of oranges. Last year you removed ten of the trees and noticed that the total yield increased to 80 bags. Assuming that the yield per tree depends linearly on the number of trees in the orchard, what should you do this year to maximize your total yield?

75. ◆ *Revenue* (based on a question on the GRE Economics Test[26]) If total revenue (TR) is specified by $TR = a + bQ - cQ^2$, where Q is quantity of output and a, b, and c are positive parameters, then TR is maximized for this firm when it produces Q equal to:

(A) $b/2ac$ **(B)** $b/4c$ **(C)** $(a + b)/c$ **(D)** $b/2c$ **(E)** $c/2b$

76. ◆ *Revenue* (based on a question on the GRE Economics Test) If total demand (Q) is specified by $Q = -aP + b$, where P is unit price and a and b are positive parameters, then

total revenue is maximized for this firm when it charges P equal to:

(A) $b/2a$ **(B)** $b/4a$ **(C)** a/b **(D)** $a/2b$ **(E)** $-b/2a$

COMMUNICATION AND REASONING EXERCISES

77. You are interested in knowing the height of the tallest condominium complex that meets the city zoning requirements that the height H should not exceed eight times the distance D from the road and that it must provide parking for at least 50 cars. The objective function of the associated optimization problem is then:

(A) H **(B)** $H - 8D$ **(C)** D **(D)** $D - 8H$

One of the constraints is:

(A) $8H = D$ **(B)** $8D = H$
(C) $H'(D) = 0$ **(D)** $D'(H) = 0$

78. You are interested in building a condominium complex with a height H of at least 8 times the distance D from the road and parking area of at least 1,000 sq ft. at the cheapest cost C. The objective function of the associated optimization problem is then:

(A) H **(B)** D **(C)** C **(D)** $H + D - C$

One of the constraints is:

(A) $H - 8D = 0$ **(B)** $H + D - C = 0$
(C) $C'(D) = 0$ **(D)** $8H = D$

79. Explain why the following problem is uninteresting: A packaging company wishes to make cardboard boxes with open tops by cutting square pieces from the corners of a square sheet of cardboard and folding up the sides. What is the box with the least surface area it can make this way?

80. Explain why finding the production level that minimizes a cost function is frequently uninteresting. What would a more interesting objective be?

81. Your friend Margo claims that all you have to do to find the absolute maxima and minima in applications is set the derivative equal to zero and solve. "All that other stuff about end-points and so-on is a waste of time just to make life hard for us," according to Margo. Explain why she is wrong, and find at least one exercise in this exercise set to illustrate your point.

82. You are having a hard time persuading your friend Marco that maximizing revenue is not the same as maximizing profit. "How on earth can you expect to obtain the largest profit if you are not taking in the largest revenue?" Explain why he is wrong, and find at least one exercise in this exercise set to illustrate your point.

83. ▼ If demand q decreases as price p increases, what does the minimum value of dq/dp measure?

84. ▼ Explain how you would solve an optimization problem of the following form. Maximize $P = f(x, y, z)$ subject to $z = g(x, y)$ and $y = h(x)$.

[25] The model is the authors' and is based on data in *Environmental and Natural Resource Economics* by Tom Tietenberg, Third Edition, (New York: HarperCollins, 1992), p. 282.

[26] Source: GRE Economics Test, by G. Gallagher, G. E. Pollock, W. J. Simeone, G. Yohe (Piscataway, NJ: Research and Education Association, 1989).

12.3 Higher Order Derivatives: Acceleration and Concavity

The **second derivative** is simply the derivative of the derivative function. To explain why we would be interested in such a thing, we start by discussing one of its interpretations.

Acceleration

Recall that if $s(t)$ represents the position of a car at time t, then its velocity is given by the derivative: $v(t) = s'(t)$. But one rarely drives a car at a constant speed; the velocity itself is changing. The rate at which the velocity is changing is the **acceleration**. Because the derivative measures the rate of change, acceleration is the derivative of velocity: $a(t) = v'(t)$. Because v is the derivative of s, we can express the acceleration in terms of s:

$$a(t) = v'(t) = (s')'(t) = s''(t)$$

That is, a is the derivative of the derivative of s, in other words, the second derivative of s, which we write as s''. (In this context you will often hear the derivative s' referred to as the **first derivative**.)

> ### Second Derivative, Acceleration
>
> If a function f has a derivative that is in turn differentiable, then its **second derivative** is the derivative of the derivative of f, written as f''. If $f''(a)$ exists, we say that f is **twice differentiable at $x = a$**.
>
> #### Quick Examples
>
> 1. If $f(x) = x^3 - x$, then $f'(x) = 3x^2 - 1$, so $f''(x) = 6x$ and $f''(-2) = -12$.
> 2. If $f(x) = 3x + 1$, then $f'(x) = 3$, so $f''(x) = 0$.
> 3. If $f(x) = e^x$, then $f'(x) = e^x$, so $f''(x) = e^x$ as well.
>
> The **acceleration** of a moving object is the derivative of its velocity—that is, the second derivative of the position function.
>
> #### Quick Example
>
> If t is time in hours and the position of a car at time t is $s(t) = t^3 + 2t^2$ miles, then the car's velocity is $v(t) = s'(t) = 3t^2 + 4t$ miles per hour and its acceleration is $a(t) = s''(t) = v'(t) = 6t + 4$ miles per hour per hour.

Differential Notation for the Second Derivative

We have written the second derivative of $f(x)$ as $f''(x)$. We could also use differential notation:

$$f''(x) = \frac{d^2f}{dx^2}$$

This notation comes from writing the second derivative as the derivative of the derivative in differential notation:

$$f''(x) = \frac{d}{dx}\left[\frac{df}{dx}\right] = \frac{d^2f}{dx^2}$$

Similarly, if $y = f(x)$, we write $f''(x)$ as $\dfrac{d}{dx}\left[\dfrac{dy}{dx}\right] = \dfrac{d^2y}{dx^2}$. For example, if $y = x^3$, then $\dfrac{d^2y}{dx^2} = 6x$.

An important example of acceleration is the acceleration due to gravity.

EXAMPLE 1 Acceleration Due to Gravity

According to the laws of physics, the height of an object near the surface of the earth falling in a vacuum from an initial rest position 100 feet above the ground under the influence of gravity is approximately

$$s(t) = 100 - 16t^2 \text{ feet}$$

in t seconds. Find its acceleration.

Solution The velocity of the object is

$$v(t) = s'(t) = -32t \text{ ft/s}. \qquad \text{Differential notation: } v = \frac{ds}{dt} = -32t \text{ ft/s.}$$

The reason for the negative sign is that the height of the object is decreasing with time, so its velocity is negative. Hence, the acceleration is

$$a(t) = s''(t) = -32 \text{ ft/s}^2. \qquad \text{Differential notation: } a = \frac{d^2s}{dt^2} = -32 \text{ ft/s}^2.$$

(We write ft/s^2 as an abbreviation for feet/second/second—that is, feet per second per second. It is often read "feet per second squared.") Thus, the *downward* velocity is increasing by 32 ft/s every second. We say that 32 ft/s^2 is the **acceleration due to gravity**. If we ignore air resistance, all falling bodies near the surface of the earth, no matter what their weight, will fall with this acceleration.*

➡ **Before we go on...** In very careful experiments using balls rolling down inclined planes, Galileo made one of his most important discoveries—that the acceleration due to gravity is constant and does not depend on the weight or composition of the object falling.† A famous, though probably apocryphal, story has him dropping cannonballs of different weights off the Leaning Tower of Pisa to prove his point.§ ∎

EXAMPLE 2 Acceleration of Sales

For the first 15 months after the introduction of a new video game, the total sales can be modeled by the curve

$$S(t) = 20e^{0.4t} \text{ units sold}$$

where t is the time in months since the game was introduced. After about 25 months total sales follow more closely the curve

$$S(t) = 100,000 - 20e^{17-0.4t}$$

How fast are total sales accelerating after 10 months? How fast are they accelerating after 30 months? What do these numbers mean?

Solution By acceleration we mean the rate of change of the rate of change, which is the second derivative. During the first 15 months, the first derivative of sales is

$$\frac{dS}{dt} = 8e^{0.4t}$$

✻ NOTE On other planets the acceleration due to gravity is different. For example, on Jupiter, it is about three times as large as on Earth.

† NOTE An interesting aside: Galileo's experiments depended on getting extremely accurate timings. Because the timepieces of his day were very inaccurate, he used the most accurate time measurement he could: He sang and used the beat as his stopwatch.

§ NOTE A true story: The point was made again during the Apollo 15 mission to the moon (July 1971) when astronaut David R. Scott dropped a feather and a hammer from the same height. The moon has no atmosphere, so the two hit the surface of the moon simultaneously.

and so the second derivative is

$$\frac{d^2 S}{dt^2} = 3.2e^{0.4t}$$

Thus, after 10 months the acceleration of sales is

$$\left.\frac{d^2 S}{dt^2}\right|_{t=10} = 3.2e^4 \approx 175 \text{ units/month/month, or units/month}^2$$

We can also compute total sales

$$S(10) = 20e^4 \approx 1,092 \text{ units}$$

and the rate of change of sales

$$\left.\frac{dS}{dt}\right|_{t=10} = 8e^4 \approx 437 \text{ units/month.}$$

What do these numbers mean? By the end of the tenth month, a total of 1,092 video games have been sold. At that time the game is selling at the rate of 437 units per month. This rate of sales is increasing by 175 units per month per month. More games will be sold each month than the month before.

To analyze the sales after 30 months is similar, using the formula

$$S(t) = 100,000 - 20e^{17-0.4t}.$$

The derivative is

$$\frac{dS}{dt} = 8e^{17-0.4t}$$

and the second derivative is

$$\frac{d^2 S}{dt^2} = -3.2e^{17-0.4t}.$$

After 30 months,

$$S(30) = 100,000 - 20e^{17-12} \approx 97,032 \text{ units}$$

$$\left.\frac{dS}{dt}\right|_{t=30} = 8e^{17-12} \approx 1,187 \text{ units/month}$$

$$\left.\frac{d^2 S}{dt^2}\right|_{t=30} = -3.2e^{17-12} \approx -475 \text{ units/month}^2.$$

By the end of the 30th month, 97,032 video games have been sold, the game is selling at a rate of 1,187 units per month, and the rate of sales is *decreasing* by 475 units per month. Fewer games are sold each month than the month before.

Geometric Interpretation of Second Derivative: Concavity

The first derivative of f tells us where the graph of f is rising [where $f'(x) > 0$] and where it is falling [where $f'(x) < 0$]. The second derivative tells in what direction the graph of f *curves* or *bends*. Consider the graphs in Figures 25 and 26.

$y = f(x)$ $y = g(x)$

Figure 25   **Figure 26**

Think of a car driving from left to right along each of the roads shown in the two figures. A car driving along the graph of f in Figure 25 will turn to the left (upward); a car driving along the graph of g in Figure 26 will turn to the right (downward). We say that the graph of f is **concave up** and the graph of g is **concave down**. Now think about the derivatives of f and g. The derivative $f'(x)$ starts small but *increases* as the graph gets steeper. Because $f'(x)$ is increasing, its derivative $f''(x)$ must be positive. On the other hand, $g'(x)$ *decreases* as we go to the right. Because $g'(x)$ is decreasing, its derivative $g''(x)$ must be negative. Summarizing, we have the following.

Concavity and the Second Derivative

A curve is **concave up** if its slope is increasing, in which case the second derivative is positive. A curve is **concave down** if its slope is decreasing, in which case the second derivative is negative. A point in the domain of f where the graph of f changes concavity, from concave up to concave down or vice versa, is called a **point of inflection**. At a point of inflection, the second derivative is either zero or undefined.

Locating Points of Inflection
To locate possible points of inflection, list points where $f''(x) = 0$ and also points where $f''(x)$ is not defined.

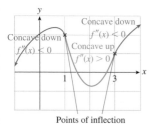

Figure 27

| Quick Examples |

1. The graph of the function f shown in Figure 27 is concave up when $1 < x < 3$, so $f''(x) > 0$ for $1 < x < 3$. It is concave down when $x < 1$ and $x > 3$, so $f''(x) < 0$ when $x < 1$ and $x > 3$. It has points of inflection at $x = 1$ and $x = 3$.
2. Consider $f(x) = x^3 - 3x$, whose graph is shown in Figure 28. $f''(x) = 6x$ is negative when $x < 0$ and positive when $x > 0$. The graph of f is concave down when $x < 0$ and concave up when $x > 0$. f has a point of inflection at $x = 0$, where the second derivative is 0.

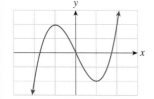

Figure 28

The following example shows one of the reasons it's useful to look at concavity.

EXAMPLE 3 Inflation

Figure 29 shows the value of the U.S. Consumer Price Index (CPI) from January 2007 through June 2008.*

Figure 29

The approximating curve shown on the figure is given by
$$I(t) = 0.0075t^3 - 0.2t^2 + 2.2t + 200 \qquad (1 \le t \le 19)$$

---

* The CPI is compiled by the Bureau of Labor Statistics and is based upon a 1982 value of 100. For instance, a CPI of 200 means the CPI has doubled since 1982. Source: InflationData.com (www.inflationdata.com).

where t is time in months ($t = 1$ represents January 2007). When the CPI is increasing, the U.S. economy is **experiencing inflation**. In terms of the model, this means that the derivative is positive: $I'(t) > 0$. Notice that $I'(t) > 0$ for the entire period shown (the graph is sloping upward), so the U.S. economy experienced inflation for $1 \le t \le 19$. We could measure **inflation** by the first derivative $I'(t)$ of the CPI, but we traditionally measure it as a ratio:

$$\text{Inflation rate} = \frac{I'(t)}{I(t)}, \qquad \text{Relative rate of change of the CPI}$$

expressed as a percentage per unit time (per month in this case).

a. Use the model to estimate the inflation rate in January 2008.

b. Was inflation slowing or speeding up in January 2008?

c. When was inflation slowing? When was inflation speeding up? When was inflation slowest?

Solution

a. We need to compute $I'(t)$:

$$I'(t) = 0.0225t^2 - 0.4t + 2.2$$

Thus, the inflation rate in January 2008 was given by

$$\text{Inflation rate} = \frac{I'(13)}{I(13)} = \frac{0.0225(13)^2 - 0.4(13) + 2.2}{0.0075(13)^3 - 0.2(13)^2 + 2.2(13) + 200}$$

$$= \frac{0.8025}{211.2775} \approx 0.00380,$$

or 0.38% per month.*

✻ NOTE The 0.38% monthly inflation rate corresponds to a $12 \times 0.38 = 4.56\%$ annual inflation rate. This result could be obtained directly by changing the units of the t-axis from months to years and then redoing the calculation.

b. We say that inflation is "slowing" when the CPI is decelerating ($I''(t) < 0$; the index rises at a slower rate). Similarly, inflation is "speeding up" when the CPI is accelerating ($I''(t) > 0$; the index rises at a faster rate). From the formula for $I'(t)$, the second derivative is

$$I''(t) = 0.045t - 0.4$$
$$I''(13) = 0.045(13) - 0.4 = 0.185.$$

Because this quantity is positive, we conclude that inflation was speeding up in January 2008.

c. When inflation is slowing, $I''(t)$ is negative, so the graph of the CPI is concave down. When inflation is speeding up, it is concave up. At the point at which it switches, there is point of inflection (Figure 30).

Figure 30

(a) Graph of S

(b) Graph of S′

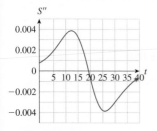

(c) Graph of S″

Figure 31

 using Technology

We can use a TI-83/84 Plus or a downloadable Excel sheet at the Web site to graph the second derivative of the function in Example 4:

TI-83/84 Plus

Y₁=1/(1+50*e^(-0.2X))
Y₂=nDeriv(Y₁,X,X)
Y₃=nDeriv(Y₂,X,X)

Web Site

www.FiniteandCalc.org

Student Web Site

→ Online Utilities

→ Excel First and Second
    Derivative Graphing Utility

Function:

1/(1+50*exp(-0.2*x))

The point of inflection occurs when $I''(t) = 0$; that is,

$$0.045t - 0.4 = 0$$

$$t = \frac{0.4}{0.45} \approx 8.9.$$

Thus, inflation was slowing when $t < 8.9$ (that is, until the end of August), and speeding up when $t > 8.9$ (after that time). Inflation was slowest at the point when it stopped slowing down and began to speed up, $t \approx 8.9$; notice that the graph has the least slope at that point.

EXAMPLE 4 The Point of Diminishing Returns

After the introduction of a new video game, the total worldwide sales are modeled by the curve

$$S(t) = \frac{1}{1 + 50e^{-0.2t}} \text{ million units sold}$$

where t is the time in months since the game was introduced (compare Example 2). The graphs of $S(t)$, $S'(t)$, and $S''(t)$ are shown in Figure 31. Where is the graph of S concave up, and where is it concave down? Where are any points of inflection? What does this all mean?

Solution Look at the graph of S. We see that the graph of S is concave up in the early months and then becomes concave down later. The point of inflection, where the concavity changes, is somewhere between 15 and 25 months.

Now look at the graph of S''. This graph crosses the t-axis very close to $t = 20$, is positive before that point, and negative after that point. Because positive values of S'' indicate S is concave up and negative values concave down, we conclude that the graph of S is concave up for about the first 20 months; that is, for $0 < t < 20$ and concave down for $20 < t < 40$. The concavity switches at the point of inflection, which occurs at about $t = 20$ (when $S''(t) = 0$; a more accurate answer is $t \approx 19.56$).

What does this all mean? Look at the graph of S', which shows sales per unit time, or monthly sales. From this graph we see that monthly sales are increasing for $t < 20$: more units are being sold each month than the month before. Monthly sales reach a peak of 0.05 million = 50,000 games per month at the point of inflection $t = 20$ and then begin to drop off. Thus, the point of inflection occurs at the time when monthly sales stop increasing and start to fall off; that is, the time when monthly sales peak. The point of inflection is sometimes called the **point of diminishing returns**. Although the total sales figure continues to rise (see the graph of S: game units continue to be sold), the *rate* at which units are sold starts to drop. (See Figure 32.)

Figure 32

The Second Derivative Test for Relative Extrema

The second derivative often gives us a way of knowing whether or not a stationary point is a relative extremum. Figure 33 shows a graph with two stationary points: a relative maximum at $x = a$ and a relative minimum at $x = b$.

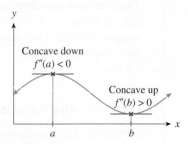

Figure 33

Notice that the curve is *concave down* at the relative maximum $(x = a)$, so that $f''(a) < 0$, and *concave up* at the relative minimum $(x = b)$, so that $f''(b) > 0$. This suggests the following (compare the First Derivative Test in Section 12.1).

Second Derivative Test for Relative Extrema

Suppose that the function f has a stationary point at $x = c$, and that $f''(c)$ exists. Determine the sign of $f''(c)$.

1. If $f''(c) > 0$ then f has a relative minimum at $x = c$.
2. If $f''(c) < 0$ then f has a relative maximum at $x = c$.

If $f''(c) = 0$ then the test is inconclusive and you need to use one of the methods of Section 12.1 (such as the first derivative test) to determine whether or not f has a relative extremum at $x = c$.

Quick Examples

1. $f(x) = x^2 - 2x$ has $f'(x) = 2x - 2$ and hence a stationary point at $x = 1$. $f''(x) = 2$, and so $f''(1) = 2$, which is positive, so f has a relative minimum at $x = 1$.
2. Let $f(x) = x^3 - 3x^2 - 9x$. Then
   $$f'(x) = 3x^2 - 6x - 9 = 3(x + 1)(x - 3)$$
   Stationary points at $x = -1, x = 3$
   $$f''(x) = 6x - 6$$
   $f''(-1) = -12$, so there is a relative maximum at $x = -1$
   $f''(3) = 12$, so there is a relative minimum at $x = 3$.
3. $f(x) = x^4$ has $f'(x) = 4x^3$ and hence a stationary point at $x = 0$. $f''(x) = 12x^2$ and so $f''(0) = 0$, telling us that the second derivative test is inconclusive. However, we can see from the graph of f or the first derivative test that f has a minimum at $x = 0$.

Higher Order Derivatives

There is no reason to stop at the second derivative; we could once again take the *derivative* of the second derivative to obtain the **third derivative**, f''', and we could take the derivative once again to obtain the **fourth derivative**, written $f^{(4)}$, and then continue to obtain $f^{(5)}$, $f^{(6)}$, and so on (assuming we get a differentiable function at each stage).

Higher Order Derivatives

We define

$$f'''(x) = \frac{d}{dx}[f''(x)]$$

$$f^{(4)}(x) = \frac{d}{dx}[f'''(x)]$$

$$f^{(5)}(x) = \frac{d}{dx}[f^{(4)}(x)],$$

and so on, assuming all these derivatives exist.

Different Notations

$$f'(x), f''(x), f'''(x), f^{(4)}(x), \ldots, f^{(n)}(x), \ldots$$

$$\frac{df}{dx}, \frac{d^2f}{dx^2}, \frac{d^3f}{dx^3}, \frac{d^4f}{dx^4}, \ldots, \frac{d^nf}{dx^n}, \ldots$$

$$\frac{dy}{dx}, \frac{d^2y}{dx^2}, \frac{d^3y}{dx^3}, \frac{d^4y}{dx^4}, \ldots, \frac{d^ny}{dx^n}, \ldots \qquad \text{When } y = f(x)$$

$$y, y', y'', y''', y^{(4)}, \ldots, y^{(n)}, \ldots \qquad \text{When } y = f(x)$$

Quick Examples

1. If $f(x) = x^3 - x$, then $f'(x) = 3x^2 - 1$, $f''(x) = 6x$, $f'''(x) = 6$, $f^{(4)}(x) = f^{(5)}(x) = \cdots = 0$.
2. If $f(x) = e^x$, then $f'(x) = e^x$, $f''(x) = e^x$, $f'''(x) = e^x$, $f^{(4)}(x) = f^{(5)}(x) = \cdots = e^x$.

Q: *We know that the second derivative can be interpreted as acceleration. How do we interpret the third derivative; and the fourth, fifth, and so on?*

A: Think of a car traveling down the road (with position $s(t)$ at time t) in such a way that its acceleration $\frac{d^2s}{dt^2}$ is changing with time (for instance, the driver may be slowly increasing pressure on the accelerator, causing the car to accelerate at a greater and greater rate). Then $\frac{d^3s}{dt^3}$ is the rate of change of acceleration. $\frac{d^4s}{dt^4}$ would then be the *acceleration* of the acceleration, and so on.

Q :*How are these higher order derivatives reflected in the graph of a function f?*

A :Because the concavity is measured by f'', its derivative f''' tells us the rate of change of concavity. Similarly, $f^{(4)}$ would tell us the *acceleration* of concavity, and so on. These properties are very subtle and hard to discern by simply looking at the curve; the higher the order, the more subtle the property. There is a remarkable theorem by Taylor* that tells us that, for a large class of functions (including polynomial, exponential, logarithmic, and trigonometric functions) the values of all orders of derivative $f(a)$, $f'(a)$, $f''(a)$, $f'''(a)$, and so on at the single point $x = a$ are enough to describe the entire graph (even at points very far from $x = a$)! In other words, the smallest piece of a graph near any point a contains sufficient information to "clone" the entire graph!

✳ **NOTE** Brook Taylor (1685–1731) was an English mathematician.

FAQs

Interpreting Points of Inflection and Using the Second Derivative Test

Q :*It says in Example 4 that monthly sales reach a maximum at the point of inflection (second derivative is zero), but the Second Derivative test says that, for a maximum, the second derivative must be positive. What is going on here?*

A :What is a maximum in Example 4 is the *rate of change of* sales: which is measured in sales per unit time (monthly sales in the example). In other words, it is the *derivative* of the total sales function that is a maximum, so we located the maximum by setting its derivative (which is the *second* derivative of total sales) equal to zero. In general: To find relative (stationary) extrema of the *original* function, set $f'(x)$ equal to zero and solve for x as usual. The second derivative test can then be used to test the stationary point obtained. To find relative (stationary) extrema of the *rate of change of* f, set $f''(x) = 0$ and solve for x.

Q :*I used the second derivative test and it was inconclusive. That means that there is neither a relative maximum nor a relative minimum at x = a, right?*

A :Wrong. If (as is often the case) the second derivative is zero at a stationary point, all it means is that the second derivative test itself cannot determine whether the given point is a relative maximum, minimum, or neither. For instance, $f(x) = x^4$ has a stationary minimum at $x = 0$, but the second derivative test is inconclusive. In such cases, one should use another test (such as the first derivative test) to decide if the point is a relative maximum, minimum, or neither.

12.3 **EXERCISES**

▼ more advanced   ◆ challenging

🖳 indicates exercises that should be solved using technology

In Exercises 1–10, calculate $\dfrac{d^2y}{dx^2}$. HINT [See Quick Examples on page 894.]

1. $y = 3x^2 - 6$

2. $y = -x^2 + x$

3. $y = \dfrac{2}{x}$

4. $y = -\dfrac{2}{x^2}$

5. $y = 4x^{0.4} - x$

6. $y = 0.2x^{-0.1}$

7. $y = e^{-(x-1)} - x$

8. $y = e^{-x} + e^x$

9. $y = \dfrac{1}{x} - \ln x$

10. $y = x^{-2} + \ln x$

In Exercises 11–16, the position s of a point (in feet) is given as a function of time t (in seconds). Find (a) its acceleration as a function of t and (b) its acceleration at the specified time. HINT [See Example 1.]

11. $s = 12 + 3t - 16t^2$; $t = 2$

12. $s = -12 + t - 16t^2$; $t = 2$

13. $s = \dfrac{1}{t} + \dfrac{1}{t^2}$; $t = 1$ **14.** $s = \dfrac{1}{t} - \dfrac{1}{t^2}$; $t = 2$

15. $s = \sqrt{t} + t^2$; $t = 4$ **16.** $s = 2\sqrt{t} + t^3$; $t = 1$

In Exercises 17–24, the graph of a function is given. Find the approximate coordinates of all points of inflection of each function (if any). HINT [See Quick Examples on page 897.]

17.

18.

19.

20.

21.

22.

23.

24.
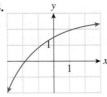

In Exercises 25–28, the graph of the derivative, $f'(x)$, is given. Determine the x-coordinates of all points of inflection of $f(x)$, if any. (Assume that $f(x)$ is defined and continuous everywhere in $[-3, 3]$.) HINT [See the **Before we go on** discussion in Example 4.]

25.

26.

27.

28.

In Exercises 29–32, the graph of the second derivative, $f''(x)$, is given. Determine the x-coordinates of all points of inflection of $f(x)$, if any. (Assume that $f(x)$ is defined and continuous everywhere in $[-3, 3]$.)

29.

30.

31.

32.

In Exercises 33–44, find the x-coordinates of all critical points of the given function. Determine whether each critical point is a relative maximum, minimum, or neither by first applying the second derivative test, and, if the test fails, by some other method. HINT [See Quick Examples on page 900.]

33. $f(x) = x^2 - 4x + 1$ **34.** $f(x) = 2x^2 - 2x + 3$

35. $g(x) = x^3 - 12x$ **36.** $g(x) = 2x^3 - 6x + 3$

37. $f(t) = t^3 - t$ **38.** $f(t) = -2t^3 + 3t$

39. $f(x) = x^4 - 4x^3$ **40.** $f(x) = 3x^4 - 2x^3$

41. $f(x) = e^{-x^2}$ **42.** $f(x) = e^{2-x^2}$

43. $f(x) = xe^{1-x^2}$ **44.** $f(x) = xe^{-x^2}$

In Exercises 45–54, calculate the derivatives of all orders: $f'(x)$, $f''(x)$, $f'''(x)$, $f^{(4)}(x)$, ..., $f^{(n)}(x)$, ... HINT [See Quick Examples on page 901.]

45. $f(x) = 4x^2 - x + 1$ **46.** $f(x) = -3x^3 + 4x$

47. $f(x) = -x^4 + 3x^2$ **48.** $f(x) = x^4 + x^3$

49. $f(x) = (2x + 1)^4$ **50.** $f(x) = (-2x + 1)^3$

51. $f(x) = e^{-x}$ **52.** $f(x) = e^{2x}$

53. $f(x) = e^{3x-1}$ **54.** $f(x) = 2e^{-x+3}$

APPLICATIONS

55. *Acceleration on Mars* If a stone is dropped from a height of 40 meters above the Martian surface, its height in meters after t seconds is given by $s = 40 - 1.9t^2$. What is its acceleration? HINT [See Example 1.]

56. *Acceleration on the Moon* If a stone is thrown up at 10 m per second from a height of 100 meters above the surface of the Moon, its height in meters after t seconds is given by $s = 100 + 10t - 0.8t^2$. What is its acceleration? HINT [See Example 1.]

57. *Motion in a Straight Line* The position of a particle moving in a straight line is given by $s = t^3 - t^2$ ft after t seconds. Find an expression for its acceleration after a time t. Is its velocity increasing or decreasing when $t = 1$?

58. *Motion in a Straight Line* The position of a particle moving in a straight line is given by $s = 3e^t - 8t^2$ ft after t seconds. Find an expression for its acceleration after a time t. Is its velocity increasing or decreasing when $t = 1$?

59. *Bottled Water Sales* Annual sales of bottled water in the United States in the period 2000–2008 can be approximated by

$$R(t) = 12t^2 + 500t + 4{,}700 \text{ million gallons} \quad (0 \le t \le 8)$$

where t is time in years since 2000.[27] Were sales of bottled water accelerating or decelerating in 2004? How quickly? HINT [See Example 2.]

60. *Bottled Water Sales* Annual U.S. per capita sales of bottled water through the period 2000–2008 can be approximated by

$$Q(t) = 0.04t^2 + 1.5t + 17 \text{ gallons} \quad (0 \le t \le 8)$$

where t is time in years since 2000.[28] Were U.S. per capita sales of bottled water accelerating or decelerating in 2006? How quickly?

61. *Embryo Development* The daily oxygen consumption of a bird embryo increases from the time the egg is laid through the time the chick hatches. In a typical galliform bird, the oxygen consumption can be approximated by

$$c(t) = -0.065t^3 + 3.4t^2 - 22t + 3.6 \text{ ml} \quad (8 \le t \le 30)$$

where t is the time (in days) since the egg was laid.[29] (An egg will typically hatch at around $t = 28$.) Use the model to estimate the following (give the units of measurement for each answer and round all answers to two significant digits):

a. The daily oxygen consumption 20 days after the egg was laid
b. The rate at which the oxygen consumption is changing 20 days after the egg was laid
c. The rate at which the oxygen consumption is accelerating 20 days after the egg was laid

62. *Embryo Development* The daily oxygen consumption of a turkey embryo increases from the time the egg is laid through the time the chick hatches. In a brush turkey, the oxygen consumption can be approximated by

$$c(t) = -0.028t^3 + 2.9t^2 - 44t + 95 \text{ ml} \quad (20 \le t \le 50)$$

where t is the time (in days) since the egg was laid.[30] (An egg will typically hatch at around $t = 50$.) Use the model to estimate the following (give the units of measurement for each answer and round all answers to two significant digits):

a. The daily oxygen consumption 40 days after the egg was laid
b. The rate at which the oxygen consumption is changing 40 days after the egg was laid
c. The rate at which the oxygen consumption is accelerating 40 days after the egg was laid

63. *Inflation* The following graph shows the approximate value of the United States Consumer Price Index (CPI) from December 2006 through July 2007.[31]

The approximating curve shown on the figure is given by

$$I(t) = -0.04t^3 + 0.4t^2 + 0.1t + 202 \quad (0 \le t \le 7)$$

where t is time in months ($t = 0$ represents December 2006).

a. Use the model to estimate the monthly inflation rate in February 2007 ($t = 2$). [Recall that the inflation *rate* is $I'(t)/I(t)$.]
b. Was inflation slowing or speeding up in February 2007?
c. When was inflation speeding up? When was inflation slowing? HINT [See Example 3.]

64. *Inflation* The following graph shows the approximate value of the U.S. Consumer Price Index (CPI) from September 2004 through November 2005.[32]

---

[27] Source for data: Beverage Marketing Corporation (www.bottledwater.org).

[28] Ibid.

[29] The model approximates graphical data published in the article "The Brush Turkey" by Roger S. Seymour, *Scientific American,* December, 1991, pp. 108–114.

[30] Ibid.

[31] The CPI is compiled by the Bureau of Labor Statistics and is based upon a 1982 value of 100. For instance, a CPI of 200 means the CPI has doubled since 1982. Source: InflationData.com (www.inflationdata.com).

[32] Ibid.

The approximating curve shown on the figure is given by

$$I(t) = -0.005t^3 + 0.12t^2 - 0.01t + 190 \quad (0 \le t \le 14)$$

where t is time in months ($t = 0$ represents September 2004).

a. Use the model to estimate the monthly inflation rate in July 2005 ($t = 10$). [Recall that the inflation *rate* is $I'(t)/I(t)$.]
b. Was inflation slowing or speeding up in July 2005?
c. When was inflation speeding up? When was inflation slowing? HINT [See Example 3.]

65. Inflation The following graph shows the approximate value of the U.S. Consumer Price Index (CPI) from July 2005 through March 2006.[33]

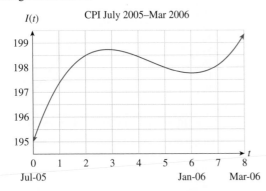

CPI July 2005–Mar 2006

The approximating curve shown on the figure is given by

$$I(t) = 0.06t^3 - 0.8t^2 + 3.1t + 195 \quad (0 \le t \le 8)$$

where t is time in months ($t = 0$ represents July 2005).

a. Use the model to estimate the monthly inflation rates in December 2005 and February 2006 ($t = 5$ and $t = 7$).
b. Was inflation slowing or speeding up in February 2006?
c. When was inflation decreasing? When was inflation increasing?

66. Inflation The following graph shows the approximate value of the U.S. Consumer Price Index (CPI) from March 2006 through May 2007.[34]

CPI Mar 2006–May 2007

The approximating curve shown on the figure is given by

$$I(t) = 0.02t^3 - 0.38t^2 + 2t + 200 \quad (0 \le t \le 14)$$

where t is time in months ($t = 0$ represents March, 2006).

a. Use the model to estimate the monthly inflation rates in September 2006 and January 2007 ($t = 6$ and $t = 10$).
b. Was inflation slowing or speeding up in January 2007?
c. When was inflation decreasing? When was inflation increasing?

67. Scientific Research The percentage of research articles in the prominent journal *Physical Review* that were written by researchers in the United States during the years 1983–2003 can be modeled by

$$P(t) = 25 + \frac{36}{1 + 0.06(0.7)^{-t}}$$

where t is time in years since 1983.[35] The graphs of P, P', and P'' are shown here:

Graph of P

Graph of P'

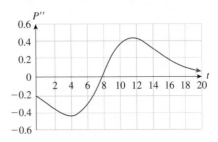

Graph of P''

[33] The CPI is compiled by the Bureau of Labor Statistics and is based upon a 1982 value of 100. For instance, a CPI of 200 means the CPI has doubled since 1982. Source: InflationData.com (www.inflationdata.com).
[34] Ibid.

[35] Source: The American Physical Society/*New York Times*, May 3, 2003, p. A1.

Determine, to the nearest whole number, the values of t for which the graph of P is concave up, and where it is concave down, and locate any points of inflection. What does the point of inflection tell you about science articles? HINT [See Example 4.]

68. **Scientific Research** The number of research articles in the prominent journal *Physical Review* that were written by researchers in Europe during the years 1983–2003 can be modeled by

$$P(t) = \frac{7.0}{1 + 5.4(1.2)^{-t}}$$

where t is time in years since 1983.[36] The graphs of P, P', and P'' are shown here:

Graph of P

Graph of P'

Graph of P''

Determine, to the nearest whole number, the values of t for which the graph of P is concave up, and where it is concave down, and locate any points of inflection. What does the point of inflection tell you about science articles?

[36] Source: The American Physical Society/*New York Times*, May 3, 2003, p. A1.

69. **Embryo Development** Here are sketches of the graphs of c, c', and c'' from Exercise 61:

Graph of c

Graph of c'

Graph of c''

Multiple choice:

a. The graph of c' (**A**) has a point of inflection (**B**) has no points of inflection in the range shown.

b. At around 18 days after the egg is laid, daily oxygen consumption is: (**A**) at a maximum, (**B**) increasing at a maximum rate, or (**C**) just beginning to decrease.

c. For $t > 18$ days, the oxygen consumption is (**A**) increasing at a decreasing rate, (**B**) decreasing at an increasing rate, or (**C**) increasing at an increasing rate.

70. **Embryo Development** Here are sketches of the graphs of c, c', and c'' from Exercise 62:

Graph of c

Graph of c'

Graph of c''

Multiple choice:

a. The graph of c: **(A)** has points of inflection, **(B)** has no points of inflection, or **(C)** may or may not have a point of inflection, but the graphs do not provide enough information.

b. At around 35 days after the egg is laid, the rate of change of daily oxygen consumption is: **(A)** at a maximum, **(B)** increasing at a maximum rate, or **(C)** just becoming negative.

c. For $t < 35$ days, the oxygen consumption is: **(A)** increasing at an increasing rate, **(B)** increasing at a decreasing rate, or **(C)** decreasing at an increasing rate.

71. 🔢 *Subprime Mortgages* The percentage of U.S.-issued mortgages that are subprime can be approximated by

$$A(t) = \frac{15.0}{1 + 8.6(1.8)^{-t}} \text{ percent } \quad (0 \le t \le 8)$$

t years after the start of 2000.[37] Graph the function as well as its first and second derivatives. Determine, to the nearest whole number, the values of t for which the graph of A is concave up and concave down, and the t-coordinate of any points of inflection. What does the point of inflection tell you about subprime mortgages? HINT [To graph the second derivative, see the note in the margin on page 899.]

72. 🔢 *Subprime Mortgage Debt* The approximate value of subprime (normally classified as risky) mortgage debt outstanding in the United States can be approximated by

$$A(t) = \frac{1{,}350}{1 + 4.2(1.7)^{-t}} \text{ billion dollars } \quad (0 \le t \le 8)$$

t years after the start of 2000.[38] Graph the function as well as its first and second derivatives. Determine, to the nearest whole number, the values of t for which the graph of A is concave up and concave down, and the t-coordinate of any points of inflection. What does the point of inflection tell you about subprime mortgages? HINT [To graph the second derivative, see the note in the margin on page 899.]

73. *Epidemics* The following graph shows the total number n of people (in millions) infected in an epidemic as a function of time t (in years):

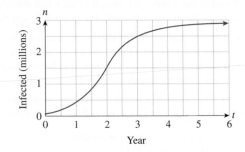

a. When to the nearest year was the rate of new infection largest?

b. When could the Centers for Disease Control and Prevention announce that the rate of new infection was beginning to drop? HINT [See Example 4.]

74. *Sales* The following graph shows the total number of Pomegranate Q4 computers sold since their release (t is in years):

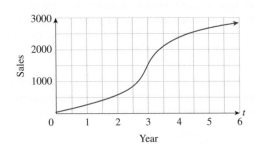

a. When were the computers selling fastest?

b. Explain why this graph might look as it does. HINT [See Example 4.]

---

[37] Sources: Mortgage Bankers Association, UBS.

[38] 2008 figure is an estimate.
Source: www.data360.org/dataset.aspx?Data_Set_Id=9549.

75. *Industrial Output* The following graph shows the yearly industrial output (measured in billions of zonars) of the Republic of Mars over a seven-year period:

P(t)   Industrial output (Republic of Mars)

Year since 2020

a. When to the nearest year did the rate of change of yearly industrial output reach a maximum?

b. When to the nearest year did the rate of change of yearly industrial output reach a minimum?

c. When to the nearest year does the graph first change from concave down to concave up? The result tells you that:

(A) In that year the rate of change of industrial output reached a minimum compared with nearby years.

(B) In that year the rate of change of industrial output reached a maximum compared with nearby years.

76. *Profits* The following graph shows the yearly profits of Gigantic Conglomerate, Inc. (GCI) from 2020 to 2035:

P(t)   Yearly profit ($ billions)

Year since 2020

a. Approximately when were the profits rising most rapidly?

b. Approximately when were the profits falling most rapidly?

c. Approximately when could GCI's board of directors legitimately tell stockholders that they had "turned the company around"?

77. ▼ *Education and Crime* The following graph shows a striking relationship between the total prison population and the average combined SAT score in the United States:

Combined SAT score (U.S. average)

Number of prisoners (thousands)

These data can be accurately modeled by

$$S(n) = 904 + \frac{1{,}326}{(n-180)^{1.325}}. \quad (192 \le n \le 563)$$

Here, $S(n)$ is the combined U.S. average SAT score at a time when the total U.S. prison population was n thousand.[39]

a. Are there any points of inflection on the graph of S?

b. What does the concavity of the graph of S tell you about prison populations and SAT scores?

78. ▼ *Education and Crime* Refer back to the model in the preceding exercise.

a. Are there any points of inflection on the graph of S'?

b. When is S'' a maximum? Interpret your answer in terms of prisoners and SAT scores.

79. ▼ *Patents* In 1965, the economist F. M. Scherer modeled the number, n, of patents produced by a firm as a function of the size, s, of the firm (measured in annual sales in millions of dollars). He came up with the following equation based on a study of 448 large firms:[40]

$$n = -3.79 + 144.42s - 23.86s^2 + 1.457s^3.$$

a. Find $\dfrac{d^2n}{ds^2}\Big|_{s=3}$. Is the rate at which patents are produced as the size of a firm goes up increasing or decreasing with size when $s = 3$? Comment on Scherer's words, ". . . we find diminishing returns dominating."

b. Find $\dfrac{d^2n}{ds^2}\Big|_{s=7}$ and interpret the answer.

c. Find the s-coordinate of any points of inflection and interpret the result.

80. ▼ *Returns on Investments* A company finds that the number of new products it develops per year depends on the size of its annual R&D budget, x (in thousands of dollars), according to the formula

$$n(x) = -1 + 8x + 2x^2 - 0.4x^3.$$

a. Find $n''(1)$ and $n''(3)$, and interpret the results.

b. Find the size of the budget that gives the largest rate of return as measured in new products per dollar (again, called the point of diminishing returns).

81. 🎛 ▼ *Oil Imports from Mexico* Daily oil production in Mexico and daily U.S. oil imports from Mexico during 2005–2009 can be approximated by

$$P(t) = 3.9 - 0.10t \text{ million barrels} \quad (5 \le t \le 9)$$
$$I(t) = 2.1 - 0.11t \text{ million barrels} \quad (5 \le t \le 9)$$

[39] The model is the authors' based on data for the years 1967–1989. Sources: *Sourcebook of Criminal Justice Statistics*, 1990, p. 604/ Educational Testing Service.

[40] Source: F. M. Scherer, "Firm Size, Market Structure, Opportunity, and the Output of Patented Inventions," *American Economic Review* 55 (December 1965): pp. 1097–1125.

where t is time in years since the start of 2000.[41]

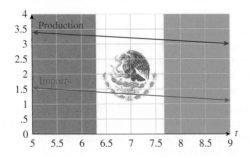

Graph the function $I(t)/P(t)$ and its derivative. Is the graph of $I(t)/P(t)$ concave up or concave down? The concavity of $I(t)/P(t)$ tells you that:

(A) The percentage of oil produced in Mexico that was exported to the United States was decreasing.
(B) The percentage of oil produced in Mexico that was not exported to the United States was increasing.
(C) The percentage of oil produced in Mexico that was exported to the United States was decreasing at a slower rate.
(D) The percentage of oil produced in Mexico that was exported to the United States was decreasing at a faster rate.

82. ▣ ▼ *Oil Imports from Mexico* Repeat Exercise 81 using instead the models for 2000–2004 shown below:

$$P(t) = 3.0 + 0.13t \text{ million barrels} \quad (0 \le t \le 4)$$
$$I(t) = 1.4 + 0.06t \text{ million barrels} \quad (0 \le t \le 4)$$

(t is time in years since the start of 2000).[42]

83. ◆ *Logistic Models* Let

$$f(x) = \frac{N}{1 + Ab^{-x}}$$

for constants N, A, and b *(A and b positive and $b \ne 1$)*. Show that f has a single point of inflection at $x = \ln A/\ln b$.

84. ◆ *Logistic Models* Let

$$f(x) = \frac{N}{1 + Ae^{-kx}}$$

for constants N, A, and k *(A and k positive)*. Show that f has a single point of inflection at $x = \ln A/k$.

85. ▣ *Population: Puerto Rico* The population of Puerto Rico in 1950–2025 can be approximated by

$$P(t) = \frac{4,500}{1 + 1.1466\,(1.0357)^{-t}} \text{ thousand people} \quad (0 \le t \le 75)$$

(t is the year since 1950).[43] Use the result of Exercise 83 to find the location of the point of inflection in the graph of P. What does the result tell you about the population of Puerto Rico?

86. ▣ *Population: Virgin Islands* The population of the Virgin Islands can be approximated by

$$P(t) = \frac{110}{1 + 2.3596\,(1.0767)^{-t}} \text{ thousand people} \quad (0 \le t \le 75)$$

(t is the year since 1950).[44] Use the result of Exercise 83 to find the location of the point of inflection in the graph of P. What does the result tell you about the population of the Virgin Islands?

87. ▣ ▼ *Asset Appreciation* You manage a small antique store that owns a collection of Louis XVI jewelry boxes. Their value v is increasing according to the formula

$$v = \frac{10,000}{1 + 500e^{-0.5t}}$$

where t is the number of years from now. You anticipate an inflation rate of 5% per year, so that the present value of an item that will be worth $\$v$ in t years' time is given by

$$p = v(1.05)^{-t}.$$

What is the greatest rate of increase of the value of your antiques, and when is this rate attained?

88. ▣ ▼ *Harvesting Forests* The following equation models the approximate volume in cubic feet of a typical Douglas fir tree of age t years[45]:

$$V = \frac{22,514}{1 + 22,514t^{-2.55}}.$$

The lumber will be sold at $10 per cubic foot, and you do not expect the price of lumber to appreciate in the foreseeable future. On the other hand, you anticipate a general inflation

---

[41] Source for data: Energy Information Administration/Pemex (http://www.eia.doe.gov)
[42] Ibid.
[43] Figures from 2010 on are U.S. census projections. Source for data: The 2008 Statistical Abstract (www.census.gov/).
[44] Ibid.
[45] The model is the authors', and is based on data in *Environmental and Natural Resource Economics* by Tom Tietenberg, Third Edition (New York: HarperCollins, 1992), p. 282.

rate of 5% per year, so that the present value of an item that will be worth $v in t years time is given by

$$p = v(1.05)^{-t}.$$

What is the largest rate of increase of the value of a fir tree, and when is this rate attained?

89. ▮ ▼ *Asset Appreciation* As the financial consultant to a classic auto dealership, you estimate that the total value of its collection of 1959 Chevrolets and Fords is given by the formula

$$v = 300,000 + 1,000t^2$$

where t is the number of years from now. You anticipate a continuous inflation rate of 5% per year, so that the discounted (present) value of an item that will be worth $v in t years' time is given by

$$p = ve^{-0.05t}.$$

When is the value of the collection of classic cars increasing most rapidly? When is it decreasing most rapidly?

90. ▮ ▼ *Plantation Management* The value of a fir tree in your plantation increases with the age of the tree according to the formula

$$v = \frac{20t}{1 + 0.05t}$$

where t is the age of the tree in years. Given a continuous inflation rate of 5% per year, the discounted (present) value of a newly planted seedling is

$$p = ve^{-0.05t}.$$

When is the discounted value of a tree increasing most rapidly? Decreasing most rapidly?

COMMUNICATION AND REASONING EXERCISES

91. Complete the following: If the graph of a function is concave up on its entire domain, then its second derivative is _____ on the domain.

92. Complete the following: If the graph of a function is concave up on its entire domain, then its first derivative is _____ on the domain.

93. Daily sales of Kent's Tents reached a maximum in January 2002 and declined to a minimum in January 2003 before starting to climb again. The graph of daily sales shows a point of inflection at June 2002. What is the significance of the point of inflection?

94. The graph of daily sales of Luddington's Wellington boots is concave down, although sales continue to increase. What properties of the graph of daily sales versus time are reflected in the following behaviors?

  a. a point of inflection next year
  b. a horizontal asymptote

95. ▼ Company A's profits satisfy $P(0) = \$1$ million, $P'(0) = \$1$ million per year, and $P''(0) = -\$1$ million per year per year. Company B's profits satisfy $P(0) = \$1$ million, $P'(0) = -\$1$ million per year, and $P''(0) = \$1$ million per year per year. There are no points of inflection in either company's profit curve. Sketch two pairs of profit curves: one in which Company A ultimately outperforms Company B and another in which Company B ultimately outperforms Company A.

96. ▼ Company C's profits satisfy $P(0) = \$1$ million, $P'(0) = \$1$ million per year, and $P''(0) = -\$1$ million per year per year. Company D's profits satisfy $P(0) = \$0$ million, $P'(0) = \$0$ million per year, and $P''(0) = \$1$ million per year per year. There are no points of inflection in either company's profit curve. Sketch two pairs of profit curves: one in which Company C ultimately outperforms Company D and another in which Company D ultimately outperforms Company C.

97. ▼ Explain geometrically why the derivative of a function has a relative extremum at a point of inflection, if it is defined there. Which points of inflection give rise to relative maxima in the derivative?

98. ▼ If we regard position, s, as a function of time, t, what is the significance of the *third* derivative, $s'''(t)$? Describe an everyday scenario in which this arises.

12.4 Analyzing Graphs

Mathematical curves are beautiful—their subtle form can be imitated by only the best of artists—and calculus gives us the tools we need to probe their secrets. While it is easy to use graphing technology to draw a graph, we must use calculus to understand what we are seeing. Following is a list of some of the most interesting features of the graph of a function.

Features of a Graph

1. ***The x- and y-intercepts:*** If $y = f(x)$, find the x-intercept(s) by setting $y = 0$ and solving for x; find the y-intercept by setting $x = 0$ and solving for y:

2. ***Extrema:*** Use the techniques of Section 12.1 to locate the maxima and minima:

3. ***Points of inflection:*** Use the techniques of Section 12.2 to locate the points of inflection:

4. ***Behavior near points where the function is not defined:*** If $f(x)$ is not defined at $x = a$, consider $\lim_{x \to a^-} f(x)$ and $\lim_{x \to a^+} f(x)$ to see how the graph of f behaves as x approaches a:

5. *Behavior at infinity:* Consider $\lim_{x \to -\infty} f(x)$ and $\lim_{x \to +\infty} f(x)$ if appropriate, to see how the graph of f behaves far to the left and right:

Note It is sometimes difficult or impossible to solve all of the equations that come up in Steps 1, 2, and 3 of the previous analysis. As a consequence, we might not be able to say exactly where the x-intercept, extrema, or points of inflection are. When this happens, we will use graphing technology to assist us in determining accurate numerical approximations. ■

$-50 \le x \le 50, -20 \le y \le 20$

$-10 \le x \le 10, -3 \le y \le 1$

Figure 34

EXAMPLE 1 Analyzing a Graph

Analyze the graph of $f(x) = \dfrac{1}{x} - \dfrac{1}{x^2}$.

Solution The graph, as drawn using graphing technology, is shown in Figure 34, using two different viewing windows. (Note that $x = 0$ is not in the domain of f.) The second window in Figure 34 seems to show the features of the graph better than the first. Does the second viewing window include *all* the interesting features of the graph? Or are there perhaps some interesting features to the right of $x = 10$ or to the left of $x = -10$? Also, where exactly do features like maxima, minima, and points of inflection occur? In our five-step process of analyzing the interesting features of the graph, we will be able to sketch the curve by hand, and also answer these questions.

1. *The x- and y-intercepts:* We consider $y = \dfrac{1}{x} - \dfrac{1}{x^2}$. To find the x-intercept(s), we set $y = 0$ and solve for x:

$$0 = \frac{1}{x} - \frac{1}{x^2}$$

$$\frac{1}{x} = \frac{1}{x^2}.$$

Multiplying both sides by x^2 (we know that x cannot be zero, so we are not multiplying both sides by 0) gives

$$x = 1.$$

Thus, there is one x-intercept (which we can see in Figure 34) at $x = 1$.

For the y-intercept, we would substitute $x = 0$ and solve for y. However, we cannot substitute $x = 0$; because $f(0)$ is not defined, the graph does not meet the y-axis.

We add features to our freehand sketch as we go. Figure 35 shows what we have so far.

Figure 35

2. *Relative extrema:* We calculate $f'(x) = -\dfrac{1}{x^2} + \dfrac{2}{x^3}$. To find any stationary points, we set the derivative equal to 0 and solve for x:

$$-\frac{1}{x^2} + \frac{2}{x^3} = 0$$

$$\frac{1}{x^2} = \frac{2}{x^3}$$

$$x = 2.$$

Thus, there is one stationary point, at $x = 2$. We can use a test point to the right to determine that this stationary point is a relative maximum:

x	1 (Intercept)	2	3 (Test point)
$y = \dfrac{1}{x} - \dfrac{1}{x^2}$	0	$\dfrac{1}{4}$	$\dfrac{2}{9}$

The only possible singular point is at $x = 0$ because $f'(0)$ is not defined. However, $f(0)$ is not defined either, so there are no singular points. Figure 36 shows our graph so far.

Figure 36

3. *Points of inflection:* We calculate $f''(x) = \dfrac{2}{x^3} - \dfrac{6}{x^4}$. To find points of inflection, we set the second derivative equal to 0 and solve for x:

$$\frac{2}{x^3} - \frac{6}{x^4} = 0$$

$$\frac{2}{x^3} = \frac{6}{x^4}$$

$$2x = 6$$

$$x = 3.$$

Figure 34 confirms that the graph of f changes from being concave down to being concave up at $x = 3$, so this is a point of inflection. $f''(x)$ is not defined at $x = 0$, but that is not in the domain, so there are no other points of inflection. In particular, the graph must be concave down in the whole region $(-\infty, 0)$, as we can see by calculating the second derivative at any one point in that interval: $f''(-1) = -8 < 0$.

Figure 37 shows our graph so far (we extended the curve near $x = 3$ to suggest a point of inflection at $x = 3$).

Figure 37

4. *Behavior near points where f is not defined:* The only point where $f(x)$ is not defined is $x = 0$. From the graph, $f(x)$ appears to go to $-\infty$ as x approaches 0 from either side. To calculate these limits, we rewrite $f(x)$:

$$f(x) = \frac{1}{x} - \frac{1}{x^2} = \frac{x - 1}{x^2}$$

Now, if x is close to 0 (on either side), the numerator $x - 1$ is close to -1 and the denominator is a very small but positive number. The quotient is therefore a negative number of very large magnitude. Therefore,

$$\lim_{x \to 0^-} f(x) = -\infty$$

and

$$\lim_{x \to 0^+} f(x) = -\infty.$$

Figure 38

Figure 39

From these limits, we see the following:

(1) Immediately to the *left* of $x = 0$, the graph plunges down toward $-\infty$.

(2) Immediately to the *right* of $x = 0$, the graph also plunges down toward $-\infty$.

Figure 38 shows our graph with these features added. We say that f has a **vertical asymptote** at $x = 0$, meaning that the points on the graph of f get closer and closer to points on a vertical line (the y-axis in this case) further and further from the origin.

5. ***Behavior at infinity:*** Both $1/x$ and $1/x^2$ go to 0 as x goes to $-\infty$ or $+\infty$; that is,

$$\lim_{x \to -\infty} f(x) = 0$$

and

$$\lim_{x \to +\infty} f(x) = 0.$$

Thus, on the extreme left and right of our picture, the height of the curve levels off toward zero. Figure 39 shows the completed freehand sketch of the graph.

We say that f has a **horizontal asymptote** at $y = 0$. (Notice another thing: We haven't plotted a single point to the left of the y-axis, and yet we have a pretty good idea of what the curve looks like there! Compare the technology-drawn curve in Figure 34.)

In summary, there is one x-intercept at $x = 1$; there is one relative maximum (which, we can now see, is also an absolute maximum) at $x = 2$; there is one point of inflection at $x = 3$, where the graph changes from being concave down to concave up. There is a vertical asymptote at $x = 0$, on both sides of which the graph goes down toward $-\infty$, and a horizontal asymptote at $y = 0$.

Technology:
2*x/3-((x-2)^2)^(1/3)

Figure 40

Figure 41

EXAMPLE 2 Analyzing a Graph

Analyze the graph of $f(x) = \dfrac{2x}{3} - (x - 2)^{2/3}$.

Solution Figure 40 shows a technology-generated version of the graph. Note that in the technology formulation $(x - 2)^{2/3}$ is written as $[(x - 2)^2]^{1/3}$ to avoid problems with some graphing calculators and Excel.

Let us now recreate this graph by hand, and in the process identify the features we see in Figure 40.

1. ***The x- and y-intercepts:*** We consider $y = \dfrac{2x}{3} - (x - 2)^{2/3}$. For the y-intercept, we set $x = 0$ and solve for y:

$$y = \frac{2(0)}{3} - (0 - 2)^{2/3} = -2^{2/3} \approx -1.59.$$

To find the x-intercept(s), we set $y = 0$ and solve for x. However, if we attempt this, we will find ourselves with a cubic equation that is hard to solve. (Try it!) Following the advice in the note on page 912, we use graphing technology to locate the x-intercept we see in Figure 40 by zooming in (Figure 41). From Figure 41, we find $x \approx 1.24$. We shall see in the discussion to follow that there can be no other x-intercepts.

Figure 42

Figure 42 shows our freehand sketch so far.

2. *Relative extrema:* We calculate

$$f'(x) = \frac{2}{3} - \frac{2}{3}(x - 2)^{-1/3}$$

$$= \frac{2}{3} - \frac{2}{3(x - 2)^{1/3}}.$$

To find any stationary points, we set the derivative equal to 0 and solve for x:

$$\frac{2}{3} - \frac{2}{3(x - 2)^{1/3}} = 0$$

$$(x - 2)^{1/3} = 1$$

$$x - 2 = 1^3 = 1$$

$$x = 3.$$

To check for singular points, look for points where $f(x)$ is defined and $f'(x)$ is not defined. The only such point is $x = 2$: $f'(x)$ is not defined at $x = 2$, whereas $f(x)$ is defined there, so we have a singular point at $x = 2$.

Figure 43

x	2 (Singular point)	3 (Stationary point)	4 (Test point)
$y = \dfrac{2x}{3} - (x - 2)^{2/3}$	$\dfrac{4}{3}$	1	1.079

Figure 43 shows our graph so far.

We see that there is a singular relative maximum at $(2, 4/3)$ (we will confirm that the graph eventually gets higher on the right) and a stationary relative minimum at $x = 3$.

3. *Points of inflection:* We calculate

$$f''(x) = \frac{2}{9(x - 2)^{4/3}}.$$

To find points of inflection, we set the second derivative equal to 0 and solve for x. But the equation

$$0 = \frac{2}{9(x - 2)^{4/3}}$$

has no solution for x, so there are no points of inflection on the graph.

4. *Behavior near points where f is not defined:* Because $f(x)$ is defined everywhere, there are no such points to consider. In particular, there are no vertical asymptotes.

5. *Behavior at infinity:* We estimate the following limits numerically:

$$\lim_{x \to -\infty} \left[\frac{2x}{3} - (x - 2)^{2/3} \right] = -\infty$$

and

$$\lim_{x \to +\infty} \left[\frac{2x}{3} - (x - 2)^{2/3} \right] = +\infty.$$

Figure 44

Thus, on the extreme left the curve goes down toward $-\infty$, and on the extreme right the curve rises toward $+\infty$. In particular, there are no horizontal asymptotes. (There can also be no other x-intercepts.)

Figure 44 shows the completed graph.

12.4 EXERCISES

▼ more advanced   ◆ challenging

T indicates exercises that should be solved using technology

In Exercises 1–26, sketch the graph of the given function, indicating (a) x- and y-intercepts, (b) extrema, (c) points of inflection, (d) behavior near points where the function is not defined, and (e) behavior at infinity. Where indicated, technology should be used to approximate the intercepts, coordinates of extrema, and/or points of inflection to one decimal place. Check your sketch using technology. HINT [See Example 1.]

1. $f(x) = x^2 + 2x + 1$

2. $f(x) = -x^2 - 2x - 1$

3. $g(x) = x^3 - 12x$, domain $[-4, 4]$

4. $g(x) = 2x^3 - 6x$, domain $[-4, 4]$

5. $h(x) = 2x^3 - 3x^2 - 36x$ [Use technology for x-intercepts.]

6. $h(x) = -2x^3 - 3x^2 + 36x$ [Use technology for x-intercepts.]

7. $f(x) = 2x^3 + 3x^2 - 12x + 1$ [Use technology for x-intercepts.]

8. $f(x) = 4x^3 + 3x^2 + 2$ [Use technology for x-intercepts.]

9. $k(x) = -3x^4 + 4x^3 + 36x^2 + 10$ [Use technology for x-intercepts.]

10. $k(x) = 3x^4 + 4x^3 - 36x^2 - 10$ [Use technology for x-intercepts.]

11. $g(t) = \frac{1}{4}t^4 - \frac{2}{3}t^3 + \frac{1}{2}t^2$

12. $g(t) = 3t^4 - 16t^3 + 24t^2 + 1$

13. $f(x) = x + \frac{1}{x}$

14. $f(x) = x^2 + \frac{1}{x^2}$

15. $g(x) = x^3/(x^2 + 3)$

16. $g(x) = x^3/(x^2 - 3)$

17. $f(t) = \frac{t^2 + 1}{t^2 - 1}$, domain $[-2, 2], t \neq \pm 1$

18. $f(t) = \frac{t^2 - 1}{t^2 + 1}$, domain $[-2, 2]$

19. $k(x) = \frac{2x}{3} + (x + 1)^{2/3}$ [Use technology for x-intercepts.

HINT [See Example 2.]

20. $k(x) = \frac{2x}{5} - (x - 1)^{2/5}$ [Use technology for x-intercepts.

HINT [See Example 2.]

21. $f(x) = x - \ln x$, domain $(0, +\infty)$

22. $f(x) = x - \ln x^2$, domain $(0, +\infty)$

23. $f(x) = x^2 + \ln x^2$ [Use technology for x-intercepts.]

24. $f(x) = 2x^2 + \ln x$ [Use technology for x-intercepts.]

25. $g(t) = e^t - t$, domain $[-1, 1]$

26. $g(t) = e^{-t^2}$

T *In Exercises 27–30, use technology to sketch the graph of the given function, labeling all relative and absolute extrema and points of inflection, and vertical and horizontal asymptotes. The coordinates of the extrema and points of inflection should be accurate to two decimal places.* HINT [To locate extrema accurately, plot the first derivative; to locate points of inflection accurately, plot the second derivative.]

27. ▼ $f(x) = x^4 - 2x^3 + x^2 - 2x + 1$

28. ▼ $f(x) = x^4 + x^3 + x^2 + x + 1$

29. ▼ $f(x) = e^x - x^3$

30. ▼ $f(x) = e^x - \frac{x^4}{4}$

APPLICATIONS

31. Home Prices The following graph shows the approximate value of the home price index as a percentage change from 2003. The locations of the maximum and the point of inflection are indicated on the graph (t is time in years since the start of 2004).[46]

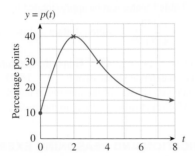

Analyze the graph's important features and interpret each feature in terms of the home price index.

32. Existing Home Sales The following graph shows the approximate value of existing home sales as a percentage change from 2003. The locations of the maximum and the point of inflection are indicated on the graph (t is time in years since the start of 2004).[47]

Analyze the graph's important features and interpret each feature in terms of the existing home sales.

33. Consumer Price Index The following graph shows the approximate value of the U.S. Consumer Price Index (CPI) from July 2005 through March 2006.[48]

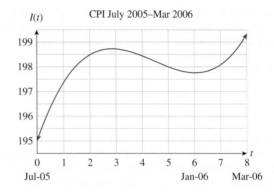

The approximating curve shown on the figure is given by

$$I(t) = 0.06t^3 - 0.8t^2 + 3.1t + 195 \quad (0 \le t \le 8)$$

where t is time in months ($t = 0$ represents July 2005).

a. Locate the intercepts, extrema, and points of inflection of the curve and interpret each feature in terms of the CPI. (Approximate all coordinates to one decimal place.)
HINT [See Example 1.]

b. Recall from Section 12.2 that the inflation rate is defined to be $\dfrac{I'(t)}{I(t)}$. What do the stationary extrema of the curve shown above tell you about the inflation rate?

34. Inflation The following graph shows the approximate value of the U.S. Consumer Price Index (CPI) from March 2006 through May 2007.[49]

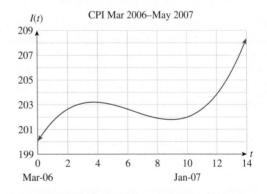

The approximating curve shown on the figure is given by

$$I(t) = 0.02t^3 - 0.38t^2 + 2t + 200 \quad (0 \le t \le 14)$$

where t is time in months ($t = 0$ represents March, 2006).

---

[46] 2008–2012 data are the authors' projections. Source for data: S&P/Case-Shiller Home Price Index. Source: Standard & Poors/*New York Times*, September 29, 2007, p. C3.

[47] 2008–2012 data are the authors' projections. Source for data: Bloomberg Finiancial Markets/*New York Times*, September 29, 2007, p. C3.

[48] The CPI is compiled by the Bureau of Labor Statistics and is based upon a 1982 value of 100. For instance, a CPI of 200 means the CPI has doubled since 1982. Source: InflationData.com (www.inflationdata.com).

[49] Ibid.

a. Locate the intercepts, extrema, and points of inflection of the curve and interpret each feature in terms of the CPI. (Approximate all coordinates to one decimal place.) HINT [See Example 1.]

b. Recall from Section 12.2 that the inflation rate is defined to be $\dfrac{I'(t)}{I(t)}$. What do the stationary extrema of the curve shown above tell you about the inflation rate?

35. *Motion in a Straight Line* The distance of a UFO from an observer is given by $s = 2t^3 - 3t^2 + 100$ feet after t seconds ($t \geq 0$). Obtain the extrema, points of inflection, and behavior at infinity. Sketch the curve and interpret these features in terms of the movement of the UFO.

36. *Motion in a Straight Line* The distance of the Mars orbiter from your location in Utarek, Mars is given by $s = 2(t - 1)^3 - 3(t - 1)^2 + 100$ km after t seconds ($t \geq 0$). Obtain the extrema, points of inflection, and behavior at infinity. Sketch the curve and interpret these features in terms of the movement of the Mars orbiter.

37. *Average Cost: iPods* Assume that it costs **Apple** approximately

$$C(x) = 22{,}500 + 100x + 0.01x^2$$

dollars to manufacture x 30-gigabyte video iPods in a day.[50] Obtain the average cost function, sketch its graph, and analyze the graph's important features. Interpret each feature in terms of iPods. HINT [Recall that the average cost function is $\bar{C}(x) = C(x)/x$.]

38. *Average Cost: Xboxes* Assume that it costs **Microsoft** approximately

$$C(x) = 14{,}400 + 550x + 0.01x^2$$

dollars to manufacture x Xbox 360s in a day.[51] Obtain the average cost function, sketch its graph, and analyze the graph's important features. Interpret each feature in terms of Xboxes. HINT [Recall that the average cost function is $\bar{C}(x) = C(x)/x$.]

39. ⊤ ▼ *Subprime Mortgages* The percentage of U.S.-issued mortgages that were subprime can be approximated by

$$A(t) = \frac{15.0}{1 + 8.6(1.8)^{-t}} \quad \text{percent} \qquad (0 \leq t \leq 8)$$

---

[50] Not the actual cost equation; the authors do not know Apple's actual cost equation. The marginal cost in the model given is in rough agreement with the actual marginal cost for reasonable values of x. Source for cost data: Manufacturing & Technology News, July 31, 2007 Volume 14, No. 14 (www.manufacturingnews.com).

[51] Not the actual cost equation; the authors do not know Microsoft's actual cost equation. The marginal cost in the model given is in rough agreement with the actual marginal cost for reasonable values of x. Source for estimate of marginal cost: iSuppli: (www.isuppli.com/news/xbox/).

t years after the start of 2000.[52] Graph the *derivative* $A'(t)$ of $A(t)$ using an extended domain of $0 \leq t \leq 15$. Determine the approximate coordinates of the maximum and determine the behavior of $A'(t)$ at infinity. What do the answers tell you?

40. ⊤ ▼ *Subprime Mortgage Debt* The approximate value of subprime (normally classified as risky) mortgage debt outstanding in the United States can be approximated by

$$A(t) = \frac{1{,}350}{1 + 4.2(1.7)^{-t}} \quad \text{billion dollars} \qquad (0 \leq t \leq 8)$$

t years after the start of 2000.[53] Graph the *derivative* $A'(t)$ of $A(t)$ using an extended domain of $0 \leq t \leq 15$. Determine the approximate coordinates of the maximum and determine the behavior of $A'(t)$ at infinity. What do the answers tell you?

COMMUNICATION AND REASONING EXERCISES

41. A function is *bounded* if its entire graph lies between two horizontal lines. Can a bounded function have vertical asymptotes? Can a bounded function have horizontal asymptotes? Explain.

42. A function is *bounded above* if its entire graph lies below some horizontal line. Can a bounded above function have vertical asymptotes? Can a bounded above function have horizontal asymptotes? Explain.

43. If the graph of a function has a vertical asymptote at $x = a$ in such a way that y increases to $+\infty$ as $x \to a$, what can you say about the graph of its derivative? Explain.

44. If the graph of a function has a horizontal asymptote at $y = a$ in such a way that y decreases to a as $x \to +\infty$, what can you say about the graph of its derivative? Explain.

45. Your friend tells you that he has found a continuous function defined on $(-\infty, +\infty)$ with exactly two critical points, each of which is a relative maximum. Can he be right?

46. Your other friend tells you that she has found a continuous function with two critical points, one a relative minimum and one a relative maximum, and no point of inflection between them. Can she be right?

47. ▼ By thinking about extrema, show that, if $f(x)$ is a polynomial, then between every pair of zeros (x-intercepts) of $f(x)$ there is a zero of $f'(x)$.

48. ▼ If $f(x)$ is a polynomial of degree 2 or higher, show that between every pair of relative extrema of $f(x)$ there is a point of inflection of $f(x)$.

---

[52] 2009 figure is an estimate. Sources: Mortgage Bankers Association, UBS.

[53] 2008–2009 figure are estimates. Source: www.data360.org/dataset.aspx?Data_Set_Id=9549.

12.5 Related Rates

We start by recalling some basic facts about the rate of change of a quantity:

Rate of Change of Q

If Q is a quantity changing over time t, then the derivative dQ/dt is the rate at which Q changes over time.

Quick Examples

1. If A is the area of an expanding circle, then dA/dt is the rate at which the area is increasing.
2. *Words:* The radius r of a sphere is currently 3 cm and increasing at a rate of 2 cm/s.

   Symbols: $r = 3$ cm and $dr/dt = 2$ cm/s.

In this section we are concerned with what are called **related rates** problems. In such a problem we have two (sometimes more) related quantities, we know the rate at which one is changing, and we wish to find the rate at which another is changing. A typical example is the following.

EXAMPLE 1 The Expanding Circle

The radius of a circle is increasing at a rate of 10 cm/s. How fast is the area increasing at the instant when the radius has reached 5 cm?

Solution We have two related quantities: the radius of the circle, r, and its area, A. The first sentence of the problem tells us that r is increasing at a certain rate. When we see a sentence referring to speed or change, it is very helpful to rephrase the sentence using the phrase "the rate of change of." Here, we can say

The rate of change of r is 10 cm/s.

Because the rate of change is the derivative, we can rewrite this sentence as the equation

$$\frac{dr}{dt} = 10.$$

Similarly, the second sentence of the problem asks how A is changing. We can rewrite that question:

What is the rate of change of A when the radius is 5 cm?

Using mathematical notation, the question is:

What is $\dfrac{dA}{dt}$ *when* $r = 5$?

Thus, knowing one rate of change, dr/dt, we wish to find a related rate of change, dA/dt. To find exactly how these derivatives are related, we need the equation relating the variables, which is

$$A = \pi r^2.$$

To find the relationship between the derivatives, we take the derivative of both sides of this equation *with respect to t*. On the left we get dA/dt. On the right we need to remember that r is a function of t and use the chain rule. We get

$$\frac{dA}{dt} = 2\pi r \frac{dr}{dt}.$$

Now we substitute the given values $r = 5$ and $dr/dt = 10$. This gives

$$\left.\frac{dA}{dt}\right|_{r=5} = 2\pi(5)(10) = 100\pi \approx 314 \text{ cm}^2/\text{s}.$$

Thus, the area is increasing at the rate of $314 \text{ cm}^2/\text{s}$ when the radius is 5 cm.

We can organize our work as follows:

Solving a Related Rates Problem

A. The Problem

1. List the related, changing quantities.
2. Restate the problem in terms of rates of change. Rewrite the problem using mathematical notation for the changing quantities and their derivatives.

B. The Relationship

1. Draw a diagram, if appropriate, showing the changing quantities.
2. Find an equation or equations relating the changing quantities.
3. Take the derivative with respect to time of the equation(s) relating the quantities to get the **derived equation(s)**, which relate the rates of change of the quantities.

C. The Solution

1. Substitute into the derived equation(s) the given values of the quantities and their derivatives.
2. Solve for the derivative required.

We can illustrate the procedure with the "ladder problem" found in almost every calculus textbook.

EXAMPLE 2 The Falling Ladder

Jane is at the top of a 5-foot ladder when it starts to slide down the wall at a rate of 3 feet per minute. Jack is standing on the ground behind her. How fast is the base of the ladder moving when it hits him if Jane is 4 feet from the ground at that instant?

Solution The first sentence talks about (the top of) the ladder sliding down the wall. Thus, one of the changing quantities is the height of the top of the ladder. The question asked refers to the motion of the base of the ladder, so another changing quantity is the distance of the base of the ladder from the wall. Let's record these variables and follow the outline above to obtain the solution.

A. The Problem

1. The changing quantities are

h = height of the top of the ladder
b = distance of the base of the ladder from the wall

2. We rephrase the problem in words, using the phrase "rate of change":

The rate of change of the height of the top of the ladder is −3 feet per minute. What is the rate of change of the distance of the base from the wall when the top of the ladder is 4 feet from the ground?

We can now rewrite the problem mathematically:

$$\frac{dh}{dt} = -3. \text{ Find } \frac{db}{dt} \text{ when } h = 4.$$

B. The Relationship

1. Figure 45 shows the ladder and the variables h and b. Notice that we put in the figure the fixed length, 5, of the ladder, but any changing quantities, like h and b, we leave as variables. We shall not use any specific values for h or b until the very end.

2. From the figure, we can see that h and b are related by the Pythagorean theorem:

$$h^2 + b^2 = 25.$$

3. Taking the derivative with respect to time of the equation above gives us the derived equation:

$$2h\frac{dh}{dt} + 2b\frac{db}{dt} = 0.$$

C. The Solution

1. We substitute the known values $dh/dt = -3$ and $h = 4$ into the derived equation:

$$2(4)(-3) + 2b\frac{db}{dt} = 0.$$

We would like to solve for db/dt, but first we need the value of b, which we can determine from the equation $h^2 + b^2 = 25$, using the value $h = 4$:

$$16 + b^2 = 25$$
$$b^2 = 9$$
$$b = 3.$$

Substituting into the derived equation, we get

$$-24 + 2(3)\frac{db}{dt} = 0.$$

2. Solving for db/dt gives

$$\frac{db}{dt} = \frac{24}{6} = 4.$$

Thus, the base of the ladder is sliding away from the wall at 4 ft/min when it hits Jack.

Figure 45

AFP/Getty Images

EXAMPLE 3 **Average Cost**

The cost to manufacture x cell phones in a day is

$$C(x) = 10,000 + 20x + \frac{x^2}{10,000} \text{ dollars.}$$

The daily production level is currently $x = 5,000$ cell phones and is increasing at a rate of 100 units per day. How fast is the average cost changing?

Solution

A. The Problem

1. The changing quantities are the production level x and the average cost, $\bar{C}$.

2. We rephrase the problem as follows:

> *The daily production level is $x = 5,000$ units and the rate of change of x is 100 units/ day. What is the rate of change of the average cost, $\bar{C}$?*

In mathematical notation,

$$x = 5,000 \text{ and } \frac{dx}{dt} = 100. \text{ Find } \frac{d\bar{C}}{dt}.$$

B. The Relationship

1. In this example the changing quantities cannot easily be depicted geometrically.

2. We are given a formula for the *total* cost. We get the *average* cost by dividing the total cost by x:

$$\bar{C} = \frac{C}{x}.$$

So,

$$\bar{C} = \frac{10,000}{x} + 20 + \frac{x}{10,000}.$$

3. Taking derivatives with respect to t of both sides, we get the derived equation:

$$\frac{d\bar{C}}{dt} = \left(-\frac{10,000}{x^2} + \frac{1}{10,000} \right) \frac{dx}{dt}.$$

C. The Solution

Substituting the values from part A into the derived equation, we get

$$\frac{d\bar{C}}{dt} = \left(-\frac{10,000}{5,000^2} + \frac{1}{10,000} \right) 100$$

$$= -0.03 \text{ dollars/day.}$$

Thus, the average cost is decreasing by 3¢ per day.

The scenario in the following example is similar to Example 5 in Section 12.2.

EXAMPLE 4 **Allocation of Labor**

The Gym Sock Company manufactures cotton athletic socks. Production is partially automated through the use of robots. The number of pairs of socks the company can manufacture in a day is given by a Cobb-Douglas production formula:

$$q = 50n^{0.6}r^{0.4}$$

where q is the number of pairs of socks that can be manufactured by n laborers and r robots. The company currently produces 1,000 pairs of socks each day and employs 20 laborers. It is bringing one new robot on line every month. At what rate are laborers being laid off, assuming that the number of socks produced remains constant?

Solution

A. The Problem

1. The changing quantities are the number of laborers n and the number of robots r.

2. $\dfrac{dr}{dt} = 1$. Find $\dfrac{dn}{dt}$ when $n = 20$.

B. The Relationship

1. No diagram is appropriate here.

2. The equation relating the changing quantities:

$$1{,}000 = 50n^{0.6}r^{0.4}$$

or

$$20 = n^{0.6}r^{0.4}.$$

(Productivity is constant at 1,000 pairs of socks each day.)

3. The derived equation is

$$0 = 0.6n^{-0.4}\left(\frac{dn}{dt}\right)r^{0.4} + 0.4n^{0.6}r^{-0.6}\left(\frac{dr}{dt}\right)$$

$$= 0.6\left(\frac{r}{n}\right)^{0.4}\left(\frac{dn}{dt}\right) + 0.4\left(\frac{n}{r}\right)^{0.6}\left(\frac{dr}{dt}\right).$$

We solve this equation for dn/dt because we shall want to find dn/dt below and because the equation becomes simpler when we do this:

$$0.6\left(\frac{r}{n}\right)^{0.4}\left(\frac{dn}{dt}\right) = -0.4\left(\frac{n}{r}\right)^{0.6}\left(\frac{dr}{dt}\right)$$

$$\frac{dn}{dt} = -\frac{0.4}{0.6}\left(\frac{n}{r}\right)^{0.6}\left(\frac{n}{r}\right)^{0.4}\left(\frac{dr}{dt}\right)$$

$$= -\frac{2}{3}\left(\frac{n}{r}\right)\left(\frac{dr}{dt}\right).$$

C. The Solution

Substituting the numbers in A into the last equation in B, we get

$$\frac{dn}{dt} = -\frac{2}{3}\left(\frac{20}{r}\right) \quad (1).$$

We need to compute r by substituting the known value of n in the original formula:

$$20 = n^{0.6}r^{0.4}$$
$$20 = 20^{0.6}r^{0.4}$$
$$r^{0.4} = \frac{20}{20^{0.6}} = 20^{0.4}$$
$$r = 20.$$

Thus,

$$\frac{dn}{dt} = -\frac{2}{3}\left(\frac{20}{20}\right)(1) = -\frac{2}{3} \text{ laborers per month.}$$

The company is laying off laborers at a rate of $2/3$ per month, or two every three months. We can interpret this result as saying that, at the current level of production and number of laborers, one robot is as productive as $2/3$ of a laborer, or 3 robots are as productive as 2 laborers.

12.5 EXERCISES

▼ more advanced   ◆ challenging
[T] indicates exercises that should be solved using technology

Rewrite the statements and questions in Exercises 1–8 in mathematical notation. HINT [See Quick Examples on page 919.]

1. The population P is currently 10,000 and growing at a rate of 1,000 per year.

2. There are presently 400 cases of Bangkok flu, and the number is growing by 30 new cases every month.

3. The annual revenue of your tie-dye T-shirt operation is currently $7,000 but is decreasing by $700 each year. How fast are annual sales changing?

4. A ladder is sliding down a wall so that the distance between the top of the ladder and the floor is decreasing at a rate of 3 feet per second. How fast is the base of the ladder receding from the wall?

5. The price of shoes is rising $5 per year. How fast is the demand changing?

6. Stock prices are rising $1,000 per year. How fast is the value of your portfolio increasing?

7. The average global temperature is 60°F and rising by 0.1°F per decade. How fast are annual sales of Bermuda shorts increasing?

8. The country's population is now 260,000,000 and is increasing by 1,000,000 people per year. How fast is the annual demand for diapers increasing?

APPLICATIONS

9. *Sun Spots* The area of a circular sun spot is growing at a rate of 1,200 km²/s.
   a. How fast is the radius growing at the instant when it equals 10,000 km? HINT [See Example 1.]
   b. How fast is the radius growing at the instant when the sun spot has an area of 640,000 km²? HINT [Use the area formula to determine the radius at that instant.]

10. *Puddles* The radius of a circular puddle is growing at a rate of 5 cm/s.
   a. How fast is its area growing at the instant when the radius is 10 cm? HINT [See Example 1.]
   b. How fast is the area growing at the instant when it equals 36 cm²? HINT [Use the area formula to determine the radius at that instant.]

11. *Balloons* A spherical party balloon is being inflated with helium pumped in at a rate of 3 cubic feet per minute. How fast is the radius growing at the instant when the radius has reached 1 foot? (The volume of a sphere of radius r is $V = \frac{4}{3}\pi r^3$.) HINT [See Example 1.]

12. *More Balloons* A rather flimsy spherical balloon is designed to pop at the instant its radius has reached 10 centimeters. Assuming the balloon is filled with helium at a rate of 10 cubic centimeters per second, calculate how fast the radius is growing at the instant it pops. (The volume of a sphere of radius r is $V = \frac{4}{3}\pi r^3$.) HINT [See Example 1.]

13. **Sliding Ladders** The base of a 50-foot ladder is being pulled away from a wall at a rate of 10 feet per second. How fast is the top of the ladder sliding down the wall at the instant when the base of the ladder is 30 feet from the wall? HINT [See Example 2.]

14. **Sliding Ladders** The top of a 5-foot ladder is sliding down a wall at a rate of 10 feet per second. How fast is the base of the ladder sliding away from the wall at the instant when the top of the ladder is 3 feet from the ground? HINT [See Example 2.]

15. **Average Cost** The average cost function for the weekly manufacture of portable CD players is given by

$$\bar{C}(x) = 150{,}000x^{-1} + 20 + 0.0001x \text{ dollars per player,}$$

where x is the number of CD players manufactured that week. Weekly production is currently 3,000 players and is increasing at a rate of 100 players per week. What is happening to the average cost? HINT [See Example 3.]

16. **Average Cost** Repeat the preceding exercise, using the revised average cost function

$$\bar{C}(x) = 150{,}000x^{-1} + 20 + 0.01x \text{ dollars per player.}$$

HINT [See Example 3.]

17. **Demand** Demand for your tie-dyed T-shirts is given by the formula

$$q = 500 - 100p^{0.5}$$

where q is the number of T-shirts you can sell each month at a price of p dollars. If you currently sell T-shirts for $15 each and you raise your price by $2 per month, how fast will the demand drop? (Round your answer to the nearest whole number.)

18. **Supply** The number of portable CD players you are prepared to supply to a retail outlet every week is given by the formula

$$q = 0.1p^2 + 3p$$

where p is the price it offers you. The retail outlet is currently offering you $40 per CD player. If the price it offers decreases at a rate of $2 per week, how will this affect the number you supply?

19. **Revenue** You can now sell 50 cups of lemonade per week at 30¢ per cup, but demand is dropping at a rate of 5 cups per week each week. Assuming that raising the price does not affect demand, how fast do you have to raise your price if you want to keep your weekly revenue constant? HINT [Revenue = Price × Quantity.]

20. **Revenue** You can now sell 40 cars per month at $20,000 per car, and demand is increasing at a rate of 3 cars per month each month. What is the fastest you could drop your price before your monthly revenue starts to drop? HINT [Revenue = Price × Quantity.]

21. ▼ **Oil Revenues** Daily oil production by **Pemex**, Mexico's national oil company, can be approximated by

$$q(t) = -0.022t^2 + 0.2t + 2.9 \text{ million barrels} \quad (1 \le t \le 9)$$

where t is time in years since the start of 2000.[54]

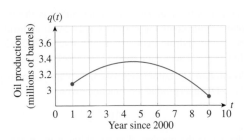

At the start of 2008 the price of oil was $90 per barrel and increasing at a rate of $80 per year.[55] How fast was **Pemex**'s oil (daily) revenue changing at that time?

22. ▼ **Oil Expenditures** Daily oil imports to the United States from Mexico can be approximated by

$$q(t) = -0.015t^2 + 0.1t + 1.4 \text{ million barrels} \quad (0 \le t \le 8)$$

where t is time in years since the start of 2000.[56]

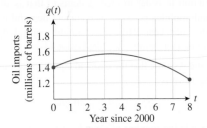

At the start of 2004 the price of oil was $30 per barrel and increasing at a rate of $40 per year.[57] How fast was (daily) oil expenditure for imports from Mexico changing at that time?

23. **Resource Allocation** Your company manufactures automobile alternators, and production is partially automated through the use of robots. In order to meet production deadlines, your company calculates that the numbers of laborers and robots must satisfy the constraint

$$xy = 10{,}000$$

where x is the number of laborers and y is the number of robots. Your company currently uses 400 robots and is increasing robot deployment at a rate of 16 per month. How fast is it laying off laborers? HINT [See Example 4.]

24. **Resource Allocation** Your company is the largest sock manufacturer in the solar system, and production is automated through the use of androids and robots. In order to meet production deadlines, your company calculates that the numbers of androids and robots must satisfy the constraint

$$xy = 1{,}000{,}000$$

---

[54] Source for data: Energy Information Administration/Pemex (http://www.eia.doe.gov).

[55] Based on NYMEX crude oil futures; average rate of change during January–June, 2008.
[56] Source for data: Energy Information Administration/Pemex (http://www.eia.doe.gov).
[57] Based on NYMEX crude oil futures; average rate of change during 2004–2005.

where x is the number of androids and y is the number of robots. Your company currently uses 5000 androids and is increasing android deployment at a rate of 200 per month. How fast is it scrapping robots? HINT [See Example 4.]

25. Production The automobile assembly plant you manage has a Cobb-Douglas production function given by

$$P = 10x^{0.3}y^{0.7}$$

where P is the number of automobiles it produces per year, x is the number of employees, and y is the daily operating budget (in dollars). You maintain a production level of 1,000 automobiles per year. If you currently employ 150 workers and are hiring new workers at a rate of 10 per year, how fast is your daily operating budget changing? HINT [See Example 4.]

26. Production Refer back to the Cobb-Douglas production formula in the preceding exercise. Assume that you maintain a constant work force of 200 workers and wish to increase production in order to meet a demand that is increasing by 100 automobiles per year. The current demand is 1000 automobiles per year. How fast should your daily operating budget be increasing? HINT [See Example 4.]

27. Demand Assume that the demand equation for tuna in a small coastal town is

$$pq^{1.5} = 50,000$$

where q is the number of pounds of tuna that can be sold in one month at the price of p dollars per pound. The town's fishery finds that the demand for tuna is currently 900 pounds per month and is increasing at a rate of 100 pounds per month each month. How fast is the price changing?

28. Demand The demand equation for rubies at Royal Ruby Retailers is

$$q + \frac{4}{3}p = 80$$

where q is the number of rubies RRR can sell per week at p dollars per ruby. RRR finds that the demand for its rubies is currently 20 rubies per week and is dropping at a rate of one ruby per week. How fast is the price changing?

29. ▼ Ships Sailing Apart The H.M.S. Dreadnaught is 40 miles north of Montauk and steaming due north at 20 miles/hour, while the U.S.S. Mona Lisa is 50 miles east of Montauk and steaming due east at an even 30 miles/hour. How fast is their distance apart increasing?

30. ▼ Near Miss My aunt and I were approaching the same intersection, she from the south and I from the west. She was traveling at a steady speed of 10 miles/hour, while I was approaching the intersection at 60 miles/hour. At a certain instant in time, I was one-tenth of a mile from the intersection, while she was one-twentieth of a mile from it. How fast were we approaching each other at that instant?

31. ▼ Baseball A baseball diamond is a square with side 90 ft.

A batter at home base hits the ball and runs toward first base with a speed of 24 ft/s. At what rate is his distance from third base increasing when he is halfway to first base?

32. ▼ Baseball Refer to Exercise 31. Another player is running from third base to home at 30 ft/s. How fast is her distance from second base increasing when she is 60 feet from third base?

33. ▼ Movement along a Graph A point on the graph of $y = 1/x$ is moving along the curve in such a way that its x-coordinate is increasing at a rate of 4 units per second. What is happening to the y-coordinate at the instant the y-coordinate is equal to 2?

34. ▼ Motion around a Circle A point is moving along the circle $x^2 + (y - 1)^2 = 8$ in such a way that its x-coordinate is decreasing at a rate of 1 unit per second. What is happening to the y-coordinate at the instant when the point has reached $(-2, 3)$?

35. ▼ Education In 1991, the expected income of an individual depended on his or her educational level according to the following formula:

$$I(n) = 2928.8n^3 - 115,860n^2 + 1,532,900n - 6,760,800.$$
$$(12 \le n \le 15)$$

Here, n is the number of school years completed and $I(n)$ is the individual's expected income.[58] You have completed 13 years of school and are currently a part-time student. Your schedule is such that you will complete the equivalent of one year of college every three years. Assuming that your salary is linked to the above model, how fast is your income going up? (Round your answer to the nearest $1.)

---

[58] The model is a best-fit cubic based on Table 358, U.S. Department of Education, *Digest of Education Statistics, 1991*, Washington, DC: Government Printing Office, 1991.

36. ▼ *Education* Refer back to the model in the preceding exercise. Assume that someone has completed 14 years of school and that her income is increasing by $10,000 per year. How much schooling per year is this rate of increase equivalent to?

37. ▼ *Employment* An employment research company estimates that the value of a recent MBA graduate to an accounting company is

$$V = 3e^2 + 5g^3$$

where V is the value of the graduate, e is the number of years of prior business experience, and g is the graduate school grade point average. A company that currently employs graduates with a 3.0 average wishes to maintain a constant employee value of $V = 200$, but finds that the grade point average of its new employees is dropping at a rate of 0.2 per year. How fast must the experience of its new employees be growing in order to compensate for the decline in grade point average?

38. ▼ *Grades*[59] A production formula for a student's performance on a difficult English examination is given by

$$g = 4hx - 0.2h^2 - 10x^2$$

where g is the grade the student can expect to obtain, h is the number of hours of study for the examination, and x is the student's grade point average. The instructor finds that students' grade point averages have remained constant at 3.0 over the years, and that students currently spend an average of 15 hours studying for the examination. However, scores on the examination are dropping at a rate of 10 points per year. At what rate is the average study time decreasing?

39. ▼ *Cones* A right circular conical vessel is being filled with green industrial waste at a rate of 100 cubic meters per second. How fast is the level rising after 200π cubic meters have been poured in? The cone has a height of 50 m and a radius of 30 m at its brim. (The volume of a cone of height h and cross-sectional radius r at its brim is given by $V = \frac{1}{3}\pi r^2 h$.)

40. ▼ *More Cones* A circular conical vessel is being filled with ink at a rate of 10 cm³/s. How fast is the level rising after 20 cm³ have been poured in? The cone has height 50 cm and radius 20 cm at its brim. (The volume of a cone of height h and cross-sectional radius r at its brim is given by $V = \frac{1}{3}\pi r^2 h$.)

41. ▼ *Cylinders* The volume of paint in a right cylindrical can is given by $V = 4t^2 - t$ where t is time in seconds and V is the volume in cm³. How fast is the level rising when the height is 2 cm? The can has a height of 4 cm and a radius of 2 cm. HINT [To get h as a function of t, first solve the volume $V = \pi r^2 h$ for h.]

42. ▼ *Cylinders* A cylindrical bucket is being filled with paint at a rate of 6 cm³ per minute. How fast is the level rising when the bucket starts to overflow? The bucket has a radius of 30 cm and a height of 60 cm.

43. ▼ *Computers vs. Income* The demand for personal computers in the home goes up with household income. For a given community, we can approximate the average number of computers in a home as

$$q = 0.3454 \ln x - 3.047 \quad 10,000 \le x \le 125,000$$

where x is mean household income.[60] Your community has a mean income of $30,000, increasing at a rate of $2,000 per year. How many computers per household are there, and how fast is the number of computers in a home increasing? (Round your answer to four decimal places.)

44. ▼ *Computers vs. Income* Refer back to the model in the preceding exercise. The average number of computers per household in your town is 0.5 and is increasing at a rate of 0.02 computers per household per year. What is the average household income in your town, and how fast is it increasing? (Round your answers to the nearest $10).

Education and Crime The following graph shows a striking relationship between the total prison population and the average combined SAT score in the U.S.

Exercises 45 and 46 are based on the following model for these data:

$$S(n) = 904 + \frac{1,326}{(n - 180)^{1.325}}. \quad (192 \le n \le 563)$$

Here, $S(n)$ is the combined average SAT score at a time when the total prison population is n thousand.[61]

45. ▼ In 1985, the U.S. prison population was 475,000 and increasing at a rate of 35,000 per year. What was the average SAT score, and how fast, and in what direction, was it changing? (Round your answers to two decimal places.)

---

[59] Based on an Exercise in *Introduction to Mathematical Economics* by A.L. Ostrosky Jr. and J.V. Koch (Waveland Press, Illinois, 1979.)

[60] The model is a regression model. Source for data: Income distribution: Computer data: Forrester Research/*The New York Times*, August 8, 1999, p. BU4.

[61] The model is the authors' based on data for the years 1967–1989. Sources: Sourcebook of Criminal Justice Statistics, 1990, p. 604/ Educational Testing Service.

46. ▼ In 1970, the U.S. combined SAT average was 940 and dropping by 10 points per year. What was the U.S. prison population, and how fast, and in what direction, was it changing? (Round your answers to the nearest 100.)

Divorce Rates *A study found that the divorce rate d (given as a percentage) appears to depend on the ratio r of available men to available women.*[62] *This function can be approximated by*

$$d(r) = \begin{cases} -40r + 74 & \text{if } r \leq 1.3 \\ \dfrac{130r}{3} - \dfrac{103}{3} & \text{if } r > 1.3 \end{cases}.$$

Exercises 47 and 48 are based on this model.

47. ◆ There are currently 1.1 available men per available woman in Littleville, and this ratio is increasing by 0.05 per year. What is happening to the divorce rate?

48. ◆ There are currently 1.5 available men per available woman in Largeville, and this ratio is decreasing by 0.03 per year. What is happening to the divorce rate?

COMMUNICATION AND REASONING EXERCISES

49. Why is this section titled "related rates"?

50. If you know how fast one quantity is changing and need to compute how fast a second quantity is changing, what kind of information do you need?

51. In a related rates problem, there is no limit to the number of changing quantities we can consider. Illustrate this by creating a related rates problem with four changing quantities.

---

[62] The cited study, by Scott J. South and associates, appeared in the *American Sociological Review* (February, 1995). Figures are rounded. Source: *The New York Times*, February 19, 1995, p. 40.

52. If three quantities are related by a single equation, how would you go about computing how fast one of them is changing based on a knowledge of the other two?

53. ▼ The demand and unit price for your store's checkered T-shirts are changing with time. Show that the percentage rate of change of revenue equals the sum of the percentage rates of change of price and demand. (The percentage rate of change of a quantity Q is $Q'(t)/Q(t)$.)

54. ▼ The number N of employees and the total floor space S of your company are both changing with time. Show that the percentage rate of change of square footage per employee equals the percentage rate of change of S minus the percentage rate of change of N. (The percentage rate of change of a quantity Q is $Q'(t)/Q(t)$.)

55. ▼ In solving a related rates problem, a key step is solving the derived equation for the unknown rate of change (once we have substituted the other values into the equation). Call the unknown rate of change X. The derived equation is what kind of equation in X?

56. ▼ On a recent exam, you were given a related rates problem based on an algebraic equation relating two variables x and y. Your friend told you that the correct relationship between dx/dt and dy/dt was given by

$$\left(\frac{dx}{dt}\right) = \left(\frac{dy}{dt}\right)^2.$$

Could he be correct?

57. ▼ Transform the following into a mathematical statement about derivatives: If my grades are improving at twice the speed of yours, then your grades are improving at half the speed of mine.

58. ▼ If two quantities x and y are related by a linear equation, how are their rates of change related?

12.6 Elasticity

You manufacture an extremely popular brand of sneakers and want to know what will happen if you increase the selling price. Common sense tells you that demand will drop as you raise the price. But will the drop in demand be enough to cause your revenue to fall? Or will it be small enough that your revenue will rise because of the higher selling price? For example, if you raise the price by 1%, you might suffer only a 0.5% loss in sales. In this case, the loss in sales will be more than offset by the increase in price and your revenue will rise. In such a case, we say that the demand is **inelastic**, because it is not very sensitive to the increase in price. On the other hand, if your 1% price increase results in a 2% drop in demand, then raising the price will cause a drop in revenues. We then say that the demand is **elastic** because it reacts strongly to a price change.

* NOTE Coming up with a good demand equation is not always easy. We saw in Chapter 1 that it is possible to find a linear demand equation if we know the sales figures at two different prices. However, such an equation is only a first approximation. To come up with a more accurate demand equation, we might need to gather data corresponding to sales at several different prices and use curve-fitting techniques like regression. Another approach would be an analytic one, based on mathematical modeling techniques that an economist might use.

We can use calculus to measure the response of demand to price changes if we have a demand equation for the item we are selling.* We need to know the *percentage drop in demand per percentage increase in price*. This ratio is called the **elasticity of demand**, or **price elasticity of demand**, and is usually denoted by E. Let's derive a formula for E in terms of the demand equation.

Assume that we have a demand equation

$$q = f(p)$$

where q stands for the number of items we would sell (per week, per month, or what have you) if we set the price per item at p. Now suppose we increase the price p by a very small amount, Δp. Then our percentage increase in price is $(\Delta p/p) \times 100\%$. This increase in p will presumably result in a decrease in the demand q. Let's denote this corresponding decrease in q by $-\Delta q$ (we use the minus sign because, by convention, Δq stands for the *increase* in demand). Thus, the percentage decrease in demand is $(-\Delta q/q) \times 100\%$.

Now E is the ratio

$$E = \frac{\text{Percentage decrease in demand}}{\text{Percentage increase in price}}$$

so

$$E = \frac{-\dfrac{\Delta q}{q} \times 100\%}{\dfrac{\Delta p}{p} \times 100\%}.$$

Canceling the 100%s and reorganizing, we get

$$E = -\frac{\Delta q}{\Delta p} \cdot \frac{p}{q}.$$

Q : *What small change in price will we use for Δp?*

A : It should probably be pretty small. If, say, we increased the price of sneakers to $1 million per pair, the sales would likely drop to zero. But knowing this tells us nothing about how the market would respond to a modest increase in price. In fact, we'll do the usual thing we do in calculus and let Δp approach 0.

In the expression for E, if we let Δp go to 0, then the ratio $\Delta q/\Delta p$ goes to the derivative dq/dp. This gives us our final and most useful definition of the elasticity.

Price Elasticity of Demand

The **price elasticity of demand E** is the percentage rate of decrease of demand per percentage increase in price. E is given by the formula

$$E = -\frac{dq}{dp} \cdot \frac{p}{q}.$$

We say that the demand is **elastic** if $E > 1$, is **inelastic** if $E < 1$, and has **unit elasticity** if $E = 1$.

✳ NOTE For another—more rigorous—argument, see Exercise 27.

✳ NOTE See, for example, Exercise 53 in Section 12.4.

Quick Example

Suppose that the demand equation is $q = 20,000 - 2p$ where p is the price in dollars. Then

$$E = -(-2)\frac{p}{20,000 - 2p} = \frac{p}{10,000 - p}.$$

If $p = \$2,000$, then $E = 1/4$, and demand is inelastic at this price.

If $p = \$8,000$, then $E = 4$, and demand is elastic at this price.

If $p = \$5,000$, then $E = 1$, and the demand has unit elasticity at this price.

We are generally interested in the price that maximizes revenue and, in ordinary cases, the price that maximizes revenue must give unit elasticity. One way of seeing this is as follows:✳ If the demand is inelastic (which ordinarily occurs at a low unit price) then raising the price by a small percentage—1% say—results in a smaller percentage drop in demand. For example, in the Quick Example above, if $p = \$2,000,$ d then the demand would drop by only $\frac{1}{4}$% for every 1% increase in price. To see the effect on revenue, we use the fact✳ that, for small changes in price,

Percentage change in revenue $\approx$ Percentage change in price
        $+$ Percentage change in demand

$$= 1 + \left(-\frac{1}{4}\right) = \frac{3}{4}\%.$$

Thus, the revenue will increase by about 3/4%. Put another way:

If the demand is inelastic, raising the price increases revenue.

On the other hand, if the price is elastic (which ordinarily occurs at a high unit price), then increasing the price slightly will lower the revenue, so:

If the demand is elastic, lowering the price increases revenue.

The price that results in the largest revenue must therefore be at unit elasticity.

EXAMPLE 1 Price Elasticity of Demand: Dolls

Suppose that the demand equation for Bobby Dolls is given by $q = 216 - p^2$, where p is the price per doll in dollars and q is the number of dolls sold per week.

a. Compute the price elasticity of demand when $p = \$5$ and $p = \$10$, and interpret the results.

b. Find the ranges of prices for which the demand is elastic and the range for which the demand is inelastic

c. Find the price at which the weekly revenue is maximized. What is the maximum weekly revenue?

Solution

a. The price elasticity of demand is

$$E = -\frac{dq}{dp} \cdot \frac{p}{q}.$$

Taking the derivative and substituting for q gives

$$E = 2p \cdot \frac{p}{216 - p^2} = \frac{2p^2}{216 - p^2}.$$

When $p = \$5$,

$$E = \frac{2(5)^2}{216 - 5^2} = \frac{50}{191} \approx 0.26.$$

Thus, when the price is set at \$5, the demand is dropping at a rate of 0.26% per 1% increase in the price. Because $E < 1$, the demand is inelastic at this price, so raising the price will increase revenue.

When $p = \$10$,

$$E = \frac{2(10)^2}{216 - 10^2} = \frac{200}{116} \approx 1.72.$$

Thus, when the price is set at \$10, the demand is dropping at a rate of 1.72% per 1% increase in the price. Because $E > 1$, demand is elastic at this price, so raising the price will decrease revenue; lowering the price will increase revenue.

b. and c. We answer part (c) first. Setting $E = 1$, we get

$$\frac{2p^2}{216 - p^2} = 1$$

$$p^2 = 72.$$

Thus, we conclude that the maximum revenue occurs when $p = \sqrt{72} \approx \$8.49$. We can now answer part (b): The demand is elastic when $p > \$8.49$ (the price is too high), and the demand is inelastic when $p < \$8.49$ (the price is too low). Finally, we calculate the maximum weekly revenue, which equals the revenue corresponding to the price of \$8.49:

$$R = qp = (216 - p^2)p = (216 - 72)\sqrt{72} = 144\sqrt{72} \approx \$1,222.$$

The concept of elasticity can be applied in other situations. In the following example we consider *income* elasticity of demand—the percentage increase in demand for a particular item per percentage increase in personal income.

EXAMPLE 2 Income Elasticity of Demand: Porsches

You are the sales director at Suburban Porsche and have noticed that demand for Porsches depends on income according to

$$q = 0.005e^{-0.05x^2 + x}. \qquad (1 \le x \le 10)$$

Here, x is the income of a potential customer in hundreds of thousands of dollars and q is the probability that the person will actually purchase a Porsche.[*] The **income elasticity of demand** is

$$E = \frac{dq}{dx}\frac{x}{q}.$$

Compute and interpret E for $x = 2$ and 9.

using Technology

See the Technology Guides at the end of the chapter to find out how to automate computations like those in part (a) of Example 1 using a graphing calculator or Excel. Here is an outline for the TI-83/84 Plus:

TI-83/84 Plus

$Y_1 = 216 - X^2$
$Y_2 = -n\text{Deriv}(Y_1, X, X) * X / Y_1$
2ND TABLE Enter $x = 5$
[More details on page 944.]

Excel

Enter values of p: 4.9, 4.91, . . . , 5.0, 5.01, . . . , 5.1 in A5–A25.
In B5 enter `216-A5^2` and copy down to B25.
In C5 enter `=(A6-A5)/A5` and paste the formula in C5–D24.
In E5 enter `=-D5/C5` and copy down to E24. This column contains the values of E for the values of p in column A.
[More details on page 944.]

✳ NOTE In other words, q is the fraction of visitors to your showroom having income x who actually purchase a Porsche.

Solution

Q : *Why is there no negative sign in the formula?*

A : Because we anticipate that the demand will increase as income increases, the ratio

$$\frac{\text{Percentage increase in demand}}{\text{Percentage increase in income}}$$

will be positive, so there is no need to introduce a negative sign.

Turning to the calculation, since $q = 0.005e^{-0.05x^2+x}$,

$$\frac{dq}{dx} = 0.005e^{-0.05x^2+x}(-0.1x+1)$$

and so

$$E = \frac{dq}{dx}\frac{x}{q}$$

$$= 0.005e^{-0.05x^2+x}(-0.1x+1)\frac{x}{0.005e^{-0.05x^2+x}}$$

$$= x(-0.1x+1).$$

When $x = 2$, $E = 2[-0.1(2)+1] = 1.6$. Thus, at an income level of $200,000, the probability that a customer will purchase a Porsche increases at a rate of 1.6% per 1% increase in income.

When $x = 9$, $E = 9[-0.1(9)+1] = 0.9$. Thus, at an income level of $900,000, the probability that a customer will purchase a Porsche increases at a rate of 0.9% per 1% increase in income.

12.6 EXERCISES

▼ more advanced   ◆ challenging
T indicates exercises that should be solved using technology

APPLICATIONS

1. **Demand for Oranges** The weekly sales of Honolulu Red Oranges is given by $q = 1,000 - 20p$. Calculate the price elasticity of demand when the price is $30 per orange (yes, $30 per orange[63]). Interpret your answer. Also, calculate the price that gives a maximum weekly revenue, and find this maximum revenue. HINT [See Example 1.]

2. **Demand for Oranges** Repeat the preceding exercise for weekly sales of $1,000 - 10p$. HINT [See Example 1.]

3. **Tissues** The consumer demand equation for tissues is given by $q = (100 - p)^2$, where p is the price per case of tissues and q is the demand in weekly sales.

a. Determine the price elasticity of demand E when the price is set at $30, and interpret your answer.
b. At what price should tissues be sold in order to maximize the revenue?
c. Approximately how many cases of tissues would be demanded at that price?

4. **Bodybuilding** The consumer demand curve for Professor Stefan Schwarzenegger dumbbells is given by $q = (100 - 2p)^2$, where p is the price per dumbbell, and q is the demand in weekly sales. Find the price Professor Schwarzenegger should charge for his dumbbells in order to maximize revenue.

5. **T-Shirts** The Physics Club sells $E = mc^2$ T-shirts at the local flea market. Unfortunately, the club's previous administration has been losing money for years, so you decide to do an analysis of the sales. A quadratic regression based on old sales data reveals the following demand equation for the T-shirts:

$$q = -2p^2 + 33p. \quad (9 \le p \le 15)$$

---

[63] They are very hard to find, and their possession confers considerable social status.

Here, p is the price the club charges per T-shirt, and q is the number it can sell each day at the flea market.

a. Obtain a formula for the price elasticity of demand for $E = mc^2$ T-shirts.
b. Compute the elasticity of demand if the price is set at $10 per shirt. *Interpret the result.*
c. How much should the Physics Club charge for the T-shirts in order to obtain the maximum daily revenue? What will this revenue be?

6. *Comics* The demand curve for original *Iguanawoman* comics is given by

$$q = \frac{(400 - p)^2}{100} \quad (0 \le p \le 400)$$

where q is the number of copies the publisher can sell per week if it sets the price at p.

a. Find the price elasticity of demand when the price is set at $40 per copy.
b. Find the price at which the publisher should sell the books in order to maximize weekly revenue.
c. What, to the nearest $1, is the maximum weekly revenue the publisher can realize from sales of *Iguanawoman* comics?

7. *College Tuition* A study of about 1,800 U.S. colleges and universities resulted in the demand equation $q = 9,900 - 2.2p$, where q is the enrollment at a college or university, and p is the average annual tuition (plus fees) it charges.[64]

a. The study also found that the average tuition charged by universities and colleges was $2,900. What is the corresponding price elasticity of demand? Is the price elastic or inelastic? Should colleges charge more or less on average to maximize revenue?
b. Based on the study, what would you advise a college to charge its students in order to maximize total revenue, and what would the revenue be?

8. *Demand for Fried Chicken* A fried chicken franchise finds that the demand equation for its new roast chicken product, "Roasted Rooster," is given by

$$p = \frac{40}{q^{1.5}}$$

where p is the price (in dollars) per quarter-chicken serving and q is the number of quarter-chicken servings that can be sold per hour at this price. Express q as a function of p and find the price elasticity of demand when the price is set at $4 per serving. Interpret the result.

9. *Paint-By-Number* The estimated monthly sales of *Mona Lisa* paint-by-number sets is given by the formula $q = 100e^{-3p^2 + p}$,

where q is the demand in monthly sales and p is the retail price in yen.

a. Determine the price elasticity of demand E when the retail price is set at ¥3 and interpret your answer.
b. At what price will revenue be a maximum?
c. Approximately how many paint-by-number sets will be sold per month at the price in part (b)?

10. *Paint-By-Number* Repeat the previous exercise using the demand equation $q = 100e^{p - 3p^2/2}$.

11. ▼ *Linear Demand Functions* A general linear demand function has the form $q = mp + b$ (m and b constants, $m \ne 0$).

a. Obtain a formula for the price elasticity of demand at a unit price of p.
b. Obtain a formula for the price that maximizes revenue.

12. ▼ *Exponential Demand Functions* A general exponential demand function has the form $q = Ae^{-bp}$ (A and b nonzero constants).

a. Obtain a formula for the price elasticity of demand at a unit price of p.
b. Obtain a formula for the price that maximizes revenue.

13. ▼ *Hyperbolic Demand Functions* A general hyperbolic demand function has the form $q = \dfrac{k}{p^r}$ (r and k nonzero constants).

a. Obtain a formula for the price elasticity of demand at unit price p.
b. How does E vary with p?
c. What does the answer to part (b) say about the model?

14. ▼ *Quadratic Demand Functions* A general quadratic demand function has the form $q = ap^2 + bp + c$ (a, b, and c constants with $a \ne 0$).

a. Obtain a formula for the price elasticity of demand at a unit price p.
b. Obtain a formula for the price or prices that could maximize revenue.

15. ▼ *Modeling Linear Demand* You have been hired as a marketing consultant to Johannesburg Burger Supply, Inc., and you wish to come up with a unit price for its hamburgers in order to maximize its weekly revenue. To make life as simple as possible, you assume that the demand equation for Johannesburg hamburgers has the linear form $q = mp + b$, where p is the price per hamburger, q is the demand in weekly sales, and m and b are certain constants you must determine.

a. Your market studies reveal the following sales figures: When the price is set at $2.00 per hamburger, the sales amount to 3,000 per week, but when the price is set at $4.00 per hamburger, the sales drop to zero. Use these data to calculate the demand equation.
b. Now estimate the unit price that maximizes weekly revenue and predict what the weekly revenue will be at that price.

---

[64] Based on a study by A.L. Ostrosky Jr. and J.V. Koch , as cited in their book, *Introduction to Mathematical Economics* (Waveland Press, Illinois, 1979) p. 133.

16. ▼ *Modeling Linear Demand* You have been hired as a marketing consultant to Big Book Publishing, Inc., and you have been approached to determine the best selling price for the hit calculus text by Whiner and Istanbul entitled *Fun with Derivatives*. You decide to make life easy and assume that the demand equation for *Fun with Derivatives* has the linear form $q = mp + b$, where p is the price per book, q is the demand in annual sales, and m and b are certain constants you'll have to figure out.

 a. Your market studies reveal the following sales figures: when the price is set at $50.00 per book, the sales amount to 10,000 per year; when the price is set at $80.00 per book, the sales drop to 1000 per year. Use these data to calculate the demand equation.

 b. Now estimate the unit price that maximizes annual revenue and predict what Big Book Publishing, Inc.'s annual revenue will be at that price.

17. *Income Elasticity of Demand: Live Drama* The likelihood that a child will attend a live theatrical performance can be modeled by

$$q = 0.01(-0.0078x^2 + 1.5x + 4.1) \quad (15 \le x \le 100)$$

Here, q is the fraction of children with annual household income x thousand dollars who will attend a live dramatic performance at a theater during the year.[65] Compute the income elasticity of demand at an income level of $20,000 and interpret the result. (Round your answer to two significant digits.) HINT [See Example 2.]

18. *Income Elasticity of Demand: Live Concerts* The likelihood that a child will attend a live musical performance can be modeled by

$$q = 0.01(0.0006x^2 + 0.38x + 35). \quad (15 \le x \le 100)$$

Here, q is the fraction of children with annual household income x who will attend a live musical performance during the year.[66] Compute the income elasticity of demand at an income level of $30,000 and interpret the result. HINT [See Example 2.]

19. *Income Elasticity of Demand: Computer Usage* The demand for personal computers in the home goes up with household income. The following graph shows some data on computer usage together with the logarithmic model $q = 0.3454 \ln(x) - 3.047$, where q is the probability that a household with annual income x will have a computer.[67]

a. Compute the income elasticity of demand for computers, to two decimal places, for a household income of $60,000 and interpret the result.

b. As household income increases, how is income elasticity of demand affected?

c. How reliable is the given model of demand for incomes well above $120,000? Explain.

d. What can you say about E for incomes much larger than those shown?

20. *Income Elasticity of Demand: Internet Usage* The demand for Internet connectivity also goes up with household income. The following graph shows some data on Internet usage, together with the logarithmic model $q = 0.2802 \ln(x) - 2.505$, where q is the probability that a home with annual household income x will have an Internet connection.[68]

a. Compute the income elasticity of demand to two decimal places for a household income of $60,000 and interpret the result.

b. As household income increases, how is income elasticity of demand affected?

c. The logarithmic model shown above is not appropriate for incomes well above $100,000. Suggest a model that might be more appropriate.

d. In the model you propose, how does E behave for very large incomes?

21. ▼ *Income Elasticity of Demand (based on a question on the GRE Economics Test)* If $Q = a P^\alpha Y^\beta$ is the individual's demand function for a commodity, where P is the (fixed) price of the commodity, Y is the individual's income, and a, α, and β are parameters, explain why β can be interpreted as the income elasticity of demand.

---

[65] Based on a quadratic regression of data from a 2001 survey. Source for data: New York Foundation of the Arts (www.nyfa.org/culturalblueprint/).

[66] Ibid.

[67] All figures are approximate. The model is a regression model, and x measures the probability that a given household will have one or more computers. Source: Income distribution computer data: Forrester Research/*The New York Times*, August 8, 1999, p. BU4.

[68] All figures are approximate, and the model is a regression model. The Internet connection figures were actually quoted as "share of consumers who use the Internet, by household income." Sources: Luxembourg Income Study/*The New York Times*, August 14, 1995, p. A9, Commerce Department, Deloitte & Touche Survey/*The New York Times*, November 24, 1999, p. C1.

22. ▼ *College Tuition (from the GRE Economics Test)* A time-series study of the demand for higher education, using tuition charges as a price variable, yields the following result:

$$\frac{dq}{dp} \cdot \frac{p}{q} = -0.4$$

where p is tuition and q is the quantity of higher education. Which of the following is suggested by the result?

(A) As tuition rises, students want to buy a greater quantity of education.

(B) As a determinant of the demand for higher education, income is more important than price.

(C) If colleges lowered tuition slightly, their total tuition receipts would increase.

(D) If colleges raised tuition slightly, their total tuition receipts would increase.

(E) Colleges cannot increase enrollments by offering larger scholarships.

23. ▼ *Modeling Exponential Demand* As the new owner of a supermarket, you have inherited a large inventory of unsold imported Limburger cheese, and you would like to set the price so that your revenue from selling it is as large as possible. Previous sales figures of the cheese are shown in the following table:

Price per Pound, p	$3.00	$4.00	$5.00
Monthly Sales in Pounds, q	407	287	223

a. Use the sales figures for the prices $3 and $5 per pound to construct a demand function of the form $q = Ae^{-bp}$, where A and b are constants you must determine. (Round A and b to two significant digits.)

b. Use your demand function to find the price elasticity of demand at each of the prices listed.

c. At what price should you sell the cheese in order to maximize monthly revenue?

d. If your total inventory of cheese amounts to only 200 pounds, and it will spoil one month from now, how should you price it in order to receive the greatest revenue? Is this the same answer you got in part (c)? If not, give a brief explanation.

24. ▼ *Modeling Exponential Demand* Repeat the preceding exercise, but this time use the sales figures for $4 and $5 per pound to construct the demand function.

COMMUNICATION AND REASONING EXERCISES

25. Complete the following: When demand is inelastic, revenue will decrease if ____ .

26. Complete the following: When demand has unit elasticity, revenue will decrease if ____ .

27. ▼ Given that the demand q is a differentiable function of the unit price p, show that the revenue $R = pq$ has a stationary point when

$$q + p\frac{dq}{dp} = 0.$$

Deduce that the stationary points of R are the same as the points of unit price elasticity of demand. (Ordinarily, there is only one such stationary point, corresponding to the absolute maximum of R.) HINT [Differentiate R with respect to p.]

28. ▼ Given that the demand q is a differentiable function of income x, show that the quantity $R = q/x$ has a stationary point when

$$q - x\frac{dq}{dx} = 0.$$

Deduce that stationary points of R are the same as the points of unit income elasticity of demand. HINT [Differentiate R with respect to x.]

29. ◆ Your calculus study group is discussing price elasticity of demand, and a member of the group asks the following question: "Since elasticity of demand measures the response of demand to change in unit price, what is the difference between elasticity of demand and the quantity $-dq/dp$?" How would you respond?

30. ◆ Another member of your study group claims that unit price elasticity of demand need not always correspond to maximum revenue. Is he correct? Explain your answer.

KEY CONCEPTS

REVIEW EXERCISES

In Exercises 1–8, find all the relative and absolute extrema of
the given functions on the given domain (if supplied) or on the
largest possible domain (if no domain is supplied).

1. $f(x) = 2x^3 - 6x + 1$ on $[-2, +\infty)$

2. $f(x) = x^3 - x^2 - x - 1$ on $(-\infty, \infty)$

3. $g(x) = x^4 - 4x$ on $[-1, 1]$

4. $f(x) = \dfrac{x+1}{(x-1)^2}$ on $[-2, 1) \cup (1, 2]$

5. $g(x) = (x-1)^{2/3}$ **6.** $g(x) = x^2 + \ln x$ on $(0, +\infty)$

7. $h(x) = \dfrac{1}{x} + \dfrac{1}{x^2}$ **8.** $h(x) = e^{x^2} + 1$

In Exercises 9–12, the graph of the function f or its derivative is
given. Find the approximate x-coordinates of all relative extrema
and points of inflection of the original function f (if any).

9. Graph of f:

10. Graph of f:

11. Graph of f':

12. Graph of f':

In Exercises 13 and 14, the graph of the second derivative of a
function f is given. Find the approximate x-coordinates of all
points of inflection of the original function f (if any).

13. Graph of f''

14. Graph of f''

In Exercises 15 and 16, the position s of a point (in meters) is given as a function of time t (in seconds). Find **(a)** its acceleration as a function of t and **(b)** its acceleration at the specified time.

15. $s = \dfrac{2}{3t^2} - \dfrac{1}{t}; t = 1$ **16.** $s = \dfrac{4}{t^2} - \dfrac{3t}{4}; t = 2$

In Exercises 17–22, sketch the graph of the given function, indicating all relative and absolute extrema and points of inflection. Find the coordinates of these points exactly, where possible. Also indicate any horizontal and vertical asymptotes.

17. $f(x) = x^3 - 12x$ on $[-2, +\infty)$

18. $g(x) = x^4 - 4x$ on $[-1, 1]$

19. $f(x) = \dfrac{x^2 - 3}{x^3}$

20. $f(x) = (x - 1)^{2/3} + \dfrac{2x}{3}$

21. $g(x) = (x - 3)\sqrt{x}$

22. $g(x) = (x + 3)\sqrt{x}$

APPLICATIONS

23. *Revenue* Demand for the latest best-seller at OHaganBooks.com, *A River Burns Through It*, is given by

$$q = -p^2 + 33p + 9 \quad (18 \le p \le 28)$$

copies sold per week when the price is p dollars. What price should the company charge to obtain the largest revenue?

24. *Revenue* Demand for *The Secret Loves of John O*, a romance novel by Margó Dufón that flopped after two weeks on the market, is given by

$$q = -2p^2 + 5p + 6 \quad (0 \le p \le 3.3)$$

copies sold per week when the price is p dollars. What price should OHaganBooks charge to obtain the largest revenue?

25. *Profit* Taking into account storage and shipping, it costs OHaganBooks.com

$$C = 9q + 100$$

dollars to sell q copies of *A River Burns Through It* in a week (see Exercise 23).

a. If demand is as in Exercise 23, express the weekly profit earned by OHaganBooks.com from the sale of *A River Burns Through It* as a function of unit price p.

b. What price should the company charge to get the largest weekly profit? What is the maximum possible weekly profit?

c. Compare your answer in part (b) with the price the company should charge to obtain the largest revenue (Exercise 23). Explain any difference.

26. *Profit* Taking into account storage and shipping, it costs OHaganBooks.com

$$C = 3q$$

dollars to sell q copies of Margó Dufón's *The Secret Loves of John O* in a week (see Exercise 24).

a. If demand is as in Exercise 24, express the weekly profit earned by OHaganBooks.com from the sale of *The Secret Loves of John O* as a function of unit price p.

b. What price should the company charge to get the largest weekly profit? What is the maximum possible weekly profit?

c. Compare your answer in part (b) with the price the company should charge to obtain the largest revenue (Exercise 24). Explain any difference.

27. *Box Design* The sales department at OHaganBooks.com, which has decided to send chocolate lobsters to each of its customers, is trying to design a shipping box with a square base. It has a roll of cardboard 36 inches wide from which to make the boxes. Each box will be obtained by cutting out corners from a rectangle of cardboard as shown in the following diagram:

(Notice that the top and bottom of each box will be square, but the sides will not necessarily be square.) What are the dimensions of the boxes with the largest volume that can be made in this way? What is the maximum volume?

28. *Box Redesign* The sales department at OHaganBooks.com was not pleased with the result of the box design in the preceding exercise; the resulting box was too large for the chocolate lobsters, so, following a suggestion by a math major student intern, the department decided to redesign the boxes to meet the following specifications: As in Exercise 27, each box would be obtained by cutting out corners from a rectangle of cardboard as shown in the following diagram:

(Notice that the top and bottom of each box would be square, but not necessarily the sides.) The dimensions would be such that the total surface area of the sides plus the bottom of the box would be as large as possible. What are the dimensions of the boxes with the largest area that can be made in this way? How does this box compare with that obtained in Exercise 27?

29. *Elasticity of Demand* (Compare Exercise 23). Demand for the latest best-seller at OHaganBooks.com, *A River Burns Through It*, is given by

$$q = -p^2 + 33p + 9 \quad (18 \leq p \leq 28)$$

copies sold per week when the price is p dollars.

a. Find the price elasticity of demand as a function of p.
b. Find the elasticity of demand for this book at a price of $20 and at a price of $25. (Round your answers to two decimal places.) Interpret the answers.
c. What price should the company charge to obtain the largest revenue?

30. *Elasticity of Demand* (Compare Exercise 24). Demand for *The Secret Loves of John O*, a romance novel by Margó Dufón that flopped after two weeks on the market, is given by

$$q = -2p^2 + 5p + 6 \quad (0 \leq p \leq 3.3)$$

copies sold per week when the price is p dollars.

a. Find the price elasticity of demand as a function of p.
b. Find the elasticity of demand for this book at a price of $2 and at a price of $3. (Round your answers to two decimal places.) Interpret the answers.
c. What price should the company charge to obtain the largest revenue?

31. *Elasticity of Demand* Last year OHaganBooks.com experimented with an online subscriber service, Red On Line (ROL), for its electronic book service. The consumer demand for ROL was modeled by the equation

$$q = 1,000e^{-p^2+p}$$

where p was the monthly access charge and q is the number of subscribers.

a. Obtain a formula for the price elasticity of demand, E, for ROL services.
b. Compute the elasticity of demand if the monthly access charge is set at $2 per month. Interpret the result.
c. How much should the company have charged in order to obtain the maximum monthly revenue? What would this revenue have been?

32. *Elasticity of Demand* JungleBooks.com (one of OHaganBooks' main competitors) responded with its own online subscriber service, Better On Line (BOL), for its electronic book service. The consumer demand for BOL was modeled by the equation

$$q = 2,000e^{-3p^2+2p}$$

where p was the monthly access charge and q is the number of subscribers.

a. Obtain a formula for the price elasticity of demand, E, for BOL services.
b. Compute the elasticity of demand if the monthly access charge is set at $2 per month. Interpret the result.
c. How much should the company have charged in order to obtain the maximum monthly revenue? What would this revenue have been?

33. *Sales* OHaganBooks.com modeled its weekly sales over a period of time with the function

$$s(t) = 6,053 + \frac{4,474}{1 + e^{-0.55(t-4.8)}}$$

where t is the time in weeks. Following are the graphs of s, s', and s'':

Graph of s

Graph of s'

Graph of s''

a. Estimate when, to the nearest week, the weekly sales were growing fastest.

b. To what features on the graphs of s, s', and s'' does your answer to part (a) correspond?

c. The graph of s has a horizontal asymptote. What is the approximate value (s-coordinate) of this asymptote, and what is its significance in terms of weekly sales at OHaganBooks.com?

d. The graph of s' has a horizontal asymptote. What is the value (s'-coordinate) of this asymptote, and what is its significance in terms of weekly sales at OHaganBooks.com?

34. *Sales* The quarterly sales of OHagan χPods (OHaganBooks' answer to the *iPod*; a portable audio book unit with an incidental music feature) from the fourth quarter of 2009 can be roughly approximated by the function

$$N(t) = \frac{1{,}100}{1 + 9(1.8)^{-t}} \quad (t \geq 0)$$

where t is time in quarters since the fourth quarter of 2009. Following are the graphs of N, N', and N'':

Graph of N

Graph of N'

Graph of N''

a. Estimate when, to the nearest quarter, the quarterly sales were growing fastest.

b. To what features on the graphs of N, N', and N'' does your answer to part (a) correspond?

c. The graph of N has a horizontal asymptote. What is the approximate value (N-coordinate) of this asymptote, and what is its significance in terms of quarterly sales of χPods?

d. The graph of N' has a horizontal asymptote. What is the value (N'-coordinate) of this asymptote, and what is its significance in terms of quarterly sales of χPods?

35. *Chance Encounter* Marjory Duffin is walking north towards the corner entrance of OHaganBooks.com company headquarters at 5 ft/s, while John O'Hagan is walking west toward the same entrance, also at 5 ft/s. How fast is their distance apart decreasing when:

a. Each of them is 2 ft from the corner?

b. Each of them is 1 ft. from the corner?

c. Each of them is h ft. from the corner?

d. They collide on the corner?

36. *Company Logos* OHaganBooks.com's Web site has an animated graphic with its name in a rectangle whose height and width change; on either side of the rectangle are semicircles, as in the figure, whose diameters are the same as the height of the rectangle.

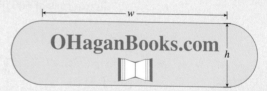

For reasons too complicated to explain, the designer wanted the combined area of the rectangle and semicircles to remain constant. At one point during the animation, the width of the rectangle is 1 inch, growing at a rate of 0.5 inches per second, while the height is 3 inches. How fast is the height changing?

Case Study   Production Lot Size Management

Your publishing company, Knockem Dead Paperbacks, Inc., is about to release its next best-seller, *Henrietta's Heaving Heart* by Celestine A. Lafleur. The company expects to sell 100,000 books each month in the next year. You have been given the job of scheduling print runs to meet the anticipated demand and minimize total costs to the company. Each print run has a setup cost of $5,000, each book costs $1 to produce, and monthly storage costs for books awaiting shipment average 1¢ per book. What will you do?

If you decide to print all 1,200,000 books (the total demand for the year, 100,000 books per month for 12 months) in a single run at the start of the year and sales run as predicted, then the number of books in stock would begin at 1,200,000 and decrease to zero by the end of the year, as shown in Figure 46.

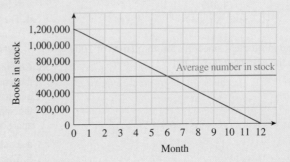

Figure 46

On average, you would be storing 600,000 books for 12 months at 1¢ per book, giving a total storage cost of $600,000 \times 12 \times .01 = \$72,000$. The setup cost for the single print run would be $5,000. When you add to these the total cost of producing 1,200,000 books at $1 per book, your total cost would be $1,277,000.

If, on the other hand, you decide to cut down on storage costs by printing the book in two runs of 600,000 each, you would get the picture shown in Figure 47.

Figure 47

Now, the storage cost would be cut in half because on average there would be only 300,000 books in stock. Thus, the total storage cost would be $36,000, and the setup cost would double to $10,000 (because there would now be two runs). The production costs would be the same: 1,200,000 books @ $1 per book. The total cost would therefore be reduced to $1,246,000, a savings of $31,000 compared to your first scenario.

"Aha!" you say to yourself, after doing these calculations. "Why not drastically cut costs by setting up a run every month?" You calculate that the setup costs alone would be $12 \times \$5,000 = \$60,000$, which is already more than the setup plus storage costs for two runs, so a run every month will cost too much. Perhaps, then, you should investigate three runs, four runs, and so on, until you find the lowest cost. This strikes you as too laborious a process, especially considering that you will have to do it all over again when planning for Lafleur's sequel, *Lorenzo's Lost Love,* due to be released next year. Realizing that this is an optimization problem, you decide to use some calculus to help you come up with a *formula* that you can use for all future plans. So you get to work.

Instead of working with the number 1,200,000, you use the letter N so that you can be as flexible as possible. (What if *Lorenzo's Lost Love* sells more copies?) Thus, you have a total of N books to be produced for the year. You now calculate the total cost of using x print runs per year. Because you are to produce a total of N books in x print runs, you will have to produce N/x books in each print run. N/x is called the **lot size**. As you can see from the diagrams above, the average number of books in storage will be half that amount, $N/(2x)$.

Now you can calculate the total cost for a year. Write P for the setup cost of a single print run ($P = \$5,000$ in your case) and c for the *annual* cost of storing a book (to convert all of the time measurements to years; $c = \$0.12$ here). Finally, write b for the cost of producing a single book ($b = \$1$ here). The costs break down as follows.

Setup Costs: x print runs @ P dollars per run: Px

Storage Costs: $N/(2x)$ books stored @ c dollars per year: $cN/(2x)$

Production Costs: N books @ b dollars per book: Nb

Total Cost: $Px + \dfrac{cN}{2x} + Nb$

Remember that P, N, c, and b are all constants and x is the only variable. Thus, your cost function is

$$C(x) = Px + \frac{cN}{2x} + Nb$$

and you need to find the value of x that will minimize $C(x)$. But that's easy! All you need to do is find the relative extrema and select the absolute minimum (if any).

The domain of $C(x)$ is $(0, +\infty)$ because there is an x in the denominator and x can't be negative. To locate the extrema, you start by locating the critical points:

$$C'(x) = P - \frac{cN}{2x^2}.$$

The only singular point would be at $x = 0$, but 0 is not in the domain. To find stationary points, you set $C'(x) = 0$ and solve for x:

$$P - \frac{cN}{2x^2} = 0$$

$$2x^2 = \frac{cN}{P}$$

so

$$x = \sqrt{\frac{cN}{2P}}.$$

There is only one stationary point, and there are no singular points or endpoints. To graph the function you will need to put in numbers for the various constants. Substituting $N = 1,200,000$, $P = 5,000$, $c = 0.12$, and $b = 1$, you get

$$C(x) = 5,000x + \frac{72,000}{x} + 1,200,000$$

with the stationary point at

$$x = \sqrt{\frac{(0.12)(1,200,000)}{2(5000)}} \approx 3.79.$$

The total cost at the stationary point is

$$C(3.79) \approx 1,240,000.$$

You now graph $C(x)$ in a window that includes the stationary point, say, $0 \le x \le 12$ and $1,100,000 \le C \le 1,500,000$, getting Figure 48.

From the graph, you can see that the stationary point is an absolute minimum. In the graph it appears that the graph is always concave up, which also tells you that your stationary point is a minimum. You can check the concavity by computing the second derivative:

$$C''(x) = \frac{cN}{x^3} > 0.$$

Figure 48

The second derivative is always positive because c, N, and x are all positive numbers, so indeed the graph is always concave up. Now you also know that it works regardless of the particular values of the constants.

So now you are practically done! You know that the absolute minimum cost occurs when you have $x \approx 3.79$ print runs per year. Don't be disappointed that the answer is not a whole number; whole number solutions are rarely found in real scenarios. What the answer (and the graph) do indicate is that either 3 or 4 print runs per year will cost the least money. If you take $x = 3$, you get a total cost of

$$C(3) = \$1,239,000$$

If you take $x = 4$, you get a total cost of

$$C(4) = \$1,238,000$$

So, four print runs per year will allow you to minimize your total costs.

EXERCISES

1. *Lorenzo's Lost Love* will sell 2,000,000 copies in a year. The remaining costs are the same. How many print runs should you use now?
2. In general, what happens to the number of runs that minimizes cost if both the setup cost and the total number of books are doubled?
3. In general, what happens to the number of runs that minimizes cost if the setup cost increases by a factor of 4?
4. Assuming that the total number of copies and storage costs are as originally stated, find the setup cost that would result in a single print run.
5. Assuming that the total number of copies and setup cost are as originally stated, find the storage cost that would result in a print run each month.

6. In Figure 47 we assumed that all the books in each run were manufactured in a very short time; otherwise the figure might have looked more like Figure 49, which shows the inventory, assuming a slower rate of production.

Figure 49

How would this affect the answer?

7. Referring to the general situation discussed in the text, find the cost as a function of the total number of books produced, assuming that the number of runs is chosen to minimize total cost. Also find the average cost per book.

8. Let $\bar{C}$ be the average cost function found in the preceding exercise. Calculate $\lim_{N \to +\infty} \bar{C}(N)$ and interpret the result.

TI-83/84 Plus   Technology Guide

Section 12.6

Example 1(a) (page 930)   Suppose that the demand equation for Bobby Dolls is given by $q = 216 - p^2$, where p is the price per doll in dollars and q is the number of dolls sold per week. Compute the price elasticity of demand when $p = \$5$ and $p = \$10$, and interpret the results.

Solution with Technology

The TI-83/84 Plus function `nDeriv` can be used to compute approximations of the elasticity E at various prices.

1. Set

$$Y_1 = 216 - X^2 \qquad \text{Demand equation}$$
$$Y_2 = -\text{nDeriv}(Y_1, X, X) * X/Y_1 \qquad \text{Formula for } E$$

2. Use the table feature to list the values of elasticity for a range of prices. For part (a) we chose values of X close to 5:

EXCEL   Technology Guide

Section 12.6

Example 1(a) (page 930)   Suppose that the demand equation for Bobby Dolls is given by $q = 216 - p^2$, where p is the price per doll in dollars and q is the number of dolls sold per week. Compute the price elasticity of demand when $p = \$5$ and $p = \$10$, and interpret the results.

Solution with Technology

To approximate E in Excel, we can use the following approximation of E.

$$E \approx \frac{\text{Percentage decrease in demand}}{\text{Percentage increase in price}} \approx -\frac{\left(\dfrac{\Delta q}{q}\right)}{\left(\dfrac{\Delta p}{p}\right)}$$

The smaller Δp is, the better the approximation. Let's use $\Delta p = 1\cent$, or 0.01 (which is small compared with the typical prices we consider—around \$5 to \$10).

1. We start by setting up our worksheet to list a range of prices, in increments of Δp, on either side of a price in which we are interested, such as $p_0 = \$5$:

We start in cell A5 with the formula for $p_0 - 10\Delta p$ and then successively add Δp going down column A. You will find that the value $p_0 = 5$ appears midway down the list.

2. Next, we compute the corresponding values for the demand q in Column B.

3. We add two new columns for the percentage changes in *p* and *q*. The formula shown in cell C5 is copied down columns C and D, to Row 24. (Why not Row 25?)

4. The elasticity can now be computed in column E as shown:

13

The Integral

Case Study Spending on Housing Construction

As a summer intern at the U.S. Department of Housing and Urban Development, you have been asked to find formulas for monthly spending on housing construction in the United States and for the average spent per month over a given period. You have data about percentage spending changes. **How will you model the trend and estimate the total?**

Bill Varie/CORBIS

Web Site
www.FiniteandCalc.org
At the Web site you will find:

- Section by section tutorials, including game tutorials with randomized quizzes

- A detailed chapter summary

- A true/false quiz

- Additional review exercises

- A numerical integration utility

- Graphing calculator programs for numerical integration

- Graphers, Excel tutorials, and other resources

- The following extra topic:
  Numerical Integration

Introduction

Roughly speaking, calculus is divided into two parts: **differential calculus** (the calculus of derivatives) and **integral calculus**, which is the subject of this chapter and the next. Integral calculus is concerned with problems that are in some sense the reverse of the problems seen in differential calculus. For example, where differential calculus shows how to compute the rate of change of a quantity, integral calculus shows how to find the quantity if we know its rate of change. This idea is made precise in the **Fundamental Theorem of Calculus**. Integral calculus and the Fundamental Theorem of Calculus allow us to solve many problems in economics, physics, and geometry, including one of the oldest problems in mathematics—computing areas of regions with curved boundaries.

13.1 The Indefinite Integral

Suppose that we knew the marginal cost to manufacture an item and we wanted to reconstruct the cost function. We would have to *reverse* the process of differentiation, to go from the derivative (the marginal cost function) back to the original function (the total cost). We'll first discuss how to do that and then look at some applications.

Here is an example: If the derivative of $F(x)$ is $4x^3$, what was $F(x)$? We recognize $4x^3$ as the derivative of x^4. So, we might have $F(x) = x^4$. However, $F(x) = x^4 + 7$ works just as well. In fact, $F(x) = x^4 + C$ works for any number C. Thus, there are *infinitely many* possible answers to this question.

In fact, we will see shortly that the formula $F(x) = x^4 + C$ covers *all* possible answers to the question. Let's give a name to what we are doing.

Antiderivative

An **antiderivative** of a function f is a function F such that $F' = f$.

Quick Examples

1. An antiderivative of $4x^3$ is x^4.   Because the derivative of x^4 is $4x^3$
2. Another antiderivative of $4x^3$ is $x^4 + 7$.   Because the derivative of $x^4 + 7$ is $4x^3$
3. An antiderivative of $2x$ is $x^2 + 12$.   Because the derivative of $x^2 + 12$ is $2x$

Thus,

If the derivative of A(x) is B(x), then an antiderivative of B(x) is A(x).

We call the set of *all* antiderivatives of a function the **indefinite integral** of the function.

Indefinite Integral

$$\int f(x)\, dx$$

is read "the **indefinite integral** of $f(x)$ with respect to x" and stands for the set of all antiderivatives of f. Thus, $\int f(x)\, dx$ is a *collection of functions*; it is not a single function or a number. The function f that is being **integrated** is called the **integrand**, and the variable x is called the **variable of integration**.

Quick Examples

1. $\displaystyle\int 4x^3\, dx = x^4 + C$ Every possible antiderivative of $4x^3$ has the form $x^4 + C$.

2. $\displaystyle\int 2x\, dx = x^2 + C$ Every possible antiderivative of $2x$ has the form $x^2 + C$.

The **constant of integration** C reminds us that we can add any constant and get a different antiderivative.

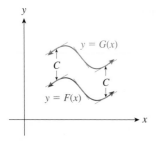

Figure 1

Q : *If $F(x)$ is one antiderivative of $f(x)$, why must all other antiderivatives have the form $F(x) + C$?*

A : Suppose $F(x)$ and $G(x)$ are both antiderivatives of $f(x)$, so that $F'(x) = G'(x)$. Consider what this means by looking at Figure 1. If $F'(x) = G'(x)$ for all x, then F and G have the *same slope* at each value of x. This means that their graphs must be *parallel* and hence remain exactly the same vertical distance apart. But that is the same as saying that the functions differ by a constant—that is, that $G(x) = F(x) + C$ for some constant C.*

✳ NOTE This argument can be turned into a more rigorous proof—that is, a proof that does not rely on geometric concepts such as "parallel graphs." We should also say that the result requires that F and G have the same derivative *on an interval* $[a, b]$.

EXAMPLE 1 Indefinite Integral

Check that $\displaystyle\int x\, dx = \frac{x^2}{2} + C$.

Solution We check our answer by taking the derivative of the right-hand side:

$$\frac{d}{dx}\left(\frac{x^2}{2} + C\right) = \frac{2x}{2} + 0 = x \qquad ✔$$

Because the derivative of the right-hand side is the integrand x, we can conclude that $\displaystyle\int x\, dx = \frac{x^2}{2} + C$, as claimed.

Now, we would like to make the process of finding indefinite integrals (antiderivatives) more mechanical. For example, it would be nice to have a power rule for indefinite integrals similar to the one we already have for derivatives. Two cases suggested by the examples above are:

$$\int x\, dx = \frac{x^2}{2} + C \qquad\qquad \int x^3\, dx = \frac{x^4}{4} + C$$

You should check the last equation by taking the derivative of its right-hand side. These cases suggest the following general statement:

Power Rule for the Indefinite Integral, Part I

$$\int x^n \, dx = \frac{x^{n+1}}{n+1} + C \qquad (\text{if } n \neq -1)$$

In Words To find the integral of x^n, add 1 to the exponent, and then divide by the new exponent. This rule works provided that n is not -1.

Quick Examples

1. $\displaystyle \int x^{55} \, dx = \frac{x^{56}}{56} + C$

2. $\displaystyle \int \frac{1}{x^{55}} \, dx = \int x^{-55} \, dx$ Exponent form

   $\displaystyle \qquad\qquad = \frac{x^{-54}}{-54} + C$ When we add 1 to -55, we get -54, *not* -56.

   $\displaystyle \qquad\qquad = -\frac{1}{54x^{54}} + C$ See marginal note.*

3. $\displaystyle \int 1 \, dx = x + C$ Because $1 = x^0$. This is an important special case.

4. $\displaystyle \int \sqrt{x} \, dx = \int x^{1/2} dx$ Exponent form

   $\displaystyle \qquad\qquad = \frac{x^{3/2}}{3/2} + C$

   $\displaystyle \qquad\qquad = \frac{2x^{3/2}}{3} + C$

✱ NOTE We are glossing over a subtlety here: The constant of integration C can be different for $x < 0$ and $x > 0$ because the graph breaks at $x = 0$. In general, our understanding will be that the constant of integration may be different on disconnected intervals of the domain.

Notes

1. The integral $\displaystyle \int 1 \, dx$ is commonly written as $\displaystyle \int dx$. Similarly, the integral $\displaystyle \int \frac{1}{x^{55}} \, dx$ may be written as $\displaystyle \int \frac{dx}{x^{55}}$.

2. We can easily check the power rule formula by taking the derivative of the right-hand side:

$$\frac{d}{dx}\left(\frac{x^{n+1}}{n+1} + C \right) = \frac{(n+1)x^n}{n+1} = x^n \qquad \checkmark \qquad \blacksquare$$

Q: *What is the reason for the restriction $n \neq -1$?*

A: The right-hand side of the power rule formula has $n + 1$ in the denominator, and thus makes no sense if $n = -1$. This leaves us not yet knowing how to compute

$$\int x^{-1} \, dx = \int \frac{1}{x} \, dx.$$

Computing this derivative amounts to finding a function whose derivative is $1/x$. Prodding our memories a little, we recall that $\ln x$ has derivative $1/x$. In fact, as we pointed out when we first discussed it, $\ln |x|$ also has derivative $1/x$, but it has the advantage that its domain is the same as that of $1/x$. Thus, we can fill in the missing case as follows:

Power Rule for the Indefinite Integral, Part II

$$\int x^{-1} \, dx = \ln |x| + C \qquad \text{Equivalently,} \int \frac{1}{x} \, dx = \ln |x| + C.$$

Two other indefinite integrals that come from formulas for differentiation are the following:

Indefinite Integral of e^x and b^x

$$\int e^x \, dx = e^x + C \qquad \text{Because } \frac{d}{dx}(e^x) = e^x$$

If b is any positive number other than 1, then

$$\int b^x \, dx = \frac{b^x}{\ln b} + C \qquad \text{Because } \frac{d}{dx}\left(\frac{b^x}{\ln b}\right) = \frac{b^x \ln b}{\ln b} = b^x$$

Quick Example

$$\int 2^x \, dx = \frac{2^x}{\ln 2} + C$$

For more complicated functions, like $2x^3 + 6x^5 - 1$, we need the following rules for integrating sums, differences, and constant multiples.

Sums, Differences, and Constant Multiples

Sum and Difference Rules

$$\int [f(x) \pm g(x)] \, dx = \int f(x) \, dx \pm \int g(x) \, dx$$

In Words: The integral of a sum is the sum of the integrals, and the integral of a difference is the difference of the integrals.

Constant Multiple Rule

$$\int kf(x)\,dx = k\int f(x)\,dx \quad (k\text{ constant})$$

In Words: The integral of a constant times a function is the constant times the integral of the function. (In other words, the constant "goes along for the ride.")

Quick Examples

Sum Rule: $\displaystyle\int (x^3 + 1)\,dx = \int x^3\,dx + \int 1\,dx = \frac{x^4}{4} + x + C$

$f(x) = x^3; g(x) = 1$

Constant Multiple Rule: $\displaystyle\int 5x^3\,dx = 5\int x^3\,dx = 5\frac{x^4}{4} + C$ $k = 5; f(x) = x^3$

Constant Multiple Rule: $\displaystyle\int 4\,dx = 4\int 1\,dx = 4x + C$ $k = 4; f(x) = 1$

Constant Multiple Rule: $\displaystyle\int 4e^x\,dx = 4\int e^x\,dx = 4e^x + C$ $k = 4; f(x) = e^x$

Proof of the Sum Rule

We saw above that if two functions have the same derivative, they differ by a (possibly zero) constant. Look at the rule for sums:

$$\int [f(x) + g(x)]\,dx = \int f(x)\,dx + \int g(x)\,dx$$

If we take the derivative of the left-hand side with respect to x, we get the integrand, $f(x) + g(x)$. If we take the derivative of the right-hand side, we get

$$\frac{d}{dx}\left[\int f(x)\,dx + \int g(x)\,dx\right] = \frac{d}{dx}\left[\int f(x)\,dx\right] + \frac{d}{dx}\left[\int g(x)\,dx\right]$$

Derivative of a sum = Sum of derivatives.

$$= f(x) + g(x)$$

Because the left- and right-hand sides have the same derivative, they differ by a constant. But, because both expressions are indefinite integrals, adding a constant does not affect their value, so they are the same as indefinite integrals.

Notice that a key step in the proof was the fact that the derivative of a sum is the sum of the derivatives.

A similar proof works for the difference and constant multiple rule.

EXAMPLE 2 **Using the Sum and Difference Rules**

Find the integrals.

a. $\int (x^3 + x^5 - 1)\, dx$ **b.** $\int \left(x^{2.1} + \dfrac{1}{x^{1.1}} + \dfrac{1}{x} + e^x\right) dx$ **c.** $\int (e^x + 3^x - 1)\, dx$

Solution

a. $\displaystyle \int (x^3 + x^5 - 1)\, dx = \int x^3\, dx + \int x^5\, dx - \int 1\, dx$ Sum/difference rule

$$= \frac{x^4}{4} + \frac{x^6}{6} - x + C \qquad\qquad \text{Power rule}$$

b. $\displaystyle \int \left(x^{2.1} + \frac{1}{x^{1.1}} + \frac{1}{x} + e^x\right) dx$

$$= \int (x^{2.1} + x^{-1.1} + x^{-1} + e^x)\, dx \qquad \text{Exponent form}$$

$$= \int x^{2.1}\, dx + \int x^{-1.1}\, dx + \int x^{-1}\, dx + \int e^x\, dx \qquad \text{Sum rule}$$

$$= \frac{x^{3.1}}{3.1} + \frac{x^{-0.1}}{-0.1} + \ln|x| + e^x + C \qquad \text{Power rule and exponential rule}$$

$$= \frac{x^{3.1}}{3.1} - \frac{10}{x^{0.1}} + \ln|x| + e^x + C$$

c. $\displaystyle \int (e^x + 3^x - 1)\, dx = \int e^x\, dx + \int 3^x\, dx - \int 1\, dx$ Sum/difference rule

$$= e^x + \frac{3^x}{\ln 3} - x + C \qquad\qquad \text{Power rule and exponential rule}$$

➡ **Before we go on...** You should check each of the answers in Example 2 by differentiating.

Q: *Why is there only a single arbitrary constant C in each of the answers?*

A: We could have written the answer to part (a) as

$$\frac{x^4}{4} + D + \frac{x^6}{6} + E - x + F$$

where D, E, and F are all arbitrary constants. Now suppose, for example, we set $D = 1$, $E = -2$, and $F = 6$. Then the particular antiderivative we get is $x^4/4 + x^6/6 - x + 5$, which has the form $x^4/4 + x^6/6 - x + C$. Thus, we could have chosen the single constant C to be 5 and obtained the same answer. In other words, the answer $x^4/4 + x^6/6 - x + C$ is just as general as the answer $x^4/4 + D + x^6/6 + E - x + F$, but simpler.

■

In practice we do not explicitly write the integral of a sum as a sum of integrals but just "integrate term by term," much as we learned to differentiate term by term.

EXAMPLE 3 **Combining the Rules**

Find the integrals.

a. $\int (10x^4 + 2x^2 - 3e^x) \, dx$ **b.** $\int \left(\frac{2}{x^{0.1}} + \frac{x^{0.1}}{2} - \frac{3}{4x} \right) dx$ **c.** $\int [3e^x - 2(1.2^x)] \, dx$

Solution

a. We need to integrate separately each of the terms $10x^4$, $2x^2$, and $3e^x$. To integrate $10x^4$ we use the rules for constant multiples and powers:

$$\int 10x^4 \, dx = 10 \int x^4 \, dx = 10 \frac{x^5}{5} + C = 2x^5 + C.$$

The other two terms are similar. We get

$$\int (10x^4 + 2x^2 - 3e^x) \, dx = 10 \frac{x^5}{5} + 2 \frac{x^3}{3} - 3e^x + C = 2x^5 + \frac{2}{3}x^3 - 3e^x + C.$$

b. We first convert to exponent form and then integrate term by term:

$$\int \left(\frac{2}{x^{0.1}} + \frac{x^{0.1}}{2} - \frac{3}{4x} \right) dx = \int \left(2x^{-0.1} + \frac{1}{2}x^{0.1} - \frac{3}{4}x^{-1} \right) dx \qquad \text{Exponent form}$$

$$= 2\frac{x^{0.9}}{0.9} + \frac{1}{2}\frac{x^{1.1}}{1.1} - \frac{3}{4}\ln|x| + C \qquad \begin{array}{l}\text{Integrate term by} \\ \text{term.}\end{array}$$

$$= \frac{20x^{0.9}}{9} + \frac{x^{1.1}}{2.2} - \frac{3}{4}\ln|x| + C. \qquad \begin{array}{l}\text{Back to rational} \\ \text{form}\end{array}$$

c. $\int [3e^x - 2(1.2^x)] \, dx = 3e^x - 2\frac{1.2^x}{\ln(1.2)} + C$

EXAMPLE 4 **Different Variable Name**

Find $\int \left(\frac{1}{u} + \frac{1}{u^2} \right) du.$

Solution This integral may look a little strange because we are using the letter u instead of x, but there is really nothing special about x. Using u as the variable of integration, we get

$$\int \left(\frac{1}{u} + \frac{1}{u^2} \right) du = \int (u^{-1} + u^{-2}) \, du \qquad \text{Exponent form.}$$

$$= \ln|u| + \frac{u^{-1}}{-1} + C \qquad \text{Integrate term by term.}$$

$$= \ln|u| - \frac{1}{u} + C. \qquad \text{Simplify the result.}$$

➡ **Before we go on...** When we compute an indefinite integral, we want the independent variable in the answer to be the same as the variable of integration. Thus, if the integral in Example 4 had been written in terms of x rather than u, we would have written

$$\int \left(\frac{1}{x} + \frac{1}{x^2} \right) dx = \ln |x| - \frac{1}{x} + C.$$ ■

APPLICATIONS

EXAMPLE 5 Finding Cost from Marginal Cost

The marginal cost to produce baseball caps at a production level of x caps is $4 - 0.001x$ dollars per cap, and the cost of producing 100 caps is $500. Find the cost function.

Solution We are asked to find the cost function $C(x)$, given that the *marginal* cost function is $4 - 0.001x$. Recalling that the marginal cost function is the derivative of the cost function, we can write

$$C'(x) = 4 - 0.001x$$

and must find $C(x)$. Now $C(x)$ must be an antiderivative of $C'(x)$, so

$$
\begin{aligned}
C(x) &= \int (4 - 0.001x)\, dx \\
&= 4x - 0.001\frac{x^2}{2} + K \qquad \text{K is the constant of integration.}* \\
&= 4x - 0.0005x^2 + K.
\end{aligned}
$$

* **NOTE** We used K and not C for the constant of integration because we are using C for cost.

Now, unless we have a value for K, we don't really know what the cost function is. However, there is another piece of information we have ignored: The cost of producing 100 baseball caps is $500. In symbols

$$C(100) = 500.$$

Substituting in our formula for $C(x)$, we have

$$
\begin{aligned}
C(100) &= 4(100) - 0.0005(100)^2 + K \\
500 &= 395 + K \\
K &= 105.
\end{aligned}
$$

Now that we know what K is, we can write down the cost function:

$$C(x) = 4x - 0.0005x^2 + 105.$$

➡ **Before we go on...** Let us consider the significance of the constant term 105 in Example 5. If we substitute $x = 0$ into the cost function, we get

$$C(0) = 4(0) - 0.0005(0)^2 + 105 = 105.$$

Thus, $105 is the cost of producing zero items; in other words, it is the **fixed cost**. ■

EXAMPLE 6 **Total Sales from Annual Sales**

By the start of 2004, **Apple** had sold a total of about 2 million iPods. From the start of 2004 through mid-2008, sales of iPods were approximately

$$s(t) = -3t^2 + 28t - 5.4 \text{ million iPods per year} \qquad (0 \le t \le 4.5)$$

where t is time in years since the start of 2004.*

a. Find an expression for the total sales of iPods up to time t.

b. Use the answer to part (a) to estimate the total sales of iPods by the start of 2008. (The actual figure was 141 million.)

Solution

a. Let $S(t)$ be the total sales of iPods up to time t, where t is measured in years since the start of 2004, so we know that $S(0) = 2$. We are also given an expression for the number of iPods sold per year. This function is the *derivative* of $S(t)$:

$$S'(t) = -3t^2 + 28t - 5.4.$$

Thus, the desired total sales function must be an antiderivative of $S'(t)$:

$$S(t) = \int (-3t^2 + 28t - 5.4)\, dt$$

$$= -\frac{3t^2}{3} + \frac{28t^2}{2} - 5.4t + C$$

$$= -t^3 + 14t^2 - 5.4t + C.$$

To calculate the value of the constant C, we can, as in the preceding example, use the known value of S: $S(0) = 2$

$$S(0) = -(0)^3 + 14(0)^2 - 5.4(0) + C = 2$$

so

$$C = 2.$$

We can now write down the total sales function:

$$S(t) = -t^3 + 14t^2 - 5.4t + 2 \text{ million iPods.}$$

b. Because the start of 2008 corresponds to $t = 4$, we calculate total sales as

$$S(4) = -(4)^3 + 14(4)^2 - 5.4(4) + 2 \approx 140 \text{ million iPods.}$$

---

* Source for data: Apple quarterly earnings reports (www.apple.com/investor/).

Motion in a Straight Line

An important application of the indefinite integral is to the study of motion. The application of calculus to problems about motion is an example of the intertwining of mathematics and physics. We begin by bringing together some facts, scattered through the last several chapters, that have to do with an object moving in a straight line, and then restating them in terms of antiderivatives.

Position, Velocity, and Acceleration: Derivative Form

If $s = s(t)$ is the **position** of an object at time t, then its **velocity** is given by the derivative

$$v = \frac{ds}{dt}.$$

In Words: Velocity is the derivative of position.

The **acceleration** of an object is given by the derivative

$$a = \frac{dv}{dt}.$$

In Words: Acceleration is the derivative of velocity.

Position, Velocity, and Acceleration: Integral Form

$$s(t) = \int v(t)\, dt \qquad \text{Because } v = \frac{ds}{dt}$$

$$v(t) = \int a(t)\, dt \qquad \text{Because } a = \frac{dv}{dt}$$

Quick Examples

1. If the velocity of a particle moving in a straight line is given by $v(t) = 4t + 1$, then its position after t seconds is given by $s(t) = \int v(t)\, dt = \int (4t + 1)\, dt = 2t^2 + t + C$.

2. If sales are accelerating at 2 golf balls/day^2, then the rate of change of sales ("velocity of sales") is $v(t) = \int a(t)\, dt = \int 2\, dt = 2t + C$ golf balls/day.

3. If the rate of change of sales is $v(t) = 2t + 5$ golf balls per day, then the total sales are $s(t) = \int v(t)\, dt = \int (2t + 5)\, dt = t^2 + 5t + C$ golf balls sold through time t.

EXAMPLE 7 Motion in a Straight Line

a. The velocity of a particle moving along in a straight line is given by $v(t) = 4t + 1$ m/s. Given that the particle is at position $s = 2$ meters at time $t = 1$, find an expression for s in terms of t.

b. For a freely falling body experiencing no air resistance and zero initial velocity, find an expression for the velocity v in terms of t. [Note: On Earth, a freely falling body experiencing no air resistance accelerates downward at approximately 9.8 meters per second per second, or 9.8 m/s^2 (or 32 ft/s^2).]

Solution

a. As we saw in the Quick Example above, the position of the particle after t seconds is given by

$$s(t) = \int v(t)\, dt$$

$$= \int (4t + 1)\, dt = 2t^2 + t + C.$$

But what is the value of C? Now, we are told that the particle is at position $s = 2$ at time $t = 1$. In other words, $s(1) = 2$. Substituting this into the expression for $s(t)$ gives

$$2 = 2(1)^2 + 1 + C$$

so

$$C = -1.$$

Hence the position after t seconds is given by

$$s(t) = 2t^2 + t - 1 \text{ meters.}$$

b. Let's measure heights above the ground as positive, so that a rising object has positive velocity and the acceleration due to gravity is negative. (It causes the upward velocity to decrease in value.) Thus, the acceleration of the stone is given by

$$a(t) = -9.8 \text{ m/s}^2.$$

We wish to know the velocity, which is an antiderivative of acceleration, so we compute

$$v(t) = \int a(t)\, dt = \int (-9.8)\, dt = -9.8t + C.$$

To find the value of C, we use the given information that at time $t = 0$ the velocity is 0: $v(0) = 0$. Substituting this into the expression for $v(t)$ gives

$$0 = -9.8(0) + C$$

so

$$C = 0.$$

Hence, the velocity after t seconds is given by

$$v(t) = -9.8t \text{ m/s.}$$

EXAMPLE 8 Vertical Motion Under Gravity

You are standing on the edge of a cliff and toss a stone upward at a speed of $v_0 = 30$ feet per second (v_0 is called the *initial velocity*).

a. Find the stone's velocity as a function of time. How fast and in what direction is it going after 5 seconds? (Neglect the effects of air resistance.)

b. Find the position of the stone as a function of time. Where will it be after 5 seconds?

c. When and where will the stone reach its zenith, its highest point?

Solution

a. This is similar to Example 7(b): Measuring height above the ground as positive, the acceleration of the stone is given by $a(t) = -32$ ft/s^2, and so

$$v(t) = \int (-32)\, dt = -32t + C.$$

To obtain C, we use the fact that you tossed the stone upward at 30 ft/s; that is, when $t = 0$, $v = 30$, or $v(0) = 30$. Thus,

$$30 = v(0) = -32(0) + C.$$

So, $C = 30$ and the formula for velocity is

$$v(t) = -32t + 30 \text{ ft.} \qquad v(t) = -32t + v_0$$

In particular, after 5 seconds the velocity will be

$$v(5) = -32(5) + 30 = -130 \text{ ft/s}.$$

After 5 seconds the stone is *falling* with a speed of 130 ft/s.

b. We wish to know the position, but position is an antiderivative of velocity. Thus,

$$s(t) = \int v(t) \, dt = \int (-32t + 30) \, dt = -16t^2 + 30t + C.$$

Now to find C, we need to know the initial position $s(0)$. We are not told this, so let's measure heights so that the initial position is zero. Then

$$0 = s(0) = C$$

and

$$s(t) = -16t^2 + 30t. \qquad s(t) = -16t^2 + v_0 t + s_0$$
$$ s_0 = \text{initial position}$$

In particular, after 5 seconds the stone has a height of

$$s(5) = -16(5)^2 + 30(5) = -250 \text{ ft}.$$

In other words, the stone is now 250 ft *below* where it was when you first threw it, as shown in Figure 2.

c. The stone reaches its zenith when its height $s(t)$ is at its maximum value, which occurs when $v(t) = s'(t)$ is zero. So we solve

$$v(t) = -32t + 30 = 0$$

getting $t = 30/32 = 15/16 = 0.9375$ s. This is the time when the stone reaches its zenith. The height of the stone at that time is

$$s(15/16) = -16(15/16)^2 + 30(15/16) = 14.0625 \text{ ft}.$$

Figure 2

➡ **Before we go on...** Here again are the formulas we obtained in Example 8, together with their metric equivalents:

Vertical Motion Under Gravity: Velocity and Position

If one ignores air resistance, the vertical velocity and position of an object moving under gravity are given by

British Units	Metric Units
Velocity: $v(t) = -32t + v_0$ ft/s	$v(t) = -9.8t + v_0$ m/s
Position: $s(t) = -16t^2 + v_0 t + s_0$ ft	$s(t) = -4.9t^2 + v_0 t + s_0$ m

$v_0 =$ initial velocity = velocity at time 0
$s_0 =$ initial position = position at time 0

Quick Example

If a ball is thrown down at 2 ft/s from a height of 200 ft, then its velocity and position after t seconds are $v(t) = -32t - 2$ ft/s and $s(t) = -16t^2 - 2t + 200$ ft. ∎

13.1 EXERCISES

▼ more advanced   ◆ challenging
T indicates exercises that should be solved using technology

Evaluate the integrals in Exercises 1–40.
HINT [for 1–6: See Quick Examples on page 949.]

1. $\int x^5 \, dx$ **2.** $\int x^7 \, dx$ **3.** $\int 6 \, dx$

4. $\int (-5) \, dx$ **5.** $\int x \, dx$ **6.** $\int (-x) \, dx$

HINT [for 7–18: See Example 2.]

7. $\int (x^2 - x) \, dx$ **8.** $\int (x + x^3) \, dx$

9. $\int (1 + x) \, dx$ **10.** $\int (4 - x) \, dx$

11. $\int x^{-5} \, dx$ **12.** $\int x^{-7} \, dx$

13. $\int (x^{2.3} + x^{-1.3}) \, dx$ **14.** $\int (x^{-0.2} - x^{0.2}) \, dx$

15. $\int (u^2 - 1/u) \, du$ HINT [See Example 4.]

16. $\int (1/v^2 + 2/v) \, dv$ HINT [See Example 4.]

17. $\int \sqrt[4]{x} \, dx$ **18.** $\int \sqrt[3]{x} \, dx$

HINT [for 19–40: See Example 3.]

19. $\int (3x^4 - 2x^{-2} + x^{-5} + 4) \, dx$ **20.** $\int (4x^7 - x^{-3} + 1) \, dx$

21. $\int \left(\dfrac{2}{u} + \dfrac{u}{4} \right) du$ **22.** $\int \left(\dfrac{2}{u^2} + \dfrac{u^2}{4} \right) du$

23. $\int \left(\dfrac{1}{x} + \dfrac{2}{x^2} - \dfrac{1}{x^3} \right) dx$ **24.** $\int \left(\dfrac{3}{x} - \dfrac{1}{x^5} + \dfrac{1}{x^7} \right) dx$

25. $\int (3x^{0.1} - x^{4.3} - 4.1) \, dx$ **26.** $\int \left(\dfrac{x^{2.1}}{2} - 2.3 \right) dx$

27. $\int \left(\dfrac{3}{x^{0.1}} - \dfrac{4}{x^{1.1}} \right) dx$ **28.** $\int \left(\dfrac{1}{x^{1.1}} - \dfrac{1}{x} \right) dx$

29. $\int \left(5.1t - \dfrac{1.2}{t} + \dfrac{3}{t^{1.2}} \right) dt$

30. $\int \left(3.2 + \dfrac{1}{t^{0.9}} + \dfrac{t^{1.2}}{3} \right) dt$

31. $\int (2e^x + 5/x + 1/4) \, dx$

32. $\int (-e^x + x^{-2} - 1/8) \, dx$

33. $\int \left(\dfrac{6.1}{x^{0.5}} + \dfrac{x^{0.5}}{6} - e^x \right) dx$

34. $\int \left(\dfrac{4.2}{x^{0.4}} + \dfrac{x^{0.4}}{3} - 2e^x \right) dx$

35. $\int (2^x - 3^x) \, dx$ **36.** $\int (1.1^x + 2^x) \, dx$

37. $\int 100(1.1^x) \, dx$ **38.** $\int 1,000(0.9^x) \, dx$

39. ▼ $\int \dfrac{x + 2}{x^3} \, dx$ **40.** ▼ $\int \dfrac{x^2 - 2}{x} \, dx$

41. Find $f(x)$ if $f(0) = 1$ and the tangent line at $(x, f(x))$ has slope x. HINT [See Example 5.]

42. Find $f(x)$ if $f(1) = 1$ and the tangent line at $(x, f(x))$ has slope $\dfrac{1}{x}$. HINT [See Example 5.]

43. Find $f(x)$ if $f(0) = 0$ and the tangent line at $(x, f(x))$ has slope $e^x - 1$.

44. Find $f(x)$ if $f(1) = -1$ and the tangent line at $(x, f(x))$ has slope $2e^x + 1$.

45. *Antiderivative of $|x|$* Show that an antiderivative of $|x|$ is $\dfrac{1}{2} x|x|$. Hence evaluate $\int (3|x| - x) \, dx$.

46. *Antiderivative of $|x|$* Use the result of Exercise 45 to evaluate $\int \left(\dfrac{|x|}{3} - \dfrac{1}{x} \right) dx$.

APPLICATIONS

47. *Marginal Cost* The marginal cost of producing the xth box of light bulbs is $5 - \dfrac{x}{10,000}$ and the fixed cost is \$20,000. Find the cost function $C(x)$. HINT [See Example 5.]

48. *Marginal Cost* The marginal cost of producing the xth box of Zip disks is $10 + \dfrac{x^2}{100,000}$ and the fixed cost is \$100,000. Find the cost function $C(x)$. HINT [See Example 5.]

49. *Marginal Cost* The marginal cost of producing the xth roll of film is $5 + 2x + \dfrac{1}{x}$. The total cost to produce one roll is \$1,000. Find the cost function $C(x)$. HINT [See Example 5.]

50. *Marginal Cost* The marginal cost of producing the xth box of CDs is $10 + x + \dfrac{1}{x^2}$. The total cost to produce 100 boxes is \$10,000. Find the cost function $C(x)$. HINT [See Example 5.]

51. Facebook *Membership* At the start of 2005, **Facebook** had 1 million members. Since that time, new members joined at a rate of approximately

$$m(t) = 12t^2 - 20t + 10 \text{ million members per year}$$
$$(0 \le t \le 3.5)$$

where t is time in years since the start of 2005.[1]

---

[1] Sources for data: www.facebook.com, www.insidehighered.com (Some data are interpolated.)

a. Find an expression for total **Facebook** membership $M(t)$ at time t. HINT [See Example 6.]

b. Use the answer to part (a) to estimate **Facebook** membership midway through 2008. (The actual figure was 80 million.)

52. **MySpace** *Membership* At the start of 2004, **MySpace** had 0.6 million members. Since that time, new members joined at a rate of approximately

$$m(t) = 10.5t^2 + 14t - 6 \text{ million members per year}$$
$$(0 \le t \le 3.5)$$

where t is time in years since the start of 2004.[2]

a. Find an expression for total **MySpace** membership $M(t)$ at time t. HINT [See Example 6.]

b. Use the answer to part (a) to estimate **MySpace** membership in January 2007. (The actual figure was 141 million.)

53. **Median Household Income** From 2000 to 2007, median household income in the United States rose by an average of approximately $1,200 per year.[3] Given that the median household income in 2000 was approximately $42,000, use an indefinite integral to find a formula for median household income I as a function of the year t ($t = 0$ represents 2000), and use your formula to estimate the median household income in 2005. HINT [See Example 6.]

54. **Mean Household Income** From 2000 to 2007, the mean household income in the United States rose by an average of approximately $1,500 per year.[4] Given that the mean household income in 2000 was approximately $57,000, use an indefinite integral to find a formula for the mean household income I as a function of the year t ($t = 0$ represents 2000), and use your formula to estimate the mean household income in 2006. HINT [See Example 6.]

55. **Bottled Water Sales** The rate of U.S. sales of bottled water for the period 2000–2008 can be approximated by

$$s(t) = 12t^2 + 500t + 4,700 \text{ million gallons per year}$$
$$(0 \le t \le 8)$$

where t is time in years since the start of 2000.[5] Use an indefinite integral to approximate the total sales $S(t)$ of bottled water since the start of 2000. Approximately how much bottled water was sold from the start of 2000 to the end of 2005? HINT [See Example 6. At the start of 2000, sales since that time are zero.]

56. **Bottled Water Sales** The rate of U.S. per capita sales of bottled water for the period 2000–2008 can be approximated by

$$s(t) = 0.04t^2 + 1.5t + 17 \text{ gallons per year} \quad (0 \le t \le 8)$$

where t is the time in years since the start of 2000.[6] Use an indefinite integral to approximate the total per capita sales $S(t)$ of bottled water since the start of 2000. Approximately how much bottled water was sold, per capita, from the start of 2000 to the end of 2007? HINT [See Example 6. At the start of 2000, sales since that time are zero.]

57. ▼ **Health Care Spending** Write $H(t)$ for the amount spent in the United States on health care in year t, where t is measured in years since 1990. The rate of increase of $H(t)$ was approximately $65 billion per year in 1990 and rose to $100 billion per year in 2000.[7]

a. Find a linear model for the rate of change $H'(t)$.

b. Given that $700 billion was spent on health care in the United States in 1990, find the function $H(t)$.

58. ▼ **Health Care Spending** Write $H(t)$ for the amount spent in the United States on health care in year t, where t is measured in years since 2000. The rate of increase of $H(t)$ was projected to rise from $100 billion per year in 2000 to approximately $190 billion per year in 2010.[8]

a. Find a linear model for the rate of change $H'(t)$.

b. Given that $1,300 billion was spent on health care in the United States in 2000, find the function $H(t)$.

59. ▼ **Subprime Mortgage Debt** At the start of 2007, the percentage of U.S. mortgages that were subprime was about 13%, was increasing at a rate of 1 percentage point per year, but was decelerating at 0.4 percentage points per year per year.[9]

a. Find an expression for the rate of change (velocity) of this percentage at time t in years since the start of 2007.

b. Use the result of part (a) to find an expression for the percentage of mortgages that were subprime at time t, and use it to estimate the rate at the start of 2008. HINT [See Quick Examples 2 and 3 on page 957.]

60. ▼ **Subprime Mortgage Debt** At the start of 2008, the value of subprime mortgage debt outstanding in the U.S. was about $1,300 billion, was increasing at a rate of 40 billion dollars per year, but was decelerating at 20 billion dollars per year per year.[10]

a. Find an expression for the rate of change (velocity) of the value of subprime mortgage debt at time t in years since the start of 2008.

---

[2] Source for data: www.swivel.com/data_sets.

[3] In current dollars, unadjusted for inflation. Source: U.S. Census Bureau; "Table H-5. Race and Hispanic Origin of Householder—Households by Median and Mean Income: 1967 to 2007" (www.census.gov/hhes/www/income/histinc/h05.html).

[4] Ibid.

[5] The 2008 figure is an estimate. Source: Beverage Marketing Corporation (www.bottledwater.org).

[6] Ibid.

[7] Source: Centers for Medicare and Medicaid Services, "National Health Expenditures," 2002 version, released January 2004 (www.cms.hhs.gov/statistics/nhe/).

[8] Source: Centers for Medicare and Medicaid Services, "National Health Expenditures 1965–2013, History and Projections" (www.cms.hhs.gov/statistics/nhe/).

[9] Sources: Mortgage Bankers Association, UBS.

[10] Source: www.data360.org/dataset.aspx?Data_Set_Id=9549.

b. Use the result of part (a) to find an expression for the value of subprime mortgage debt at time t, and use it to estimate the value at the start of 2009. HINT [See Quick Examples 2 and 3 on page 957.]

61. *Motion in a Straight Line* The velocity of a particle moving in a straight line is given by $v(t) = t^2 + 1$.

   a. Find an expression for the position s after a time t.
   b. Given that $s = 1$ at time $t = 0$, find the constant of integration C, and hence find an expression for s in terms of t without any unknown constants. HINT [See Example 7.]

62. *Motion in a Straight Line* The velocity of a particle moving in a straight line is given by $v = 3e^t + t$.

   a. Find an expression for the position s after a time t.
   b. Given that $s = 3$ at time $t = 0$, find the constant of integration C, and hence find an expression for s in terms of t without any unknown constants. HINT [See Example 7.]

63. *Vertical Motion under Gravity* If a stone is dropped from a rest position above the ground, how fast (in feet per second) and in what direction will it be traveling after 10 seconds? (Neglect the effects of air resistance.) HINT [See Example 8.]

64. *Vertical Motion under Gravity* If a stone is thrown upward at 10 feet per second, how fast (in feet per second) and in what direction will it be traveling after 10 seconds? (Neglect the effects of air resistance.) HINT [See Example 8.]

65. *Vertical Motion under Gravity* Your name is Galileo Galilei and you toss a weight upward at 16 feet per second from the top of the Leaning Tower of Pisa (height 185 ft).

   a. Neglecting air resistance, find the weight's velocity as a function of time t in seconds.
   b. Find the height of the weight above the ground as a function of time. Where and when will it reach its zenith? HINT [See Example 8.]

66. *Vertical Motion under Gravity* Your name is Spaghettini Bologna (an assistant of Galileo Galilei) and, to impress your boss, you toss a weight upward at 24 feet per second from the top of the Leaning Tower of Pisa (height 185 ft).

   a. Neglecting air resistance, find the weight's velocity as a function of time t in seconds.
   b. Find the height of the weight above the ground as a function of time. Where and when will it reach its zenith? HINT [See Example 8.]

67. ▼ *Tail Winds* The ground speed of an airliner is obtained by adding its air speed and the tail-wind speed. On your recent trip from Mexico to the United States your plane was traveling at an air speed of 500 miles per hour and experienced tail winds of $25 + 50t$ miles per hour, where t is the time in hours since takeoff.

   a. Obtain an expression for the distance traveled in terms of the time since takeoff. HINT [Ground speed = Air speed + Tail-wind speed.]
   b. Use the result of part (a) to estimate the time of your 1,800-mile trip.
   c. The equation solved in part (b) leads mathematically to two solutions. Explain the meaning of the solution you rejected.

68. ▼ *Head Winds* The ground speed of an airliner is obtained by subtracting its head-wind speed from its air speed. On your recent trip to Mexico from the United States your plane was traveling at an air speed of 500 miles per hour and experienced head winds of $25 + 50t$ miles per hour, where t is the time in hours since takeoff. HINT [Ground speed = Air speed − Head-wind speed.]

   a. Obtain an expression for the distance traveled in terms of the time since takeoff.
   b. Use the result of part (a) to estimate the time of your 1,500-mile trip.
   c. The equation solved in part (b) leads mathematically to two solutions. Explain the meaning of the solution you rejected.

69. ▼ *Vertical Motion* Show that if a projectile is thrown upward with a velocity of v_0 ft/s, then (neglecting air resistance) it will reach its highest point after $v_0/32$ seconds. HINT [See the formulas after Example 8.]

70. ▼*Vertical Motion* Use the result of the preceding exercise to show that if a projectile is thrown upward with a velocity of v_0 ft/s, its highest point will be $v_0^2/64$ feet above the starting point (if we neglect the effects of air resistance).

Exercises 71–76 use the results in the preceding two exercises.

71. ▼ I threw a ball up in the air to a height of 20 feet. How fast was the ball traveling when it left my hand?

72. ▼ I threw a ball up in the air to a height of 40 feet. How fast was the ball traveling when it left my hand?

73. ▼ A piece of chalk is tossed vertically upward by Prof. Schwarzenegger and hits the ceiling 100 feet above with a *BANG*.

   a. What is the minimum speed the piece of chalk must have been traveling to enable it to hit the ceiling?
   b. Assuming that Prof. Schwarzenegger in fact tossed the piece of chalk up at 100 ft/s, how fast was it moving when it struck the ceiling?
   c. Assuming that Prof. Schwarzenegger tossed the chalk up at 100 ft/s, and that it recoils from the ceiling with the same speed it had at the instant it hit, how long will it take the chalk to make the return journey and hit the ground?

74. ▼ A projectile is fired vertically upward from ground level at 16,000 feet per second.

   a. How high does the projectile go?
   b. How long does it take to reach its zenith (highest point)?
   c. How fast is it traveling when it hits the ground?

75. ▼ *Strength* Prof. Strong can throw a 10-pound dumbbell twice as high as Professor Weak can. How much faster can Prof. Strong throw it?

76. ▼ *Weakness* Prof. Weak can throw a computer disk three times as high as Professor Strong can. How much faster can Prof. Weak throw it?

COMMUNICATION AND REASONING EXERCISES

77. Why is this section called "The *Indefinite* Integral?"

78. If the derivative of Julius is Augustus, then Augustus is _____ of Julius.

79. Linear functions are antiderivatives of what kind of function? Explain.

80. Constant functions are antiderivatives of what kind of function? Explain.

81. If we know the *derivative* of a function, do we know the function? Explain. If not, what further informaion will suffice?

82. If we know an *antiderivative* of a function, do we know the function? Explain. If not, what further informaion will suffice?

83. If $F(x)$ and $G(x)$ are both antiderivatives of $f(x)$, how are $F(x)$ and $G(x)$ related?

84. Your friend Marco claims that once you have one antiderivative of $f(x)$, you have all of them. Explain what he means.

85. Complete the following: The total cost function is a(n) _____ of the _____ cost function.

86. Complete the following: The distance covered is an antiderivative of the _____ function, and the velocity is an antiderivative of the _____ function.

87. If x represents the number of items manufactured and $f(x)$ represents dollars per item, what does $\int f(x)\,dx$ represent? In general, how are the units of $f(x)$ and the units of $\int f(x)\,dx$ related?

88. Complete the following: $-\dfrac{1}{x}$ is a(n) _____ of $\dfrac{1}{x^2}$, whereas $\ln x^2$ is not. Also, $-\dfrac{1}{x} + C$ is the _____ of $\dfrac{1}{x^2}$, because the _____ of $-\dfrac{1}{x} + C$ is _____.

89. ▼ Give an argument for the rule that the integral of a sum is the sum of the integrals.

90. ▼ Is it true that $\displaystyle\int \frac{1}{x^3}\,dx = \ln(x^3) + C$? Give a reason for your answer.

91. ▼ Give an example to show that the integral of a product is not the product of the integrals.

92. ▼ Give an example to show that the integral of a quotient is not the quotient of the integrals.

93. ▼ Complete the following: If you take the _____ of the _____ of $f(x)$, you obtain $f(x)$ back. On the other hand, if you take the _____ of the _____ of $f(x)$, you obtain $f(x) + C$.

94. ▼ If a Martian told you that the Institute of Alien Mathematics, after a long and difficult search, has announced the discovery of a new antiderivative of $x - 1$ called $M(x)$ [the formula for $M(x)$ is classified information and cannot be revealed here], how would you respond?

13.2 Substitution

The chain rule for derivatives gives us an extremely useful technique for finding antiderivatives. This technique is called **change of variables** or **substitution**.

Recall that to differentiate a function like $(x^2 + 1)^6$, we first think of the function as $g(u)$ where $u = x^2 + 1$ and $g(u) = u^6$. We then compute the derivative, using the chain rule, as

$$\frac{d}{dx}g(u) = g'(u)\frac{du}{dx}.$$

Any rule for derivatives can be turned into a technique for finding antiderivatives by writing it in integral form. The integral form of the above formula is

$$\int g'(u)\frac{du}{dx}\,dx = g(u) + C.$$

But, if we write $g(u) + C = \int g'(u)\,du$, we get the following interesting equation:

$$\int g'(u)\frac{du}{dx}\,dx = \int g'(u)\,du.$$

This equation is the one usually called the *change of variables formula.* We can turn it into a more useful integration technique as follows. Let $f = g'(u)(du/dx)$. We can rewrite the above change of variables formula using f:

$$\int f \, dx = \int \left(\frac{f}{du/dx} \right) du.$$

In essence, we are making the formal substitution

$$dx = \frac{1}{du/dx} \, du.$$

Here's the technique:

Substitution Rule

If u is a function of x, then we can use the following formula to evaluate an integral:

$$\int f \, dx = \int \left(\frac{f}{du/dx} \right) du.$$

Rather than use the formula directly, we use the following step-by-step procedure:

1. Write u as a function of x.

2. Take the derivative du/dx and solve for the quantity dx in terms of du.

3. Use the expression you obtain in step 2 to substitute for dx in the given integral and substitute u for its defining expression.

Now let's see how this procedure works in practice.

EXAMPLE 1 Substitution

Find $\int 4x(x^2 + 1)^6 \, dx$.

Solution To use substitution we need to choose an expression to be u. There is no hard and fast rule, but here is one hint that often works:

Take u to be an expression that is being raised to a power.

In this case, let's set $u = x^2 + 1$. Continuing the procedure above, we place the calculations for step 2 in a box.

$u = x^2 + 1$	Write u as a function of x.
$\dfrac{du}{dx} = 2x$	Take the derivative of u with respect to x.
$dx = \dfrac{1}{2x} \, du$	Solve for dx: $dx = \dfrac{1}{du/dx} \, du$.

Now we *substitute u for its defining expression and substitute for dx* in the original integral:

✱ NOTE This step is equivalent to using the formula stated in the Substitution Rule box. If it should bother you that the integral contains both x and u, note that x is now a function of u.

$$\int 4x(x^2 + 1)^6 \, dx = \int 4xu^6 \frac{1}{2x} \, du \qquad \text{Substitute* for } u \text{ and } dx.$$

$$= \int 2u^6 \, du. \qquad \text{Cancel the } x\text{s and simplify.}$$

We have boiled the given integral down to the much simpler integral $\int 2u^6 \, du$, and we can now write down the solution:

$$2\frac{u^7}{7} + C = \frac{2(x^2 + 1)^7}{7} + C. \qquad \text{Substitute } (x^2 + 1) \text{ for } u \text{ in the answer.}$$

➡ **Before we go on...** There are two points to notice in Example 1. First, before we can actually integrate with respect to u, *we must eliminate all xs from the integrand.* If we cannot, we may have chosen the wrong expression for u. Second, after integrating, we must substitute back to obtain an expression involving x.

It is easy to check our answer. We differentiate:

$$\frac{d}{dx}\left[\frac{2(x^2 + 1)^7}{7}\right] = \frac{2(7)(x^2 + 1)^6(2x)}{7} = 4x(x^2 + 1)^6. \qquad ✔$$

Notice how we used the chain rule to check the result obtained by substitution. ∎

When we use substitution, the first step is always to decide what to take as u. Again, there are no set rules, but we see some common cases in the examples.

EXAMPLE 2 More Substitution

Calculate $\int x^2(x^3 + 1)^2 \, dx.$

Solution As we said in Example 1, it often works to take u to be an expression that is being raised to a power. We usually also want to see the derivative of u as a factor in the integrand so that we can cancel terms involving x. In this case, $x^3 + 1$ is being raised to a power, so let's set $u = x^3 + 1$. Its derivative is $3x^2$; in the integrand is x^2, which is missing the factor 3, but missing or incorrect constant factors are not a problem.

$$u = x^3 + 1 \qquad \text{Write } u \text{ as a function of } x.$$

$$\frac{du}{dx} = 3x^2 \qquad \text{Take the derivative of } u \text{ with respect to } x.$$

$$dx = \frac{1}{3x^2} \, du \qquad \text{Solve for } dx\text{: } dx = \frac{1}{du/dx} \, du.$$

$$\int x^2(x^3+1)^2\,dx = \int x^2 u^2 \frac{1}{3x^2}\,du \qquad \text{Substitute for } u \text{ and } dx.$$

$$= \int \frac{1}{3} u^2\,du \qquad \text{Cancel the terms with } x.$$

$$= \frac{1}{9} u^3 + C \qquad \text{Take the antiderivative.}$$

$$= \frac{1}{9}(x^3+1)^3 + C \qquad \text{Substitute for } u \text{ in the answer.}$$

EXAMPLE 3   **An Expression in the Exponent**

Evaluate $\int 3x e^{x^2}\,dx$.

Solution   When we have an exponential with an expression in the exponent, it often works to substitute u for that expression. In this case, let's set $u = x^2$.

$$u = x^2$$

$$\frac{du}{dx} = 2x$$

$$dx = \frac{1}{2x}\,du$$

Substituting into the integral, we have

$$\int 3x e^{x^2}\,dx = \int 3x e^u \frac{1}{2x}\,du = \int \frac{3}{2} e^u\,du$$

$$= \frac{3}{2} e^u + C = \frac{3}{2} e^{x^2} + C.$$

EXAMPLE 4   **A Special Power**

Evaluate: **a.** $\int \frac{1}{2x+5}\,dx$ **b.** $\int \left(\frac{1}{2x+5} + 4x^2 + 1 \right) dx$

Solution

a. We begin by rewriting the integrand as a power.

$$\int \frac{1}{2x+5}\,dx = \int (2x+5)^{-1}\,dx$$

Now we take our earlier advice and set u equal to the expression that is being raised to a power:

$$u = 2x+5$$

$$\frac{du}{dx} = 2$$

$$dx = \frac{1}{2}\,du$$

Substituting into the integral, we have

$$\int \frac{1}{2x+5}\,dx = \int \frac{1}{2} u^{-1}\,du = \frac{1}{2} \ln|u| + C$$

$$= \frac{1}{2} \ln|2x+5| + C.$$

b. Here, the substitution $u = 2x + 5$ works for the first part of the integrand, $1/(2x + 5)$, but not for the rest of it, so we break up the integral:

$$\int \left(\frac{1}{2x + 5} + 4x^2 + 1 \right) dx = \int \frac{1}{2x + 5} \, dx + \int (4x^2 + 1) \, dx.$$

For the first integral we can use the substitution $u = 2x + 5$ [which we did in part (a)], and for the second, no substitution is necessary:

$$\int \frac{1}{2x + 5} \, dx + \int (4x^2 + 1) \, dx = \frac{1}{2} \ln|2x + 5| + \frac{4x^3}{3} + x + C.$$

EXAMPLE 5 Choosing *u*

Evaluate $\int (x + 3)\sqrt{x^2 + 6x} \, dx$.

Solution There are two parenthetical expressions. Notice, however, that the derivative of the expression $(x^2 + 6x)$ is $2x + 6$, which is twice the term $(x + 3)$ in front of the radical. Recall that we would like the derivative of *u* to appear as a factor. Thus, let's take $u = x^2 + 6x$.

$$u = x^2 + 6x$$

$$\frac{du}{dx} = 2x + 6 = 2(x + 3)$$

$$dx = \frac{1}{2(x + 3)} \, du$$

Substituting into the integral, we have

$$\int (x + 3)\sqrt{x^2 + 6x} \, dx$$

$$= \int (x + 3)\sqrt{u} \left(\frac{1}{2(x + 3)} \right) du$$

$$= \int \frac{1}{2}\sqrt{u} \, du = \frac{1}{2} \int u^{1/2} du$$

$$= \frac{1}{2} \frac{2}{3} u^{3/2} + C = \frac{1}{3}(x^2 + 6x)^{3/2} + C.$$

Some cases require a little more work.

EXAMPLE 6 When the *x* Terms Do Not Cancel

Evaluate $\int \frac{2x}{(x - 5)^2} \, dx$.

Solution We first rewrite

$$\int \frac{2x}{(x - 5)^2} \, dx = \int 2x(x - 5)^{-2} \, dx.$$

This suggests that we should set $u = x - 5$.

$$\boxed{\begin{array}{l} u = x - 5 \\[4pt] \dfrac{du}{dx} = 1 \\[4pt] dx = du \end{array}}$$

Substituting, we have

$$\int \frac{2x}{(x-5)^2}\, dx = \int 2xu^{-2}\, du.$$

Now, there is nothing in the integrand to cancel the x that appears. If, as here, there is still an x in the integrand after substituting, we go back to the expression for u, solve for x, and substitute the expression we obtain for x in the integrand. So, we take $u = x - 5$ and solve for $x = u + 5$. Substituting, we get

$$\int 2xu^{-2}\, du = \int 2(u + 5)u^{-2}\, du$$

$$= 2 \int (u^{-1} + 5u^{-2})\, du$$

$$= 2 \ln |u| - \frac{10}{u} + C$$

$$= 2 \ln |x - 5| - \frac{10}{x - 5} + C.$$

EXAMPLE 7 **Application: Bottled Water for Pets**

Annual sales of bottled spring water for pets can be modeled by the logistic function

$$s(t) = \frac{3{,}000e^{0.5t}}{3 + e^{0.5t}} \text{ million gallons per year} \qquad (0 \le t \le 8)$$

where t is time in years since the start of 2000.*

a. Find an expression for the total amount of bottled spring water for pets sold since the start of 2000.

b. How much bottled spring water for pets was sold from the start of 2005 to the start of 2008?

Solution

a. If we write the total amount of pet spring water sold since the start of 2000 as $S(t)$, then the information we are given says that

$$S'(t) = s(t) = \frac{3{,}000e^{0.5t}}{3 + e^{0.5t}}.$$

Thus,

$$S(t) = \int \frac{3{,}000e^{0.5t}}{3 + e^{0.5t}}\, dt$$

---

* Source for data: Beverage Marketing Corporation (www.beveragemarketing.com).

is the function we are after. To integrate the expression, take u to be the denominator of the integrand:

$$u = 3 + e^{0.5t}$$

$$\frac{du}{dt} = 0.5e^{0.5t}$$

$$dt = \frac{1}{0.5e^{0.5t}} \, du$$

$$S(t) = \int \frac{3,000e^{0.5t}}{3 + e^{0.5t}} \, dt$$

$$= \int \frac{3,000e^{0.5t}}{u} \cdot \frac{1}{0.5e^{0.5t}} \, du$$

$$= \frac{3,000}{0.5} \int \frac{1}{u} \, du$$

$$= 6,000 \ln |u| + C = 6,000 \ln(3 + e^{0.5t}) + C.$$

(Why could we drop the absolute value in the last step?)

Now what is C? Because $S(t)$ represents the total amount of bottled spring water for pets sold *since time* $t = 0$, we have $S(0) = 0$ (because that is when we started counting). Thus,

$$0 = 6,000 \ln(3 + e^{0.5(0)}) + C$$

$$= 6,000 \ln(4) + C$$

$$C = -6,000 \ln(4) \approx -8,318.$$

Therefore, the total sales from the start of 2000 is approximately

$$S(t) = 6,000 \ln(3 + e^{0.5t}) - 8,318 \text{ million gallons.}$$

b. The period from the start of 2005 to the start of 2008 is represented by the interval $[5, 8]$. From part (a):

Sales through the start of $2005 = S(5)$
$$= 6,000 \ln(3 + e^{0.5(5)}) - 8,318 \approx 8,003 \text{ million gallons.}$$

Sales through the start of $2008 = S(8)$
$$= 6,000 \ln(3 + e^{0.5(8)}) - 8,318 \approx 16,003 \text{ million gallons.}$$

Therefore, sales over the period were about $16,003 - 8,003 = 8,000$ million gallons.

➡ **Before we go on...** You might wonder why we are writing a logistic function in the form we used in Example 7 rather than in one of the "standard" forms $\dfrac{N}{1 + Ab^{-t}}$ or $\dfrac{N}{1 + Ae^{-kt}}$. Our only reason for doing this is to make the substitution work. To convert from the second "standard" form to the form we used in the example, multiply top and bottom by e^{kt}. (See Exercises 81 and 82 in Section 13.4 for further discussion.) ■

Shortcuts

The following shortcuts allow us to simply write down the antiderivative in cases where we would otherwise need the substitution $u = ax + b$, as in Example 4. (a and b are constants with $a \neq 0$.) All of the shortcuts can be obtained using the substitution $u = ax + b$. Their derivation will appear in the exercises.

Shortcuts: Integrals of Expressions Involving (*ax* + *b*)

Rule	Quick Example
$\displaystyle\int (ax+b)^n\,dx = \frac{(ax+b)^{n+1}}{a(n+1)} + C$ (if $n \neq -1$)	$\displaystyle\int (3x-1)^2\,dx = \frac{(3x-1)^3}{3(3)} + C$ $\displaystyle = \frac{(3x-1)^3}{9} + C$
$\displaystyle\int (ax+b)^{-1}\,dx = \frac{1}{a}\ln|ax+b| + C$	$\displaystyle\int (3-2x)^{-1}\,dx = \frac{1}{(-2)}\ln|3-2x| + C$ $\displaystyle = -\frac{1}{2}\ln|3-2x| + C$
$\displaystyle\int e^{ax+b}\,dx = \frac{1}{a}e^{ax+b} + C$	$\displaystyle\int e^{-x+4}\,dx = \frac{1}{(-1)}e^{-x+4} + C$ $\displaystyle = -e^{-x+4} + C$
$\displaystyle\int c^{ax+b}\,dx = \frac{1}{a\ln c}c^{ax+b} + C$	$\displaystyle\int 2^{-3x+4}\,dx = \frac{1}{(-3\ln 2)}2^{-3x+4} + C$ $\displaystyle = -\frac{1}{3\ln 2}2^{-3x+4} + C$
$\displaystyle\int |ax+b|\,dx$ $\displaystyle = \frac{1}{2a}(ax+b)|ax+b| + C^{*}$	$\displaystyle\int |2x-1|\,dx$ $\displaystyle = \frac{1}{4}(2x-1)|2x-1| + C$

✳ NOTE Recall that
$$\int |x|\,dx = \frac{1}{2}x|x| + C.$$
(See Exercise 45 of Section 13.1 on page 960.)

FAQs

When to Use Substitution and What to Use for *u*

Q : *If I am asked to calculate an antiderivative, how do I know when to use a substitution and when not to use one?*

A : Do *not* use substitution when integrating sums, differences, and/or constant multiples of powers of *x* and exponential functions, such as $2x^3 - \dfrac{4}{x^2} + \dfrac{1}{2x} + 3^x + \dfrac{2^x}{3}$.

To recognize when you should try a substitution, pretend that you are *differentiating* the given expression instead of integrating it. If differentiating the expression would require use of the chain rule, then integrating that expression may well require a substitution, as in, say, $x(3x^2 - 4)^3$ or $(x+1)e^{x^2+2x-1}$. (In the first we have a *quantity* cubed, and in the second we have *e* raised to a *quantity*.)

Q : *If an integral seems to call for a substitution, what should I use for u?*

A : There are no set rules for deciding what to use for u, but the preceding examples show some common patterns:

- If you see a linear expression raised to a power, try setting u equal to that linear expression. For example, in $(3x - 2)^{-3}$, set $u = 3x - 2$. (Alternatively, try using the shortcuts above.)
- If you see a constant raised to a linear expression, try setting u equal to that linear expression. For example, in $3^{(2x+1)}$, set $u = 2x + 1$. (Alternatively, try a shortcut.)
- If you see an expression raised to a power multiplied by the derivative of that expression (or a constant multiple of the derivative), try setting u equal to that expression. For example, in $x^2(3x^3 - 4)^{-1}$, set $u = 3x^3 - 4$.
- If you see a constant raised to an expression, multiplied by the derivative of that expression (or a constant multiple of its derivative), try setting u equal to that expression. For example, in $5(x + 1)e^{x^2+2x-1}$, set $u = x^2 + 2x - 1$.
- If you see an expression in the denominator and its derivative (or a constant multiple of its derivative) in the numerator, try setting u equal to that expression. For example, in $\dfrac{2^{3x}}{3 - 2^{3x}}$, set $u = 3 - 2^{3x}$.

Persistence often pays off: If a certain substitution does not work, try another approach or a different substitution.

13.2 EXERCISES

▼ more advanced   ◆ challenging
T indicates exercises that should be solved using technology

In Exercises 1–10, evaluate the given integral using the substitution (or method) indicated.

1. $\displaystyle\int (3x - 5)^3 \, dx; u = 3x - 5$

2. $\displaystyle\int (2x + 5)^{-2} \, dx; u = 2x + 5$

3. $\displaystyle\int (3x - 5)^3 \, dx;$ shortcut page 970

4. $\displaystyle\int (2x + 5)^{-2} \, dx;$ shortcut page 970

5. $\displaystyle\int e^{-x} \, dx; u = -x$

6. $\displaystyle\int e^{x/2} \, dx; u = x/2$

7. $\displaystyle\int e^{-x} \, dx;$ shortcut page 970

8. $\displaystyle\int e^{x/2} \, dx;$ shortcut page 970

9. $\displaystyle\int (x + 1)e^{(x+1)^2} \, dx; u = (x + 1)^2$

10. $\displaystyle\int (x - 1)^2 e^{(x-1)^3} \, dx; u = (x - 1)^3$

In Exercises 11–48, decide on what substitution to use, and then evaluate the given integral using a substitution. HINT [See Example 1.]

11. $\displaystyle\int (3x + 1)^5 \, dx$

12. $\displaystyle\int (-x - 1)^7 \, dx$

13. $\displaystyle\int (-2x + 2)^{-2} \, dx$

14. $\displaystyle\int (2x)^{-1} \, dx$

15. $\displaystyle\int 7.2\sqrt{3x - 4} \, dx$

16. $\displaystyle\int 4.4e^{(-3x+4)} \, dx$

17. $\displaystyle\int 1.2e^{(0.6x+2)} \, dx$

18. $\displaystyle\int 8.1\sqrt{-3x + 4} \, dx$

19. $\displaystyle\int x(3x^2 + 3)^3 \, dx$

20. $\displaystyle\int x(-x^2 - 1)^3 \, dx$

21. $\displaystyle\int x(x^2 + 1)^{1.3} \, dx$

22. $\displaystyle\int \frac{x}{(3x^2 - 1)^{0.4}} \, dx$

23. $\displaystyle\int (1 + 9.3e^{3.1x-2}) \, dx$

24. $\displaystyle\int (3.2 - 4e^{1.2x-3}) \, dx$

25. $\int 2x\sqrt{3x^2 - 1}\,dx$

26. $\int 3x\sqrt{-x^2 + 1}\,dx$

27. $\int xe^{-x^2+1}\,dx$

28. $\int xe^{2x^2-1}\,dx$

29. $\int (x + 1)e^{-(x^2+2x)}\,dx$ HINT [See Example 5.]

30. $\int (2x - 1)e^{2x^2-2x}\,dx$ HINT [See Example 5.]

31. $\int \dfrac{-2x - 1}{(x^2 + x + 1)^3}\,dx$

32. $\int \dfrac{x^3 - x^2}{3x^4 - 4x^3}\,dx$

33. $\int \dfrac{x^2 + x^5}{\sqrt{2x^3 + x^6 - 5}}\,dx$ HINT [See Example 6.]

34. $\int \dfrac{2(x^3 - x^4)}{(5x^4 - 4x^5)^5}\,dx$ HINT [See Example 6.]

35. $\int x(x - 2)^5\,dx$

36. $\int x(x - 2)^{1/3}\,dx$

37. $\int 2x\sqrt{x + 1}\,dx$

38. $\int \dfrac{x}{\sqrt{x + 1}}\,dx$

39. $\int \dfrac{e^{-0.05x}}{1 - e^{-0.05x}}\,dx$ HINT [See Example 7.]

40. $\int \dfrac{3e^{1.2x}}{2 + e^{1.2x}}\,dx$ HINT [See Example 7.]

41. ▼ $\int \dfrac{3e^{-1/x}}{x^2}\,dx$

42. ▼ $\int \dfrac{2e^{2/x}}{x^2}\,dx$

43. ▼ $\int \dfrac{e^x + e^{-x}}{2}\,dx$ HINT [See Example 4(b).]

44. ▼ $\int \left(e^{x/2} + e^{-x/2}\right)\,dx$ HINT [See Example 4(b).]

45. ▼ $\int \dfrac{e^x - e^{-x}}{e^x + e^{-x}}\,dx$

46. ▼ $\int \dfrac{e^{x/2} + e^{-x/2}}{e^{x/2} - e^{-x/2}}\,dx$

47. ▼ $\int \left((2x - 1)e^{2x^2-2x} + xe^{x^2}\right)\,dx$

48. ▼ $\int \left(xe^{-x^2+1} + e^{2x}\right)\,dx$

In Exercises 49–52, derive the given equation, where a and b are constants with $a \neq 0$.

49. $\int (ax + b)^n\,dx = \dfrac{(ax + b)^{n+1}}{a(n + 1)} + C$ (if $n \neq -1$)

50. $\int (ax + b)^{-1}\,dx = \dfrac{1}{a}\ln|ax + b| + C$

51. $\int |ax + b|\,dx = \dfrac{1}{2a}(ax + b)|ax + b| + C$

52. $\int e^{ax+b}\,dx = \dfrac{1}{a}e^{ax+b} + C$

In Exercises 53–68, use the shortcut formulas (see page 970 and Exercises 49–52) to calculate the given integral.

53. $\int e^{-x}\,dx$

54. $\int e^{x-1}\,dx$

55. $\int e^{2x-1}\,dx$

56. $\int e^{-3x}\,dx$

57. $\int (2x + 4)^2\,dx$

58. $\int (3x - 2)^4\,dx$

59. $\int \dfrac{1}{5x - 1}\,dx$

60. $\int (x - 1)^{-1}\,dx$

61. $\int (1.5x)^3\,dx$

62. $\int e^{2.1x}\,dx$

63. $\int 1.5^{3x}\,dx$

64. $\int 4^{-2x}\,dx$

65. $\int |2x + 4|\,dx$

66. $\int |3x - 2|\,dx$

67. $\int (2^{3x+4} + 2^{-3x+4})\,dx$ HINT [See Example 4(b).]

68. $\int (1.1^{-x+4} + 1.1^{x+4})\,dx$ HINT [See Example 4(b).]

69. Find $f(x)$ if $f(0) = 0$ and the tangent line at $(x, f(x))$ has slope $x(x^2 + 1)^3$.

70. Find $f(x)$ if $f(1) = 0$ and the tangent line at $(x, f(x))$ has slope $\dfrac{x}{x^2 + 1}$.

71. Find $f(x)$ if $f(1) = 1/2$ and the tangent line at $(x, f(x))$ has slope xe^{x^2-1}.

72. Find $f(x)$ if $f(2) = 1$ and the tangent line at x has slope $(x - 1)e^{x^2-2x}$.

APPLICATIONS

73. *Economic Growth* The value of sold goods in Mexico can be approximated by

$$v(t) = 210 - 62e^{-0.05t} \text{ trillion pesos per month } \quad (t \geq 0)$$

where t is time in months since January 2005.[11] Find an expression for the total value $V(t)$ of sold goods in Mexico from January 2005 to time t. HINT [Use the shortcut on page 970.]

74. *Economic Contraction* The number of housing starts in the United States can be approximated by

$$n(t) = \dfrac{1}{12}(1.1 + 1.2e^{-0.08t}) \text{ million homes per month } \quad (t \geq 0)$$

where t is time in months from the start of 2006.[12] Find an expression for the total number $N(t)$ of housing starts in the United States from January 2006 to time t. HINT [Use the shortcut on page 970.]

---

[11] Source: Instituto Nacional de Estadística y Geografía (INEGI) (www.inegi.gob.mx).

[12] Source for data: *New York Times*, February 17, 2007, p. C3.

75. Casino Revenues Annual revenues in 1996–2006 from slot machines and video poker machines at **Foxwoods** casino in Connecticut can be modeled by

$$R(t) = 825 - 240e^{-0.4t} \text{ million dollars} \quad (0 \le t \le 10)$$

where t is time in years since 1996.[13] Find an expression for the total revenue earned since 1996, and hence estimate the total revenue earned over the period 1996–2006. (Round your answer to the nearest $10 million.)

76. Casino Revenues Annual revenues in 1996–2006 from slot machines and video poker machines at the **Mohegan Sun** casino in Connecticut can be modeled by

$$R(t) = 1{,}260 - 1{,}030e^{-0.1t} \text{ million dollars} \quad (0 \le t \le 10)$$

where t is time in years since 1996.[14] Find an expression for the total revenue earned since 1996, and hence estimate the total revenue earned over the period 1996–2006. (Round your answer to the nearest $10 million.)

77. Cost The marginal cost of producing the xth roll of film is given by $5 + 1/(x + 1)^2$. The total cost to produce one roll is $1,000. Find the total cost function $C(x)$.

78. Cost The marginal cost of producing the xth box of CDs is given by $10 - x/(x^2 + 1)^2$. The total cost to produce 2 boxes is $1,000. Find the total cost function $C(x)$.

79. Scientific Research The number of research articles in the prominent journal *Physical Review* written by researchers in Europe can be approximated by

$$E(t) = \frac{7e^{0.2t}}{5 + e^{0.2t}} \text{ thousand articles per year} \quad (t \ge 0)$$

where t is time in years ($t = 0$ represents 1983).[15]

a. Find an (approximate) expression for the total number of articles written by researchers in Europe since 1983 ($t = 0$). HINT [See Example 7.]

b. Roughly how many articles were written by researchers in Europe from 1983 to 2003? (Round your answer to the nearest 1,000 articles.)

80. Scientific Research The number of research articles in the prominent journal *Physical Review* written by researchers in the United States can be approximated by

$$U(t) = \frac{4.6e^{0.6t}}{0.4 + e^{0.6t}} \text{ thousand articles per year} \quad (t \ge 0)$$

where t is time in years ($t = 0$ represents 1983).[16]

a. Find an (approximate) expression for the total number of articles written by researchers in the United States since 1983 ($t = 0$). HINT [See Example 7.]

b. Roughly how many articles were written by researchers in the United States from 1983 to 2003?

81. Sales The rate of sales of your company's Jackson Pollock Advanced Paint-by-Number sets can be modeled by

$$s(t) = \frac{900e^{0.25t}}{3 + e^{0.25t}} \text{ sets per month}$$

t months after their introduction. Find an expression for the total number of paint-by-number sets $S(t)$ sold t months after their introduction, and use it to estimate the total sold in the first 12 months. HINT [See Example 7.]

82. Sales The rate of sales of your company's Jackson Pollock Beginners Paint-by-Number sets can be modeled by

$$s(t) = \frac{1{,}800e^{0.75t}}{10 + e^{0.75t}} \text{ sets per month}$$

t months after their introduction. Find an expression for the total number of paint-by-number sets $S(t)$ sold t months after their introduction, and use it to estimate the total sold in the first 12 months. HINT [See Example 7.]

83. Motion in a Straight Line The velocity of a particle moving in a straight line is given by $v = t(t^2 + 1)^4 + t$.

a. Find an expression for the position s after a time t. HINT [See Example 4(b).]

b. Given that $s = 1$ at time $t = 0$, find the constant of integration C and hence an expression for s in terms of t without any unknown constants.

84. Motion in a Straight Line The velocity of a particle moving in a straight line is given by $v = 3te^{t^2} + t$.

a. Find an expression for the position s after a time t. HINT [See Example 4(b).]

b. Given that $s = 3$ at time $t = 0$, find the constant of integration C and hence an expression for s in terms of t without any unknown constants.

85. Bottled Water Sales (Compare Exercise 55 in Section 13.1.) The rate of U.S. sales of bottled water for the period 2000–2008 can be approximated by

$$s(t) = 12(t - 2000)^2 + 500(t - 2000) + 4{,}700 \text{ million gallons per year} \quad (2000 \le t \le 2008)$$

where t is the year.[17] Use an indefinite integral to approximate the total sales $S(t)$ of bottled water since 2003 ($t = 2003$). Approximately how much bottled water was sold from $t = 2003$ to $t = 2008$?

---

[13] Source for data: Connecticut Division of Special Revenue/*New York Times*, Sept. 23, 2007, p. C1.

[14] Ibid.

[15] Based on data from 1983 to 2003. Source: The American Physical Society/*New York Times*, May 3, 2003, p. A1.

[16] Ibid.

---

[17] The 2008 figure is an estimate. Source: Beverage Marketing Corporation (www.bottledwater.org).

86. *Bottled Water Sales* (Compare Exercise 56 in Section 13.1.) The rate of U.S. per capita sales of bottled water for the period 2000–2008 can be approximated by

$$s(t) = 0.04(t - 2000)^2 + 1.5(t - 2000) + 17 \text{ gallons per year}$$
$$(2000 \le t \le 2008)$$

where t is the year.[18] Use an indefinite integral to approximate the total per capita sales $S(t)$ of bottled water since the start of 2006. Approximately how much bottled water was sold, per capita, from $t = 2006$ to $t = 2008$?

COMMUNICATION AND REASONING EXERCISES

87. Are there any circumstances in which you should use the substitution $u = x$? Illustrate your answer by giving an example that shows the effect of this substitution.

88. At what stage of a calculation using a u substitution should you substitute back for u in terms of x: before or after taking the antiderivative?

89. Consider $\int \left(\dfrac{x}{x^2 - 1} + \dfrac{3x}{x^2 + 1} \right) dx$. To compute it, you should use which of the following?

(A) $u = x^2 - 1$ **(B)** $u = x^2 + 1$ **(C)** Neither **(D)** Both

Explain your answer.

---

[18] The 2008 figure is an estimate. Source: Beverage Marketing Corporation (www.bottledwater.org).

90. If the substitution $u = x^2 - 1$ works in $\int \dfrac{x}{x^2 - 1} dx$, why does it not work nearly so easily in $\int \dfrac{x^2 - 1}{x} dx$? How would you do the second integral most simply?

91. You are asked to calculate $\int \dfrac{u}{u^2 + 1} du$. What is wrong with the substitution $u = u^2 + 1$?

92. What is wrong with the following "calculation" of $\int \dfrac{1}{x^2 - 1} dx$?

$$\int \frac{1}{x^2 - 1} = \int \frac{1}{u} \qquad \text{Using the substitution } u = x^2 - 1$$
$$= \ln |u| + C$$
$$= \ln |x^2 - 1| + C$$

93. Give an example of an integral that can be calculated by using the substitution $u = x^2 + 1$, and then carry out the calculation.

94. ▼Give an example of an integral that can be calculated either by using the power rule for antiderivatives or by using the substitution $u = x^2 + x$, and then carry out the calculations.

95. ▼Show that *none* of the following substitutions work for $\int e^{-x^2} dx$: $u = -x, u = x^2, u = -x^2$. (The antiderivative of e^{-x^2} involves the *error function* erf(x).)

96. ▼Show that *none* of the following substitutions work for $\int \sqrt{1 - x^2} dx$: $u = 1 - x^2, u = x^2$, and $u = -x^2$. (The antiderivative of $\sqrt{1 - x^2}$ involves inverse trigonometric functions, discussion of which is beyond the scope of this book.)

13.3 The Definite Integral: Numerical and Graphical Approaches

In Sections 13.1 and 13.2, we discussed the indefinite integral. There is an older, related concept called the **definite integral**. Let's introduce this new idea with an example. (We'll drop hints now and then about how the two types of integral are related. In Section 13.4 we discuss the exact relationship, which is one of the most important results in calculus.)

In Section 13.1, we used antiderivatives to answer questions of the form "Given the marginal cost, compute the total cost." (See Example 5 in Section 13.1.) In this section we approach such questions more directly, and we will forget about antiderivatives for now.

EXAMPLE 1 Total Cost

Your cell phone company offers you an innovative pricing scheme. When you make a call, the *marginal* cost is

$$c(t) = \frac{5}{10t + 1} \text{ dollars per hour.}$$

Use a numerical calculation to estimate the total cost of a 2-hour phone call.

Solution The graph of $c(t)$ is shown in Figure 3.

Figure 3

Let's start with a very crude estimate of the total cost, using the graph as a guide. The marginal cost at the beginning of your call is $c(0) = 5/(0 + 1) = \$5$ per hour. If this cost were to remain constant for the length of your call, the total cost of the call would be

Cost of call = Cost per hour × Number of hours $= 5 \times 2 = \$10$.

Figure 4 shows how we can represent this calculation on the graph of $c(t)$.

Figure 4

The cost per hour based on $c(0) = 5$ is represented by the y-coordinate of the graph at its left edge, while the number of hours is represented by the width of the interval $[0, 2]$ on the x-axis. Therefore, computing the area of the shaded rectangle in the figure gives the same calculation:

Area of rectangle = Cost per hour × Number of hours
$$= 5 \times 2 = \$10 = \text{Cost of call.}$$

But, as we see in the graph, the marginal cost does not remain constant, but goes down quite dramatically over the course of the call. We can obtain a somewhat more accurate estimate of the total cost by looking at the call hour by hour—that is, by dividing the length of the call into two equal intervals, or subdivisions. We estimate the cost of each one-hour subdivision, using the marginal cost at the beginning of that hour.

Cost of first hour = Cost per hour × Number of hours
$$= c(0) \times 1 = 5 \times 1 = \$5$$
Cost of second hour = Cost per hour × Number of hours
$$= c(1) \times 1 = 5/11 \times 1 \approx \$0.45$$

Adding these costs gives us the more accurate estimate

$c(0) \times 1 + c(1) \times 1 = \$5.45.$ Calculation using 2 subdivisions

In Figure 5 we see that we are computing the combined area of two rectangles, each of whose heights is determined by the height of the graph at its left edge:

Number of hours

The areas of the rectangles are estimates of the costs for successive one-hour periods.

Figure 5

$$\text{Area of first rectangle} = \text{Cost per hour} \times \text{Number of hours}$$
$$= c(0) \times 1 = \$5 = \text{Cost of first hour}$$
$$\text{Area of second rectangle} = \text{Cost per hour} \times \text{Number of hours}$$
$$= c(1) \times 1 \approx \$0.45 = \text{Cost of second hour}$$

If we assume that the phone company is honest about $c(t)$ being the marginal cost and is actually calculating your cost more than once an hour, we get an even better estimate of the cost by looking at the call by using four divisions of a half-hour each. The calculation for this estimate is

$$c(0) \times 0.5 + c(0.5) \times 0.5 + c(1) \times 0.5 + c(1.5) \times 0.5$$
$$\approx 2.500 + 0.417 + 0.227 + 0.156 = \$3.30. \qquad \text{Calculation using 4 subdivisions}$$

As we see in Figure 6, we have now computed the combined area of *four* rectangles, each of whose heights is again determined by the height of the graph at its left edge.

Estimated Cost Using 4 Subdivisions.

The areas of the rectangles are estimates of the costs for successive half-hour periods.

Figure 6

Estimated Cost Using 8 Subdivisions.

The areas of the rectangles are estimates of the costs for successive quarter-hour periods.

Figure 7

Notice how the cost seems to be decreasing as we use more subdivisions. More importantly, total cost seems to be getting closer to the area under the graph. Figure 7 illustrates the calculation for 8 equal subdivisions. The approximate total cost using 8 subdivisions is the total area of the shaded region in Figure 7:

$$c(0) \times 0.25 + c(0.25) \times 0.25 + c(0.5) \times 0.25 + \cdots + c(1.75) \times 0.25 \approx \$2.31.$$

Calculation using 8 subdivisions

Looking at Figure 7, one still gets the impression that we are being overcharged, especially for the first period. If the phone company wants to be *really* honest about $c(t)$ being the marginal cost, it should really be calculating your cost *continuously*, minute by minute or, better yet, second-by-second, as illustrated in Figure 8.

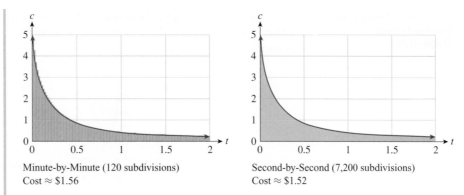

Minute-by-Minute (120 subdivisions)
Cost ≈ $1.56

Second-by-Second (7,200 subdivisions)
Cost ≈ $1.52

Figure 8

Figure 8 strongly suggests that the more accurately we calculate the total cost, the closer the answer gets to the exact area under the portion of the graph of $c(t)$ with $0 \leq t \leq 2$, and leads us to the conclusion that the *exact* total cost is the exact area under the marginal cost curve for $0 \leq t \leq 2$. In other words, we have made the following remarkable discovery:

Total cost is the area under the marginal cost curve!

➡ **Before we go on...** The minute-by-minute calculation in Example 1 is tedious to do by hand, and no one in his or her right mind would even *attempt* to do the second-by-second calculation by hand! Below we discuss ways of doing these calculations with the aid of technology. ∎

The type of calculation done in Example 1 is useful in many applications. Let's look at the general case and give the result a name.

In general, we have a function f (such as the function c in the example), and we consider an interval $[a, b]$ of possible values of the independent variable x. We subdivide the interval $[a, b]$ into some number of segments of equal length. Write n for the number of segments, or **subdivisions**.

Next, we label the endpoints of these subdivisions x_0 for a, x_1 for the end of the first subdivision, x_2 for the end of the second subdivision, and so on until we get to x_n, the end of the nth subdivision, so that $x_n = b$. Thus,

$$a = x_0 < x_1 < \cdots < x_n = b.$$

The first subdivision is the interval $[x_0, x_1]$, the second subdivision is $[x_1, x_2]$, and so on until we get to the last subdivision, which is $[x_{n-1}, x_n]$. We are dividing the interval $[a, b]$ into n subdivisions of equal length, so each segment has length $(b - a)/n$. We write Δx for $(b - a)/n$ (Figure 9).

$$
\begin{array}{ccccccc}
x_0 & x_1 & x_2 & x_3 & \cdots & x_{n-1} & x_n \\
\vdash & + & + & + & & + & \dashv \\
a & & |\!\leftarrow \Delta x \rightarrow\! | & & & & b
\end{array}
$$

Figure 9

Having established this notation, we can write the calculation that we want to do as follows: For each subdivision $[x_{k-1}, x_k]$, compute $f(x_{k-1})$, the value of the function f at the left endpoint. Multiply this value by the length of the interval, which is Δx. Then add together all n of these products to get the number

$$f(x_0)\Delta x + f(x_1)\Delta x + \cdots + f(x_{n-1})\Delta x.$$

✱ NOTE After Georg Friedrich
Bernhard Riemann
(1826–1866).

This sum is called a **(left) Riemann✱ sum** for f. In Example 1 we computed several different Riemann sums. Here is the computation for $n = 4$ we used in the cell phone example (see Figure 10):

$$\Delta x = 0.5$$

Figure 10

$$\text{Left Riemann sum} = f(x_0)\Delta x + f(x_1)\Delta x + \cdots + f(x_{n-1})\Delta x$$
$$= f(0)(0.5) + f(0.5)(0.5) + f(1)(0.5) + f(1.5)(0.5)$$
$$\approx (5)(0.5) + (0.833)(0.5) + (0.455)(0.5) + (0.313)(0.5) \approx 3.30$$

Because sums are often used in mathematics, mathematicians have developed a shorthand notation for them. We write

$$f(x_0)\Delta x + f(x_1)\Delta x + \cdots + f(x_{n-1})\Delta x \text{ as } \sum_{k=0}^{n-1} f(x_k)\Delta x.$$

The symbol $\sum$ is the Greek letter sigma and stands for **summation**. The letter k here is called the index of summation, and we can think of it as counting off the segments. We read the notation as "the sum from $k = 0$ to $n - 1$ of the quantities $f(x_k)\Delta x$." Think of it as a set of instructions:

Set $k = 0$, and calculate $f(x_0)\Delta x$. $f(0)(0.5)$ in the above calculation

Set $k = 1$, and calculate $f(x_1)\Delta x$. $f(0.5)(0.5)$ in the above calculation

$\cdots$

Set $k = n - 1$, and calculate $f(x_{n-1})\Delta x$. $f(1.5)(0.5)$ in the above calculation

Then sum all the quantities so calculated.

Riemann Sum

If f is a continuous function, the **left Riemann sum** with n equal subdivisions for f over the interval $[a, b]$ is defined to be

$$\text{Left Riemann sum} = \sum_{k=0}^{n-1} f(x_k)\Delta x$$
$$= f(x_0)\Delta x + f(x_1)\Delta x + \cdots + f(x_{n-1})\Delta x$$
$$= [f(x_0) + f(x_1) + \cdots + f(x_{n-1})]\Delta x$$

where $a = x_0 < x_1 < \cdots < x_n = b$ are the subdivisions, and $\Delta x = (b - a)/n$.

Interpretation of the Riemann Sum

If f is the rate of change of a quantity F (that is, $f = F'$), then the Riemann sum of f approximates the total change of F from $x = a$ to $x = b$. The approximation improves as the number of subdivisions increases toward infinity.

Quick Example

If $f(t)$ is the rate of change in the number of bats in a belfry and $[a, b] = [2, 3]$, then the Riemann sum approximates the total change in the number of bats in the belfry from time $t = 2$ to time $t = 3$.

Visualizing a Left Riemann Sum (Non-negative Function)

Graphically, we can represent a left Riemann sum of a non-negative function as an approximation of the area under a curve:

Riemann sum = Shaded area = Area of first rectangle + Area of second rectangle $+ \cdots +$
Area of nth rectangle $= f(x_0)\Delta x + f(x_1)\Delta x + f(x_2)\Delta x + \cdots + f(x_{n-1})\Delta x$

Quick Example

In Example 1 we computed several Riemann sums, including these:

$n = 1$:   Riemann sum $= c(0)\Delta t = 5 \times 2 = \$10$

$n = 2$:   Riemann sum $= [c(t_0) + c(t_1)]\Delta t$
$= [c(0) + c(1)] \cdot (1) \approx \$5.45$

$n = 4$:   Riemann sum $= [c(t_0) + c(t_1) + c(t_2) + c(t_3)]\Delta t$
$= [c(0) + c(0.5) + c(1) + c(1.5)] \cdot (0.5) \approx \$3.30$

$n = 8$:   Riemann sum $= [c(t_0) + c(t_1) + \cdots + c(t_7)]\Delta t$
$= [c(0) + c(0.25) + \cdots + c(1.75)] \cdot (0.25) \approx \$2.31$

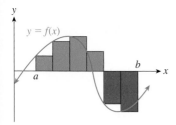

Riemann sum = Area above x-axis
– Area below x-axis

Figure 11

Note To visualize the Riemann sum of a function that is negative, look again at the formula $f(x_0)\Delta x + f(x_1)\Delta x + f(x_2)\Delta x + \cdots + f(x_{n-1})\Delta x$ for the Riemann sum. Each term $f(x_k)\Delta x_k$ represents the area of one rectangle in the figure above. So, the areas of the rectangles with negative values of $f(x_k)$ are automatically counted as negative. They appear as red rectangles in Figure 11. ∎

Figure 12

Figure 13

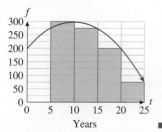

Right Riemann Sum = (300)(5)
+ (275)(5) + (200)(5) + (75)(5)
= 4,250

Height of each rectangle is determined by height of graph at right edge.

Figure 14

Figure 15

EXAMPLE 2 **Computing a Riemann Sum From a Graph**

Figure 12 shows the approximate rate f at which convicts have been given the death sentence in the United States since 1980 (t is time in years since 1980.)* Use a left Riemann sum with 4 subdivisions to estimate the total number of death sentences handed down from 1985 to 2005.

Solution Let us represent the total number of death sentences handed down since the institution of the death sentence up to time t (measured in years since 1980) by $F(t)$. The total number of death sentences handed down from 1985 to 2005 is then the total change in F over the interval [5, 25]. In view of the above discussion, we can approximate the total change in F using a Riemann sum of its rate of change f. Because $n = 4$ subdivisions are specified, the width of each subdivision is

$$\Delta x = \frac{b - a}{n} = \frac{25 - 5}{4} = 5.$$

We can therefore represent the left Riemann sum by the shaded area shown in Figure 13:
From the graph,

$$\text{Left sum} = f(5)\Delta t + f(10)\Delta t + f(15)\Delta t + f(20)\Delta t$$
$$= (275)(5) + (300)(5) + (275)(5) + (200)(5) = 5,250.$$

So, we estimate that a total of 5,250 death sentences were handed down during the given period.

---

* The death penalty was reinstated by the U.S. Supreme Court in 1976. Source for data through 2003: Bureau of Justice Statistics, NAACP Defense Fund Inc./*New York Times*, September 15, 2004, p. A16.

➡ **Before we go on...** Although in this section we focus primarily on left Riemann sums, we could also approximate the total in Example 2 using a **right Riemann sum**, as shown in Figure 14. For continuous functions, the distinction between these two types of Riemann sums approaches zero as the number of subdivisions approaches infinity. (See below.) ∎

EXAMPLE 3 **Computing a Riemann Sum From a Formula**

Compute the left Riemann sum for $f(x) = x^2 + 1$ over the interval $[-1, 1]$, using $n = 5$ subdivisions.

Solution Because the interval is $[a, b] = [-1, 1]$ and $n = 5$, we have

$$\Delta x = \frac{b - a}{n} = \frac{1 - (-1)}{5} = 0.4.\qquad\text{Width of subdivisions}$$

Thus, the subdivisions of $[-1, 1]$ are given by

$$-1 < -0.6 < -0.2 < 0.2 < 0.6 < 1.\qquad\text{Start with } -1 \text{ and keep adding } \Delta x = 0.4.$$

Figure 15 shows the graph with a representation of the Riemann sum.
The Riemann sum we want is

$$[f(x_0) + f(x_1) + \cdots + f(x_4)]\Delta x$$
$$= [f(-1) + f(-0.6) + f(-0.2) + f(0.2) + f(0.6)]0.4.$$

We can conveniently organize this calculation in a table as follows:

x	-1	-0.6	-0.2	0.2	0.6	**Total**
$f(x) = x^2 + 1$	2	1.36	1.04	1.04	1.36	6.8

The Riemann sum is therefore

$$6.8\Delta x = 6.8 \times 0.4 = 2.72.$$

✳ **NOTE** This applies to some other functions as well, including "piecewise continuous" functions discussed in the next section.

As in Example 1, we're most interested in what happens to the Riemann sum when we let n get very large. When f is continuous,✳ its Riemann sums will always approach a limit as n goes to infinity. (This is not meant to be obvious. Proofs may be found in advanced calculus texts.) We give the limit a name.

The Definite Integral

If f is a continuous function, the **definite integral of f from a to b** is defined to be the limit of the Riemann sums as the number of subdivisions approaches infinity:

$$\int_a^b f(x)\, dx = \lim_{n\to\infty} \sum_{k=0}^{n-1} f(x_k)\, \Delta x.$$

In Words: The integral, from a to b, of $f(x)\, dx$ equals the limit, as $n \to \infty$, of the Riemann Sum with a partition of n subdivisions.

The function f is called the **integrand**, the numbers a and b are the **limits of integration**, and the variable x is the **variable of integration**. A Riemann sum with a large number of subdivisions may be used to approximate the definite integral.

Interpretation of the Definite Integral
If f is the rate of change of a quantity F (that is, $f = F'$), then $\int_a^b f(x)\, dx$ is the (exact) total change of F from $x = a$ to $x = b$.

Quick Examples

1. If $f(t)$ is the rate of change in the number of bats in a belfry and $[a, b] = [2, 3]$, then $\int_2^3 f(t)\, dt$ is the total change in the number of bats in the belfry from time $t = 2$ to time $t = 3$.

2. If, at time t hours, you are selling wall posters at a rate of $s(t)$ posters per hour, then

$$\text{Total number of posters sold from hour 3 to hour 5} = \int_3^5 s(t)\, dt.$$

Visualizing the Definite Integral

Non-negative Functions: If $f(x) \geq 0$ for all x in $[a, b]$, then $\int_a^b f(x)\,dx$ is the area under the graph of f over the interval $[a, b]$, as shaded in the figure.

General Functions: $\int_a^b f(x)\,dx$ is the area between $x = a$ and $x = b$ that is above the x-axis and below the graph of f, minus the area that is below the x-axis and above the graph of f:

$$\int_a^b f(x)\,dx = \text{Area above } x\text{-axis} - \text{Area below } x\text{-axis}$$

Quick Examples

1.

$$\int_1^4 2\,dx = \text{Area of rectangle} = 6$$

2.

$$\int_0^2 x\,dx = \text{Area of triangle} = \frac{1}{2}\text{ base} \times \text{height} = 2$$

3.

$$\int_{-1}^1 x\,dx = 0 \qquad \text{The areas above and below the } x\text{-axis are equal.}$$

Notes

1. Remember that $\int_a^b f(x)\,dx$ stands for a number that depends on f, a, and b. The variable x that appears is called a **dummy variable** because it has no effect on the answer. In other words,

$$\int_a^b f(x)\,dx = \int_a^b f(t)\,dt. \qquad \text{x or t is just a name we give the variable.}$$

2. The notation for the definite integral (due to Leibniz) comes from the notation for the Riemann sum. The integral sign $\int$ is an elongated S, the Roman equivalent of the Greek $\sum$. The d in dx is the lowercase Roman equivalent of the Greek Δ.

3. The definition above is adequate for continuous functions, but more complicated definitions are needed to handle other functions. For example, we broke the interval $[a, b]$ into n subdivisions of equal length, but other definitions allow a **partition** of the interval into subdivisions of possibly unequal lengths. We have evaluated f at the left endpoint of each subdivision, but we could equally well have used the right endpoint or any other point in the subdivision. All of these variations lead to the same answer when f is continuous.

4. The similarity between the notations for the definite integral and the indefinite integral is no mistake. We will discuss the exact connection in the next section. ■

Computing Definite Integrals

In some cases, we can compute the definite integral directly from the graph (see the quick examples above and the next example below). In general, the only method of computing definite integrals we have discussed so far is numerical estimation: compute the Riemann sums for larger and larger values of n and then estimate the number it seems to be approaching as we did in Example 1. (In the next section we will discuss an algebraic method for computing them.)

EXAMPLE 4 Estimating a Definite Integral From a Graph

Figure 16 shows the graph of the (approximate) rate $f'(t)$, at which the United States has been consuming gasoline from 2000 through 2008. (t is time in years since 2000.)*

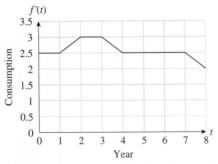

$f'(t)$ = Gasoline consumption (100 million gals per year)

Figure 16

Use the graph to estimate the total U.S. consumption of gasoline over the period shown.

---

*Source: Energy Information Administration (Department of Energy), (http://www.eia.doe.gov).

Solution The derivative $f'(t)$ represents the rate of change of the total U.S. consumption of gasoline, and so the total U.S. consumption of gasoline over the given period $[0, 8]$ is given by the definite integral:

$$\text{Total U.S. consumption of gasoline} = \text{Total change in } f(t) = \int_0^8 f'(t)\, dt$$

and is given by the area under the graph (Figure 17).

Figure 17

One way to determine the area is to count the number of filled rectangles as defined by the grid. Each rectangle has an area of $1 \times 0.5 = 0.5$ units (and the half-rectangles determined by diagonal portions of the graph have half that area). Counting rectangles, we find a total of 41.5 complete rectangles, so

$$\text{Total area} = 20.75.$$

Because $f'(t)$ is in 100 million gallons per year, we conclude that the total U.S. consumption of gasoline over the given period was about 2,075 million gallons, or 2.075 billion gallons.

While counting rectangles might seem easy, it becomes awkward in cases involving large numbers of rectangles or partial rectangles whose area is not easy to determine. Rather than counting rectangles, we can get the area by averaging the left and right Riemann sums whose subdivisions are determined by the grid:

$$\text{Left sum} = (2.5 + 2.5 + 3 + 3 + 2.5 + 2.5 + 2.5 + 2.5)(1) = 21$$
$$\text{Right sum} = (2.5 + 3 + 3 + 2.5 + 2.5 + 2.5 + 2.5 + 2)(1) = 20.5$$
$$\text{Average} = \frac{21 + 20.5}{2} = 20.75.$$

To see why this works, look at the single interval $[1, 2]$. The left sum contributes $2.5 \times 1 = 2.5$ and the right sum contributes $3 \times 1 = 3$. The exact area is their average, 2.75 (Figure 18).

Left sum   Right sum   Average

Figure 18

➡ **Before we go on...** It is important to check that the units we are using in Example 4 match up correctly: t is given in *years* and $f'(t)$ is given in 100 million gallons per *year*. The integral is then given in

$$\text{Years} \times \frac{100 \text{ million gallons}}{\text{Year}} = 100 \text{ million gallons}$$

If we had specified $f'(t)$ in, say, 100 million gallons per *day* but t in years, then we would have needed to convert either t or $f'(t)$ so that the units of time match. ■

The next example illustrates the use of technology in estimating definite integrals using Riemann sums.

EXAMPLE 5   Using Technology to Approximate the Definite Integral

Use technology to estimate the area under the graph of $f(x) = 1 - x^2$ over the interval $[0, 1]$ using $n = 100$, $n = 200$, and $n = 500$ subdivisions.

Solution We need to estimate the area under the parabola shown in Figure 19.

From the discussion above,

$$\text{Area} = \int_0^1 (1 - x^2)\, dx.$$

The Riemann sum with $n = 100$ has $\Delta x = (b - a)/n = (1 - 0)/100 = 0.01$ and is given by

$$\sum_{k=0}^{99} f(x_k)\Delta x = [f(0) + f(0.01) + \cdots + f(0.99)](0.01).$$

Similarly, the Riemann sum with $n = 200$ has $\Delta x = (b - a)/n = (1 - 0)/200 = 0.005$ and is given by

$$\sum_{k=0}^{199} f(x_k)\Delta x = [f(0) + f(0.005) + \cdots + f(0.995)](0.005).$$

For $n = 500$, $x = (b - a)/n = (1 - 0)/500 = 0.002$ and the Riemann sum is

$$\sum_{k=0}^{499} f(x_k)\Delta x = [f(0) + f(0.002) + \cdots + f(0.998)](0.002).$$

Using technology to evaluate these Riemann sums, we find:

$$n = 100: \sum_{k=0}^{99} f(x_k)\Delta x = 0.67165$$

$$n = 200: \sum_{k=0}^{199} f(x_k)\Delta x = 0.6691625$$

$$n = 500: \sum_{k=0}^{499} f(x_k)\Delta x = 0.667666$$

so we estimate that the area under the curve is about 0.667. (The exact answer is $2/3$, as we will be able to verify using the techniques in the next section.)

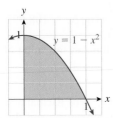

Figure 19

using Technology

See the Technology Guides at the end of the chapter to find out how to compute these sums on a TI-83/84 Plus and Excel.

Web Site
www.FiniteandCalc.org
Follow the path

Chapter 13

→ Math Tools for Chapter 13

→ Numerical Integration
    Utility

to obtain a utility that computes left and right Riemann sums. In the utilities, there is also a downloadable Excel spreadsheet that computes and also graphs Riemann sums (Riemann Sum Grapher).

EXAMPLE 6 **Motion**

A fast car has velocity $v(t) = 6t^2 + 10t$ ft/s after t seconds (as measured by a radar gun). Use several values of n to find the distance covered by the car from time $t = 3$ seconds to time $t = 4$ seconds.

Solution Because the velocity $v(t)$ is rate of change of position, the total change in position over the interval $[3, 4]$ is

$$\text{Distance covered} = \text{Total change in position} = \int_3^4 v(t)\,dt = \int_3^4 (6t^2 + 10t)\,dt.$$

As in Examples 1 and 5, we can subdivide the one-second interval $[3, 4]$ into smaller and smaller pieces to get more and more accurate approximations of the integral. By computing Riemann sums for various values of n, we get the following results.

$$n = 10: \sum_{k=0}^{9} v(t_k)\Delta t = 106.41 \qquad n = 100: \sum_{k=0}^{99} v(t_k)\Delta t \approx 108.740$$

$$n = 1{,}000: \sum_{k=0}^{999} v(t_k)\Delta t \approx 108.974 \qquad n = 10{,}000: \sum_{k=0}^{9999} v(t_k)\Delta t \approx 108.997$$

These calculations suggest that the total distance covered by the car, the value of the definite integral, is approximately 109 feet.

Web Site
www.FiniteandCalc.org
At the Web site you will find the following optional online interactive section: Internet Topic: Numerical Integration.

➡ **Before we go on...** Do Example 6 using antiderivatives instead of Riemann sums, as in Section 13.1. Do you notice a relationship between antiderivatives and definite integrals? This will be explored in the next section. ∎

13.3 EXERCISES

▼ more advanced   ◆ challenging
Ⅰ indicates exercises that should be solved using technology

In Exercises 1–8, use the given graph to estimate the left Riemann sum for the given interval with the stated number of subdivisions. HINT [See Example 2.]

1. $[0, 5], n = 5$

2. $[0, 8], n = 4$

3. $[1, 9], n = 4$

4. $[0.5, 2.5], n = 4$

5. $[1, 3.5], n = 5$

6. $[0.5, 3.5], n = 3$

7. $[0, 3]; n = 3$

8. $[0.5, 3]; n = 5$

Calculate the left Riemann sums for the given functions over the given interval in Exercises 9–18, using the given values of n. (When rounding, round answers to four decimal places.) HINT [See Example 3.]

9. $f(x) = 4x - 1$ over $[0, 2]$, $n = 4$

10. $f(x) = 1 - 3x$ over $[-1, 1]$, $n = 4$

11. $f(x) = x^2$ over $[-2, 2]$, $n = 4$

12. $f(x) = x^2$ over $[1, 5]$, $n = 4$

13. $f(x) = \dfrac{1}{1+x}$ over $[0, 1]$, $n = 5$

14. $f(x) = \dfrac{x}{1+x^2}$ over $[0, 1]$, $n = 5$

15. $f(x) = e^{-x}$ over $[0, 10]$, $n = 5$

16. $f(x) = e^{-x}$ over $[-5, 5]$, $n = 5$

17. $f(x) = e^{-x^2}$ over $[0, 10]$, $n = 4$

18. $f(x) = e^{-x^2}$ over $[0, 100]$, $n = 4$

Use geometry (not Riemann sums) to compute the integrals in Exercises 19–28. HINT [See Quick Examples page 982.]

19. $\displaystyle\int_0^1 1 \, dx$

20. $\displaystyle\int_0^2 5 \, dx$

21. $\displaystyle\int_0^1 x \, dx$

22. $\displaystyle\int_1^2 x \, dx$

23. $\displaystyle\int_0^1 \dfrac{x}{2} \, dx$

24. $\displaystyle\int_1^2 \dfrac{x}{2} \, dx$

25. $\displaystyle\int_2^4 (x - 2) \, dx$

26. $\displaystyle\int_3^6 (x - 3) \, dx$

27. $\displaystyle\int_{-1}^1 x^3 \, dx$

28. $\displaystyle\int_{-2}^2 \dfrac{x}{2} \, dx$

In Exercises 29–34, the graph of the derivative $f'(t)$ of $f(t)$ is shown. Compute the total change of $f(t)$ over the given interval. HINT [See Example 4.]

29. $[1, 5]$

30. $[2, 6]$

31. $[2, 6]$

32. $[0, 5]$

33. $[-1, 2]$

34. $[-1, 2]$

T *In Exercises 35–38, use technology to approximate the given integrals with Riemann sums, using **(a)** $n = 10$, **(b)** $n = 100$, and **(c)** $n = 1{,}000$. Round all answers to four decimal places.* HINT [See Example 5.]

35. ▼ $\displaystyle\int_0^1 4\sqrt{1 - x^2} \, dx$

36. ▼ $\displaystyle\int_0^1 \dfrac{4}{1 + x^2} \, dx$

37. ▼ $\displaystyle\int_2^3 \dfrac{2x^{1.2}}{1 + 3.5x^{4.7}} \, dx$

38. ▼ $\displaystyle\int_3^4 3x e^{1.3x} \, dx$

APPLICATIONS

39. *Cost* The marginal cost function for the manufacture of portable MP3 players is given by

$$C'(x) = 20 - \frac{x}{200}$$

where x is the number of MP3 players manufactured. Use a Riemann sum with $n = 5$ to estimate the cost of producing the first 5 MP3 players. HINT [See Examples 1 and 3.]

40. *Cost* Repeat the preceding exercise using the marginal cost function

$$C'(x) = 25 - \frac{x}{50}.$$

HINT [See Examples 1 and 3.]

41. *Bottled Water Sales* The rate of U.S. sales of bottled water for the period 2000–2008 can be approximated by

$$s(t) = 12t^2 + 500t + 4{,}700 \text{ million gallons per year}$$
$$(0 \le t \le 8)$$

where t is time in years since the start of 2000.[19] Use a Riemann sum with $n = 5$ to estimate the total U.S. sales of bottled water from the start of 2000 to the start of 2005. (Round your answer to the nearest billion gallons.) HINT [See Example 3.]

---

[19] The 2008 figure is an estimate. Source: Beverage Marketing Corporation (www.bottledwater.org).

42. *Bottled Water Sales* The rate of U.S. per capita sales of bottled water for the period 2000–2008 can be approximated by

$$s(t) = 0.04t^2 + 1.5t + 17 \text{ gallons per year} \quad (0 \le t \le 8)$$

where t is the time in years since the start of 2000.[20] Use a Riemann sum with $n = 5$ to estimate the total U.S. per capita sales of bottled water from the start of 2003 to the start of 2008. (Round your answer to the nearest gallon.) HINT [See Example 3.]

43. *Online Auctions: United States* The following graph shows the approximate rate of change $n(t)$ of the number of items listed on **eBay**, in millions (t is time in quarters; $t = 1$ represents the first quarter in 2005).[21]

Use the graph to estimate the total number of items listed on **eBay** from Q2 2006 to Q2 2008 (the interval [6, 14]). Use a left Riemann sum with four subdivisions. HINT [See Example 2.]

44. *Online Stores: United States* The following graph shows the approximate rate of change $s(t)$ of the number of **eBay** stores (t is time in quarters; $t = 1$ represents the first quarter in 2005).[22]

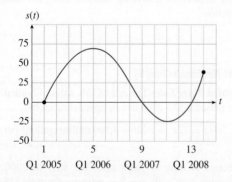

Use the graph to estimate the total net number of **eBay** stores opened between Q3 2006 and Q1 2008 (the interval [7, 13]). Use a left Riemann sum with three subdivisions. HINT [See Example 2.]

45. *Scientific Research* The rate of change $r(t)$ of the total number of research articles in the prominent journal *Physical Review* written by researchers in Europe is shown in the following graph:

Here, t is time in years ($t = 0$ represents the start of 1983).[23]

a. Use both left and right Riemann sums with eight subdivisions to estimate the total number of articles in *Physical Review* written by researchers in Europe during the 16-year period beginning at the start of 1983. (Estimate each value of $r(t)$ to the nearest 0.5.) HINT [See Example 2.]

b. Use the answers from part (a) to obtain an estimate of $\int_0^{16} r(t)\, dt$. HINT [See Example 4.] Interpret the result.

46. *Scientific Research* The rate of change $r(t)$ of the total number of research articles in the prominent journal *Physical Review* written by researchers in the United States is shown in the following graph:

Here, t is time in years ($t = 0$ represents the start of 1983).[24]

a. Use both left and right Riemann sums with six subdivisions to estimate the total number of articles in *Physical Review* written by researchers in the United States during the 12-year period beginning at the start of 1993. (Estimate each value of $r(t)$ to the nearest 0.25.) HINT [See Example 2.]

b. Use the answers from part (a) to obtain an estimate of $\int_{10}^{22} r(t)\, dt$. HINT [See Example 4.] Interpret the result.

[20] The 2008 figure is an estimate. Source: Beverage Marketing Corporation (www.bottledwater.org).

[21] Source for data: eBay company report (www.investor.ebay.com).

[22] Ibid.

[23] Based on data from 1983 to 2003. Source: The American Physical Society/*New York Times*, May 3, 2003, p. A1.

[24] Ibid.

47. Graduate Degrees: Women The following graph shows the approximate number $f'(t)$ of doctoral degrees per year awarded to women in the United States during 2005–2014 ($t = 0$ represents 2005 and each unit of the y-axis represents 10,000 degrees).[25]

Use the graph to estimate the total number of doctoral degrees awarded to women from 2005 to 2010. HINT [See Example 4.]

48. Graduate Degrees: Men The following graph shows the approximate number $m'(t)$ of doctoral degrees per year awarded to men in the United States during 2005–2014 ($t = 0$ represents 2005 and each unit of the y-axis represents 10,000 degrees).[26]

Use the graph to estimate the total number of doctoral degrees awarded to men from 2009 to 2014. HINT [See Example 4.]

Net Income: General Electric. *Exercises 49 and 50 are based on the following graph, which shows* **GE**'s *approximate net income in billions of dollars each quarter from 2006 through the middle of 2008.*[27]

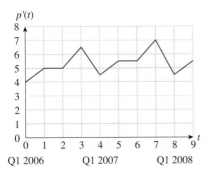

Q1 2006   Q1 2007   Q1 2008

[25] Source for data and projections: National Center for Education Statistics (www.nces.ed.gov).

[26] Ibid.

[27] Source: Company reports (www.ge.com/investors).

49. Compute the left- and right-Riemann sum estimates of $\int_0^4 p'(t)\,dt$ using $\Delta x = 1$. Which of these two sums gives the actual total net income earned by **GE** during 2006? Explain.

50. Compute the left- and right-Riemann sum estimates of $\int_3^7 p'(t)\,dt$ using $\Delta x = 1$. Which of these two sums gives the actual total net income earned by **GE** during 2007? Explain.

51. Visiting Students The following graph shows the approximate rate of change $c'(t)$ in the number of students from China who have taken the GRE exam required for admission to U.S. universities (t is time in years since 2000):[28]

Use the graph to estimate, to the nearest 1,000, the total number of students from China who took the GRE exams during the period 2002–2004.

52. Visiting Students Repeat Exercise 51, using the following graph for students from India:[29]

53. Motion under Gravity The velocity of a stone moving under gravity t seconds after being thrown up at 30 ft/s is given by $v(t) = -32t + 30$ ft/s. Use a Riemann sum with 5 subdivisions to estimate $\int_0^4 v(t)\,dt$. What does the answer represent? HINT [See Example 6.]

54. Motion under Gravity The velocity of a stone moving under gravity t seconds after being thrown up at 4 m/s is given by $v(t) = -9.8t + 4$ m/s. Use a Riemann sum with 5 subdivisions to estimate $\int_0^1 v(t)\,dt$. What does the answer represent? HINT [See Example 6.]

55. Motion A model rocket has upward velocity $v(t) = 40t^2$ ft/s, t seconds after launch. Use a Riemann sum with $n = 10$ to estimate how high the rocket is 2 seconds after launch. HINT [See Example 6.]

[28] Source: Educational Testing Services/Shanghai and Jiao Tong University/*New York Times*, December 21, 2004, p. A25.

[29] Ibid.

56. *Motion* A race car has a velocity of $v(t) = 600(1 - e^{-0.5t})$ ft/s, t seconds after starting. Use a Riemann sum with $n = 10$ to estimate how far the car has traveled in the first 4 seconds. (Round your answer to the nearest whole number.) HINT [See Example 6.]

57. ▣ *Oil Production in Mexico* The rate of oil production by **Pemex**, Mexico's national oil company, can be approximated by

$$p(t) = -8.03t^2 + 73t + 1{,}060 \text{ million barrels per year}$$
$$(1 \le t \le 9)$$

where t is time in years since the start of 2000.[30] Estimate $\int_1^9 p(t)\, dt$ using a Riemann sum with $n = 150$. (Round your answer to three significant digits.) Interpret the answer. HINT [See Example 5.]

58. ▣ *Oil Imports from Mexico* The rate of oil imports to the U.S. from Mexico can be approximated by

$$r(t) = -5.48t^2 + 36.5t + 510 \text{ million barrels per year}$$
$$(0 \le t \le 8)$$

where t is time in years since the start of 2000.[31] Estimate $\int_0^8 r(t)\, dt$ using a Riemann sum with $n = 150$. (Round your answer to three significant digits.) Interpret the answer. HINT [See Example 5.]

59. ▣ *Big Brother* The total number of wiretaps authorized each year by U.S. state and federal courts from 1990 to 2010 can be approximated by

$$w(t) = 820e^{0.051t} \quad (0 \le t \le 20)$$

(t is time in years since the start of 1990).[32] Estimate $\int_0^{15} w(t)\, dt$ using a (left) Riemann sum with $n = 100$. (Round your answer to the nearest 10.) Interpret the answer. HINT [See Example 5.]

60. ▣ *Big Brother* The number of wiretaps authorized each year by U.S. state courts from 1990 to 2010 can be approximated by

$$w(t) = 440e^{0.06t} \quad (0 \le t \le 20)$$

(t is time in years since the start of 1990).[33] Estimate $\int_{10}^{15} w(t)\, dt$ using a (left) Riemann sum with $n = 100$. (Round your answer to the nearest 10.) Interpret the answer. HINT [See Example 5.]

61. ▼ *Surveying* My uncle intends to build a kidney-shaped swimming pool in his small yard, and the town zoning board will approve the project only if the total area of the pool does not exceed 500 square feet. The accompanying figure shows a diagram of the planned swimming pool, with measurements of its width at the indicated points. Will my uncle's plans be approved? Use a (left) Riemann sum to approximate the area.

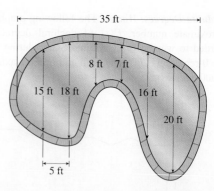

62. ▼ *Pollution* An aerial photograph of an ocean oil spill shows the pattern in the accompanying diagram. Assuming that the oil slick has a uniform depth of 0.01 m, how many cubic meters of oil would you estimate to be in the spill? (Volume = Area × Thickness. Use a (left) Riemann sum to approximate the area.)

63. ▣ ▼ *Oil Consumption: United States* During the period 1980–2008 the United States was consuming oil at a rate of about

$$q(t) = 76t + 5{,}540 \text{ million barrels per year} \quad (0 \le t \le 28)$$

where t is time in years since the start of 1980.[34] During the same period, the price per barrel of crude oil in constant 2008 dollars was about

$$p(t) = 0.45t^2 - 12t + 105 \text{ dollars}[35] \quad (0 \le t \le 28).$$

a. Graph the function $r(t) = p(t)q(t)$ for $0 \le t \le 28$, indicating the area that represents $\int_{10}^{20} r(t)\, dt$. What does this area signify?

---

[30] Source for data: Energy Information Administration/Pemex (http://www.eia.doe.gov.)

[31] Ibid.

[32] Source for data: 2007 Wiretap Report, Administrative Office of the United States Courts (www.uscourts.gov/wiretap07/2007WTText.pdf).

[33] Ibid.

[34] Source for data: BP Statistical Review of World Energy (www.bp.com/statisticalreview).

[35] Source for data: www.inflationdata.com.

b. Estimate the area in part (a) using a Riemann sum with $n = 200$. (Round the answer to 3 significant digits.) Interpret the answer.

64. ☐ ▼ *Oil Consumption: China* Repeat Exercise 63 using instead the rate of consumption of oil in China: During the period 1980–2008 China was consuming oil at a rate of about

$$q(t) = 82t + 221 \text{ million barrels per year}^{36} \quad (0 \le t \le 28).$$

The Normal Curve *The normal distribution curve, which models the distributions of data in a wide range of applications, is given by the function*

$$p(x) = \frac{1}{\sqrt{2\pi}\sigma} e^{-(x-\mu)^2/2\sigma^2}$$

where $\pi = 3.14159265\ldots$ *and* σ *and* μ *are constants called the* ***standard deviation*** *and the* ***mean****, respectively. Its graph (when* $\sigma = 1$ *and* $\mu = 2$*) is shown in the figure. Exercises 65 and 66 illustrate its use.*

65. ☐ ▼ *Test Scores* Enormous State University's Calculus I test scores are modeled by a normal distribution with $\mu = 72.6$ and $\sigma = 5.2$. The percentage of students who obtained scores between a and b on the test is given by

$$\int_a^b p(x)\,dx.$$

a. Use a Riemann sum with $n = 40$ to estimate the percentage of students who obtained between 60 and 100 on the test.

b. What percentage of students scored less than 30?

66. ☐ ▼ *Consumer Satisfaction* In a survey, consumers were asked to rate a new toothpaste on a scale of 1–10. The resulting data are modeled by a normal distribution with $\mu = 4.5$ and $\sigma = 1.0$. The percentage of consumers who rated the toothpaste with a score between a and b on the test is given by

$$\int_a^b p(x)\,dx.$$

a. Use a Riemann sum with $n = 10$ to estimate the percentage of customers who rated the toothpaste 5 or above. (Use the range 4.5 to 10.5.)

b. What percentage of customers rated the toothpaste 0 or 1? (Use the range −0.5 to 1.5.)

---

[36] Source for data: BP Statistical Review of World Energy (www.bp.com/statisticalreview).

COMMUNICATION AND REASONING EXERCISES

67. If $f(x) = 6$, then the left Riemann sum _____ (increases/decreases/stays the same) as n increases.

68. If $f(x) = -1$, then the left Riemann sum _____ (increases/decreases/stays the same) as n increases.

69. If f is an increasing function of x, then the left Riemann sum _____ (increases/decreases/stays the same) as n increases.

70. If f is a decreasing function of x, then the left Riemann sum _____ (increases/decreases/stays the same) as n increases.

71. If $\int_a^b f(x)\,dx = 0$, what can you say about the graph of f?

72. Sketch the graphs of two (different) functions $f(x)$ and $g(x)$ such that $\int_a^b f(x)\,dx = \int_a^b g(x)\,dx$.

73. ▼ The definite integral counts the area under the x-axis as negative. Give an example that shows how this can be useful in applications.

74. ▼ Sketch the graph of a nonconstant function whose Riemann sum with $n = 1$ gives the exact value of the definite integral.

75. ▼ Sketch the graph of a nonconstant function whose Riemann sums with $n = 1, 5$, and 10 are all zero.

76. ▼ Besides left and right Riemann sums, another approximation of the integral is the **mid-point** approximation, in which we compute the sum

$$\sum_{k=1}^{n} f(\bar{x}_k)\,\Delta x$$

where $\bar{x}_k = (x_{k-1} + x_k)/2$ is the point midway between the left and right endpoints of the interval $[x_{k-1}, x_k]$. Why is it true that the midpoint approximation is exact if f is linear? (Draw a picture.)

77. ▼ Your cell phone company charges you $c(t) = \dfrac{20}{t + 100}$ dollars for the tth minute. You make a 60-minute phone call. What kind of (left) Riemann sum represents the total cost of the call? Explain.

78. ▼ Your friend's cell phone company charges her $c(t) = \dfrac{20}{t + 100}$ dollars for the $(t + 1)$st minute. Your friend makes a 60-minute phone call. What kind of (left) Riemann sum represents the total cost of the call? Explain.

79. ▼ Give a formula for the **right Riemann Sum** with n equal subdivisions $a = x_0 < x_1 < \cdots < x_n = b$ for f over the interval $[a, b]$.

80. ▼ Refer to Exercise 79. If f is continuous, what happens to the difference between the left and right Riemann sums as $n \to \infty$? Explain.

81. ▼ When approximating a definite integral by computing Riemann sums, how might you judge whether you have chosen n large enough to get your answer accurate to, say, three decimal places?

13.4 The Definite Integral: Algebraic Approach and the Fundamental Theorem of Calculus

In Section 13.3 we saw that the definite integral of the marginal cost function gives the total cost. However, in Section 13.1 we used antiderivatives to recover the cost function from the marginal cost function, so we *could* use antiderivatives to compute total cost. The following example, based on Example 5 in Section 13.1, compares these two approaches.

EXAMPLE 1 Finding Cost from Marginal Cost

The marginal cost of producing baseball caps at a production level of x caps is $4 - 0.001x$ dollars per cap. Find the total change of cost if production is increased from 100 to 200 caps.

Solution

Method 1: Using an Antiderivative (based on Example 5 in Section 13.1): Let $C(x)$ be the cost function. Because the marginal cost function is the derivative of the cost function, we have $C'(x) = 4 - 0.001x$ and so

$$C(x) = \int (4 - 0.001x)\, dx$$

$$= 4x - 0.001\frac{x^2}{2} + K \qquad K \text{ is the constant of integration.}$$

$$= 4x - 0.0005x^2 + K.$$

Although we do not know what to use for the value of the constant K, we can say:

Cost at production level of 100 caps $= C(100)$

$$= 4(100) - 0.0005(100)^2 + K$$
$$= \$395 + K$$

Cost at production level of 200 caps $= C(200)$

$$= 4(200) - 0.0005(200)^2 + K$$
$$= \$780 + K.$$

Therefore,

Total change in cost $= C(200) - C(100)$

$$= (\$780 + K) - (\$395 + K) = \$385.$$

Notice how the constant of integration simply canceled out! So, we could choose any value for K that we wanted (such as $K = 0$) and still come out with the correct total change. Put another way, we could use *any antiderivative* of $C'(x)$, such as

$$F(x) = 4x - 0.0005x^2 \qquad \begin{array}{l} F(x) \text{ is } any \text{ antiderivative of } C'(x) \\ \text{whereas } C(x) \text{ is the actual cost function.} \end{array}$$

or

$$F(x) = 4x - 0.0005x^2 + 4$$

compute $F(200) - F(100)$, and obtain the total change, $385.

Summarizing this method: To compute the total change of $C(x)$ over the interval $[100, 200]$, use any antiderivative $F(x)$ of $C'(x)$, and compute $F(200) - F(100)$.

Method 2: Using a Definite Integral (based on Example 1 in Section 13.3): Because the marginal cost $C'(x)$ is the rate of change of the total cost function $C(x)$, the total change in $C(x)$ over the interval $[100, 200]$ is given by

Total change in cost = Area under the marginal cost function curve

$$= \int_{100}^{200} C'(x)\,dx$$

$$= \int_{100}^{200} (4 - 0.001x)\,dx \qquad \text{See Figure 20.}$$

$$= \$385. \qquad\qquad \text{Using geometry or Riemann sums}$$

Figure 20

Putting these two methods together gives us the following surprising result:

$$\int_{100}^{200} C'(x)\,dx = F(200) - F(100)$$

where $F(x)$ is any antiderivative of $C'(x)$.

Now, there is nothing special in Example 1 about the specific function $C'(x)$ or the choice of end-points of integration. So if we replace $C'(x)$ by a general continuous function $f(x)$, we can write

$$\int_{a}^{b} f(x)\,dx = F(b) - F(a)$$

where $F(x)$ is any antiderivative of $f(x)$. This result is known as the **Fundamental Theorem of Calculus**.

The Fundamental Theorem of Calculus (FTC)

Let f be a continuous function defined on the interval $[a, b]$ and let F be *any* antiderivative of f defined on $[a, b]$. Then

$$\int_{a}^{b} f(x)\,dx = F(b) - F(a).$$

Moreover, an antiderivative of f is guaranteed to exist.

In Words: Every continuous function has an antiderivative. To compute the definite integral of $f(x)$ over $[a, b]$, first find an antiderivative $F(x)$, then evaluate it at $x = b$, evaluate it at $x = a$, and subtract the two answers.

Quick Example

Because $F(x) = x^2$ is an antiderivative of $f(x) = 2x$,

$$\int_{0}^{1} 2x\,dx = F(1) - F(0) = 1^2 - 0^2 = 1.$$

Note The Fundamental Theorem of Calculus actually applies to some other functions besides the continuous ones. The function f is **piecewise continuous** on $[a, b]$ if it is defined and continuous at all but finitely many points in the interval, and at each point where the function is not defined or is discontinuous, the left and right limits of f exist and are finite. (See Figure 21.)

$$f(x) = \frac{|x|}{x}$$

$$f(x) = \begin{cases} 1 + \frac{x^2}{8} & \text{if } x < 1 \\ 3 - \frac{x^2}{8} & \text{if } x > 1 \end{cases}$$

$$f(x) = \frac{1}{2}\left[\frac{|x - 1|}{x - 1} + \frac{|x - 2|}{x - 2}\right]$$

Figure 21

The FTC also applies to any piecewise continuous function f, as long as we specify that the antiderivative F that we choose be continuous. To be precise, to say that F is an antiderivative of f means here that $F'(x) = f(x)$ except at the points at which f is discontinuous or not defined, where $F'(x)$ may not exist. For example, if f is the step function $f(x) = |x|/x$, shown on the left in Figure 21, then we can use $F(x) = |x|$. (Note that F is continuous, and $F'(x) = |x|/x$ except when $x = 0$.) ∎

EXAMPLE 2 Using the FTC to Calculate a Definite Integral

Calculate $\displaystyle\int_0^1 (1 - x^2)\, dx$.

Solution To use the FTC, we need to find an antiderivative of $1 - x^2$. But we know that

$$\int (1 - x^2)\, dx = x - \frac{x^3}{3} + C.$$

We need only one antiderivative, so let's take $F(x) = x - x^3/3$. The FTC tells us that

$$\int_0^1 (1 - x^2)\, dx = F(1) - F(0) = \left(1 - \frac{1}{3}\right) - (0) = \frac{2}{3}$$

which is the value we estimated in Section 13.3.

✱ NOTE There seem to be several notations in use, actually. Another common notation is $F(x)\Big|_a^b$.

➡ **Before we go on...** A useful piece of notation is often used here. We write✱

$$\big[F(x)\big]_a^b = F(b) - F(a).$$

Thus, we can rewrite the computation in Example 2 as

$$\int_0^1 (1 - x^2)\, dx = \left[x - \frac{x^3}{3}\right]_0^1$$

Substitute $x = 1$.   Substitute $x = 0$.

$$= \left(1 - \frac{1}{3}\right) - \left(0 - \frac{0}{3}\right)$$

$$= \left(1 - \frac{1}{3}\right) - (0) = \frac{2}{3}.$$ ∎

EXAMPLE 3 More Use of the FTC

Compute the following definite integrals.

a. $\displaystyle\int_0^1 (2x^3 + 10x + 1)\,dx$ **b.** $\displaystyle\int_1^5 \left(\frac{1}{x^2} + \frac{1}{x}\right)dx$

Solution

a. $\displaystyle\int_0^1 (2x^3 + 10x + 1)\,dx = \left[\frac{1}{2}x^4 + 5x^2 + x\right]_0^1$

$$\underset{\text{Substitute } x = 1.}{\qquad\qquad} \underset{\text{Substitute } x = 0.}{\qquad\qquad}$$

$$= \left(\frac{1}{2} + 5 + 1\right) - \left(\frac{1}{2}(0) + 5(0) + 0\right)$$

$$= \left(\frac{1}{2} + 5 + 1\right) - (0) = \frac{13}{2}$$

b. $\displaystyle\int_1^5 \left(\frac{1}{x^2} + \frac{1}{x}\right)dx = \int_1^5 (x^{-2} + x^{-1})\,dx$

$$= [-x^{-1} + \ln|x|]_1^5$$

$$\underset{\text{Substitute } x = 5.}{\qquad\qquad} \underset{\text{Substitute } x = 1.}{\qquad\qquad}$$

$$= \left(-\frac{1}{5} + \ln 5\right) - (-1 + \ln 1)$$

$$= \frac{4}{5} + \ln 5$$

When calculating a definite integral, we may have to use substitution to find the necessary antiderivative. We could substitute, evaluate the indefinite integral with respect to u, express the answer in terms of x, and then evaluate at the limits of integration. However, there is a shortcut, as we shall see in the next example.

EXAMPLE 4 Using the FTC with Substitution

Evaluate $\displaystyle\int_1^2 (2x - 1)e^{2x^2 - 2x}\,dx$.

Solution The shortcut we promised is to put *everything* in terms of u, including the limits of integration.

$$u = 2x^2 - 2x$$

$$\frac{du}{dx} = 4x - 2$$

$$dx = \frac{1}{4x - 2}\,du$$

When $x = 1$, $u = 0$.   Substitute $x = 1$ in the formula for u.
When $x = 2$, $u = 4$.   Substitute $x = 2$ in the formula for u.

We get the value $u = 0$, for example, by substituting $x = 1$ in the equation $u = 2x^2 - 2x$. We can now rewrite the integral.

$$\int_1^2 (2x - 1)e^{2x^2 - 2x}\, dx = \int_0^4 (2x - 1)e^u \frac{1}{4x - 2}\, du$$

$$= \int_0^4 \frac{1}{2} e^u\, du$$

$$= \left[\frac{1}{2} e^u\right]_0^4 = \frac{1}{2} e^4 - \frac{1}{2}$$

➡ **Before we go on...** The alternative, longer calculation in Example 4 is first to calculate the indefinite integral:

$$\int (2x - 1)e^{2x^2 - 2x}\, dx = \int \frac{1}{2} e^u\, du$$

$$= \frac{1}{2} e^u + C = \frac{1}{2} e^{2x^2 - 2x} + C.$$

Then we can say that

$$\int_1^2 (2x - 1)e^{2x^2 - 2x}\, dx = \left[\frac{1}{2} e^{2x^2 - 2x}\right]_1^2 = \frac{1}{2} e^4 - \frac{1}{2}.$$ ∎

■■■ **using** Technology

The TI-83/84 Plus and the
Web site use numerical methods that give good quite accurate approximations for definite
integrals, and so we can use
them to check our answers.

TI-83/84 Plus

Home Screen:
fnInt(5/(10*x+1),x,0,2)
(fnInt is MATH → 9)

Web Site
www.FiniteandCalc.org
Follow the path

  Chapter 13

  → Math Tools for Chapter 13

  → Numerical Integration
    Utility

Enter 5/(10*x+1) for f(x),
0 and 2 for the left and right
end points, and press
"Adaptive Quadrature."

APPLICATIONS

EXAMPLE 5 Total Cost

In Section 13.3 we considered the following example. Your cell phone company offers you an innovative pricing scheme. When you make a call, the marginal cost is

$$c(t) = \frac{5}{10t + 1} \text{ dollars per hour.}$$

Compute the total cost of a 2-hour phone call.

Solution We calculate

$$\text{Total Cost} = \int_0^2 \frac{5}{10t + 1}\, dt = 5 \int_0^2 \frac{1}{10t + 1}\, dt$$

$$= 5 \left[\frac{1}{10} \ln(10t + 1)\right]_0^2 \qquad \text{See the shortcuts on page 970.}$$

$$= \frac{5}{10} [\ln(21) - \ln(1)]$$

$$= \frac{1}{2} \ln 21 \approx \$1.52.$$

Compare this with Example 1 of Section 13.3, where we found the same answer by approximating with Riemann sums.

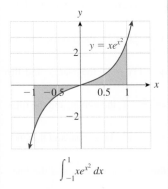

$$\int_{-1}^{1} xe^{x^2}\,dx$$

Figure 22

EXAMPLE 6 Computing Area

Find the total area of the region enclosed by the graph of $y = xe^{x^2}$, the x-axis, and the vertical lines $x = -1$ and $x = 1$.

Solution The region whose area we want is shown in Figure 22. Notice the symmetry of the graph. Also, half the region we are interested in is above the x-axis, while the other half is below. If we calculated the integral $\int_{-1}^{1} xe^{x^2}\,dx$, the result would be

Area above x-axis − Area below x-axis = 0,

which does not give us the total area. To prevent the area below the x-axis from being combined with the area above the axis, we do the calculation in two parts, as illustrated in Figure 23.

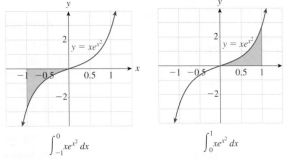

$$\int_{-1}^{0} xe^{x^2}\,dx \qquad \int_{0}^{1} xe^{x^2}\,dx$$

Figure 23

(In Figure 23 we broke the integral at $x = 0$ because that is where the graph crosses the x-axis.) These integrals can be calculated using the substitution $u = x^2$:

$$\int_{-1}^{0} xe^{x^2}\,dx = \frac{1}{2}\left[e^{x^2}\right]_{-1}^{0} = \frac{1}{2}(1 - e) \approx -0.85914 \qquad \text{Why is it negative?}$$

$$\int_{0}^{1} xe^{x^2}\,dx = \frac{1}{2}\left[e^{x^2}\right]_{0}^{1} = \frac{1}{2}(e - 1) \approx 0.85914$$

To obtain the total area, we should add the *absolute* values of these answers because we don't wish to count any area as negative. Thus,

Total area $\approx 0.85914 + 0.85914 = 1.71828$.

13.4 EXERCISES

▼ more advanced   ◆ challenging
T indicates exercises that should be solved using technology

Evaluate the integrals in Exercises 1–44. HINT [See Example 2.]

1. $\int_{-1}^{1} (x^2 + 2)\,dx$

2. $\int_{-2}^{1} (x - 2)\,dx$

3. $\int_{0}^{1} (12x^5 + 5x^4 - 6x^2 + 4)\,dx$

4. $\int_{0}^{1} (4x^3 - 3x^2 + 4x - 1)\,dx$

5. $\int_{-2}^{2} (x^3 - 2x)\,dx$

6. $\int_{-1}^{1} (2x^3 + x)\,dx$

7. $\int_{1}^{3} \left(\frac{2}{x^2} + 3x\right)dx$

8. $\int_{2}^{3} \left(x + \frac{1}{x}\right)dx$

9. $\int_{0}^{1} (2.1x - 4.3x^{1.2})\,dx$

10. $\int_{-1}^{0} (4.3x^2 - 1)\,dx$

11. $\int_0^1 2e^x \, dx$

12. $\int_{-1}^0 3e^x \, dx$

13. $\int_0^1 \sqrt{x} \, dx$

14. $\int_{-1}^1 \sqrt[3]{x} \, dx$

15. $\int_0^1 2^x \, dx$

16. $\int_0^1 3^x \, dx$

17. $\int_0^1 18(3x+1)^5 \, dx$

18. $\int_0^1 8(-x+1)^7 \, dx$

HINT [for Exercises 19–44: See Example 4 or use a shortcut (page 970) if applicable.]

19. $\int_{-1}^1 e^{2x-1} \, dx$

20. $\int_0^2 e^{-x+1} \, dx$

21. $\int_0^2 2^{-x+1} \, dx$

22. $\int_{-1}^1 3^{2x-1} \, dx$

23. $\int_0^{50} e^{-0.02x-1} \, dx$

24. $\int_{-20}^0 3e^{2.2x} \, dx$

25. $\int_0^4 |-3x+4| \, dx$

26. $\int_{-4}^4 |-x-2| \, dx$

27. $\int_{-1.1}^{1.1} e^{x+1} \, dx$

28. $\int_0^{\sqrt{2}} x\sqrt{2x^2+1} \, dx$

29. $\int_{-\sqrt{2}}^{\sqrt{2}} 3x\sqrt{2x^2+1} \, dx$

30. $\int_{-1.2}^{1.2} e^{-x-1} \, dx$

31. $\int_0^1 5xe^{x^2+2} \, dx$

32. $\int_0^2 \frac{3x}{x^2+2} \, dx$

33. $\int_2^3 \frac{x^2}{x^3-1} \, dx$

34. $\int_2^3 \frac{x}{2x^2-5} \, dx$

35. $\int_0^1 x(1.1)^{-x^2} \, dx$

36. $\int_0^1 x^2(2.1)^{x^3} \, dx$

37. $\int_1^2 \frac{e^{1/x}}{x^2} \, dx$

38. $\int_1^2 \frac{\sqrt{\ln x}}{x} \, dx$

39. ▼ $\int_0^2 \frac{x}{x+1} \, dx$

40. ▼ $\int_{-1}^1 \frac{2x}{x+2} \, dx$

41. ▼ $\int_1^2 x(x-2)^5 \, dx$

42. ▼ $\int_1^2 x(x-2)^{1/3} \, dx$

43. ▼ $\int_0^1 x\sqrt{2x+1} \, dx$

44. ▼ $\int_{-1}^0 2x\sqrt{x+1} \, dx$

Calculate the total area of the regions described in Exercises 45–54. Do not count area beneath the x-axis as negative. HINT [See Example 6.]

45. Bounded by the line $y=x$, the x-axis, and the lines $x=0$ and $x=1$

46. Bounded by the line $y=2x$, the x-axis, and the lines $x=1$ and $x=2$

47. Bounded by the curve $y=\sqrt{x}$, the x-axis, and the lines $x=0$ and $x=4$

48. Bounded by the curve $y=2\sqrt{x}$, the x-axis, and the lines $x=0$ and $x=16$

49. Bounded by the graph of $y=|2x-3|$, the x-axis, and the lines $x=0$ and $x=3$

50. Bounded by the graph of $y=|3x-2|$, the x-axis, and the lines $x=0$ and $x=3$

51. ▼ Bounded by the curve $y=x^2-1$, the x-axis, and the lines $x=0$ and $x=4$

52. ▼ Bounded by the curve $y=1-x^2$, the x-axis, and the lines $x=-1$ and $x=2$

53. ▼ Bounded by the x-axis, the curve $y=xe^{x^2}$, and the lines $x=0$ and $x=(\ln 2)^{1/2}$

54. ▼ Bounded by the x-axis, the curve $y=xe^{x^2-1}$, and the lines $x=0$ and $x=1$

APPLICATIONS

55. *Cost* The marginal cost of producing the xth box of light bulbs is $5+x^2/1{,}000$ dollars. Determine how much is added to the total cost by a change in production from $x=10$ to $x=100$ boxes. HINT [See Example 5.]

56. *Revenue* The marginal revenue of the xth box of flash cards sold is $100e^{-0.001x}$ dollars. Find the revenue generated by selling items 101 through 1,000. HINT [See Example 5.]

57. *Motion* A car traveling down a road has a velocity of $v(t)=60-e^{-t/10}$ mph at time t hours. Find the distance it has traveled from time $t=1$ hour to time $t=6$ hours. (Round your answer to the nearest mile.)

58. *Motion* A ball thrown in the air has a velocity of $v(t)=100-32t$ ft/s at time t seconds. Find the total displacement of the ball between times $t=1$ second and $t=7$ seconds, and interpret your answer.

59. *Motion* A car slows to a stop at a stop sign, then starts up again, in such a way that its speed at time t seconds after it starts to slow is $v(t)=|-10t+40|$ ft/s. How far does the car travel from time $t=0$ to time $t=10$ s?

60. *Motion* A truck slows, doesn't quite stop at a stop sign, and then speeds up again in such a way that its speed at time t seconds is $v(t)=10+|-5t+30|$ ft/s. How far does the truck travel from time $t=0$ to time $t=10$?

61. *Bottled Water Sales* (Compare Exercise 41 in Section 13.3.) The rate of U.S. sales of bottled water for the period 2000–2008 can be approximated by

$$s(t)=12t^2+500t+4{,}700 \text{ million gallons per year}$$
$$(0 \le t \le 8),$$

where t is time in years since the start of 2000.[37] Use the FTC to estimate the total U.S. sales of bottled water from the start of 2000 to the start of 2005. (Round your answer to the nearest billion gallons.)

---

[37] The 2008 figure is an estimate. Source: Beverage Marketing Corporation (www.bottledwater.org).

62. *Bottled Water Sales* (Compare Exercise 42 in Section 13.3.) The rate of U.S. per capita sales of bottled water for the period 2000–2008 can be approximated by

$$s(t) = 0.04t^2 + 1.5t + 17 \text{ gallons per year} \quad (0 \le t \le 8),$$

where t is the time in years since the start of 2000.[38] Use the FTC to estimate the total U.S. per capita sales of bottled water from the start of 2003 to the start of 2008. (Round your answer to the nearest gallon.)

63. *Oil Production in Mexico* (Compare Exercise 57 in Section 13.3.) The rate of oil production by **Pemex**, Mexico's national oil company, can be approximated by

$$p(t) = -8.03t^2 + 73t + 1{,}060 \text{ million barrels per year,}$$
$$(1 \le t \le 9)$$

where t is time in years since the start of 2000.[39] Use a definite integral to estimate total production of oil from the start of 2001 to the start of 2009.

64. *Oil Imports from Mexico* (Compare Exercise 58 in Section 13.3.) The rate of oil imports to the United States from Mexico can be approximated by

$$r(t) = -5.48t^2 + 36.5t + 510 \text{ million barrels per year}$$
$$(0 \le t \le 8)$$

where t is time in years since the start of 2000.[40] Use a definite integral to estimate total oil imports from the start of 2000 to the start of 2008.

65. *Big Brother* (Compare Exercise 59 in Section 13.3.) The total number of wiretaps authorized each year by U.S. state and federal courts from 1990 to 2010 can be approximated by

$$w(t) = 820e^{0.051t} \quad (0 \le t \le 20)$$

(t is time in years since the start of 1990).[41] Compute $\int_0^{15} w(t)\, dt$. (Round your answer to the nearest 10.) Interpret the answer.

66. *Big Brother* (Compare Exercise 60 in Section 13.3.) The number of wiretaps authorized each year by U.S. state courts from 1990 to 2010 can be approximated by

$$w(t) = 440e^{0.06t} \quad (0 \le t \le 20)$$

(t is time in years since the start of 1990).[42] Compute $\int_{10}^{15} w(t)\, dt$. (Round your answer to the nearest 10.) Interpret the answer.

67. *Economic Growth* The value of sold goods in Mexico can be approximated by

$$v(x) = 210 - 62e^{-0.05x} \text{ trillion pesos per month} \quad (x \ge 0)$$

where x is time in months since January 2005.[43] Find an expression for the total value $V(t)$ of sold goods in Mexico from January 2005 to time t. HINT [Use the shortcut on page 970.]

68. *Economic Contraction* The number of housing starts in the United States can be approximated by

$$n(t) = \frac{1}{12}(1.1 + 1.2e^{-0.08x}) \text{ million homes per month}$$
$$(x \ge 0)$$

where x is time in months since January 2006.[44] Find an expression for the total number $N(t)$ of housing starts in the United States from January 2006 to time t. HINT [Use the shortcut on page 970.]

69. *Fuel Consumption* The way Professor Waner drives, he burns gas at the rate of $1 - e^{-t}$ gallons each hour, t hours after a fill-up. Find the number of gallons of gas he burns in the first 10 hours after a fill-up.

70. *Fuel Consumption* The way Professor Costenoble drives, he burns gas at the rate of $1/(t + 1)$ gallons each hour, t hours after a fill-up. Find the number of gallons of gas he burns in the first 10 hours after a fill-up.

71. ▼ *Sales* Weekly sales of your *Lord of the Rings* T-shirts have been falling by 5% per week. Assuming you are now selling 50 T-shirts per week, how many shirts will you sell during the coming year? (Round your answer to the nearest shirt.)

72. ▼ *Sales* Annual sales of fountain pens in Littleville are 4,000 per year and are increasing by 10% per year. How many fountain pens will be sold over the next five years?

73. ◻ *Embryo Development* The oxygen consumption of a bird embryo increases from the time the egg is laid through the time the chick hatches. In a typical galliform bird, the oxygen consumption can be approximated by

$$c(t) = -0.065t^3 + 3.4t^2 - 22t + 3.6 \text{ milliliters per day}$$
$$(8 \le t \le 30)$$

where t is the time (in days) since the egg was laid.[45] (An egg will typically hatch at around $t = 28$.) Use technology to estimate the total amount of oxygen consumed during the ninth and tenth days ($t = 8$ to $t = 10$). Round your answer to the nearest milliliter. HINT [See the technology note in the margin on page 996.]

74. ◻ *Embryo Development* The oxygen consumption of a turkey embryo increases from the time the egg is laid through the

---

[38] The 2008 figure is an estimate. Source: Beverage Marketing Corporation (www.bottledwater.org).

[39] Source for data: Energy Information Administration/Pemex (http://www.eia.doe.gov).

[40] Ibid.

[41] Source for data: 2007 Wiretap Report, Administrative Office of the United States Courts (www.uscourts.gov/wiretap07/2007WTText.pdf).

[42] Ibid.

[43] Source: Instituto Nacional de Estadística y Geografía (INEGI) (www.inegi.org.mx).

[44] Source for data: *New York Times*, February 17, 2007, p. C3.

[45] The model approximates graphical data published in the article "The Brush Turkey" by Roger S. Seymour, *Scientific American*, December 1991, pp. 108–114.

time the chick hatches. In a brush turkey, the oxygen consumption can be approximated by

$$c(t) = -0.028t^3 + 2.9t^2 - 44t + 95 \text{ milliliters per day}$$
$$(20 \leq t \leq 50)$$

where t is the time (in days) since the egg was laid.[46] (An egg will typically hatch at around $t = 50$.) Use technology to estimate the total amount of oxygen consumed during the 21st and 22nd days ($t = 20$ to $t = 22$). Round your answer to the nearest 10 milliliters. HINT [See the technology note in the margin on page 996.]

75. ▉ **Online Auctions: United States** The rate of change $n(t)$ of the number of items listed on **eBay** can be approximated by

$$n(t) = 0.07t^4 - 1.7t^3 + 9.9t^2 + 17t + 390 \text{ million items/}$$
$$\text{quarter} \quad (1 \leq t \leq 14)$$

(t is time in quarters; $t = 1$ represents the start of the first quarter in 2005.)[47] Use technology to compute $\int_1^9 n(t)\, dt$ correct to the nearest 100. Interpret your answer.

76. ▉ **Online Stores: United States** The rate of change $s(t)$ of the number of **eBay** stores can be approximated by

$$s(t) = 0.035t^4 - 0.55t^3 - 1.45t^2 + 37t - 36 \text{ stores/quarter}$$
$$(1 \leq t \leq 14)$$

(t is time in quarters; $t = 1$ represents the start of the first quarter in 2005).[48] Use technology to compute $\int_5^{13} s(t)\, dt$ correct to the nearest whole number. Interpret your answer.

77. ▼ **Total Cost** Use the Fundamental Theorem of Calculus to show that if $m(x)$ is the marginal cost at a production level of x items, then the cost function $C(x)$ is given by

$$C(x) = C(0) + \int_0^x m(t)\, dt.$$

What do we call $C(0)$?

78. ▼ **Total Sales** The total cost of producing x items is given by

$$C(x) = 246.76 + \int_0^x 5t\, dt.$$

Find the fixed cost and the marginal cost of producing the 10th item.

79. **Scientific Research** (Compare Exercise 79 in Section 13.2.) The number of research articles in the prominent journal *Physical Review* written by researchers in Europe can be approximated by

$$E(t) = \frac{7e^{0.2t}}{5 + e^{0.2t}} \text{ thousand articles per year} \quad (t \geq 0)$$

where t is time in years ($t = 0$ represents 1983).[49] Use a definite integral to estimate the number of articles were written by researchers in Europe from 1983 to 2003. (Round your answer to the nearest 1,000 articles.) HINT [See Example 7 in Section 13.2.]

80. **Scientific Research** (Compare Exercise 80 in Section 13.2.) The number of research articles in the prominent journal *Physical Review* written by researchers in the United States can be approximated by

$$U(t) = \frac{4.6e^{0.6t}}{0.4 + e^{0.6t}} \text{ thousand articles per year} \quad (t \geq 0)$$

where t is time in years ($t = 0$ represents 1983).[50] Use a definite integral to estimate the total number of articles written by researchers in the United States from 1983 to 2003. HINT [See Example 7 in Section 13.2.]

81. ▼ **The Logistic Function and High School Graduates**
a. Show that the logistic function $f(x) = \dfrac{N}{1 + Ab^{-x}}$ can be written in the form

$$f(x) = \frac{Nb^x}{A + b^x}.$$

HINT [See the note after Example 7 in Section 13.2.]
b. Use the result of part (a) and a suitable substitution to show that

$$\int \frac{N}{1 + Ab^{-x}}\, dx = \frac{N \ln(A + b^x)}{\ln b} + C.$$

c. The rate of graduation of private high school students in the United States for the period 1994–2008 was approximately

$$r(t) = 220 + \frac{110}{1 + 3.8(1.27)^{-t}} \text{ thousand students per year}$$
$$(0 \leq t \leq 14)$$

t years since 1994.[51] Use the result of part (b) to estimate the total number of private high school graduates over the period 2000–2008.

82. ▼ **The Logistic Function and Grant Spending**
a. Show that the logistic function $f(x) = \dfrac{N}{1 + Ae^{-kx}}$ can be written in the form

$$f(x) = \frac{Ne^{kx}}{A + e^{kx}}.$$

HINT [See the note after Example 7 in Section 13.2.]
b. Use the result of part (a) and a suitable substitution to show that

$$\int \frac{N}{1 + Ae^{-kx}}\, dx = \frac{N \ln(A + e^{kx})}{k} + C.$$

---

[46] The model approximates graphical data published in the article "The Brush Turkey" by Roger S. Seymour, *Scientific American*, December 1991, pp. 108–114.

[47] Source for data: eBay company report (www.investor.ebay.com).

[48] Ibid.

[49] Based on data from 1983 to 2003. Source: The American Physical Society/*New York Times*, May 3, 2003, p. A1.

[50] Ibid.

[51] Based on a logistic regression. Source for data: National Center for Educational Statistics (www.nces.ed.gov/).

c. The rate of spending on grants by U.S. foundations in the period 1993–2003 was approximately

$$s(t) = 11 + \frac{20}{1 + 1,800e^{-0.9t}} \text{ billion dollars per year}$$

$$(3 \le t \le 13)$$

where t is the number of years since 1990.[52] Use the result of part (b) to estimate, to the nearest $10 billion, the total spending on grants from 1998 to 2003.

83. ◆ Kinetic Energy The work done in accelerating an object from velocity v_0 to velocity v_1 is given by

$$W = \int_{v_0}^{v_1} v \frac{dp}{dv} \, dv$$

where p is its momentum, given by $p = mv$ (m = mass). Assuming that m is a constant, show that

$$W = \frac{1}{2}mv_1^2 - \frac{1}{2}mv_0^2.$$

The quantity $\frac{1}{2}mv^2$ is referred to as the **kinetic energy** of the object, so the work required to accelerate an object is given by its change in kinetic energy.

84. ◆ Einstein's Energy Equation According to the special theory of relativity, the apparent mass of an object depends on its velocity according to the formula

$$m = \frac{m_0}{\left(1 - \dfrac{v^2}{c^2}\right)^{1/2}}$$

where v is its velocity, m_0 is the "rest mass" of the object (that is, its mass when $v = 0$), and c is the velocity of light: approximately 3×10^8 meters per second.

a. Show that, if $p = mv$ is the momentum,

$$\frac{dp}{dv} = \frac{m_0}{\left(1 - \dfrac{v^2}{c^2}\right)^{3/2}}.$$

b. Use the integral formula for W in the preceding exercise, together with the result in part (a) to show that the work required to accelerate an object from a velocity of v_0 to v_1 is given by

$$W = \frac{m_0 c^2}{\sqrt{1 - \dfrac{v_1^2}{c^2}}} - \frac{m_0 c^2}{\sqrt{1 - \dfrac{v_0^2}{c^2}}}.$$

We call the quantity $\dfrac{m_0 c^2}{\sqrt{1 - \frac{v^2}{c^2}}}$ the **total relativistic energy** of an object moving at velocity v. Thus, the work to accelerate an object from one velocity to another is given by the change in its total relativistic energy.

c. Deduce (as Albert Einstein did) that the total relativistic energy E of a body at rest with rest mass m is given by the famous equation

$$E = mc^2.$$

COMMUNICATION AND REASONING EXERCISES

85. Explain how the indefinite integral and the definite integral are related.

86. What is "definite" about the definite integral?

87. The total change of a quantity from time a to time b can be obtained from its rate of change by doing what?

88. Complete the following: The total sales from time a to time b are obtained from the marginal sales by taking its _____ _____ from _____ to _____ .

89. What does the Fundamental Theorem of Calculus permit one to do?

90. If Felice and Philipe have different antiderivatives of f and each uses his or her own antiderivative to compute $\int_a^b f(x)\,dx$, they might get different answers, right?

91. ▼Give an example of a nonzero velocity function that will produce a displacement of 0 from time $t = 0$ to time $t = 10$.

92. ▼Give an example of a nonzero function whose definite integral over the interval [4, 6] is zero.

93. ▼Give an example of a decreasing function $f(x)$ with the property that $\int_a^b f(x)\,dx$ is positive for every choice of a and $b > a$.

94. ▼Explain why, in computing the total change of a quantity from its rate of change, it is useful to have the definite integral subtract area below the x-axis.

95. ◆ If $f(x)$ is a continuous function defined for $x \ge a$, define a new function $F(x)$ by the formula

$$F(x) = \int_a^x f(t)\,dt.$$

Use the Fundamental Theorem of Calculus to deduce that $F'(x) = f(x)$. What, if anything, is interesting about this result?

96. ⊞ ◆ Use the result of Exercise 95 and technology to compute a table of values for $x = 1, 2, 3$ for an antiderivative $A(x)$ of e^{-x^2} with the property that $A(0) = 0$. (Round answers to two decimal places.)

---

[52] Based on a logistic regression. Source for data: The Foundation Center, *Foundation Growth and Giving Estimates*, 2004, downloaded from the Center's Web site (www.fdncenter.org).

KEY CONCEPTS

Web Site www.FiniteandCalc.org
Go to the student Web site at
www.FiniteandCalc.org to find a
comprehensive and interactive
Web-based summary of Chapter 13.

13.1 The Indefinite Integral

An antiderivative of a function f is a
function F such that $F' = f$. *p. 948*
Indefinite integral $\int f(x)\,dx$ *p. 948*
Power rule for the indefinite integral:

$$\int x^n\,dx = \frac{x^{n+1}}{n+1} + C$$

$$\text{(if } n \ne -1) \text{ *p. 950*}$$

$$\int x^{-1}\,dx = \ln|x| + C \quad \text{*p. 951*}$$

Indefinite Integral of e^x and b^x:

$$\int e^x\,dx = e^x + C$$

$$\int b^x\,dx = \frac{b^x}{\ln b} + C \quad \text{*p. 951*}$$

Sums, differences, and constant
multiples:

$$\int [f(x) \pm g(x)]\,dx$$

$$= \int f(x)\,dx \pm \int g(x)\,dx$$

$$\int kf(x)\,dx = k \int f(x)\,dx$$

$$\text{(} k \text{ constant) *p. 951*}$$

Combining the rules *p. 954*
Position, velocity, and acceleration:

$$v = \frac{ds}{dt} \qquad s(t) = \int v(t)\,dt$$

$$a = \frac{dv}{dt} \qquad v(t) = \int a(t)\,dt \quad \text{*p. 957*}$$

Motion in a straight line *p. 957*
Vertical motion under gravity *p. 959*

13.2 Substitution

Substitution rule:

$$\int f\,dx = \int \left(\frac{f}{du/dx}\right) du \quad \text{*p. 964*}$$

Using the substitution rule *p. 964*
Shortcuts: integrals of expressions
involving $(ax + b)$:

$$\int (ax+b)^n\,dx = \frac{(ax+b)^{n+1}}{a(n+1)} + C$$

$$\text{(if } n \ne -1)$$

$$\int (ax+b)^{-1}\,dx = \frac{1}{a}\ln|ax+b| + C$$

$$\int e^{ax+b}\,dx = \frac{1}{a}e^{ax+b} + C$$

$$\int c^{ax+b}\,dx = \frac{1}{a \ln c}c^{ax+b} + C$$

$$\int |ax+b|\,dx$$

$$= \frac{1}{2a}(ax+b)|ax+b| + C \quad \text{*p. 970*}$$

13.3 The Definite Integral: Numerical and Graphical Approaches

Left Riemann sum:

$$\sum_{k=0}^{n-1} f(x_k)\Delta x$$

$$= [f(x_0) + f(x_1) + \cdots + f(x_{n-1})]\Delta x$$

p. 978

Computing the Riemann sum from a
graph *p. 980*
Computing the Riemann sum from a
formula *p. 980*
Definite integral of f from a to b:

$$\int_a^b f(x)\,dx = \lim_{n \to \infty} \sum_{k=0}^{n-1} f(x_k)\Delta x. \quad \text{*p. 981*}$$

Estimating the definite integral from a
graph *p. 983*
Estimating the definite integral using
technology *p. 985*
Application to motion in a straight line
p. 986

13.4 The Definite Integral: Algebraic Approach and the Fundamental Theorem of Calculus

The Fundamental Theorem of Calculus
(FTC) *p. 993*
Using the FTC to compute definite
integrals *p. 994*
Computing total cost from marginal cost
p. 996
Computing area *p. 997*

REVIEW EXERCISES

Evaluate the indefinite integrals in Exercises 1–12.

1. $\int (x^2 - 10x + 2)\,dx$ **2.** $\int (e^x + \sqrt{x})\,dx$

3. $\int \left(\frac{4x^2}{5} - \frac{4}{5x^2}\right) dx$ **4.** $\int \left(\frac{3x}{5} - \frac{3}{5x}\right) dx$

5. $\int e^{-2x+11}\,dx$ **6.** $\int \frac{dx}{(4x-3)^2}$

7. $\int x(x^2 + 4)^{10}\,dx$ **8.** $\int \frac{x^2+1}{(x^3+3x+2)^2}\,dx$

9. $\int 5e^{-2x}\,dx$ **10.** $\int xe^{-x^2/2}\,dx$

11. $\int \frac{x+1}{x+2}\,dx$ **12.** $\int x\sqrt{x-1}\,dx$

In Exercises 13 and 14, use the given graph to estimate the left Riemann sum for the given interval with the stated number of subdivisions.

13. $[0, 3]$, $n = 6$ **14.** $[1, 3]$, $n = 4$

Calculate the left Riemann sums for the given functions over the given interval in Exercises 15–18, using the given values of n. (When rounding, round answers to four decimal places.)

15. $f(x) = x^2 + 1$ over $[-1, 1]$, $n = 4$

16. $f(x) = (x - 1)(x - 2) - 2$ over $[0, 4]$, $n = 4$

17. $f(x) = x(x^2 - 1)$ over $[0, 1]$, $n = 5$

18. $f(x) = \dfrac{x - 1}{x - 2}$ over $[0, 1.5]$, $n = 3$

 In Exercises 19 and 20, use technology to approximate the given definite integrals using left Riemann sums with $n = 10$, 100, and 1,000. (Round answers to four decimal places.)

19. $\displaystyle\int_0^1 e^{-x^2}\, dx$

20. $\displaystyle\int_1^3 x^{-x}\, dx$

In Exercises 21 and 22 the graph of the derivative $f'(x)$ of $f(x)$ is shown. Compute the total change of $f(x)$ over the given interval.

21. $[-1, 2]$

22. $[0, 2]$

Evaluate the definite integrals in Exercises 23–30, using the Fundamental Theorem of Calculus.

23. $\displaystyle\int_0^1 (x - x^3)\, dx$

24. $\displaystyle\int_0^9 \dfrac{1}{x + 1}\, dx$

25. $\displaystyle\int_{-1}^1 (1 + e^x)\, dx$

26. $\displaystyle\int_0^9 (x + \sqrt{x})\, dx$

27. $\displaystyle\int_0^2 x^2\sqrt{x^3 + 1}\, dx$

28. $\displaystyle\int_{-1}^1 3^{2x-2}\, dx$

29. $\displaystyle\int_0^{\ln 2} \dfrac{e^{-2x}}{1 + 4e^{-2x}}\, dx$

30. $\displaystyle\int_0^1 3xe^{-x^2}\, dx$

In Exercises 31–34, find the areas of the specified regions. (Do not count area below the x-axis as negative.)

31. The area bounded by $y = 4 - x^2$, the x-axis, and the lines $x = -2$ and $x = 2$

32. The area bounded by $y = 4 - x^2$, the x-axis, and the lines $x = 0$ and $x = 5$

33. The area bounded by $y = xe^{-x^2}$, the x-axis, and the lines $x = 0$ and $x = 5$

34. The area bounded by $y = |2x|$, the x-axis, and the lines $x = -1$ and $x = 1$

APPLICATIONS

35. Sales The rate of net sales (sales minus returns) of *The Secret Loves of John O*, a romance novel by Margó Dufón, can be approximated by

$$n(t) = 196 + t^2 - 0.16t^5 \text{ copies per week}$$

t weeks since its release.

  a. Find the total net sales N as a function of time t.

  b. How many books are still held by customers after 6 weeks? (Round your answer to the nearest book.)

36. Demand If OHaganBooks.com were to give away its latest bestseller, *A River Burns Through It*, the demand q would be 100,000 books. The marginal demand (dq/dp) for the book is $-20p$ at a price of p dollars.

  a. What is the demand function for this book?

  b. At what price does demand drop to zero?

37. Motion Under Gravity Billy-Sean O'Hagan's friend Juan (Billy-Sean is John O'Hagan's son, currently a senior in college) says he can throw a baseball vertically upward at 100 feet per second. Assuming Juan's claim is true,

  a. Where would the baseball be at time t seconds?

  b. How high would the ball go?

  c. When would it return to Juan's hand?

38. Motion Under Gravity An overworked employee at OHaganBooks.com goes to the top of the company's 100 foot tall headquarters building and flings a book up into the air at a speed of 60 feet per second.

  a. When will the book hit the ground 100 feet below? (Neglect air resistance.)

  b. How fast will it be traveling when it hits the ground?

  c. How high will the book go?

39. Sales Sales at the OHaganBooks.com Web site of *Larry Potter and the Riemann Sum* fluctuated rather wildly in the first 5 months of last year as the following graph shows:

Puzzled by the graph, CEO John O'Hagan asks Jimmy Duffin[53] to estimate the total sales over the entire 5-month period shown. Jimmy decides to use a left Riemann sum with 10 partitions to estimate the total sales. What does he find?

40. Sales The following graph shows the approximate rate of change $s(t)$ of the total value, in thousands of dollars, of Spanish books sold online at OHaganBooks.com (t is the number of months since January 1):

---

[53] Marjory Duffin's nephew, currently at OHaganBooks.com on a summer internship.

Use the graph to estimate the total value of Spanish books sold from March 1 through June 1. (Use a left Riemann sum with three subdivisions.)

41. Promotions Unlike sales of *Larry Potter and the Riemann Sum*, sales at OHaganBooks.com of the special leather-bound gift editions of *Lord of the Rings* have been suffering lately, as shown in the following graph (negative sales indicate returns by dissatisfied customers; t is time in months since January 1 of this year):

Use the graph to compute the total (net) sales over the period shown.

42. Sales Even worse than with the leather-bound *Lord of the Rings*, sales of *Investing in Real Estate* have been dismal, as shown in the following graph (negative sales indicate returns by dissatisfied customers; t is time in months since January 1 of this year):

Use the graph to compute the total (net) sales over the period shown.

43. Web Site Activity The number of "hits" on the OHaganBooks.com Web site has been steadily increasing over the past month in response to recent publicity over a software glitch that caused the company to pay customers for buying books online. The activity can be modeled by

$$n(t) = 1{,}000t - 10t^2 + t^3 \text{ hits per day}$$

where t is time in days since news about the software glitch was first publicized on GrungeReport.com. Use a left Riemann sum with five partitions to estimate the total number of hits during the first 10 days of the period.

44. Web Site Crashes The latest DoorsXL servers OHaganBooks.com has been using for its Web site have been crashing with increasing frequency lately. One of the student summer interns has estimated the number of crashes to be

$$q(t) = 0.05t^2 + 0.4t + 9 \text{ crashes per week} \quad (0 \le t \le 10).$$

where t is the number of weeks since the DoorsXL system was first installed. Use a Riemann sum with five partitions to estimate the total number of crashes from the start of week 5 to the start of week 10. (Round your answer to the nearest crash.)

45. Student Intern Costs The marginal monthly cost of maintaining a group of summer student interns at OHaganBooks.com is calculated to be

$$c(x) = \frac{1{,}000(x+3)^2}{(8+(x+3)^3)^{3/2}} \text{ thousand dollars per additional student.}$$

Compute, to the nearest \$100, the total monthly cost if O'HaganBooks increases the size of the student intern program from five students to seven students.

46. Legal Costs The legal team maintained by OHaganBooks.com to handle the numerous lawsuits brought against the company by disgruntled clients may have to be expanded. The marginal monthly cost to maintain a team of x lawyers is estimated (by a method too complicated to explain) as

$$c(x) = (x-2)^2[8-(x-2)^3]^{3/2} \text{ thousand dollars per additional lawyer.}$$

Compute, to the nearest \$1,000, the total monthly cost if O'HaganBooks goes ahead with a proposal to increase the size of the legal team from two to four.

47. Projected Sales When OHaganBooks.com was about to go online, it estimated that its weekly sales would begin at about 6,400 books per week, with sales increasing at such a rate that weekly sales would double about every 2 weeks. If these estimates had been correct, how many books would the company have sold in the first 5 weeks? (Round your answer to the nearest 1,000 books.)

48. Projected Sales Once OHaganBooks.com actually went online, its weekly sales began at about 7,500 books per week, with weekly sales doubling every 3 weeks. How many books did the company actually sell in the first 5 weeks? (Round your answer to the nearest 1,000 books.)

49. Actual Sales OHaganBooks.com modeled its revised weekly sales over a period of time after it went online with the function

$$s(t) = 6{,}053 + \frac{4{,}474e^{0.55t}}{e^{0.55t} + 14.01}$$

where t is the time in weeks after it went online. According to this model, how many books did it actually sell in the first 5 weeks?

50. Computer Usage A consultant recently hired by OHaganBooks.com estimates total weekly computer usage as

$$w(t) = 620 + \frac{900e^{0.25t}}{3 + e^{0.25t}} \text{ hours} \quad (0 \le t \le 20)$$

where t is time in weeks since January 1 of this year. Use the model to estimate the total computer usage during the first 14 weeks of the year.

Case Study   Spending on Housing Construction

You are a summer intern at the U.S. Department of Housing and Urban Development, which has begun an ambitious public works program under the direction of the new administration. Yesterday you received the following memo from the senior aide to the Assistant Undersecretary:

TO: SW

FROM: SC

SUBJECT: Residential Construction Spending. Urgent!

Help! There is a subcommittee meeting in two hours and the office of the Undersecretary has asked me to immediately produce some mathematical formulas to (1) model the trend in residential construction spending since January 2006, when it was $618.7 billion, and (2) estimate the average spent per month on residential construction over a specified period of time. All I have on hand so far is data giving the month-over-month percentage changes (attached). Do you have any ideas?

ATTACHMENT*

Month	% Change	Month	% Change
1	1.16	16	−1.59
2	1.17	17	−1.62
3	1.33	18	−1.58
4	0.67	19	−1.67
5	0.42	20	−1.77
6	−0.04	21	−1.92
7	−0.24	22	−2.06
8	−0.44	23	−2.19
9	−0.70	24	−2.45
10	−0.94	25	−2.50
11	−1.31	26	−2.65
12	−1.34	27	−2.85
13	−1.49	28	−2.65
14	−1.75	29	−2.66
15	−1.74	30	−2.66

*Based on 12-month moving average. Source for data: U.S. Census Bureau: Manufacturing, Mining and Construction Statistics, Data 360 (www.data360.org/dataset.aspx?Data_Set_Id=3627).

Getting to work, you decide that the first thing to do is fit these data to a mathematical curve that you can use to project future changes in construction spending. You graph the data to get a sense of what mathematical models might be appropriate (Figure 24).

Figure 24

Figure 25

The graph suggests a decreasing trend, leveling off at about -3%. You recall that there are many curves that behave this way. One of the simplest is the curve

$$y = \frac{a}{t^c} + b \qquad (t \geq 1)$$

where a, b, and c are constants (Figure 25).[54]

You convert all the percentages to decimals, giving the following table of data:

t	y	t	y
1	0.0116	16	−0.0159
2	0.0117	17	−0.0162
3	0.0133	18	−0.0158
4	0.0067	19	−0.0167
5	0.0042	20	−0.0177
6	−0.0004	21	−0.0192
7	−0.0024	22	−0.0206
8	−0.0044	23	−0.0219
9	−0.0070	24	−0.0245
10	−0.0094	25	−0.0250
11	−0.0131	26	−0.0265
12	−0.0134	27	−0.0285
13	−0.0149	28	−0.0265
14	−0.0175	29	−0.0266
15	−0.0174	30	−0.0266

✱ **NOTE** To do this, you can use Excel's Solver, for example. However, the exact results may vary slightly, even when using the same program, depending on the settings and initial guesses for the coefficients.

You then find the values of a, b, and c that best fit the given data:*

$$a = 3.867405726, \quad b = -3.844754206, \quad c = 0.003685514$$

These values give you the following model for construction spending (with figures rounded to five significant digits):

$$y = \frac{3.8674}{t^{0.0036855}} - 3.8448.$$

---

[54] There is a good mathematical reason for choosing a curve of this form: It is a first approximation (for $t \geq 1$) to a general rational function that approaches a constant as $t \to +\infty$.

(It is interesting that the model predicts the change in construction spending leveling off to about -3.84%.) Figure 26 shows the graph of y superimposed on the data.

Figure 26

Now that you have a model for the month-over-month change in construction spending, you must use it to find the actual spending on construction. First, you realize that the model gives the *fractional rate of increase* of construction spending (because it is specified as a percentage, or fraction, of the total spending). In other words, if $p(t)$ represents the construction cost in month t, Then

$$y = \frac{dp/dt}{p} = \frac{d}{dt}(\ln p). \qquad \text{By the chain rule for derivatives}$$

You find an equation for actual monthly construction cost at time t by solving for p:

$$\ln p = \int y\, dt$$

$$= \int \left(\frac{a}{t^c} + b\right) dt$$

$$= \frac{at^{1-c}}{1-c} + bt + K$$

$$= dt^{1-c} + bt + K,$$

where

$$d = \frac{a}{1-c} = \frac{3.867405726}{1 - 0.003685514} \approx 3.8817,$$

a and b are as above, and K is the constant of integration. So

$$p(t) = e^{dt^{1-c}+bt+K}.$$

To compute K, you substitute the initial data from the memo: $p(1) = 618.7$. Thus,

$$618.7 = e^{d+b+K} = e^{3.8817-3.8448+K} = e^{0.0369+K}.$$

Thus,

$$\ln(618.7) = 0.0369 + K,$$

which gives

$$K = \ln(618.7) - 0.0369 \approx 6.3907 \text{ (to five significant digits)}.$$

Now you can write down the following formula for the monthly spending on residential construction as a function of t, the number of months since the beginning of 2006:

$$p(t) = e^{dt^{1-c}+bt+K} = e^{(3.8817t^{1-0.0036855}-3.8448t+6.3907)}.$$

What remains is the calculation of the average spent per month over a specified period $[r, s]$. Since p is the rate of change of the total spent, the total spent on housing construction over this period is

$$P = \int_r^s p(t)\, dt$$

and so the average spent per month is

$$\bar{P} = \frac{1}{s-r}\int_r^s p(t)\, dt. \qquad \frac{1}{\text{Number of months}} \times \text{Total spent}$$

Substituting the formula for $p(t)$ gives

$$\bar{P} = \frac{1}{s-r}\int_r^s e^{(3.8817t^{1-0.0036855}-3.8448t+6.3907)}\, dt.$$

You cannot find an explicit antiderivative for the integrand, so you decide that the only way to compute it is numerically. You send the following memo to SC.

TO: SC

FROM: SW

SUBJECT: The formula you wanted

Spending in the United States on housing construction in the tth month of 2006 can be modeled by

$$p(t) = e^{(3.8817t^{1-0.0036855}-3.8448t+6.3907)} \text{ million dollars.}$$

Further, the average spent per month from month r to month s (since the start of January 2006) can be computed as

$$\bar{P} = \frac{1}{s-r}\int_r^s e^{(3.8817t^{1-0.0036855}-3.8448t+6.3907)}\, dt.$$

To calculate it easily (and impress the subcommittee members), I suggest you have a graphing calculator on hand and enter the following on your graphing calculator (watch the parentheses!):

```
Y₁=1/(S-R)*fnInt(e^(3.8817T^(1-0.0036855)-3.8448T+6.3907),T,R,S)
```

Then suppose, for example, you need to estimate the average for the period March 1, 2006 ($t = 3$) to February 1, 2007 ($t = 14$) All you do is enter

```
3→R
14→S
Y₁
```

and your calculator will give you the result: The average spending was $624 million per month.

Good luck with the meeting!

EXERCISES

1. Use the actual January 2006 spending figure of $618.7 million and the percentage changes in the table to compute the actual spending in February, March, and April of that year. Also use the model of monthly spending to estimate those figures, and compare the predicted values with the actual figures. Is it unacceptable that the April figures agree to only one significant digit? Explain.

2. Use the model developed above to estimate the average monthly spending on residential construction over the 12-month period beginning June 1, 2006. (Round your answer to the nearest $1 million.)

3. What (if any) advantages are there to using a model for residential construction spending when the actual residential construction spending figures are available?

4. The formulas for $p(t)$ and $\bar{P}$ were based on the January 2006 spending figure of $618.7 million. Change the models to allow for a possibly revised January 2006 spending figure of p_0 million.

5. If we had used quadratic regression to model the construction spending data, we would have obtained

$$y = 0.00005t^2 - 0.0028t + 0.158.$$

(See the graph.)

Use this formula and the given January 2006 spending figure to obtain corresponding models for $p(t)$ and $\bar{P}$.

6. Compare the model in the text with the quadratic model in Exercise 5 in terms of both short- and long-term predictions; in particular, when does the quadratic model predict construction spending will have reached its biggest monthly decrease? Are either of these models realistic in the near-term? in the long term?

TI-83/84 Plus **Technology Guide**

Section 13.3

Example 5 (page 985) Estimate the area under the graph of $f(x) = 1 - x^2$ over the interval $[0, 1]$ using $n = 100$, $n = 200$, and $n = 500$ partitions.

Solution with Technology

There are several ways to compute Riemann sums with a graphing calculator. We illustrate one method. For $n = 100$, we need to compute the sum

$$\sum_{k=0}^{99} f(x_k)\Delta x = [f(0) + f(0.01) + \cdots + f(0.99)](0.01).$$

See discussion in Example 5.

Thus, we first need to calculate the numbers $f(0)$, $f(0.01)$, and so on, and add them up. The TI-83/84 Plus has a built-in `sum` function (available in the LIST MATH menu), which, like the SUM function in a spreadsheet, sums the entries in a list.

1. To generate a list that contains the numbers we want to add together, use the `seq` function (available in the LIST OPS menu). If we enter

$$\texttt{seq(1-X\textasciicircum 2,X,0,0.99,0.01)}$$

seq: 2ND LIST OPS 5

   the calculator will calculate a list by evaluating `1-X^2` for values of `X` from 0 to 0.99 in steps of 0.01.

2. To take the sum of all these numbers, we wrap the `seq` function in a call to `sum`:

$$\texttt{sum(seq(1-X\textasciicircum 2,X,0,0.99,0.01))}$$

sum: 2ND LIST MATH 5

   This gives the sum

$$f(0) + f(0.01) + \cdots + f(0.99) = 67.165.$$

3. To obtain the Riemann sum, we need to multiply this sum by $\Delta x = 0.01$, and we obtain the estimate of $67.165 \times 0.01 = 0.67165$ for the Riemann sum:

We obtain the other Riemann sums similarly, as shown here:

$n = 200$ $n = 500$

One disadvantage of this method is that the TI-83/84 Plus can generate and sum a list of at most 999 entries. The LEFTSUM program below calculates left Riemann sums for any n. The TI-83/84 Plus also has a built-in function `fnInt`, which finds a very accurate approximation of a definite integral, using a more sophisticated technique than the one we are discussing here.

The LEFTSUM program for the TI-83/84 Plus

The following program calculates (left) Riemann sums for any n. The latest version of this program (and others) is available at the Web site.

```
PROGRAM: LEFTSUM
:Input "LEFT ENDPOINT? ",A
```
Prompts for the left end-point a

```
:Input "RIGHT ENDPOINT? ",B
```
Prompts for the right end-point b

```
:Input "N? ",N
```
Prompts for the number
of rectangles

```
:(B-A)/N→D
```
D is $\Delta x = (b-a)/n$.

```
:∅→L
```
L will eventually be the left sum.

```
:A→X
```
X is the current x-coordinate.

```
:For(I,1,N)
```
Start of a loop—recall the sigma
notation.

```
:L+Y₁→L
```
Add $f(x_{i-1})$ to L.

```
:A+I*D→X
```
Uses formula $x_i = a + i\Delta x$

```
:End
```
End of loop.

```
:L*D→L
```
Multiply by Δx.

```
:Disp "LEFT SUM IS ",L
:Stop
```

EXCEL Technology Guide

Section 13.3

Example 5 (page 985) Estimate the area under the graph of $f(x) = 1 - x^2$ over the interval $[0, 1]$ using $n = 100$, $n = 200$, and $n = 500$ partitions.

Solution with Technology

We need to compute various sums:

$$\sum_{k=0}^{99} f(x_k)\Delta x = [f(0) + f(0.01) + \cdots + f(0.99)](0.01)$$

See discussion in Example 5.

$$\sum_{k=0}^{199} f(x_k)\Delta x = [f(0) + f(0.005) + \cdots + f(0.995)](0.005)$$

$$\sum_{k=0}^{499} f(x_k)\Delta x = [f(0) + f(0.002) + \cdots + f(0.998)](0.002).$$

Here is how you can compute them all on the same spreadsheet.

1. Enter the values for the end-points a and b, the number of subdivisions n, and the formula $\Delta x = (b - a)/n$:

	A	B	C	D
1	x	f(x)	a	0
2			b	1
3			n	100
4			Delta x	=(D2-D1)/D3

2. Next, we compute all the x-values we might need in column A. Because the largest value of n that we will be using is 500, we will need a total of 501 values of x. Note that the value in each cell below A3 is obtained from the one above by adding Δx.

	A	B	C	D
1	x	f(x)	a	0
2	=D1		b	1
3	=A2+$D$4		n	100
4			Delta x	0.01
5				
501				
502				

	A	B	C	D
1	x	f(x)	a	0
2	0		b	1
3	0.01		n	100
4	0.02		Delta x	0.01
5				
501	4.99			
502	5			

(The fact that the values of x currently go too far will be corrected in the next step.)

3. We need to calculate the numbers $f(0)$, $f(0.01)$, and so on, but only those for which the corresponding x-value is less than b. To do this, we use a logical formula like we did with piecewise-defined functions in Chapter 1:

When the value of x is b or above, the function will evaluate to zero, because we do not want to count it.

4. Finally, we compute the Riemann sum by adding up everything in Column B and multiplying by Δx:

	A	B	C	D
1	x	f(x)	a	0
2	0	1	b	1
3	0.01	0.9999	n	100
4	0.02	0.9996	Delta x	0.01
5	0.03	0.9991	Left Sum	=SUM(B:B)*D4
6	0.04	0.9984		

↓

	A	B	C	D
1	x	f(x)	a	0
2	0	1	b	1
3	0.01	0.9999	n	100
4	0.02	0.9996	Delta x	0.01
5	0.03	0.9991	Left Sum	0.67165
6	0.04	0.9984		

Now it is easy to obtain the sums for $n = 200$ and $n = 500$: Simply change the value of n in cell D3:

	A	B	C	D
1	x	f(x)	a	0
2	0	1	b	1
3	0.005	0.999975	n	200
4	0.01	0.9999	Delta x	0.005
5	0.015	0.999775	Left Sum	0.6691625
6	0.02	0.9996		

	A	B	C	D
1	x	f(x)	a	0
2	0	1	b	1
3	0.002	0.999996	n	500
4	0.004	0.999984	Delta x	0.002
5	0.006	0.999964	Left Sum	0.667666
6	0.008	0.999936		

14

Further Integration Techniques and Applications of the Integral

Web Site

www.FiniteandCalc.org

At the Web site you will find:

- A detailed chapter summary
- A true/false quiz
- Additional review exercises
- A numerical integration utility
- Graphing calculator programs for numerical integration
- Graphers, Excel tutorials, and other resources

Case Study Estimating Tax Revenues

You have just been hired by the incoming administration to coordinate national tax policy, and the so-called experts on your staff can't seem to agree on which of two tax proposals will result in more revenue for the government. The data you have are the two income tax proposals (graphs of tax vs. income) and the distribution of incomes in the country. **How do you use this information to decide which tax policy will result in more revenue?**

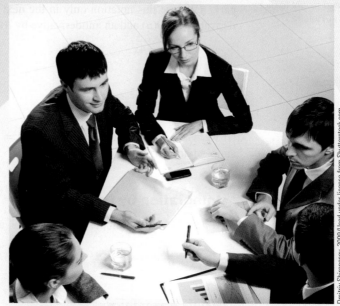

Dmitriy Shironosov, 2009/Used under license from Shutterstock.com

Introduction

In the preceding chapter, we learned how to compute many integrals and saw some of the applications of the integral. In this chapter, we look at some further techniques for computing integrals and then at more applications of the integral. We also see how to extend the definition of the definite integral to include integrals over infinite intervals, and show how such integrals can be used for long-term forecasting. Finally, we introduce the beautiful theory of differential equations and some of its numerous applications.

14.1 Integration by Parts

Integration by parts is an integration technique that comes from the product rule for derivatives. The tabular method we present here has been around for some time and makes integration by parts quite simple, particularly in problems where it has to be used several times.*

We start with a little notation to simplify things while we introduce integration by parts. (We use this notation only in the next few pages.) If u is a function, denote its derivative by $D(u)$ and an antiderivative by $I(u)$. Thus, for example, if $u = 2x^2$, then

$$D(u) = 4x$$

and

$$I(u) = \frac{2x^3}{3}.$$

[If we wished, we could instead take $I(u) = \frac{2x^3}{3} + 46$, but we usually opt to take the simplest antiderivative.]

* **NOTE** The version of the tabular method we use was developed and taught to us by Dan Rosen at Hofstra University.

Integration by Parts

If u and v are continuous functions of x, and u has a continuous derivative, then

$$\int u \cdot v \, dx = u \cdot I(v) - \int D(u) I(v) \, dx.$$

Quick Example

(Discussed more fully in Example 1 below)

$$\int x \cdot e^x \, dx = x I(e^x) - \int D(x) I(e^x) \, dx$$

$$= x e^x - \int 1 \cdot e^x \, dx \qquad I(e^x) = e^x; \ D(x) = 1$$

$$= x e^x - e^x + C. \qquad \int e^x \, dx = e^x + C$$

As the Quick Example shows, although we could not immediately integrate $u \cdot v = x \cdot e^x$, we could easily integrate $D(u)I(v) = 1 \cdot e^x = e^x$.

Derivation of Integration by Parts Formula

As we mentioned, the integration-by-parts formula comes from the product rule for derivatives. We apply the product rule to the function $uI(v)$

$$D[u \cdot I(v)] = D(u)I(v) + uD(I(v))$$
$$= D(u)I(v) + uv$$

because $D(I(v))$ is the derivative of an antiderivative of v, which is v. Integrating both sides gives

$$u \cdot I(v) = \int D(u)I(v)\, dx + \int uv\, dx.$$

A simple rearrangement of the terms now gives us the integration-by-parts formula.

The integration-by-parts formula is easiest to use via the tabular method illustrated in the following example, where we repeat the calculation we did in the Quick Example above.

EXAMPLE 1 Integration by Parts: Tabular Method

Calculate $\int xe^x\, dx$.

Solution First, the reason we *need* to use integration by parts to evaluate this integral is that none of the other techniques of integration that we've talked about up to now will help us. Furthermore, we cannot simply find antiderivatives of x and e^x and multiply them together. [You should check that $(x^2/2)e^x$ is *not* an antiderivative of xe^x.] However, as we saw above, this integral can be found by integration by parts. We want to find the integral of the *product* of x and e^x. We must make a decision: Which function will play the role of u and which will play the role of v in the integration-by-parts formula? Because the derivative of x is just 1, differentiating makes it simpler, so we try letting x be u and letting e^x be v. We need to calculate $D(u)$ and $I(v)$, which we record in the following table.

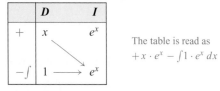

The table is read as
$$+x \cdot e^x - \int 1 \cdot e^x\, dx$$

Below x in the D column, we put $D(x) = 1$; below e^x in the I column, we put $I(e^x) = e^x$. The arrow at an angle connecting x and $I(e^x)$ reminds us that the product $xI(e^x)$ will appear in the answer; the plus sign on the left of the table reminds us that it is $+xI(e^x)$ that appears. The integral sign and the horizontal arrow connecting $D(x)$ and $I(e^x)$ remind us that the *integral* of the product $D(x)I(e^x)$ also appears in the answer; the minus sign on the left reminds us that we need to subtract this integral. Combining these two contributions, we get

$$\int xe^x\, dx = xe^x - \int e^x\, dx.$$

The integral that appears on the right is much easier than the one we began with, so we can complete the problem:

$$\int xe^x\, dx = xe^x - \int e^x\, dx = xe^x - e^x + C.$$

➡ **Before we go on...** In Example 1, what if we had made the opposite decision and put e^x in the D column and x in the I column? Then we would have had the following table:

	D	I
$+$	e^x	x
$-\int$	e^x ⟶	$x^2/2$

This gives

$$\int xe^x \, dx = \frac{x^2}{2}e^x - \int \frac{x^2}{2}e^x \, dx.$$

The integral on the right is harder than the one we started with, not easier! How do we know beforehand which way to go? We don't. We have to be willing to do a little trial and error: We try it one way, and if it doesn't make things simpler, we try it another way. *Remember, though, that the function we put in the I column must be one that we can integrate.* ■

EXAMPLE 2 Repeated Integration by Parts

Calculate $\int x^2 e^{-x} \, dx$.

Solution Again, we have a product—the integrand is the product of x^2 and e^{-x}. Because differentiating x^2 makes it simpler, we put it in the D column and get the following table:

	D	I
$+$	x^2	e^{-x}
$-\int$	$2x$ ⟶	$-e^{-x}$

This table gives us

$$\int x^2 e^{-x} \, dx = x^2(-e^{-x}) - \int 2x(-e^{-x}) \, dx.$$

The last integral is simpler than the one we started with, but it still involves a product. It's a good candidate for another integration by parts. The table we would use would start with $2x$ in the D column and $-e^{-x}$ in the I column, which is exactly what we see in the last row of the table we've already made. Therefore, we *continue the process*, elongating the table above:

	D	I
$+$	x^2	e^{-x}
$-$	$2x$	$-e^{-x}$
$+\int$	2 ⟶	e^{-x}

(Notice how the signs on the left alternate. Here's why: To compute $-\int 2x(-e^{-x})\,dx$ we use the negative of the following table:

	D	**I**
$+$	$2x$	$-e^{-x}$
$-\int$	2	e^{-x}

so we reverse all the signs.)

Now, we still have to compute an integral (the integral of the product of the functions in the bottom row) to complete the computation. But why stop here? Let's continue the process one more step:

	D	**I**
$+$	x^2	e^{-x}
$-$	$2x$	$-e^{-x}$
$+$	2	e^{-x}
$-\int$	0	$-e^{-x}$

In the bottom line we see that all that is left to integrate is $0(-e^{-x}) = 0$. Because the indefinite integral of 0 is C, we can read the answer from the table as

$$\int x^2 e^{-x}\,dx = x^2(-e^{-x}) - 2x(e^{-x}) + 2(-e^{-x}) + C$$
$$= -x^2 e^{-x} - 2x e^{-x} - 2e^{-x} + C$$
$$= -e^{-x}(x^2 + 2x + 2) + C.$$

In Example 2 we saw a technique that we can summarize as follows:

Integrating a Polynomial Times a Function

If one of the factors in the integrand is a polynomial and the other factor is a function that can be integrated repeatedly, put the polynomial in the D column and keep differentiating until you get zero. Then complete the I column to the same depth, and read off the answer.

For practice, redo Example 1 using this technique.

It is not always the case that the integrand is a polynomial times something easy to integrate, so we can't always expect to end up with a zero in the D column. In that case we hope that at some point we will be able to integrate the product of the functions in the last row. Here are some examples.

EXAMPLE 3 **Polynomial Times a Logarithm**

Calculate: **a.** $\int x \ln x \, dx$ **b.** $\int (x^2 - x) \ln x \, dx$ **c.** $\int \ln x \, dx$

Solution

a. This is a product and therefore a good candidate for integration by parts. Our first impulse is to differentiate x, but that would mean integrating $\ln x$, and we do not (yet) know how to do that. So we try it the other way around and hope for the best.

	D	*I*
$+$	$\ln x$	x
$-\int$	$\dfrac{1}{x}$	$\dfrac{x^2}{2}$

Why did we stop? If we continued the table, both columns would get more complicated. However, if we stop here we get

$$\int x \ln x \, dx = (\ln x)\left(\frac{x^2}{2}\right) - \int \left(\frac{1}{x}\right)\left(\frac{x^2}{2}\right) dx$$

$$= \frac{x^2}{2}\ln x - \frac{1}{2}\int x \, dx$$

$$= \frac{x^2}{2}\ln x - \frac{x^2}{4} + C.$$

b. We can use the same technique we used in part (a) to integrate any polynomial times the logarithm of x:

	D	*I*
$+$	$\ln x$	$x^2 - x$
$-\int$	$\dfrac{1}{x}$	$\dfrac{x^3}{3} - \dfrac{x^2}{2}$

$$\int (x^2 - x) \ln x \, dx = (\ln x)\left(\frac{x^3}{3} - \frac{x^2}{2}\right) - \int \left(\frac{1}{x}\right)\left(\frac{x^3}{3} - \frac{x^2}{2}\right) dx$$

$$= \left(\frac{x^3}{3} - \frac{x^2}{2}\right)\ln x - \int \left(\frac{x^2}{3} - \frac{x}{2}\right) dx$$

$$= \left(\frac{x^3}{3} - \frac{x^2}{2}\right)\ln x - \frac{x^3}{9} + \frac{x^2}{4} + C.$$

c. The integrand $\ln x$ is not a product. We can, however, *make* it into a product by thinking of it as $1 \cdot \ln x$. Because this is a polynomial times $\ln x$, we proceed as in parts (a) and (b):

	D	*I*
$+$	$\ln x$	1
$-\int$	$1/x$	x

We notice that the product of $1/x$ and x is just 1, which we know how to integrate, so we can stop here:

$$\int \ln x \, dx = x \ln x - \int \left(\frac{1}{x}\right) x \, dx$$

$$= x \ln x - \int 1 \, dx$$

$$= x \ln x - x + C.$$

FAQs

Whether to Use Integration by Parts, and What Goes in the *D* and *I* Columns

Q: *Will integration by parts always work to integrate a product?*

A: No. Although integration by parts often works for products in which one factor is a polynomial, it will almost *never* work in the examples of products we saw when discussing substitution in Section 13.2. For example, although integration by parts can be used to compute $\int (x^2 - x) e^{2x-1} \, dx$ (put $x^2 - x$ in the *D* column and e^{2x-1} in the *I* column), it *cannot* be used to compute $\int (2x - 1) e^{x^2 - x} \, dx$ (put $u = x^2 - x$). Recognizing when to use integration by parts is best learned by experience.

Q: *When using integration by parts, which expression goes in the D column, and which in the I column?*

A: Although there is no general rule, the following guidelines are useful:

- To integrate a product in which one factor is a polynomial and the other can be integrated several times, put the polynomial in the *D* column and the other factor in the *I* column. Then differentiate the polynomial until you get zero.
- If one of the factors is a polynomial but the other factor cannot be integrated easily, put the polynomial in the *I* column and the other factor in the *D* column. Stop when the product of the functions in the bottom row can be integrated.
- If neither factor is a polynomial, put the factor that seems easier to integrate in the *I* column and the other factor in the *D* column. Again, stop the table as soon as the product of the functions in the bottom row can be integrated.
- If your method doesn't work, try switching the functions in the *D* and *I* columns or try breaking the integrand into a product in a different way. If none of this works, maybe integration by parts isn't the technique to use on this problem.

14.1 EXERCISES

▼ more advanced   ◆ challenging
T indicates exercises that should be solved using technology

Evaluate the integrals in Exercises 1–40 using integration by parts where possible. HINT [See Examples 1–3.]

1. $\int 2x e^x \, dx$

2. $\int 3x e^{-x} \, dx$

3. $\int (3x - 1) e^{-x} \, dx$

4. $\int (1 - x) e^x \, dx$

5. $\int (x^2 - 1) e^{2x} \, dx$

6. $\int (x^2 + 1) e^{-2x} \, dx$

7. $\int (x^2 + 1) e^{-2x+4} \, dx$

8. $\int (x^2 + 1) e^{3x+1} \, dx$

9. $\int (2 - x)2^x \, dx$

10. $\int (3x - 2)4^x \, dx$

11. $\int (x^2 - 1)3^{-x} \, dx$

12. $\int (1 - x^2)2^{-x} \, dx$

13. ▼ $\int \dfrac{x^2 - x}{e^x} \, dx$

14. ▼ $\int \dfrac{2x + 1}{e^{3x}} \, dx$

15. $\int x(x + 2)^6 \, dx$ (See note.[1])

16. $\int x^2(x - 1)^6 \, dx$ (See note.[1])

17. ▼ $\int \dfrac{x}{(x - 2)^3} \, dx$

18. ▼ $\int \dfrac{x}{(x - 1)^2} \, dx$

19. $\int x^3 \ln x \, dx$

20. $\int x^2 \ln x \, dx$

21. $\int (t^2 + 1) \ln(2t) \, dt$

22. $\int (t^2 - t) \ln(-t) \, dt$

23. $\int t^{1/3} \ln t \, dt$

24. $\int t^{-1/2} \ln t \, dt$

25. $\int \log_3 x \, dx$

26. $\int x \log_2 x \, dx$

27. ▼ $\int (x e^{2x} - 4 e^{3x}) \, dx$

28. ▼ $\int (x^2 e^{-x} + 2 e^{-x+1}) \, dx$

29. ▼ $\int \left(x^2 e^x - x e^{x^2} \right) \, dx$

30. ▼ $\int \left[(2x + 1) e^{x^2 + x} - x^2 e^{2x+1} \right] dx$

31. $\int_0^1 (x + 1) e^x \, dx$

32. $\int_{-1}^1 (x^2 + x) e^{-x} \, dx$

33. $\int_0^1 x^2(x + 1)^{10} \, dx$

34. $\int_0^1 x^3(x + 1)^{10} \, dx$

35. ▼ $\int (3x - 4)\sqrt{2x - 1} \, dx$ (See note.[1])

36. ▼ $\int \dfrac{2x + 1}{\sqrt{3x - 2}} \, dx$ (See note.[1])

37. $\int_1^2 x \ln(2x) \, dx$

38. $\int_1^2 x^2 \ln(3x) \, dx$

39. $\int_0^1 x \ln(x + 1) \, dx$

40. $\int_0^1 x^2 \ln(x + 1) \, dx$

41. Find the area bounded by the curve $y = x e^{-x}$, the x-axis, and the lines $x = 0$ and $x = 10$.

42. Find the area bounded by the curve $y = x \ln x$, the x-axis, and the lines $x = 1$ and $x = e$.

43. Find the area bounded by the curve $y = (x + 1) \ln x$, the x-axis, and the lines $x = 1$ and $x = 2$.

44. Find the area bounded by the curve $y = (x - 1)e^x$, the x-axis, and the lines $x = 0$ and $x = 2$.

---

[1] Several exercises, including these, can also be done by using substitution, although integration by parts is easier and should be used instead.

Integrals of Functions Involving Absolute Values In Exercises 45–52, use integration by parts to evaluate the given integral using the following integral formulas where necessary. (You have seen some of these before; all can be checked by differentiating.)

Integral Formula	Shortcut Version
$\int \dfrac{\|x\|}{x} \, dx = \|x\| + C$	$\int \dfrac{\|ax + b\|}{ax + b} \, dx = \dfrac{1}{a}\|ax + b\| + C$
	Because $\dfrac{d}{dx}\|x\| = \dfrac{\|x\|}{x}$.
$\int \|x\| \, dx = \dfrac{1}{2}x\|x\| + C$	$\int \|ax + b\| \, dx$
	$= \dfrac{1}{2a}(ax + b)\|ax + b\| + C$
$\int x\|x\| \, dx = \dfrac{1}{3}x^2\|x\| + C$	$\int (ax + b)\|ax + b\| \, dx$
	$= \dfrac{1}{3a}(ax + b)^2\|ax + b\| + C$
$\int x^2\|x\| \, dx = \dfrac{1}{4}x^3\|x\| + C$	$\int (ax + b)^2\|ax + b\| \, dx$
	$= \dfrac{1}{4a}(ax + b)^3\|ax + b\| + C$

45. $\int x\|x - 3\| \, dx$

46. $\int x\|x + 4\| \, dx$

47. $\int 2x \dfrac{\|x - 3\|}{x - 3} \, dx$

48. $\int 3x \dfrac{\|x + 4\|}{x + 4} \, dx$

49. ▼ $\int 2x^2\|-x + 4\| \, dx$

50. ▼ $\int 3x^2\|2x - 3\| \, dx$

51. ▼ $\int (x^2 - 2x + 3)\|x - 4\| \, dx$

52. ▼ $\int (x^2 - x + 1)\|2x - 4\| \, dx$

APPLICATIONS

53. *Displacement* A rocket rising from the ground has a velocity of $2{,}000t e^{-t/120}$ ft/s, after t seconds. How far does it rise in the first two minutes?

54. *Sales* Weekly sales of graphing calculators can be modeled by the equation

$$s(t) = 10 - t e^{-t/20}$$

where s is the number of calculators sold per week after t weeks. How many graphing calculators (to the nearest unit) will be sold in the first 20 weeks?

55. *Total Cost* The marginal cost of the xth box of light bulbs is $10 + [\ln(x + 1)]/(x + 1)^2$, and the fixed cost is $5{,}000$. Find the total cost to make x boxes of bulbs.

56. *Total Revenue* The marginal revenue for selling the xth box of light bulbs is $10 + 0.001x^2 e^{-x/100}$. Find the total revenue generated by selling 200 boxes of bulbs.

57. *Spending on Gasoline* During 2000–2008, the United States consumed gasoline at a rate of about

$$q(t) = -3.5t + 280 \text{ billion gallons per year.} \quad (0 \le t \le 8)$$

(t is the number of years since 2000.)[2] During the same period, the price of gasoline was approximately

$$p(t) = 1.2e^{0.12t} \text{ dollars per gallon.}$$

Use an integral to estimate, to the nearest billion dollars, the total spent on gasoline during the given period. HINT [Rate of spending $= p(t)q(t)$.]

58. Spending on Gasoline During 1992–2000, the United States consumed gasoline at a rate of about

$$q(t) = 3.2t + 240 \text{ billion gallons per year.}   (0 \le t \le 8)$$

(t is the number of years since 1992.)[3] During the same period, the price of gasoline was approximately

$$p(t) = 1.0e^{0.02t} \text{ dollars per gallon.}$$

Use an integral to estimate, to the nearest billion dollars, the total spent on gasoline during the given period. HINT [Rate of spending $= p(t)q(t)$.]

59. Bottled Water Sales The rate of U.S. sales of bottled water for the period 2000–2008 can be approximated by

$$s(t) = 600t + 4{,}600 \text{ million gallons per year}   (0 \le t \le 8)$$

where t is time in years since the start of 2000.[4] After conducting a survey of sales in your town, you estimate that consumption in gyms accounts for a fraction

$$f(t) = \sqrt{0.1 + 0.02t}$$

of all bottled water sold. Assuming your model is correct, estimate, to the nearest million gallons, the total amount of bottled water consumed in gyms from the start of 2000 to the start of 2005. HINT [Rate of consumption $= s(t)f(t)$. Also see Exercise 35.]

60. Bottled Water Sales The rate of U.S. per capita sales of bottled water for the period 2000–2008 can be approximated by

$$s(t) = 1.8t + 16 \text{ gallons per year}   (0 \le t \le 8)$$

where t is the time in years since the start of 2000.[5] After conducting a survey of sales in your state, you estimate that consumption in gyms accounts for a fraction

$$f(t) = \sqrt{0.2 + 0.04t}$$

of all bottled water consumed. Assuming your model is correct, estimate, to the nearest gallon, the total amount of bottled water consumed per capita in gyms from the start of 2000 to the start of 2005. HINT [Rate of consumption $= s(t)f(t)$. Also see Exercise 36.]

61. Housing The following graph shows the annual number of housing starts in the United States during 2000–2008 together with a quadratic approximating model

$$s(t) = -30t^2 + 240t + 800 \text{ thousand homes per year.}$$
$$(0 \le t \le 8)$$

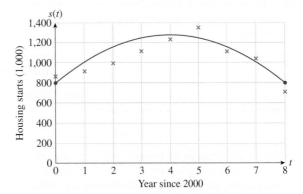

(t is the time in years since 2000.)[6] At the same time, the homes being built were getting larger: The average area per home was approximately

$$a(t) = 40t + 2{,}000 \text{ square feet.}$$

Use the given models to estimate the total housing area under construction over the given period. (Use integration by parts to evaluate the integral and round your answer to the nearest billion square feet.) HINT [Rate of change of area under construction $= s(t)a(t)$.]

62. Housing for Sale The following graph shows the number of housing starts for sale purposes in the United States during 2000–2008 together with a quadratic approximating model

$$s(t) = -33t^2 + 240t + 700 \text{ thousand homes per year.}$$
$$(0 \le t \le 8)$$

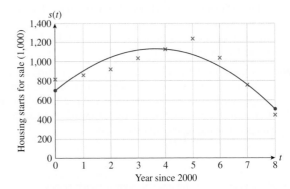

(t is the time in years since 2000.)[7] At the same time, the homes being built were getting larger: The average area per home was approximately

$$a(t) = 40t + 2{,}000 \text{ square feet.}$$

[2] Source for data: Energy Information Administration (Department of Energy) (http://www.eia.doe.gov).

[3] Ibid.

[4] Source for data: *Beverage Marketing Corporation* (www.bottledwater.org) (The 2008 figure is an estimate.)

[5] Ibid.

[6] Source for data: U.S. Census Bureau (www.census.gov).

[7] Ibid.

Use the given models to estimate the total housing area under construction for sale purposes over the given period. (Use integration by parts to evaluate the integral and round your answer to the nearest billion square feet.) HINT [Rate of change of area under construction = $s(t)a(t)$.]

63. ▼ *Oil Production in Mexico:* **Pemex** The rate of oil production by **Pemex**, Mexico's national oil company, can be approximated by

$$q(t) = -8t^2 + 70t + 1,000 \text{ million barrels per year}$$
$$(0 \le t \le 9)$$

where t is time in years since the start of 2000.[8] During that time, the price of oil was approximately[9]

$$p(t) = 25e^{0.1t} \text{ dollars per barrel.}$$

Obtain an expression for **Pemex**'s total oil revenue $R(x)$ since the start of 2000 to the start of year x as a function of x. (Do not simplify the answer.) HINT [Rate of revenue = $p(t)q(t)$.]

64. ▼ *Oil Imports from Mexico* The rate of oil imports to the United States from Mexico can be approximated by

$$r(t) = -5t^2 + 40t + 500 \text{ million barrels per year}$$
$$(0 \le t \le 8)$$

where t is time in years since the start of 2000.[10] During that time, the price of oil was approximately[11]

$$p(t) = 25e^{0.1t} \text{ dollars per barrel.}$$

Obtain an expression for the total oil revenue $R(t)$ Mexico earned from the United States since the start of 2000. HINT [Rate of revenue = $p(t)q(t)$.]

65. ▼ *Revenue* You have been raising the price of your *Lord of the Rings* T-shirts by 50¢ per week, and sales have been falling continuously at a rate of 2% per week. Assuming you are now selling 50 T-shirts per week and charging $10 per T-shirt, how much revenue will you generate during the coming year? (Round your answer to the nearest dollar.) HINT [Weekly revenue = weekly sales × price per T-shirt.]

66. ▼ *Revenue* Luckily, sales of your *Star Wars* T-shirts are now 50 T-shirts per week and increasing continuously at a rate of 5% per week. You are now charging $10 per T-shirt and are decreasing the price by 50¢ per week. How much revenue will you generate during the next six weeks?

---

[8] Source for data: Energy Information Administration/Pemex (http://www.eia.doe.gov).

[9] Source for data: BP Statistical Review of World Energy (www.bp.com/statisticalreview).

[10] Source for data: Energy Information Administration/Pemex (http://www.eia.doe.gov).

[11] Source for data: BP Statistical Review of World Energy (www.bp.com/statisticalreview).

Integrals of Piecewise Linear Functions Exercises 67 and 68 are based on the following formula that can be used to represent a piecewise linear function as a closed form function:

$$\begin{cases} p(x) & \text{if } x < a \\ q(x) & \text{if } x > a \end{cases} = p(x) + \frac{1}{2}[q(x) - p(x)]\left[1 + \frac{|x-a|}{x-a}\right]$$

Such functions can then be integrated using the technique of Exercises 45–52.

67. ◆ *Population: Mexico* The rate of change of population in Mexico over 1990–2010 was approximately

$$r(t) = \begin{cases} -0.1t + 3 & \text{if } 0 \le t \le 10 \\ -0.05t + 2.5 & \text{if } 10 \le t \le 20 \end{cases} \quad \begin{array}{l} \text{million people} \\ \text{per year} \end{array}$$

where t is time in years since 1990.

a. Use the formula given before the exercise to represent $r(t)$ as a closed-form function. HINT [Use the formula with $a = 10$.]

b. Use the result of part (a) and a definite integral to estimate the total increase in population over the given 20-year period. HINT [Break up the integral into two, and use the technique of Exercises 45–52 to evaluate one of them.]

68. ◆ *Population: Mexico* The rate of change of population in Mexico over 1950–1990 was approximately

$$r(t) = \begin{cases} 0.05t + 2.5 & \text{if } 0 \le t \le 20 \\ -0.075t + 5 & \text{if } 20 \le t \le 40 \end{cases} \quad \begin{array}{l} \text{million people} \\ \text{per year} \end{array}$$

where t is time in years since 1950.

a. Use the formula given before the exercise to represent $r(t)$ as a closed-form function. HINT [Use the formula with $a = 20$.]

b. Use the result of part (a) and a definite integral to estimate the total increase in population over the given 40-year period. HINT [Break up the integral into two, and use the technique of Exercises 45–52 to evaluate one of them.]

COMMUNICATION AND REASONING EXERCISES

69. Your friend Janice claims that integration by parts allows one to integrate any product of two functions. Prove her wrong by giving an example of a product of two functions that cannot be integrated using integration by parts.

70. Complete the following sentence in words: The integral of $u\,v$ is the first times the integral of the second minus the integral of _____.

71. Give an example of an integral that can be computed in two ways: by substitution or integration by parts.

72. Give an example of an integral that can be computed by substitution but not by integration by parts. (You need not compute the integral.)

In Exercises 73–80, indicate whether the given integral calls for integration by parts or substitution.

73. $\displaystyle\int (6x - 1)e^{3x^2 - x}\,dx$ 74. $\displaystyle\int \frac{x^2 - 3x + 1}{e^{2x-3}}\,dx$

75. $\int (3x^2 - x)e^{6x-1}\, dx$

76. $\int \dfrac{2x - 3}{e^{x^2-3x+1}}\, dx$

77. $\int \dfrac{1}{(x + 1)\ln(x + 1)}\, dx$

78. $\int \dfrac{\ln(x + 1)}{x + 1}\, dx$

79. $\int \ln(x^2)\, dx$

80. $\int (x + 1)\,\ln(x + 1)\, dx$

81. ▼ If $p(x)$ is a polynomial of degree n and $f(x)$ is some function of x, how many times do we generally have to integrate $f(x)$ to compute $\int p(x) f(x)\, dx$?

82. ▼ Use integration by parts to show that $\int (\ln x)^2\, dx = x(\ln x)^2 - 2x \ln x + 2x + C$.

83. ◆ *Hermite's Identity* If $f(x)$ is a polynomial of degree n, show that

$$\int_0^b f(x)e^{-x}\, dx = F(0) - F(b)e^{-b}$$

where $F(x) = f(x) + f'(x) + f''(x) + \cdots + f^{(n)}(x)$. (This is the sum of f and all of its derivatives.)

84. ◆ Write down a formula similar to Hermite's identity for $\int_0^b f(x)e^x\, dx$ when $f(x)$ is a polynomial of degree n.

14.2 Area Between Two Curves and Applications

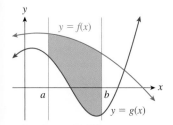

Figure 1

As we saw in the preceding chapter, we can use the definite integral to calculate the area between the graph of a function and the x-axis. With only a little more work, we can use it to calculate the area between two graphs. Figure 1 shows the graphs of two functions, $f(x)$ and $g(x)$, with $f(x) \geq g(x)$ for every x in the interval $[a, b]$.

To find the shaded area between the graphs of the two functions, we use the following formula.

Area Between Two Graphs

If $f(x) \geq g(x)$ for all x in $[a, b]$ (so that the graph of f does not move below that of g), then the area of the region between the graphs of f and g and between $x = a$ and $x = b$ is given by

$$A = \int_a^b [f(x) - g(x)]\, dx.$$

Caution If the graphs of f and g cross in the interval, the above formula does not hold; for instance, if $f(x) = x$ and $g(x) = -x$ then the total area shown in the figure is 2 square units, whereas $\int_{-1}^1 [f(x) - g(x)]\, dx = 0$.

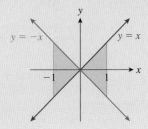

Let's look at an example and then discuss why the formula works.

Figure 2

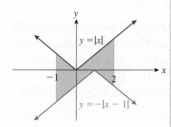

Figure 3

EXAMPLE 1 The Area Between Two Curves

Find the areas of the following regions:

a. Between $f(x) = -x^2 - 3x + 4$ and $g(x) = x^2 - 3x - 4$ and between $x = -1$ and $x = 1$

b. Between $f(x) = |x|$ and $g(x) = -|x - 1|$ over $[-1, 2]$

Solution

a. The area in question is shown in Figure 2. Because the graph of f lies above the graph of g in the interval $[-1, 1]$, we have $f(x) \geq g(x)$ for all x in $[-1, 1]$. Therefore, we can use the formula given above and calculate the area as follows:

$$A = \int_{-1}^{1} [f(x) - g(x)]\, dx$$

$$= \int_{-1}^{1} [(-x^2 - 3x + 4) - (x^2 - 3x - 4)]\, dx$$

$$= \int_{-1}^{1} (8 - 2x^2)\, dx$$

$$= \left[8x - \frac{2}{3}x^3 \right]_{-1}^{1}$$

$$= \frac{44}{3}$$

b. The given area can be broken up into triangles and rectangles (see Figure 3), but we already know a formula for the antiderivative of $|ax + b|$ for constants a and b, so we can use calculus instead:

$$A = \int_{-1}^{2} [f(x) - g(x)]\, dx$$

$$= \int_{-1}^{2} [|x| - (-|x - 1|)]\, dx$$

$$= \int_{-1}^{2} [|x| + |x - 1|]\, dx$$

$$= \frac{1}{2}[x|x| + (x - 1)|x - 1|]_{-1}^{2} \qquad \int |ax + b|\, dx = \frac{1}{2a}(ax + b)|ax + b| + C$$

$$= \frac{1}{2}[(4 + 1) - (-1 - 4)]$$

$$= \frac{1}{2}(10) = 5$$

Q: *Why does the formula for the area between two curves work?*

A: Let's go back once again to the general case illustrated in Figure 1, where we were given two functions f and g with $f(x) \geq g(x)$ for every x in the interval $[a, b]$. To avoid complicating the argument by the fact that the graph of g, or f, or both, may dip below the x-axis in the interval $[a, b]$ (as occurs in Figure 1 and also in Example 1), we shift both graphs vertically upward by adding a big enough constant M to lift them both above the x-axis in the interval $[a, b]$, as shown in Figure 4.

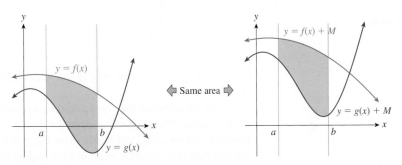

Figure 4

As the figure illustrates, the area of the region between the graphs is not affected, so we will calculate the area of the region shown on the right of Figure 4. That calculation is shown in Figure 5.

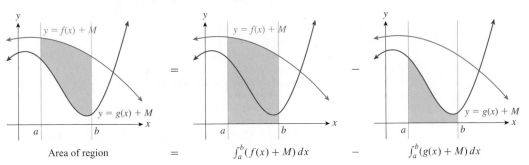

Figure 5

From the figure, the area we want is

$$\int_a^b (f(x) + M)\, dx - \int_a^b (g(x) + M)\, dx = \int_a^b [(f(x) + M) - (g(x) + M)]\, dx$$

$$= \int_a^b [f(x) - g(x)]\, dx,$$

which is the formula we gave originally.

So far, we've been assuming that $f(x) \geq g(x)$, so that the graph of f never dips below the graph of g and so the graphs cannot cross (although they can touch). Example 2 shows how we compute the area between graphs that *do* cross.

EXAMPLE 2 Regions Enclosed by Crossing Curves

Find the area of the region between $y = 3x^2$ and $y = 1 - x^2$ and between $x = 0$ and $x = 1$.

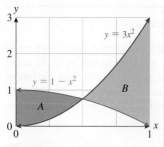

Figure 6

Solution The area we wish to calculate is shown in Figure 6. From the figure, we can see that neither graph lies above the other over the whole interval. To get around this, we break the area into the two pieces on either side of the point at which the graphs cross and then compute each area separately. To do this, we need to know exactly where that crossing point is. The crossing point is where $3x^2 = 1 - x^2$, so we solve for x:

$$3x^2 = 1 - x^2$$
$$4x^2 = 1$$
$$x^2 = \frac{1}{4}$$
$$x = \pm\frac{1}{2}.$$

Because we are interested only in the interval $[0, 1]$, the crossing point we're interested in is at $x = 1/2$.

Now, to compute the areas A and B, we need to know which graph is on top in each of these areas. We can see that from the figure, but what if the functions were more complicated and we could not easily draw the graphs? To be sure, we can test the values of the two functions at some point in each region. But we really need not worry. If we make the wrong choice for the top function, the integral will yield the negative of the area (why?), so we can simply take the absolute value of the integral to get the area of the region in question. For this example, we have

$$A = \int_0^{1/2} [(1 - x^2) - 3x^2]\, dx = \int_0^{1/2} (1 - 4x^2)\, dx$$

$$= \left[x - \frac{4x^3}{3} \right]_0^{1/2}$$

$$= \left(\frac{1}{2} - \frac{1}{6} \right) - (0 - 0) = \frac{1}{3}$$

and

$$B = \int_{1/2}^1 [3x^2 - (1 - x^2)]\, dx = \int_{1/2}^1 (4x^2 - 1)\, dx$$

$$= \left[\frac{4x^3}{3} - x \right]_{1/2}^1$$

$$= \left(\frac{4}{3} - 1 \right) - \left(\frac{1}{6} - \frac{1}{2} \right) = \frac{2}{3}.$$

This gives a total area of $A + B = \dfrac{1}{3} + \dfrac{2}{3} = 1$.

➡ **Before we go on...** What would have happened in Example 2 if we had not broken the area into two pieces but had just calculated the integral of the difference of the two functions? We would have calculated

$$\int_0^1 [(1 - x^2) - 3x^2]\, dx = \int_0^1 [1 - 4x^2]\, dx = \left[x - \frac{4x^3}{3} \right]_0^1 = -\frac{1}{3},$$

which is not even close to the right answer. What this integral calculated was actually $A - B$ rather than $A + B$. Why? ∎

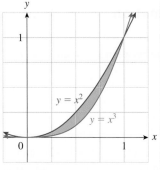

Figure 7

EXAMPLE 3 The Area Enclosed by Two Curves

Find the area enclosed by $y = x^2$ and $y = x^3$.

Solution This example has a new wrinkle: we are not told what interval to use for x. However, if we look at the graph in Figure 7, we see that the question can have only one meaning.

We are being asked to find the area of the shaded sliver, which is the only region that is actually *enclosed* by the two graphs. This sliver is bounded on either side by the two points where the graphs cross, so our first task is to find those points. They are the points where $x^2 = x^3$, so we solve for x:

$$x^2 = x^3$$
$$x^3 - x^2 = 0$$
$$x^2(x - 1) = 0$$
$$x = 0 \quad \text{or} \quad x = 1$$

Thus, we must integrate over the interval $[0, 1]$. Although we see from the diagram (or by substituting $x = 1/2$) that the graph of $y = x^2$ is above that of $y = x^3$, if we didn't notice that we might calculate

$$\int_0^1 (x^3 - x^2)\, dx = \left[\frac{x^4}{4} - \frac{x^3}{3} \right]_0^1 = -\frac{1}{12}.$$

This tells us that the required area is $1/12$ square units and also that we had our integral reversed. Had we calculated $\int_0^1 (x^2 - x^3)\, dx$ instead, we would have found the correct answer, $1/12$.

We can summarize the procedure we used in the preceding two examples.

Finding the Area Between the Graphs of $f(x)$ and $g(x)$

1. Find all points of intersection by solving $f(x) = g(x)$ for x. This either determines the interval over which you will integrate or breaks up a given interval into regions between the intersection points.
2. Determine the area of each region you found by integrating the difference of the larger and the smaller function. (If you accidentally take the smaller minus the larger, the integral will give the negative of the area, so just take the absolute value.)
3. Add together the areas you found in step 2 to get the total area.

Q: *Is there any quick and easy method to find the area between two graphs without having to find all points of intersection? What if it is hard or impossible to find out where the curves intersect?*

A: We *can* use technology to give the approximate area between two graphs. First recall that, if $f(x) \geq g(x)$ for all x in $[a, b]$, then the area between their graphs over $[a, b]$ is given by $\int_a^b [f(x) - g(x)]\, dx$, whereas if $g(x) \geq f(x)$, the area is given by $\int_a^b [g(x) - f(x)]\, dx$. Notice that both expressions are equal to

$$\int_a^b |f(x) - g(x)|\, dx$$

telling us that we can use this same formula in both cases.

T Area Between Two Graphs: Approximation using Technology

The area of the region between the graphs of f and g and between $x = a$ and $x = b$ is given by

$$A = \int_a^b |f(x) - g(x)|\, dx.$$

Quick Example

To approximate the area of the region between $y = 3x^2$ and $y = 1 - x^2$ and between $x = 0$ and $x = 1$ we calculated in Example 2, use technology to compute

$$\int_0^1 |3x^2 - (1 - x^2)|\, dx = 1.$$

TI-83/84 Plus   `fnInt(abs(3x^2-(1-x^2)),X,0,1)`

Web Site   Online Utilities → Numerical Integration Utility

---

f(x) = |abs(3x^2-(1-x^2))|

Left End-Point: |0   Right End-Point: |1

14.2 EXERCISES

▼ more advanced   ◆ challenging

T indicates exercises that should be solved using technology

Find the area of the shaded region in Exercises 1–8. (We suggest you use technology to check your answers.)

1.
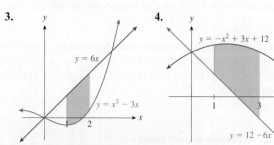
$y = x^2 - 4$
$y = 0$

2.
$y = 0$

3.

$y = 6x$
$y = x^3 - 3x$

4.
$y = -x^2 + 3x + 12$
$y = 12 - 6x$

5.
$y = |x - 1|$
$y = -|x - 1|$

6.
$y = |x - 1|$
$y = -|x|$

7. ▼
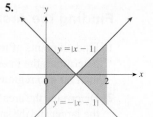
$y = x^2 - 2x + 1$
$y = 5 - x^2$

8. ▼
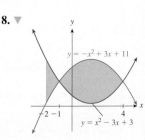
$y = -x^2 + 3x + 11$
$y = x^2 - 3x + 3$

Find the area of the indicated region in Exercises 9–42. We suggest you graph the curves to check whether one is above the other or whether they cross, and that you use technology to check your answers.

9. Between $y = x^2$ and $y = -1$ for x in $[-1, 1]$ HINT [See Example 1.]

10. Between $y = x^3$ and $y = -1$ for x in $[-1, 1]$ HINT [See Example 1.]

11. Between $y = -x$ and $y = x$ for x in $[0, 2]$

12. Between $y = -x$ and $y = x/2$ for x in $[0, 2]$

13. Between $y = |x|$ and $y = x^2$ in $[-1, 1]$

14. Between $y = -|x|$ and $y = x^2 - 2$ in $[-1, 1]$

15. Between $y = x$ and $y = x^2$ for x in $[-1, 1]$ HINT [See Example 2.]

16. Between $y = x$ and $y = x^3$ for x in $[-1, 1]$ HINT [See Example 2.]

17. Between $y = x^2 - 2x$ and $y = -x^2 + 4x - 4$ for x in $[0, 2]$

18. Between $y = x^2 - 4x + 2$ and $y = -x^2 + 4x - 4$ for x in $[0, 3]$

19. Between $y = 2x^2 + 10x - 5$ and $y = -x^2 + 4x + 4$ for x in $[-3, 2]$

20. Between $y = 2x^2 + 7x - 2$ and $y = -x^2 + 4x + 4$ for x in $[-2, 2]$

21. Between $y = e^x$ and $y = x$ for x in $[0, 1]$

22. Between $y = e^{-x}$ and $y = -x$ for x in $[0, 1]$

23. Between $y = (x - 1)^2$ and $y = -(x - 1)^2$ for x in $[0, 1]$

24. Between $y = x^2(x^3 + 1)^{10}$ and $y = -x(x^2 + 1)^{10}$ for x in $[0, 1]$

25. Enclosed by $y = x$ and $y = x^4$ HINT [See Example 3.]

26. Enclosed by $y = x$ and $y = -x^4$ HINT [See Example 3.]

27. Enclosed by $y = x^3$ and $y = x^4$

28. Enclosed by $y = x$ and $y = x^3$

29. Enclosed by $y = x^2$ and $y = x^4$

30. Enclosed by $y = x^4 - x^2$ and $y = x^2 - x^4$

31. Enclosed by $y = x^2 - 2x$ and $y = -x^2 + 4x - 4$

32. Enclosed by $y = x^2 - 4x + 2$ and $y = -x^2 + 4x - 4$

33. Enclosed by $y = 2x^2 + 10x - 5$ and $y = -x^2 + 4x + 4$

34. Enclosed by $y = 2x^2 + 7x - 2$ and $y = -x^2 + 4x + 4$

35. Enclosed by $y = e^x$, $y = 2$, and the y-axis

36. Enclosed by $y = e^{-x}$, $y = 3$, and the y-axis

37. Enclosed by $y = \ln x$, $y = 2 - \ln x$, and $x = 4$

38. Enclosed by $y = \ln x$, $y = 1 - \ln x$, and $x = 4$

39. ⊞ Enclosed by $y = e^x$, $y = 2x + 1$, $x = -1$, and $x = 1$ (Round answer to four significant digits.) HINT [See Quick Example page 1028.]

40. ⊞ Enclosed by $y = 2^x$, $y = x + 2$, $x = -2$, and $x = 2$ (Round answer to four significant digits.) HINT [See Quick Example page 1028.]

41. ⊞ Enclosed by $y = \ln x$ and $y = \dfrac{x}{2} - \dfrac{1}{2}$ (Round answer to four significant digits.) [First use technology to determine approximately where the graphs cross.]

42. ⊞ Enclosed by $y = \ln x$ and $y = x - 2$ (Round answer to four significant digits.) [First use technology to determine approximately where the graphs cross.]

APPLICATIONS

43. **Revenue and Cost** Suppose your daily revenue from selling used DVDs is
$$R(t) = 100 + 10t \quad (0 \le t \le 5)$$
dollars per day, where t represents days from the beginning of the week, while your daily costs are
$$C(t) = 90 + 5t \quad (0 \le t \le 5)$$
dollars per day. Find the area between the graphs of $R(t)$ and $C(t)$ for $0 \le t \le 5$. What does your answer represent?

44. **Income and Expenses** Suppose your annual income is
$$I(t) = 50{,}000 + 2{,}000t \quad (0 \le t \le 3)$$
dollars per year, where t represents the number of years since you began your job, while your annual expenses are
$$E(t) = 45{,}000 + 1{,}500t \quad (0 \le t \le 3)$$
dollars per year. Find the area between the graphs of $I(t)$ and $E(t)$ for $0 \le t \le 3$. What does your answer represent?

45. **Housing** The total number of housing starts in the United States during 2000–2008 was approximately
$$h(t) = -30t^2 + 240t + 800 \text{ thousand homes per year}$$
$$(0 \le t \le 8)$$
where t is time in years since the start of 2000.[12] During that time, the number of housing starts for sale purposes in the United States was approximately
$$s(t) = -33t^2 + 240t + 700 \text{ thousand homes per year.}$$
$$(0 \le t \le 8)$$
Compute the area shown in the graph, and interpret the answer.

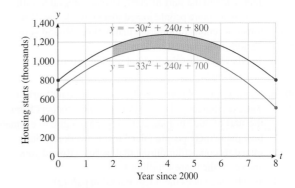

46. **Oil Production in Mexico: Pemex** The rate of oil production by **Pemex**, Mexico's national oil company, can be approximated by
$$q(t) = -8t^2 + 70t + 1{,}000 \text{ million barrels per year}$$
$$(0 \le t \le 9)$$

_____
[12] Source for data: U.S. Census Bureau (www.census.gov).

where t is time in years since the start of 2000.[13] During that time, Mexico exported oil to the United States at a rate of

$$r(t) = -5t^2 + 40t + 500 \text{ million barrels per year.}$$
$$(0 \le t \le 8)$$

Compute the area shown in the graph, and interpret the answer.

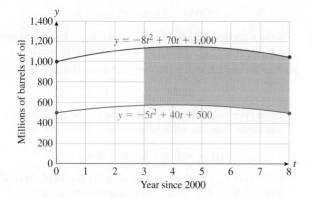

Year since 2000

MySpace *and* **Facebook** *Exercises 47 and 48 are based on the following models, which show: the rate at which new members joined* **Facebook** *and* **MySpace**:

Facebook:[14]　$f(t) = 12t^2 - 20t + 10$ *million members per year*　$(0 \le t \le 3.5)$

MySpace:[15]　$m(t) = 10.5t^2 + 25t + 18.5$ *million members per year*　$(0 \le t \le 3.5)$

(t is time in years since the start of 2005.)

47. a. Use a graph to determine which of the two network sites was experiencing a larger influx of new members from June 2005 to the start of 2007. Use an integral to estimate how many more people joined that network site than joined its competitor during that period. (Round your answer to the nearest million.)

　　b. To what area does the integral used in part (a) correspond?

48. a. Use a graph to determine which of the two network sites was experiencing a larger influx of new members from the start of 2007 to June 2008. Use an integral to estimate how many more people joined that network site than joined its competitor during that period. (Round your answer to the nearest million.)

　　b. To what area does the integral used in part (a) correspond?

---

[13] Source for data: Energy Information Administration/Pemex (http://www.eia.doe.gov).

[14] Sources for data: Some data are interpolated (www.facebook.com/, www.insidehighered.com).

[15] Source for data: www.swivel.com/data_sets.

Big Brother *Exercises 49 and 50 are based on the following models, which show the total number of wiretaps authorized per year by all state and federal courts in the United States and the number authorized by state courts.*

State and federal courts:　$a(t) = 820e^{0.051t}$　$(0 \le t \le 20)$
　　State courts:　$s(t) = 440e^{0.06t}$　$(0 \le t \le 20)$

(t is time in years since the start of 1990.)[16]

49. ▼ Estimate the area between the graphs of the two functions over the interval $[0, t]$. Interpret your answer.

50. ▼ Estimate the area between the graphs of the two functions over the interval $[t, 20]$. Interpret your answer.

COMMUNICATION AND REASONING EXERCISES

51. If f and g are continuous functions with $\int_a^b [f(x) - g(x)]\, dx = 0$, it follows that the area between the graphs of f and g is zero, right?

52. You know that f and g are continuous and their graphs do not cross on the interval $[a, b]$, so you calculate $\int_a^b [f(x) - g(x)]\, dx$ and find that the answer is -40. Why is it negative, and what is the area between the curves?

53. The following graph shows annual U.S. exports and imports for the period 1960–2007.[17]

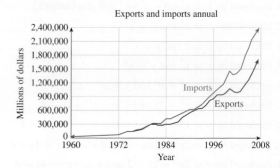

Exports and imports annual

What does the area between the export and import curves represent?

54. The following graph shows a fictitious country's monthly exports and imports for the period 1997–2001.

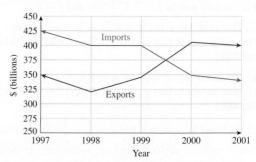

---

[16] Source for data: 2007 Wiretap Report, Administrative Office of the United States Courts (www.uscourts.gov/wiretap07/2007WTText.pdf).

[17] Source: Data 360 (www.data360.org).

What does the total area enclosed by the export and import curves represent, and what does the definite integral of the difference, Exports − Imports, represent?

55. ▼ The following graph shows the daily revenue and cost in your Adopt-a-Chia operation *t* days from its inception.

Multiple choice: The area between the cost and revenue curves represents:

(A) The accumulated loss through day 4 plus the accumulated profit for days 5 through 7

(B) The accumulated profit for the week

(C) The accumulated loss for the week

(D) The accumulated cost through day 4 plus the accumulated revenue for days 5 through 7

56. ▼ The following graph shows daily orders and inventory (stock on hand) for your Jackson Pollock paint-by-number sets *t* days into last week.

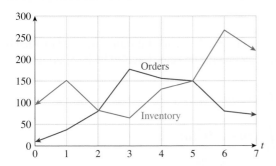

a. Multiple choice: Which is greatest?

(A) $\int_0^7 (\text{Orders} - \text{Inventory})\, dt$

(B) $\int_0^7 (\text{Inventory} - \text{Orders})\, dt$

(C) The area between the Orders and Inventory curves.

b. Multiple choice: The answer to part (a) measures

(A) The accumulated gap between orders and inventory

(B) The accumulated surplus through day 3 minus the accumulated shortage for days 3 through 5 plus the accumulated surplus through days 6 through 7

(C) The total net surplus

(D) The total net loss

57. ▼ What is wrong with the following claim: "I purchased **Novartis AG** shares for $50 at the beginning of March 2008. My total profit per share from this investment from March through August is represented by the area between the stock price curve and the purchase price curve as shown on the following graph, where *t* is time in months since March 1, 2008."[18]

58. ▼ Your pharmaceutical company monitors the amount of medication in successive batches of 100 mg tetracycline capsules, and obtains the following graph.

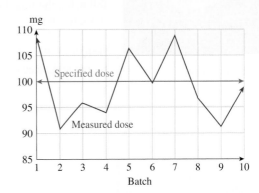

Your production manager claims that the batches of tetracycline conform to the exact dosage requirement because half of the area between the graphs is above the Specified dose line and half is below it. Comment on this reasoning.

─────────

[18] Source: www.finance.google.com.

14.3 Averages and Moving Averages

Averages

To find the average of, say, 20 numbers, we simply add them up and divide by 20. More generally, if we want to find the **average**, or **mean**, of the n numbers $y_1, y_2, y_3, \ldots y_n$, we add them up and divide by n. We write this average as $\bar{y}$ ("y-bar").

Average, or Mean, of a Collection of Values

$$\bar{y} = \frac{y_1 + y_2 + \cdots + y_n}{n}$$

Quick Example

The average of $\{0, 2, -1, 5\}$ is $\bar{y} = \dfrac{0 + 2 - 1 + 5}{4} = \dfrac{6}{4} = 1.5.$

But, we also use the word *average* in other senses. For example, we speak of the average speed of a car during a trip.

Vladimir Pcholkin/Getty Images

EXAMPLE 1 Average Speed

Over the course of 2 hours, my speed varied from 50 miles per hour to 60 miles per hour, following the function $v(t) = 50 + 2.5t^2$, $0 \le t \le 2$. What was my average speed over those two hours?

Solution Recall that average speed is simply the total distance traveled divided by the time it took. Recall, also, that we can find the distance traveled by integrating the speed:

$$
\begin{aligned}
\text{Distance traveled} &= \int_0^2 v(t)\, dt \\
&= \int_0^2 (50 + 2.5t^2)\, dt \\
&= \left[50t + \frac{2.5}{3}t^3 \right]_0^2 \\
&= 100 + \frac{20}{3} \\
&\approx 106.67 \text{ miles}
\end{aligned}
$$

It took 2 hours to travel this distance, so the average speed was

$$\text{Average speed} \approx \frac{106.67}{2} \approx 53.3 \text{ mph}$$

In general, if we travel with velocity $v(t)$ from time $t = a$ to time $t = b$, we will travel a distance of $\int_a^b v(t)\,dt$ in time $b - a$, which gives an average velocity of

$$\text{Average velocity} = \frac{1}{b-a} \int_a^b v(t)\,dt.$$

Thinking of this calculation as finding the average value of the velocity function, we generalize and make the following definition.

Average Value of a Function

The **average**, or **mean**, of a function $f(x)$ on an interval $[a, b]$ is

$$\bar{f} = \frac{1}{b-a} \int_a^b f(x)\,dx.$$

Quick Example

The average of $f(x) = x$ on $[1, 5]$ is

$$\bar{f} = \frac{1}{b-a} \int_a^b f(x)\,dx$$

$$= \frac{1}{5-1} \int_1^5 x\,dx$$

$$= \frac{1}{4}\left[\frac{x^2}{2}\right]_1^5 = \frac{1}{4}\left(\frac{25}{2} - \frac{1}{2}\right) = 3.$$

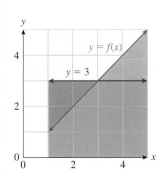

Figure 8

Interpreting the Average of a Function Geometrically

The average of a function has a geometric interpretation. Referring to the Quick Example above, we can compare the graph of $y = f(x)$ with the graph of $y = 3$, both over the interval $[1, 5]$ (Figure 8). We can find the area under the graph of $f(x) = x$ by geometry or by calculus; it is 12. The area in the rectangle under $y = 3$ is also 12.

In general, the average $\bar{f}$ of a positive function over the interval $[a, b]$ gives the height of the rectangle over the interval $[a, b]$ that has the same area as the area under the graph of $f(x)$ as illustrated in Figure 9. The equality of these areas follows from the equation

$$(b-a)\bar{f} = \int_a^b f(x)\,dx.$$

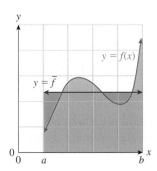

Figure 9

EXAMPLE 2 Average Balance

A savings account at the People's Credit Union pays 3% interest, compounded continuously, and at the end of the year you get a bonus of 1% of the average balance in the account during the year. If you deposit $10,000 at the beginning of the year, how much interest and how large a bonus will you get?

Solution We can use the continuous compound interest formula to calculate the amount of money you have in the account at time t:

$$A(t) = 10,000e^{0.03t}$$

where t is measured in years. At the end of 1 year, the account will have

$$A(1) = \$10,304.55$$

so you will have earned $304.55 interest. To compute the bonus, we need to find the average amount in the account, which is the average of $A(t)$ over the interval $[0, 1]$. Thus,

$$\bar{A} = \frac{1}{b-a} \int_a^b A(t)\, dt$$

$$= \frac{1}{1-0} \int_0^1 10,000e^{0.03t}\, dt = \frac{10,000}{0.03} \left[e^{0.03t} \right]_0^1$$

$$\approx \$10,151.51$$

The bonus is 1% of this, or $101.52.

➡ **Before we go on...** The 1% bonus in Example 2 was one-third of the total interest. Why did this happen? What fraction of the total interest would the bonus be if the interest rate was 4%, 5%, or 10%? ∎

Moving Averages

Suppose you follow the performance of a company's stock by recording the daily closing prices. The graph of these prices may seem jagged or "jittery" due to random day-to-day fluctuations. To see any trends, you would like a way to "smooth out" these data. The **moving average** is one common way to do that.

EXAMPLE 3 Stock Prices

The following table shows Colossal Conglomerate's closing stock prices for 20 consecutive trading days.

Day	1	2	3	4	5	6	7	8	9	10
Price	20	22	21	24	24	23	25	26	20	24
Day	11	12	13	14	15	16	17	18	19	20
Price	26	26	25	27	28	27	29	27	25	24

Plot these prices and the 5-day moving average.

Solution The 5-day moving average is the average of each day's price together with the prices of the preceding 4 days. We can compute the 5-day moving averages starting on the fifth day. We get these numbers:

Day	1	2	3	4	5	6	7	8	9	10
Moving Average					22.2	22.8	23.4	24.4	23.6	23.6
Day	11	12	13	14	15	16	17	18	19	20
Moving Average	24.2	24.4	24.2	25.6	26.4	26.6	27.2	27.6	27.2	26.4

The closing stock prices and moving averages are plotted in Figure 10.

Figure 10

As you can see, the moving average is less volatile than the closing price. Because the moving average incorporates the stock's performance over 5 days at a time, a single day's fluctuation is smoothed out. Look at day 9 in particular. The moving average also tends to lag behind the actual performance because it takes past history into account. Look at the downturns at days 6 and 18 in particular.

The period of 5 days for a moving average, as used in Example 3, is arbitrary. Using a longer period of time would smooth the data more but increase the lag. For data used as economic indicators, such as housing prices or retail sales, it is common to compute the 4-quarter moving average to smooth out seasonal variations.

It is also sometimes useful to compute moving averages of continuous functions. We may want to do this if we use a mathematical model of a large collection of data. Also, some physical systems have the effect of converting an input function (an electrical signal, for example) into its moving average. By an *n*-**unit moving average** of a function $f(x)$ we mean the function $\bar{f}$ for which $\bar{f}(x)$ is the average of the value of $f(x)$ on $[x - n, x]$. Using the formula for the average of a function, we get the following formula.

n-Unit Moving Average of a Function

The *n*-unit moving average of a function f is

$$\bar{f}(x) = \frac{1}{n} \int_{x-n}^{x} f(t)\, dt.$$

Quick Example

The 2-unit moving average of $f(x) = x^2$ is

$$\bar{f}(x) = \frac{1}{2} \int_{x-2}^{x} t^2\, dt = \frac{1}{6} \left[t^3 \right]_{x-2}^{x} = x^2 - 2x + \frac{4}{3}.$$

The graphs of $f(x)$ and $\bar{f}(x)$ are shown in Figure 11.

using Technology

See the Technology Guides at the end of the chapter to find out how to tabulate and graph moving averages on a TI-83/84 Plus or Excel. Here is an outline:

TI-83/84 Plus

STAT EDIT; enter the days in L_1, and the prices in L_2.
Home screen:

`seq((L₂(X)+L₂(X-1)`
`+L₂(X-2)+L₂(X-3)`
`+L₂(X-4))/5,X,5,20)`
`→L₃`

[More details on page 1077.]

Excel

Day data in A2–A21
Price data in B2–B21
Enter =AVERAGE(B2:B6)
in C6, and copy down to C21.
Graph: Highlight columns A–C and insert a Scatter Chart.
[More details on page 1078.]

Figure 11

$$f(x) = |x| - |x-1| + |x-2|$$

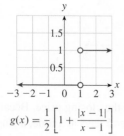

$$g(x) = \frac{1}{2}\left[1 + \frac{|x-1|}{x-1}\right]$$

Figure 12

using Technology

TI-83/84 Plus

We can graph the moving average of *f* in Example 4 on a TI-83/84 Plus as follows:

```
Y₁=abs(X)-abs(X-1)
+abs(X-2)
Y₂=fnInt(Y1(T),T,
X-1,X)
ZOOM 0
```

For *g*, change Y₁ to

```
Y₁=.5*(1+abs(X-1)/
(X-1))
```

Figure 14

EXAMPLE 4 Moving Averages: Saw Tooth and Step Functions

Graph the following functions, and then compute and graph their 1-unit moving averages.

$$f(x) = |x| - |x-1| + |x-2| \qquad \text{Saw tooth}$$

$$g(x) = \frac{1}{2}\left[1 + \frac{|x-1|}{x-1}\right] \qquad \text{Unit step at } x = 1$$

Solution The graphs of *f* and *g* are shown in Figure 12. (Notice that the step function is not defined at $x = 1$. Most graphers will show the step function as an actual step by connecting the points $(1, 0)$ and $(1, 1)$ with a vertical line.)

The 1-step moving averages are:

$$\bar{f}(x) = \int_{x-1}^{x} f(t)\,dt = \int_{x-1}^{x} [|t| - |t-1| + |t-2|]\,dt$$

$$= \frac{1}{2}\left[t|t| - (t-1)|t-1| + (t-2)|t-2|\right]_{x-1}^{x}$$

$$= \frac{1}{2}([x|x| - (x-1)|x-1| + (x-2)|x-2|]$$
$$\qquad - [(x-1)|x-1| - (x-2)|x-2| + (x-3)|x-3|])$$

$$= \frac{1}{2}[x|x| - 2(x-1)|x-1| + 2(x-2)|x-2| - (x-3)|x-3|]$$

$$\bar{g}(x) = \int_{x-1}^{x} g(t)\,dt = \int_{x-1}^{x} \frac{1}{2}\left[1 + \frac{|t-1|}{t-1}\right]dt$$

$$= \frac{1}{2}[t + |t-1|]_{x-1}^{x}$$

$$= \frac{1}{2}[(x + |x-1|) - (x-1 + |x-2|)]$$

$$= \frac{1}{2}[1 + |x-1| - |x-2|]$$

The graphs of $\bar{f}$ and $\bar{g}$ are shown in Figure 13.

Figure 13

Notice how the graph of $\bar{f}$ smooths out the zig-zags of the sawtooth function.

➡ **Before we go on...** Figure 14 shows the 2-unit moving average of *f* in Example 4,

$$\bar{f}(x) = \frac{1}{2}\int_{x-2}^{x} f(t)\,dt$$

$$= \frac{1}{4}(x|x| - (x-1)|x-1| + (x-3)|x-3| - (x-4)|x-4|)$$

Notice how the 2-point moving average has completely eliminated the zig-zags, illustrating how moving averages can be used to remove seasonal fluctuations in real-life situations. ■

14.3 EXERCISES

▼ more advanced   ◆ challenging
⊤ indicates exercises that should be solved using technology

Find the averages of the functions in Exercises 1–8 over the given intervals. Plot each function and its average on the same graph (as in Figure 8). HINT [See Quick Example page 1033.]

1. $f(x) = x^3$ over $[0, 2]$ **2.** $f(x) = x^3$ over $[-1, 1]$

3. $f(x) = x^3 - x$ over $[0, 2]$ **4.** $f(x) = x^3 - x$ over $[0, 1]$

5. $f(x) = e^{-x}$ over $[0, 2]$ **6.** $f(x) = e^x$ over $[-1, 1]$

7. $f(x) = |2x - 5|$ over $[0, 4]$

8. $f(x) = |-x + 2|$ over $[-1, 3]$

In Exercises 9 and 10, complete the given table with the values of the 3-unit moving average of the given function. HINT [See Example 3.]

9.

x	0	1	2	3	4	5	6	7
$r(x)$	3	5	10	3	2	5	6	7
$\bar{r}(x)$								

10.

x	0	1	2	3	4	5	6	7
$s(x)$	2	9	7	3	2	5	7	1
$\bar{s}(x)$								

In Exercises 11 and 12, some values of a function and its 3-unit moving average are given. Supply the missing information.

11.

x	0	1	2	3	4	5	6	7
$r(x)$	1	2			11		10	2
$\bar{r}(x)$			3	5		11		

12.

x	0	1	2	3	4	5	6	7
$s(x)$	1	5		1				
$\bar{s}(x)$			5		5	2	3	2

Calculate the 5-unit moving average of each function in Exercises 13–24. Plot each function and its moving average on the same graph, as in Example 4. (You may use graphing technology for these plots, but you should compute the moving averages analytically.) HINT [See Quick Example page 1035, and Example 4.]

13. $f(x) = x^3$ **14.** $f(x) = x^3 - x$

15. $f(x) = x^{2/3}$ **16.** $f(x) = x^{2/3} + x$

17. $f(x) = e^{0.5x}$ **18.** $f(x) = e^{-0.02x}$

19. $f(x) = \sqrt{x}$ **20.** $f(x) = x^{1/3}$

21. $f(x) = 1 - \dfrac{|2x - 1|}{2x - 1}$ **22.** $f(x) = 2 + \dfrac{|3x + 1|}{3x + 1}$

23. ▼ $f(x) = 2 - |x + 1| + |x|$ [Do not simplify the answer.]

24. ▼ $f(x) = |2x + 1| - |2x| - 2$ [Do not simplify the answer.]

⊤ *In Exercises 25–34, use graphing technology to plot the given functions together with their 3-unit moving averages.* HINT [See Technology Note for Example 4.]

25. $f(x) = \dfrac{10x}{1 + 5|x|}$ **26.** $f(x) = \dfrac{1}{1 + e^x}$

27. $f(x) = \ln(1 + x^2)$ **28.** $f(x) = e^{1 - x^2}$

29. $f(x) = |x| - |x - 1| + |x - 2| - |x - 3| + |x - 4|$

30. $f(x) = |x| - 2|x - 1| + 2|x - 2| - 2|x - 3| + |x - 4|$

31. $f(x) = \dfrac{|x|}{x} - \dfrac{|x - 1|}{x - 1} + \dfrac{|x - 2|}{x - 2} - \dfrac{|x - 3|}{x - 3}$

32. $f(x) = \dfrac{|x|}{x} - 2\dfrac{|x - 1|}{x - 1} + 2\dfrac{|x - 2|}{x - 2} - \dfrac{|x - 3|}{x - 3}$

33. $f(x) = \dfrac{|x|}{x} + \dfrac{|x - 1|}{x - 1} + \dfrac{|x - 2|}{x - 2} + \dfrac{|x - 3|}{x - 3}$

34. $f(x) = 4 - \dfrac{|x|}{x} - \dfrac{|x - 1|}{x - 1} - \dfrac{|x - 2|}{x - 2} - \dfrac{|x - 3|}{x - 3}$

APPLICATIONS

35. *Profits:* British Petroleum The following table shows **BP**'s quarterly profits for a 5-quarter period beginning the second quarter of 2007:[19]

Quarter	2007 Q2	2007 Q3	2007 Q4	2008 Q1	2008 Q2
Profit ($ million)	7,441	4,478	4,504	7,583	9,588

What was the average quarterly profit earned by **BP** during the given period? HINT [See Quick Example page 1032.]

36. *Revenues:* British Petroleum The following table shows **BP**'s quarterly revenues for a 5-quarter period beginning the second quarter of 2007:[20]

Quarter	2007 Q2	2007 Q3	2007 Q4	2008 Q1	2008 Q2
Revenue ($ million)	73,083	72,610	81,222	89,223	110,903

What was the average quarterly profit earned by **BP** during the given period? HINT [See Quick Example page 1032.]

37. *Television Advertising* The cost, in millions of dollars, of a 30-second television ad during the Super Bowl in the years 2000 to 2007 can be approximated by

$$C(t) = 0.13t + 1.5 \text{ million dollars.} \quad (0 \le t \le 7)$$

---

[19] Source: British Petroleum (www.bp.com).
[20] Ibid.

(t is the number of years since 2000).[21] What was the average cost of a Super Bowl ad during the given period? HINT [See Example 1.]

38. *Television Advertising* The cost, in millions of dollars, of a 30-second television ad during the Super Bowl in the years 1990 to 1998 can be approximated by

$$C(t) = 0.08t + 0.6 \text{ million dollars.} (0 \le t \le 8)$$

(t is the number of years since 1990).[22] What was the average cost of a Super Bowl ad during the given period? HINT [See Example 1.]

39. *Membership:* Facebook The number of new members joining **Facebook** each year can be modeled by

$$m(t) = 12t^2 - 20t + 10 \text{ million members per year}$$
$$(0 \le t \le 3.5)$$

where t is time in years since the start of 2005.[23] What was the average number of new members joining **Facebook** each year from the start of 2005 to the start of 2008?

40. *Membership:* MySpace The number of new members joining **MySpace** each year can be modeled by

$$m(t) = 10.5t^2 + 14t - 6 \text{ million members per year}$$
$$(0 \le t \le 3.5)$$

where t is time in years since the start of 2004.[24] What was the average number of new members joining **MySpace** each year from the start of 2004 to the start of 2007?

41. *Freon Production* Annual production of ozone-layer damaging Freon 22 (chlorodifluoromethane) in developing countries from 2000 to 2010 can be modeled by

$$F(t) = 97.2(1.20)^t \text{ tons.} (0 \le t \le 10)$$

(t is the number of years since 2000).[25] What was the average annual production over the period shown? (Round your answer to the nearest ton.) HINT [See Example 2.]

42. *Health Expenditures* Annual expenditure on health in the United States from 1980 to 2010 can be modeled by

$$F(t) = 282(1.08)^t \text{ billion dollars.} (0 \le t \le 30)$$

(t is the number of years since 1980).[26] What was the average annual expenditure over the period shown? (Round your answer to the nearest billion dollars.) HINT [See Example 2.]

43. *Investments* If you invest $10,000 at 8% interest compounded continuously, what is the average amount in your account over one year?

44. *Investments* If you invest $10,000 at 12% interest compounded continuously, what is the average amount in your account over one year?

45. ▼ *Average Balance* Suppose you have an account (paying no interest) into which you deposit $3,000 at the beginning of each month. You withdraw money continuously so that the amount in the account decreases linearly to 0 by the end of the month. Find the average amount in the account over a period of several months. (Assume that the account starts at $0 at $t = 0$ months.)

46. ▼ *Average Balance* Suppose you have an account (paying no interest) into which you deposit $4,000 at the beginning of each month. You withdraw $3,000 during the course of each month, in such a way that the amount decreases linearly. Find the average amount in the account in the first two months. (Assume that the account starts at $0 at $t = 0$ months.)

47. ▣ *Online Auctions:* eBay The number of items sold each quarter on **eBay** from the first quarter of 2005 through the second quarter of 2008 can be approximated by

$$n(t) = 0.07t^4 - 1.7t^3 + 9.9t^2 + 17t + 390 \text{ million items.}$$
$$(1 \le t \le 14)$$

(t is time in quarters; $t = 1$ represents the start of first quarter in 2005).[27] Use technology to estimate the average number of items sold per quarter on **eBay** during the given period. (Round your answer to the nearest million.)

48. ▣ *Online Stores:* eBay The number of stores opened on **eBay** each quarter from the first quarter of 2005 through the second quarter of 2008 can be approximated by

$$s(t) = 0.035t^4 - 0.55t^3 - 1.45t^2 + 37t - 36 \text{ stores.}$$
$$(1 \le t \le 14)$$

(t is time in quarters; $t = 1$ represents the start of first quarter in 2005).[28] Use technology to estimate the average number of stores opened per quarter on **eBay** during the given period. (Round your answer to the nearest whole number.)

---

[21] Source: Advertising Age (www.adage.com/SuperBowlBuyers/superbowlhistory07.html).

[22] Ibid.

[23] Sources for data: Some data are interpolated. (www.facebook.com, www.insidehighered.com).

[24] Source for data: www.swivel.com/data_sets.

[25] Figures are approximate. Source: Lampert Kuijpers (Panel of the Montreal Protocol), National Bureau of Statistics in China, via CEIC DSata/*New York Times*, February 23, 2007, p. C1.

[26] Data are rounded. 2005 and 2010 figures are projections. Source: Centers for Medicare and Medicaid Services, "National Health Expenditures," 2002 version, released January 2004 (www.cms.hhs.gov/statistics/nhe/).

[27] Source for data: eBay company report (www.investor.ebay.com).

[28] Ibid.

49. Stock Prices: Exxon Mobil The following table shows the approximate price of **Exxon Mobil** stock in October of each year from 1999 through 2008. Complete the table by computing the 4-year moving averages. (Note the steep drop in October 2008.) Round each average to the nearest dollar.

Year t	1999	2000	2001	2002	2003	2004	2005	2006	2007	2008
Stock Price	36	44	41	36	38	49	56	71	92	62
Moving Average (rounded)										

The stock price spiked in 2007 and then dropped steeply in 2008. What happened to the corresponding moving average? HINT [See Example 3.]

50. Stock Prices: Nokia The following table shows the approximate price of **Nokia Corporation** stocks in October of each year from 1999 through 2008. Complete the table by computing the 4-year moving averages. (Note the steep drop in October 2008.) Round each average to the nearest dollar.

Year t	1999	2000	2001	2002	2003	2004	2005	2006	2007	2008
Stock Price	25	38	20	13	16	15	16	20	40	15
Moving Average (rounded)										

How does the average year-by-year change in the moving average compare with the average year-by-year change in the stock price? HINT [See Example 3.]

51. ▼ Cancun The *Playa Loca Hotel* in Cancun has an advertising brochure with the following chart, showing the year-round temperature.

Source: http://www.holiday-weather.com (Temperatures are rounded.)

a. Estimate and plot the year-round 6-month moving average. (Use graphing technology, if available, to check your graph.)
b. What can you say about the 12-month moving average?

52. ▼ Reykjavik Repeat the preceding exercise, using the following data from the brochure of the *Tough Traveler Lodge* in Reykjavik.

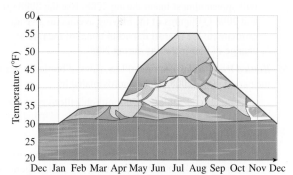

Source: www.holiday-weather.com (Temperatures are rounded.)

53. ▣ ▼ Sales: Apple The following table shows approximate quarterly sales of iPods in millions of units, starting in the first quarter of 2004.[29]

Quarter	2004 Q1	2004 Q2	2004 Q3	2004 Q4	2005 Q1	2005 Q2	2005 Q3	2005 Q4	2006 Q1	2006 Q2
Housing Starts (1,000)	345	456	440	370	369	485	471	392	382	433
Quarter	2006 Q3	2006 Q4	2007 Q1	2007 Q2	2007 Q3	2007 Q4	2008 Q1	2008 Q2	2008 Q3	2008 Q4
Housing Starts (1,000)	372	278	260	333	265	188	162	193	162	116

a. Use technology to compute and plot the 4-quarter moving average of these data.
b. The graph of the moving average for the last four quarters will appear almost linear during 2008. Use the 2008 Q1 and 2008 Q4 figures of the moving average to give an estimate (to the nearest 0.1 million units) of the rate of change of iPod sales during 2008.

54. ▣ ▼ Housing Starts The following table shows the number of housing starts for one-family units, in thousands of units, starting in the first quarter of 2004.[30]

Quarter	2004 Q1	2004 Q2	2004 Q3	2004 Q4	2005 Q1	2005 Q2	2005 Q3	2005 Q4	2006 Q1	2006 Q2
Sales (millions)	0.8	0.9	2	4.5	5.3	6.2	6.5	14	8.5	8.1
Quarter	2006 Q3	2006 Q4	2007 Q1	2007 Q2	2007 Q3	2007 Q4	2008 Q1	2008 Q2	2008 Q3	2008 Q4
Sales (millions)	8.7	21.1	10.5	9.7	10.3	22.1	10.6	11	11.3	23.9

---

[29] Source for data: Apple quarterly earnings reports (www.apple.com/investor/).

[30] Source for data: U.S. Census Bureau (www.census.gov).

a. Use technology to compute and plot the 4-quarter moving average of these data.

b. The graph of the moving average for the last four quarters will appear almost linear during 2008. Use the 2008 Q1 and 2008 Q4 figures of the moving average to give an estimate (to the nearest thousand units) of the rate of change of housing starts during 2008.

55. *Bottled Water Sales* The rate of U.S. sales of bottled water for the period 2000–2008 can be approximated by

$$s(t) = 12t^2 + 500t + 4{,}700 \text{ million gallons per year}$$
$$(0 \le t \le 8)$$

where t is time in years since the start of 2000.[31]

a. Estimate the average annual sales of bottled water over the period 2000–2008, to the nearest 100 million gallons per year. HINT [See Quick Example page 1033.]

b. Compute the two-year moving average of s. (You need not simplify the answer.) HINT [See Quick Example page 1035.]

c. Without simplifying the answer in part (b), say what kind of function the moving average is.

56. *Bottled Water Sales* The rate of U.S. per capita sales of bottled water for the period 2000–2008 can be approximated by

$$s(t) = 0.04t^2 + 1.5t + 17 \text{ gallons per year} \quad (0 \le t \le 8)$$

where t is the time in years since the start of 2000.[32] Repeat the preceding exercise as applied to per capita sales. (Give your answer to (a) to the nearest gallon per year.)

57. *Medicare Spending* Annual federal spending on Medicare (in constant 2000 dollars) was projected to increase from $240 billion in 2000 to $600 billion in 2025.[33]

a. Use this information to express s, the annual spending on Medicare (in billions of dollars), as a linear function of t, the number of years since 2000.

b. Find the 4-year moving average of your model.

c. What can you say about the slope of the moving average?

58. *Pasta Imports in the 90s* In 1990, the United States imported 290 million pounds of pasta. From 1990 to 2000 imports increased by an average of 40 million pounds per year.[34]

a. Use these data to express q, the annual U.S. imports of pasta (in millions of pounds), as a linear function of t, the number of years since 1990.

b. Find the 4-year moving average of your model.

c. What can you say about the slope of the moving average?

59. ▼ *Moving Average of a Linear Function* Find a formula for the a-unit moving average of a general linear function $f(x) = mx + b$.

60. ▼ *Moving Average of an Exponential Function* Find a formula for the a-unit moving average of a general exponential function $f(x) = Ae^{kx}$.

COMMUNICATION AND REASONING EXERCISES

61. Explain why it is sometimes more useful to consider the moving average of a stock price rather than the stock price itself.

62. Sales this month were sharply lower than they were last month, but the 12-unit moving average this month was higher than it was last month. How can that be?

63. Your company's six-month moving average of sales is constant. What does that say about the sales figures?

64. Your monthly salary has been increasing steadily for the past year, and your average monthly salary over the past year was x dollars. Would you have earned more money if you had been paid x dollars per month? Explain your answer.

65. ▼ What property does a (nonconstant) function have if its average value over an interval is zero? Sketch a graph of such a function.

66. ▼ Can the average value of a function f on an interval be greater than its value at every point in that interval? Explain.

67. ▼ Criticize the following claim: The average value of a function on an interval is midway between its highest and lowest value.

68. ▼ Your manager tells you that 12-month moving averages gives at least as much information as shorter-term moving averages and very often more. How would you argue that he is wrong?

69. ▼ Which of the following most closely approximates the original function, (A) its 10-unit moving average, (B) its 1-unit moving average, or (C) its 0.8-unit moving average? Explain your answer.

70. ▼ Is an increasing function larger or smaller than its 1-unit moving average? Explain.

---

[31] Source for data: *Beverage Marketing Corporation* (www.bottledwater .org) (The 2008 figure is an estimate.)

[32] Ibid.

[33] Data are rounded. Source: The Urban Institute's Analysis of the 1999 Trustee's Report (www.urban.org).

[34] Data are rounded. Sources: Department of Commerce/*New York Times*, September 5, 1995, p. D4, International Trade Administration (www.ita.doc.gov/) March 31, 2002.

14.4 Applications to Business and Economics: Consumers' and Producers' Surplus and Continuous Income Streams

Consumers' Surplus

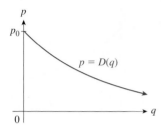

Figure 15

Consider a general demand curve presented, as is traditional in economics, as $p = D(q)$, where p is unit price and q is demand measured, say, in annual sales (Figure 15). Thus, $D(q)$ is the price at which the demand will be q units per year. The price p_0 shown on the graph is the highest price that customers are willing to pay.

Suppose, for example, that the graph in Figure 15 is the demand curve for a particular new model of computer. When the computer first comes out and supplies are low (q is small), "early adopters" will be willing to pay a high price. This is the part of the graph on the left, near the p-axis. As supplies increase and the price drops, more consumers will be willing to pay and more computers will be sold. We can ask the following question: How much are consumers willing to spend for the first $\bar{q}$ units?

Consumers' Willingness to Spend

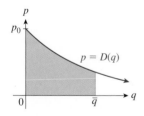

Figure 16

We can approximate consumers' willingness to spend on the first $\bar{q}$ units as follows. We partition the interval $[0, \bar{q}]$ into n subintervals of equal length, as we did when discussing Riemann sums. Figure 16 shows a typical subinterval, $[q_{k-1}, q_k]$.

The price consumers are willing to pay for each of units q_{k-1} through q_k is approximately $D(q_{k-1})$, so the total that consumers are willing to spend for these units is approximately $D(q_{k-1})(q_k - q_{k-1}) = D(q_{k-1})\Delta q$, the area of the shaded region in Figure 16. Thus, the total amount that consumers are willing to spend for items 0 through $\bar{q}$ is

$$W \approx D(q_0)\Delta q + D(q_1)\Delta q + \cdots + D(q_{n-1})\Delta q = \sum_{k=0}^{n-1} D(q_k)\Delta q,$$

which is a Riemann sum. The approximation becomes better the larger n becomes, and in the limit the Riemann sums converge to the integral

$$W = \int_0^{\bar{q}} D(q)\, dq.$$

Figure 17

This quantity, the area shaded in Figure 17, is the total consumers' willingness to spend to buy the first $\bar{q}$ units.

Consumers' Expenditure

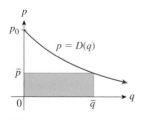

Figure 18

Now suppose that the manufacturer simply sets the price at $\bar{p}$, with a corresponding demand of $\bar{q}$, so $D(\bar{q}) = \bar{p}$. Then the amount that consumers will actually spend to buy these $\bar{q}$ is $\bar{p}\bar{q}$, the product of the unit price and the quantity sold. This is the area of the rectangle shown in Figure 18. Notice that we can write $\bar{p}\bar{q} = \int_0^{\bar{q}} \bar{p}\, dq$, as suggested by the figure.

The difference between what consumers are willing to pay and what they actually pay is money in their pockets and is called the **consumers' surplus**.

Consumers' Surplus

If demand for an item is given by $p = D(q)$, the selling price is $\bar{p}$, and $\bar{q}$ is the corresponding demand [so that $D(\bar{q}) = \bar{p}$], then the **consumers' surplus** is the difference between willingness to spend and actual expenditure:

$$CS = \int_0^{\bar{q}} D(q)\,dq - \bar{p}\bar{q} = \int_0^{\bar{q}} (D(q) - \bar{p})\,dq$$

Graphically, it is the area between the graphs of $p = D(q)$ and $p = \bar{p}$, as shown in the figure.

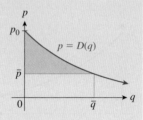

EXAMPLE 1 Consumers' Surplus

Your used-CD store has an exponential demand equation of the form

$$p = 15e^{-0.01q}$$

where q represents daily sales of used CDs and p is the price you charge per CD. Calculate the daily consumers' surplus if you sell your used CDs at $5 each.

Solution We are given $D(q) = 15e^{-0.01q}$ and $\bar{p} = 5$. We also need $\bar{q}$. By definition,

$$D(\bar{q}) = \bar{p}$$

or $15e^{-0.01\bar{q}} = 5$

which we must solve for $\bar{q}$:

$$e^{-0.01\bar{q}} = \frac{1}{3}$$

$$-0.01\bar{q} = \ln\left(\frac{1}{3}\right) = -\ln 3$$

$$\bar{q} = \frac{\ln 3}{0.01} \approx 109.8612$$

We now have

$$CS = \int_0^{\bar{q}} (D(q) - \bar{p})\,dq$$

$$= \int_0^{109.8612} (15e^{-0.01q} - 5)\,dq$$

$$= \left[\frac{15}{-0.01}e^{-0.01q} - 5q\right]_0^{109.8612}$$

$$\approx (-500 - 549.31) - (-1,500 - 0)$$

$$= \$450.69 \text{ per day}$$

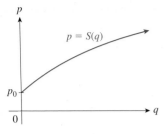

Figure 19

Producers' Surplus

We can also calculate extra income earned by producers. Consider a supply equation of the form $p = S(q)$, where $S(q)$ is the price at which a supplier is willing to supply q items (per time period). Because a producer is generally willing to supply more units at a higher price per unit, a supply curve usually has a positive slope, as shown in Figure 19. The price p_0 is the lowest price that a producer is willing to charge.

Arguing as before, we see that the minimum amount of money producers are willing to receive in exchange for $\bar{q}$ items is $\int_0^{\bar{q}} S(q)\,dq$. On the other hand, if the producers charge $\bar{p}$ per item for $\bar{q}$ items, their actual revenue is $\bar{p}\bar{q} = \int_0^{\bar{q}} \bar{p}\,dq$.

The difference between the producers' actual revenue and the minimum they would have been willing to receive is the **producers' surplus**.

Producers' Surplus

The **producers' surplus** is the extra amount earned by producers who were willing to charge less than the selling price of $\bar{p}$ per unit and is given by

$$PS = \int_0^{\bar{q}} [\bar{p} - S(q)]\,dq$$

where $S(\bar{q}) = \bar{p}$. Graphically, it is the area of the region between the graphs of $p = \bar{p}$ and $p = S(q)$ for $0 \le q \le \bar{q}$, as in the figure.

EXAMPLE 2 Producers' Surplus

My tie-dye T-shirt enterprise has grown to the extent that I am now able to produce T-shirts in bulk, and several campus groups have begun placing orders. I have informed one group that I am prepared to supply $20\sqrt{p-4}$ T-shirts at a price of p dollars per shirt. What is my total surplus if I sell T-shirts to the group at $8 each?

Solution We need to calculate the producers' surplus when $\bar{p} = 8$. The supply equation is

$$q = 20\sqrt{p-4}$$

but in order to use the formula for producers' surplus, we need to express p as a function of q. First, we square both sides to remove the radical sign:

$$q^2 = 400(p-4)$$

so

$$p - 4 = \frac{q^2}{400}$$

giving

$$p = S(q) = \frac{q^2}{400} + 4.$$

We now need the value of $\bar{q}$ corresponding to $\bar{p} = 8$. Substituting $p = 8$ in the original equation, gives

$$\bar{q} = 20\sqrt{8-4} = 20\sqrt{4} = 40.$$

Thus,

$$PS = \int_0^{\bar{q}} (\bar{p} - S(q))\, dq$$

$$= \int_0^{40} \left[8 - \left(\frac{q^2}{400} + 4 \right) \right] dq$$

$$= \int_0^{40} \left(4 - \frac{q^2}{400} \right) dq$$

$$= \left[4q - \frac{q^3}{1{,}200} \right]_0^{40} \approx \$106.67$$

Thus, I earn a surplus of \$106.67 if I sell T-shirts to the group at \$8 each.

EXAMPLE 3 Equilibrium

To continue the preceding example: A representative informs me that the campus group is prepared to order only $\sqrt{200(16 - p)}$ T-shirts at p dollars each. I would like to produce as many T-shirts for them as possible but avoid being left with unsold T-shirts. Given the supply curve from the preceding example, what price should I charge per T-shirt, and what are the consumers' and producers' surpluses at that price?

Solution The price that guarantees neither a shortage nor a surplus of T-shirts is the **equilibrium price**, the price where supply equals demand. We have

Supply: $q = 20\sqrt{p - 4}.$

Demand: $q = \sqrt{200(16 - p)}.$

Equating these gives

$$20\sqrt{p - 4} = \sqrt{200(16 - p)}$$

$$400(p - 4) = 200(16 - p),$$

$$400p - 1{,}600 = 3{,}200 - 200p$$

$$600p = 4{,}800$$

$$p = \$8 \text{ per T-shirt.}$$

We therefore take $\bar{p} = 8$ (which happens to be the price we used in the preceding example). We get the corresponding value for q by substituting $p = 8$ into either the demand or supply equation:

$$\bar{q} = 20\sqrt{8-4} = 40.$$

Thus, $\bar{p} = 8$ and $\bar{q} = 40.$

We must now calculate the consumers' surplus and the producers' surplus. We calculated the producers' surplus for $\bar{p} = 8$ in the preceding example:

$$PS = \$106.67.$$

For the consumers' surplus, we must first express p as a function of q for the demand equation. Thus, we solve the demand equation for p as we did for the supply equation and we obtain

Demand: $D(q) = 16 - \dfrac{q^2}{200}.$

Therefore,

$$
\begin{aligned}
CS &= \int_0^{\bar{q}} (D(q) - \bar{p})\,dq \\
&= \int_0^{40} \left[\left(16 - \frac{q^2}{200} \right) - 8 \right] dq \\
&= \int_0^{40} \left(8 - \frac{q^2}{200} \right) dq \\
&= \left[8q - \frac{q^3}{600} \right]_0^{40} \approx \$213.33
\end{aligned}
$$

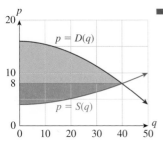

Figure 20

➡ **Before we go on...** Figure 20 shows both the consumers' surplus (top portion) and the producers' surplus (bottom portion) from Example 3. Because extra money in people's pockets is a good thing, the total of the consumers' and the producers' surpluses is called the **total social gain**. In this case it is

Social gain $= CS + PS = 213.33 + 106.67 = \$320.00.$

As you can see from the figure, the total social gain is also the area between two curves and equals

$$\int_0^{40} (D(q) - S(q))\,dq. \qquad\blacksquare$$

Continuous Income Streams

For purposes of calculation, it is often convenient to assume that a company with a high sales volume receives money continuously. In such a case, we have a function $R(t)$ that represents the rate at which money is being received by the company at time t.

EXAMPLE 4 Continuous Income

An ice cream store's business peaks in late summer; the store's summer revenue is approximated by

$$R(t) = 300 + 4.5t - 0.05t^2 \text{ dollars per day} \quad (0 \le t \le 92)$$

where t is measured in days after June 1. What is its total revenue for the months of June, July, and August?

Solution Let's approximate the total revenue by breaking up the interval $[0, 92]$ representing the three months into n subintervals $[t_{k-1}, t_k]$, each with length Δt. In the interval $[t_{k-1}, t_k]$ the store receives money at a rate of approximately $R(t_{k-1})$ dollars per day for Δt days, so it will receive a total of $R(t_{k-1})\Delta t$ dollars. Over the whole summer, then, the store will receive approximately

$$R(t_0)\Delta t + R(t_1)\Delta t + \cdots + R(t_{n-1})\Delta t \text{ dollars.}$$

As we let n become large to better approximate the total revenue, this Riemann sum approaches the integral

$$\text{Total revenue} = \int_0^{92} R(t)\, dt.$$

Substituting the function we were given, we get

$$\text{Total revenue} = \int_0^{92} (300 + 4.5t - 0.05t^2)\, dt$$

$$= \left[300t + 2.25t^2 - \frac{0.05}{3}t^3 \right]_0^{92}$$

$$\approx \$33{,}666.$$

➡ **Before we go on...** We could approach the calculation in Example 4 another way: $R(t) = S'(t)$ where $S(t)$ is the total revenue earned up to day t. By the Fundamental Theorem of Calculus,

$$\text{Total revenue} = S(92) - S(0) = \int_0^{92} R(t)\, dt.$$

We did the calculation using Riemann sums mainly as practice for the next example. ∎

Generalizing Example 4, we can say the following:

Total Value of a Continuous Income Stream

If the rate of receipt of income is $R(t)$ dollars per unit of time, then the total income received from time $t = a$ to $t = b$ is

$$\text{Total value} = TV = \int_a^b R(t)\, dt$$

EXAMPLE 5 **Future Value**

Suppose the ice cream store in the preceding example deposits its receipts in an account paying 5% interest per year compounded continuously. How much money will it have in its account at the end of August?

Solution Now we have to take into account not only the revenue but also the interest it earns in the account. Again, we break the interval $[0, 92]$ into n subintervals. During the interval $[t_{k-1}, t_k]$, approximately $R(t_{k-1})\Delta t$ dollars are deposited in the account. That money will earn interest until the end of August, a period of $92 - t_{k-1}$ days, or

$(92 - t_{k-1})/365$ years. The formula for continuous compounding tells us that by the end of August, those $R(t_{k-1})\Delta t$ dollars will have turned into

$$R(t_{k-1})\Delta t e^{0.05(92-t_{k-1})/365} = R(t_{k-1})e^{0.05(92-t_{k-1})/365}\Delta t \text{ dollars.}$$

(Recall that 5% is the *annual* interest rate.) Adding up the contributions from each subinterval, we see that the total in the account at the end of August will be approximately

$$R(t_0)e^{0.05(92-t_0)/365}\Delta t + R(t_1)e^{0.05(92-t_1)/365}\Delta t + \cdots + R(t_{n-1})e^{0.05(92-t_{n-1})/365}\Delta t.$$

This is a Riemann sum; as n gets large the sum approaches the integral

$$\text{Future value} = FV = \int_0^{92} R(t)e^{0.05(92-t)/365}\,dt.$$

Substituting $R(t) = 300 + 4.5t - 0.05t^2$, we obtain

$$FV = \int_0^{92} (300 + 4.5t - 0.05t^2)e^{0.05(92-t)/365}\,dt$$

$$\approx \$33,880. \qquad \text{\small Using technology or integration by parts}$$

➡ **Before we go on...** The interest earned in the account in Example 5 was fairly small. (Compare this answer to that in Example 4.) Not only was the money in the account for only three months, but much of it was put in the account toward the end of that period, so had very little time to earn interest. ∎

Generalizing again, we have the following:

Future Value of a Continuous Income Stream

If the rate of receipt of income from time $t = a$ to $t = b$ is $R(t)$ dollars per unit of time and the income is deposited as it is received in an account paying interest at rate r per unit of time, compounded continuously, then the amount of money in the account at time $t = b$ is

$$\text{Future value} = FV = \int_a^b R(t)e^{r(b-t)}\,dt.$$

EXAMPLE 6 **Present Value**

You are thinking of buying the ice cream store discussed in the preceding two examples. What is its income stream worth to you on June 1? Assume that you have access to the same account paying 5% per year compounded continuously.

Solution The value of the income stream on June 1 is the amount of money that, if deposited June 1, would give you the same future value as the income stream will. If we let PV denote this "present value," its value after 92 days will be

$$PVe^{0.05 \times 92/365}.$$

We equate this with the future value of the income stream to get

$$PVe^{0.05 \times 92/365} = \int_0^{92} R(t)e^{0.05(92-t)/365} \, dt$$

so

$$PV = \int_0^{92} R(t)e^{-0.05t/365} \, dt.$$

Substituting the formula for $R(t)$ and integrating using technology or integration by parts, we get

$$PV \approx \$33,455.$$

The general formula is the following:

Present Value of a Continuous Income Stream

If the rate of receipt of income from time $t = a$ to $t = b$ is $R(t)$ dollars per unit of time and the income is deposited as it is received in an account paying interest at rate r per unit of time, compounded continuously, then the value of the income stream at time $t = a$ is

$$\text{Present value} = PV = \int_a^b R(t)e^{r(a-t)} \, dt.$$

We can derive this formula from the relation

$$FV = PVe^{r(b-a)}$$

because the present value is the amount that would have to be deposited at time $t = a$ to give a future value of FV at time $t = b$.

Note These formulas are more general than we've said. They still work when $R(t) < 0$ if we interpret negative values as money flowing *out* rather than in. That is, we can use these formulas for income we receive or for payments that we make, or for situations where we sometimes receive money and sometimes pay it out. These formulas can also be used for flows of quantities other than money. For example, if we use an exponential model for population growth and we let $R(t)$ represent the rate of immigration $[R(t) > 0]$ or emigration $[R(t) < 0]$, then the future value formula gives the future population. ■

14.4 EXERCISES

▼ more advanced   ◆ challenging
T indicates exercises that should be solved using technology

Calculate the consumers' surplus at the indicated unit price $\bar{p}$ for each of the demand equations in Exercises 1–12. HINT [See Example 1.]

1. $p = 10 - 2q$; $\bar{p} = 5$ **2.** $p = 100 - q$; $\bar{p} = 20$

3. $p = 100 - 3\sqrt{q}$; $\bar{p} = 76$ **4.** $p = 10 - 2q^{1/3}$; $\bar{p} = 6$

5. $p = 500e^{-2q}$; $\bar{p} = 100$ **6.** $p = 100 - e^{0.1q}$; $\bar{p} = 50$

7. $q = 100 - 2p$; $\bar{p} = 20$ **8.** $q = 50 - 3p$; $\bar{p} = 10$

9. $q = 100 - 0.25p^2$; $\bar{p} = 10$ **10.** $q = 20 - 0.05p^2$; $\bar{p} = 5$

11. $q = 500e^{-0.5p} - 50$; $\bar{p} = 1$ **12.** $q = 100 - e^{0.1p}$; $\bar{p} = 20$

Calculate the producers' surplus for each of the supply equations in Exercises 13–24 at the indicated unit price $\bar{p}$. HINT [See Example 2.]

13. $p = 10 + 2q$; $\bar{p} = 20$ **14.** $p = 100 + q$; $\bar{p} = 200$

15. $p = 10 + 2q^{1/3}$; $\bar{p} = 12$ **16.** $p = 100 + 3\sqrt{q}$; $\bar{p} = 124$

17. $p = 500e^{0.5q}$; $\bar{p} = 1,000$ **18.** $p = 100 + e^{0.01q}$; $\bar{p} = 120$

19. $q = 2p - 50$; $\bar{p} = 40$

20. $q = 4p - 1{,}000$; $\bar{p} = 1{,}000$

21. $q = 0.25p^2 - 10$; $\bar{p} = 10$

22. $q = 0.05p^2 - 20$; $\bar{p} = 50$

23. $q = 500e^{0.05p} - 50$; $\bar{p} = 10$

24. $q = 10(e^{0.1p} - 1)$; $\bar{p} = 5$

In Exercises 25–30, find the total value of the given income stream and also find its future value (at the end of the given interval) using the given interest rate. HINT [See Examples 4, 5.]

25. $R(t) = 30{,}000$, $0 \le t \le 10$, at 7%

26. $R(t) = 40{,}000$, $0 \le t \le 5$, at 10%

27. $R(t) = 30{,}000 + 1{,}000t$, $0 \le t \le 10$, at 7%

28. $R(t) = 40{,}000 + 2{,}000t$, $0 \le t \le 5$, at 10%

29. $R(t) = 30{,}000e^{0.05t}$, $0 \le t \le 10$, at 7%

30. $R(t) = 40{,}000e^{0.04t}$, $0 \le t \le 5$, at 10%

In Exercises 31–36, find the total value of the given income stream and also find its present value (at the beginning of the given interval) using the given interest rate. HINT [See Examples 4, 6.]

31. $R(t) = 20{,}000$, $0 \le t \le 5$, at 8%

32. $R(t) = 50{,}000$, $0 \le t \le 10$, at 5%

33. $R(t) = 20{,}000 + 1{,}000t$, $0 \le t \le 5$, at 8%

34. $R(t) = 50{,}000 + 2{,}000t$, $0 \le t \le 10$, at 5%

35. $R(t) = 20{,}000e^{0.03t}$, $0 \le t \le 5$, at 8%

36. $R(t) = 50{,}000e^{0.06t}$, $0 \le t \le 10$, at 5%

APPLICATIONS

37. *College Tuition* A study of U.S. colleges and universities resulted in the demand equation $q = 20{,}000 - 2p$, where q is the enrollment at a public college or university and p is the average annual tuition (plus fees) it charges.[35] Officials at Enormous State University have developed a policy whereby the number of students it will accept per year at a tuition level of p dollars is given by $q = 7{,}500 + 0.5p$. Find the equilibrium tuition price $\bar{p}$ and the consumers' and producers' surpluses at this tuition level. What is the total social gain at the equilibrium price? HINT [See Example 3.]

38. *Fast Food* A fast-food outlet finds that the demand equation for its new side dish, "Sweetdough Tidbit," is given by

$$p = \frac{128}{(q + 1)^2}$$

where p is the price (in cents) per serving and q is the number of servings that can be sold per hour at this price. At the same

time, the franchise is prepared to sell $q = 0.5p - 1$ servings per hour at a price of p cents. Find the equilibrium price $\bar{p}$ and the consumers' and producers' surpluses at this price level. What is the total social gain at the equilibrium price? HINT [See Example 3.]

39. ▼ *Linear Demand* Given a linear demand equation $q = -mp + b$ ($m > 0$), find a formula for the consumers' surplus at a price level of $\bar{p}$ per unit.

40. ▼ *Linear Supply* Given a linear supply equation of the form $q = mp + b$ ($m > 0$), find a formula for the producers' surplus at a price level of $\bar{p}$ per unit.

41. *Revenue:* Nokia The annual net sales (revenue) earned by Nokia in the years starting January 2000 to January 2008 can be approximated by

$$R(t) = 0.6t^2 - 2t + 30 \text{ billion euros per year}$$
$$(0 \le t \le 8)$$

where t is time in years ($t = 0$ represents January 2000).[36] Estimate, to the nearest €10 billion, Nokia's total revenue from January 2002 to January 2008. HINT [See Example 4.]

42. *Revenue:* Nintendo The annual net sales (revenue) earned by Nintendo Co., Ltd., in the fiscal years ending March 31, 2000 to March 31, 2008, can be approximated by

$$R(t) = 12t^3 - 100t^2 + 180t + 500 \text{ billion yen per year}$$
$$(0 \le t \le 8)$$

where t is time in years ($t = 0$ represents March 31, 2000).[37] Estimate, to the nearest ¥100 billion, Nintendo's total revenue from March 31, 2002 to March 31, 2006. HINT [See Example 4.]

43. *Revenue:* Wal-Mart The annual revenue earned by Wal-Mart in the years starting January 2000 to January 2008 can be approximated by

$$R(t) = 162e^{0.11t} \text{ billion dollars per year} \quad (0 \le t \le 8)$$

where t is time in years ($t = 0$ represents January 2000).[38] Estimate, to the nearest $10 billion, Wal-Mart's total revenue from January 2000 to January 2006.

44. *Revenue:* Target The annual revenue earned by Target for fiscal years 1998 through 2008 can be approximated by

$$R(t) = 27e^{0.11t} \text{ billion dollars per year} \quad (0 \le t \le 8)$$

where t is time in years ($t = 0$ represents the beginning of fiscal year 2000).[39] Estimate, to the nearest $10 billion, Target's total revenue from the beginning of fiscal year 2004 to the beginning of fiscal year 2008.

---

[35] Idea based on a study by A. L. Ostrosky, Jr. and J. V. Koch, as cited in their book, *Introduction to Mathematical Economics* (Waveland Press, Illinois, 1979, p. 133). The data used here are fictitious, however.

[36] Source for data: Nokia financial statements (www.investors.nokia.com).

[37] Source for data: Nintendo annual reports (www.nintendo.com/corp).

[38] Source for data: Wal-Mart annual reports (www.walmartstores.com/Investors).

[39] The model is based on an exponential regression. Source for data: Target 2003 annual report (www.targetcorp.com).

45. ▼ *Revenue* Refer to Exercise 41. Suppose that, from January 2000 on, **Nokia** invested its revenue in an investment yielding 4% compounded continuously. What, to the nearest €10 billion, would the total value of **Nokia**'s revenue from January 2002 to January 2008 have been as of January 2008? HINT [See Example 5.]

46. ▼ *Revenue* Refer to Exercise 42. Suppose that, from March 2000 on, **Nintendo** invested its revenue in an investment yielding 5% compounded continuously. What, to the nearest ¥100 billion, would the total value of **Nintendo**'s revenue from March 31, 2002 to March 31, 2006 have been as of March 31, 2006? HINT [See Example 5.]

47. ▼ *Revenue* Refer to Exercise 43. Suppose that, from January 2000 on, **Wal-Mart** invested its revenue in an investment that depreciated continuously at a rate of 5% per year. What, to the nearest $10 billion, would the total value of **Wal-Mart**'s revenues from January 2000 to January 2006 have been?

48. ▼ *Revenue* Refer to Exercise 44. Suppose that, from the start of fiscal year 2004 on, **Target** invested its revenue in an investment that depreciated continuously at a rate of 3% per year. What, to the nearest $10 billion, would the total value of **Target**'s revenue from the beginning of fiscal year 2004 to the beginning of fiscal year 2008 have been?

49. ▼ *Saving for Retirement* You are saving for your retirement by investing $700 per month in an annuity with a guaranteed interest rate of 6% per year. With a continuous stream of investment and continuous compounding, how much will you have accumulated in the annuity by the time you retire in 45 years?

50. ▼ *Saving for College* When your first child is born, you begin to save for college by depositing $400 per month in an account paying 12% interest per year. With a continuous stream of investment and continuous compounding, how much will you have accumulated in the account by the time your child enters college 18 years later?

51. ▼ *Saving for Retirement* You begin saving for your retirement by investing $700 per month in an annuity with a guaranteed interest rate of 6% per year. You increase the amount you invest at the rate of 3% per year. With continuous investment and compounding, how much will you have accumulated in the annuity by the time you retire in 45 years?

52. ▼ *Saving for College* When your first child is born, you begin to save for college by depositing $400 per month in an account paying 12% interest per year. You increase the amount you save by 2% per year. With continuous investment and compounding, how much will have accumulated in the account by the time your child enters college 18 years later?

53. ▼ *Bonds* The U.S. Treasury issued a 30-year bond on October 15, 2001, paying 3.375% interest.[40] Thus, if you bought

$100,000 worth of these bonds you would receive $3,375 per year in interest for 30 years. An investor wishes to buy the rights to receive the interest on $100,000 worth of these bonds. The amount the investor is willing to pay is the present value of the interest payments, assuming a 4% rate of return. Assuming (incorrectly, but approximately) that the interest payments are made continuously, what will the investor pay? HINT [See Example 6.]

54. ▼ *Bonds* The Megabucks Corporation is issuing a 20-year bond paying 7% interest. (See the preceding exercise.) An investor wishes to buy the rights to receive the interest on $50,000 worth of these bonds, and seeks a 6% rate of return. Assuming that the interest payments are made continuously, what will the investor pay? HINT [See Example 6.]

55. ▼ *Valuing Future Income* Inga was injured and can no longer work. As a result of a lawsuit, she is to be awarded the present value of the income she would have received over the next 20 years. Her income at the time she was injured was $100,000 per year, increasing by $5,000 per year. What will be the amount of her award, assuming continuous income and a 5% interest rate?

56. ▼ *Valuing Future Income* Max was injured and can no longer work. As a result of a lawsuit, he is to be awarded the present value of the income he would have received over the next 30 years. His income at the time he was injured was $30,000 per year, increasing by $1,500 per year. What will be the amount of his award, assuming continuous income and a 6% interest rate?

COMMUNICATION AND REASONING EXERCISES

57. Complete the following: The future value of a continuous income stream earning 0% interest is the same as the _____ value.

58. Complete the following: The present value of a continuous income stream earning 0% interest is the same as the _____ value.

59. ▼ Your study group friend says that the future value of a continuous stream of income is always greater than the total value, assuming a positive rate of return. Is she correct? Why?

60. ▼ Your other study group friend says that the present value of a continuous stream of income can sometimes be greater than the total value, depending on the (positive) interest rate. Is he correct? Explain.

61. ▼ Arrange from smallest to largest: Total Value, Future Value, Present Value of a continuous stream of income (assuming a positive income and positive rate of return).

62. ▼ **a.** Arrange the following functions from smallest to largest: $R(t)$, $R(t)e^{r(b-t)}$, $R(t)e^{r(a-t)}$, where $a \le t \le b$, and r and $R(t)$ are positive.
b. Use the result from part (a) to justify your answers in Exercises 59–61.

---

[40]Note: The U.S. Treasury suspended selling Treasury Bonds after October 2001, but resumed issuing them in February, 2006. Source: The Bureau of the Public Debt (www.publicdebt.treas.gov).

14.5 Improper Integrals and Applications

All the definite integrals we have seen so far have had the form $\int_a^b f(x)\,dx$, with a and b finite and $f(x)$ piecewise continuous on the closed interval $[a, b]$. If we relax one or both of these requirements somewhat, we obtain what are called **improper integrals**. There are various types of improper integrals.

Integrals in Which a Limit of Integration is Infinite

Integrals in which one or more limits of integration are infinite can be written as

$$\int_a^{+\infty} f(x)\,dx, \quad \int_{-\infty}^b f(x)\,dx, \quad \text{or} \quad \int_{-\infty}^{+\infty} f(x)\,dx.$$

Let's concentrate for a moment on the first form, $\int_a^{+\infty} f(x)\,dx$. What does the $+\infty$ mean here? As it often does, it means that we are to take a limit as something gets large. Specifically, it means the limit as the upper bound of integration gets large.

Improper Integral with an Infinite Limit of Integration

We define

$$\int_a^{+\infty} f(x)\,dx = \lim_{M \to +\infty} \int_a^M f(x)\,dx,$$

provided the limit exists. If the limit exists, we say that $\int_a^{+\infty} f(x)\,dx$ **converges**. Otherwise, we say that $\int_a^{+\infty} f(x)\,dx$ **diverges**. Similarly, we define

$$\int_{-\infty}^b f(x)\,dx = \lim_{M \to -\infty} \int_M^b f(x)\,dx,$$

provided the limit exists. Finally, we define

$$\int_{-\infty}^{+\infty} f(x)\,dx = \int_{-\infty}^a f(x)\,dx + \int_a^{+\infty} f(x)\,dx$$

for some convenient a, provided *both* integrals on the right converge.

Quick Examples

1. $\displaystyle \int_1^{+\infty} \frac{dx}{x^2} = \lim_{M \to +\infty} \int_1^M \frac{dx}{x^2} = \lim_{M \to +\infty} \left[-\frac{1}{x} \right]_1^M = \lim_{M \to +\infty} \left(-\frac{1}{M} + 1 \right) = 1$

    Converges

2. $\displaystyle \int_1^{+\infty} \frac{dx}{x} = \lim_{M \to +\infty} \int_1^M \frac{dx}{x} = \lim_{M \to +\infty} \left[\ln|x| \right]_1^M = \lim_{M \to +\infty} (\ln M - \ln 1) = +\infty$

    Diver

3. $\displaystyle \int_{-\infty}^{-1} \frac{dx}{x^2} = \lim_{M \to -\infty} \int_M^{-1} \frac{dx}{x^2} = \lim_{M \to -\infty} \left[-\frac{1}{x} \right]_M^{-1} = \lim_{M \to -\infty} \left(1 + \frac{1}{M} \right)$

4. $\displaystyle\int_{-\infty}^{+\infty} e^{-x}\,dx = \int_{-\infty}^{0} e^{-x}\,dx + \int_{0}^{+\infty} e^{-x}\,dx$

$\displaystyle= \lim_{M\to-\infty} \int_{M}^{0} e^{-x}\,dx + \lim_{M\to+\infty} \int_{0}^{M} e^{-x}\,dx$

$\displaystyle= \lim_{M\to-\infty} -[e^{-x}]_{M}^{0} + \lim_{M\to+\infty} -[e^{-x}]_{0}^{M}$

$\displaystyle= \lim_{M\to-\infty} (e^{-M} - 1) + \lim_{M\to+\infty} (1 - e^{-M})$

$\displaystyle= +\infty + 1$ 　　　　　　　　　　　　　　　　　　Diverges

5. $\displaystyle\int_{-\infty}^{+\infty} xe^{-x^2}\,dx = \int_{-\infty}^{0} xe^{-x^2}\,dx + \int_{0}^{+\infty} xe^{-x^2}\,dx$

$\displaystyle= \lim_{M\to-\infty} \int_{M}^{0} xe^{-x^2}\,dx + \lim_{M\to+\infty} \int_{0}^{M} xe^{-x^2}\,dx$

$\displaystyle= \lim_{M\to-\infty} \left[-\frac{1}{2}e^{-x^2}\right]_{M}^{0} + \lim_{M\to+\infty} \left[-\frac{1}{2}e^{-x^2}\right]_{0}^{M}$

$\displaystyle= \lim_{M\to-\infty} \left(-\frac{1}{2} + \frac{1}{2}e^{-M^2}\right) + \lim_{M\to+\infty} \left(-\frac{1}{2}e^{-M^2} + \frac{1}{2}\right)$

$\displaystyle= -\frac{1}{2} + \frac{1}{2} = 0$ 　　　　　　　　　　　　　　Converges

Q: *We learned that the integral can be interpreted as the area under the curve. Is this still true for improper integrals?*

A: Yes. Figure 21 illustrates how we can represent an improper integral as the area of an infinite region.

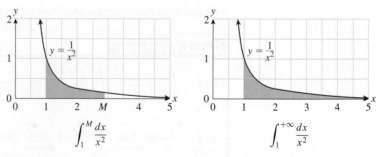

Figure 21

On the left we see the area represented by $\int_{1}^{M} dx/x^2$. As M gets larger, the integral approaches $\int_{1}^{+\infty} dx/x^2$. In the picture, think of M being moved farther and farther along the x-axis in the direction of increasing x, resulting in the region shown on the right.

Q :*Wait! We calculated $\int_{1}^{+\infty} dx/x^2 = 1$. Does this mean that the infinitely long area in Figure 21 has an area of only 1 square unit?*

A :That is exactly what it means. If you had enough paint to cover 1 square unit, you would never run out of paint while painting the region in Figure 21. This is one of the places where mathematics seems to contradict common sense. But common sense is notoriously unreliable when dealing with infinities.

EXAMPLE 1 Future Sales of CDs

In 2006, music downloads were starting to make inroads into the sales of CDs.* Approximately 140 million CD albums were sold in the first quarter of 2006, and sales declined by about 3.5% per quarter for the following 2 years. Suppose that this rate of decrease were to continue indefinitely. How many CD albums, total, would be sold from the first quarter of 2006 on?

Solution Recall that the total sales between two dates can be computed as the definite integral of the rate of sales. So, if we wanted the sales between the first quarter of 2006 and a time far in the future, we would compute $\int_{0}^{M} s(t)\, dt$ with a large M, where $s(t)$ is the quarterly sales t quarters after the first quarter of 2006. Because we want to know the *total* number of CD albums sold from the first quarter of 2006 on, we let $M \to +\infty$; that is, we compute $\int_{0}^{+\infty} s(t)\, dt$.

Because sales of CD albums are decreasing by 3.5% per quarter, we can model $s(t)$ by

$$s(t) = 140(0.965)^t \text{ million CD albums}$$

where t is the number of quarters since the first quarter of 2006.

$$
\begin{aligned}
\text{Total sales from the first quarter of 2006 on} &= \int_{0}^{+\infty} 140(0.965)^t\, dt \\
&= \lim_{M \to +\infty} \int_{0}^{M} 140(0.965)^t\, dt \\
&= \frac{140}{\ln 0.965} \lim_{M \to +\infty} [0.965^t]_0^M \\
&= \frac{140}{\ln 0.965} \lim_{M \to +\infty} (0.965^M - 0.965^0) \\
&= \frac{140}{\ln 0.965}(-1) \\
&\approx 3929.6 \text{ million CD albums.}
\end{aligned}
$$

*Source: "Album sales decline, but is the slump slowing?" USA Today, (www.usatoday.com/life/music/news/2008-04-02-album-sales_N.htm) April 3, 2008.

Getty Images

using Technology

You can estimate the integral in Example 1 with technology by computing $\int_{0}^{M} 140(0.965)^t\, dt$ for $M = 10, 100, 1000, \ldots$. You will find that the resulting values appear to converge to about 3,929.6. (Stop when the effect of further increases of M has no effect at this level of accuracy.)

TI-83/84 Plus
Y₁=140*0.965^X
Home screen:
fnInt(Y₁,X,0,10)
fnInt(Y₁,X,0,100)
fnInt(Y₁,X,0,1000)

Web Site
www.FiniteandCalc.org:
  Online Utilities
  → Numerical Integration
    Utility
Enter
140*0.965^X
for $f(x)$. Enter 0 and 10 for the left and right end-points and press "Adaptive Quadrature" for the most accurate estimate of the integral. Repeat with the right end-point set to 100, 1000, and higher.

Integrals in Which the Integrand Becomes Infinite

We can sometimes compute integrals $\int_{a}^{b} f(x)\, dx$ in which $f(x)$ becomes infinite. As we'll see in Example 4, the Fundamental Theorem of Calculus does not work for such integrals. The first case to consider is when $f(x)$ approaches $\pm\infty$ at either a or b.

Figure 22

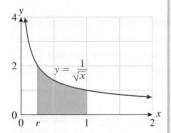

Figure 23

EXAMPLE 2 Integrand Infinite at One Endpoint

Calculate $\int_0^1 \dfrac{1}{\sqrt{x}}\,dx$.

Solution Notice that the integrand approaches $+\infty$ as x approaches 0 from the right and is not defined at 0. This makes the integral an improper integral. Figure 22 shows the region whose area we are trying to calculate; it extends infinitely vertically rather than horizontally.

Now, if $0 < r < 1$, the integral $\int_r^1 (1/\sqrt{x})\,dx$ is a proper integral because we avoid the bad behavior at 0. This integral gives the area shown in Figure 23. If we let r approach 0 from the right, the area in Figure 23 will approach the area in Figure 22. So, we calculate

$$\int_0^1 \frac{1}{\sqrt{x}}\,dx = \lim_{r \to 0^+} \int_r^1 \frac{1}{\sqrt{x}}\,dx$$

$$= \lim_{r \to 0^+} [2\sqrt{x}]_r^1$$

$$= \lim_{r \to 0^+} (2 - 2\sqrt{r})$$

$$= 2.$$

Thus, we again have an infinitely long region with finite area.

Generalizing, we make the following definition.

Improper Integral in Which the Integrand Becomes Infinite

If $f(x)$ is defined for all x with $a < x \le b$ but approaches $\pm\infty$ as x approaches a, we define

$$\int_a^b f(x)\,dx = \lim_{r \to a^+} \int_r^b f(x)\,dx$$

provided the limit exists. Similarly, if $f(x)$ is defined for all x with $a \le x < b$ but approaches $\pm\infty$ as x approaches b, we define

$$\int_a^b f(x)\,dx = \lim_{r \to b^-} \int_a^r f(x)\,dx$$

provided the limit exists. In either case, if the limit exists, we say that $\int_a^b f(x)\,dx$ **converges**. Otherwise, we say that $\int_a^b f(x)\,dx$ **diverges**.

Note We saw in Chapter 13 that the Fundamental Theorem of Calculus applies to piecewise continuous functions as well as continuous ones. Examples are $f(x) = |x|/x$ and $(x^2 - 1)/(x - 1)$. The integrals of such functions are not improper, and we can use the Fundamental Theorem of Calculus to evaluate such integrals in the usual way. ∎

EXAMPLE 3 Testing for Convergence

Does $\int_{-1}^{3} \dfrac{x}{x^2 - 9}\, dx$ converge? If so, to what?

Solution We first check to see where, if anywhere, the integrand approaches $\pm\infty$. That will happen where the denominator becomes 0, so we solve $x^2 - 9 = 0$.

$$x^2 - 9 = 0$$
$$x^2 = 9$$
$$x = \pm 3$$

The solution $x = -3$ is outside of the range of integration, so we ignore it. The solution $x = 3$ is, however, the right endpoint of the range of integration, so the integral is improper. We need to investigate the following limit:

$$\int_{-1}^{3} \frac{x}{x^2 - 9}\, dx = \lim_{r \to 3^-} \int_{-1}^{r} \frac{x}{x^2 - 9}\, dx.$$

Now, to calculate the integral we use a substitution:

$$u = x^2 - 9$$
$$\frac{du}{dx} = 2x$$
$$dx = \frac{1}{2x}\, du$$
$$\text{when } x = r,\, u = r^2 - 9$$
$$\text{when } x = -1,\, u = (-1)^2 - 9 = -8$$

Thus,

$$\int_{-1}^{r} \frac{x}{x^2 - 9}\, dx = \int_{-8}^{r^2 - 9} \frac{1}{2u}\, du$$

$$= \frac{1}{2}\left[\ln |u|\right]_{-8}^{r^2 - 9}$$

$$= \frac{1}{2}\left(\ln |r^2 - 9| - \ln 8\right).$$

Now we take the limit:

$$\int_{-1}^{3} \frac{x}{x^2 - 9}\, dx = \lim_{r \to 3^-} \int_{-1}^{r} \frac{x}{x^2 - 9}\, dx$$

$$= \lim_{r \to 3^-} \frac{1}{2}\left(\ln |r^2 - 9| - \ln 8\right)$$

$$= -\infty$$

because, as $r \to 3$, $r^2 - 9 \to 0$, and so $\ln |r^2 - 9| \to -\infty$. Thus, this integral diverges.

EXAMPLE 4 **Integrand Infinite Between the Endpoints**

Does $\displaystyle\int_{-2}^{3} \frac{1}{x^2}\, dx$ converge? If so, to what?

Solution Again we check to see if there are any points at which the integrand approaches $\pm\infty$. There is such a point, at $x = 0$. This is between the endpoints of the range of integration. To deal with this we break the integral into two integrals:

$$\int_{-2}^{3} \frac{1}{x^2}\, dx = \int_{-2}^{0} \frac{1}{x^2}\, dx + \int_{0}^{3} \frac{1}{x^2}\, dx.$$

Each integral on the right is an improper integral with the integrand approaching $\pm\infty$ at an endpoint. If both of the integrals on the right converge, we take the sum as the value of the integral on the left. So now we compute

$$\int_{-2}^{0} \frac{1}{x^2}\, dx = \lim_{r \to 0^-} \int_{-2}^{r} \frac{1}{x^2}\, dx$$

$$= \lim_{r \to 0^-} \left[-\frac{1}{x} \right]_{-2}^{r}$$

$$= \lim_{r \to 0^-} \left(-\frac{1}{r} - \frac{1}{2} \right),$$

which diverges to $+\infty$. There is no need now to check $\int_{0}^{3}(1/x^2)\, dx$; because one of the two pieces of the integral diverges, we simply say that $\int_{-2}^{3}(1/x^2)\, dx$ diverges.

➡**Before we go on...**   What if we had been sloppy in Example 4 and had not checked first whether the integrand approached $\pm\infty$ somewhere? Then we probably would have applied the Fundamental Theorem of Calculus and done the following:

$$\int_{-2}^{3} \frac{1}{x^2}\, dx = \left(-\frac{1}{x} \right)_{-2}^{3} = \left(-\frac{1}{3} - \frac{1}{2} \right) = -\frac{5}{6} \qquad \text{✗ } \textit{WRONG!}$$

Notice that the answer this "calculation" gives is patently ridiculous. Because $1/x^2 > 0$ for all x for which it is defined, any definite integral of $1/x^2$ must give a positive answer. *Moral:* Always check to see whether the integrand blows up anywhere in the range of integration. If it does, the FTC does not apply, and we must use the methods of this example. ∎

We end with an example of what to do if an integral is improper for more than one reason.

EXAMPLE 5 **An Integral Improper in Two Ways**

Does $\int_0^{+\infty} \dfrac{1}{\sqrt{x}}\, dx$ converge? If so, to what?

Solution This integral is improper for two reasons. First, the range of integration is infinite. Second, the integrand blows up at the endpoint 0. In order to separate these two problems, we break up the integral at some convenient point:

$$\int_0^{+\infty} \frac{1}{\sqrt{x}}\, dx = \int_0^1 \frac{1}{\sqrt{x}}\, dx + \int_1^{+\infty} \frac{1}{\sqrt{x}}\, dx$$

We chose to break the integral at 1. Any positive number would have sufficed, but 1 is generally easier to use in calculations.

   The first piece, $\int_0^1 (1/\sqrt{x})\, dx$, we discussed in Example 2; it converges to 2. For the second piece we have

$$\int_1^{+\infty} \frac{1}{\sqrt{x}}\, dx = \lim_{M \to +\infty} \int_1^M \frac{1}{\sqrt{x}}\, dx$$
$$= \lim_{M \to +\infty} [2\sqrt{x}]_1^M$$
$$= \lim_{M \to +\infty} (2\sqrt{M} - 2),$$

which diverges to $+\infty$. Because the second piece of the integral diverges, we conclude that $\int_0^{+\infty} (1/\sqrt{x})\, dx$ diverges.

14.5 EXERCISES

▼ more advanced   ◆ challenging
⊞ indicates exercises that should be solved using technology

Note: For some of the exercises in this section you need to assume the fact that $\lim_{M \to +\infty} M^n e^{-M} = 0$ *for all n.*

In Exercises 1–26, decide whether or not the given integral converges. If the integral converges, compute its value. HINT [See Quick Examples page 1051.]

1. $\int_1^{+\infty} x\, dx$

2. $\int_0^{+\infty} e^{-x}\, dx$

3. $\int_{-2}^{+\infty} e^{-0.5x}\, dx$

4. $\int_1^{+\infty} \dfrac{1}{x^{1.5}}\, dx$

5. $\int_{-\infty}^2 e^x\, dx$

6. $\int_{-\infty}^{-1} \dfrac{1}{x^{1/3}}\, dx$

7. $\int_{-\infty}^{-2} \dfrac{1}{x^2}\, dx$

8. $\int_{-\infty}^0 e^{-x}\, dx$

9. $\int_0^{+\infty} x^2 e^{-6x}\, dx$

10. $\int_0^{+\infty} (2x - 4)e^{-x}\, dx$

11. $\int_0^5 \dfrac{2}{x^{1/3}}\, dx$ HINT [See Example 2.]

12. $\int_0^2 \dfrac{1}{x^2}\, dx$

13. $\int_{-1}^2 \dfrac{3}{(x + 1)^2}\, dx$ HINT [See Example 3.]

14. $\int_{-1}^2 \dfrac{3}{(x + 1)^{1/2}}\, dx$

15. $\int_{-1}^2 \dfrac{3x}{x^2 - 1}\, dx$ HINT [See Example 4.]

16. $\int_{-1}^2 \dfrac{3}{x^{1/3}}\, dx$

17. $\int_{-2}^2 \dfrac{1}{(x + 1)^{1/5}}\, dx$

18. $\int_{-2}^2 \dfrac{2x}{\sqrt{4 - x^2}}\, dx$

19. $\int_{-1}^1 \dfrac{2x}{x^2 - 1}\, dx$

20. $\int_{-1}^2 \dfrac{2x}{x^2 - 1}\, dx$

21. $\displaystyle\int_{-\infty}^{+\infty} x e^{-x^2}\, dx$

22. $\displaystyle\int_{-\infty}^{\infty} x e^{1-x^2}\, dx$

23. $\displaystyle\int_{0}^{+\infty} \frac{1}{x \ln x}\, dx$ HINT [See Example 5.]

24. $\displaystyle\int_{0}^{+\infty} \ln x\, dx$

25. ▼ $\displaystyle\int_{0}^{+\infty} \frac{2x}{x^2 - 1}\, dx$

26. ▼ $\displaystyle\int_{-\infty}^{0} \frac{2x}{x^2 - 1}\, dx$

▣ *In Exercises 27–34 use technology to approximate the given integrals with $M = 10, 100, 1,000,\ldots$ and hence decide whether the associated improper integral converges and estimate its value to four significant digits if it does.* HINT [See the Technology Note for Example 1.]

27. $\displaystyle\int_{1}^{M} \frac{1}{x^2}\, dx$

28. $\displaystyle\int_{0}^{M} e^{-x^2}\, dx$

29. $\displaystyle\int_{0}^{M} \frac{x}{1+x}\, dx$

30. $\displaystyle\int_{1/M}^{1} \frac{1}{\sqrt{x}}\, dx$

31. $\displaystyle\int_{1+1/M}^{2} \frac{1}{\sqrt{x-1}}\, dx$

32. $\displaystyle\int_{1}^{M} \frac{1}{x}\, dx$

33. $\displaystyle\int_{0}^{1-1/M} \frac{1}{(1-x)^2}\, dx$

34. $\displaystyle\int_{0}^{2-1/M} \frac{1}{(2-x)^3}\, dx$

APPLICATIONS

35. *New Home Sales* Sales of new homes in the United States decreased dramatically from 2006 to 2008, as shown in the model

$$n(t) = 1.05 e^{-0.376t} \text{ million homes per year}\quad (0 \le t \le 2)$$

where t is the year since 2006.[41] If this trend were to have continued into the indefinite future, estimate the total number of new homes that would have been sold in the United States from 2006 on. HINT [See Example 1.]

36. *Revenue from New Home Sales* Revenue from the sale of new homes in the United States decreased dramatically from 2006 to 2008 as shown in the model

$$r(t) = 321 e^{-0.429t} \text{ billion dollars per year}\quad (0 \le t \le 2)$$

where t is the year since 2006.[42] If this trend were to have continued into the indefinite future, estimate the total revenue

from the sale of new homes in the United States from 2006 on. HINT [See Example 1.]

37. *Cigarette Sales* According to data published by the Federal Trade Commission, the number of cigarettes sold domestically has been decreasing by about 3% per year from the 2000 total of about 415 billion.[43] Use an exponential model to forecast the total number of cigarettes sold from 2000 on. (Round your answer to the nearest 100 billion cigarettes.) HINT [Use a model of the form Ab^t.]

38. *Sales* Sales of the text *Calculus and You* have been declining continuously at a rate of 5% per year. Assuming that *Calculus and You* currently sells 5,000 copies per year and that sales will continue this pattern of decline, calculate total future sales of the text. HINT [Use a model of the form Ae^{rt}.]

39. ▼ *Sales* My financial adviser has predicted that annual sales of Frodo T-shirts will continue to decline by 10% each year. At the moment, I have 3,200 of the shirts in stock and am selling them at a rate of 200 per year. Will I ever sell them all?

40. ▼ *Revenue* Alarmed about the sales prospects for my Frodo T-shirts (see the preceding exercise), I will try to make up lost revenues by increasing the price by $1 each year. I now charge $10 per shirt. What is the total amount of revenue I can expect to earn from sales of my T-shirts, assuming the sales levels described in the previous exercise? (Give your answer to the nearest $1,000.)

41. ▼ *Education* Let $N(t)$ be the number of high school students graduated in the United States in year t. This number is projected to change at a rate of about

$$N'(t) = 0.20 t^{-0.93} \text{ million graduates per year}\quad (1 \le t \le 21)$$

where t is time in years since 2000.[44] In 2001, there were about 2.8 million high school students graduated. By extrapolating the model, what can you say about the number of high school students graduated in a year far in the future?

42. ▼ *Education, Martian* Let $M(t)$ be the number of high school students graduated in the Republic of Mars in year t. This number is projected to change at a rate of about

$$M'(t) = 0.321 t^{-1.10} \text{ thousand graduates per year}$$
$$(1 \le t \le 50)$$

where t is time in years since 2020. In 2021, there were about 1,300 high school students graduated. By extrapolating the model, what can you say about the number of high school students graduated in a year far in the future?

---

[41] Based on new home sales data at www.census.gov.

[42] Ibid.

[43] Source for data: Federal Trade Commission Cigarette Report for 2004 and 2005 available at www.ftc.gov.

[44] Based on a regression model. Source for data: U.S. Department of Education, 2002 (www.nces.ed.gov/).

43. ▼ *Cell Phone Revenues* The number of cell phone subscribers in China in the early 2000s was projected to follow the equation,[45]

$$N(t) = 39t + 68 \text{ million subscribers}$$

in year t ($t = 0$ represents 2000). The average annual revenue per cell phone user was \$350 in 2000.

a. Assuming that, due to competition, the revenue per cell phone user decreases continuously at an annual rate of 10%, give a formula for the annual revenue in year t.

b. Using the model you obtained in part (a) as an estimate of the rate of change of total revenue, estimate the total revenue from 2000 into the indefinite future.

44. ▼ *Vid Phone Revenues* The number of vid phone subscribers in the Republic of Mars for the period 2200–2300 was projected to follow the equation

$$N(t) = 18t - 10 \text{ thousand subscribers}$$

in year t ($t = 0$ represents 2200). The average annual revenue per vid phone user was $\overline{Z}40$ in 2200.[46]

a. Assuming that, due to competition, the revenue per vid phone user decreases continuously at an annual rate of 20%, give a formula for the annual revenue in year t.

b. Using the model you obtained in part (a) as an estimate of the rate of change of total revenue, estimate the total revenue from 2200 into the indefinite future.

45. ⊞ *Development Assistance* According to data published by the World Bank, development assistance to low income countries from 2000 through 2008 was approximately

$$q(t) = 0.2t^2 + 3.5t + 60 \text{ billion dollars per year}$$

where t is time in years since 2000.[47] Assuming a world-wide inflation rate of 3% per year, and that the above model remains accurate into the indefinite future, find the value of all development assistance to low income countries from 2000 on in constant dollars. (The constant dollar value of $q(t)$ dollars t years from now is given by $q(t)e^{-rt}$, where r is the fractional rate of inflation. Give your answer to the nearest \$100 billion.) HINT [See Technology Note for Example 1.]

46. ⊞ *Humanitarian Aid* Repeat the preceding exercise, using the following model for humanitarian aid.[48]

$$q(t) = 0.07t^2 + 0.3t + 5 \text{ billion dollars per year}$$

---

[45] Based on a regression of projected figures (coefficients are rounded). Source: Intrinsic Technology/*New York Times*, Nov. 24, 2000, p. C1.

[46] $\overline{Z}$ designates Zonars, the designated currency for the city-state of Utarek, Mars. Source: (www.marsnext.com/comm/zonars.html).

[47] The authors' approximation, based on data from the World Bank, obtained from www.worldbank.org.

[48] Ibid.

47. ▼ *Hair Mousse Sales* The amount of extremely popular hair mousse sold online at your Web site can be approximated by

$$N(t) = \frac{80(7)^t}{20 + 7^t} \text{ million gallons per year.}$$

($t = 0$ represents the current year.) Investigate the integrals $\int_0^{+\infty} N(t)\, dt$ and $\int_{-\infty}^0 N(t)\, dt$ and interpret your answers.

48. ▼ *Chocolate Mousse Sales* The weekly demand for your company's Lo-Cal Mousse is modeled by the equation

$$q(t) = \frac{50e^{2t-1}}{1 + e^{2t-1}} \text{ gallons per week}$$

where t is time from now in weeks. Investigate the integrals $\int_0^{+\infty} q(t)\, dt$ and $\int_{-\infty}^0 q(t)\, dt$ and interpret your answers.

⊞ *The Normal Curve* Exercises 49–52 require the use of a graphing calculator or computer programmed to do numerical integration. The normal distribution curve, which models the distributions of data in a wide range of applications, is given by the function

$$p(x) = \frac{1}{\sqrt{2\pi}\,\sigma} e^{-(x-\mu)^2/2\sigma^2}$$

where $\pi = 3.14159265....$ and σ and μ are constants called the standard deviation and the mean, respectively. Its graph (for $\sigma = 1$ and $\mu = 2$) is shown in the figure.

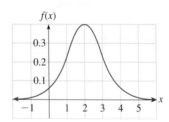

49. ▼ With $\sigma = 4$ and $\mu = 1$, approximate $\int_{-\infty}^{+\infty} p(x)\, dx$. HINT [See Example 5 and Technology Note for Example 1.]

50. ▼ With $\sigma = 1$ and $\mu = 0$, approximate $\int_0^{+\infty} p(x)\, dx$.

51. ▼ With $\sigma = 1$ and $\mu = 0$, approximate $\int_1^{+\infty} p(x)\, dx$.

52. ▼ With $\sigma = 1$ and $\mu = 0$, approximate $\int_{-\infty}^1 p(x)\, dx$.

53. ◆ *Variable Sales* The value of your Chateau Petit Mont Blanc 1963 vintage burgundy is increasing continuously at an annual rate of 40%, and you have a supply of 1,000 bottles worth \$85 each at today's prices. In order to ensure a steady income, you have decided to sell your wine at a diminishing rate—starting at 500 bottles per year, and then decreasing this figure continuously at a fractional rate of 100% per year. How much income (to the nearest dollar) can you expect to generate by this scheme? HINT [Use the formula for continuously compounded interest.]

54. ◆ Panic Sales Unfortunately, your large supply of Chateau Petit Mont Blanc is continuously turning to vinegar at a fractional rate of 60% per year! You have thus decided to sell off your Petit Mont Blanc at $50 per bottle, but the market is a little thin, and you can only sell 400 bottles per year. Because you have no way of knowing which bottles now contain vinegar until they are opened, you shall have to give refunds for all the bottles of vinegar. What will your net income be before all the wine turns to vinegar?

55. ◆ Meteor Impacts The frequency of meteor impacts on earth can be modeled by

$$n(k) = \frac{1}{5.6997k^{1.081}}$$

where $n(k) = N'(k)$, and $N(k)$ is the average number of meteors of energy less than or equal to k megatons that will hit the earth in one year.[49] (A small nuclear bomb releases on the order of one megaton of energy.)

a. How many meteors of energy at least $k = 0.2$ hit the earth each year?

b. Investigate and interpret the integral $\int_0^1 n(k)\, dk$.

56. ◆ Meteor Impacts (continuing the previous exercise)

a. Explain why the integral

$$\int_a^b kn(k)\, dk$$

computes the total energy released each year by meteors with energies between a and b megatons.

b. Compute and interpret

$$\int_0^1 kn(k)\, dk.$$

c. Compute and interpret

$$\int_1^{+\infty} kn(k)\, dk.$$

57. ◆ The Gamma Function The gamma function is defined by the formula

$$\Gamma(x) = \int_0^{+\infty} t^{x-1}e^{-t}\, dt.$$

a. Find $\Gamma(1)$ and $\Gamma(2)$.

b. Use integration by parts to show that for every positive integer n, $\Gamma(n + 1) = n\Gamma(n)$.

c. Deduce that $\Gamma(n) = (n - 1)! \left[= (n - 1)(n - 2)\cdots 2 \cdot 1\right]$ for every positive integer n.

---

[49] The authors' model, based on data published by NASA International Near-Earth-Object Detection Workshop (*The New York Times*, Jan. 25, 1994, p. C1).

58. ◆ Laplace Transforms The Laplace Transform $F(x)$ of a function $f(t)$ is given by the formula

$$F(x) = \int_0^{+\infty} f(t)e^{-xt}\, dt \quad (x > 0).$$

a. Find $F(x)$ for $f(t) = 1$ and for $f(t) = t$.

b. Find a formula for $F(x)$ if $f(t) = t^n$ ($n = 1, 2, 3, \ldots$).

c. Find a formula for $F(x)$ if $f(t) = e^{at}$ (a constant).

COMMUNICATION AND REASONING EXERCISES

59. Why can't the Fundamental Theorem of Calculus be used to evaluate $\int_{-1}^{1} \frac{1}{x}\, dx$?

60. Why can't the Fundamental Theorem of Calculus be used to evaluate $\int_1^{+\infty} \frac{1}{x^2}\, dx$?

61. It sometimes happens that the Fundamental Theorem of Calculus gives the correct answer for an improper integral. Does the FTC give the correct answer for improper integrals of the form

$$\int_{-a}^{a} \frac{1}{x^{1/r}}\, dx$$

if $r = 3, 5, 7, \ldots$?

62. Does the FTC give the correct answer for improper integrals of the form

$$\int_{-a}^{a} \frac{1}{x^r}\, dx$$

if $r = 3, 5, 7, \ldots$?

63. Which of the following integrals are improper, and why? (Do not evaluate any of them.)

a. $\int_{-1}^{1} \frac{|x|}{x}\, dx$ **b.** $\int_{-1}^{1} x^{-1/3}\, dx$ **c.** $\int_0^2 \frac{x - 2}{x^2 - 4x + 4}\, dx$

64. Which of the following integrals are improper, and why? (Do not evaluate any of them.)

a. $\int_{-1}^{1} \frac{|x - 1|}{x - 1}\, dx$ **b.** $\int_0^1 \frac{1}{x^{2/3}}\, dx$ **c.** $\int_0^2 \frac{x^2 - 4x + 4}{x - 2}\, dx$

65. ⊣ ▼ How could you use technology to approximate improper integrals? (Your discussion should refer to each type of improper integral.)

66. ⊣ ▼ Use technology to approximate the integrals $\int_0^M e^{-(x-10)^2}\, dx$ for larger and larger values of M, using Riemann sums with 500 subdivisions. What do you find? Comment on the answer.

67. ▼ Make up an interesting application whose solution is $\int_{10}^{+\infty} 100te^{-0.2t}\, dt = \$1,015.01$.

68. ▼ Make up an interesting application whose solution is $\int_{100}^{+\infty} \frac{1}{r^2}\, dr = 0.01$.

14.6 Differential Equations and Applications

A **differential equation** is an equation that involves a derivative of an unknown function. A **first-order differential equation** involves only the first derivative of the unknown function. A **second-order differential equation** involves the second derivative of the unknown function (and possibly the first derivative). Higher-order differential equations are defined similarly. In this book, we will deal only with first-order differential equations.

To **solve** a differential equation means to find the unknown function. Many of the laws of science and other fields describe how things change. When expressed mathematically, these laws take the form of equations involving derivatives—that is, differential equations. The field of differential equations is a large and very active area of study in mathematics, and we shall see only a small part of it in this section.

Jon Ferrey /Allsport/Getty Images

EXAMPLE 1 Motion

A dragster accelerates from a stop so that its speed t seconds after starting is $40t$ ft/s. How far will the car go in 8 seconds?

Solution We wish to find the car's position function $s(t)$. We are told about its speed, which is ds/dt. Precisely, we are told that

$$\frac{ds}{dt} = 40t.$$

This is the differential equation we have to solve to find $s(t)$. But we already know how to solve this kind of differential equation; we integrate

$$s(t) = \int 40t\, dt = 20t^2 + C.$$

We now have the **general solution** to the differential equation. By letting C take on different values, we get all the possible solutions. We can specify the one **particular solution** that gives the answer to our problem by imposing the **initial condition** that $s(0) = 0$. Substituting into $s(t) = 20t^2 + C$, we get

$$0 = s(0) = 20(0)^2 + C = C$$

so $C = 0$ and $s(t) = 20t^2$. To answer the question, the car travels $20(8)^2 = 1{,}280$ feet in 8 seconds.

We did not have to work hard to solve the differential equation in Example 1. In fact, any differential equation of the form $dy/dx = f(x)$ can (in theory) be solved by integrating. (Whether we can actually carry out the integration is another matter!)

Simple Differential Equations

A **simple** differential equation has the form

$$\frac{dy}{dx} = f(x).$$

Its general solution is

$$y = \int f(x)\, dx.$$

Quick Example

The differential equation

$$\frac{dy}{dx} = 2x^2 - 4x^3$$

is simple and has general solution

$$y = \int f(x)\, dx = \frac{2x^3}{3} - x^4 + C.$$

Not all differential equations are simple, as the next example shows.

EXAMPLE 2 Separable Differential Equation

Consider the differential equation $\dfrac{dy}{dx} = \dfrac{x}{y^2}$.

a. Find the general solution.

b. Find the particular solution that satisfies the initial condition $y(0) = 2$.

Solution

a. This is not a simple differential equation because the right-hand side is a function of both x and y. We cannot solve this equation by just integrating; the solution to this problem is to "separate" the variables.

Step 1: *Separate the variables algebraically.* We rewrite the equation as

$$y^2\, dy = x\, dx.$$

Step 2: *Integrate both sides.*

$$\int y^2\, dy = \int x\, dx$$

giving

$$\frac{y^3}{3} = \frac{x^2}{2} + C.$$

Step 3: *Solve for the dependent variable.* We solve for y:

$$y^3 = \frac{3}{2}x^2 + 3C = \frac{3}{2}x^2 + D$$

(Rewriting $3C$ as D, an equally arbitrary constant), so

$$y = \left(\frac{3}{2}x^2 + D\right)^{1/3}.$$

This is the general solution of the differential equation.

b. We now need to find the value for D that will give us the solution satisfying the condition $y(0) = 2$. Substituting 0 for x and 2 for y in the general solution, we get

$$2 = \left(\frac{3}{2}(0)^2 + D\right)^{1/3} = D^{1/3}$$

so

$$D = 2^3 = 8.$$

Thus, the particular solution we are looking for is

$$y = \left(\frac{3}{2}x^2 + 8\right)^{1/3}.$$

➡ **Before we go on...** We can check the general solution in Example 2 by calculating both sides of the differential equation and comparing.

$$\frac{dy}{dx} = \frac{d}{dx}\left(\frac{3}{2}x^2 + D\right)^{1/3} = x\left(\frac{3}{2}x^2 + D\right)^{-2/3}$$

$$\frac{x}{y^2} = \frac{x}{\left(\frac{3}{2}x^2 + 8\right)^{2/3}} = x\left(\frac{3}{2}x^2 + D\right)^{-2/3} \qquad ✔ \qquad ∎$$

Q: *In Example 2, we wrote $y^2\,dy$ and $x\,dx$. What do they mean?*

A: Although it is possible to give meaning to these symbols, for us they are just a notational convenience. We could have done the following instead:

$$y^2\frac{dy}{dx} = x$$

Now we integrate both sides with respect to x.

$$\int y^2\frac{dy}{dx}\,dx = \int x\,dx$$

We can use substitution to rewrite the left-hand side:

$$\int y^2\frac{dy}{dx}\,dx = \int y^2\,dy,$$

which brings us back to the equation

$$\int y^2\,dy = \int x\,dx.$$

We were able to separate the variables in the preceding example because the right-hand side, x/y^2, was a *product* of a function of x and a function of y—namely,

$$\frac{x}{y^2} = x\left(\frac{1}{y^2}\right).$$

In general, we can say the following:

Separable Differential Equation

A **separable** differential equation has the form

$$\frac{dy}{dx} = f(x)g(y).$$

We solve a separable differential equation by separating the xs and the ys algebraically, writing

$$\frac{1}{g(y)}\,dy = f(x)\,dx$$

and then integrating:

$$\int \frac{1}{g(y)}\,dy = \int f(x)\,dx.$$

EXAMPLE 3   Rising Medical Costs

Spending on Medicare from 2000 to 2025 was projected to rise continuously at an instantaneous rate of 3.7% per year.* Find a formula for Medicare spending y as a function of time t in years since 2000.

Solution When we say that Medicare spending y was going up continuously at an instantaneous rate of 3.7% per year, we mean that

the instantaneous rate of increase of y *was 3.7% of its value*

or $\dfrac{dy}{dt} = 0.037y.$

This is a separable differential equation. Separating the variables gives

$$\frac{1}{y}\,dy = 0.037\,dt.$$

Integrating both sides, we get

$$\int \frac{1}{y}\,dy = \int 0.037\,dt$$

so $\ln y = 0.037t + C.$

(We should write $\ln |y|$, but we know that the medical costs are positive.) We now solve for y.

$$y = e^{0.037t+C} = e^C e^{0.037t} = Ae^{0.037t}$$

where A is a positive constant. This is the formula we used before for continuous percentage growth.

---

* Spending is in constant 2000 dollars. Source for projected data: The Urban Institute's Analysis of the 1999 Trustee's Report (www.urban.org).

➡ **Before we go on...** To determine A in Example 3 we need to know, for example, Medicare spending at time $t = 0$ (the initial condition). The source cited estimates Medicare spending as \$239.6 billion in 2000. Substituting $t = 0$ in the equation above gives

$$239.6 = Ae^0 = A.$$

Thus, projected Medicare spending is

$$y = 239.6e^{0.037t} \text{ billion dollars}$$

t years after 2000. ■

EXAMPLE 4 Newton's Law of Cooling

Newton's Law of Cooling states that a hot object cools at a rate proportional to the difference between its temperature and the temperature of the surrounding environment (the **ambient temperature**). If a hot cup of coffee, at 170°F, is left to sit in a room at 70°F, how will the temperature of the coffee change over time?

Solution We let $H(t)$ denote the temperature of the coffee at time t. Newton's Law of Cooling tells us that $H(t)$ *decreases* at a rate proportional to the difference between $H(t)$ and 70°F, the ambient temperature. In other words,

$$\frac{dH}{dt} = -k(H - 70)$$

✱ NOTE When we say that a quantity Q is *proportional* to a quantity R, we mean that $Q = kR$ for some constant k. The constant k is referred to as the **constant of proportionality**.

where k is some positive constant.✱ Note that $H \geq 70$: The coffee will never cool to less than the ambient temperature.

The variables here are H and t, which we can separate as follows:

$$\frac{dH}{H - 70} = -k\,dt.$$

Integrating, we get

$$\int \frac{dH}{H - 70} = \int (-k)\,dt$$

so $\ln(H - 70) = -kt + C.$

(Note that $H - 70$ is positive, so we don't need absolute values.) We now solve for H:

$$H - 70 = e^{-kt+C}$$
$$= e^C e^{-kt}$$
$$= Ae^{-kt}$$

so

$$H(t) = 70 + Ae^{-kt}$$

where A is some positive constant. We can determine the constant A using the initial condition $H(0) = 170$:

$$170 = 70 + Ae^0 = 70 + A$$

so $A = 100.$

Therefore,

$$H(t) = 70 + 100e^{-kt}$$

Figure 24

Q: But what is k?

A: The constant k determines the rate of cooling. Its value depends on the units of time we are using, on the substance cooling—in this case the coffee—and its container. Because k depends so heavily on the particular circumstances, it's usually easiest to determine it experimentally. Figure 24 shows two possible graphs, one with $k = 0.1$ and the other with $k = 0.03$ ($k \approx 0.03$ would be reasonable for a cup of coffee in a polystyrene container with t measured in minutes).

In any case, we can see from the graph or the formula for $H(t)$ that the temperature of the coffee will approach the ambient temperature exponentially.

➡ **Before we go on...** Notice that the calculation in Example 4 shows that the temperature of an object cooling according to Newton's law is given in general by

$$H(t) = T_a + (T_0 - T_a)e^{-kt}$$

where T_a is the ambient temperature (70° in the example) and T_0 is the initial temperature (170° in the example). The formula also holds if the ambient temperature is higher than the initial temperature ("Newton's Law of Heating"). ∎

14.6 EXERCISES

▼ more advanced   ◆ challenging
Ⅱ indicates exercises that should be solved using technology

Find the general solution of each differential equation in Exercises 1–10. Where possible, solve for y as a function of x.

1. $\dfrac{dy}{dx} = x^2 + \sqrt{x}$

HINT [See Quick Example page 1072.]

2. $\dfrac{dy}{dx} = \dfrac{1}{x} + 3$

HINT [See Quick Example page 1072.]

3. $\dfrac{dy}{dx} = \dfrac{x}{y}$

HINT [See Example 2a.]

4. $\dfrac{dy}{dx} = \dfrac{y}{x}$

HINT [See Example 2a.]

5. $\dfrac{dy}{dx} = xy$

6. $\dfrac{dy}{dx} = x^2 y$

7. $\dfrac{dy}{dx} = (x+1)y^2$

8. $\dfrac{dy}{dx} = \dfrac{1}{(x+1)y^2}$

9. $x\dfrac{dy}{dx} = \dfrac{1}{y}\ln x$

10. $\dfrac{1}{x}\dfrac{dy}{dx} = \dfrac{1}{y}\ln x$

For each differential equation in Exercises 11–20, find the particular solution indicated. HINT [See Example 2b.]

11. $\dfrac{dy}{dx} = x^3 - 2x$; $y = 1$ when $x = 0$

12. $\dfrac{dy}{dx} = 2 - e^{-x}$; $y = 0$ when $x = 0$

13. $\dfrac{dy}{dx} = \dfrac{x^2}{y^2}$; $y = 2$ when $x = 0$

14. $\dfrac{dy}{dx} = \dfrac{y^2}{x^2}$; $y = \dfrac{1}{2}$ when $x = 1$

15. $x\dfrac{dy}{dx} = y$; $y(1) = 2$

16. $x^2\dfrac{dy}{dx} = y$; $y(1) = 1$

17. $\dfrac{dy}{dx} = x(y+1)$; $y(0) = 0$

18. $\dfrac{dy}{dx} = \dfrac{y+1}{x}$; $y(1) = 2$

19. $\dfrac{dy}{dx} = \dfrac{xy^2}{x^2+1}$; $y(0) = -1$

20. $\dfrac{dy}{dx} = \dfrac{xy}{(x^2+1)^2}$; $y(0) = 1$

APPLICATIONS

21. *Sales* Your monthly sales of Green Tea Ice Cream are falling at an instantaneous rate of 5% per month. If you currently sell 1,000 quarts per month, find the differential equation describing your change in sales, and then solve it to predict your monthly sales. HINT [See Example 3.]

22. *Profit* Your monthly profit on sales of Avocado Ice Cream is rising at an instantaneous rate of 10% per month. If you currently make a profit of $15,000 per month, find the differential equation describing your change in profit, and solve it to predict your monthly profits. HINT [See Example 3.]

23. *Newton's Law of Cooling* For coffee in a ceramic cup, suppose $k \approx 0.05$ with time measured in minutes. **(a)** Use Newton's Law of Cooling to predict the temperature of the coffee, initially at a temperature of 200°F, that is left to sit in a room at 75°F. **(b)** When will the coffee have cooled to 80°F? HINT [See Example 4.]

24. *Newton's Law of Cooling* For coffee in a paper cup, suppose $k \approx 0.08$ with time measured in minutes. **(a)** Use Newton's Law of Cooling to predict the temperature of the coffee, initially at a temperature of 210°F, that is left to sit in a room at

60°F. **(b)** When will the coffee have cooled to 70°F? HINT [See Example 4.]

25. ***Cooling*** A bowl of clam chowder at 190°F is placed in a room whose air temperature is 75°F. After 10 minutes, the soup has cooled to 150°F. Find the value of k in Newton's Law of Cooling, and hence find the temperature of the chowder as a function of time.

26. ***Heating*** Suppose that a pie, at 20°F, is put in an oven at 350°F. After 15 minutes, its temperature has risen to 80°F. Find the value of k in Newton's Law of Heating (see the note after Example 4), and hence find the temperature of the pie as a function of time.

27. ***Market Saturation*** You have just introduced a new flat-screen monitor to the market. You predict that you will eventually sell 100,000 monitors and that your monthly rate of sales will be 10% of the difference between the saturation value of 100,000 and the total number you have sold up to that point. Find a differential equation for your total sales (as a function of the month) and solve. (What are your total sales at the moment when you first introduce the monitor?)

28. ***Market Saturation*** Repeat the preceding exercise, assuming that monthly sales will be 5% of the difference between the saturation value (of 100,000 monitors) and the total sales to that point, and assuming that you sell 5,000 monitors to corporate customers before placing the monitor on the open market.

29. ***Determining Demand*** Nancy's Chocolates estimates that the elasticity of demand for its dark chocolate truffles is $E = 0.05p - 1.5$ where p is the price per pound. Nancy's sells 20 pounds of truffles per week when the price is $20 per pound. Find the formula expressing the demand q as a function of p. Recall that the elasticity of demand is given by

$$E = -\frac{dq}{dp} \times \frac{p}{q}.$$

30. ***Determining Demand*** Nancy's Chocolates estimates that the elasticity of demand for its chocolate strawberries is $E = 0.02p - 0.5$ where p is the price per pound. It sells 30 pounds of chocolate strawberries per week when the price is $30 per pound. Find the formula expressing the demand q as a function of p. Recall that the elasticity of demand is given by

$$E = -\frac{dq}{dp} \times \frac{p}{q}.$$

Linear Differential Equations *Exercises 31–36 are based on **first order linear differential equations with constant coefficients**. These have the form*

$$\frac{dy}{dt} + py = f(t) \quad (p \; constant)$$

and the general solution is

$$y = e^{-pt} \int f(t) e^{pt} \, dt. \quad (Check \; this \; by \; substituting!)$$

31. Solve the linear differential equation
$$\frac{dy}{dt} + y = e^{-t}; \; y = 1 \text{ when } t = 0.$$

32. Solve the linear differential equation
$$\frac{dy}{dt} - y = e^{2t}; \; y = 2 \text{ when } t = 0.$$

33. Solve the linear differential equation
$$2\frac{dy}{dt} - y = 2t; \; y = 1 \text{ when } t = 0.$$
HINT [First rewrite the differential equation in the form $\frac{dy}{dt} + py = f(t)$.]

34. Solve the linear differential equation
$$2\frac{dy}{dt} + y = -t. \quad y = 1 \text{ when } t = 0$$
HINT [First rewrite the differential equation in the form $\frac{dy}{dt} + py = f(t)$.]

35. ▼ ***Electric Circuits*** The flow of current $i(t)$ in an electric circuit without capacitance satisfies the linear differential equation

$$L\frac{di}{dt} + Ri = V(t)$$

where L and R are constants (the *inductance* and *resistance* respectively) and $V(t)$ is the applied voltage. (See figure.)

If the voltage is supplied by a 10-volt battery and the switch is turned on at time $t = 1$, then the voltage V is a step function that jumps from 0 to 10 at $t = 1$: $V(t) = 5\left[1 + \frac{|t-1|}{t-1}\right]$. Find the current as a function of time for $L = R = 1$. Use a grapher to plot the resulting current as a function of time. (Assume there is no current flowing at time $t = 0$.) [Use the following integral formula: $\int \left[1 + \frac{|t-1|}{t-1}\right] e^t \, dt = \left[1 + \frac{|t-1|}{t-1}\right] (e^t - e) + C.$]

36. ▼ ***Electric Circuits*** Repeat Exercise 35 for $L = 1$, $R = 5$, and $V(t) = 5\left[1 + \frac{|t-2|}{t-2}\right]$. (The switch flipped on at time $t = 2$). [Use the following integral formula: $\int \left[1 + \frac{|t-2|}{t-2}\right] e^{5t} \, dt = \left(1 + \frac{|t-2|}{t-2}\right)\left(\frac{e^{5t} - e^{10}}{5}\right) + C.$]

37. ▼ ***Approach to Equilibrium*** The Extrasoft Toy Co. has just released its latest creation, a plush platypus named "Eggbert." The demand function for Eggbert dolls is $D(p) = 50,000 - 500p$ dolls per month when the price is p dollars. The supply function

is $S(p) = 30,000 + 500p$ dolls per month when the price is p dollars. This makes the equilibrium price \$20. The Evans price adjustment model assumes that if the price is set at a value other than the equilibrium price, it will change over time in such a way that its rate of change is proportional to the shortage $D(p) - S(p)$.

a. Write the differential equation given by the Evans price adjustment model for the price p as a function of time.
b. Find the general solution of the differential equation you wrote in (a). (You will have two unknown constants, one being the constant of proportionality.)
c. Find the particular solution in which Eggbert dolls are initially priced at \$10 and the price rises to \$12 after one month.

38. ▼ Approach to Equilibrium Spacely Sprockets has just released its latest model, the Dominator. The demand function is $D(p) = 10,000 - 1,000p$ sprockets per year when the price is p dollars. The supply function is $S(p) = 8,000 + 1,000p$ sprockets per year when the price is p dollars.

a. Using the Evans price adjustment model described in the preceding exercise, write the differential equation for the price $p(t)($ as a function of time.
b. Find the general solution of the differential equation you wrote in (a).
c. Find the particular solution in which Dominator sprockets are initially priced at \$5 each but fall to \$3 each after one year.

39. ▼ Logistic Equation There are many examples of growth in which the rate of growth is slow at first, becomes faster, and then slows again as a limit is reached. This pattern can be described by the differential equation

$$\frac{dy}{dt} = ay(L - y)$$

where a is a constant and L is the limit of y. Show by substitution that

$$y = \frac{CL}{e^{-aLt} + C}$$

is a solution of this equation, where C is an arbitrary constant.

40. ▼ Logistic Equation Using separation of variables and integration with a table of integrals or a symbolic algebra program, solve the differential equation in the preceding exercise to derive the solution given there.

T *Exercises 41–44 require the use of technology.*

41. ▼ Market Saturation You have just introduced a new model of DVD player. You predict that the market will saturate at 2,000,000 DVD players and that your total sales will be governed by the equation

$$\frac{dS}{dt} = \frac{1}{4}S(2 - S)$$

where S is the total sales in millions of DVD players and t is measured in months. If you give away 1,000 DVD players when you first introduce them, what will S be? Sketch the graph of S as a function of t. About how long will it take to saturate the market? (See Exercise 39.)

42. ▼ Epidemics A certain epidemic of influenza is predicted to follow the function defined by

$$\frac{dA}{dt} = \frac{1}{10}A(20 - A)$$

where A is the number of people infected in millions and t is the number of months after the epidemic starts. If 20,000 cases are reported initially, find $A(t)$ and sketch its graph. When is A growing fastest? How many people will eventually be affected? (See Exercise 39.)

43. ▼ Growth of Tumors The growth of tumors in animals can be modeled by the Gompertz equation:

$$\frac{dy}{dt} = -ay \ln\left(\frac{y}{b}\right)$$

where y is the size of a tumor, t is time, and a and b are constants that depend on the type of tumor and the units of measurement.

a. Solve for y as a function of t.
b. If $a = 1$, $b = 10$, and $y(0) = 5$ cm^3 (with t measured in days), find the specific solution and graph it.

44. ▼ Growth of Tumors Refer back to the preceding exercise. Suppose that $a = 1$, $b = 10$, and $y(0) = 15$ cm^3. Find the specific solution and graph it. Comparing its graph to the one obtained in the preceding exercise, what can you say about tumor growth in these instances?

COMMUNICATION AND REASONING EXERCISES

45. What is the difference between a particular solution and the general solution of a differential equation? How do we get a particular solution from the general solution?

46. Why is there always an arbitrary constant in the general solution of a differential equation? Why are there not two or more arbitrary constants in a first-order differential equation?

47. ▼ Show by example that a **second-order** differential equation, one involving the second derivative y'', usually has two arbitrary constants in its general solution.

48. ▼ Find a differential equation that is not separable.

49. ▼ Find a differential equation whose general solution is $y = 4e^{-x} + 3x + C$.

50. ▼ Explain how, knowing the elasticity of demand as a function of either price or demand, you may find the demand equation. (See Exercise 29.)

KEY CONCEPTS

Web Site www.FiniteandCalc.org
Go to the student Web site at
www.FiniteandCalc.org to find a
comprehensive and interactive
Web-based summary of Chapter 14.

14.1 Integration by Parts
Integration by parts formula:
$$\int u \cdot v \, dx = u \cdot I(v) - \int D(u)I(v) \, dx$$
p. 1014

Tabular method for integration by parts
p. 1015

Integrating a polynomial times a
logarithm p. 1017

14.2 Area Between Two Curves and Applications
If $f(x) \geq g(x)$ for all x in $[a, b]$, then the
area of the region between the graphs
of f and g and between $x = a$ and
$x = b$ is given by
$$A = \int_a^b [f(x) - g(x)] \, dx \quad p. 1023$$

Regions enclosed by crossing curves
p. 1025
Area enclosed by two curves p. 1027
General instructions for finding the area
between the graphs of $f(x)$ and $g(x)$
p. 1027
Approximating the area between two
curves using technology:
$$A = \int_a^b |f(x) - g(x)| \, dx \quad p. 1028$$

14.3 Averages and Moving Averages
Average, or mean, of a collection of
values
$$\bar{y} = \frac{y_1 + y_2 + \cdots + y_n}{n} \quad p. 1032$$
The *average*, or *mean*, of a function $f(x)$
on an interval $[a, b]$ is
$$\bar{f} = \frac{1}{b-a} \int_a^b f(x) \, dx \quad p. 1033$$
Average balance p. 1033
Computing the moving average of a set
of data p. 1034
n-Unit moving average of a function:
$$\bar{f}(x) = \frac{1}{n} \int_{x-n}^x f(t) \, dt \quad p. 1035$$
Computing moving averages of saw tooth
and step functions p. 1036

14.4 Applications to Business and Economics: Consumers' and Producers' Surplus and Continuous Income Streams
Consumers' surplus:
$$CS = \int_0^{\bar{q}} [D(q) - \bar{p}] \, dq \quad p. 1042$$
Producers' surplus:
$$PS = \int_0^{\bar{q}} [\bar{p} - S(q)] \, dq \quad p. 1043$$
Equilibrium price p. 1044
Social gain $= CS + PS$ p. 1045
Total value of a continuous income
stream: $TV = \int_a^b R(t) \, dt \quad p. 1046$

Future value of a continuous income
stream: $FV = \int_a^b R(t)e^{r(b-t)} \, dt$
p. 1047

Present value of a continuous income
stream: $PV = \int_a^b R(t)e^{r(a-t)} \, dt$
p. 1048

14.5 Improper Integrals and Applications
Improper integral with an infinite limit of
integration:
$$\int_a^{+\infty} f(x) \, dx, \int_{-\infty}^b f(x) \, dx,$$
$$\int_{-\infty}^{+\infty} f(x) \, dx \quad p. 1051$$
Improper integral in which the integrand
becomes infinite p. 1054
Testing for convergence p. 1055
Integrand infinite between the endpoints
p. 1056
Integral improper in two ways p. 1057

14.6 Differential Equations and Applications
Simple differential equations:
$$\frac{dy}{dx} = f(x) \quad p. 1062$$
Separable differential equations:
$$\frac{dy}{dx} = f(x)g(y) \quad p. 1064$$
Newton's Law of Cooling p. 1065

REVIEW EXERCISES

Evaluate the integrals in Exercises 1–10.

1. $\int (x^2 + 2)e^x \, dx$

2. $\int (x^2 - x)e^{-3x+1} \, dx$

3. $\int x^2 \ln(2x) \, dx$

4. $\int \log_5 x \, dx$

5. $\int 2x|2x + 1| \, dx$

6. $\int 3x|-x + 5| \, dx$

7. $\int 5x \frac{|-x + 3|}{-x + 3} \, dx$

8. $\int 2x \frac{|3x + 1|}{3x + 1} \, dx$

9. $\int_{-2}^2 (x^3 + 1)e^{-x} \, dx$

10. $\int_1^e x^2 \ln x \, dx$

In Exercises 11–14, find the areas of the given regions.

11. Between $y = x^3$ and $y = 1 - x^3$ for x in $[0, 1]$
12. Between $y = e^x$ and $y = e^{-x}$ for x in $[0, 2]$
13. Enclosed by $y = 1 - x^2$ and $y = x^2$
14. Between $y = x$ and $y = xe^{-x}$ for x in $[0, 2]$

In Exercises 15–18, find the average value of the given function over the indicated interval.

15. $f(x) = x^3 - 1$ over $[-2, 2]$
16. $f(x) = \frac{x}{x^2 + 1}$ over $[0, 1]$
17. $f(x) = x^2 e^x$ over $[0, 1]$
18. $f(x) = (x + 1) \ln x$ over $[1, 2e]$

In Exercises 19–22, find the 2-unit moving averages of the given function.

19. $f(x) = 3x + 1$

20. $f(x) = 6x^2 + 12$

21. $f(x) = x^{4/3}$

22. $f(x) = \ln x$

In Exercises 23 and 24, calculate the consumers' surplus at the indicated unit price $\bar{p}$ for the given demand equation.

23. $p = 50 - \dfrac{1}{2}q;\ \bar{p} = 10$

24. $p = 10 - q^{1/2};\ \bar{p} = 4$

In Exercises 25 and 26, calculate the producers' surplus at the indicated unit price $\bar{p}$ for the given supply equation.

25. $p = 50 + \dfrac{1}{2}q;\ \bar{p} = 100$

26. $p = 10 + q^{1/2};\ \bar{p} = 40$

In Exercises 27–32 decide whether the given integral converges. If the integral converges, compute its value.

27. $\displaystyle\int_1^\infty \frac{1}{x^5}\, dx$

28. $\displaystyle\int_0^1 \frac{1}{x^5}\, dx$

29. $\displaystyle\int_{-1}^1 \frac{x}{(x^2-1)^{5/3}}\, dx$

30. $\displaystyle\int_0^2 \frac{x}{(x^2-1)^{1/3}}\, dx$

31. $\displaystyle\int_0^{+\infty} 2xe^{-x^2}\, dx$

32. $\displaystyle\int_0^{+\infty} x^2 e^{-6x^3}\, dx$

Solve the differential equations in Exercises 33–36.

33. $\dfrac{dy}{dx} = x^2 y^2$

34. $\dfrac{dy}{dx} = xy + 2x$

35. $xy\dfrac{dy}{dx} = 1;\ y(1) = 1$

36. $y(x^2+1)\dfrac{dy}{dx} = xy^2;\ y(0) = 2$

APPLICATIONS

37. *Spending on Stationery* Alarmed by the volume of pointless memos and reports being copied and circulated by management at OHaganBooks.com, John O'Hagan ordered a 5-month audit of paper usage at the company. He found that management consumed paper at a rate of

$$q(t) = 45t + 200 \text{ thousand sheets per month} \quad (0 \le t \le 5)$$

(t is the time in months since the audit began). During the same period, the price of paper was escalating; the company was charged approximately

$$p(t) = 9e^{0.09t} \text{ dollars per thousand sheets.}$$

Use an integral to estimate, to the nearest hundred dollars, the total spent on paper for management during the given period.

38. *Spending on Shipping* During the past 10 months, OHaganBooks.com shipped orders at a rate of about

$$q(t) = 25t + 3{,}200 \text{ packages per month} \quad (0 \le t \le 10)$$

(t is the time in months since the beginning of the year). During the same period, the cost of shipping a package averaged approximately

$$p(t) = 4e^{0.04t} \text{ dollars per package.}$$

Use an integral to estimate, to the nearest thousand dollars, the total spent on shipping orders during the given period.

39. *Education Costs* Billy-Sean O'Hagan, having graduated *summa cum laude* from college, has been accepted by the doctoral program in biophysics at Oxford. John O'Hagan estimates that the total cost (minus scholarships) he will need to pay is $2,000 per month, but that this cost will escalate at a continuous compounding rate of 1% per month.

  a. What, to the nearest dollar, is the average monthly cost over the course of two years?

  b. Find the four-month moving average of the monthly cost.

40. *Investments* OHaganBooks.com keeps its cash reserves in a hedge fund paying 6% compounded continuously. It starts a year with $1 million in reserves and does not withdraw or deposit any money.

  a. What is the average amount it will have in the fund over the course of two years?

  b. Find the one-month moving average of the amount it has in the fund.

41. *Consumers' and Producers' Surplus* Currently, the hottest selling item at OHaganBooks.com is *Mensa for Dummies*[50] with a demand curve of $q = 20{,}000(28 - p)^{1/3}$ books per week, and a supply curve of $q = 40{,}000(p - 19)^{1/3}$ books per week.

  a. Find the equilibrium price and demand.

  b. Find the consumers' and producers' surpluses at the equilibrium price.

42. *Consumers' and Producers' Surplus* OHaganBooks.com is about to start selling a new coffee table book, *Computer Designs of the Late Twentieth Century*. It estimates the demand curve to be $q = 1{,}000\sqrt{200 - 2p}$, and its willingness to order books from the publisher is given by the supply curve $q = 1{,}000\sqrt{10p - 400}$.

  a. Find the equilibrium price and demand.

  b. Find the consumers' and producers' surpluses at the equilibrium price.

43. *Revenue* Sales of the bestseller *A River Burns Through It* are dropping at OHaganBooks.com. To try to bolster sales, the company is dropping the price of the book, now $40, at a rate of $2 per week. As a result, this week OHaganBooks.com will sell 5,000 copies, and it estimates that sales will fall continuously at a rate of 10% per week. How much revenue will it earn on sales of this book over the next 8 weeks?

44. *Foreign Investments* Panicked by the performance of the U.S. stock market, Marjory Duffin is investing her 401(k) money in a Russian hedge fund at a rate of approximately

$$q(t) = 1.7t^2 - 0.5t + 8 \text{ thousand shares per month}$$

where t is time in months since the stock market began to plummet. At the time she started making the investments, the hedge fund was selling for $1 per share, but subsequently

[50] The actual title is: *Let Us Just Have A Ball! Mensa for Dummies* by Wendu Mekbib (Author) Silhouette Publishing Corporation.

declined in value at a continuous rate of 5% per month. What was the total amount of money Marjory Duffin invested after one year? (Answer to the nearest $1,000.)

45. *Investments* OHaganBooks.com CEO John O'Hagan has started a gift account for the Marjory Duffin Foundation. The account pays 6% compounded continuously and is initially empty. OHaganBooks .com deposits money continuously into it, starting at the rate of $100,000 per month and increasing continuously by $10,000 per month.

    a. How much money will the company have in the account at the end of two years?

    b. How much of the amount you found in part (a) was principal deposited and how much was interest earned? (Round answers to the nearest $1,000.)

46. *Savings* John O'Hagan had been saving money for Billy-Sean's education since he had been a wee lad. O'Hagan began depositing money at the rate of $1,000 per month and increased his deposits continuously by $50 per month. If the account earned 5% compounded continuously and O'Hagan continued these deposits for 15 years,

    a. How much money did he accumulate?

    b. How much was money deposited and how much was interest?

47. *Acquisitions* The Megabucks Corporation is considering buying OHaganBooks.com. They estimate OHaganBooks.com's revenue stream at $50 million per year, growing continuously

at a 10% rate. Assuming interest rates of 6%, how much is OHaganBooks.com's revenue for the next year worth now?

48. *More Acquisitions* OHaganBooks.com is thinking of buying JungleBooks and would like to recoup its investment after three years. The estimated net profit for JungleBooks is $40 million per year, growing linearly by $5 million per year. Assuming interest rates of 4%, how much should OHaganBooks.com pay for JungleBooks?

49. *Incompetence* OHaganBooks.com is shopping around for a new bank. A junior executive at one bank offers them the following interesting deal: The bank will pay them interest continuously at a rate numerically equal to 0.01% of the square of the amount of money they have in the account at any time. By considering what would happen if $10,000 was deposited in such an account, explain why the junior executive was fired shortly after this offer was made.

50. *Shrewd Bankers* The new junior officer at the bank (who replaced the one fired in the preceding exercise) offers OHaganBook.com the following deal for the $800,000 they plan to deposit: While the amount in the account is less than $1 million, the bank will pay interest continuously at a rate equal to 10% of the difference between $1 million and the amount of money in the account. When it rises over $1 million, the bank will pay interest of 20%. Why should OHaganBooks.com not take this offer?

Case Study   Estimating Tax Revenues

from Shutterstock.com

✳ NOTE To simplify our discussion, we are assuming that (1) all tax revenues are based on earned income and that (2) everyone in the population we consider earns some income.

You have just been hired by the incoming administration of your country as chief consultant for national tax policy, and you have been getting conflicting advice from the finance experts on your staff. Several of them have come up with plausible suggestions for new tax structures, and your job is to choose the plan that results in more revenue for the government.

    Before you can evaluate their plans, you realize that it is essential to know your country's income distribution—that is, how many people earn how much money.* One might think that the most useful way of specifying income distribution would be to use a function that gives the exact number $f(x)$ of people who earn a given salary x. This would necessarily be a discrete function—it makes sense only if x happens to be a whole number of cents. There is, after all, no one earning a salary of exactly $22,000.142567! Furthermore, this function would behave rather erratically, because there are, for example, probably many more people making a salary of exactly $30,000 than exactly $30,000.01. Given these problems, it is far more convenient to start with the function defined by

$$N(x) = \text{the total number of people earning between 0 and } x \text{ dollars.}$$

Actually, you would want a "smoothed" version of this function. The graph of $N(x)$ might look like the one shown in Figure 25.

Figure 25

If we take the *derivative* of $N(x)$, we get an income distribution function. Its graph might look like the one shown in Figure 26.

Figure 26

✱ **NOTE** A very similar idea is used in probability. See the optional chapter "Calculus Applied to Probability and Statistics" on the Web site.

✱ **NOTE** Gamma distributions are often good models for income distributions. The one used in the text is the authors' approximation of the income distribution in the United States in 2007. Source for data: U.S. Census Bureau, Current Population Survey, 2008 Annual Social and Economic Supplement.

Because the derivative measures the rate of change, its value at x is the additional number of taxpayers per \$1 increase in salary. Thus, the fact that $N'(25,000) \approx 3,800$ tells us that approximately 3,800 people are earning a salary of between \$20,000 and \$20,001. In other words, N' shows the distribution of incomes among the population—hence, the name "distribution function."✱

You thus send a memo to your experts requesting the income distribution function for the nation. After much collection of data, they tell you that the income distribution function is

$$N'(x) = 100x^{0.466}e^{-x/23,000}.$$

This is in fact the function whose graph is shown in Figure 26 and is an example of a **gamma distribution**.✱ (You might find it odd that you weren't given the original function N, but it will turn out that you don't need it. How would you compute it?)

Given this income distribution, your financial experts have come up with the two possible tax policies illustrated in Figures 27 and 28.

Figure 27

Figure 28

In the first alternative, all taxpayers pay 20% of their income in taxes, except that no one pays more than $20,000 in taxes. In the second alternative, there are three tax brackets, described by the following table:

Income	Marginal tax rate
$0–20,000	0%
$20,000–100,000	20%
Above $100,000	30%

Now you must determine which alternative will generate more annual tax revenue.

Each of Figures 27 and 28 is the graph of a function, T. Rather than using the formulas for these particular functions, you begin by working with the general situation. You have an income distribution function N' and a tax function T, both functions of annual income. You need to find a formula for total tax revenues. First you decide to use a cutoff so that you need to work only with incomes in some finite bracket $[0, M]$; you might use, for example, $M = \$10$ million. (Later you will let M approach $+\infty$.) Next, you subdivide the interval $[0, M]$ into a large number of intervals of small width, Δx. If $[x_{k-1}, x_k]$ is a typical such interval, you wish to calculate the approximate tax revenue from people whose total incomes lie between x_{k-1} and x_k. You will then sum over k to get the total revenue.

You need to know how many people are making incomes between x_{k-1} and x_k. Because $N(x_k)$ people are making incomes *up to* x_k and $N(x_{k-1})$ people are making incomes up to x_{k-1}, the number of people making incomes between x_{k-1} and x_k is $N(x_k) - N(x_{k-1})$. Because x_k is very close to x_{k-1}, the incomes of these people are all approximately equal to x_{k-1} dollars, so each of these taxpayers is paying an annual tax of about $T(x_{k-1})$. This gives a tax revenue of

$$[N(x_k) - N(x_{k-1})]T(x_{k-1}).$$

Now you do a clever thing. You write $x_k - x_{k-1} = \Delta x$ and replace $N(x_k) - N(x_{k-1})$ by

$$\frac{N(x_k) - N(x_{k-1})}{\Delta x}\Delta x.$$

This gives you a tax revenue of about

$$\frac{N(x_k) - N(x_{k-1})}{\Delta x}T(x_{k-1})\Delta x$$

from wage-earners in the bracket $[x_{k-1}, x_k]$. Summing over k gives an approximate total revenue of

$$\sum_{k=1}^{n} \frac{N(x_k) - N(x_{k-1})}{\Delta x}T(x_{k-1})\Delta x$$

where n is the number of subintervals. The larger n is, the more accurate your estimate will be, so you take the limit of the sum as $n \to \infty$. When you do this, two things happen. First, the quantity

$$\frac{N(x_k) - N(x_{k-1})}{\Delta x}$$

approaches the derivative, $N'(x_{k-1})$. Second, the sum, which you recognize as a Riemann sum, approaches the integral

$$\int_0^M N'(x)T(x)\,dx.$$

You now take the limit as $M \to +\infty$ to get

$$\text{Total tax revenue} = \int_0^{+\infty} N'(x)T(x)\,dx.$$

This improper integral is fine in theory, but the actual calculation will have to be done numerically, so you stick with the upper limit of \$10 million for now. You will have to check that it is reasonable at the end. (Notice that, by the graph of N', it appears that extremely few, if any, people earn that much.) Now you already have a formula for $N'(x)$, but you still need to write formulas for the tax functions $T(x)$ for both alternatives.

Alternative 1 The graph in Figure 27 rises linearly from 0 to 20,000 as x ranges from 0 to 100,000, and then stays constant at 20,000. The slope of the first part is $20{,}000/100{,}000 = 0.2$. The taxation function is therefore

$$T_1(x) = \begin{cases} 0.2x & \text{if } 0 \le x < 100{,}000 \\ 20{,}000 & \text{if } x \ge 100{,}000 \end{cases}.$$

For use of technology, it's convenient to express this in closed form using absolute values:

$$T_1(x) = 0.2x + \frac{1}{2}\left(1 + \frac{|x - 100,000|}{x - 100,000}\right)(20,000 - 0.2x)$$

The total revenue generated by this tax scheme is, therefore,

$$R_1 = \int_0^{10,000,000} (100x^{0.466}e^{-x/23,000})$$
$$\times \left[0.2x + \frac{1}{2}\left(1 + \frac{|x - 100,000|}{x - 100,000}\right)(20,000 - 0.2x)\right]dx$$

You decide not to attempt this by hand! You use numerical integration software to obtain a grand total of $R_1 = \$1,445,860,000,000$, or $1.44586 trillion (rounded to six significant digits).

Alternative 2 The graph in Figure 28 rises with a slope of 0.2 from 0 to 16,000 as x ranges from 20,000 to 100,000, then rises from that point on with a slope of 0.3. (This is why we say that the *marginal* tax rates are 20% and 30%, respectively.) The taxation function is therefore

$$T_2(x) = \begin{cases} 0 & \text{if } 0 \leq x < 20,000 \\ 0.2(x - 20,000) & \text{if } 20,000 \leq x < 100,000 \\ 16,000 + 0.3(x - 100,000) & \text{if } x \geq 100,000 \end{cases}.$$

Again, you express this in closed form using absolute values:

$$T_2(x) = [0.2(x - 20,000)]\frac{1}{2}\left(\frac{|x - 20,000|}{x - 20,000} - \frac{|x - 100,000|}{x - 100,000}\right)$$
$$+ [16,000 + 0.3(x - 100,000)]\frac{1}{2}\left(1 + \frac{|x - 100,000|}{x - 100,000}\right)$$
$$= 0.1(x - 20,000)\left(\frac{|x - 20,000|}{x - 20,000} - \frac{|x - 100,000|}{x - 100,000}\right)$$
$$+ [8,000 + 0.15(x - 100,000)]\left(1 + \frac{|x - 100,000|}{x - 100,000}\right)$$

Values of x between 0 and 20,000 do not contribute to the integral, so

$$R_2 = \int_{20,000}^{10,000,000} 100x^{0.466}e^{-x/23,000}T_2(x)\,dx$$

with $T_2(x)$ as above. Numerical integration software gives $R_2 = \$0.777589$ trillion—considerably less than Alternative 1. Thus, even though Alternative 2 taxes the wealthy more heavily, it yields less total revenue.

Now what about the cutoff at $10 million annual income? If you try either integral again with an upper limit of $100 million, you will see no change in either result to six significant digits. There simply are not enough taxpayers earning an income above $10,000,000 to make a difference. You conclude that your answers are sufficiently accurate and that the first alternative provides more tax revenue.

EXERCISES

In Exercises 1–4, calculate the total tax revenue for a country with the given income distribution and tax policies (all currency in dollars).

1. ⊞ $N'(x) = 100x^{0.466}e^{-x/23,000}$; 25% tax on all income
2. ⊞ $N'(x) = 100x^{0.4}e^{-x/30,000}$; 45% tax on all income
3. ⊞ $N'(x) = 100x^{0.466}e^{-x/23,000}$; tax brackets as in the following tax table:

Income	*Marginal tax rate*
$0–30,000	0%
$30,000–250,000	10%
Above $250,000	80%

4. ⊞ $N'(x) = 100x^{0.4}e^{-x/30,000}$; no tax on any income below $250,000, 100% marginal tax rate on any income above $250,000

5. Let $N'(x)$ be an income distribution function.

   a. If $0 \le a < b$, what does $\int_a^b N'(x)\,dx$ represent? HINT [Use the Fundamental Theorem of Calculus.]
   b. What does $\int_0^{+\infty} N'(x)\,dx$ represent?

6. Let $N'(x)$ be an income distribution function. What does $\int_0^{+\infty} x N'(x)\,dx$ represent? HINT [Argue as in the text.]

7. Let $P(x)$ be the number of people earning more than x dollars.

   a. What is $N(x) + P(x)$?
   b. Show that $P'(x) = -N'(x)$.
   c. Use integration by parts to show that, if $T(0) = 0$, then the total tax revenue is

   $$\int_0^{+\infty} P(x)T'(x)\,dx.$$

   [Note: You may assume that $T'(x)$ is continuous, but the result is still true if we assume only that $T(x)$ is continuous and piecewise continuously differentiable.]

8. Income tax functions T are most often described, as in the text, by tax brackets and marginal tax rates.

   a. If one tax bracket is $a < x \le b$, show that $\int_a^b P(x)\,dx$ is the total income earned in the country that falls into that bracket (P as in the preceding exercise).
   b. Use (a) to explain directly why $\int_0^{+\infty} P(x)T'(x)\,dx$ gives the total tax revenue in the case where T is described by tax brackets and constant marginal tax rates in each bracket.

TI-83/84 Plus   Technology Guide

Section 14.3

Example 3 (page 1034)   The following table shows Colossal Conglomerate's closing stock prices for 20 consecutive trading days:

Day	1	2	3	4	5	6	7	8	9	10
Price	20	22	21	24	24	23	25	26	20	24
Day	11	12	13	14	15	16	17	18	19	20
Price	26	26	25	27	28	27	29	27	25	24

Plot these prices and the 5-day moving average.

Solution with Technology

Here is how to automate this calculation on a TI-83 Plus.

1. Use

$$\mathtt{seq(X,X,1,20)} \to L_1 \qquad \boxed{\text{2ND}}\;\boxed{\text{STAT}} \to \text{OPS} \to 5$$
$$\boxed{\text{STO}}\;\boxed{\text{2ND}}\;\boxed{\text{STAT}} \to L_1$$

to enter the sequence of numbers 1 through 20 into the list L_1, representing the trading days.

2. Using the list editor accessible through the $\boxed{\text{STAT}}$ menu, enter the daily stock prices in list L_2.

3. Calculate the list of 5-day moving averages by using the following command:

$$\mathtt{seq(\,(L_2\,(X)+L_2\,(X-1)+L_2\,(X-2)+L_2\,(X-3)}$$
$$\mathtt{+L_2\,(X-4)\,)/5\,,X\,,5\,,20)} \to L_3$$

This has the effect of putting the moving averages into elements 1 through 15 of list L_3.

4. If you wish to plot the moving average on the same graph as the daily prices, you will want the averages in L_3 to match up with the prices in L_2. One way to do this is to put four more entries at the beginning of L_3—say, copies of the first four entries of L_2. The following command accomplishes this:

$$\mathtt{augment(seq(L_2\,(X)\,,X\,,1\,,4)\,,L_3)} \to L_3$$
$$\boxed{\text{2ND}}\;\boxed{\text{STAT}} \to \text{OPS} \to 9$$

5. You can now graph the prices and moving averages by creating an xyLine scatter plot through the $\boxed{\text{STAT PLOT}}$ menu, with L_1 being the Xlist and L_2 being the Ylist for `Plot1`, and L_1 being the Xlist and L_3 the Ylist for `Plot2`:

EXCEL **Technology Guide**

Section 14.3

Example 3 (page 1034)   The following table shows Colossal Conglomerate's closing stock prices for 20 consecutive trading days:

Day	1	2	3	4	5	6	7	8	9	10
Price	20	22	21	24	24	23	25	26	20	24
Day	11	12	13	14	15	16	17	18	19	20
Price	26	26	25	27	28	27	29	27	25	24

Plot these prices and the 5-day moving average.

Solution with Technology

1. Compute the moving averages in a column next to the daily prices, as shown here:

	A	B	C
1	Day	Price	Moving Average
2	1	20	
3	2	22	
4	3	21	
5	4	24	
6	5	24	=AVERAGE(B2:B6)
7	6	23	
21	20	24	

→

	A	B	C
1	Day	Price	Moving Average
2	1	20	
3	2	22	
4	3	21	
5	4	24	
6	5	24	22.2
7	6	23	22.8
21	20	24	26.4

2. You can then graph the price and moving average using a scatter plot.

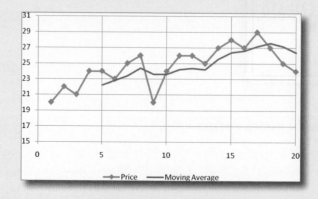

15 Functions of Several Variables

Web Site
www.FiniteandCalc.org
At the Web site you will find:

- A detailed chapter summary
- A true/false quiz
- A surface grapher
- An Excel surface grapher
- A linear multiple regression utility
- The following optional extra sections:

    Maxima and Minima: Boundaries and the Extreme Value Theorem

    The Chain Rule for Functions of Several Variables

Case Study Modeling College Population

College Malls Inc. is planning to build a national chain of shopping malls in college neighborhoods. The company is planning to lease only to stores that target the specific age demographics of the national college student population. To decide which age brackets to target, the company has asked you, a paid consultant, for an analysis of the college population by student age, and of its trends over time. **How can you analyze the relevant data?**

David Pearson/Alamy

Introduction

We have studied functions of a single variable extensively. But not every useful function is a function of only one variable. In fact, most are not. For example, if you operate an online bookstore in competition with **Amazon.com**, **BN.com**, and Booksamillion.com, your sales may depend on those of your competitors. Your company's daily revenue might be modeled by a function such as

$$R(x, y, z) = 10{,}000 - 0.01x - 0.02y - 0.01z + 0.00001yz$$

where x, y, and z are the online daily revenues of **Amazon.com**, **BN.com**, and Booksamillion.com, respectively. Here, R is a function of three variables because it *depends on* x, y, and z. As we shall see, the techniques of calculus extend readily to such functions. Among the applications we shall look at is optimization: finding, where possible, the maximum or minimum of a function of two or more variables.

15.1 Functions of Several Variables from the Numerical, Algebraic, and Graphical Viewpoints

Numerical and Algebraic Viewpoints

Recall that a function of one variable is a rule for manufacturing a new number $f(x)$ from a single independent variable x. A function of two or more variables is similar, but the new number now depends on more than one independent variable.

Function of Several Variables

A **real-valued function**, f, **of** $x, y, z, \ldots$ is a rule for manufacturing a new number, written $f(x, y, z, \ldots)$, from the values of a sequence of independent variables $(x, y, z, \ldots)$. The function f is called a **real-valued function of two variables** if there are two independent variables, a **real-valued function of three variables** if there are three independent variables, and so on.

Quick Examples

1. $f(x, y) = x - y$	Function of two variables
$f(1, 2) = 1 - 2 = -1$	Substitute 1 for x and 2 for y.
$f(2, -1) = 2 - (-1) = 3$	Substitute 2 for x and -1 for y.
$f(y, x) = y - x$	Substitute y for x and x for y.
2. $g(x, y) = x^2 + y^2$	Function of two variables
$g(-1, 3) = (-1)^2 + 3^2 = 10$	Substitute -1 for x and 3 for y.
3. $h(x, y, z) = x + y + xz$	Function of three variables
$h(2, 2, -2) = 2 + 2 + 2(-2) = 0$	Substitute 2 for x, 2 for y, and -2 for z.

Note It is often convenient to use $x_1, x_2, x_3, \ldots$ for the independent variables, so that, for instance, the third example above would be $h(x_1, x_2, x_3) = x_1 + x_2 + x_1x_3$. ∎

Figure 1 illustrates the concept of a function of two variables: In goes a pair of numbers and out comes a single number.

$$(x, y) \longrightarrow \boxed{g} \longrightarrow x^2 + y^2 \qquad (2, -1) \longrightarrow \boxed{g} \longrightarrow 5$$

Figure 1

As with functions of one variable, functions of several variables can be represented numerically (using a table of values), algebraically (using a formula as in the above examples), and sometimes graphically (using a graph).

Let's now look at a number of examples of interesting functions of several variables.

EXAMPLE 1 Cost Function

You own a company that makes two models of speakers: the Ultra Mini and the Big Stack. Your total monthly cost (in dollars) to make x Ultra Minis and y Big Stacks is given by

$$C(x, y) = 10{,}000 + 20x + 40y.$$

What is the significance of each term in this formula?

Solution The terms have meanings similar to those we saw for linear cost functions of a single variable. Let us look at the terms one at a time.

Constant Term Consider the monthly cost of making no speakers at all ($x = y = 0$). We find

$$C(0, 0) = 10{,}000. \qquad \text{\footnotesize Cost of making no speakers is \$10,000.}$$

Thus, the constant term 10,000 is the **fixed cost**, the amount you have to pay each month even if you make no speakers.

Coefficients of x and y Suppose you make a certain number of Ultra Minis and Big Stacks one month and the next month you increase production by one Ultra Mini. The costs are

$$\begin{aligned} C(x, y) &= 10{,}000 + 20x + 40y & \text{\footnotesize First month} \\ C(x + 1, y) &= 10{,}000 + 20(x + 1) + 40y & \text{\footnotesize Second month} \\ &= 10{,}000 + 20x + 20 + 40y \\ &= C(x, y) + 20. \end{aligned}$$

Thus, each Ultra Mini adds $20 to the total cost. We say that $20 is the **marginal cost** of each Ultra Mini. Similarly, because of the term $40y$, each Big Stack adds $40 to the total cost. The marginal cost of each Big Stack is $40.

This cost function is an example of a *linear function of two variables*. The coefficients of x and y play roles similar to that of the slope of a line. In particular, they give the rates of change of the function as each variable increases while the other stays constant (think about it). We shall say more about linear functions below.

using Technology

See the Technology Guides at the end of the chapter to see how you can use a TI-83/84 Plus and Excel to display various values of $C(x, y)$ in Example 1. Here is an outline:

TI-83/84 Plus

Y₁=10000+20X+40Y

To evaluate C(10, 30):

10 → X

30 → Y

Y₁ [More details on page 1142.]

Excel

x-values down column A starting in A2

y-values down column B starting in B2

=10000+20*A2+40*B2 in C2; copy down column C. [More details on page 1142.]

Figure 2

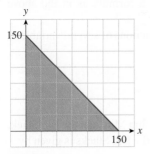

Figure 3

➡ **Before we go on...** In Example 1 which values of x and y may we substitute into $C(x, y)$? Certainly we must have $x \geq 0$ and $y \geq 0$ because it makes no sense to speak of manufacturing a negative number of speakers. Also, there is certainly some upper bound to the number of speakers that can be made in a month. The bound might take one of several forms. The number of each model may be bounded—say $x \leq 100$ and $y \leq 75$. The inequalities $0 \leq x \leq 100$ and $0 \leq y \leq 75$ describe the region in the plane shaded in Figure 2.

Another possibility is that the *total* number of speakers is bounded—say, $x + y \leq 150$. This, together with $x \geq 0$ and $y \geq 0$, describes the region shaded in Figure 3.

In either case, the region shown represents the pairs (x, y) for which $C(x, y)$ is defined. Just as with a function of one variable, we call this region the **domain** of the function. As before, when the domain is not given explicitly, we agree to take the largest domain possible. ■

EXAMPLE 2   Faculty Salaries

David Katz came up with the following function for the salary of a professor with 10 years of teaching experience in a large university.

$$S(x, y, z) = 13{,}005 + 230x + 18y + 102z$$

Here, S is the salary in 1969–1970 in dollars per year, x is the number of books the professor has published, y is the number of articles published, and z is the number of "excellent" articles published.[*] What salary do you expect that a professor with 10 years' experience earned in 1969–1970 if she published 2 books, 20 articles, and 3 "excellent" articles?

Solution All we need to do is calculate

$$S(2, 20, 3) = 13{,}005 + 230(2) + 18(20) + 102(3)$$
$$= \$14{,}131.$$

---

[*] David A. Katz, "Faculty Salaries, Promotions and Productivity at a Large University," *American Economic Review*, June 1973, pp. 469–477. Prof. Katz's equation actually included other variables, such as the number of dissertations supervised; our equation assumes that all of these are zero.

➡ **Before we go on...** In Example 1, we gave a linear function of two variables. In Example 2 we have a linear function of three variables. Katz came up with his model by surveying a large number of faculty members and then finding the linear function "best" fitting the data. Such models are called **multiple linear regression** models. In the Case Study at the end of this chapter, we shall see a spreadsheet method of finding the coefficients of a multiple regression model from a set of observed data.

What does this model say about the value of a single book or a single article? If a book takes 15 times as long to write as an article, how would you recommend that a professor spend her writing time? ■

Here are two simple kinds of functions of several variables.

Linear Function

A function f of n variables is **linear** if f has the property that

$$f(x_1, x_2, \ldots, x_n) = a_0 + a_1 x_1 + \cdots + a_n x_n. \qquad (a_0, a_1, a_2, \ldots, a_n \text{ constants})$$

Quick Examples

1. $f(x, y) = 3x - 5y$ Linear function of x and y

2. $C(x, y) = 10{,}000 + 20x + 40y$ Example 1

3. $S(x_1, x_2, x_3) = 13{,}005 + 230x_1 + 18x_2 + 102x_3$ Example 2

Interaction Function

If we add to a linear function one or more terms of the form $bx_i x_j$ (b a nonzero constant and $i \neq j$), we get a **second-order interaction function**.

Quick Examples

1. $C(x, y) = 10{,}000 + 20x + 40y + 0.1xy$

2. $R(x_1, x_2, x_3) = 10{,}000 - 0.01x_1 - 0.02x_2 - 0.01x_3 + 0.00001x_2x_3$

So far, we have been specifying functions of several variables **algebraically**—by using algebraic formulas. If you have ever studied statistics, you are probably familiar with statistical tables. These tables may also be viewed as representing functions **numerically**, as the next example shows.

EXAMPLE 3 Function Represented Numerically: Body Mass Index

The following table lists some values of the "body mass index," which gives a measure of the massiveness of your body, taking height into account.* The variable w represents your weight in pounds, and h represents your height in inches. An individual with a body mass index of 25 or above is generally considered overweight.

✳ NOTE It is interesting that weight-lifting competitions are usually based on weight, rather than body mass index. As a consequence, taller people are at a significant disadvantage in these competitions because they must compete with shorter, stockier people of the same weight. (An extremely thin, very tall person can weigh as much as a muscular short person, although his body mass index would be significantly lower.)

$w \rightarrow$

h ↓		130	140	150	160	170	180	190	200	210
	60	25.2	27.1	29.1	31.0	32.9	34.9	36.8	38.8	40.7
	61	24.4	26.2	28.1	30.0	31.9	33.7	35.6	37.5	39.4
	62	23.6	25.4	27.2	29.0	30.8	32.7	34.5	36.3	38.1
	63	22.8	24.6	26.4	28.1	29.9	31.6	33.4	35.1	36.9
	64	22.1	23.8	25.5	27.2	28.9	30.7	32.4	34.1	35.8
	65	21.5	23.1	24.8	26.4	28.1	29.7	31.4	33.0	34.7
	66	20.8	22.4	24.0	25.6	27.2	28.8	30.4	32.0	33.6
	67	20.2	21.8	23.3	24.9	26.4	28.0	29.5	31.1	32.6
	68	19.6	21.1	22.6	24.1	25.6	27.2	28.7	30.2	31.7
	69	19.0	20.5	22.0	23.4	24.9	26.4	27.8	29.3	30.8
	70	18.5	19.9	21.4	22.8	24.2	25.6	27.0	28.5	29.9
	71	18.0	19.4	20.8	22.1	23.5	24.9	26.3	27.7	29.1
	72	17.5	18.8	20.2	21.5	22.9	24.2	25.6	26.9	28.3
	73	17.0	18.3	19.6	20.9	22.3	23.6	24.9	26.2	27.5
	74	16.6	17.8	19.1	20.4	21.7	22.9	24.2	25.5	26.7
	75	16.1	17.4	18.6	19.8	21.1	22.3	23.6	24.8	26.0
	76	15.7	16.9	18.1	19.3	20.5	21.7	22.9	24.2	25.4

using Technology

See the Technology Guides at the end of the chapter to see how to use Excel to create the table in Example 3. Here is an outline:

Excel

w-values 130 to 210 in B1–J1

h-values 60 to 76 in A2–A18

=0.45*B$1/
(0.0254*$A2)^2

in B2; copy down and across through J18. [More details on page 1142.]

As the table shows, the value of the body mass index depends on two quantities: w and h. Let us write $M(w, h)$ for the body mass index function. What are $M(140, 62)$ and $M(210, 63)$?

Solution We can read the answers from the table:

$$M(140, 62) = 25.4 \qquad w = 140 \text{ lb}, h = 62 \text{ in}$$

and $$M(210, 63) = 36.9. \qquad w = 210 \text{ lb}, h = 63 \text{ in}$$

The function $M(w, h)$ is actually given by the formula

$$M(w, h) = \frac{0.45w}{(0.0254h)^2}.$$

[The factor 0.45 converts the weight to kilograms, and 0.0254 converts the height to meters. If w is in kilograms and h is in meters, the formula is simpler: $M(w, h) = w/h^2$.]

Geometric Viewpoint: Three-Dimensional Space and the Graph of a Function of Two Variables

Just as functions of a single variable have graphs, so do functions of two or more variables. Recall that the graph of $f(x)$ consists of all points $(x, f(x))$ in the xy-plane. By analogy, we would like to say that the graph of a function of *two* variables, $f(x, y)$, consists of all points of the form $(x, y, f(x, y))$. Thus, we need three axes: the x-, y-, and z-axes. In other words, our graph will live in **three-dimensional space**, or **3-space**.*

Just as we had two mutually perpendicular axes in two-dimensional space (the xy-plane; see Figure 4(a)), so we have three mutually perpendicular axes in three-dimensional space (Figure 4(b)).

* NOTE If we were dealing instead with a function of *three* variables, then we would need to go to *four-dimensional* space. Here we run into visualization problems (to say the least!) so we won't discuss the graphs of functions of three or more variables in this text.

Two-dimensional space	Three-dimensional space	
Figure 4(a)	**Figure 4(b)**	**Figure 5**

In both 2-space and 3-space, the axis labeled with the last letter goes up. Thus, the z-direction is the "up" direction in 3-space, rather than the y-direction.

Three important planes are associated with these axes: the xy-plane, the yz-plane, and the xz-plane. These planes are shown in Figure 5. Any two of these planes intersect in one of the axes (for example, the xy- and xz-planes intersect in the x-axis) and all three meet at the origin. Notice that the xy-plane consists of all points with z-coordinate zero, the xz-plane consists of all points with $y = 0$, and the yz-plane consists of all points with $x = 0$.

In 3-space, each point has *three* coordinates, as you might expect: the x-coordinate, the y-coordinate, and the z-coordinate. To see how this works, look at the following examples.

The z-coordinate of a point is its height above the xy-plane.

EXAMPLE 4 Plotting Points in Three Dimensions

Locate the points $P(1, 2, 3)$, $Q(-1, 2, 3)$, $R(1, -1, 0)$, and $S(1, 2, -2)$ in 3-space.

Solution To locate P, the procedure is similar to the one we used in 2-space: Start at the origin, proceed one unit in the x direction, then proceed two units in the y direction, and finally, proceed three units in the z direction. We wind up at the point P shown in Figures 6(a) and 6(b).

Here is another, extremely useful way of thinking about the location of P. First, look at the x- and y-coordinates, obtaining the point $(1, 2)$ in the xy-plane. The point we want is then three units vertically above the point $(1, 2)$ because the z-coordinate of a point is just its height above the xy-plane. This strategy is shown in Figure 6(c).

Figure 6(a)   **Figure 6(b)**   **Figure 6(c)**

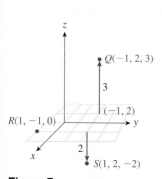

Figure 7

Plotting the points Q, R, and S is similar, using the convention that negative coordinates correspond to moves back, left, or down. (See Figure 7.)

Our next task is to describe the graph of a function $f(x, y)$ of two variables.

Graph of a Function of Two Variables

The **graph of the function f of two variables** is the set of all points $(x, y, f(x, y))$ in three-dimensional space, where we restrict the values of (x, y) to lie in the domain of f. In other words, the graph is the set of all the points (x, y, z) with $z = f(x, y)$.

For *every* point (x, y) in the domain of f, the z-coordinate of the corresponding point on the graph is given by evaluating the function at (x, y). Thus, there will be a point on the graph above *every* point in the domain of f, so that the graph is usually a *surface* of some sort.

EXAMPLE 5   Graph of a Function of Two Variables

Describe the graph of $f(x, y) = x^2 + y^2$.

Solution   Your first thought might be to make a table of values. You could choose some values for x and y and then, for each such pair, calculate $z = x^2 + y^2$. For example, you might get the following table:

		$x \rightarrow$		
		−1	**0**	**1**
y ↓	**−1**	2	1	2
	0	1	0	1
	1	2	1	2

$$f(x, y) = x^2 + y^2$$

This gives the following nine points on the graph of f: $(-1, -1, 2), (-1, 0, 1), (-1, 1, 2),$ $(0, -1, 1), (0, 0, 0), (0, 1, 1), (1, -1, 2), (1, 0, 1),$ and $(1, 1, 2)$. These points are shown in Figure 8.

The points on the xy-plane we chose for our table are the grid points in the xy-plane, and the corresponding points on the graph are marked with solid dots. The problem is that this small number of points hardly tells us what the surface looks like, and even if we plotted more points, it is not clear that we would get anything more than a mass of dots on the page.

What can we do? There are several alternatives. One place to start is to use technology to draw the graph. (See the technology note on the next page.) We then obtain something like Figure 9. This particular surface is called a **paraboloid**.

Figure 8

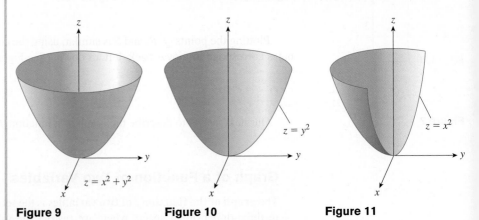

Figure 9	Figure 10	Figure 11

If we slice vertically through this surface along the yz-plane, we get the picture in Figure 10. The shape of the front edge, where we cut, is a parabola. To see why, note that the yz-plane is the set of points where $x = 0$. To get the intersection of $x = 0$ and $z = x^2 + y^2$, we substitute $x = 0$ in the second equation, getting $z = y^2$. This is the equation of a parabola in the yz-plane.

Similarly, we can slice through the surface with the xz-plane by setting $y = 0$. This gives the parabola $z = x^2$ in the xz-plane (Figure 11).

✴ **NOTE** See Section 0.7 for a discussion of equations of circles.

 using Technology

We can use technology to obtain the graph of the function in Example 5:

Excel
Table of values:
x-values −3 to 3 in B1–H1
y-values −3 to 3 in A2–A8
=B1^2+A2^2
in B2; copy down and across through H8.
Graph: Highlight A1 through H8 and insert a Surface chart.
[More details on page 1143.]

Web Site
www.FiniteandCalc.org
  Everything for Calculus
  → Chapter 15
  → Math Tools (Surface Graphing Utility)
Enter x^2+y^2 for $f(x, y)$
Set xMin = −3, xMax = 3, yMin = −3, yMax = 3
Press "Graph."

We can also look at horizontal slices through the surface, that is, slices by planes parallel to the xy-plane. These are given by setting $z = c$ for various numbers c. For example, if we set $z = 1$, we will see only the points with height 1. Substituting in the equation $z = x^2 + y^2$ gives the equation

$$1 = x^2 + y^2,$$

which is the equation of a circle of radius 1.✴ If we set $z = 4$, we get the equation of a circle of radius 2:

$$4 = x^2 + y^2.$$

In general, if we slice through the surface at height $z = c$, we get a circle (of radius $\sqrt{c}$). Figure 12 shows several of these circles.

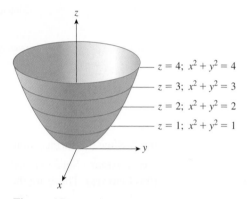

$z = 4;\ x^2 + y^2 = 4$
$z = 3;\ x^2 + y^2 = 3$
$z = 2;\ x^2 + y^2 = 2$
$z = 1;\ x^2 + y^2 = 1$

Figure 12

Looking at these circular slices, we see that this surface is the one we get by taking the parabola $z = x^2$ and spinning it around the z-axis. This is an example of what is known as a **surface of revolution**.

➡ **Before we go on...** The graph of any function of the form $f(x, y) = Ax^2 + By^2 + Cxy + Dx + Ey + F$ ($A, B, \ldots, F$ constants), with $4AB - C^2$ positive, can be shown to be a paraboloid of the same general shape as that in Example 5 if A and B are positive, or upside-down if A and B are negative. If $A \neq B$, the horizontal slices will be ellipses rather than circles.

Notice that each horizontal slice through the surface in Example 5 was obtained by putting $z = constant$. This gave us an equation in x and y that described a curve. These curves are called the **level curves** of the surface $z = f(x, y)$. In Example 5, the equations are of the form $x^2 + y^2 = c$ (c constant), and so the level curves are circles. Figure 13 shows the level curves for $c = 0, 1, 2, 3,$ and 4.

The level curves give a contour map or topographical map of the surface. Each curve shows all of the points on the surface at a particular height c. You can use this contour map to visualize the shape of the surface. Imagine moving the contour at $c = 1$ to a height of 1 unit above the xy-plane, the contour at $c = 2$ to a height of 2 units above the xy-plane, and so on. You will end up with something like Figure 12. ∎

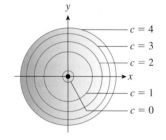

$c = 4$
$c = 3$
$c = 2$
$c = 1$
$c = 0$

Level curves of the paraboloid
$z = x^2 + y^2$

Figure 13

The following summary includes the techniques we have just used plus some additional ones:

Analyzing the Graph of a Function of Two Variables

If possible, use technology to render the graph of a given function $z = f(x, y)$. Given the function $z = f(x, y)$, you can analyze its graph as follows:

Step 1 Obtain the **x-, y-, and z-intercepts** (the places where the surface crosses the coordinate axes).

x-Intercept(s):   Set $y = 0$ and $z = 0$ and solve for x.

y-Intercept(s):   Set $x = 0$ and $z = 0$ and solve for y.

z-Intercept: Set $x = 0$ and $y = 0$ and compute z.

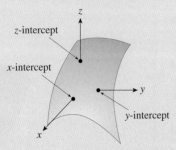

Step 2 Slice the surface along planes parallel to the xy-, yz-, and xz-planes.

z = constant   Set $z = constant$ and analyze the resulting curves.
(level curves)   These are the curves resulting from horizontal slices.

x = constant   Set $x = constant$ and analyze the resulting curves.
                      These are the curves resulting from slices parallel to the yz-plane.

y = constant   Set $y = constant$ and analyze the resulting curves.
                      These are the curves resulting from slices parallel to the xz-plane.

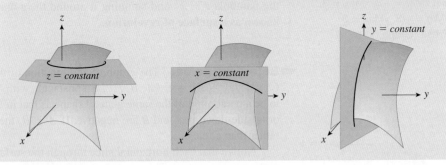

Spreadsheets often have built-in features to render surfaces such as the paraboloid in Example 5. In the following example, we use Excel to graph another surface and then analyze it as above.

EXAMPLE 6 ▪ Analyzing a Surface

Describe the graph of $f(x, y) = x^2 - y^2$.

Solution First we obtain a picture of the graph using technology. Figure 14 shows two graphs obtained using resources at the Web site.

Chapter 15 → Math Tools for Chapter 15   Chapter 15 → Math Tools for Chapter 15
→ Surface Graphing Utility   → Excel Surface Graphing Utility

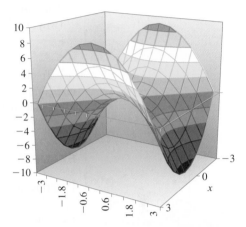

Figure 14

See the Technology Guides at the end of the chapter to find out how to obtain a similar graph from scratch on an ordinary Excel sheet.

The graph shows an example of a "saddle point" at the origin. (We return to this idea in Section 15.3.) To analyze the graph for the features shown in the box above, replace $f(x, y)$ by z to obtain

$$z = x^2 - y^2.$$

Step 1: *Intercepts* Setting any two of the variables x, y, and z equal to zero results in the third also being zero, so the x-, y-, and z-intercepts are all 0. In other words, the surface touches all three axes in exactly one point, the origin.

Step 1: *Slices* Slices in various directions show more interesting features.

Slice by $x = c$ This gives $z = c^2 - y^2$, which is the equation of a parabola that opens downward. You can see two of these slices ($c = -3, c = 3$) as the front and back edges of the surface in Figure 14. (More are shown in Figure 15(a).)

Slice by $y = c$ This gives $z = x^2 - c^2$, which is the equation of a parabola once again—this time, opening upward. You can see two of these slices ($c = -3, c = 3$) as the left and right edges of the surface in Figure 14. (More are shown in Figure 15(b).)

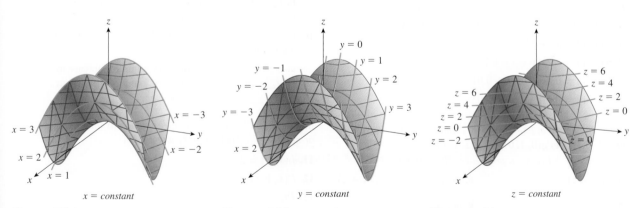

Figure 15(a)   **Figure 15(b)**   **Figure 15(c)**

Slice by $z = c$ This gives $x^2 - y^2 = c$, which is a hyperbola. The level curves for various values of c are visible in Figure 14 as the horizontal slices. (See Figure 15(c).) The case $c = 0$ is interesting: The equation $x^2 - y^2 = 0$ can be rewritten as $x = \pm y$ (why?), which represents two lines at right-angles to each other.

To obtain really beautiful renderings of surfaces, you could use one of the commercial computer algebra software packages, such as Mathematica® or Maple®, or, if you use a Mac, the built-in grapher (grapher.app located in the Utilities folder).

EXAMPLE 7 **Graph of a Linear Function**

Describe the graph of $g(x, y) = \dfrac{1}{2}x + \dfrac{1}{3}y - 1$.

Solution   Notice first that g is a linear function of x and y. Figure 16 shows a portion of the graph, which is a plane.

We can get a good idea of what plane this is by looking at the x-, y-, and z-intercepts.

x-intercept Set $y = z = 0$, which gives $x = 2$.

y-intercept Set $x = z = 0$, which gives $y = 3$.

z-intercept Set $x = y = 0$, which gives $z = -1$.

Three points are enough to define a plane, so we can say that the plane is the one passing through the three points $(2, 0, 0)$, $(0, 3, 0)$, and $(0, 0, -1)$.

Note It can be shown that the graph of every linear function of two variables is a plane. What do the level curves look like? ■

$z = \dfrac{1}{2}x + \dfrac{1}{3}y - 1$

Figure 16

15.1 EXERCISES

▼ more advanced   ◆ challenging
T indicates exercises that should be solved using technology

For each function in Exercises 1–4, evaluate (a) $f(0, 0)$;
(b) $f(1, 0)$; (c) $f(0, -1)$; (d) $f(a, 2)$; (e) $f(y, x)$;
(f) $f(x + h, y + k)$ HINT [See Quick Examples page 1080.]

1. $f(x, y) = x^2 + y^2 - x + 1$

2. $f(x, y) = x^2 - y - xy + 1$

3. $f(x, y) = 0.2x + 0.1y - 0.01xy$

4. $f(x, y) = 0.4x - 0.5y - 0.05xy$

For each function in Exercises 5–8, evaluate (a) $g(0, 0, 0)$;
(b) $g(1, 0, 0)$; (c) $g(0, 1, 0)$; (d) $g(z, x, y)$;
(e) $g(x + h, y + k, z + l)$, provided such a value exists.

5. $g(x, y, z) = e^{x+y+z}$

6. $g(x, y, z) = \ln(x + y + z)$

7. $g(x, y, z) = \dfrac{xyz}{x^2 + y^2 + z^2}$

8. $g(x, y, z) = \dfrac{e^{xyz}}{x + y + z}$

9. Let $f(x, y, z) = 1.5 + 2.3x - 1.4y - 2.5z$. Complete the following sentences. HINT [See Example 1.]

   a. f ___ by ___ units for every 1 unit of increase in x.
   b. f ___ by ___ units for every 1 unit of increase in y.
   c. _____ by 2.5 units for every _____.

10. Let $g(x, y, z) = 0.01x + 0.02y - 0.03z - 0.05$. Complete the following sentences.

   a. g ___ by ___ units for every 1 unit of increase in z.
   b. g ___ by ___ units for every 1 unit of increase in x.
   c. _____ by 0.02 units for every _____.

In Exercises 11–18, classify each function as linear, interaction, or neither. HINT [See Quick Examples page 1083.]

11. $L(x, y) = 3x - 2y + 6xy - 4y^2$

12. $L(x, y, z) = 3x - 2y + 6xz$

13. $P(x_1, x_2, x_3) = 0.4 + 2x_1 - x_3$

14. $Q(x_1, x_2) = 4x_2 - 0.5x_1 - x_1^2$

15. $f(x, y, z) = \dfrac{x + y - z}{3}$

16. $g(x, y, z) = \dfrac{xz - 3yz + z^2}{4z}$ $(z \neq 0)$

17. $g(x, y, z) = \dfrac{xz - 3yz + z^2 y}{4z}$ $(z \neq 0)$

18. $f(x, y) = x + y + xy + x^2 y$

In Exercises 19 and 20, use the given tabular representation of the function f to compute the quantities asked for. HINT [See Example 3.]

19.

	$x \rightarrow$			
	10	**20**	**30**	**40**
$y \downarrow$ **10**	-1	107	162	-3
20	-6	194	294	-14
30	-11	281	426	-25
40	-16	368	558	-36

a. $f(20, 10)$ **b.** $f(40, 20)$ **c.** $f(10, 20) - f(20, 10)$

20.

	$x \rightarrow$			
	10	**20**	**30**	**40**
$y \downarrow$ **10**	162	107	-5	-7
20	294	194	-22	-30
30	426	281	-39	-53
40	558	368	-56	-76

a. $f(10, 30)$ **b.** $f(20, 10)$ **c.** $f(10, 40) + f(10, 20)$

T *In Exercises 21 and 22, use a spreadsheet or some other method to complete the given tables.*

21. $P(x, y) = x - 0.3y + 0.45xy$

	$x \rightarrow$			
	10	**20**	**30**	**40**
$y \downarrow$ **10**				
20				
30				
40				

22. $Q(x, y) = 0.4x + 0.1y - 0.06xy$

	$x \rightarrow$			
	10	**20**	**30**	**40**
$y \downarrow$ **10**				
20				
30				
40				

23. **T** ▼ The following statistical table lists some values of the "Inverse F distribution" ($\alpha = 0.5$):

	$n \rightarrow$									
	1	**2**	**3**	**4**	**5**	**6**	**7**	**8**	**9**	**10**
$d \downarrow$ **1**	161.4	199.5	215.7	224.6	230.2	234.0	236.8	238.9	240.5	241.9
2	18.51	19.00	19.16	19.25	19.30	19.33	19.35	19.37	19.39	19.40
3	10.13	9.552	9.277	9.117	9.013	8.941	8.887	8.812	8.812	8.785
4	7.709	6.944	6.591	6.388	6.256	6.163	6.094	5.999	5.999	5.964
5	6.608	5.786	5.409	5.192	5.050	4.950	4.876	4.772	4.772	4.735
6	5.987	5.143	4.757	4.534	4.387	4.284	4.207	4.099	4.099	4.060
7	5.591	4.737	4.347	4.120	3.972	3.866	3.787	3.677	3.677	3.637
8	5.318	4.459	4.066	3.838	3.688	3.581	3.500	3.388	3.388	3.347
9	5.117	4.256	3.863	3.633	3.482	3.374	3.293	3.179	3.179	3.137
10	4.965	4.103	3.708	3.478	3.326	3.217	3.135	3.020	3.020	2.978

In Excel, you can compute the value of this function at (n, d) by the formula

$= \text{FINV}(0.05, \text{ n}, \text{ d})$ The 0.05 is the value of alpha (α).

Use Excel to re-create this table.

24. **T** ▼ The formula for body mass index $M(w, h)$, if w is given in kilograms and h is given in meters, is

$$M(w, h) = \dfrac{w}{h^2} \quad \text{See Example 3.}$$

Use this formula to complete the following table in Excel:

	$w \rightarrow$						
	70	**80**	**90**	**100**	**110**	**120**	**130**
$h \downarrow$ **1.8**							
1.85							
1.9							
1.95							
2							
2.05							
2.1							
2.15							
2.2							
2.25							
2.3							

1 In Exercises 25–28, use either a graphing calculator or a spreadsheet to complete each table. Express all your answers as decimals rounded to four decimal places.

25.

x	y	$f(x, y) = x^2\sqrt{1 + xy}$
3	1	
1	15	
0.3	0.5	
56	4	

26.

x	y	$f(x, y) = x^2 e^y$
0	2	
−1	5	
1.4	2.5	
11	9	

27.

x	y	$f(x, y) = x\ln(x^2 + y^2)$
3	1	
1.4	−1	
e	0	
0	e	

28.

x	y	$f(x, y) = \dfrac{x}{x^2 - y^2}$
−1	2	
0	0.2	
0.4	2.5	
10	0	

29. ▼ Brand Z's annual sales are affected by the sales of related products X and Y as follows: Each $1 million increase in sales of brand X causes a $2.1 million decline in sales of brand Z, whereas each $1 million increase in sales of brand Y results in an increase of $0.4 million in sales of brand Z. Currently, brands X, Y, and Z are each selling $6 million per year. Model the sales of brand Z using a linear function.

30. ▼ Let $f(x, y, z) = 43.2 - 2.3x + 11.3y - 4.5z$. Complete the following: An increase of 1 in the value of y causes the value of f to ___ by ___, whereas increasing the value of x by 1 and ___ the value of z by ___ causes a decrease of 11.3 in the value of f.

31. Sketch the cube with vertices $(0, 0, 0)$, $(1, 0, 0)$, $(0, 1, 0)$, $(0, 0, 1)$, $(1, 1, 0)$, $(1, 0, 1)$, $(0, 1, 1)$, and $(1, 1, 1)$. HINT [See Example 4.]

32. Sketch the cube with vertices $(-1, -1, -1)$, $(1, -1, -1)$, $(-1, 1, -1)$, $(-1, -1, 1)$, $(1, 1, -1)$, $(1, -1, 1)$, $(-1, 1, 1)$, and $(1, 1, 1)$. HINT [See Example 4.]

33. Sketch the pyramid with vertices $(1, 1, 0)$, $(1, -1, 0)$, $(-1, 1, 0)$, $(-1, -1, 0)$, and $(0, 0, 2)$.

34. Sketch the solid with vertices $(1, 1, 0)$, $(1, -1, 0)$, $(-1, 1, 0)$, $(-1, -1, 0)$, $(0, 0, -1)$, and $(0, 0, 1)$.

Sketch the planes in Exercises 35–40.

35. $z = -2$ 36. $z = 4$

37. $y = 2$ 38. $y = -3$

39. $x = -3$ 40. $x = 2$

Match each equation in Exercises 41–48 with one of the graphs below. (If necessary, use technology to render the surfaces.) HINT [See Examples 5, 6, and 7.]

41. $f(x, y) = 1 - 3x + 2y$ 42. $f(x, y) = 1 - \sqrt{x^2 + y^2}$

43. $f(x, y) = 1 - (x^2 + y^2)$ 44. $f(x, y) = y^2 - x^2$

45. $f(x, y) = -\sqrt{1 - (x^2 + y^2)}$

46. $f(x, y) = 1 + (x^2 + y^2)$

47. $f(x, y) = \dfrac{1}{x^2 + y^2}$ 48. $f(x, y) = 3x - 2y + 1$

(A)   **(B)**

(C)   **(D)**

(E)   **(F)**

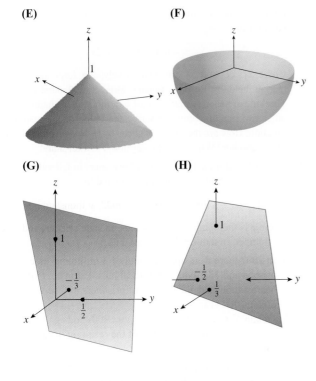

(G)   **(H)**

In Exercises 49–54 sketch the level curves $f(x, y) = c$ for the given function and values of c. HINT [See Example 5.]

49. $f(x, y) = 2x^2 + 2y^2; c = 0, 2, 18$

50. $f(x, y) = 3x^2 + 3y^2; c = 0, 3, 27$

51. $f(x, y) = y + 2x^2; c = -2, 0, 2$

52. $f(x, y) = 2y - x^2; c = -2, 0, 2$

53. $f(x, y) = 2xy - 1; c = -1, 0, 1$

54. $f(x, y) = 2 + xy; c = -2, 0, 2$

Sketch the graphs of the functions in Exercises 55–76. HINT [See Example 7.]

55. $f(x, y) = 1 - x - y$ **56.** $f(x, y) = x + y - 2$

57. $g(x, y) = 2x + y - 2$ **58.** $g(x, y) = 3 - x + 2y$

59. $h(x, y) = x + 2$ **60.** $h(x, y) = 3 - y$

61. $r(x, y) = x + y$ **62.** $r(x, y) = x - y$

▨ *Use of technology is suggested in Exercises 63–76.* HINT [See Example 6.]

63. $s(x, y) = 2x^2 + 2y^2$. Show cross sections at $z = 1$ and $z = 2$.

64. $s(x, y) = -(x^2 + y^2)$. Show cross sections at $z = -1$ and $z = -2$.

65. $t(x, y) = x^2 + 2y^2$. Show cross sections at $x = 0$ and $z = 1$.

66. $t(x, y) = \frac{1}{2}x^2 + y^2$. Show cross sections at $x = 0$ and $z = 1$.

67. $f(x, y) = 2 + \sqrt{x^2 + y^2}$. Show cross sections at $z = 3$ and $y = 0$.

68. $f(x, y) = 2 - \sqrt{x^2 + y^2}$. Show cross sections at $z = 0$ and $y = 0$.

69. $f(x, y) = -2\sqrt{x^2 + y^2}$. Show cross sections at $z = -4$ and $y = 1$.

70. $f(x, y) = 2 + 2\sqrt{x^2 + y^2}$. Show cross sections at $z = 4$ and $y = 1$.

71. $f(x, y) = y^2$ **72.** $g(x, y) = x^2$

73. $h(x, y) = \frac{1}{y}$ **74.** $k(x, y) = e^y$

75. $f(x, y) = e^{-(x^2+y^2)}$ **76.** $g(x, y) = \frac{1}{\sqrt{x^2 + y^2}}$

APPLICATIONS

77. *Marginal Cost* Your weekly cost (in dollars) to manufacture x cars and y trucks is

$$C(x, y) = 240,000 + 6,000x + 4,000y.$$

a. What is the marginal cost of a car? Of a truck? HINT [See Example 1.]

b. Describe the graph of the cost function C. HINT [See Example 7.]

c. Describe the slice $x = 10$. What cost function does this slice describe?

d. Describe the level curve $z = 480,000$. What does this curve tell you about costs?

78. *Marginal Cost* Your weekly cost (in dollars) to manufacture x bicycles and y tricycles is

$$C(x, y) = 24,000 + 60x + 20y.$$

a. What is the marginal cost of a bicycle? Of a tricycle? HINT [See Example 1.]

b. Describe the graph of the cost function C. HINT [See Example 7.]

c. Describe the slice by $y = 100$. What cost function does this slice describe?

d. Describe the level curve $z = 72,000$. What does this curve tell you about costs?

79. *Marginal Cost* Your sales of online video and audio clips are booming. Your Internet provider, Moneydrain.com, wants to get in on the action and has offered you unlimited technical assistance and consulting if you agree to pay Moneydrain 3¢ for every video clip and 4¢ for every audio clip you sell on the site. Further, Moneydrain agrees to charge you only $10 per month to host your site. Set up a (monthly) cost function for the scenario, and describe each variable.

80. *Marginal Cost* Your Cabaret nightspot "Jazz on Jupiter" has become an expensive proposition: You are paying monthly costs of $50,000 just to keep the place running. On top of that, your regular cabaret artist is charging you $3,000 per performance, and your jazz ensemble is charging $1,000 per hour. Set up a (monthly) cost function for the scenario, and describe each variable.

81. *Scientific Research* In each year from 1983 to 2003, the percentage y of research articles in *Physical Review* written by researchers in the United States can be approximated by

$$y = 82 - 0.78t - 1.02x \text{ percentage points} \quad (0 \le t \le 20)$$

where t is the year since 1983 and x is the percentage of articles written by researchers in Europe.[1]

a. In 2003, researchers in Europe wrote 38% of the articles published by the journal that year. What percentage was written by researchers in the United States?

b. In 1983, researchers in the United States wrote 61% of the articles published that year. What percentage was written by researchers in Europe?

c. What are the units of measurement of the coefficient of t?

82. *Scientific Research* The number z of research articles in *Physical Review* that were written by researchers in the United States from 1993 through 2003 can be approximated by

$$z = 5,960 - 0.71x + 0.50y \quad (3,000 \le x, y \le 6,000)$$

articles each year, where x is the number of articles written by researchers in Europe and y is the number written by researchers in other countries (excluding Europe and the United States).[2]

a. In the year 2000, approximately 5,500 articles were written by researchers in Europe, and 4,500 by researchers in other countries. How many (to the nearest 100) were written by researchers in the United States?

b. According to the model, if 5,000 articles were written in Europe and an equal number by researchers in the United States and other countries, what would that number be?

c. What is the significance of the fact that the coefficient of x is negative?

83. *Market Share in the 1900s:* Chrysler, Ford, General Motors In the late 1900s, the relationship between the domestic market shares of three major U.S. manufacturers of cars and light trucks could be modeled by

$$x_3 = 0.66 - 2.2x_1 - 0.02x_2$$

where x_1, x_2, and x_3 are, respectively, the fractions of the market held by **Chrysler, Ford,** and **General Motors.**[3] Thinking of **General Motors'** market share as a function of the shares of the other two manufacturers, describe the graph of the resulting function. How are the different slices by $x_1 = constant$ related to one another? What does this say about market share?

84. *Market Share in the 1900s:* Kellogg, General Mills, General Foods In the late 1900s, the relationship among the domestic market shares of three major manufacturers of breakfast cereal was

$$x_1 = -0.4 + 1.2x_2 + 2x_3$$

where x_1, x_2, and x_3 are, respectively, the fractions of the market held by **Kellogg, General Mills,** and **General Foods.**[4] Thinking of **Kellogg's** market share as a function of shares of the other two manufacturers, describe the graph of the resulting function. How are the different slices by $x_2 = constant$ related to one another? What does this say about market share?

85. *Prison Population* The number of prisoners in federal prisons in the United States can be approximated by

$$N(x, y) = 27 - 0.08x + 0.08y + 0.0002xy \text{ thousand inmates}$$

where x is the number, in thousands, in state prisons, and y is the number, in thousands, in local jails.[5]

a. In 2007 there were approximately 1.3 million in state prisons and 781 thousand in local jails. Estimate, to the nearest thousand, the number of prisoners in federal prisons that year.

b. Obtain N as a function of x for $y = 300$, and again for $y = 500$. Interpret the slopes of the resulting linear functions.

86. *Prison Population* The number of prisoners in state prisons in the United States can be approximated by

$$N(x, y) = -260 + 7x + 2y - 0.009xy \text{ thousand inmates}$$

where x is the number, in thousands, in federal prisons, and y is the number, in thousands, in local jails.[6]

a. In 2007 there were approximately 189 thousand in federal prisons and 781 thousand in local jails. Estimate, to the nearest 0.1 million, the number of prisoners in state prisons that year.

b. Obtain N as a function of y for $x = 80$, and again for $x = 100$. Interpret the slopes of the resulting linear functions.

87. *Marginal Cost (Interaction Model)* Your weekly cost (in dollars) to manufacture x cars and y trucks is

$$C(x, y) = 240,000 + 6,000x + 4,000y - 20xy.$$

(Compare with Exercise 77.)

a. Describe the slices $x = constant$ and $y = constant$.

b. Is the graph of the cost function a plane? How does your answer relate to part (a)?

c. What are the slopes of the slices $x = 10$ and $x = 20$? What does this say about cost?

---

[1] Source: The American Physical Society/*New York Times*, May 3, 2003, p. A1.

[2] Ibid.

[3] The model is based on a linear regression. Source of data: Ward's AutoInfoBank/*The New York Times*, July 29, 1998, p. D6.

[4] The models are based on a linear regression. Source of data: Bloomberg Financial Markets/*The New York Times*, November 28, 1998, p. C1.

[5] Source for data: Sourcebook of Criminal Justice Statistics Online (www.albany.edu/sourcebook/wk1/t6132007.wk1).

[6] Ibid.

88. Marginal Cost (Interaction Model) Repeat the preceding exercise using the weekly cost to manufacture x bicycles and y tricycles given by

$$C(x, y) = 24{,}000 + 60x + 20y + 0.3xy.$$

(Compare with Exercise 78.)

89. ▼ Online Revenue Let us look once again at the example we used to introduce the chapter. Your major online bookstore is in direct competition with **Amazon.com**, **BN.com**, and **Borders.com**. Your company's daily revenue in dollars is given by

$$R(x, y, z) = 10{,}000 - 0.01x - 0.02y - 0.01z + 0.00001yz,$$

where x, y, and z are the online daily revenues of **Amazon.com**, **BN.com**, and **Borders.com** respectively.

a. If, on a certain day, **Amazon.com** shows revenue of $12,000, while **BN.com** and **Borders.com** each show $5,000, what does the model predict for your company's revenue that day?

b. If **Amazon.com** and **BN.com** each show daily revenue of $5,000, give an equation showing how your daily revenue depends on that of **Borders.com**.

90. ▼ Online Revenue Repeat the preceding exercise, using the revised revenue function

$$R(x, y, z) = 20{,}000 - 0.02x - 0.04y - 0.01z + 0.00001yz.$$

91. ▼ Profits: Walmart, Target The following table shows the approximate net earnings, in billions of dollars, of **Walmart** and **Target** in 2000, 2004, and 2008.[7]

	2000	**2004**	**2008**
Walmart	160	250	370
Target	27	42	62

Model **Walmart**'s net earnings as a function of **Target**'s net earnings and time, using a linear function of the form

$$f(x, t) = Ax + Bt + C \quad (A, B, C \text{ constants})$$

where f is **Walmart**'s net earnings (in billions of dollars), x is **Target**'s net earnings (in billions of dollars), and t is time in years since 2000. In 2006 **Target**'s net earnings were about $52.5 billion. What does your model estimate as **Walmart**'s net earnings that year?

92. ▼ Profits: Nintendo, Nokia The following table shows the approximate net earnings of **Nintendo** (in billions of yen) and **Nokia** (in billions of euro) in 2000, 2004, and 2008.[8]

	2000	**2004**	**2008**
Nintendo	530	510	1700
Nokia	30	30	52

Model **Nintendo**'s net earnings as a function of **Nokia**'s net earnings and time, using a linear function of the form

$$f(x, t) = Ax + Bt + C \quad (A, B, C \text{ constants})$$

where f is **Nintendo**'s net earnings (in billions of yen), x is **Nokia**'s net earnings (in billions of euro), and t is time in years since 2000. In 2007 **Nokia**'s net earnings were about €50 billion. What does your model estimate as **Nokia**'s net earnings that year?

93. ▼ Utility Suppose your newspaper is trying to decide between two competing desktop publishing software packages, Macro Publish and Turbo Publish. You estimate that if you purchase x copies of Macro Publish and y copies of Turbo Publish, your company's daily productivity will be

$$U(x, y) = 6x^{0.8}y^{0.2} + x$$

where $U(x, y)$ is measured in pages per day (U is called a *utility function*). If $x = y = 10$, calculate the effect of increasing x by one unit, and interpret the result.

94. ▼ Housing Costs[9] The cost C (in dollars) of building a house is related to the number k of carpenters used and the number e of electricians used by

$$C(k, e) = 15{,}000 + 50k^2 + 60e^2.$$

If $k = e = 10$, compare the effects of increasing k by one unit and of increasing e by one unit. Interpret the result.

95. ▼ Volume The volume of an ellipsoid with cross-sectional radii a, b, and c is $V(a, b, c) = \frac{4}{3}\pi abc$.

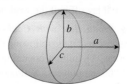

a. Find at least two sets of values for a, b, and c such that $V(a, b, c) = 1$.

b. Find the value of a such that $V(a, a, a) = 1$, and describe the resulting ellipsoid.

96. ▼ Volume The volume of a right elliptical cone with height h and radii a and b of its base is $V(a, b, h) = \frac{1}{3}\pi abh$.

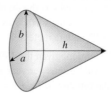

a. Find at least two sets of values for a, b, and h such that $V(a, b, h) = 1$.

b. Find the value of a such that $V(a, a, a) = 1$, and describe the resulting cone.

---

[7] Sources: www.walmartstores.com/Investors, www.investors.target.com

[8] Sources: www.nintendo.com/corp/, www.investors.nokia.com

[9] Based on an Exercise in *Introduction to Mathematical Economics* by A. L. Ostrosky Jr. and J. V. Koch (Waveland Press, Illinois, 1979).

Exercises 97–100 involve "Cobb-Douglas" productivity functions. These functions have the form

$$P(x, y) = Kx^a y^{1-a}$$

where P stands for the number of items produced per year, x is the number of employees, and y is the annual operating budget. (The numbers K and a are constants that depend on the situation we are looking at, with $0 \le a \le 1$.)

97. Productivity How many items will be produced per year by a company with 100 employees and an annual operating budget of $500,000 if $K = 1,000$ and $a = 0.5$? (Round your answer to one significant digit.)

98. Productivity How many items will be produced per year by a company with 50 employees and an annual operating budget of $1,000,000 if $K = 1,000$ and $a = 0.5$? (Round your answer to one significant digit.)

99. ▼ **Modeling Production with Cobb-Douglas** Two years ago my piano manufacturing plant employed 1,000 workers, had an operating budget of $1 million, and turned out 100 pianos. Last year, I slashed the operating budget to $10,000, and production dropped to 10 pianos.

   a. Use the data for each of the two years and the Cobb-Douglas formula to obtain two equations in K and a.

   b. Take logs of both sides in each equation and obtain two linear equations in a and log K.

   c. Solve these equations to obtain values for a and K.

   d. Use these values in the Cobb-Douglas formula to predict production if I increase the operating budget back to $1 million but lay off half the work force.

100. ▼ **Modeling Production with Cobb-Douglas** Repeat the preceding exercise using the following data: Two years ago— 1,000 employees, $1 million operating budget, 100 pianos; last year—1,000 employees, $100,000 operating budget, 10 pianos.

101. ▼ **Pollution** The burden of man-made aerosol sulfate in the earth's atmosphere, in grams per square meter, is

$$B(x, n) = \frac{xn}{A}$$

where x is the total weight of aerosol sulfate emitted into the atmosphere per year and n is the number of years it remains in the atmosphere. A is the surface area of the earth, approximately 5.1×10^{14} square meters.[10]

   a. Calculate the burden, given the 1995 estimated values of $x = 1.5 \times 10^{14}$ grams per year, and $n = 5$ days.

   b. What does the function $W(x, n) = xn$ measure?

102. ▼ **Pollution** The amount of aerosol sulfate (in grams) was approximately 45×10^{12} grams in 1940 and has been increasing exponentially ever since, with a doubling time of

approximately 20 years.[11] Use the model from the preceding exercise to give a formula for the atmospheric burden of aerosol sulfate as a function of the time t in years since 1940 and the number of years n it remains in the atmosphere.

103. ▼ **Alien Intelligence** Frank Drake, an astronomer at the University of California at Santa Cruz, devised the following equation to estimate the number of planet-based civilizations in our Milky Way galaxy willing and able to communicate with Earth:[12]

$$N(R, f_p, n_e, f_l, f_i, f_c, L) = Rf_p n_e f_l f_i f_c L$$

$R =$ the number of new stars formed in our galaxy each year

$f_p =$ the fraction of those stars that have planetary systems

$n_e =$ the average number of planets in each such system that can support life

$f_l =$ the fraction of such planets on which life actually evolves

$f_i =$ the fraction of life-sustaining planets on which intelligent life evolves

$f_c =$ the fraction of intelligent-life-bearing planets on which the intelligent beings develop the means and the will to communicate over interstellar distances

$L =$ the average lifetime of such technological civilizations (in years)

   a. What would be the effect on N if any one of the variables were doubled?

   b. How would you modify the formula if you were interested only in the number of intelligent-life-bearing planets in the galaxy?

   c. How could one convert this function into a linear function?

   d. (For discussion) Try to come up with an estimate of N.

104. ▼ **More Alien Intelligence** The formula given in the preceding exercise restricts attention to planet-based civilizations in our galaxy. Give a formula that includes intelligent planet-based aliens from the galaxy Andromeda. (Assume that all the variables used in the formula for the Milky Way have the same values for Andromeda.)

COMMUNICATION AND REASONING EXERCISES

105. Let $f(x, y) = \dfrac{x}{y}$. How are $f(x, y)$ and $f(y, x)$ related?

106. Let $f(x, y) = x^2 y^3$. How are $f(x, y)$ and $f(-x, -y)$ related?

---

[11] Ibid.

[12] Source: "First Contact" (Plume Books/Penguin Group)/*The New York Times*, October 6, 1992, p. C1.

[10] Source: Robert J. Charlson and Tom M. L. Wigley, "Sulfate Aerosol and Climatic Change," *Scientific American*, February, 1994, pp. 48–57.

107. Give an example of a function of the two variables x and y with the property that interchanging x and y has no effect.

108. Give an example of a function f of the two variables x and y with the property that $f(x, y) = -f(y, x)$.

109. Give an example of a function f of the three variables x, y, and z with the property that $f(x, y, z) = f(y, x, z)$ and $f(-x, -y, -z) = -f(x, y, z)$.

110. Give an example of a function f of the three variables x, y, and z with the property that $f(x, y, z) = f(y, x, z)$ and $f(-x, -y, -z) = f(x, y, z)$.

111. Illustrate by means of an example how a real-valued function of the two variables x and y gives different real-valued functions of one variable when we restrict y to be different constants.

112. Illustrate by means of an example how a real-valued function of one variable x gives different real-valued functions of the two variables y and z when we substitute for x suitable functions of y and z.

113. ▼ If f is a linear function of x and y, show that if we restrict y to be a fixed constant, then the resulting function of x is linear. Does the slope of this linear function depend on the choice of y?

114. ▼ If f is an interaction function of x and y, show that if we restrict y to be a fixed constant, then the resulting function of x is linear. Does the slope of this linear function depend on the choice of y?

115. ▼ Suppose that $C(x, y)$ represents the cost of x CDs and y cassettes. If $C(x, y + 1) < C(x + 1, y)$ for every $x \geq 0$ and $y \geq 0$, what does this tell you about the cost of CDs and cassettes?

116. ▼ Suppose that $C(x, y)$ represents the cost of renting x DVDs and y video games. If $C(x + 2, y) < C(x, y + 1)$ for every $x \geq 0$ and $y \geq 0$, what does this tell you about the cost of renting DVDs and video games?

117. Complete the following: The graph of a linear function of two variables is a _____ .

118. Complete the following: The level curves of a linear function of two variables are _____ .

119. ▼ **Heat-Seeking Missiles** The following diagram shows some level curves of the temperature, in degrees Fahrenheit, of a region in space, as well as the location, on the 100-degree curve, of a heat-seeking missile moving through the region. (These level curves are called **isotherms**.) In which of the three directions shown should the missile be traveling so as to experience the fastest rate of increase in temperature at the given point? Explain your answer.

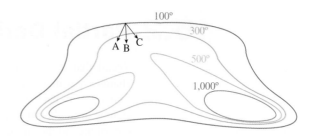

120. ▼ **Hiking** The following diagram shows some level curves of the altitude of a mountain valley, as well as the location, on the 2,000-ft curve, of a hiker. The hiker is currently moving at the greatest possible rate of descent. In which of the three directions shown is he moving? Explain your answer.

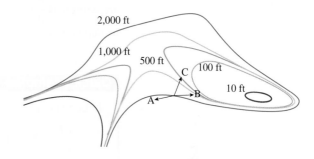

121. Your study partner Slim claims that because the surface $z = f(x, y)$ you have been studying is a plane, it follows that all the slices $x = constant$ and $y = constant$ are straight lines. Do you agree or disagree? Explain.

122. Your other study partner Shady just told you that the surface $z = xy$ you have been trying to graph must be a plane because you've already found that the slices $x = constant$ and $y = constant$ are all straight lines. Do you agree or disagree? Explain.

123. Why do we not sketch the graphs of functions of three or more variables?

124. The surface of a mountain can be thought of as the graph of what function?

125. Why is three-dimensional space used to represent the graph of a function of two variables?

126. Why is it that we can sketch the graphs of functions of two variables on the two-dimensional flat surfaces of these pages?

15.2 Partial Derivatives

Recall that if f is a function of x, then the derivative df/dx measures how fast f changes as x increases. If f is a function of two or more variables, we can ask how fast f changes as each variable increases while the others remain fixed. These rates of change are called the "partial derivatives of f," and they measure how each variable contributes to the change in f. Here is a more precise definition.

Partial Derivatives

The **partial derivative of f with respect to x** is the derivative of f with respect to x, when all other variables are treated as constant. Similarly, the **partial derivative of f with respect to y** is the derivative of f with respect to y, with all other variables treated as constant, and so on for other variables. The partial derivatives are written as $\dfrac{\partial f}{\partial x}, \dfrac{\partial f}{\partial y}$, and so on. The symbol ∂ is used (instead of d) to remind us that there is more than one variable and that we are holding the other variables fixed.

Quick Examples

1. Let $f(x, y) = x^2 + y^2$.

$$\frac{\partial f}{\partial x} = 2x + 0 = 2x \qquad \text{Because } y^2 \text{ is treated as a constant}$$

$$\frac{\partial f}{\partial y} = 0 + 2y = 2y \qquad \text{Because } x^2 \text{ is treated as a constant}$$

2. Let $z = x^2 + xy$.

$$\frac{\partial z}{\partial x} = 2x + y \qquad \frac{\partial}{\partial x}(xy) = \frac{\partial}{\partial x}(x \cdot \text{constant}) = \text{constant} = y$$

$$\frac{\partial z}{\partial y} = 0 + x \qquad \frac{\partial}{\partial y}(xy) = \frac{\partial}{\partial x}(\text{constant} \cdot y) = \text{constant} = x$$

3. Let $f(x, y) = x^2 y + y^2 x - xy + y$.

$$\frac{\partial f}{\partial x} = 2xy + y^2 - y \qquad y \text{ is treated as a constant.}$$

$$\frac{\partial f}{\partial y} = x^2 + 2xy - x + 1 \qquad x \text{ is treated as a constant.}$$

Interpretation

$\dfrac{\partial f}{\partial x}$ is the rate at which f changes as x changes, for a fixed (constant) y.

$\dfrac{\partial f}{\partial y}$ is the rate at which f changes as y changes, for a fixed (constant) x.

EXAMPLE 1 Marginal Cost: Linear Model

We return to Example 1 from Section 15.1. Suppose that you own a company that makes two models of speakers, the Ultra Mini and the Big Stack. Your total monthly cost (in dollars) to make x Ultra Minis and y Big Stacks is given by

$$C(x, y) = 10{,}000 + 20x + 40y.$$

What is the significance of $\dfrac{\partial C}{\partial x}$ and of $\dfrac{\partial C}{\partial y}$?

Solution First we compute these partial derivatives:

$$\frac{\partial C}{\partial x} = 20$$

$$\frac{\partial C}{\partial y} = 40.$$

We interpret the results as follows: $\dfrac{\partial C}{\partial x} = 20$ means that the cost is increasing at a rate of $20 per additional Ultra Mini (if production of Big Stacks is held constant); $\dfrac{\partial C}{\partial y} = 40$ means that the cost is increasing at a rate of $40 per additional Big Stack (if production of Ultra Minis is held constant). In other words, these are the **marginal costs** of each model of speaker.

➡ **Before we go on...** How much does the cost rise if you increase x by Δx and y by Δy? In Example 1, the change in cost is given by

$$\Delta C = 20\Delta x + 40\Delta y = \frac{\partial C}{\partial x}\Delta x + \frac{\partial C}{\partial y}\Delta y.$$

This suggests the **chain rule for several variables**. Part of this rule says that if x and y are both functions of t, then C is a function of t through them, and the rate of change of C with respect to t can be calculated as

$$\frac{dC}{dt} = \frac{\partial C}{\partial x}\cdot\frac{dx}{dt} + \frac{\partial C}{\partial y}\cdot\frac{dy}{dt}.$$

See the optional section on the chain rule for several variables for further discussion and applications of this interesting result. ∎

EXAMPLE 2 Marginal Cost: Interaction Model

Another possibility for the cost function in the preceding example is the interaction model

$$C(x, y) = 10{,}000 + 20x + 40y + 0.1xy.$$

a. *Now* what are the marginal costs of the two models of speakers?

b. What is the marginal cost of manufacturing Big Stacks at a production level of 100 Ultra Minis and 50 Big Stacks per month?

Solution

a. We compute the partial derivatives:

$$\frac{\partial C}{\partial x} = 20 + 0.1y$$

$$\frac{\partial C}{\partial y} = 40 + 0.1x.$$

Thus, the marginal cost of manufacturing Ultra Minis increases by $0.1 or 10¢ for each Big Stack that is manufactured. Similarly, the marginal cost of manufacturing Big Stacks increases by 10¢ for each Ultra Mini that is manufactured.

b. From part (a), the marginal cost of manufacturing Big Stacks is

$$\frac{\partial C}{\partial y} = 40 + 0.1x.$$

At a production level of 100 Ultra Minis and 50 Big Stacks per month, we have $x = 100$ and $y = 50$. Thus, the marginal cost of manufacturing Big Stacks at these production levels is

$$\left.\frac{\partial C}{\partial y}\right|_{(100,50)} = 40 + 0.1(100) = \$50 \text{ per Big Stack.}$$

Partial derivatives of functions of three variables are obtained in the same way as those for functions of two variables, as the following example shows.

EXAMPLE 3 Function of Three Variables

Calculate $\dfrac{\partial f}{\partial x}, \dfrac{\partial f}{\partial y}$, and $\dfrac{\partial f}{\partial z}$ if $f(x, y, z) = xy^2z^3 - xy$.

Solution Although we now have three variables, the calculation remains the same: $\partial f/\partial x$ is the derivative of f with respect to x, with *both* other variables, y and z, held constant:

$$\frac{\partial f}{\partial x} = y^2z^3 - y.$$

Similarly, $\partial f/\partial y$ is the derivative of f with respect to y, with both x and z held constant:

$$\frac{\partial f}{\partial y} = 2xyz^3 - x.$$

Finally, to find $\partial f/\partial z$, we hold both x and y constant and take the derivative with respect to z.

$$\frac{\partial f}{\partial z} = 3xy^2z^2.$$

Note The procedure for finding a partial derivative is the same for any number of variables: To get the partial derivative with respect to any one variable, we treat all the others as constants. ∎

Tangent line along the slice through $y = b$

$\dfrac{\partial f}{\partial x}\Big|_{(a,b)}$ is the slope of the tangent line at the point $P(a, b, f(a, b))$ along the slice through $y = b$.

Figure 17

Geometric Interpretation of Partial Derivatives

Recall that if f is a function of one variable x, then the derivative df/dx gives the slopes of the tangent lines to its graph. Now, suppose that f is a function of x and y. By definition, $\partial f/\partial x$ is the derivative of the function of x we get by holding y fixed. If we evaluate this derivative at the point (a, b), we are holding y fixed at the value b, taking the ordinary derivative of the resulting function of x, and evaluating this at $x = a$. Now, holding y fixed at b amounts to slicing through the graph of f along the plane $y = b$, resulting in a curve. Thus, the partial derivative is the slope of the tangent line to this curve at the point where $x = a$ and $y = b$, along the plane $y = b$ (Figure 17). This fits with our interpretation of $\partial f/\partial x$ as the rate of increase of f with increasing x when y is held fixed at b.

The other partial derivative, $\partial f/\partial y|_{(a,b)}$ is, similarly, the slope of the tangent line at the same point $P(a, b, f(a, b))$ but along the slice by the plane $x = a$. You should draw the corresponding picture for this on your own.

Second-Order Partial Derivatives

Just as for functions of a single variable, we can calculate second derivatives. Suppose, for example, that we have a function of x and y, say, $f(x, y) = x^2 - x^2y^2$. We know that

$$\frac{\partial f}{\partial x} = 2x - 2xy^2.$$

If we take the partial derivative with respect to x once again, we obtain

$$\frac{\partial}{\partial x}\left(\frac{\partial f}{\partial x}\right) = 2 - 2y^2. \qquad \text{Take } \frac{\partial}{\partial x} \text{ of } \frac{\partial f}{\partial x}.$$

(The symbol $\partial/\partial x$ means "the partial derivative with respect to x," just as d/dx stands for "the derivative with respect to x.") This is called the **second-order partial derivative** and is written $\dfrac{\partial^2 f}{\partial x^2}$. We get the following derivatives similarly:

$$\frac{\partial f}{\partial y} = -2x^2y$$

$$\frac{\partial^2 f}{\partial y^2} = -2x^2. \qquad \text{Take } \frac{\partial}{\partial y} \text{ of } \frac{\partial f}{\partial y}.$$

Now what if we instead take the partial derivative with respect to y of $\partial f/\partial x$?

$$\frac{\partial^2 f}{\partial y\partial x} = \frac{\partial}{\partial y}\left(\frac{\partial f}{\partial x}\right) \qquad \text{Take } \frac{\partial}{\partial y} \text{ of } \frac{\partial f}{\partial x}.$$

$$= \frac{\partial}{\partial y}[2x - 2xy^2] = -4xy.$$

Here, $\dfrac{\partial^2 f}{\partial y\partial x}$ means "first take the partial derivative with respect to x and then with respect to y," and is called a **mixed partial derivative**. If we differentiate in the opposite order, we get

$$\frac{\partial^2 f}{\partial x\partial y} = \frac{\partial}{\partial x}\left(\frac{\partial f}{\partial y}\right) = \frac{\partial}{\partial x}[-2x^2y] = -4xy,$$

the same expression as $\dfrac{\partial^2 f}{\partial y \partial x}$. This is no coincidence: The mixed partial derivatives $\dfrac{\partial^2 f}{\partial x \partial y}$ and $\dfrac{\partial^2 f}{\partial y \partial x}$ are always the same as long as the first partial derivatives are both differentiable functions of x and y and the mixed partial derivatives are continuous. Because all the functions we shall use are of this type, we can take the derivatives in any order we like when calculating mixed derivatives.

Here is another notation for partial derivatives that is especially convenient for second-order partial derivatives:

$$f_x \text{ means } \frac{\partial f}{\partial x}$$

$$f_y \text{ means } \frac{\partial f}{\partial y}$$

$$f_{xy} \text{ means } (f_x)_y = \frac{\partial^2 f}{\partial y \partial x} \quad \text{(Note the order in which the derivatives are taken.)}$$

$$f_{yx} \text{ means } (f_y)_x = \frac{\partial^2 f}{\partial x \partial y}.$$

15.2 EXERCISES

▼ more advanced   ◆ challenging

T indicates exercises that should be solved using technology

In Exercises 1–18, calculate $\dfrac{\partial f}{\partial x}, \dfrac{\partial f}{\partial y}, \dfrac{\partial f}{\partial x}\bigg|_{(1,-1)}$, *and* $\dfrac{\partial f}{\partial y}\bigg|_{(1,-1)}$

when defined. HINT [See Quick Examples page 1098.]

1. $f(x, y) = 10{,}000 - 40x + 20y$

2. $f(x, y) = 1{,}000 + 5x - 4y$

3. $f(x, y) = 3x^2 - y^3 + x - 1$

4. $f(x, y) = x^{1/2} - 2y^4 + y + 6$

5. $f(x, y) = 10{,}000 - 40x + 20y + 10xy$

6. $f(x, y) = 1{,}000 + 5x - 4y - 3xy$

7. $f(x, y) = 3x^2 y$

8. $f(x, y) = x^4 y^2 - x$

9. $f(x, y) = x^2 y^3 - x^3 y^2 - xy$

10. $f(x, y) = x^{-1} y^2 + xy^2 + xy$

11. $f(x, y) = (2xy + 1)^3$ **12.** $f(x, y) = \dfrac{1}{(xy+1)^2}$

13. ▼ $f(x, y) = e^{x+y}$ **14.** ▼ $f(x, y) = e^{2x+y}$

15. ▼ $f(x, y) = 5x^{0.6} y^{0.4}$ **16.** ▼ $f(x, y) = -2x^{0.1} y^{0.9}$

17. ▼ $f(x, y) = e^{0.2xy}$ **18.** ▼ $f(x, y) = xe^{xy}$

In Exercises 19–28, find $\dfrac{\partial^2 f}{\partial x^2}, \dfrac{\partial^2 f}{\partial y^2}, \dfrac{\partial^2 f}{\partial x \partial y}$, *and* $\dfrac{\partial^2 f}{\partial y \partial x}$, *and*

evaluate them all at $(1, -1)$ *if possible.* HINT [See Discussion on page 1101.]

19. $f(x, y) = 10{,}000 - 40x + 20y$

20. $f(x, y) = 1{,}000 + 5x - 4y$

21. $f(x, y) = 10{,}000 - 40x + 20y + 10xy$

22. $f(x, y) = 1{,}000 + 5x - 4y - 3xy$

23. $f(x, y) = 3x^2 y$ **24.** $f(x, y) = x^4 y^2 - x$

25. ▼ $f(x, y) = e^{x+y}$ **26.** ▼ $f(x, y) = e^{2x+y}$

27. ▼ $f(x, y) = 5x^{0.6} y^{0.4}$ **28.** ▼ $f(x, y) = -2x^{0.1} y^{0.9}$

In Exercises 29–40, find $\dfrac{\partial f}{\partial x}, \dfrac{\partial f}{\partial y}, \dfrac{\partial f}{\partial z}$, *and their values at* $(0, -1, 1)$

if possible. HINT [See Example 3.]

29. $f(x, y, z) = xyz$

30. $f(x, y, z) = xy + xz - yz$

31. ▼ $f(x, y, z) = -\dfrac{4}{x+y+z^2}$

32. ▼ $f(x, y, z) = \dfrac{6}{x^2 + y^2 + z^2}$

33. ▼ $f(x, y, z) = xe^{yz} + ye^{xz}$

34. ▼ $f(x, y, z) = xye^z + xe^{yz} + e^{xyz}$

35. ▼ $f(x, y, z) = x^{0.1} y^{0.4} z^{0.5}$

36. ▼ $f(x, y, z) = 2x^{0.2} y^{0.8} + z^2$

37. ▼ $f(x, y, z) = e^{xyz}$

38. ▼ $f(x, y, z) = \ln(x + y + z)$

39. ▼ $f(x, y, z) = \dfrac{2{,}000z}{1 + y^{0.3}}$

40. ▼ $f(x, y, z) = \dfrac{e^{0.2x}}{1 + e^{-0.1y}}$

APPLICATIONS

41. Marginal Cost (Linear Model) Your weekly cost (in dollars) to manufacture x cars and y trucks is

$$C(x, y) = 240{,}000 + 6{,}000x + 4{,}000y.$$

Calculate and interpret $\dfrac{\partial C}{\partial x}$ and $\dfrac{\partial C}{\partial y}$. HINT [See Example 1.]

42. Marginal Cost (Linear Model) Your weekly cost (in dollars) to manufacture x bicycles and y tricycles is

$$C(x, y) = 24{,}000 + 60x + 20y.$$

Calculate and interpret $\dfrac{\partial C}{\partial x}$ and $\dfrac{\partial C}{\partial y}$.

43. Scientific Research In each year from 1983 to 2003, the percentage y of research articles in *Physical Review* written by researchers in the United States can be approximated by

$$y = 82 - 0.78t - 1.02x \text{ percentage points} \quad (0 \le t \le 20)$$

where t is the year since 1983 and x is the percentage of articles written by researchers in Europe.[13] Calculate and interpret $\dfrac{\partial y}{\partial t}$ and $\dfrac{\partial y}{\partial x}$.

44. Scientific Research The number z of research articles in *Physical Review* that were written by researchers in the United States from 1993 through 2003 can be approximated by

$$z = 5{,}960 - 0.71x + 0.50y \quad (3{,}000 \le x, y \le 6{,}000)$$

articles each year, where x is the number of articles written by researchers in Europe and y is the number written by researchers in other countries (excluding Europe and the United States).[14] Calculate and interpret $\dfrac{\partial z}{\partial x}$ and $\dfrac{\partial z}{\partial y}$.

45. Marginal Cost (Interaction Model) Your weekly cost (in dollars) to manufacture x cars and y trucks is

$$C(x, y) = 240{,}000 + 6{,}000x + 4{,}000y - 20xy.$$

(Compare with Exercise 77.) Compute the marginal cost of manufacturing cars at a production level of 10 cars and 20 trucks. HINT [See Example 2.]

46. Marginal Cost (Interaction Model) Your weekly cost (in dollars) to manufacture x bicycles and y tricycles is

$$C(x, y) = 24{,}000 + 60x + 20y + 0.3xy.$$

(Compare with Exercise 78.) Compute the marginal cost of manufacturing tricycles at a production level of 10 bicycles and 20 tricycles. HINT [See Example 2.]

47. Brand Loyalty: Mazda The fraction of **Mazda** car owners who chose another new **Mazda** can be modeled by the following function:[15]

$$M(c, f, g, h, t) = 1.1 - 3.8c + 2.2f + 1.9g - 1.7h - 1.3t.$$

Here, c is the fraction of **Chrysler** car owners who remained loyal to **Chrysler**, f is the fraction of **Ford** car owners remaining loyal to **Ford**, g the corresponding figure for **General Motors**, h the corresponding figure for **Honda**, and t for **Toyota**.

a. Calculate $\dfrac{\partial M}{\partial c}$ and $\dfrac{\partial M}{\partial f}$ and interpret the answers.

b. One year it was observed that $c = 0.56$, $f = 0.56$, $g = 0.72$, $h = 0.50$, and $t = 0.43$. According to the model, what percentage of **Mazda** owners remained loyal to **Mazda**? (Round your answer to the nearest percentage point.)

48. Brand Loyalty The fraction of **Mazda** car owners who chose another new **Mazda** can be modeled by the following function:[16]

$$M(c, f) = 9.4 + 7.8c + 3.6c^2 - 38f - 22cf + 43f^2$$

where c is the fraction of **Chrysler** car owners who remained loyal to **Chrysler** and f is the fraction of **Ford** car owners remaining loyal to **Ford**.

a. Calculate $\dfrac{\partial M}{\partial c}$ and $\dfrac{\partial M}{\partial f}$ evaluated at the point $(0.7, 0.7)$, and interpret the answers.

b. One year it was observed that $c = 0.56$, and $f = 0.56$. According to the model, what percentage of **Mazda** owners remained loyal to **Mazda**? (Round your answer to the nearest percentage point.)

49. ▼ Income Gap The following model is based on data on the median family incomes of Hispanic and white families in the United States for the period 1980–2008:[17]

$$z(t, x) = 31{,}200 + 270t + 13{,}500x + 140xt$$

where

$z(t, x) = $ median family income
$t = $ year ($t = 0$ represents 1980)
$$x = \begin{cases} 0 & \text{if the income was for a Hispanic family} \\ 1 & \text{if the income was for a white family.} \end{cases}$$

---

[13] Source: The American Physical Society/*New York Times*, May 3, 2003, p. A1.

[14] Ibid.

[15] The model is an approximation of a linear regression based on data from the period 1988–1995. Source for data: Chrysler, Maritz Market Research, Consumer Attitude Research, and Strategic Vision/*The New York Times*, November 3, 1995, p. D2.

[16] The model is an approximation of a second order regression based on data from the period 1988–1995. Source for data: Chrysler, Maritz Market Research, Consumer Attitude Research, and Strategic Vision/*The New York Times*, November 3, 1995, p. D2.

[17] Incomes are in 2007 dollars. Source for data: U.S. Census Bureau (www.census.gov).

a. Use the model to estimate the median income of a Hispanic family and of a white family in 2000.

b. According to the model, how fast was the median income for a Hispanic family increasing in 2000? How fast was the median income for a white family increasing in 2000?

c. Do the answers in part (b) suggest that the income gap between white and Hispanic families was widening or narrowing during the given period?

d. What does the coefficient of xt in the formula for $z(t, x)$ represent in terms of the income gap?

50. ▼ *Income Gap* The following model is based on data on the median family incomes of black and white families in the United States for the period 1980–2008:[18]

$$z(t, x) = 24,500 + 390t + 20,200x + 20xt$$

where

$z(t, x) = $ median family income

$t = $ year ($t = 0$ represents 1980)

$x = \begin{cases} 0 & \text{if the income was for a black family} \\ 1 & \text{if the income was for a white family.} \end{cases}$

a. Use the model to estimate the median income of a black family and of a white family in 2000.

b. According to the model, how fast was the median income for a black family increasing in 2000? How fast was the median income for a white family increasing in 2000?

c. Do the answers in part (b) suggest that the income gap between white and black families was widening or narrowing during the given period?

d. What does the coefficient of xt in the formula for $z(t, x)$ represent in terms of the income gap?

51. ▼ *Marginal Cost* Your weekly cost (in dollars) to manufacture x cars and y trucks is

$$C(x, y) = 200,000 + 6,000x + 4,000y - 100,000e^{-0.01(x+y)}.$$

What is the marginal cost of a car? Of a truck? How do these marginal costs behave as total production increases?

52. ▼ *Marginal Cost* Your weekly cost (in dollars) to manufacture x bicycles and y tricycles is

$$C(x, y) = 20,000 + 60x + 20y + 50\sqrt{xy}.$$

What is the marginal cost of a bicycle? Of a tricycle? How do these marginal costs behave as x and y increase?

53. ▼ *Average Cost* If you average your costs over your total production, you get the **average cost**, written $\bar{C}$:

$$\bar{C}(x, y) = \frac{C(x, y)}{x + y}.$$

Find the average cost for the cost function in Exercise 51. Then find the marginal average cost of a car and the marginal average cost of a truck at a production level of 50 cars and 50 trucks. Interpret your answers.

[18] Incomes are in 2007 dollars. Source for data: U.S. Census Bureau (www.census.gov).

54. ▼ *Average Cost* Find the average cost for the cost function in Exercise 52. (See the preceding exercise.) Then find the marginal average cost of a bicycle and the marginal average cost of a tricycle at a production level of five bicycles and five tricycles. Interpret your answers.

55. ▼ *Marginal Revenue* As manager of an auto dealership, you offer a car rental company the following deal: You will charge $15,000 per car and $10,000 per truck, but you will then give the company a discount of $5,000 times the square root of the total number of vehicles it buys from you. Looking at your marginal revenue, is this a good deal for the rental company?

56. ▼ *Marginal Revenue* As marketing director for a bicycle manufacturer, you come up with the following scheme: You will offer to sell a dealer x bicycles and y tricycles for

$$R(x, y) = 3,500 - 3,500e^{-0.02x-0.01y} \text{ dollars.}$$

Find your marginal revenue for bicycles and for tricycles. Are you likely to be fired for your suggestion?

57. ▼ *Research Productivity* Here we apply a variant of the Cobb-Douglas function to the modeling of research productivity. A mathematical model of research productivity at a particular physics laboratory is

$$P = 0.04x^{0.4}y^{0.2}z^{0.4}$$

where P is the annual number of groundbreaking research papers produced by the staff, x is the number of physicists on the research team, y is the laboratory's annual research budget, and z is the annual National Science Foundation subsidy to the laboratory. Find the rate of increase of research papers per government-subsidy dollar at a subsidy level of $1,000,000 per year and a staff level of 10 physicists if the annual budget is $100,000.

58. ▼ *Research Productivity* A major drug company estimates that the annual number P of patents for new drugs developed by its research team is best modeled by the formula

$$P = 0.3x^{0.3}y^{0.4}z^{0.3}$$

where x is the number of research biochemists on the payroll, y is the annual research budget, and z is the size of the bonus awarded to discoverers of new drugs. Assuming that the company has 12 biochemists on the staff, has an annual research budget of $500,000 and pays $40,000 bonuses to developers of new drugs, calculate the rate of growth in the annual number of patents per new research staff member.

59. ▼ *Utility* Your newspaper is trying to decide between two competing desktop publishing software packages, Macro Publish and Turbo Publish. You estimate that if you purchase x copies of Macro Publish and y copies of Turbo Publish, your company's daily productivity will be

$$U(x, y) = 6x^{0.8}y^{0.2} + x.$$

$U(x, y)$ is measured in pages per day.

a. Calculate $\left.\dfrac{\partial U}{\partial x}\right|_{(10,5)}$ and $\left.\dfrac{\partial U}{\partial y}\right|_{(10,5)}$ to two decimal places, and interpret the results.

b. What does the ratio $\left.\dfrac{\partial U}{\partial x}\right|_{(10,5)} \Big/ \left.\dfrac{\partial U}{\partial y}\right|_{(10,5)}$ tell about the usefulness of these products?

60. ▼ **Grades**[19] A production formula for a student's performance on a difficult English examination is given by

$$g(t, x) = 4tx - 0.2t^2 - x^2$$

where g is the grade the student can expect to get, t is the number of hours of study for the examination, and x is the student's grade point average.

a. Calculate $\left.\dfrac{\partial g}{\partial t}\right|_{(10,3)}$ and $\left.\dfrac{\partial g}{\partial x}\right|_{(10,3)}$ and interpret the results.

b. What does the ratio $\left.\dfrac{\partial g}{\partial t}\right|_{(10,3)} \Big/ \left.\dfrac{\partial g}{\partial x}\right|_{(10,3)}$ tell about the relative merits of study and grade point average?

61. ▼ **Electrostatic Repulsion** If positive electric charges of Q and q coulombs are situated at positions (a, b, c) and (x, y, z) respectively, then the force of repulsion they experience is given by

$$F = K \frac{Qq}{(x - a)^2 + (y - b)^2 + (z - c)^2}$$

where $K \approx 9 \times 10^9$, F is given in newtons, and all positions are measured in meters. Assume that a charge of 10 coulombs is situated at the origin, and that a second charge of 5 coulombs is situated at $(2, 3, 3)$ and moving in the y-direction at one meter per second. How fast is the electrostatic force it experiences decreasing? (Round the answer to one significant digit.)

62. ▼ **Electrostatic Repulsion** Repeat the preceding exercise, assuming that a charge of 10 coulombs is situated at the origin and that a second charge of 5 coulombs is situated at $(2, 3, 3)$ and moving in the negative z direction at one meter per second. (Round the answer to one significant digit.)

63. ▼ **Investments** Recall that the compound interest formula for annual compounding is

$$A(P, r, t) = P(1 + r)^t$$

where A is the future value of an investment of P dollars after t years at an interest rate of r.

a. Calculate $\dfrac{\partial A}{\partial P}$, $\dfrac{\partial A}{\partial r}$, and $\dfrac{\partial A}{\partial t}$, all evaluated at $(100, 0.10, 10)$. (Round your answers to two decimal places.) Interpret your answers.

b. What does the function $\left.\dfrac{\partial A}{\partial P}\right|_{(100,0.10,t)}$ of t tell about your investment?

64. ▼ **Investments** Repeat the preceding exercise, using the formula for continuous compounding:

$$A(P, r, t) = Pe^{rt}$$

65. ▼ **Modeling with the Cobb-Douglas Production Formula** Assume you are given a production formula of the form

$$P(x, y) = Kx^a y^b \quad (a + b = 1).$$

a. Obtain formulas for $\dfrac{\partial P}{\partial x}$ and $\dfrac{\partial P}{\partial y}$, and show that

$$\frac{\partial P}{\partial x} = \frac{\partial P}{\partial y} \text{ precisely when } x/y = a/b.$$

b. Let x be the number of workers a firm employs and let y be its monthly operating budget in thousands of dollars. Assume that the firm currently employs 100 workers and has a monthly operating budget of $200,000. If each additional worker contributes as much to productivity as each additional $1,000 per month, find values of a and b that model the firm's productivity.

66. ▼ **Housing Costs**[20] The cost C of building a house is related to the number k of carpenters used and the number e of electricians used by

$$C(k, e) = 15,000 + 50k^2 + 60e^2.$$

If three electricians are currently employed in building your new house and the marginal cost per additional electrician is the same as the marginal cost per additional carpenter, how many carpenters are being used? (Round your answer to the nearest carpenter.)

67. ▼ **Nutrient Diffusion** Suppose that one cubic centimeter of nutrient is placed at the center of a circular petri dish filled with water. We might wonder how the nutrient is distributed after a time of t seconds. According to the classical theory of diffusion, the concentration of nutrient (in parts of nutrient per part of water) after a time t is given by

$$u(r, t) = \frac{1}{4\pi Dt} e^{-\frac{r^2}{4Dt}}.$$

Here D is the *diffusivity*, which we will take to be 1, and r is the distance from the center in centimeters. How fast is the concentration increasing at a distance of 1 cm from the center 3 seconds after the nutrient is introduced?

68. ▼ **Nutrient Diffusion** Refer back to the preceding exercise. How fast is the concentration increasing at a distance of 4 cm from the center 4 seconds after the nutrient is introduced?

COMMUNICATION AND REASONING EXERCISES

69. Given that $f(a, b) = r$, $f_x(a, b) = s$, and $f_y(a, b) = t$, complete the following: _____ is increasing at a rate of _____ units per unit of x, _____ is increasing at a rate of _____ units per unit of y, and the value of _____ is _____ when $x = $ _____ and $y = $ _____.

70. A firm's productivity depends on two variables, x and y. Currently, $x = a$ and $y = b$, and the firm's productivity is 4,000 units. Productivity is increasing at a rate of 400 units per unit *decrease* in x, and is decreasing at a rate of 300 units per unit increase in y. What does all of this information tell you about the firm's productivity function $g(x, y)$?

71. Complete the following: Let $f(x, y, z)$ be the cost to build a development of x cypods (one-bedroom units) in the city-state of Utarek, Mars, y argaats (two-bedroom units) and z orbici

---

[19] Based on an Exercise in *Introduction to Mathematical Economics* by A. L. Ostrosky Jr. and J. V. Koch (Waveland Press, Illinois, 1979).

[20] Ibid.

(singular: orbicus; three-bedroom units) in $\bar{\bar{Z}}$ (zonars, the designated currency in Utarek).[21] Then $\dfrac{\partial f}{\partial z}$ measures _____ and has units _____ .

72. Complete the following: Let $f(t, x, y)$ be the projected number of citizens of the Principality State of Voodice, Luna[22] in year t since its founding, assuming the presence of x lunar vehicle factories and y domed settlements. Then $\dfrac{\partial f}{\partial x}$ measures _____ and has units _____ .

73. Give an example of a function $f(x, y)$ with $f_x(1, 1) = -2$ and $f_y(1, 1) = 3$.

74. Give an example of a function $f(x, y, z)$ that has all of its partial derivatives equal to nonzero constants.

---

[21] Source: www.marsnext.com/comm/zonars.html

[22] Source: www.voodice.info

75. ▼ The graph of $z = b + mx + ny$ ($b, m,$ and n constants) is a plane.

   a. Explain the geometric significance of the numbers $b, m,$ and n.

   b. Show that the equation of the plane passing through (h, k, l) with slope m in the x direction (in the sense of $\partial/\partial x$) and slope n in the y direction is

$$z = l + m(x - h) + n(y - k).$$

76. ▼ The **tangent plane** to the graph of $f(x, y)$ at $P(a, b, f(a, b))$ is the plane containing the lines tangent to the slice through the graph by $y = b$ (as in Figure 17) and the slice through the graph by $x = a$. Use the result of the preceding exercise to show that the equation of the tangent plane is

$$z = f(a, b) + f_x(a, b)(x - a) + f_y(a, b)(y - b).$$

15.3 Maxima and Minima

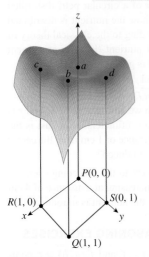

Figure 18

In Chapter 12, on applications of the derivative, we saw how to locate relative extrema of a function of a single variable. In this section we extend our methods to functions of two variables. Similar techniques work for functions of three or more variables.

Figure 18 shows a portion of the graph of the function $f(x, y) = 2(x^2 + y^2) - (x^4 + y^4) + 1$. The graph in Figure 18 resembles a "flying carpet," and several interesting points, marked $a, b, c,$ and d are shown.

1. The point a has coordinates $(0, 0, f(0, 0))$, is directly above the origin $(0, 0)$, and is the lowest point in its vicinity; water would puddle there. We say that f has a **relative minimum** at $(0, 0)$ because $f(0, 0)$ is smaller than $f(x, y)$ for any (x, y) near $(0, 0)$.

2. Similarly, the point b is higher than any point in its vicinity. Thus, we say that f has a **relative maximum** at $(1, 1)$.

3. The points c and d represent a new phenomenon and are called **saddle points**. They are neither relative maxima nor relative minima but seem to be a little of both.

To see more clearly what features a saddle point has, look at Figure 19, which shows a portion of the graph near the point d.

If we slice through the graph along $y = 1$, we get a curve on which d is the *lowest* point. Thus, d looks like a relative minimum along this slice. On the other hand, if we slice through the graph along $x = 0$, we get another curve, on which d is the *highest* point, so d looks like a relative maximum along this slice. This kind of behavior characterizes a saddle point: f has a **saddle point** at (r, s) if f has a relative minimum at (r, s) along some slice through that point and a relative maximum along another slice through that point. If you look at the other saddle point, c, in Figure 18, you see the same characteristics.

While numerical information can help us locate the approximate positions of relative extrema and saddle points, calculus permits us to locate these points accurately, as we did for functions of a single variable. Look once again at Figure 18, and notice the following:

- The points $P, Q, R,$ and S are all in the **interior** of the domain of f; that is, none lie on the boundary of the domain. Said another way, we can move some distance in any direction from any of these points without leaving the domain of f.

Figure 19

- The tangent lines along the slices through these points parallel to the x- and y-axes are *horizontal*. Thus, the partial derivatives $\partial f/\partial x$ and $\partial f/\partial y$ are zero when evaluated at any of the points P, Q, R, and S. This gives us a way of locating candidates for relative extrema and saddle points.

The following summary generalizes and also expands on some of what we have just said:

Relative and Absolute Maxima and Minima

The function f of n variables has a **relative maximum** at $(x_1, x_2, \ldots, x_n) = (r_1, r_2, \ldots, r_n)$ if $f(r_1, r_2, \ldots, r_n) \geq f(x_1, x_2, \ldots, x_n)$ for every point $(x_1, x_2, \ldots, x_n)$ near* $(r_1, r_2, \ldots, r_n)$ in the domain of f. We say that f has an **absolute maximum** at $(r_1, r_2, \ldots, r_n)$ if $f(r_1, r_2, \ldots, r_n) \geq f(x_1, x_2, \ldots, x_n)$ for every point $(x_1, x_2, \ldots, x_n)$ in the domain of f. The terms **relative minimum** and **absolute minimum** are defined in a similar way.

✱ **NOTE** For $(x, y, \ldots)$ to be near $(r, s, \ldots)$ we mean that x is in some open interval $(r - h_1, r + h_1)$ centered at r, y is in some open interval $(s - h_2, s + h_2)$ centered at s, and so on.

Locating Candidates for Relative Extrema and Saddle Points in the Interior of the Domain of f:

- Set $\dfrac{\partial f}{\partial x_1} = 0$, $\dfrac{\partial f}{\partial x_2} = 0, \ldots, \dfrac{\partial f}{\partial x_n} = 0$, simultaneously, and solve for $x_1, x_2, \ldots, x_n$.

- Check that the resulting points $(x_1, x_2, \ldots, x_n)$ are in the interior of the domain of f.

Points at which all the partial derivatives of f are zero are called **critical points**. The critical points are the only candidates for relative extrema and saddle points in the interior of the domain of f, assuming that its partial derivatives are defined at every point.*

✱ **NOTE** One can use the techniques of the next section to find extrema on the *boundary* of the domain of a function; for a complete discussion, see the optional extra section: *Maxima and Minima: Boundaries and the Extreme Value Theorem.* (We shall not consider the analogs of the singular points.)

Quick Examples

In each of the following Quick Examples, the domain is the whole Cartesian plane, and the partial derivatives are defined at every point, so the critical points give us the only candidates for relative extrema and saddle points:

1. Let $f(x, y) = x^3 + (y - 1)^2$. Then $\dfrac{\partial f}{\partial x} = 3x^2$ and $\dfrac{\partial f}{\partial y} = 2(y - 1)$. Thus, we solve the system

$$3x^2 = 0 \quad \text{and} \quad 2(y - 1) = 0.$$

The first equation gives $x = 0$, and the second gives $y = 1$. Thus, the only critical point is $(0, 1)$.

2. Let $f(x, y) = x^2 - 4xy + 8y$. Then $\dfrac{\partial f}{\partial x} = 2x - 4y$ and $\dfrac{\partial f}{\partial y} = -4x + 8$.

Thus, we solve

$$2x - 4y = 0 \quad \text{and} \quad -4x + 8 = 0.$$

The second equation gives $x = 2$, and the first then gives $y = 1$. Thus, the only critical point is $(2, 1)$.

3. Let $f(x, y) = e^{-(x^2+y^2)}$. Taking partial derivatives and setting them equal to zero gives

$$-2xe^{-(x^2+y^2)} = 0 \qquad \text{We set } \frac{\partial f}{\partial x} = 0.$$

$$-2ye^{-(x^2+y^2)} = 0. \qquad \text{We set } \frac{\partial f}{\partial y} = 0.$$

The first equation implies that $x = 0$,* and the second implies that $y = 0$. Thus, the only critical point is $(0, 0)$.

✳ NOTE Recall that if a product of two numbers is zero, then one or the other must be zero. In this case the number $e^{-(x^2+y^2)}$ can't be zero (because e^u is never zero), which gives the result claimed.

In the next example we first locate all critical points, and then classify each one as a relative maximum, minimum, saddle point, or none of these.

EXAMPLE 1 Locating and Classifying Critical Points

Locate all critical points of $f(x, y) = x^2 y - x^2 - 2y^2$. Graph the function to classify the critical points as relative maxima, minima, saddle points, or none of these.

Solution The partial derivatives are

$$f_x = 2xy - 2x = 2x(y - 1)$$
$$f_y = x^2 - 4y.$$

Setting these equal to zero gives

$$x = 0 \text{ or } y = 1$$
$$x^2 = 4y.$$

We get a solution by choosing either $x = 0$ or $y = 1$ and substituting into $x^2 = 4y$.

Case 1: $x = 0$ Substituting into $x^2 = 4y$ gives $0 = 4y$ and hence $y = 0$. Thus, the critical point for this case is $(x, y) = (0, 0)$.

Case 2: $y = 1$ Substituting into $x^2 = 4y$ gives $x^2 = 4$ and hence $x = \pm 2$. Thus, we get two critical points for this case: $(2, 1)$ and $(-2, 1)$.

We now have three critical points altogether: $(0, 0)$, $(2, 1)$, and $(-2, 1)$. Because the domain of f is the whole Cartesian plane and the partial derivatives are defined at every point, these critical points are the only candidates for relative extrema and saddle points. We get the corresponding points on the graph by substituting for x and y in the equation for f to get the z-coordinates. The points are $(0, 0, 0)$, $(2, 1, -2)$, and $(-2, 1, -2)$.

🕵 Classifying the Critical Points Graphically   To classify the critical points graphically, we look at the graph of f shown in Figure 20.

Examining the graph carefully, we see that the point $(0, 0, 0)$ is a relative maximum. As for the other two critical points, are they saddle points or are they relative maxima? They are relative maxima along the y-direction, but they are relative minima along the lines $y = \pm x$ (see the top edge of the picture, which shows a dip at $(-2, 1, 2)$) and so they are saddle points. If you don't believe this, we will get more evidence following and in a later example.

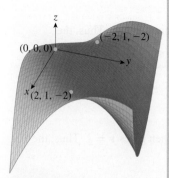

Figure 20

T *Classifying the Critical Points Numerically*   We can use a tabular representation of the function to classify the critical points numerically. The following tabular representation of the function can be obtained using Excel. (See the Excel Technology Guide discussion of Section 15.1 Example 3 at the end of the chapter for information on using Excel to generate such a table.)

	$x \rightarrow$						
$y \downarrow$		**−3**	**−2**	**−1**	**0**	**1**	**2**	**3**
−3	−54	−34	−22	−18	−22	−34	−54
−2	−35	−20	−11	−8	−11	−20	−35
−1	−20	−10	−4	−2	−4	−10	−20
0	−9	−4	−1	0	−1	−4	−9
1	−2	−2	−2	−2	−2	−2	−2
2	1	−4	−7	−8	−7	−4	1
3	0	−10	−16	−18	−16	−10	0

The shaded and colored cells show rectangular neighborhoods of the three critical points $(0, 0)$, $(2, 1)$, and $(−2, 1)$. (Notice that they overlap.) The values of f at the points are at the centers of these rectangles. Looking at the gray neighborhood of $(x, y) = (0, 0)$, we see that $f(0, 0) = 0$ is the largest value of f in the shaded cells, suggesting that f has a maximum at $(0, 0)$. The shaded neighborhood of $(2, 1)$ on the right shows $f(2, 1) = −2$ as the maximum along some slices (e.g., the vertical slice), and a minimum along the diagonal slice from top left to bottom right. This is what results in a saddle point on the graph. The point $(−2, 1)$ is similar, and thus f also has a saddle point at $(−2, 1)$.

Q : *Is there an algebraic way of deciding whether a given point is a relative maximum, relative minimum, or saddle point?*

A : There is a "second derivative test" for functions of two variables, stated as follows.

Second Derivative Test for Functions of Two Variables

Suppose (a, b) is a critical point in the interior of the domain of the function f of two variables. Let H be the quantity

$$H = f_{xx}(a, b)f_{yy}(a, b) - [f_{xy}(a, b)]^2. \qquad \text{\textit{H} is called the \textit{Hessian.}}$$

Then, if H is *positive*,

- f has a relative minimum at (a, b) if $f_{xx}(a, b) > 0$.
- f has a relative maximum at (a, b) if $f_{xx}(a, b) < 0$.

If H is *negative*,

- f has a saddle point at (a, b).

If $H = 0$, the test tells us nothing, so we need to look at the graph or a numerical table to see what is going on.

Quick Examples

1. Let $f(x, y) = x^2 - y^2$. Then

$$f_x = 2x \quad \text{and} \quad f_y = -2y,$$

which gives $(0, 0)$ as the only critical point. Also,

$$f_{xx} = 2, f_{xy} = 0, \quad \text{and} \quad f_{yy} = -2, \qquad \text{Note that these are constant.}$$

which gives $H = (2)(-2) - 0^2 = -2$. Because H is negative, we have a saddle point at $(0, 0)$.

2. Let $f(x, y) = x^2 + 2y^2 + 2xy + 4x$. Then

$$f_x = 2x + 2y + 4 \quad \text{and} \quad f_y = 2x + 4y.$$

Setting these equal to zero gives a system of two linear equations in two unknowns:

$$x + y = -2$$
$$x + 2y = 0.$$

This system has solution $(-4, 2)$, so this is our only critical point. The second partial derivatives are $f_{xx} = 2$, $f_{xy} = 2$, and $f_{yy} = 4$, so $H = (2)(4) - 2^2 = 4$. Because $H > 0$ and $f_{xx} > 0$, we have a relative minimum at $(-4, 2)$.

Note There is a second derivative test for functions of three or more variables, but it is considerably more complicated. We stick with functions of two variables for the most part in this book. The justification of the second derivative test is beyond the scope of this book. ∎

EXAMPLE 2 Using the Second Derivative Test

Use the second derivative test to analyze the function $f(x, y) = x^2 y - x^2 - 2y^2$ discussed in Example 1, and confirm the results we got there.

Solution We saw in Example 1 that the first-order derivatives are

$$f_x = 2xy - 2x = 2x(y - 1)$$
$$f_y = x^2 - 4y$$

and the critical points are $(0, 0)$, $(2, 1)$, and $(-2, 1)$. We also need the second derivatives:

$$f_{xx} = 2y - 2$$
$$f_{xy} = 2x$$
$$f_{yy} = -4.$$

The point $(0, 0)$: $f_{xx}(0, 0) = -2$, $f_{xy}(0, 0) = 0$, $f_{yy}(0, 0) = -4$, so $H = 8$. Because $H > 0$ and $f_{xx}(0, 0) < 0$, the second derivative test tells us that f has a relative maximum at $(0, 0)$.

The point $(2, 1)$: $f_{xx}(2, 1) = 0$, $f_{xy}(2, 1) = 4$ and $f_{yy}(2, 1) = -4$, so $H = -16$. Because $H < 0$, we know that f has a saddle point at $(2, 1)$.

The point $(-2, 1)$: $f_{xx}(-2, 1) = 0$, $f_{xy}(-2, 1) = -4$ and $f_{yy}(-2, 1) = -4$, so once again $H = -16$, and f has a saddle point at $(-2, 1)$.

Deriving the Regression Formulas

Back in Section 1.4, we presented the following set of formulas for the **regression** or **best-fit** line associated with a given set of data points $(x_1, y_1), (x_2, y_2), \ldots, (x_n, y_n)$.

Regression Line

The line that best fits the n data points $(x_1, y_1), (x_2, y_2), \ldots, (x_n, y_n)$ has the form

$$y = mx + b$$

where

$$m = \frac{n\left(\sum xy\right) - \left(\sum x\right)\left(\sum y\right)}{n\left(\sum x^2\right) - \left(\sum x\right)^2}$$

$$b = \frac{\sum y - m\left(\sum x\right)}{n}$$

n = number of data points.

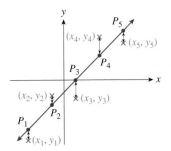

Figure 21

Derivation of the Regression Line Formulas

Recall that the regression line is defined to be the line that minimizes the sum of the squares of the **residuals**, measured by the vertical distances shown in Figure 21, which shows a regression line associated with $n = 5$ data points. In the figure, the points $P_1, \ldots, P_n$ on the regression line have coordinates $(x_1, mx_1 + b), (x_2, mx_2 + b), \ldots, (x_n, mx_n + b)$. The residuals are the quantities $y_{\text{Observed}} - y_{\text{Predicted}}$:

$$y_1 - (mx_1 + b), \ y_2 - (mx_2 + b), \ \ldots, \ y_n - (mx_n + b).$$

The sum of the squares of the residuals is therefore

$$S(m, b) = [y_1 - (mx_1 + b)]^2 + [y_2 - (mx_2 + b)]^2 + \cdots + [y_n - (mx_n + b)]^2$$

and this is the quantity we must minimize by choosing m and b. Because we reason that there is a line that minimizes this quantity, there must be a relative minimum at that point. We shall see in a moment that the function S has at most one critical point, which must therefore be the desired absolute minimum. To obtain the critical points of S, we set the partial derivatives equal to zero and solve:

$$S_m = 0: \quad -2x_1[y_1 - (mx_1 + b)] - \cdots - 2x_n[y_n - (mx_n + b)] = 0$$
$$S_b = 0: \quad -2[y_1 - (mx_1 + b)] - \cdots - 2[y_n - (mx_n + b)] = 0.$$

Dividing by -2 and gathering terms allows us to rewrite the equations as

$$m\left(x_1^2 + \cdots + x_n^2\right) + b(x_1 + \cdots + x_n) = x_1 y_1 + \cdots + x_n y_n$$
$$m(x_1 + \cdots + x_n) + nb \qquad\qquad = y_1 + \cdots + y_n.$$

We can rewrite these equations more neatly using $\sum$-notation:

$$m\left(\sum x^2\right) + b\left(\sum x\right) = \sum xy$$
$$m\left(\sum x\right) + nb \qquad = \sum y.$$

This is a system of two linear equations in the two unknowns m and b. It may or may not have a unique solution. When there is a unique solution, we can conclude that the best fit line is given by solving these two equations for m and b. Alternatively, there is a general formula for the solution of any system of two equations in two unknowns, and if we apply this formula to our two equations, we get the regression formulas above.

15.3 EXERCISES

▼ more advanced   ◆ challenging
T indicates exercises that should be solved using technology

In Exercises 1–4, classify each labeled point on the graph as one of the following:

    a. a relative maximum
    b. a relative minimum
    c. a saddle point
    d. a critical point but neither a relative extremum nor a saddle point
    e. none of the above HINT [See Example 1.]

1.

2.

3.

4.

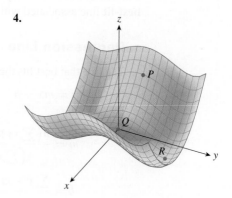

In Exercises 5–10, classify the shaded value in each table as one of the following:

    a. a relative maximum
    b. a relative minimum
    c. a saddle point
    d. neither a relative extremum nor a saddle point

5.

$y \downarrow$	$x \rightarrow$					
		−3	**−2**	**−1**	**0**	**1**	**2**
−3		10	5	2	1	2	5
−2		9	4	1	0	1	4
−1		10	5	2	1	2	5
0		13	8	5	4	5	8
1		18	13	10	9	10	13
2		25	20	17	16	17	20
3		34	29	26	25	26	29

6.

$y \downarrow$	$x \rightarrow$					
		−3	**−2**	**−1**	**0**	**1**	**2**
−3		5	0	−3	−4	−3	0
−2		8	3	0	−1	0	3
−1		9	4	1	0	1	4
0		8	3	0	−1	0	3
1		5	0	−3	−4	−3	0
2		0	−5	−8	−9	−8	−5
3		−7	−12	−15	−16	−15	−12

7.

$x \rightarrow$						
	−3	**−2**	**−1**	**0**	**1**	**2**
y ↓ **−3**	5	0	−3	−4	−3	0
−2	8	3	0	−1	0	3
−1	9	4	1	0	1	4
0	8	3	0	−1	0	3
1	5	0	−3	−4	−3	0
2	0	−5	−8	−9	−8	−5
3	−7	−12	−15	−16	−15	−12

8.

$x \rightarrow$						
	−3	**−2**	**−1**	**0**	**1**	**2**
y ↓ **−3**	2	3	2	−1	−6	−13
−2	3	4	3	0	−5	−12
−1	2	3	2	−1	−6	−13
0	−1	0	−1	−4	−9	−16
1	−6	−5	−6	−9	−14	−21
2	−13	−12	−13	−16	−21	−28
3	−22	−21	−22	−25	−30	−37

9.

$x \rightarrow$						
	−3	**−2**	**−1**	**0**	**1**	**2**
y ↓ **−3**	4	5	4	1	−4	−11
−2	3	4	3	0	−5	−12
−1	4	5	4	1	−4	−11
0	7	8	7	4	−1	−8
1	12	13	12	9	4	−3
2	19	20	19	16	11	4
3	28	29	28	25	20	13

10.

$x \rightarrow$						
	−3	**−2**	**−1**	**0**	**1**	**2**
y ↓ **−3**	100	101	100	97	92	85
−2	99	100	99	96	91	84
−1	98	99	98	95	90	83
0	91	92	91	88	83	76
1	72	73	72	69	64	57
2	35	36	35	32	27	20
3	−26	−25	−26	−29	−34	−41

Locate and classify all the critical points of the functions in Exercises 11–36. HINT [See Example 2.]

11. $f(x, y) = x^2 + y^2 + 1$

12. $f(x, y) = 4 - (x^2 + y^2)$

13. $g(x, y) = 1 - x^2 - x - y^2 + y$

14. $g(x, y) = x^2 + x + y^2 - y - 1$

15. $k(x, y) = x^2 - 3xy + y^2$

16. $k(x, y) = x^2 - xy + 2y^2$

17. $f(x, y) = x^2 + 2xy + 2y^2 - 2x + 4y$

18. $f(x, y) = x^2 + xy - y^2 + 3x - y$

19. $g(x, y) = -x^2 - 2xy - 3y^2 - 3x - 2y$

20. $g(x, y) = -x^2 - 2xy + y^2 + x - 4y$

21. $h(x, y) = x^2y - 2x^2 - 4y^2$

22. $h(x, y) = x^2 + y^2 - y^2x - 4$

23. $f(x, y) = x^2 + 2xy^2 + 2y^2$

24. $f(x, y) = x^2 + x^2y + y^2$

25. $s(x, y) = e^{x^2 + y^2}$ **26.** $s(x, y) = e^{-(x^2+y^2)}$

27. $t(x, y) = x^4 + 8xy^2 + 2y^4$ **28.** $t(x, y) = x^3 - 3xy + y^3$

29. $f(x, y) = x^2 + y - e^y$ **30.** $f(x, y) = xe^y$

31. $f(x, y) = e^{-(x^2+y^2+2x)}$ **32.** $f(x, y) = e^{-(x^2+y^2-2x)}$

33. ▼ $f(x, y) = xy + \dfrac{2}{x} + \dfrac{2}{y}$ **34.** ▼ $f(x, y) = xy + \dfrac{4}{x} + \dfrac{2}{y}$

35. ▼ $g(x, y) = x^2 + y^2 + \dfrac{2}{xy}$ **36.** ▼ $g(x, y) = x^3 + y^3 + \dfrac{3}{xy}$

37. ▼ Refer back to Exercise 11. Which (if any) of the critical points of $f(x, y) = x^2 + y^2 + 1$ are absolute extrema?

38. ▼ Refer back to Exercise 12. Which (if any) of the critical points of $f(x, y) = 4 - (x^2 + y^2)$ are absolute extrema?

39. ▣ ▼ Refer back to Exercise 21. Which (if any) of the critical points of $h(x, y) = x^2y - 2x^2 - 4y^2$ are absolute extrema?

40. ▣ ▼ Refer back to Exercise 22. Which (if any) of the critical points of $h(x, y) = x^2 + y^2 - y^2x - 4$ are absolute extrema?

APPLICATIONS

41. *Brand Loyalty* Suppose the fraction of **Mazda** car owners who chose another new **Mazda** can be modeled by the following function:[23]

$$M(c, f) = 11 + 8c + 4c^2 - 40f - 20cf + 40f^2$$

where c is the fraction of **Chrysler** car owners who remained loyal to **Chrysler** and f is the fraction of **Ford** car owners

---

[23] This model is not accurate, although it was inspired by an approximation of a second order regression based on data from the period 1988–1995. Source for original data: Chrysler, Maritz Market Research, Consumer Attitude Research, and Strategic Vision/*The New York Times*, November 3, 1995, p. D2.

remaining loyal to **Ford**. Locate and classify all the critical points and interpret your answer. HINT [See Example 2.]

42. *Brand Loyalty* Repeat the preceding exercise using the function:

$$M(c, f) = -10 - 8f - 4f^2 + 40c + 20fc - 40c^2$$

HINT [See Example 2.]

43. ▼ *Pollution Control* The cost of controlling emissions at a firm goes up rapidly as the amount of emissions reduced goes up. Here is a possible model:

$$C(x, y) = 4,000 + 100x^2 + 50y^2$$

where x is the reduction in sulfur emissions, y is the reduction in lead emissions (in pounds of pollutant per day), and C is the daily cost to the firm (in dollars) of this reduction. Government clean-air subsidies amount to $500 per pound of sulfur and $100 per pound of lead removed. How many pounds of pollutant should the firm remove each day in order to minimize *net* cost (cost minus subsidy)?

44. ▼ *Pollution Control* Repeat the preceding exercise using the following information:

$$C(x, y) = 2,000 + 200x^2 + 100y^2$$

with government subsidies amounting to $100 per pound of sulfur and $500 per pound of lead removed per day.

45. ▼ *Revenue* Your company manufactures two models of speakers, the Ultra Mini and the Big Stack. Demand for each depends partly on the price of the other. If one is expensive, then more people will buy the other. If p_1 is the price of the Ultra Mini, and p_2 is the price of the Big Stack, demand for the Ultra Mini is given by

$$q_1(p_1, p_2) = 100,000 - 100p_1 + 10p_2$$

where q_1 represents the number of Ultra Minis that will be sold in a year. The demand for the Big Stack is given by

$$q_2(p_1, p_2) = 150,000 + 10p_1 - 100p_2.$$

Find the prices for the Ultra Mini and the Big Stack that will maximize your total revenue.

46. ▼ *Revenue* Repeat the preceding exercise, using the following demand functions:

$$q_1(p_1, p_2) = 100,000 - 100p_1 + p_2$$
$$q_2(p_1, p_2) = 150,000 + p_1 - 100p_2.$$

47. ▼ *Luggage Dimensions: American Airlines* American Airlines requires that the total outside dimensions (length + width + height) of a checked bag not exceed 62 inches.[24] What are the dimensions of the largest volume bag that you can check on an American flight?

48. ▼ *Carry-on Bag Dimensions: American Airlines* American Airlines requires that the total outside dimensions (length + width + height) of a carry-on bag not exceed 45 inches.[25] What are the dimensions of the largest volume bag that you can carry on an American flight?

49. ▼ *Package Dimensions: USPS* The **U.S. Postal Service (USPS)** will accept only packages with a length plus girth no more than 108 inches.[26] (See the figure.)

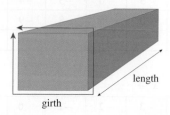

length

girth

What are the dimensions of the largest volume package that the **USPS** will accept? What is its volume?

50. ▼ *Package Dimensions: UPS* United Parcel Service (**UPS**) will accept only packages with length no more than 108 inches and length plus girth no more than 165 inches.[27] (See figure for the preceding exercise.) What are the dimensions of the largest volume package that **UPS** will accept? What is its volume?

COMMUNICATION AND REASONING EXERCISES

51. Sketch the graph of a function that has one extremum and no saddle points.

52. Sketch the graph of a function that has one saddle point and one extremum.

53. ▼ Sketch the graph of a function that has one relative extremum, no absolute extrema, and no saddle points.

54. ▼ Sketch the graph of a function that has infinitely many absolute maxima.

55. Let $H = f_{xx}(a, b)f_{yy}(a, b) - f_{xy}(a, b)^2$. What condition on H guarantees that f has a relative extremum at the point (a, b)?

56. Let H be as in the preceding exercise. Give an example to show that it is possible to have $H = 0$ and a relative minimum at (a, b).

57. ▼ Suppose that when the graph of $f(x, y)$ is sliced by a vertical plane through (a, b) parallel to either the xz-plane or the yz-plane, the resulting curve has a relative maximum at (a, b). Does this mean that f has a relative maximum at (a, b)? Explain your answer.

---

[24] According to information on its Web site (www.aa.com).

[25] Ibid.

[26] The requirement for packages sent other than Parcel Post, as of September 2008 (www.usps.com).

[27] The requirement as of September 2008 (www.ups.com).

58. ▼Suppose that f has a relative maximum at (a, b). Does it follow that, if the graph of f is sliced by a vertical plane parallel to either the xz-plane or the yz-plane, the resulting curve has a relative maximum at (a, b)? Explain your answer.

59. ▼*Average Cost* Let $C(x, y)$ be any cost function. Show that when the average cost is minimized, the marginal costs C_x and C_y both equal the average cost. Explain why this is reasonable.

60. ▼*Average Profit* Let $P(x, y)$ be any profit function. Show that when the average profit is maximized, the marginal

profits P_x and P_y both equal the average profit. Explain why this is reasonable.

61. ◆ The tangent plane to a graph was introduced in Exercise 76 in the preceding section. Use the equation of the tangent plane given there to explain why the tangent plane is parallel to the xy-plane at a relative maximum or minimum of $f(x, y)$.

62. ◆ Use the equation of the tangent plane given in Exercise 76 in the preceding section to explain why the tangent plane is parallel to the xy-plane at a saddle point of $f(x, y)$.

15.4 Constrained Maxima and Minima and Applications

So far we have looked only at the relative extrema of functions with no constraints. However, in Section 12.2 we saw examples in which we needed to find the maximum or minimum of an objective function subject to one or more constraints on the independent variables. For instance, consider the following problem:

$$\text{Minimize } S = xy + 2xz + 2yz \quad \text{subject to } xyz = 4 \text{ with } x > 0, \, y > 0, \, z > 0.$$

One strategy for solving such problems is essentially the same as the strategy we used earlier: Solve the constraint equation for one of the variables, substitute into the objective function, and then optimize the resulting function using the methods of the preceding section. We will call this the *substitution method.* An alternative method, called the *method of Lagrange multipliers,* is useful when it is difficult or impossible to solve the constraint equation for one of the variables, and even when it is possible to do so.

Substitution Method

EXAMPLE 1 **Using Substitution**

Minimize $S = xy + 2xz + 2yz$ subject to $xyz = 4$ with $x > 0, \, y > 0, \, z > 0$.

Solution As suggested in the above discussion, we proceed as follows:

Solve the constraint equation for one of the variables and then substitute in the objective function. The constraint equation is $xyz = 4$. Solving for z gives

$$z = \frac{4}{xy}.$$

The objective function is $S = xy + 2xz + 2yz$, so substituting $z = 4/xy$ gives

$$S = xy + 2x\frac{4}{xy} + 2y\frac{4}{xy}$$

$$= xy + \frac{8}{y} + \frac{8}{x}.$$

Minimize the resulting function of two variables. We use the method in Section 15.4 to find the minimum of $S = xy + \dfrac{8}{y} + \dfrac{8}{x}$ for $x > 0$ and $y > 0$. We look for critical points:

$$S_x = y - \frac{8}{x^2} \qquad S_y = x - \frac{8}{y^2}$$

$$S_{xx} = \frac{16}{x^3} \qquad S_{xy} = 1 \qquad S_{yy} = \frac{16}{y^3}.$$

We now equate the first partial derivatives to zero:

$$y = \frac{8}{x^2} \qquad \text{and} \qquad x = \frac{8}{y^2}.$$

To solve for x and y, we substitute the first of these equations in the second, getting

$$x = \frac{x^4}{8}$$

$$x^4 - 8x = 0$$

$$x(x^3 - 8) = 0.$$

The two solutions are $x = 0$, which we reject because x cannot be zero, and $x = 2$. Substituting $x = 2$ in $y = 8/x^2$ gives $y = 2$ also. Thus, the only critical point is $(2, 2)$. To apply the second derivative test, we compute

$$S_{xx}(2, 2) = 2 \qquad S_{xy}(2, 2) = 1 \qquad S_{yy}(2, 2) = 2$$

and find that $H = 3 > 0$, so we have a relative minimum at $(2, 2)$. The corresponding value of z is given by the constraint equation:

$$z = \frac{4}{xy} = \frac{4}{4} = 1.$$

The corresponding value of the objective function is

$$S = xy + \frac{8}{y} + \frac{8}{x} = 4 + \frac{8}{2} + \frac{8}{2} = 12.$$

Figure 22 shows a portion of the graph of $S = xy + \dfrac{8}{y} + \dfrac{8}{x}$ for positive x and y (drawn using the Excel Surface Grapher in the Chapter 15 utilities at the Web site), and suggests that there is a single absolute minimum, which must be at our only candidate point $(2, 2)$.

We conclude that the minimum of S is 12 and occurs at $(2, 2, 1)$.

Graph of $S = xy + \dfrac{8}{y} + \dfrac{8}{x}$

$(0.2 \le x \le 5, 0.2 \le y \le 5)$

Figure 22

The Method of Lagrange Multipliers

As we mentioned above, the method of Lagrange multipliers has the advantage that it can be used in constrained optimization problems when it is difficult or impossible to solve a constraint equation for one of the variables. We restrict attention to the case of a single constraint equation, although the method also generalizes to any number of constraint equations.

Locating Relative Extrema Using the Method of Lagrange Multipliers

To locate the candidates for relative extrema of a function $f(x, y, \ldots)$ subject to the constraint $g(x, y, \ldots) = 0$:

1. Construct the **Lagrangian function**

$$L(x, y, \ldots) = f(x, y, \ldots) - \lambda g(x, y, \ldots)$$

where λ is a new unknown called a **Lagrange multiplier.**

2. The candidates for the relative extrema occur at the critical points of $L(x, y, \ldots)$. To find them, set all the partial derivatives of $L(x, y, \ldots)$ equal to zero and solve the resulting system, together with the constraint equation $g(x, y, \ldots) = 0$, for the unknowns $x, y, \ldots$ and λ.

The points $(x, y, \ldots)$ that occur in solutions are then the candidates for the relative extrema of f subject to $g = 0$.

Although the justification for the method of Lagrange multipliers is beyond the scope of this text (a derivation can be found in many vector calculus textbooks), we will demonstrate by example how it is used.

EXAMPLE 2 Using Lagrange Multipliers

Use the method of Lagrange multipliers to find the maximum value of $f(x, y) = 2xy$ subject to $x^2 + 4y^2 = 32$.

Solution We start by rewriting the problem with the constraint in the form $g(x, y) = 0$:

Maximize $f(x, y) = 2xy$ subject to $x^2 + 4y^2 - 32 = 0$.

Here, $g(x, y) = x^2 + 4y^2 - 32$, and the Lagrangian function is

$$
\begin{aligned}
L(x, y) &= f(x, y) - \lambda g(x, y) \\
&= 2xy - \lambda(x^2 + 4y^2 - 32).
\end{aligned}
$$

The system of equations we need to solve is thus

$$
\begin{aligned}
L_x = 0: &\quad 2y - 2\lambda x = 0 \\
L_y = 0: &\quad 2x - 8\lambda y = 0 \\
g = 0: &\quad x^2 + 4y^2 - 32 = 0.
\end{aligned}
$$

It is often convenient to solve such a system by first solving one of the equations for λ and then substituting in the remaining equations. Thus, we start by solving the first equation to obtain

$$\lambda = \frac{y}{x}.$$

(A word of caution: Because we divided by x, we made the implicit assumption that $x \neq 0$, so before continuing we should check what happens if $x = 0$. But if $x = 0$, then the first equation, $2y = 2\lambda x$, tells us that $y = 0$ as well, and this contradicts the third

1118	Chapter 15	Functions of Several Variables

equation: $x^2 + 4y^2 - 32 = 0$. Thus, we can rule out the possibility that $x = 0$.) Substituting the value of λ in the second equation gives

$$2x - 8\left(\frac{y}{x}\right)y = 0 \quad \text{or} \quad x^2 = 4y^2.$$

We can now substitute $x^2 = 4y^2$ in the constraint equation, obtaining

$$4y^2 + 4y^2 - 32 = 0$$
$$8y^2 = 32$$
$$y = \pm 2.$$

We now substitute back to obtain

$$x^2 = 4y^2 = 16,$$

or $\qquad x = \pm 4.$

We don't need the value of λ, so we won't solve for it. Thus, the candidates for relative extrema are given by $x = \pm 4$ and $y = \pm 2$, that is, the four points $(-4, -2)$, $(-4, 2)$, $(4, -2)$, and $(4, 2)$. Recall that we are seeking the values of x and y that give the maximum value for $f(x, y) = 2xy$. Because we now have only four points to choose from, we compare the values of f at these four points and conclude that the maximum value of f occurs when $(x, y) = (-4, -2)$ or $(4, 2)$.

Something is suspicious in Example 2. We didn't check to see whether these candidates were relative extrema to begin with, let alone absolute extrema! How do we justify this omission? One of the difficulties with using the method of Lagrange multipliers is that it does not provide us with a test analogous to the second derivative test for functions of several variables. However, if you grant that the function in question does have an absolute maximum, then we require no test, because one of the candidates must give this maximum.

Q: *But how do we know that the given function has an absolute maximum?*

A: The best way to see this is by giving a geometric interpretation. The constraint $x^2 + 4y^2 = 32$ tells us that the point (x, y) must lie on the ellipse shown in Figure 23. The function $f(x, y) = 2xy$ gives the area of the rectangle shaded in Figure 23. There must be a largest such rectangle, because the area varies continuously from 0 when (x, y) is on the x-axis, to positive when (x, y) is in the first quadrant, to 0 again when (x, y) is on the y-axis, so f must have an absolute maximum for at least one pair of coordinates (x, y).

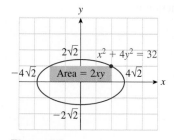

Figure 23

We now show how to use Lagrange multipliers to solve the minimization problem in Example 1:

EXAMPLE 3 Using Lagrange Multipliers: Function of Three Variables

Use the method of Lagrange multipliers to find the minimum value of $S = xy + 2xz + 2yz$ subject to $xyz = 4$ with $x > 0$, $y > 0$, $z > 0$.

Solution We start by rewriting the problem in standard form:

$$\text{Maximize } f(x, y, z) = xy + 2xz + 2yz$$
$$\text{subject to } xyz - 4 = 0 \text{ (with } x > 0, y > 0, z > 0).$$

Here, $g(x, y, z) = xyz - 4$, and the Lagrangian function is

$$L(x, y, z) = f(x, y, z) - \lambda g(x, y, z)$$
$$= xy + 2xz + 2yz - \lambda(xyz - 4).$$

The system of equations we need to solve is thus

$$
\begin{aligned}
L_x &= 0: & y + 2z - \lambda yz &= 0 \\
L_y &= 0: & x + 2z - \lambda xz &= 0 \\
L_z &= 0: & 2x + 2y - \lambda xy &= 0 \\
g &= 0: & xyz - 4 &= 0.
\end{aligned}
$$

As in the last example, we solve one of the equations for λ and substitute in the others. The first equation gives

$$\lambda = \frac{1}{z} + \frac{2}{y}.$$

Substituting this into the second equation gives

$$x + 2z = x + \frac{2xz}{y}$$

or
$$2 = \frac{2x}{y}, \qquad \text{Subtract } x \text{ from both sides and then divide by } z.$$

giving
$$y = x.$$

Substituting the expression for λ into the third equation gives

$$2x + 2y = \frac{xy}{z} + 2x$$

or
$$2 = \frac{x}{z}, \qquad \text{Subtract } 2x \text{ from both sides and then divide by } y.$$

giving
$$z = \frac{x}{2}.$$

Now we have both y and z in terms of x. We substitute these values in the last (constraint) equation:

$$x(x)\left(\frac{x}{2}\right) - 4 = 0$$
$$x^3 = 8$$
$$x = 2.$$

Thus, $y = x = 2$, and $z = \dfrac{x}{2} = 1$. Therefore, the only critical point occurs at $(2, 2, 1)$ as we found in Example 1, and the corresponding value of S is

$$S = xy + 2xz + 2yz = (2)(2) + 2(2)(1) + 2(2)(1) = 12.$$

➡ **Before we go on...** Again, the method of Lagrange multipliers does not tell us whether the critical point in Example 3 is a maximum, minimum, or neither. However, if you grant that the function in question does have an absolute minimum, then the values we found must give this minimum value. ∎

APPLICATIONS

EXAMPLE 4 **Minimizing Area**

Find the dimensions of an open-top rectangular box that has a volume of 4 cubic feet and the smallest possible surface area.

Solution Our first task is to rephrase this request as a mathematical optimization problem. Figure 24 shows a picture of the box with dimensions x, y, and z. We want to minimize the total surface area, which is given by

$$S = xy + 2xz + 2yz. \qquad \text{Base + Sides + Front and Back}$$

This is our objective function. We can't simply choose x, y, and z to all be zero, however, because the enclosed volume must be 4 cubic feet. So,

$$xyz = 4. \qquad \text{Constraint}$$

This is our constraint equation. Other unstated constraints are $x > 0$, $y > 0$, and $z > 0$, because the dimensions of the box must be positive. We now restate the problem as follows:

$$\text{Minimize } S = xy + 2xz + 2yz \quad \text{subject to } xyz = 4, x > 0, y > 0, z > 0.$$

But this is exactly the problem in Examples 1 and 3, and has a solution $x = 2$, $y = 2$, $z = 1$, $S = 12$. Thus, the required dimensions of the box are

$$x = 2 \text{ ft}, y = 2 \text{ ft}, z = 1 \text{ ft},$$

requiring a total surface area of 12 ft².

z

y

x

Figure 24

Q: *In Example 1 we checked that we had a relative minimum at $(x, y) = (2, 2)$ and we were persuaded graphically that this was probably an absolute minimum. Can we be sure that this relative minimum is an absolute minimum?*

A: Yes. There must be a least surface area among all boxes that hold 4 cubic feet. (Why?) Because this would give a relative minimum of S and because the only possible relative minimum of S occurs at $(2, 2)$, this is the absolute minimum.

EXAMPLE 5 **Maximizing productivity**

An electric motor manufacturer uses workers and robots on its assembly line, and has a Cobb-Douglas productivity function* of the form

$$P(x, y) = 10x^{0.2}y^{0.8} \text{ motors manufactured per day}$$

where x is the number of assembly-line workers and y is the number of robots. Daily operating costs amount to \$100 per worker and \$16 per robot. How many workers and robots should be used to maximize productivity if the manufacturer has a daily budget of \$4,000?

Solution Our objective function is the productivity $P(x, y)$, and the constraint is

$$100x + 16y = 4,000.$$

✳ **NOTE** Cobb-Douglas production formulas were discussed in Section 11.6.

So, the optimization problem is:

Maximize $P(x, y) = 10x^{0.2}y^{0.8}$ subject to $100x + 16y = 4{,}000$ ($x \geq 0$, $y \geq 0$).

Here, $g(x, y) = 100x + 16y - 4{,}000$, and the Lagrangian function is

$$
\begin{aligned}
L(x, y) &= P(x, y) - \lambda g(x, y)\\
&= 10x^{0.2}y^{0.8} - \lambda(100x + 16y - 4{,}000).
\end{aligned}
$$

The system of equations we need to solve is thus

$$
\begin{aligned}
L_x = 0: \quad & 2x^{-0.8}y^{0.8} - 100\lambda = 0\\
L_y = 0: \quad & 8x^{0.2}y^{-0.2} - 16\lambda = 0\\
g = 0: \quad & 100x + 16y = 4{,}000.
\end{aligned}
$$

We can rewrite the first two equations as:

$$
2\left(\frac{y}{x}\right)^{0.8} = 100\lambda \qquad 8\left(\frac{x}{y}\right)^{0.2} = 16\lambda.
$$

Dividing the first by the second to eliminate λ gives

$$
\frac{1}{4}\left(\frac{y}{x}\right)^{0.8}\left(\frac{y}{x}\right)^{0.2} = \frac{100}{16}
$$

that is,

$$
\frac{1}{4}\frac{y}{x} = \frac{25}{4},
$$

giving

$$
y = 25x.
$$

Substituting this result into the constraint equation gives

$$
\begin{aligned}
& 100x + 16(25x) = 4{,}000\\
& 500x = 4{,}000
\end{aligned}
$$

so

$$
x = 8 \text{ workers}, \quad y = 25x = 200 \text{ robots}
$$

for a productivity of

$$
P(8, 200) = 10(8)^{0.2}(200)^{0.8} \approx 1{,}051 \text{ motors manufactured per day.}
$$

FAQ

When to Use Lagrange Multipliers

Q : *When can I use the method of Lagrange multipliers? When should I use it?*

A : We have discussed the method only when there is a single equality constraint. There is a generalization, which we have not discussed, that works when there are more equality constraints (we need to introduce one multiplier for each constraint). So, if you have a problem with more than one equality constraint, or with any inequality constraints, you must use the substitution method. On the other hand, if you have one equality constraint, and it would be difficult to solve it for one of the variables, then you should use Lagrange multipliers.

15.4 EXERCISES

▼ more advanced   ◆ challenging
🔢 indicates exercises that should be solved using technology

In Exercises 1–6, solve the given optimization problem by using substitution. HINT [See Example 1.]

1. Find the maximum value of $f(x, y, z) = 1 - x^2 - y^2 - z^2$ subject to $z = 2y$. Also find the corresponding point(s) (x, y, z).

2. Find the minimum value of $f(x, y, z) = x^2 + y^2 + z^2 - 2$ subject to $x = y$. Also find the corresponding point(s) (x, y, z).

3. Find the maximum value of $f(x, y, z) = 1 - x^2 - x - y^2 + y - z^2 + z$ subject to $3x = y$. Also find the corresponding point(s) (x, y, z).

4. Find the maximum value of $f(x, y, z) = 2x^2 + 2x + y^2 - y + z^2 - z - 1$ subject to $z = 2y$. Also find the corresponding point(s) (x, y, z).

5. Minimize $S = xy + 4xz + 2yz$ subject to $xyz = 1$ with $x > 0$, $y > 0, z > 0$.

6. Minimize $S = xy + xz + yz$ subject to $xyz = 2$ with $x > 0$, $y > 0, z > 0$.

In Exercises 7–18, use Lagrange multipliers to solve the given optimization problem. HINT [See Example 2.]

7. Find the maximum value of $f(x, y) = xy$ subject to $x + 2y = 40$. Also find the corresponding point(s) (x, y).

8. Find the maximum value of $f(x, y) = xy$ subject to $3x + y = 60$. Also find the corresponding point(s) (x, y).

9. Find the maximum value of $f(x, y) = 4xy$ subject to $x^2 + y^2 = 8$. Also find the corresponding point(s) (x, y).

10. Find the maximum value of $f(x, y) = xy$ subject to $y = 3 - x^2$. Also find the corresponding point(s) (x, y).

11. Find the minimum value of $f(x, y) = x^2 + y^2$ subject to $x + 2y = 10$. Also find the corresponding point(s) (x, y).

12. Find the minimum value of $f(x, y) = x^2 + y^2$ subject to $xy^2 = 16$. Also find the corresponding point(s) (x, y).

13. The problem in Exercise 1. HINT [See Example 3.]

14. The problem in Exercise 2. HINT [See Example 3.]

15. The problem in Exercise 3.

16. The problem in Exercise 4.

17. The problem in Exercise 5.

18. The problem in Exercise 6.

APPLICATIONS

Exercises 19–22 were solved in Section 12.2. This time, use the method of Lagrange multipliers to solve them.

19. **Fences** I want to fence in a rectangular vegetable patch. The fencing for the east and west sides costs $4 per foot, and the fencing for the north and south sides costs only $2 per foot.

I have a budget of $80 for the project. What is the largest area I can enclose?

20. **Fences** My orchid garden abuts my house so that the house itself forms the northern boundary. The fencing for the southern boundary costs $4 per foot, and the fencing for the east and west sides costs $2 per foot. If I have a budget of $80 for the project, what is the largest area I can enclose?

21. **Revenue** Hercules Films is deciding on the price of the video release of its film *Son of Frankenstein*. Its marketing people estimate that at a price of p dollars, it can sell a total of $q = 200,000 - 10,000p$ copies. What price will bring in the greatest revenue?

22. **Profit** Hercules Films is also deciding on the price of the video release of its film *Bride of the Son of Frankenstein*. Again, marketing estimates that at a price of p dollars it can sell $q = 200,000 - 10,000p$ copies, but each copy costs $4 to make. What price will give the greatest *profit*?

23. **Geometry** At what points on the sphere $x^2 + y^2 + z^2 = 1$ is the product xyz a maximum? (The method of Lagrange multipliers can be used.)

24. **Geometry** At what point on the surface $z = (x^2 + x + y^2 + 4)^{1/2}$ is the quantity $x^2 + y^2 + z^2$ a minimum? (The method of Lagrange multipliers can be used.)

25. ▼ **Geometry** What point on the surface $z = x^2 + y - 1$ is closest to the origin? HINT [Minimize the square of the distance from (x, y, z) to the origin.]

26. ▼ **Geometry** What point on the surface $z = x + y^2 - 3$ is closest to the origin? HINT [Minimize the square of the distance from (x, y, z) to the origin.]

27. ▼ **Geometry** Find the point on the plane $-2x + 2y + z - 5 = 0$ closest to $(-1, 1, 3)$. HINT [Minimize the square of the distance from the given point to a general point on the plane.]

28. ▼ **Geometry** Find the point on the plane $2x - 2y - z + 1 = 0$ closest to $(1, 1, 0)$.

29. **Construction Cost** A closed rectangular box is made with two kinds of materials. The top and bottom are made with heavy-duty cardboard costing 20¢ per square foot, and the sides are made with lightweight cardboard costing 10¢ per square foot. Given that the box is to have a capacity of 2 cubic feet, what should its dimensions be if the cost is to be minimized? HINT [See Example 4.]

30. **Construction Cost** Repeat the preceding exercise assuming that the heavy-duty cardboard costs 30¢ per square foot, the lightweight cardboard costs 5¢ per square foot, and the box is to have a capacity of 6 cubic feet. HINT [See Example 4.]

31. **Package Dimensions: USPS** The **U.S. Postal Service (USPS)** will accept only packages with a length plus girth no more than 108 inches.[28] (See the figure.)

---

[28] The requirement for packages sent other than Parcel Post, as of September 2008 (www.usps.com).

length

girth

What are the dimensions of the largest volume package that the **USPS** will accept? What is its volume? (This exercise is the same as Exercise 49 in the preceding section. This time, solve it using Lagrange multipliers.)

32. **Package Dimensions: UPS** United Parcel Service (**UPS**) will accept only packages with length no more than 108 inches and length plus girth no more than 165 inches.[29] (See figure for the preceding exercise.) What are the dimensions of the largest volume package that **UPS** will accept? What is its volume? (This exercise is the same as Exercise 50 in the preceding section. This time, solve it using Lagrange multipliers.)

33. ▼ **Construction Cost** My company wishes to manufacture boxes similar to those described in Exercise 29 as cheaply as possible, but unfortunately the company that manufactures the cardboard is unable to give me price quotes for the heavy-duty and lightweight cardboard. Find formulas for the dimensions of the box in terms of the price per square foot of heavy-duty and lightweight cardboard.

34. ▼ **Construction Cost** Repeat the preceding exercise, assuming that only the bottoms of the boxes are to be made using heavy-duty cardboard.

35. ▼ **Geometry** Find the dimensions of the rectangular box with largest volume that can be inscribed above the xy-plane and under the paraboloid $z = 1 - (x^2 + y^2)$.

36. ▼ **Geometry** Find the dimensions of the rectangular box with largest volume that can be inscribed above the xy-plane and under the paraboloid $z = 2 - (2x^2 + y^2)$.

37. **Productivity** The Gym Shirt Company manufactures cotton socks. Production is partially automated through the use of robots. Daily operating costs amount to $150 per laborer and $60 per robot. The number of pairs of socks the company can manufacture in a day is given by a Cobb-Douglas production formula

$$q = 50n^{0.6}r^{0.4}$$

where q is the number of pairs of socks that can be manufactured by n laborers and r robots. Assuming that the company has a daily operating budget of $1,500 and wishes to maximize productivity, how many laborers and how many robots should it use? What is the productivity at these levels? HINT [See Example 5.]

---

[29] The requirement as of September 2008 (www.ups.com).

38. **Productivity** Your automobile assembly plant has a Cobb-Douglas production function given by

$$q = 100x^{0.3}y^{0.7}$$

where q is the number of automobiles it produces per year, x is the number of employees, and y is the monthly assembly-line budget (in thousands of dollars). Annual operating costs amount to an average of $60 thousand per employee plus the operating budget of $12y$ thousand. Your annual budget is $1,200,000. How many employees should you hire and what should your assembly-line budget be to maximize productivity? What is the productivity at these levels?

COMMUNICATION AND REASONING EXERCISES

39. Outline two methods of solution of the problem "*Maximize $f(x, y, z)$ subject to $g(x, y, z) = 0$*" and give an advantage and disadvantage of each.

40. Suppose we know that $f(x, y)$ has both partial derivatives in its domain D: $x > 0$, $y > 0$, and that (a, b) is the only point in D such that $f_x(a, b) = f_y(a, b) = 0$. Must it be the case that, if f has an absolute maximum, it occurs at (a, b)? Explain.

41. Under what circumstances would it be necessary to use the method of Lagrange multipliers?

42. Under what circumstances would the method of Lagrange multipliers not apply?

43. Restate the following problem as a maximization problem of the form *Maximize $f(x, y)$ subject to $g(x, y) = 0$*":

Find the maximum value of $h(x) = 1 - 2x^2$.

44. Restate the following problem as a maximization problem of the form *Maximize $f(x, y, z)$ subject to $g(x, y, z) = 0$*":

Find the maximum value of $h(x, y) = 1 - 2(x^2 + y^2)$.

45. ▼ If the partial derivatives of a function of several variables are never 0, is it possible for the function to have relative extrema on some domain? Explain your answer.

46. ◆ A **linear programming problem in two variables** is a problem of the form: *Maximize (or minimize) $f(x, y)$ subject to constraints of the form $C(x, y) \geq 0$ or $C(x, y) \leq 0$. Here, the objective function f and the constraints C are linear functions. There may be several linear constraints in one problem. Explain why the solution cannot occur in the interior of the domain of f.

47. ◆ Refer back to Exercise 46. Explain why the solution will actually be at a corner of the domain of f (where two or more of the line segments that make up the boundary meet). This result—or rather a slight generalization of it—is known as the Fundamental Theorem of Linear Programming.

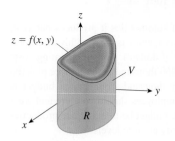

Figure 25

15.5 Double Integrals and Applications

When discussing functions of one variable, we computed the area under a graph by integration. The analog for the graph of a function of two variables is the *volume V* under the graph, as in Figure 25. Think of the region R in the xy-plane as the "shadow" under the portion of the surface $z = f(x, y)$ shown.

By analogy with the definite integral of a function of one variable, we make the following definition:

Geometric Definition of the Double Integral

The **double integral of $f(x, y)$ over the region R in the xy-plane** is defined as

(Volume *above* the region R and under the graph of f)

− (Volume *below* the region R and above the graph of f)

We denote the double integral of $f(x, y)$ over the region R by $\iint_R f(x, y)\, dx\, dy$.

Quick Example

Take $f(x, y) = 2$ and take R to be the rectangle $0 \le x \le 1, 0 \le y \le 1$. Then the graph of f is a flat horizontal surface $z = 2$, and

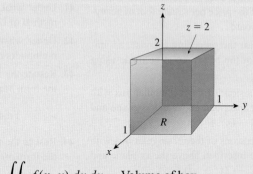

$$\iint_R f(x, y)\, dx\, dy = \text{Volume of box}$$
$$= \text{Width} \times \text{Length} \times \text{Height} = 1 \times 1 \times 2 = 2.$$

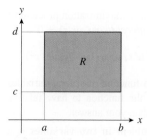

Figure 26

As we saw in the case of the definite integral of a function of one variable, we also desire *numerical* and *algebraic* definitions for two reasons: (1) to make the mathematical definition more precise, so as not to rely on the notion of "volume," and (2) for direct computation of the integral using technology or analytical tools.

We start with the simplest case, when the region R is a rectangle $a \le x \le b$ and $c \le y \le d$. (See Figure 26.) To compute the volume over R, we mimic what we did to find the area under the graph of a function of one variable. We break up the interval $[a, b]$ into m intervals all of width $\Delta x = (b - a)/m$, and we break up $[c, d]$ into n intervals all of width $\Delta y = (d - c)/n$. Figure 27 shows an example with $m = 4$ and $n = 5$.

This gives us mn rectangles defined by $x_{i-1} \le x \le x_i$ and $y_{j-1} \le y \le y_j$. Over one of these rectangles, f is approximately equal to its value at one corner—say $f(x_i, y_j)$. The volume under f over this small rectangle is then approximately the volume of the

Figure 27

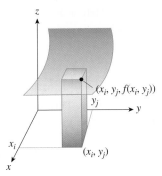

Figure 28

rectangular brick (size exaggerated) shown in Figure 28. This brick has height $f(x_i, y_j)$, and its base is Δx by Δy. Its volume is therefore $f(x_i, y_j)\Delta x \Delta y$. Adding together the volumes of all of the bricks over the small rectangles in R, we get

$$\iint_R f(x, y) \, dx \, dy \approx \sum_{j=1}^{n} \sum_{i=1}^{m} f(x_i, y_j)\Delta x \, \Delta y.$$

This double sum is called a **double Riemann sum**. We define the double integral to be the limit of the Riemann sums as m and n go to infinity.

Algebraic Definition of the Double Integral

$$\iint_R f(x, y) \, dx \, dy = \lim_{n \to \infty} \lim_{m \to \infty} \sum_{j=1}^{n} \sum_{i=1}^{m} f(x_i, y_j)\Delta x \, \Delta y$$

Note This definition is adequate (the limit exists) when f is continuous. More elaborate definitions are needed for general functions. ∎

This definition also gives us a clue about how to compute a double integral. The innermost sum is $\sum_{i=1}^{m} f(x_i, y_j)\Delta x$, which is a Riemann sum for $\int_a^b f(x, y_j) \, dx$. The innermost limit is therefore

$$\lim_{m \to \infty} \sum_{i=1}^{m} f(x_i, y_j)\Delta x = \int_a^b f(x, y_j) \, dx.$$

The outermost limit is then also a Riemann sum, and we get the following way of calculating double integrals:

Computing the Double Integral over a Rectangle

If R is the rectangle $a \leq x \leq b$ and $c \leq y \leq d$, then

$$\iint_R f(x, y) \, dx \, dy = \int_c^d \left(\int_a^b f(x, y) \, dx \right) dy = \int_a^b \left(\int_c^d f(x, y) \, dy \right) dx.$$

The second formula comes from switching the order of summation in the double sum.

Quick Example

If R is the rectangle $1 \leq x \leq 2$ and $1 \leq y \leq 3$, then

$$\iint_R 1 \, dx \, dy = \int_1^3 \left(\int_1^2 1 \, dx \right) dy$$

$$= \int_1^3 \left[x \right]_{x=1}^2 dy \qquad \text{Evaluate the inner integral.}$$

$$= \int_1^3 1 \, dy \qquad \left[x \right]_{x=1}^2 = 2 - 1 = 1.$$

$$= \left[y \right]_{y=1}^3 = 3 - 1 = 2.$$

The Quick Example used a constant function for the integrand. Here is an example in which the integrand is not constant.

$z = xy, 0 \le x \le 1$ and $0 \le y \le 2$

Figure 29

EXAMPLE 1 Double Integral over a Rectangle

Let R be the rectangle $0 \le x \le 1$ and $0 \le y \le 2$. Compute $\iint_R xy \, dx \, dy$. This integral gives the volume of the part of the boxed region under the surface $z = xy$ shown in Figure 29.

Solution

$$\iint_R xy \, dx \, dy = \int_0^2 \int_0^1 xy \, dx \, dy$$

(We usually drop the parentheses around the inner integral like this.) As in the Quick Example, we compute this iterated integral from the inside out. First we compute

$$\int_0^1 xy \, dx.$$

To do this computation, we do as we did when finding partial derivatives: We treat y as a constant. This gives

$$\int_0^1 xy \, dx = \left[\frac{x^2}{2} \cdot y \right]_{x=0}^{1} = \frac{1}{2}y - 0 = \frac{y}{2}.$$

We can now calculate the outer integral.

$$\int_0^2 \int_0^1 xy \, dx \, dy = \int_0^2 \frac{y}{2} \, dy = \left[\frac{y^2}{4} \right]_0^2 = 1$$

➡ **Before we go on...** We could also reverse the order of integration in Example 1.

$$\int_0^1 \int_0^2 xy \, dy \, dx = \int_0^1 \left(\left[x \cdot \frac{y^2}{2} \right]_{y=0}^{2} \right) dx = \int_0^1 2x \, dx = \left[x^2 \right]_0^1 = 1 \qquad ■$$

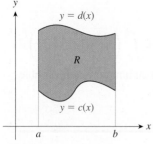

Figure 30

Often we need to integrate over regions R that are not rectangular. There are two cases that come up. The first is a region like the one shown in Figure 30. In this region, the bottom and top sides are defined by functions $y = c(x)$ and $y = d(x)$, respectively, so that the whole region can be described by the inequalities $a \le x \le b$ and $c(x) \le y \le d(x)$. To evaluate a double integral over such a region, we have the following formula:

Computing the Double Integral over a Nonrectangular Region

If R is the region $a \le x \le b$ and $c(x) \le y \le d(x)$ (Figure 30), then we integrate over R according to the following equation:

$$\iint_R f(x, y) \, dx \, dy = \int_a^b \int_{c(x)}^{d(x)} f(x, y) \, dy \, dx.$$

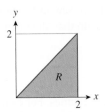

Figure 31

EXAMPLE 2 Double Integral over a Nonrectangular Region

R is the triangle shown in Figure 31. Compute $\iint_R x \, dx \, dy$.

Solution R is the region described by $0 \leq x \leq 2, 0 \leq y \leq x$. We have

$$
\iint_R x \, dx \, dy = \int_0^2 \int_0^x x \, dy \, dx
$$

$$
= \int_0^2 [xy]_{y=0}^x \, dx
$$

$$
= \int_0^2 x^2 \, dx
$$

$$
= \left[\frac{x^3}{3} \right]_0^2 = \frac{8}{3}.
$$

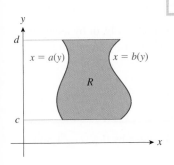

Figure 32

The second type of region is shown in Figure 32. This is the region described by $c \leq y \leq d$ and $a(y) \leq x \leq b(y)$. To evaluate a double integral over such a region, we have the following formula:

Double Integral over a Nonrectangular Region (continued)

If R is the region $c \leq y \leq d$ and $a(y) \leq x \leq b(y)$ (Figure 32), then we integrate over R according to the following equation:

$$
\iint_R f(x, y) \, dx \, dy = \int_c^d \int_{a(y)}^{b(y)} f(x, y) \, dx \, dy.
$$

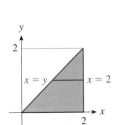

Figure 33

EXAMPLE 3 Double Integral over a Nonrectangular Region

Redo Example 2, integrating in the opposite order.

Solution We can integrate in the opposite order if we can describe the region in Figure 31 in the way shown in Figure 32. In fact, it is the region $0 \leq y \leq 2$ and $y \leq x \leq 2$. To see this, we draw a horizontal line through the region, as in Figure 33. The line extends from $x = y$ on the left to $x = 2$ on the right, so $y \leq x \leq 2$. The possible heights for such a line are $0 \leq y \leq 2$. We can now compute the integral:

$$
\iint_R x \, dx \, dy = \int_0^2 \int_y^2 x \, dx \, dy
$$

$$
= \int_0^2 \left[\frac{x^2}{2} \right]_{x=y}^2 \, dy
$$

$$
= \int_0^2 \left(2 - \frac{y^2}{2} \right) dy
$$

$$
= \left[2y - \frac{y^3}{6} \right]_0^2 = \frac{8}{3}.
$$

Note Many regions can be described in two different ways, as we saw in Examples 2 and 3. Sometimes one description will be much easier to work with than the other, so it pays to consider both. ∎

APPLICATIONS

There are many applications of double integrals besides finding volumes. For example, we can use them to find *averages*. Remember that the average of $f(x)$ on $[a, b]$ is given by $\int_a^b f(x)\,dx$ divided by $(b - a)$, the length of the interval.

Average of a Function of Two Variables

The average of $f(x, y)$ on the region R is

$$\bar{f} = \frac{1}{A} \iint_R f(x, y)\,dx\,dy.$$

Here, A is the area of R. We can compute the area A geometrically, or by using the techniques from the chapter on applications of the integral, or by computing

$$A = \iint_R 1\,dx\,dy.$$

Quick Example

The average value of $f(x, y) = xy$ on the rectangle given by $0 \le x \le 1$ and $0 \le y \le 2$ is

$$\bar{f} = \frac{1}{2} \iint_R xy\,dx\,dy \qquad \text{The area of the rectangle is 2.}$$

$$= \frac{1}{2} \int_0^2 \int_0^1 xy\,dx\,dy$$

$$= \frac{1}{2} \cdot 1 = \frac{1}{2}. \qquad \text{We calculated the integral in Example 1.}$$

EXAMPLE 4 **Average Revenue**

Your company is planning to price its new line of subcompact cars at between \$10,000 and \$15,000. The marketing department reports that if the company prices the cars at p dollars per car, the demand will be between $q = 20,000 - p$ and $q = 25,000 - p$ cars sold in the first year. What is the average of all the possible revenues your company could expect in the first year?

Solution Revenue is given by $R = pq$ as usual, and we are told that

$$10,000 \le p \le 15,000$$

and $\qquad 20,000 - p \le q \le 25,000 - p.$

This domain D of prices and demands is shown in Figure 34.

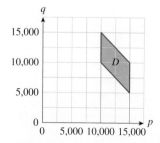

Figure 34

To average the revenue R over the domain D, we need to compute the area A of D. Using either calculus or geometry, we get $A = 25,000,000$. We then need to integrate R over D:

$$\iint_D pq \, dp \, dq = \int_{10,000}^{15,000} \int_{20,000-p}^{25,000-p} pq \, dq \, dp$$

$$= \int_{10,000}^{15,000} \left[\frac{pq^2}{2} \right]_{q=20,000-p}^{25,000-p} dp$$

$$= \frac{1}{2} \int_{10,000}^{15,000} [p(25,000-p)^2 - p(20,000-p)^2] \, dp$$

$$= \frac{1}{2} \int_{10,000}^{15,000} [225,000,000p - 10,000p^2] \, dp$$

$$\approx 3,072,900,000,000,000.$$

The average of all the possible revenues your company could expect in the first year is therefore

$$\bar{R} = \frac{3,072,900,000,000,000}{25,000,000} \approx \$122,900,000.$$

➡ **Before we go on...** To check that the answer obtained in Example 4 is reasonable, notice that the revenues at the corners of the domain are $100,000,000 per year, $150,000,000 per year (at two corners), and $75,000,000 per year. Some of these are smaller than the average and some larger, as we would expect. ∎

Another useful application of the double integral comes about when we consider density. For example, suppose that $P(x, y)$ represents the population density (in people per square mile, say) in the city of Houston, shown in Figure 35.

If we break the city up into small rectangles (for example, city blocks), then the population in the small rectangle $x_{i-1} \leq x \leq x_i$ and $y_{j-1} \leq y \leq y_j$ is approximately $P(x_i, y_j)\Delta x \Delta y$. Adding up all of these population estimates, we get

$$\text{Total population} \approx \sum_{j=1}^{n} \sum_{i=1}^{m} P(x_i, y_j) \, \Delta x \, \Delta y.$$

Because this is a double Riemann sum, when we take the limit as m and n go to infinity, we get the following calculation of the population of the city:

$$\text{Total population} = \iint_{\text{City}} P(x, y) \, dx \, dy.$$

Darker regions have higher population density

Figure 35

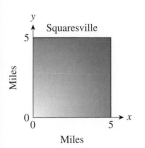

Figure 36

EXAMPLE 5 **Population**

Squaresville is a city in the shape of a square 5 miles on a side. The population density at a distance of x miles east and y miles north of the southwest corner is $P(x, y) = x^2 + y^2$ thousand people per square mile. Find the total population of Squaresville.

Solution Squaresville is pictured in Figure 36, in which we put the origin in the southwest corner of the city.

To compute the total population, we integrate the population density over the city S.

$$\text{Total population} = \iint_{\text{Squaresville}} P(x, y) \, dx \, dy$$

$$= \int_0^5 \int_0^5 (x^2 + y^2) \, dx \, dy$$

$$= \int_0^5 \left[\frac{x^3}{3} + xy^2 \right]_{x=0}^5 \, dy$$

$$= \int_0^5 \left[\frac{125}{3} + 5y^2 \right] \, dy$$

$$= \frac{1{,}250}{3} \approx 417 \text{ thousand people}$$

➡ **Before we go on...** Note that the average population density is the total population divided by the area of the city, which is about 17,000 people per square mile. Compare this calculation with the calculations of averages in the previous two examples. ∎

15.5 EXERCISES

▼ more advanced   ◆ challenging
Ⓣ indicates exercises that should be solved using technology

Compute the integrals in Exercises 1–16. HINT [See Example 1.]

1. $\int_0^1 \int_0^1 (x - 2y) \, dx \, dy$ **2.** $\int_{-1}^1 \int_0^2 (2x + 3y) \, dx \, dy$

3. $\int_0^1 \int_0^2 (ye^x - x - y) \, dx \, dy$ **4.** $\int_1^2 \int_2^3 \left(\frac{1}{x} + \frac{1}{y} \right) dx \, dy$

5. $\int_0^2 \int_0^3 e^{x+y} \, dx \, dy$ **6.** $\int_0^1 \int_0^1 e^{x-y} \, dx \, dy$

7. $\int_0^1 \int_0^{2-y} x \, dx \, dy$ **8.** $\int_0^1 \int_0^{2-y} y \, dx \, dy$

9. $\int_{-1}^1 \int_{y-1}^{y+1} e^{x+y} \, dx \, dy$ **10.** $\int_0^1 \int_y^{y+2} \frac{1}{\sqrt{x+y}} \, dx \, dy$

HINT [See Example 2.]   HINT [See Example 2.]

11. $\int_0^1 \int_{-x^2}^{x^2} x \, dy \, dx$ **12.** $\int_1^4 \int_{-\sqrt{x}}^{\sqrt{x}} \frac{1}{x} \, dy \, dx$

13. $\int_0^1 \int_0^x e^{x^2} \, dy \, dx$ **14.** $\int_0^1 \int_0^{x^2} e^{x^3+1} \, dy \, dx$

15. $\int_0^2 \int_{1-x}^{8-x} (x+y)^{1/3} \, dy \, dx$ **16.** $\int_1^2 \int_{1-2x}^{x^2} \frac{x+1}{(2x+y)^3} \, dy \, dx$

In Exercises 17–24, find $\iint_R f(x, y) \, dx \, dy$, where R is the indicated domain. (Remember that you often have a choice as to the order of integration.) HINT [See Example 2.]

17. $f(x, y) = 2$

18. $f(x, y) = x$

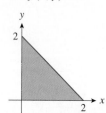

19. $f(x, y) = 1 + y$
HINT [See Example 3.]

20. $f(x, y) = e^{x+y}$
HINT [See Example 3.]

21. $f(x, y) = xy^2$

22. $f(x, y) = xy^2$

23. $f(x, y) = x^2 + y^2$

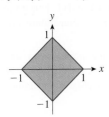

24. $f(x, y) = x^2$

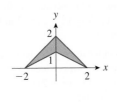

In Exercises 25–30, find the average value of the given function over the indicated domain. HINT [See Quick Examples page 1128.]

25. $f(x, y) = y$

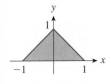

26. $f(x, y) = 2 + x$

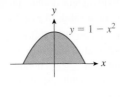

$y = 1 - x^2$

27. $f(x, y) = e^y$

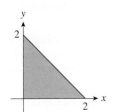

28. $f(x, y) = y$

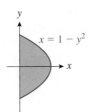

$x = 1 - y^2$

29. $f(x, y) = x^2$

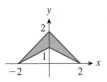

30. $f(x, y) = x^2 + y^2$

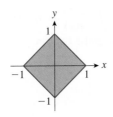

In Exercises 31–36, sketch the region over which you are integrating, and then write down the integral with the order of integration reversed (changing the limits of integration as necessary).

31. ▼ $\displaystyle\int_0^1 \int_0^{1-y} f(x, y)\, dx\, dy$

32. ▼ $\displaystyle\int_{-1}^1 \int_0^{1+y} f(x, y)\, dx\, dy$

33. ▼ $\displaystyle\int_{-1}^1 \int_0^{\sqrt{1+y}} f(x, y)\, dx\, dy$

34. ▼ $\displaystyle\int_{-1}^1 \int_0^{\sqrt{1-y}} f(x, y)\, dx\, dy$

35. ▼ $\displaystyle\int_1^2 \int_1^{4/x^2} f(x, y)\, dy\, dx$

36. ▼ $\displaystyle\int_1^{e^2} \int_0^{\ln x} f(x, y)\, dy\, dx$

37. Find the volume under the graph of $z = 1 - x^2$ over the region $0 \le x \le 1$ and $0 \le y \le 2$.

38. Find the volume under the graph of $z = 1 - x^2$ over the triangle $0 \le x \le 1$ and $0 \le y \le 1 - x$.

39. ▼ Find the volume of the tetrahedron shown in the figure. Its corners are $(0, 0, 0)$, $(1, 0, 0)$, $(0, 1, 0)$, and $(0, 0, 1)$.

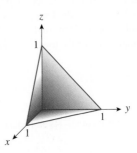

40. ▼ Find the volume of the tetrahedron with corners at $(0, 0, 0)$, $(a, 0, 0)$, $(0, b, 0)$, and $(0, 0, c)$.

APPLICATIONS

41. *Productivity* A productivity model at the Handy Gadget Company is

$$P = 10{,}000x^{0.3}y^{0.7}$$

where P is the number of gadgets the company turns out per month, x is the number of employees at the company, and y is the monthly operating budget in thousands of dollars. Because the company hires part-time workers, it uses anywhere between 45 and 55 workers each month, and its operating budget varies from \$8,000 to \$12,000 per month. What is the average of the possible numbers of gadgets it can turn out per month? (Round the answer to the nearest 1,000 gadgets.) HINT [See Quick Examples page 1128.]

42. *Productivity* Repeat the preceding exercise using the productivity model

$$P = 10{,}000x^{0.7}y^{0.3}.$$

43. *Revenue* Your latest CD-ROM of clip art is expected to sell between $q = 8{,}000 - p^2$ and $q = 10{,}000 - p^2$ copies if priced at p dollars. You plan to set the price between \$40 and \$50. What is the average of all the possible revenues you can make? HINT [See Example 4.]

44. *Revenue* Your latest DVD drive is expected to sell between $q = 180{,}000 - p^2$ and $q = 200{,}000 - p^2$ units if priced at p dollars. You plan to set the price between \$300 and \$400. What is the average of all the possible revenues you can make? HINT [See Example 4.]

45. *Revenue* Your self-published novel has demand curves between $p = 15{,}000/q$ and $p = 20{,}000/q$. You expect to sell between 500 and 1,000 copies. What is the average of all the possible revenues you can make?

46. *Revenue* Your self-published book of poetry has demand curves between $p = 80{,}000/q^2$ and $p = 100{,}000/q^2$. You expect to sell between 50 and 100 copies. What is the average of all the possible revenues you can make?

47. *Population Density* The town of West Podunk is shaped like a rectangle 20 miles from west to east and 30 miles from north to south. (See the figure.) It has a population density of $P(x, y) = e^{-0.1(x+y)}$ hundred people per square mile x miles east and y miles north of the southwest corner of town. What is the total population of the town? HINT [See Example 5.]

30 miles   West Podunk

←——— 20 miles ———→

48. *Population Density* The town of East Podunk is shaped like a triangle with an east-west base of 20 miles and a north-south height of 30 miles. (See the figure.) It has a population density of $P(x, y) = e^{-0.1(x+y)}$ hundred people per square mile x miles east and y miles north of the southwest corner of town. What is the total population of the town? HINT [See Example 5.]

30 miles   East Podunk

←——— 20 miles ———→

49. *Temperature* The temperature at the point (x, y) on the square with vertices $(0, 0)$, $(0, 1)$, $(1, 0)$, and $(1, 1)$ is given by $T(x, y) = x^2 + 2y^2$. Find the average temperature on the square.

50. *Temperature* The temperature at the point (x, y) on the square with vertices $(0, 0)$, $(0, 1)$, $(1, 0)$, and $(1, 1)$ is given by $T(x, y) = x^2 + 2y^2 - x$. Find the average temperature on the square.

COMMUNICATION AND REASONING EXERCISES

51. Explain how double integrals can be used to compute the area between two curves in the xy plane.

52. Explain how double integrals can be used to compute the volume of solids in 3-space.

53. Complete the following: The first step in calculating an integral of the form $\int_a^b \int_{r(x)}^{s(x)} f(x, y)\, dy\, dx$ is to evaluate the integral _____, obtained by holding ____ constant and integrating with respect to ____ .

54. If the units of $f(x, y)$ are zonars per square meter, and x and y are given in meters, what are the units of $\int_a^b \int_{r(x)}^{s(x)} f(x, y)\, dy\, dx$?

55. If the units of $\int_a^b \int_{r(x)}^{s(x)} f(x, y)\, dy\, dx$ are paintings, the units of x are picassos, and the units of y are dalis, what are the units of $f(x, y)$?

56. Complete the following: If the region R is bounded on the left and right by vertical lines and on the top and bottom by the graphs of functions of x, then we integrate over R by first integrating with respect to _____ and then with respect to ____.

57. ▼ Show that if a, b, c, and d are constant, then $\int_a^b \int_c^d f(x) g(y)\, dx\, dy = \int_c^d f(x)\, dx \int_a^b g(y)\, dy$. Test this result on the integral $\int_0^1 \int_1^2 y e^x\, dx\, dy$.

58. ▼ Refer to Exercise 57. If a, b, c, and d are constants, can $\int_a^b \int_c^d \dfrac{f(x)}{g(y)}\, dx\, dy$ be expressed as a product of two integrals? Explain.

KEY CONCEPTS

Web Site www.FiniteandCalc.org
Go to the student Web site at
www.FiniteandCalc.org to find a
comprehensive and interactive
Web-based summary of Chapter 15.

15.1 Functions of Several Variables from the Numerical, Algebraic, and Graphical Viewpoints

A real-valued function, f, of $x, y, z, \ldots$
p. 1080
Cost functions p. 1081
A linear function of the variables
$x_1, x_2, \ldots, x_n$ is a function of the form
$f(x_1, x_2, \ldots, x_n) = a_0 + a_1 x_1 + \ldots$
$+ a_n x_n$ ($a_0, a_1, \ldots, a_n$ constants)
p. 1082
Representing functions of two variables
numerically p. 1083
Using Excel to represent a function of
two variables p. 1084
Plotting points in three dimensions p. 1085
Graph of a function of two variables
p. 1086
Analyzing the graph of a function of two
variables p. 1088
Graph of a linear function p. 1090

15.2 Partial Derivatives

Definition of partial derivatives p. 1098

Application to marginal cost: linear cost
function p. 1099
Application to marginal cost: interaction
cost function p. 1099
Geometric interpretation of partial
derivatives p. 1101
Second order partial derivatives
p. 1101

15.3 Maxima and Minima

Definition of relative maximum and
minimum p. 1107
Locating candidates for relative maxima
and minima p. 1107
Classifying critical points graphically
p. 1108
Classifying critical points numerically
p. 1109
Second derivative test for a function of
two variables p. 1109
Using the second derivative test
p. 1110
Deriving the regression formulas:

$$m = \frac{n\left(\sum xy\right) - \left(\sum x\right)\left(\sum y\right)}{n\left(\sum x^2\right) - \left(\sum x\right)^2}$$

$$b = \frac{\sum y - m\left(\sum x\right)}{n}$$

n = number of data points p. 1111

15.4 Constrained Maxima and Minima and Applications

Constrained maximum and minimum
problem p. 1115
Solving constrained maxima and minima
problems using substitution p. 1115
The method of Lagrange multipliers
p. 1116
Using Lagrange multipliers p. 1117

15.5 Double Integrals and Applications

Geometric definition of the double
integral p. 1124
Algebraic definition of the double integral

$$\iint_R f(x, y)\, dx\, dy =$$

$$\lim_{n \to \infty} \lim_{m \to \infty} \sum_{j=1}^{n} \sum_{i=1}^{m} f(x_i, y_j) \Delta x \Delta y$$

p. 1125
Computing the double integral over a
rectangle p. 1125
Computing the double integral over
nonrectangular regions p. 1126
Average of $f(x, y)$ on the region R:

$$\bar{f} = \frac{1}{A} \iint_R f(x, y)\, dx\, dy \quad \text{p. 1128}$$

REVIEW EXERCISES

1. Let $f(x, y, z) = \dfrac{x}{y + xz} + x^2 y$. Evaluate $f(0, 1, 1), f(2, 1, 1),$
$f(-1, 1, -1), f(z, z, z),$ and $f(x + h, y + k, z + l)$.

2. Let $g(x, y, z) = xy(x + y - z) + x^2$. Evaluate $g(0, 0, 0),$
$g(1, 0, 0), g(0, 1, 0), g(x, x, x),$ and $g(x, y + k, z)$.

3. Let $f(x, y, z) = 2.72 - 0.32x - 3.21y + 12.5z$. Complete
the following: f ___ by ___ units for every 1 unit of increase
in x, and ___ by ___ units for every unit of increase in z.

4. Let $g(x, y, z) = 2.16x + 11y - 1.53z + 31.4$. Complete the
following: g ___ by ___ units for every 1 unit of increase in y,
and ___ by ___ units for every unit of increase in z.

In Exercises 5–6 complete the given table for values for $h(x, y) = 2x^2 + xy - x$.

5.

		$x \to$		
		-1	0	1
y	-1			
$\downarrow$	0			
	1			

6.

		$x \to$		
		-2	2	3
y	-2			
$\downarrow$	2			
	3			

7. Give a formula for a (single) function f with the property that
$f(x, y) = -f(y, x)$ and $f(1, -1) = 3$.

8. Let $f(x, y) = x^2 + (y + 1)^2$. Show that $f(y, x) = f(x + 1, y - 1)$.

In Exercises 9–14, compute the partial derivatives shown for the given function.

9. $f(x, y) = x^2 + xy$; find $f_x, f_y,$ and f_{yy}

10. $f(x, y) = \dfrac{6}{xy} + \dfrac{xy}{6}$; find $f_x, f_y,$ and f_{yy}

11. $f(x, y) = 4x + 5y - 6xy$; find $f_{xx}(1, 0) - f_{xx}(3, 2)$

12. $f(x, y) = e^{xy} + e^{3x^2 - y^2}$; find $\dfrac{\partial f}{\partial x}$ and $\dfrac{\partial^2 f}{\partial x \partial y}$

13. $f(x, y, z) = \dfrac{x}{x^2 + y^2 + z^2}$; find $\dfrac{\partial f}{\partial x}, \dfrac{\partial f}{\partial y}, \dfrac{\partial f}{\partial z}$ and $\dfrac{\partial f}{\partial x}\Big|_{(0,1,0)}$

14. $f(x, y, z) = x^2 + y^2 + z^2 + xyz$; find $f_{xx} + f_{yy} + f_{zz}$

In Exercises 15–19, locate and classify all critical points.

15. $f(x, y) = (x - 1)^2 + (2y - 3)^2$

16. $g(x, y) = (x - 1)^2 - 3y^2 + 9$

17. $h(x, y) = e^{xy}$

18. $j(x, y) = xy + x^2$

19. $f(x, y) = \ln(x^2 + y^2) - (x^2 + y^2)$

In Exercises 20–23, solve the following constrained optimization problems by using substitution to eliminate a variable. (Do not use Lagrange multipliers.)

20. Find the minimum value of $f(x, y, z) = x^2 + y^2 + z^2 - 1$ subject to $x = y + z$. Also find the corresponding point(s) (x, y, z).

21. Find the largest value of xyz subject to $x + y + z = 1$ with $x > 0, y > 0, z > 0$. Also find the corresponding point(s) (x, y, z).

22. Minimize $S = xy + x^2z^2 + 4yz$ subject to $xyz = 1$ with $x > 0, y > 0, z > 0$.

23. Find the point on the surface $z = \sqrt{x^2 + 2(y - 3)^2}$ closest to the origin.

In Exercises 24–28, use Lagrange multipliers to solve the given optimization problem.

24. Find the maximum value of $f(x, y) = xy$ subject to $y = e^{-x}$. Also find the corresponding point(s) (x, y).

25. Find the minimum value of $f(x, y) = x^2 + y^2$ subject to $xy = 2$. Also find the corresponding point(s) (x, y).

26. The problem in Exercise 20.

27. The problem in Exercise 22.

28. The problem in Exercise 23.

In Exercises 29–34, compute the given quantities.

29. $\displaystyle\int_0^1 \int_0^2 (2xy)\, dx\, dy$

30. $\displaystyle\int_1^2 \int_0^1 xy e^{x+y}\, dx\, dy$

31. $\displaystyle\int_0^2 \int_0^{2x} \dfrac{1}{x^2 + 1}\, dy\, dx$

32. The average value of xye^{x+y} over the rectangle $0 \le x \le 1$, $1 \le y \le 2$

33. $\iint_R (x^2 - y^2)\, dx\, dy$, where R is the region shown in the figure

34. The volume under the graph of $z = 1 - y$ over the region in the xy plane between the parabola $y = 1 - x^2$ and the x-axis.

APPLICATIONS

35. *Web Site Traffic* OHaganBooks.com has two principal competitors: JungleBooks.com and FarmerBooks.com. Current Web site traffic at OHaganBooks.com is estimated at 5,000 hits per day. This number is predicted to decrease by 0.8 for every new customer of JungleBooks.com and by 0.6 for every new customer of FarmerBooks.com.

  a. Use this information to model the daily Web site traffic at OHaganBooks.com as a linear function of the new customers of its two competitors.

  b. According to the model, if Junglebooks.com gets 100 new customers and OHaganBooks.com traffic drops to 4,770 hits per day, how many new customers has FarmerBooks .com obtained?

  c. The model in part (a) did not take into account the growth of the total online consumer base. OHaganBooks .com expects to get approximately one additional hit per day for every 10,000 new Internet shoppers. Modify your model in part (a) so as to include this information using a new independent variable.

  d. How many new Internet shoppers would it take to offset the effects on traffic at OHaganBooks.com of 100 new customers at each of its competitor sites?

36. *Productivity* Billy-Sean O'Hagan is writing up his Ph.D. thesis in biophysics but finds that his productivity is affected by the temperature and the number of text messages he receives per hour. On a brisk winter's day when the temperature is 0°C and there are no text messages, Billy-Sean can produce 15 pages of his thesis. His productivity goes down by 0.3 pages per degree Celsius increase in the temperature and by 1.2 pages for each additional text message per hour.

  a. Use this information to model Billy-Sean's productivity p as a function of the temperature and the hourly rate of text messages.

  b. The other day the temperature was 20°C and Billy-Sean managed to produce only three pages of his thesis. What was the hourly rate of incoming text messages?

  c. Billy reasons that each cup of coffee he drinks per hour can counter the effect on his productivity of two text messages per hour. Modify the model in part (a) to take consumption of coffee into account.

  d. What would the domain of your function look like to ensure that p is never negative?

37. *Internet Advertising* To increase business at OHaganBooks .com, you have purchased banner ads at well-known Internet portals and have advertised on television. The following interaction model shows the average number h of hits per day as a function of monthly expenditures x on banner ads and y on television advertising (x and y are in dollars).

$$h(x, y) = 1,800 + 0.05x + 0.08y + 0.00003xy$$

a. Based on your model, how much traffic can you anticipate if you spend $2,000 per month for banner ads and $3,000 per month on television advertising?

b. Evaluate $\dfrac{\partial h}{\partial y}$, specify its units of measurement, and indicate whether it increases or decreases with increasing x.

c. How much should the company spend on banner ads to obtain 1 hit per day for each $5 spent per month on television advertising?

38. *Company Retreats* Their companies having recently been bailed out by the government at taxpayer expense, Marjory Duffin and John O'Hagan are planning a joint winter business retreat in Cancun, but they are not sure how many sales reps to take along. The following interaction model shows the estimated cost C to their companies (in dollars) as a function of the number of sales reps x and the length of time t in days.

$$C(x, t) = 20,000 - 100x + 600t + 300xt$$

a. Based on the model, how much would it cost to take five sales reps along for a 10-day retreat?

b. Evaluate $\dfrac{\partial C}{\partial t}$, specify its units of measurement, and indicate whether it increases or decreases with increasing x.

c. How many reps should they take along if they wish to limit the marginal daily cost to $1,200?

39. *Internet Advertising* Refer to the model in Exercise 37. One or more of the following statements is correct. Identify which one(s).

(A) If nothing is spent on television advertising, one more dollar spent per month in banner ads will buy approximately 0.05 hits per day at OHaganBooks.com.

(B) If nothing is spent on television advertising, one more hit per day at OHaganBooks.com will cost the company about 5¢ per month in banner ads.

(C) If nothing is spent on banner ads, one more hit per day at OHaganBooks.com will cost the company about 5¢ per month in banner ads.

(D) If nothing is spent on banner ads, one more dollar spent per month in banner ads will buy approximately 0.05 hits per day at OHaganBooks.com.

(E) Hits at OHaganBooks.com cost approximately 5¢ per month spent on banner ads, and this cost increases at a rate of 0.003¢ per month, per hit.

40. *Company Retreats* Refer to the model in Exercise 38. One or more of the following statements is correct. Identify which one(s).

(A) If the retreat lasts for 10 days, the daily cost per sales rep is $400.

(B) If the retreat lasts for 10 days, each additional day will cost the company $2,900.

(C) If the retreat lasts for 10 days, each additional sales rep will cost the company $800.

(D) If the retreat lasts for 10 days, the daily cost per sales rep is $2,900.

(E) If the retreat lasts for 10 days, each additional sales rep will cost the company $2,900.

41. *Productivity* The holiday season is now at its peak and OHaganBooks.com has been understaffed and swamped with orders. The current backlog (orders unshipped for two or more days) has grown to a staggering 50,000, and new orders are coming in at a rate of 5,000 per day. Research based on productivity data at OHaganBooks.com results in the following model:

$$P(x, y) = 1,000x^{0.9}y^{0.1} \text{ additional orders filled per day}$$

where x is the number of additional personnel hired and y is the daily budget (excluding salaries) allocated to eliminating the backlog.

a. How many additional orders will be filled per day if the company hires 10 additional employees and budgets an additional $1,000 per day? (Round the answer to the nearest 100.)

b. In addition to the daily budget, extra staffing costs the company $150 per day for every new staff member hired. In order to fill at least 15,000 additional orders per day at a minimum total daily cost, how many new staff members should the company hire? (Use the method of Lagrange multipliers.)

42. *Productivity* The holiday season has now ended, and orders at OHaganBooks.com have plummeted, leaving staff members in the shipping department with little to do besides spend their time on their Facebook pages, so the company is considering laying off a number of personnel and slashing the shipping budget. Research based on productivity data at OHaganBooks.com results in the following model:

$$C(x, y) = 1,000x^{0.8}y^{0.2} \text{ fewer orders filled per day}$$

where x is the number of personnel laid off and y is the cut in the shipping budget (excluding salaries).

a. How many fewer orders will be filled per day if the company lays off 15 additional employees and cuts the budget by an additional $2,000 per day? (Round the answer to the nearest 100.)

b. In addition to the cut in the shipping budget, the layoffs will save the company $200 per day for every new staff member laid off. The company needs to meet a target of 20,000 fewer orders per day but, for tax reasons, it must minimize the total resulting savings. How many new staff members should the company lay off? (Use the method of Lagrange multipliers.)

43. *Profit* If OHaganBooks.com sells x paperback books and y hardcover books per week, it will make an average weekly profit of

$$P(x, y) = 3x + 10y \text{ dollars.}$$

If it sells between 1,200 and 1,500 paperback books and between 1,800 and 2,000 hardcover books per week, what is the average of all its possible weekly profits?

44. *Cost* It costs Duffin publishers

$$C(x, y) = x^2 + 2y \text{ dollars}$$

to produce x coffee table art books and y paperback books per week. If it produces between 100 and 120 art books and between 800 and 1,000 paperbacks per week, what is the average of all its possible weekly costs?

Case Study   Modeling College Population

College Malls, Inc. is planning to build a national chain of shopping malls in college neighborhoods. However, malls in general have been experiencing large numbers of store closings due to, among other things, misjudgments of the shopper demographics. As a result, the company is planning to lease only to stores that target the specific age demographics of the national college student population.

As a marketing consultant to College Malls, you will be providing the company with a report that addresses the following specific issues:

- A quick way of estimating the number of students of any specified age and in any particular year, and the effect of increasing age on the college population
- The ages that correspond to relatively high and low college populations
- How fast the 20-year-old and 25-year-old student populations are increasing
- Some near-term projections of the student population trend

You decide that a good place to start would be with a visit to the Census Bureau's Web site at www.census.gov. After some time battling with search engines, all you can find is some data on college enrollment for three age brackets for the period 1980–2005, as shown in the following table:[30]

College Enrollment (thousands)

Year	1980	1985	1990	1995	1999	2000	2001	2002	2003	2004	2005
18–24	7,229	7,537	7,964	8,541	9,260	9,451	9,629	10,033	10,364	10,608	10,831
25–34	2,703	3,063	3,161	3,349	3,095	3,207	3,422	3,401	3,494	3,695	3,601
35–41	1,207	1,661	2,318	2,669	2,699	2,507	2,684	2,868	2,630	2,883	2,857

The data are inadequate for several reasons: The data are given only for certain years, and in age brackets rather than year-by-year; nor is it obvious as to how you would project the figures. However, you notice that the table is actually a numerical representation of a function of two variables: year and age. Since the age brackets are of different sizes, you "normalize" the data by dividing each figure by the number of years represented in the corresponding age bracket; for instance, you divide the 1980 figure for the first age group by 7 in order to obtain the average enrollment for each year of age in that group.

---

[30] Source: Bureau of the Census, 2008 (www.census.gov/population/www/socdemo/school.html).

You then rewrite the resulting table representing the years by values of t and each age bracket by the age x at its center (enrollment values are rounded):

$t \rightarrow$

x	0	5	10	15	19	20	21	22	23	24	25
21	1,033	1,077	1,138	1,220	1,323	1,350	1,376	1,433	1,481	1,515	1,547
29.5	270	306	316	335	310	321	342	340	349	370	360
38	172	237	331	381	386	358	383	410	376	412	408

Figure 37

In order to see a visual representation of what the data are saying, you use Excel to graph the data as a surface (Figure 37). It is important to notice that Excel does not scale the t-axis as you would expect: It uses one subdivision for each year shown in the chart, and the result is an uneven scaling of the t-axis. Despite this drawback, you do see two trends after looking at views of the graph from various angles. First, enrollment of 38-year-olds (the front edge of the graph) seems to be increasing faster than enrollment of 21-year-olds. Second, the enrollment for all ages seem to be increasing approximately linearly with time since 1999, although at different rates for different age groups; for instance, the front and rear edges rise more-or-less linearly, but do not seem to be parallel.

At this point you realize that a mathematical model of these data would be useful; not only would it "smooth out the bumps" but it would give you a way to estimate enrollment N at each specific age, project the enrollments, and thereby complete the project for College Malls. Although technology can give you a regression model for data such as this, it is up to you to decide on the form of the model. It is in choosing an appropriate model that your analysis of the graph comes in handy. Because N should vary linearly with time t for each value of x, you would like

$$N = mt + k$$

for each value of x. Also, because there are three values of x for every value of time, you try a quadratic model for N as a function of x:

$$N = a + bx + cx^2$$

Putting these together, you get the following candidate model

$$N(t, x) = a_1 + a_2 t + a_3 x + a_4 x^2$$

where a_1, a_2, a_3, and a_4 are constants. However, for each specific age $x = k$, you get

$$N(t, k) = a_1 + a_2 t + a_3 k + a_4 k^2 = \text{Constant} + a_2 t$$

with the same slope a_2 for every choice of the age k, contrary to your observation that enrollment for different age groups is rising at different rates, so you will need a more elaborate model. You recall from your applied calculus course that interaction functions give a way to model the effect of one variable on the rate of change of another, so, as an experiment, you try adding interaction terms to your model:

Model 1: $N(t, x) = a_1 + a_2 t + a_3 x + a_4 x^2 + a_5 xt$ Second order model

Model 2: $N(t, x) = a_1 + a_2 t + a_3 x + a_4 x^2 + a_5 xt + a_6 x^2 t$.   Third order model

(Model 1 is referred to as a second order model because it contains no products of more than two independent variables, whereas Model 2 contains the third order term $x^2 t = x \cdot x \cdot t$.) If you study these two models for specific values k of x you get:

Model 1: $N = \text{Constant} + (a_2 + a_5 k)t$ Slope depends linearly on age

Model 2: $N = \text{Constant} + (a_2 + a_5 k + a_6 k^2)t$.   Slope depends quadratically on age

	A	B	C
1	N	t	x
2	1033	0	21
3	1077	5	21
4	1138	10	21
5	1220	15	21
6	1323	19	21
7	1350	20	21
8	1376	21	21
9	1433	22	21
10	1481	23	21
11	1515	24	21
12	1547	25	21
13	270	0	29.5
14	306	5	29.5
15	316	10	29.5
16	335	15	29.5
17	310	19	29.5
18	321	20	29.5
19	342	21	29.5
20	340	22	29.5
21	349	23	29.5
22	370	24	29.5
23	360	25	29.5
24	172	0	38
25	237	5	38
26	331	10	38
27	381	15	38
28	386	19	38
29	358	20	38
30	383	21	38
31	410	22	38
32	376	23	38
33	412	24	38
34	408	25	38

Figure 38

This is encouraging: Both models show different slopes for different ages. Model 1 would predict that the slope either increases with increasing age (a_5 positive) or decreases with increasing age (a_5 negative). However, the graph suggests that the slope is larger for both younger and older students, but smaller for students of intermediate age, contrary to what Model 1 predicts. So you decide to go with the more flexible Model 2, which permits the slope to decrease and then increase with increasing age. This is exactly what you observe on the graph.

You decide to use Excel to generate your model. However, the data as shown in the table are not in a form Excel can use for regression. The data need to be organized into columns: Column A for the dependent variable N and Columns B–C for the independent variables, as shown in Figure 38. You then add columns for the higher order terms x^2, xt, and $x^2 t$ as shown below:

	A	B	C	D	E	F
1	N	t	x	x^2	x*t	x^2*t
2	1033	0	21	=C2^2	=C2*B2	=C2^2*B2
3	1077	5	21			
4	1138	10	21			
5	1220	15	21			
6	1323	19	21			
7	1350	20	21			
8	1376	21	21			
9						

↓

	A	B	C	D	E	F
1	N	t	x	x^2	x*t	x^2*t
2	1033	0	21	441	0	0
3	1077	5	21	441	105	2205
4	1138	10	21	441	210	4410
5	1220	15	21	441	315	6615
6	1323	19	21	441	399	8379
7	1350	20	21	441	420	8820
8	1376	21	21	441	441	9261
9						

Next, in the "Analysis" section of the Data tab, choose "Data analysis." (If this command is not available, you will need to load the Analysis ToolPak add-in.) Choose "Regression" from the list that appears, and in the resulting dialogue box enter the location of the data and where you want to put the results as shown in Figure 39; identify where the dependent and independent variables are (A1–A34 for the Y range, and B1–F34 for the X range), check "Labels," and click "OK."

Figure 39

A portion of the output is shown below, with some of the important statistics highlighted.

37	SUMMARY OUTPUT					
38						
39	*Regression Statistics*					
40	Multiple R	0.99807463				
41	R Square	0.99615297				
42	Adjusted R Square	0.99544056				
43	Standard Error	32.4693397				
44	Observations	33				
45						
46	ANOVA					
47		*df*	*SS*	*MS*	*F*	*Significance F*
48	Regression	5	7370748.67	1474149.73	1398.28173	1.0623E-31
49	Residual	27	28464.96658	1054.25802		
50	Total	32	7399213.636			
51						
52		*Coefficients*	*Standard Error*	*t Stat*	*P-value*	*Lower 95%*
53	Intercept	5317.742	324.3264401	16.3962642	1.4646E-15	4652.279561
54	t	165.703742	17.52824924	9.45352497	4.6746E-10	129.7387692
55	x	-296.5247	22.98384198	-12.901442	4.6484E-13	-343.6836131
56	x^2	4.26166483	0.38821602	10.9775605	1.8505E-11	3.465111887
57	x*t	-10.325579	1.242163638	-8.3125755	6.3811E-09	-12.87428658
58	x^2*t	0.16304663	0.020981167	7.77109439	2.3426E-08	0.119996859

The desired constants a_1, a_2, a_3, a_4, and a_5 appear in the coefficients column at the bottom left, in the correct order: a_1 is the "intercept," a_2 is the coefficient of t, and so on. Thus, if we round to five significant digits, we have

$$a_1 = 5,317.7 \quad a_2 = 165.70 \quad a_3 = -296.52$$
$$a_4 = 4.2617 \quad a_5 = -10.326 \quad a_6 = 0.16305$$

which gives our regression model:

$$N(t, x) = 5,317.7 + 165.70t - 296.52x + 4.2617x^2 - 10.326xt + 0.16305x^2t.$$

Fine, you say to yourself, now you have the model, but how good a fit is it to the data? That is where the "Multiple R" at the top of the data analysis comes in. R is called the **multiple coefficient of correlation,** and generalizes the coefficient of correlation discussed in the section on regression in Chapter 1: The closer R is to 1, the better the fit. We can interpret its square, given in the table as "R Square" with value 0.996, as indicating that approximately 99.6% of the variation in college enrollment is explained by the regression model, indicating an excellent fit. The "P-values" at bottom right are also indicators of the appropriateness of the model; a P-value close to zero indicates a high degree of confidence that the corresponding independent variable contributes significantly to the value of the college enrollment (a P-value less than 0.05 would indicate, for example, that the corresponding coefficient is statistically significant at a level of more than 95% confidence) whereas a P-value close to 1 indicates low confidence; there is a P-value for each coefficient. Because all the values are extremely tiny, you are confident indeed that the model is an appropriate one. Another statistical indicator is the value of "F" on the right—an indicator of confidence in the model as a whole. The fact that it too is large and its "Significance F" is tiny is yet another good sign.*

* **NOTE** We are being deliberately vague about the exact meaning of these statistics, which are discussed fully in many applied statistics texts.

As comforting as these statistics are, nothing can be quite as persuasive as a graph. You turn to the graphing software of your choice and notice that the graph of the model appears to be a faithful representation of the data. (See Figure 40.)

Figure 40

Now you get to work, using the model to address the questions posed by College Malls.

1. *A quick way of estimating the number of students of any specified age and in any particular year, and the effect of increasing age on the college population.* You already have a quantitative relationship in the form of the regression model. As for the second part of the question, the rate of change of college enrollment with respect to age is given by the partial derivative:

$$\frac{\partial N}{\partial x} = -296.52 + 8.5234x - 10.326t + 0.32610xt \text{ thousand students per}$$
$$\text{additional year of age.}$$

Thus, for example, with $x = 20$ in 2004 ($t = 24$), we have

$$\frac{\partial N}{\partial x} = -296.52 + 8.5234(20) - 10.326(24) + 0.32610(20)(24)$$

$$\approx -217 \text{ thousand students per additional year of age,}$$

so there were about 217,000 fewer students of age 21 than age 20 in 2004.
On the other hand, when $x = 38$ in the same year, one has

$$\frac{\partial N}{\partial x} = -296.52 + 8.5234(38) - 10.326(24) + 0.32610(38)(24)$$

$$\approx 77 \text{ thousand students per additional year of age,}$$

so there were about 77,000 more students of age 39 than age 38 that year.

2. *The ages that correspond to relatively high and low college populations.* Although a glance at the graph shows you that there are no relative maxima, holding t constant (that is, on any given year) gives a parabola along the corresponding slice and hence a minimum somewhere along the slice.

$$\frac{\partial N}{\partial x} = 0$$

when $-296.52 + 8.5234x - 10.326t + 0.32610xt = 0,$

which gives $x = \dfrac{296.52 + 10.326t}{8.5234 + 0.32610t}$ years of age.

For instance, in 2000 ($t = 20$), the age at which there are the fewest students (in the given range) is 33.4 years of age. The relative maxima for each slice occur at the front and back edges of the surface, meaning that there are relatively more students of the lowest and highest ages represented. The absolute maximum for each slice occurs, as expected, at the lowest age. In short, a mall catering to college students should focus mostly on freshman-age students, least on 33-year-olds, and somewhat more on people around age 40.

3. *How fast the 20-year-old and 25-year-old student populations are increasing.* The rate of change of student population with respect to time is

$$\frac{\partial N}{\partial t} = 165.70 - 10.326x + 0.16305x^2 \text{ thousand students per year.}$$

For the three age groups in question, we obtain

$$x = 20: 165.70 - 10.326(20) + 0.16305(20)^2 = 24.4 \text{ thousand students/year}$$
$$x = 25: 165.70 - 10.326(25) + 0.16305(25)^2 \approx 9.5 \text{ thousand students/year.}$$

(Note that these rates of change are independent of time as we chose a model that is linear in time.)

4. *Some near-term projections of the student population trend.* As we have seen throughout the book, extrapolation can be a risky venture; however, *near-term* extrapolation from a good model can be reasonable. You enter the model in an Excel spreadsheet to obtain the following predicted college enrollments (in thousands) for the years 2006–2010:

$t \rightarrow$ x $\downarrow$	26	27	28	29	30
21	1,510	1,531	1,551	1,572	1,593
29.5	357	359	362	365	368
38	431	440	449	458	467

EXERCISES

1. Use Excel to obtain Model 1:

$$N(t, x) = a_1 + a_2 t + a_3 x + a_4 x^2 + a_5 xt.$$

Compare the fit of this model with that of the quadratic model above. Comment on the result.

2. How much is there to be gained by adding an additional term of the form $a_7 t^2$ to the original model? (Perform the regression and analyze the result by referring to the P-value for the resulting coefficient of t^2.) How does the addition of this term affect the slices $x = $ constant?

3. Compute and interpret $\left.\dfrac{\partial N}{\partial t}\right|_{(10,18)}$ and $\left.\dfrac{\partial^2 N}{\partial t \partial x}\right|_{(10,18)}$ for the model in the text. What are their units of measurement?

4. Notice that the derivatives in the preceding exercise do not depend on time. What additional polynomial term(s) would make both $\partial N/\partial t$ and $\partial^2 N/\partial t \partial x$ depend on time? (Write down the entire model.) Of what order is your model?

5. Test the model you constructed in the preceding question by discussing the P-values of the additional coefficients.

TI-83/84 Plus Technology Guide

Section 15.1

Example 1 (page 1081)   You own a company that makes two models of speakers: the Ultra Mini and the Big Stack. Your total monthly cost (in dollars) to make x Ultra Minis and y Big Stacks is given by

$$C(x, y) = 10,000 + 20x + 40y.$$

Compute several values of this function.

Solution with Technology

You can have a TI-83/84 Plus compute $C(x, y)$ numerically as follows:

1. In the "Y=" screen, enter

$$Y_1 = 10000 + 20X + 40Y$$

2. To evaluate, say, $C(10, 30)$ (the cost to make 10 Ultra Minis and 30 Big Stacks), enter

$$10 \rightarrow X$$
$$30 \rightarrow Y$$
$$Y_1$$

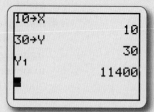

and the calculator will evaluate the function and give the answer $C(10, 30) = 11,400$.

  This procedure is too laborious if you want to calculate $f(x, y)$ for a large number of different values of x and y.

EXCEL Technology Guide

Section 15.1

Example 1 (page 1081)   You own a company that makes two models of speakers: the Ultra Mini and the Big Stack. Your total monthly cost (in dollars) to make x Ultra Minis and y Big Stacks is given by

$$C(x, y) = 10,000 + 20x + 40y.$$

Compute several values of this function.

Solution with Technology

Excel handles functions of several variables easily. The following setup shows how a table of values of C can be created, using values of x and y you enter:

	A	B	C
1	x	y	C(x, y)
2	10	30	=10000+20*A2+40*B2
3	20	30	
4	15	0	
5	0	30	
6	30	30	

↓

	A	B	C
1	x	y	C(x, y)
2	10	30	11400
3	20	30	11600
4	15	0	10300
5	0	30	11200
6	30	30	11800

A disadvantage of this layout is that it's not easy to enter values of x and y systematically in two columns. Can you find a way to remedy this? (See Example 3 for one method.)

Example 3 (page 1083)   Use technology to create a table of values of the body mass index

$$M(w, h) = \frac{0.45w}{(0.0254h)^2}.$$

Solution with Technology

We can use this formula to recreate a table in Excel, as follows:

	A	B	C	D
1		130	140	150
2	60	=0.45*B$1/(0.0254*$A2)^2		
3	61			
4	62			
5	63			
6	64			
7	65			
8	66			
9	67			

In the formula in cell B2 we have used B$1 instead of B1 for the w-coordinate because we want all references to w to use the same row (1). Similarly, we want all references to h to refer to the same column (A), so we used $A2 instead of A2.

3.6 Determinants

We said in Section 3.3 that a 2×2 matrix $\begin{bmatrix} a & b \\ c & d \end{bmatrix}$ is invertible if and only if its *determinant, ad − bc,* is nonzero, and we saw the determinant used in the formula for the inverse of a 2×2 matrix. In this section we see how to compute the determinant of $n \times n$ matrices for arbitrary n and also, in the case of 2×2 and 3×3 matrices, how to interpret it geometrically. In the next section we will see one of its important applications: we can use it to write down explicit formulas for solutions of systems of linear equations.

Determinant of an $n \times n$ Matrix

Although it is possible to write down a formula for the determinant of an $n \times n$ matrix in terms of its entries, this formula is rarely actually used to *calculate* determinants. From the point of view of calculation, it is better to specify the determinant of an $n \times n$ matrix *recursively*—we state how to find the determinant of a larger matrix in terms of the determinants of smaller matrices.

If A is a square matrix, we will write its determinant as $\det(A)$. We already know from Section 3.3 how to calculate the determinant of a 2×2 matrix: If

$$A = \begin{bmatrix} a & b \\ c & d \end{bmatrix}$$

then

$$\det(A) = ad - bc.$$

The determinant of a 1×1 matrix is even simpler: If $A = [a]$, then

$$\det(A) = a.$$

Before generalizing to $n \times n$ matrices, we introduce a new term:

The Minor Matrix and Minor of an Entry

If A is an $n \times n$ matrix with $n \geq 2$ and a_{ij} is one of its entries, the associated **minor matrix** m_{ij} is the $(n-1) \times (n-1)$ matrix obtained by deleting both the row and the column passing through a_{ij}. The *determinant* of the minor matrix m_{ij} is called the minor M_{ij}. Thus,

m_{ij} = Minor matrix (delete row and column through a_{ij})
M_{ij} = Minor = $\det(m_{ij})$

Quick Examples

1. If $A = \begin{bmatrix} 1 & -1 \\ 2 & -2 \end{bmatrix}$, then

$m_{11} = \begin{bmatrix} 1 & -1 \\ 2 & -2 \end{bmatrix} = [-2]$ Delete the row and column through a_{11}.

$$M_{11} = \det(m_{11}) = \det([-2]) = -2$$

The determinant of a 1×1 matrix is its only entry.

$$m_{12} = \begin{bmatrix} 1 & -1 \\ 2 & -2 \end{bmatrix} = [2]$$

Delete the row and column through a_{12}.

$$M_{12} = \det(m_{12}) = \det([2]) = 2$$

$$m_{21} = \begin{bmatrix} 1 & -1 \\ 2 & -2 \end{bmatrix} = [-1]$$

Delete the row and column through a_{21}.

$$M_{21} = \det(m_{21}) = \det([-1]) = -1$$

$$m_{22} = \begin{bmatrix} 1 & -1 \\ 2 & -2 \end{bmatrix} = [1]$$

Delete the row and column through a_{22}.

$$M_{22} = \det(m_{22}) = \det([1]) = 1$$

2. If $A = \begin{bmatrix} 3 & 1 & -1 \\ 2 & -2 & 0 \\ 7 & 5 & 1 \end{bmatrix}$, then

$$m_{12} = \begin{bmatrix} 3 & 1 & -1 \\ 2 & -2 & 0 \\ 7 & 5 & 1 \end{bmatrix} = \begin{bmatrix} 2 & 0 \\ 7 & 1 \end{bmatrix}$$

Delete the row and column through a_{12}.

$$M_{12} = \det(m_{12}) = \det\begin{bmatrix} 2 & 0 \\ 7 & 1 \end{bmatrix} = (2)(1) - (0)(7) = 2$$

$$m_{31} = \begin{bmatrix} 3 & 1 & -1 \\ 2 & -2 & 0 \\ 7 & 5 & 1 \end{bmatrix} = \begin{bmatrix} 1 & -1 \\ -2 & 0 \end{bmatrix}$$

Delete the row and column through a_{31}.

$$M_{31} = \det(m_{31}) = \det\begin{bmatrix} 1 & -1 \\ -2 & 0 \end{bmatrix} = (1)(0) - (-1)(-2) = -2$$

We now give the promised recursive definition of the determinant of a matrix. Since we know how to compute the determinants of 1×1 and 2×2 matrices, we start with the determinants of 3×3 matrices.

Computing the Determinant of a Square Matrix

The **determinant** of the $n \times n$ matrix A, written $\det(A)$ or sometimes $|A|$, is an associated real number computed for 1×1 and 2×2 matrices as above, and for larger matrices as follows:

3 × 3 Matrix

The determinant of the 3×3 matrix $A = \begin{bmatrix} a_{11} & a_{12} & a_{13} \\ a_{21} & a_{22} & a_{23} \\ a_{31} & a_{32} & a_{33} \end{bmatrix}$ is given by

$$\det(A) = a_{11} \times M_{11} - a_{12} \times M_{12} + a_{13} \times M_{13}.$$

(The formula involves computing 2×2 minors.)

Quick Example

Let $A = \begin{bmatrix} 3 & 1 & -1 \\ 2 & -2 & 0 \\ 7 & 5 & 1 \end{bmatrix}$. Then

$$\det(A) = a_{11} \times M_{11} - a_{12} \times M_{12} + a_{13} \times M_{13}$$

$$= 3 \times \det \begin{bmatrix} -2 & 0 \\ 5 & 1 \end{bmatrix} - 1 \times \det \begin{bmatrix} 2 & 0 \\ 7 & 1 \end{bmatrix} + (-1) \times \det \begin{bmatrix} 2 & -2 \\ 7 & 5 \end{bmatrix}$$

$$= 3 \times (-2) - 1 \times 2 + (-1) \times 24 = -32.$$

4 × 4 Matrix

The determinant of the 4×4 matrix $A = \begin{bmatrix} a_{11} & a_{12} & a_{13} & a_{14} \\ a_{21} & a_{22} & a_{23} & a_{24} \\ a_{31} & a_{32} & a_{33} & a_{34} \\ a_{41} & a_{42} & a_{43} & a_{44} \end{bmatrix}$ is given by

$$\det(A) = a_{11} \times M_{11} - a_{12} \times M_{12} + a_{13} \times M_{13} - a_{14} \times M_{14}.$$

Notice the alternating pattern in the signs.

(The formula involves computing 3×3 minors.)

Quick Example

Let $A = \begin{bmatrix} 1 & 0 & 0 & 0 \\ 2 & 4 & 0 & 0 \\ -1 & 2 & 2 & 0 \\ 1 & 2 & 3 & 4 \end{bmatrix}$. Then

$$\det(A) = a_{11} \times M_{11} - a_{12} \times M_{12} + a_{13} \times M_{13} - a_{14} \times M_{14}$$

$$= 1 \times \det \begin{bmatrix} 4 & 0 & 0 \\ 2 & 2 & 0 \\ 2 & 3 & 4 \end{bmatrix} - 0 \times \det \begin{bmatrix} 2 & 0 & 0 \\ -1 & 2 & 0 \\ 1 & 3 & 4 \end{bmatrix}$$

$$+ 0 \times \det \begin{bmatrix} 2 & 4 & 0 \\ -1 & 2 & 0 \\ 1 & 2 & 4 \end{bmatrix} - 0 \times \det \begin{bmatrix} 2 & 4 & 0 \\ -1 & 2 & 2 \\ 1 & 2 & 3 \end{bmatrix}$$

$$= 1 \times 4 \times 2 \times 4 = 32.$$

Notice that the determinant of a lower triangular matrix like this (no entries above the main diagonal) is just the product of the entries on the main diagonal.

n × n Matrix

In general, the determinant of an $n \times n$ matrix is given by the following formula with alternating signs:

$$\det(A) = a_{11} \times M_{11} - a_{12} \times M_{12} + a_{13} \times M_{13} - \cdots \pm a_{1n} \times M_{1n}$$

The formula involves computing $(n-1) \times (n-1)$ minors.

Technology: Computing Determinants with the TI-83/84 Plus

On a TI-83/84, you can find the inverse of the square matrix [A] by entering

$$\text{det([A])} \boxed{\text{ENTER}}$$

det is found in the $\boxed{\text{MATRX}}$ MATH menu

Computing Determinants with Excel

The formula `MDETERM` can be used to compute the determinant of any square matrix.

In the following worksheet, the determinant of $\begin{bmatrix} 3 & 1 & -1 \\ 2 & -2 & 0 \\ 7 & 5 & 1 \end{bmatrix}$ is computed in cell E3 by entering the formula shown:

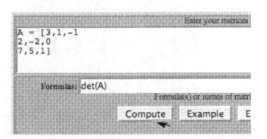

	A	B	C	D	E	F	G
1	3	1	-1				
2	2	-2	0				
3	7	5	1		=MDETERM(A1:C3)		
4							

Computing Determinants with the Online Matrix Algebra Tool

On the Web site, follow On-Line Utilities → Matrix Algebra Tool. There, enter your matrix A and the formula det(A) as shown, and press "Compute." The figure shows how one would compute the determinant of $A = \begin{bmatrix} 3 & 1 & -1 \\ 2 & -2 & 0 \\ 7 & 5 & 1 \end{bmatrix}$:

Enter your matrices
```
A = [3,1,-1
2,-2,0
7,5,1]
```

Formulas: det(A)

Formula(s) or names of matri

Compute   Example   E

Q : *Now we know how to compute the determinant, but what is it good for?*

A : Determinants give us a method to compute volumes, to determine whether a square matrix is singular, and to compute the inverse of a nonsingular matrix. In the next section we will see how they give us explicit solutions for systems of linear equations. There are also numerous theoretical applications that go beyond the scope of this book.

Computing Areas and Volumes

Consider the parallelogram shown on the left in Figure 1. Notice that its shape and size are completely determined by the coordinates of the two points (a, b) and (c, d)—once we know these points, we can draw in the rest of the parallelogram, as shown on the right.

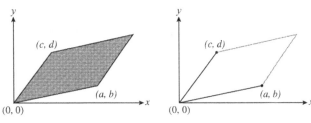

Figure 1

It follows that the *area* of this parallelogram is also determined by the four numbers a, b, c, and d, and, in fact, the area is the absolute value of the following determinant:

$$\text{Area of parallelogram} = \left| \det \begin{bmatrix} a & b \\ c & d \end{bmatrix} \right| = |ad - bc|$$

Q : *Why?*

A : Figure 2 shows the parallelogram inside a rectangle. The area of the rectangle is

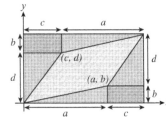

Figure 2

$$(a + c)(b + d) = ab + cb + ad + cd$$

To obtain the area of the parallelogram we subtract the combined area of the four (green) triangles and two (pink) rectangles, which is

$$2\left(\frac{1}{2}ab\right) + 2\left(\frac{1}{2}cd\right) + 2bc = ab + cd + 2bc$$

So, the area of the parallelogram is

$$ab + cb + ad + cd - (ab + cd + 2bc) = ad - bc.$$

EXAMPLE 1 Computing Areas

Use determinants to compute the areas of the following regions:

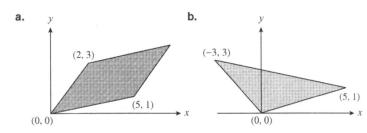

Solution

a. We are given a parallelogram with $(a, b) = (5, 1)$ and $(c, d) = (2, 3)$. (You could also reverse the choice by taking $(a, b) = (2, 3)$ and $(c, d) = (5, 1)$—see *Before we go on* below). Therefore,

$$\text{Area} = \left| \det \begin{bmatrix} 5 & 1 \\ 2 & 3 \end{bmatrix} \right| = |(5)(3) - (1)(2)| = |13| = 13 \text{ square units}$$

b. Although the figure is not a parallelogram, it can be thought of as *half* a parallelogram (Figure 3).

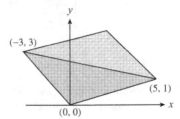

Figure 3

The area of the complete parallelogram is

$$\text{Area of parallelogram} = \left| \det \begin{bmatrix} 5 & 1 \\ -3 & 3 \end{bmatrix} \right| = |18| = 18 \text{ square units}.$$

Therefore, the area of the original triangle is half of that:

$$\textit{Area of triangle} = \frac{1}{2}18 = 9 \text{ square units}.$$

➡ **Before we go on...**

Q : *In Example 1, which point do I take as (a, b) and which point do I take as (c, d)?*

A : It makes no difference. If we reverse our choice, we get

$$\text{Area} = \left| \det \begin{bmatrix} 2 & 3 \\ 5 & 1 \end{bmatrix} \right| = |(2)(1) - (3)(5)| = |-13| = 13 \text{ square units}.$$

This is always true: Changing the order of the rows does not affect the absolute value of the determinant, only its sign.

■

Parallelepipeds are three-dimensional versions of parallelograms: You can form one by taking two identical parallelograms that are parallel to each other, and then joining corresponding corners (Figure 4).

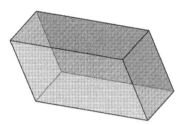

Figure 4

To specify a parallelepiped, one of whose corners is at the origin, we use three points as shown in Figure 5.

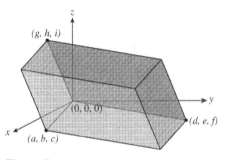

Figure 5

Notice that the three labeled points are on the ends of the three edges that contain the origin (0, 0, 0).

Q: *Why are we labeling points with 3 coordinates now?*

A: Answer We need 3 coordinates to specify a point in 3-dimensional space. Look at the point (a, b, c). We get to this point from the origin $(0, 0, 0)$ as follows: Move a units in the x-direction (towards you if a is positive, away from you if a is negative), then move b units in the y-direction (to the right if a is positive, to the left if a is negative), and finally move c units in the z-direction (straight up if a is positive, down if a is negative).

Just as the area of a parallelogram is given by the determinant of a 2×2 matrix, so the volume of a parallelepiped is given by the determinant of a 3×3 matrix:

$$\text{Volume of parallelepiped} = \left| \det \begin{bmatrix} a & b & c \\ d & e & f \\ g & h & i \end{bmatrix} \right|$$

Q: *Does it matter in what order we write the rows?*

A: No. Changing the order of the rows in a matrix effects only the *sign* of its determinant, not the absolute value.

EXAMPLE 2 **Computing Volumes**

Use determinants to compute the volumes of the following solids:

a.

b.

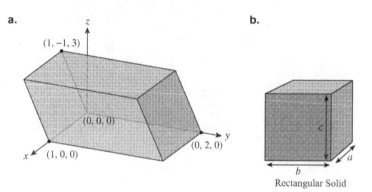

Rectangular Solid

Solution

a. Since we are given the coordinates of the three points on the ends of the three edges containing the origin, we can use the formula directly:

$$\text{Volume of parallelepiped} = \left| \det \begin{bmatrix} 1 & 0 & 0 \\ 0 & 2 & 0 \\ 1 & -1 & 3 \end{bmatrix} \right| = (1)(2)(3) = 6.$$

Notice that we arranged the three points in such a way as to obtain an upper triangular matrix, so that the determinant is just the product of the diagonal entries. As we said above, the determinant of a matrix does not change in absolute value if we rearrange the rows.

b. Since the figure is a rectangular solid, we know that its volume is

$$\text{depth} \times \text{width} \times \text{height} = abc$$

However, we were asked to compute it using determinants. To do this we first place one corner at the origin and find the coordinates of the three adjacent points. Figure 6 shows a way of doing that.

   We have placed the far corner at the origin so that the point a has coordinates $(a, 0, 0)$, the point b has coordinates $(0, b, 0)$, and the point c has coordinates $(0, 0, c)$.

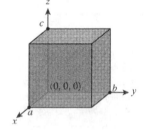

Figure 6

Q : *Why?*

A : To get to the point labeled a, just move a units in the x-direction, and no units in any of the other directions. Therefore, its coordinates are $(a, 0, 0)$. The coordinates of the other points are computed in a similar way.

   We now have

$$\text{Volume of parallelepiped} = \left| \det \begin{bmatrix} a & 0 & 0 \\ 0 & b & 0 \\ 0 & 0 & c \end{bmatrix} \right| = abc,$$

as expected.

Some Shortcuts

There are quicker ways of calculating the determinants of matrices of certain types. The justifications of the following shortcuts are beyond the scope of this book, but can be found in standard linear algebra texts.

Shortcuts and Special Cases

- The determinant of a triangular matrix (one in which either all the entries above the main diagonal are zero or all the entries below it are) is the product of the entries on the diagonal.

Quick Example

$$\det \begin{bmatrix} 5 & 198 & 44 \\ 0 & 2 & -101 \\ 0 & 0 & 1 \end{bmatrix} = (5)(2)(1) = 10 \qquad \text{Check this by calculating minors.}$$

- The determinant of a matrix is the same as the determinant of its transpose: $\det(A) = \det(A^T)$

Quick Example

$$\det \begin{bmatrix} 0 & 30 & -1 \\ 1 & 200 & 4 \\ 0 & 0 & 1 \end{bmatrix} = \det \begin{bmatrix} 0 & 1 & 0 \\ 30 & 200 & 0 \\ -1 & 4 & 1 \end{bmatrix} = -30$$

- Switching two rows changes the sign of the determinant, but leaves its magnitude unchanged. (The same is true if we switch two columns.)

Quick Example

$$\det \begin{bmatrix} -99 & 13 & 4 \\ 6 & 1 & 0 \\ 3 & 0 & 0 \end{bmatrix} = -\det \begin{bmatrix} 3 & 0 & 0 \\ 6 & 1 & 0 \\ -99 & 13 & 4 \end{bmatrix} = -12 \qquad R_1 \leftrightarrow R_3$$

- If a matrix has a row or column of zeros, or if one row or column is a multiple of another, then its determinant is zero.

Quick Examples

$$\det \begin{bmatrix} -99 & 0 & 4 \\ 0 & 0 & 1 \\ 3 & 0 & 1 \end{bmatrix} = 0 \qquad \text{Second column is zero}$$

$$\det \begin{bmatrix} 3 & 0 & 0 \\ 6 & 1 & 0 \\ 12 & 2 & 0 \end{bmatrix} = 0 \qquad R_3 \text{ is twice } R_2$$

EXAMPLE 3 Shortcuts & Special Cases

Compute the determinant of each of the following matrices.

a. $A = \begin{bmatrix} 3 & 0 & 0 \\ 6 & -1 & 0 \\ -99 & 0 & 4 \end{bmatrix}$ **b.** $B = \begin{bmatrix} 1 & 2 & -3 \\ -2 & -4 & 6 \\ 99 & 40 & 1 \end{bmatrix}$ **c.** $C = \begin{bmatrix} 1 & 2 & 3 & 4 \\ 0 & 0 & -1 & 0 \\ 1 & 0 & 1 & 3 \\ 0 & 0 & 3 & 4 \end{bmatrix}$

Solution

a. The matrix $A = \begin{bmatrix} 3 & 0 & 0 \\ 6 & -1 & 0 \\ -99 & 0 & 4 \end{bmatrix}$ is lower triangular (it has only zeros above the main diagonal). Therefore, its determinant is the product of the diagonal entries:

$$\det(A) = (3)(-1)(4) = -12.$$

b. Notice that in the matrix $B = \begin{bmatrix} 1 & 2 & -3 \\ -2 & -4 & 6 \\ 99 & 40 & 1 \end{bmatrix}$, Row 2 is (-2) times Row 1. Therefore its determinant is zero:

$$\det(B) = 0.$$

c. We notice that the second row of $C = \begin{bmatrix} 1 & 2 & 3 & 4 \\ 0 & 0 & -1 & 0 \\ 1 & 0 & 1 & 3 \\ 0 & 0 & 3 & 4 \end{bmatrix}$, is almost all zero. It would therefore be easier to compute the determinant if we first switched Rows 1 and 2:

$$\det(C) = \det \begin{bmatrix} 1 & 2 & 3 & 4 \\ 0 & 0 & -1 & 0 \\ 1 & 0 & 1 & 3 \\ 0 & 0 & 3 & 4 \end{bmatrix} = -\det \begin{bmatrix} 0 & 0 & -1 & 0 \\ 1 & 2 & 3 & 4 \\ 1 & 0 & 1 & 3 \\ 0 & 0 & 3 & 4 \end{bmatrix} \qquad \text{Rows 1 and 2 switched}$$

$$= -[a_{11} \times M_{11} - a_{12} \times M_{12} + a_{13} \times M_{13} - a_{14} \times M_{14}]$$

$$= -[(-1) \times M_{13}] \qquad \text{All the other terms are zero.}$$

$$= \det \begin{bmatrix} 1 & 2 & 4 \\ 1 & 0 & 3 \\ 0 & 0 & 4 \end{bmatrix}$$

$$= -\det \begin{bmatrix} 0 & 0 & 4 \\ 1 & 0 & 3 \\ 1 & 2 & 4 \end{bmatrix} \qquad \text{Rows 1 and 3 switched}$$

$$= -4 \times \det \begin{bmatrix} 1 & 0 \\ 1 & 2 \end{bmatrix} = -4 \times 2 = -8$$

3.6 EXERCISES

▼ more advanced

Let $A = \begin{bmatrix} -1 & 0 & 5 \\ 3 & -1 & 5 \\ 2 & 0 & 1 \end{bmatrix}$. In Exercises 1–6, write the associated

minor matrix and then compute the indicated minor.

1. M_{23} **2.** M_{32} **3.** M_{22}

4. M_{11} **5.** M_{12} **6.** M_{21}

In Exercises 7–16 compute the determinant of the given matrix directly (no shortcuts).

7. $\begin{bmatrix} 1 & 0 & -1 \\ -1 & 1 & -1 \\ 5 & 0 & 2 \end{bmatrix}$ **8.** $\begin{bmatrix} 2 & 1 & 0 \\ -2 & 1 & 0 \\ 0 & 1 & 2 \end{bmatrix}$

9. $\begin{bmatrix} 1 & -2 & 3 \\ 0 & 1 & 3 \\ 2 & 0 & 0 \end{bmatrix}$ **10.** $\begin{bmatrix} 1 & 0 & 2 \\ -2 & 1 & 0 \\ 3 & 3 & 0 \end{bmatrix}$

11. $\begin{bmatrix} 1 & 2 & 3 \\ -1 & 3 & 1 \\ 3 & 4 & 5 \end{bmatrix}$ **12.** $\begin{bmatrix} 1 & 2 & 3 \\ 2 & -3 & 4 \\ 3 & -4 & 5 \end{bmatrix}$

13. $\begin{bmatrix} 1 & 0 & 1 & 0 \\ 2 & 0 & 1 & 0 \\ 1 & 1 & 1 & 1 \\ 0 & 2 & 0 & 1 \end{bmatrix}$ **14.** $\begin{bmatrix} 0 & 2 & 0 & 1 \\ 2 & 0 & 1 & 0 \\ 1 & 1 & 1 & 1 \\ 1 & 0 & 0 & 1 \end{bmatrix}$

15. $\begin{bmatrix} 1 & 3 & -2 & 1 \\ 0 & 1 & 3 & 1 \\ 0 & 0 & 6 & -3 \\ 0 & 0 & 0 & -4 \end{bmatrix}$ **16.** $\begin{bmatrix} 1 & 0 & 0 & 0 \\ 3 & 4 & 0 & 0 \\ -2 & 3 & 1 & 0 \\ 1 & 1 & -3 & -1 \end{bmatrix}$

In Exercises 17–22, use a determinant to compute the area of the given region.

17.

18.

19.

20.

21.

22.

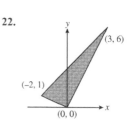

In Exercises 23–28, use a determinant to compute the volume of the given solid.

23.

24.

25.

26.

27. ▼

28. ▼

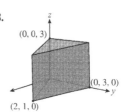

In Exercises 29–44, use shortcuts to find the determinant of the given matrix.

29. $\begin{bmatrix} 1 & -2 & 0 \\ 0 & 1 & 0 \\ 2 & 0 & 0 \end{bmatrix}$ **30.** $\begin{bmatrix} 1 & 0 & 0 \\ 0 & -3 & 0 \\ 0 & 0 & 4 \end{bmatrix}$

31. $\begin{bmatrix} -1 & 0 & 0 \\ 2 & 3 & 0 \\ 1 & 0 & 4 \end{bmatrix}$ **32.** $\begin{bmatrix} 1 & 2 & 3 \\ 0 & 0 & 0 \\ 0 & 0 & -4 \end{bmatrix}$

33. $\begin{bmatrix} 1 & -2 & 3 \\ 0 & 1 & 3 \\ -2 & 4 & -6 \end{bmatrix}$

34. $\begin{bmatrix} 4 & -2 & 3 \\ 0 & 1 & 3 \\ 0 & 0 & -1 \end{bmatrix}$

35. $\begin{bmatrix} 1 & -2 & 0 \\ 0 & 1 & 0 \\ 2 & 0 & 0 \end{bmatrix}$

36. $\begin{bmatrix} -2 & 0 & 0 \\ 0 & 0 & 5 \\ 0 & -2 & 0 \end{bmatrix}$

37. $\begin{bmatrix} 0 & -3 & 0 \\ 4 & 0 & 0 \\ 0 & 0 & -5 \end{bmatrix}$

38. $\begin{bmatrix} -3 & 3 & 2 \\ 1 & -1 & -2 \\ 2 & -2 & 0 \end{bmatrix}$

39. $\begin{bmatrix} 2 & 0 & 0 & 0 \\ 0 & 0 & 3 & 1 \\ 0 & 0 & 6 & -3 \\ 0 & 0 & 0 & -4 \end{bmatrix}$

40. $\begin{bmatrix} 4 & -1 & 2 & 3 \\ 3 & 4 & 0 & 0 \\ -2 & 3 & 1 & 0 \\ -8 & 2 & -4 & -6 \end{bmatrix}$

41. $\begin{bmatrix} 1 & 3 & -2 & 2 \\ 1 & -1 & 2 & -2 \\ 1 & -1 & 4 & -4 \\ 1 & -1 & 1 & -1 \end{bmatrix}$

42. $\begin{bmatrix} 1 & 0 & 0 & 0 \\ 0 & 4 & 0 & 0 \\ 0 & 0 & 0 & 1 \\ 0 & 0 & -3 & 0 \end{bmatrix}$

43. $\begin{bmatrix} 1 & 3 & 1 & 1 \\ 0 & 0 & 1 & 2 \\ 0 & 1 & 4 & 1 \\ 0 & 0 & 0 & 4 \end{bmatrix}$

44. $\begin{bmatrix} 3 & 0 & 0 & 0 \\ 3 & 4 & 0 & 0 \\ -1 & 1 & 1 & 0 \\ 1 & 5 & -3 & -1 \end{bmatrix}$

COMMUNICATION AND REASONING EXERCISES

45. Multiple Choice: If the $n \times n$ matrix B is obtained from A by switching two rows, then:

(A) $\det(B) = -\det(A)$
(B) $\det(B) = \det(A)$
(C) $\det(B) = 1/\det(A)$
(D) $\det(B) = 2\det(A)$

46. Multiple Choice: If A is an $n \times n$ matrix all of whose entries are 1s, then:

(A) $\det(A) = 1$
(B) $\det(A) = 0$
(C) $\det(A) = n^2$
(D) $\det(A) = n$

47. ▼ Thinking of 3×3 matrices as volumes, explain why the determinant of a matrix is zero if two rows are identical.

48. ▼ Thinking of 3×3 matrices as volumes, decide what effect doubling all the entries in one row has on the magnitude of the determinant.

3.7 Using Determinants to Solve Systems: Cramer's Rule

As we claimed, determinants can be used to write down formulas for solutions of systems of linear equations. To see how, let us first take a look at a general system of two linear equations in two unknowns:

$$a_{11}x + a_{12}y = b_1$$
$$a_{21}x + a_{22}y = b_2$$

Matrix form $\overset{A}{\begin{bmatrix} a_{11} & a_{12} \\ a_{21} & a_{22} \end{bmatrix}} \overset{X}{\begin{bmatrix} x \\ y \end{bmatrix}} = \overset{B}{\begin{bmatrix} b_1 \\ b_2 \end{bmatrix}}$

We can solve the system by the elimination method described in Section 2.1: To eliminate y, multiply the first equation by a_{22} and the second by a_{12} and subtract:

$$a_{22}a_{11}x + a_{22}a_{12}y = a_{22}b_1$$
$$\underline{a_{12}a_{21}x + a_{12}a_{22}y = a_{12}b_2}$$
$$(a_{22}a_{11} - a_{12}a_{21})x = a_{22}b_1 - a_{12}b_2$$

so $\quad x = \dfrac{a_{22}b_1 - a_{12}b_2}{a_{11}a_{22} - a_{12}a_{21}}$ Assuming that $a_{11}a_{22} - a_{12}a_{21} \neq 0$

If we instead eliminate x by multiplying the first equation by a_{21} and the second by a_{11} and subtracting, we similarly obtain

$$y = \dfrac{a_{11}b_2 - a_{21}b_1}{a_{11}a_{22} - a_{12}a_{21}}$$ Again assuming that $a_{11}a_{22} - a_{12}a_{21} \neq 0$

The denominator in both cases, $a_{11}a_{22} - a_{12}a_{21}$, you might recognize as the determinant of the coefficient matrix $A = \begin{bmatrix} a_{11} & a_{12} \\ a_{21} & a_{22} \end{bmatrix}$. The numerators are also determinants:

$$a_{22}b_1 - a_{12}b_2 = \det \begin{bmatrix} b_1 & a_{12} \\ b_2 & a_{22} \end{bmatrix} \qquad a_{11}b_2 - a_{21}b_1 = \det \begin{bmatrix} a_{11} & b_1 \\ a_{21} & b_2 \end{bmatrix}$$

Numerator of solution for x Numerator of solution for y

In the first, we have replaced the first column of the coefficient matrix A by the column B of right-hand sides, and in the second, we have replaced the second column of A by B. We can now write the solutions as follows:

Cramer's Rule for Solution of a System of 2 Linear Equations in 2 Unknowns

The system of two linear equations in two unknowns

$$\begin{aligned} a_{11}x + a_{12}y &= b_1 \\ a_{21}x + a_{22}y &= b_2 \end{aligned}$$

Matrix form $\quad \overset{A}{\begin{bmatrix} a_{11} & a_{12} \\ a_{21} & a_{22} \end{bmatrix}} \overset{X}{\begin{bmatrix} x \\ y \end{bmatrix}} = \overset{B}{\begin{bmatrix} b_1 \\ b_2 \end{bmatrix}}$

has a unique solution if and only if $\det(A) = \det \begin{bmatrix} a_{11} & a_{12} \\ a_{21} & a_{22} \end{bmatrix} = a_{11}a_{22} - a_{12}a_{21} \neq 0$, in which case the solution is given by

$$x = \frac{\det \begin{bmatrix} b_1 & a_{12} \\ b_2 & a_{22} \end{bmatrix}}{\det(A)} \qquad y = \frac{\det \begin{bmatrix} a_{11} & b_1 \\ a_{21} & b_2 \end{bmatrix}}{\det(A)}$$

Quick Examples

1. The system

$$\begin{aligned} x + 2y &= 3 \\ 3x + 4y &= 5 \end{aligned}$$

has $\det(A) = \det \begin{bmatrix} 1 & 2 \\ 3 & 4 \end{bmatrix} = (1)(4) - (2)(3) = -2 \neq 0$. Therefore the system has the unique solution

$$x = \frac{\det \begin{bmatrix} b_1 & a_{12} \\ b_2 & a_{22} \end{bmatrix}}{\det(A)} = \frac{\det \begin{bmatrix} 3 & 2 \\ 5 & 4 \end{bmatrix}}{-2} = \frac{(3)(4) - (2)(5)}{-2} = \frac{2}{-2} = -1$$

$$x = \frac{\det \begin{bmatrix} a_{11} & b_1 \\ b_{21} & a_2 \end{bmatrix}}{\det(A)} = \frac{\det \begin{bmatrix} 1 & 3 \\ 3 & 5 \end{bmatrix}}{-2} = \frac{(1)(5) - (3)(3)}{-2} = \frac{-4}{-2} = 2$$

2. The system

$$\begin{aligned} x - y &= 3 \\ 2x - 2y &= 5 \end{aligned}$$

has det $\begin{bmatrix} a_{11} & a_{12} \\ a_{21} & a_{22} \end{bmatrix}$ = det $\begin{bmatrix} 1 & -1 \\ 2 & -2 \end{bmatrix}$ = $(1)(-2) - (-1)(2) = 0$

As the coefficient matrix is singular, Cramer's rule does not apply (in fact the given system is inconsistent), and so we would need to analyze the system using the methods of Chapter 2.

Q: *What happens when the determinant of the coefficient matrix is zero?*

A: Notice first that in this case the Cramer's rule formulas have zero in their denominators and hence make no sense. In general, the coefficient matrix of a system of n linear equations in n unknowns has determinant zero if and only if the system is inconsistent (there is no solution) or underdetermined (there are infinitely many solutions). In either case, we would need to analyze the system using a method like row-reduction discussed in Section 2.2.

One advantage of Cramer's rule over row reduction is that the explicit formulas it gives allow us to write down the solution of a linear system even when the coefficients are parameters (algebraic variables) instead of numbers. (In such cases, attempting to solve the system by row-reduction might be extremely messy.) The next example illustrates the use of Cramer's rule for solving such a system.

EXAMPLE 1   Using Cramer's Rule with Parameters: Regression

We shall see in Chapter 15 that the equations for the slope m and intercept b of the regression line associated with a set of data points are given by solving the system

$$m \sum(x^2) + b \sum x = \sum xy$$
$$m \sum x + nb = \sum y$$

for m and b. Here, n is the number of data points, $\sum x$ is the sum of their x-coordinates, $\sum xy$ is the sum of the products xy, and $\sum(x^2)$ is the sum of the squares of the x-coordinates. What are m and b, and what condition is necessary to ensure a unique solution?

Solution

The determinant of the coefficient matrix is

$$\det(A) = \det \begin{bmatrix} \sum(x^2) & \sum x \\ \sum x & n \end{bmatrix} = n \sum(x^2) - \left(\sum x\right)^2$$

For a unique solution, we require that $n \sum(x^2) - \left(\sum x\right)^2 \neq 0$. (It can be shown that this condition holds whenever there is more than a single x-coordinate.) When this condition is satisfied, the unique solution is given by

$$m = \frac{\det \begin{bmatrix} b_1 & a_{12} \\ b_2 & a_{22} \end{bmatrix}}{\det(A)} = \frac{\det \begin{bmatrix} \sum xy & \sum x \\ \sum y & n \end{bmatrix}}{\det(A)} = \frac{n \sum xy - \left(\sum x\right)\left(\sum y\right)}{n \sum(x^2) - \left(\sum x\right)^2}$$

$$b = \frac{\det\begin{bmatrix} a_{11} & b_1 \\ a_{21} & b_2 \end{bmatrix}}{\det(A)} = \frac{\det\begin{bmatrix} \sum(x^2) & \sum xy \\ \sum x & \sum y \end{bmatrix}}{\det(A)} = \frac{\sum(x^2)\sum y - (\sum xy)(\sum x)}{n\sum(x^2) - (\sum x)^2}$$

The method described above can be extended to systems of n linear equations in n unknowns. To see how to extend it, is useful to look first a general system of three equations in three unknowns:

$$a_{11}x + a_{12}y + a_{13}z = b_1$$
$$a_{21}x + a_{22}y + a_{23}z = b_2$$
$$a_{31}x + a_{32}y + a_{33}z = b_3$$

As in the case of two equations in two unknowns, it is possible to solve this system by elimination: First eliminate z from the first two equations by multiplying the first by a_{23} and the second by a_{13} and subtracting. Then eliminate z from the second and third equations in a similar way (multiply the second by a_{33} and the third by a_{23} and subtract). This will leave us with two equations in x and y:

$$(a_{11}a_{23} - a_{21}a_{13})x + (a_{12}a_{23} - a_{13}a_{22})y = a_{23}b_1 - a_{13}b_2$$
$$(a_{21}a_{33} - a_{31}a_{23})x + (a_{22}a_{33} - a_{23}a_{32})y = a_{33}b_2 - a_{23}b_3$$

At this point we can calculate x and y as we did earlier: Eliminate y by multiplying each equation by the coefficient of y in the other and subtracting to obtain x, and similarly we can obtain y by eliminating x. To obtain z with this method, we would start all over again by first eliminating x and then y. If we actually went through these remaining steps we would find that the results can again be expressed in terms of determinants:

Cramer's Rule for Solution of System of 3 Linear Equations in 3 Unknowns

The system of 3 linear equations in 3 unknowns

$$a_{11}x + a_{12}y + a_{13}z = b_1$$
$$a_{21}x + a_{22}y + a_{23}z = b_2$$
$$a_{31}x + a_{32}y + a_{33}z = b_3$$

Matrix form
$$\overset{A}{\begin{bmatrix} a_{11} & a_{12} & a_{13} \\ a_{21} & a_{22} & a_{23} \\ a_{31} & a_{32} & a_{33} \end{bmatrix}} \overset{X}{\begin{bmatrix} x \\ y \\ z \end{bmatrix}} = \overset{B}{\begin{bmatrix} b_1 \\ b_2 \\ b_3 \end{bmatrix}}$$

has a unique solution if and only if $\det(A) = \det\begin{bmatrix} a_{11} & a_{12} & a_{13} \\ a_{21} & a_{22} & a_{23} \\ a_{31} & a_{32} & a_{33} \end{bmatrix} \neq 0$, in which case the solution is given by

$$x = \frac{\det\begin{bmatrix} b_1 & a_{12} & a_{13} \\ b_2 & a_{22} & a_{23} \\ b_3 & a_{32} & a_{33} \end{bmatrix}}{\det(A)}, \quad y = \frac{\det\begin{bmatrix} a_{11} & b_1 & a_{13} \\ a_{21} & b_2 & a_{23} \\ a_{31} & b_3 & a_{33} \end{bmatrix}}{\det(A)}, \quad z = \frac{\det\begin{bmatrix} a_{11} & a_{12} & b_1 \\ a_{21} & a_{22} & b_2 \\ a_{31} & a_{32} & b_3 \end{bmatrix}}{\det(A)}$$

Notice again that the matrices in the numerators are obtained from the coefficient matrix A by replacing each column in turn by the column B of right-hand sides.

Cramer's Rule for Solution of a System of n Linear Equations in n Unknowns

If A is an $n \times n$ matrix, then the system of linear equations $AX = B$ has a unique solution if and only if $\det(A) \neq 0$, in which case the unique solution is given by

$$x_1 = \frac{\det \begin{bmatrix} b_1 & a_{12} & \cdots & a_{1n} \\ b_2 & a_{22} & \cdots & a_{2n} \\ \cdots & \cdots & & \cdots \\ b_n & a_{n2} & \cdots & a_{nn} \end{bmatrix}}{\det(A)}$$

$$x_2 = \frac{\det \begin{bmatrix} a_{11} & b_1 & a_{13} & \cdots & a_{1n} \\ a_{21} & b_2 & a_{23} & \cdots & a_{2n} \\ \cdots & \cdots & \cdots & & \cdots \\ a_{n1} & b_n & a_{n3} & \cdots & a_{nn} \end{bmatrix}}{\det(A)}$$

$\cdots$

$$x_n = \frac{\det \begin{bmatrix} a_{11} & \cdots & a_{1(n-1)} & b_1 \\ a_{21} & \cdots & a_{2(n-1)} & b_2 \\ \cdots & & \cdots & \cdots \\ a_{n1} & \cdots & a_{n(n-1)} & b_n \end{bmatrix}}{\det(A)}$$

EXAMPLE 2   Using Cramer's Rule: 3 Equations in 3 Unknowns

Use Cramer's rule to solve the system

$$\begin{aligned} 2x \quad\;\; + z &= 1 \\ 2x + y - z &= 1 \\ 3x + y - z &= 1 \end{aligned}$$

Solution

We first compute the determinant of the coefficient matrix:

$$\det(A) = \det \begin{bmatrix} 2 & 0 & 1 \\ 2 & 1 & -1 \\ 3 & 1 & -1 \end{bmatrix}$$

$$= (2) \det \begin{bmatrix} 1 & -1 \\ 1 & -1 \end{bmatrix} - (0) \det \begin{bmatrix} 2 & -1 \\ 3 & -1 \end{bmatrix} + (1) \det \begin{bmatrix} 2 & 1 \\ 3 & 1 \end{bmatrix}$$

$$= (2)(0) - (0)(1) + (1)(-1) = -1$$

Since the determinant is nonzero, the system has a unique solution. The unknowns are

$$x = \frac{\det \begin{bmatrix} 1 & 0 & 1 \\ 1 & 1 & 1 \\ 1 & 1 & 1 \end{bmatrix}}{\det(A)}$$

$$= \frac{(1)\det\begin{bmatrix} 1 & -1 \\ 1 & -1 \end{bmatrix} - (0)\det\begin{bmatrix} 1 & -1 \\ 1 & -1 \end{bmatrix} + (1)\det\begin{bmatrix} 1 & 1 \\ 1 & 1 \end{bmatrix}}{-1}$$

$$= \frac{(1)(0) - (0)(0) + (1)(0)}{-1} = \frac{0}{-1} = 0$$

$$y = \frac{\det\begin{bmatrix} 2 & 1 & 1 \\ 2 & 1 & -1 \\ 3 & 1 & -1 \end{bmatrix}}{\det(A)}$$

$$= \frac{(2)\det\begin{bmatrix} 1 & -1 \\ 1 & -1 \end{bmatrix} - (1)\det\begin{bmatrix} 2 & -1 \\ 3 & -1 \end{bmatrix} + (1)\det\begin{bmatrix} 2 & 1 \\ 3 & 1 \end{bmatrix}}{-1}$$

$$= \frac{(2)(0) - (1)(1) + (1)(-1)}{-1} = \frac{-2}{-1} = 2$$

$$z = \frac{\det\begin{bmatrix} 2 & 0 & 1 \\ 2 & 1 & 1 \\ 3 & 1 & 1 \end{bmatrix}}{\det(A)}$$

$$= \frac{(2)\det\begin{bmatrix} 1 & 1 \\ 1 & 1 \end{bmatrix} - (0)\det\begin{bmatrix} 2 & 1 \\ 3 & 1 \end{bmatrix} + (1)\det\begin{bmatrix} 2 & 1 \\ 3 & 1 \end{bmatrix}}{1}$$

$$= \frac{(2)(0) - (0)(-1) + (1)(-1)}{-1} = \frac{-1}{-1} = 1$$

Thus, the unique solution is $(x, y, z) = (0, 2, 1)$.

In the next example we solve a system of four linear equations in four unknowns with the aid of a spreadsheet. From the general case for $n \times n$ systems, we can write down the solution of the 4×4 system

$$a_{11}x + a_{12}y + a_{13}z + a_{14}t = b_1$$
$$a_{21}x + a_{22}y + a_{23}z + a_{24}t = b_2$$
$$a_{31}x + a_{32}y + a_{33}z + a_{34}t = b_3$$
$$a_{41}x + a_{42}y + a_{43}z + a_{44}t = b_4$$

as

$$x = \frac{\det\begin{bmatrix} b_1 & a_{12} & a_{13} & a_{14} \\ b_2 & a_{22} & a_{23} & a_{24} \\ b_3 & a_{32} & a_{33} & a_{34} \\ b_4 & a_{42} & a_{43} & a_{44} \end{bmatrix}}{\det(A)}, \quad y = \frac{\det\begin{bmatrix} a_{11} & b_1 & a_{13} & a_{14} \\ a_{21} & b_2 & a_{23} & a_{24} \\ a_{31} & b_3 & a_{33} & a_{34} \\ a_{41} & b_4 & a_{43} & a_{44} \end{bmatrix}}{\det(A)}$$

$$z = \frac{\det\begin{bmatrix} a_{11} & a_{12} & b_1 & a_{14} \\ a_{21} & a_{22} & b_2 & a_{24} \\ a_{31} & a_{32} & b_3 & a_{34} \\ a_{41} & a_{42} & b_4 & a_{44} \end{bmatrix}}{\det(A)}, \quad z = \frac{\det\begin{bmatrix} a_{11} & a_{12} & a_{13} & b_1 \\ a_{21} & a_{22} & a_{23} & b_2 \\ a_{31} & a_{32} & a_{33} & b_3 \\ a_{41} & a_{42} & a_{43} & b_4 \end{bmatrix}}{\det(A)}$$

$$\text{provided } \det(A) = \det \begin{bmatrix} a_{11} & a_{12} & a_{13} & a_{14} \\ a_{21} & a_{22} & a_{23} & a_{24} \\ a_{31} & a_{32} & a_{33} & a_{34} \\ a_{41} & a_{42} & a_{43} & a_{44} \end{bmatrix} \neq 0,$$

▣ EXAMPLE 3 Four Equations in Four Unknowns with Excel

Use Cramer's rule to solve the system

$$\begin{aligned} x \quad\;\; + z - t &= 1 \\ 2x - y - z \quad\;\; &= 1 \\ x + y + z - t &= 2 \\ x + y + z + t &= 1 \end{aligned}$$

Solution

Doing this calculation by hand would be tedious. We show how to use Excel to help. First enter the coefficients and the right-hand sides in your spreadsheet:

◇	A	B	C	D	E
1	1	0	1	-1	1
2	2	-1	-1	0	1
3	1	1	1	-1	2
4	1	1	1	1	1

The formulas for the solution shown above require the determinants of four more matrices, each obtained from the original coefficient matrix (A1:D4) by changing a single column. We therefore make four copies of (A1:D4) (this takes seconds using copy-and-paste) and then paste the column (E1:E4) in the appropriate place of each (again using copy-and-paste):

◇	A	B	C	D	E
1	1	0	1	-1	1
2	2	-1	-1	0	1
3	1	1	1	-1	2
4	1	1	1	1	1
5					
6	1	0	1	-1	
7	1	-1	-1	0	
8	2	1	1	-1	
9	1	1	1	1	
10					
11	1	1	1	-1	
12	2	1	-1	0	
13	1	2	1	-1	
14	1	1	1	1	
15					
16	1	0	1	-1	
17	2	-1	1	0	
18	1	1	2	-1	
19	1	1	1	1	
20					
21	1	0	1	1	
22	2	-1	-1	1	
23	1	1	1	2	
24	1	1	1	1	

Next, we compute the determinant of the coefficient matrix in cell A5 using the MDETERM function we saw on p. 4:

	A	B	C	D	E
1	1	0	1	-1	1
2	2	-1	-1	0	1
3	1	1	1	-1	2
4	1	1	1	1	1
5	=MDETERM(A1:D4)				
6					

↓ Control+Shift+Enter

	A	B	C	D	E
1	1	0	1	-1	1
2	2	-1	-1	0	1
3	1	1	1	-1	2
4	1	1	1	1	1
5	6				

Since the determinant is nonzero, the system has a unique solution. We next obtain the numerators of the solutions for x, y, z, and t by copying and pasting the formula of cell A5 into cells A10, A15, A20, and A25:

	A	B	C	D	E
1	1	0	1	-1	1
2	2	-1	-1	0	1
3	1	1	1	-1	2
4	1	1	1	1	1
5	6				
6	1	0	1	-1	
7	1	-1	-1	0	
8	2	1	1	-1	
9	1	1	1	1	
10	6				
11	1	1	1	-1	
12	2	1	-1	0	
13	1	2	1	-1	
14	1	1	1	1	
15	6				
16	1	0	1	-1	
17	2	-1	1	0	
18	1	1	2	-1	
19	1	1	1	1	
20	2				
21	1	0	1	1	
22	2	-1	-1	1	
23	1	1	1	2	
24	1	1	1	1	
25	-3				

Finally, the solution for x is computed in cell B10 and then pasted into B15, B20, and B25. Note the use of the absolute reference to cell $A$5:

◇	A	B	C
1	1	0	1
2	2	-1	-1
3	1	1	1
4	1	1	1
5	6		
6	1	0	1
7	1	-1	-1
8	2	1	1
9	1	1	1
10	5	=A10/$A$5	
11	1	1	1
12	2	1	-1
13	1	2	1
14	1	1	1
15	6	=A15/$A$5	
16	1	0	1
17	2	-1	1
18	1	1	2
19	1	1	1
20	-2	=A20/$A$5	
21	1	0	1
22	2	-1	-1
23	1	1	1
24	1	1	1
25	-3	=A25/$A$5	

→

◇	A	B	C
1	1	0	1
2	2	-1	-1
3	1	1	1
4	1	1	1
5	6		
6	1	0	1
7	1	-1	-1
8	2	1	1
9	1	1	1
10	5	0.83333333	
11	1	1	1
12	2	1	-1
13	1	2	1
14	1	1	1
15	6	1	
16	1	0	1
17	2	-1	1
18	1	1	2
19	1	1	1
20	-2	-0.3333333	
21	1	0	1
22	2	-1	-1
23	1	1	1
24	1	1	1
25	-3	-0.5	

so we conclude that $(x, y, z, t) = \left(\frac{5}{6}, \frac{6}{6}, \frac{2}{6}, \frac{3}{6}\right) \approx (0.8333, 1, -0.3333, -0.5)$

3.7 EXERCISES

▼ more advanced

▮ indicates exercises that should be solved using technology

In Exercises 1–12 solve the given system of linear equations using Cramer's Rule.

1. $x + y = 4$
$x - y = 1$

2. $2x + y = 2$
$2x - 3y = 2$

3. $0.1x - 0.2y = 0$
$0.4x + 0.2y = 1.2$

4. $0.5x - 0.1y = 0.3$
$2.5x + 0.3y = 2.2$

5. $\dfrac{x}{3} + \dfrac{y}{2} = 0$
$\dfrac{x}{2} + y = 1$

6. $\dfrac{2x}{3} - \dfrac{y}{2} = \dfrac{1}{6}$
$\dfrac{x}{2} - \dfrac{y}{2} = -1$

7. $-x + 2y + z = 0$
$-x - y + 2z = 0$
$2x - z = 7$

8. $x + 2y = 4$
$y - z = 0$
$x + 3y - 2z = 5$

9. $-x - 4y + 2z = 4$
$x + 2y - z = 3$
$x + y - z = 8$

10. $-x - 4y + 2z = 8$
$x - z = 3$
$x + y - z = 2$

11. $-0.1x + 0.2z = 4$
$0.2y - 1.1z = 2$
$x + z = 2$

12. $0.1x - 0.2z = 6$
$y - z = 6$
$0.1x - 1.1y = 3$

▮ *In Exercises 13–18 use Cramer's Rule with technology to solve the given system of linear equations in the event that is has*

a unique solution. If there is no unique solution, indicate why.
HINT [See Example 3.]

13. ▮ $x + y + 5z = 1$
$y + 2z + w = 1$
$x + 3y + 7z + 2w = 2$
$x + y + 5z + w = 1$

14. ▮ $x + y + 4w = 1$
$2x - 2y - 3z + 2w = -1$
$4y + 6z + w = 4$
$2x + 4y + 9z = 6$

15. ▮ $x + y + 5z = 1$
$y + 2z + w = 1$
$x + y + 5z + w = 1$
$x + 2y + 7z + 2w = 2$

16. ▮ $x + y + 4w = 1$
$2x - 2y - 3z + 2w = -1$
$4y + 6z + w = 4$
$3x + 3y + 3z + 6w = 4$

17. ▮ $x + y + 5z = 1$
$y + 2z + w = 1$
$x + y + 5z + w = 1$
$x + 2y + 7z + 2w = 2$

18. ▮ $x + y + 4w = 1$
$2x - 2y - 3z + 2w = -1$
$4y + 6z + w = 4$
$3x + 3y + 3z + 6w = 4$

In Exercises 19–22, write down an equation the parameters must satisfy for there to be a unique solution, and then solve for the indicated variables assuming that condition is met.
HINT [See Example 1.]

19. $(a + b)p + cq = a - b$
$cp - (a - b)q = b - a$
Solve for p and q.

20. $a^2 p - (r + s)q = a^3$
$(r + s)q - \dfrac{q}{a^2} = r$
Solve for p and q.

21. $ax_1 \qquad + qx_3 = q$
$rx_1 + x_2 \qquad = 0$
$r^2 x_1 - x_2 + ax_3 = a$
Solve for x_1, x_2, and x_3.

22. $bx_1 + \quad ax_2 + qx_3 = 2a$
$a^2 x_2 + qx_3 = 2a^2$
$bx_1 + \qquad qx_3 = 0$
Solve for x_1, x_2, and x_3.

APPLICATIONS

Some of the following exercises are similar or identical to exercises and examples in Section 3.3. All should be solved using Cramer's Rule.

23. *Resource Allocation* You manage an ice cream factory that makes three flavors: Creamy Vanilla, Continental Mocha, and Succulent Strawberry. Into each batch of Creamy Vanilla go two eggs, one cup of milk, and two cups of cream. Into each batch of Continental Mocha go one egg, one cup of milk, and two cups of cream. Into each batch of Succulent Strawberry go one egg, two cups of milk, and one cup of cream. Your stocks of eggs, milk, and cream vary from day to day. How many batches of each flavor should you make in order to use up all of your ingredients if you have the following amounts in stock?

(a) 350 eggs, 350 cups of milk, and 400 cups of cream

(b) 400 eggs, 500 cups of milk, and 400 cups of cream

24. *Resource Allocation* The Arctic Juice Company makes three juice blends: PineOrange, using 2 quarts of pineapple juice and 2 quarts of orange juice per gallon; PineKiwi, using 3 quarts of pineapple juice and 1 quart of kiwi juice per gallon; and OrangeKiwi, using 3 quarts of orange juice and 1 quart of kiwi juice per gallon. The amount of each kind of juice the company has on hand varies from day to day. How many gallons of each blend can it make on a day with the following stocks?

(a) 800 quarts of pineapple juice, 650 quarts of orange juice, 350 quarts of kiwi juice.

(b) 650 quarts of pineapple juice, 800 quarts of orange juice, 350 quarts of kiwi juice.

Investing In Mutual Funds Exercises 25 and 26 are based on the following data on three mutual funds.[1]

	2007 Yield
FHIFX (Fidelity Focused High Income Fund)	6%
FFRHX (Fidelity Floating Rate High Income Fund)	5%
FASIX (Fidelity Asset Manager 20%)	7%

25. You invested a total of $9,000 in the three funds at the beginning of 2007, including an equal amount in FFRHX and FASIX. Your 2007 yield for the year from the first two funds amounted to $400. How much did you invest in each of the three funds?

26. You invested a total of $6,000 in the three funds at the beginning of 2007, including an equal amount in FHIFX and FFRHX. Your total yields for 2007 amounted to $360. How much did you invest in each of the three funds?

Investing in Stocks Exercises 27 and 28 are based on the following data on three computer-related stocks.[2]

	Price per Share	Dividend Yield
MSFT (Microsoft)	$30	1.5%
INTC (Intel)	25	1.8
YHOO (Yahoo)	25	0

27. You invested a total of $5,400 in Microsoft, Intel, and Yahoo shares at the above prices, and expected to earn $45 in annual dividends. If you purchased a total of 200 shares, how many shares of each stock did you purchase?

28. You invested a total of $5,800 in Microsoft, Intel, and Yahoo shares at the above prices, and expected to earn $54 in annual dividends. If you purchased a total of 220 shares, how many shares of each stock did you purchase?

COMMUNICATION AND REASONING EXERCISES

29. Name one advantage and one disadvantage of Cramer's rule versus row-reduction for solving a system of linear equations.

30. What does it mean about a system of n linear equations in n unknowns when the determinant of the coefficient matrix is zero?

31. Multiple Choice: If the determinant of the coefficient matrix is zero for a system of linear equations, then:

(A) Cramer's Rule yields the exact solution.

(B) Cramer's Rule fails, but we can obtain the solution by row-reducing the augmented matrix.

(C) Cramer's Rule fails, but we can obtain the solution by using the inverse of the coefficient matrix.

(D) There is only the zero solution.

32. Multiple Choice: If the determinant of the coefficient matrix is nonzero for a system of linear equations, but the right-hand sides are zero, then:

(A) There are infinitely many solutions.

(B) Cramer's Rule fails, but we can obtain the solution by row-reducing the augmented matrix.

(C) Cramer's Rule fails, but we can obtain the solution by using the inverse of the coefficient matrix.

(D) There is only the zero solution.

---

[1] Yields are for the year ending September, 2007 and rounded. Source: http://money.excite.com, October 2007

[2] Stocks were trading at or near the given prices in September, 2007. Dividends are rounded. Source: http://money.excite.com, October 2007.

Answers to Odd-Numbered Exercises

3.6

1. $m_{23} = \begin{bmatrix} -1 & 0 \\ 2 & 0 \end{bmatrix}$; $M_{23} = 0$ **3.** $m_{22} = \begin{bmatrix} -1 & 5 \\ 2 & 1 \end{bmatrix}$; $M_{22} = -11$

5. $m_{12} = \begin{bmatrix} 3 & 5 \\ 2 & 1 \end{bmatrix}$; $M_{12} = -7$ **7.** 7 **9.** -18 **11.** -12

13. -1 **15.** -24 **17.** 6 **19.** 8 **21.** 5 **23.** 18 **25.** 12 **27.** 4 **29.** 0 **31.** -12 **33.** 0 **35.** 0 **37.** -60 **39.** 0 **41.** 0 **43.** -4 **45.** (A) **47.** The determinant a 3×3 matrix gives the volume of the solid parallelepiped obtained with corner points the three rows of the matrix. If two are the same, then two of the three edges are on top of each other, and the solid has zero volume.

3.7

1. (2.5, 1.5) **3.** (2.4, 1.2) **5.** (6, -4) **7.** (5, 1, 3) **9.** (10, -5, -3) **11.** (-12, 87, 14) **13.** (-1.5, 0, 0.5, 0) **15.** No unique solution as det(A) = 0 **17.** (0, 1, 0, 0)

19. $-a^2 + b^2 - c^2 \neq 0$; $p = \dfrac{(a - b)(-a + b + c)}{-a^2 + b^2 - c^2}$,

$q = \dfrac{(b - a)(a + b + c)}{-a^2 + b^2 - c^2}$.

21. $a^2 - rq(1 + r) \neq 0$; $(x_1, x_2, x_3) = (0, 0, 1)$ **23. (a)** 100 batches of vanilla, 50 batches of mocha, 100 batches of straw-berry **(b)** 100 batches of vanilla, no mocha, 200 batches of strawberry. **25.** $5,000 in FHIFX, $2,000 in FFRHX, $2,000 in FASIX **27.** 80 MSFT, 20 INTC, 100 YHOO **29.** Advantage: Cramer's Rule allows us to write own the solution explicitly, and this is useful when, for instance, the coefficients are parameters. Disadvantage: Cramer's Rule applies only to systems in which the number of equations equals the number of unknowns and then only when there is a unique solution. Row reduction can be used to analyze any system of linear equations. **31.** (B)

P

Calculus Applied to Probability and Statistics

Case Study: Creating a Family Trust

You are a financial planning consultant at a neighborhood bank. A 22-year-old client asks you the following question: "I would like to set up my own insurance policy by opening a trust account into which I can make monthly payments starting now, so that upon my death or my ninety-fifth birthday—whichever comes sooner—the trust can be expected to be worth $500,000. How much should I invest each month?" Assuming a 5% rate of return on investments, how should you respond?

Introduction

To answer the question on the previous page, we must know something about the probability of the client's dying at various ages. There are so many possible ages to consider (particularly because we should consider the possibilities month by month) that it would be easier to treat his age at death as a *continuous* variable, one that can take on any real value (between 22 and 95 in this case). The mathematics needed to do probability and statistics with continuous variables is calculus.

The material on statistics in this chapter is accessible to any reader with a "common-sense" knowledge of probability, but it also supplements any previous study you may have made of probability and statistics without using calculus.

 # Continuous Random Variables and Histograms

Suppose that you have purchased stock in Colossal Conglomerate, Inc., and each day you note the closing price of the stock. The result each day is a real number X (the closing price of the stock) in the unbounded interval $[0, +\infty)$. Or, suppose that you time several people running a 50-meter dash. The result for each runner is a real number X, the race time in seconds. In both cases, the value of X is somewhat random. Moreover, X can take on essentially any real value in some interval, rather than, say, just integer values. For this reason, we refer to X as a **continuous random variable**. Here is the formal definition.

Continuous Random Variable

A **random variable** is a function X that assigns to each possible outcome in an experiment a real number. If X may assume any value in some given interval I (the interval may be bounded or unbounded), it is called a **continuous** random variable. If it can assume only a number of separated values, it is called a **discrete** random variable.

Quick Examples

1. Roll a die and take X to be the number on the uppermost face. Then X is a discrete random variable with possible values 1, 2, 3, 4, 5, and 6.

2. Locate a star in the cosmos and take X to be its distance from the solar system in light years. Then X is a continuous random variable whose values are real numbers in the interval $(0, +\infty)$.

3. Open the business section of your newspaper and take X to be the closing price of Colossal Conglomerate stock. Then X can take on essentially any positive real value, so we can think of X as a continuous random variable.

If X is a random variable, we are usually interested in the **probability** that X takes on a value in a certain range. For instance, if X is the closing price of Colossal

Conglomerate stock and we find that 60% of the time the price is between $10 and $20, we would say

The probability that X is between $10 and $20 is .6.

We can write this statement mathematically as follows:

$$P(10 \leq X \leq 20) = .6$$ The probability that $10 \leq X \leq 20$ is .6.

We can use a bar chart, called a **probability distribution histogram**, to display the probabilities that X lies in selected ranges. This is shown in the following example:

EXAMPLE 1 College Population by Age

The following table shows the distribution according to age of U.S. residents (16 years old and over) attending college in 1980.[1]

Age (years)	15–19	20–24	25–29	30–34	35–?
Number in 1980 (millions)	2.7	4.8	1.9	1.2	1.8

Draw the probability distribution histogram for X = the age of a randomly chosen college student.

Solution The Summing the entries in the bottom row, we see that the total number of students in 1980 was 12.4 million. We can therefore convert all the data in the table to probabilities by dividing by this total.

X = Age (years)	15–19	20–24	25–29	30–34	35–?
Probability	.22	.39	.15	.10	.15

The probabilities in the above table have been rounded, with the consequence that they add to 1.01 instead of the expected 1. In the category 15–19, we have actually included anyone at least 15 years old and less than 20 years old. For example, someone $19\frac{1}{2}$ years old would be in this range. We would like to write 15–20 instead, but this would be ambiguous, because we would not know where to count someone who was exactly 20 years old. However, the probability that a college student is *exactly* 20 years old (and not, say, 20 years and 1 second) is essentially 0, so it doesn't matter.[2] We can therefore rewrite the table with the following ranges.

X = Age (years)	15–20	20–25	25–30	30–35	≥ 35
Probability	.22	.39	.15	.10	.15

---

[1]Source: 1980 Census of Population, U.S. Department of Commerce/Bureau of the Census.
[2]Also see the discussion after Example 2 below.

The table tells us that, for instance,

$$P(15 \le X \le 20) = .22$$

and

$$P(X \ge 35) = .15.$$

The probability distribution histogram is the bar graph we get from these data (Figure 1).

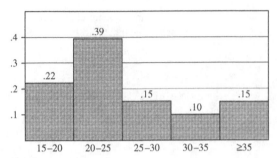

Figure 1

➡ **Before we go on...** Had the grouping into ranges been finer—for instance into divisions of 1 year instead of 5, then the histogram would appear smoother, and with lower bars, as in Figure 2. (Why?)

Figure 2

This smoother-looking distribution suggests a smooth curve. It is this kind of curve that we shall be studying in the next section. ■

EXAMPLE 2 Age of a Rented Car

A survey finds the following probability distribution for the age of a rented car.[3]

Age (years)	0–1	1–2	2–3	3–4	4–5	5–6	6–7
Probability	.20	.28	.20	.15	.10	.05	.02

---

[3] As in the preceeding example, we allow the brackets to intersect. However, because the probability that a car is *exactly* 1 or 2 or 3 or . . . years old (to a fraction of a second) is essentially zero, we can ignore the apparent overlap. The discussion at the end of this example further clarifies this point.

Plot the associated probability distribution histogram, and use it to evaluate (or estimate) the following:

(a) $P(0 \le X \le 4)$ (b) $P(X \ge 4)$

(c) $P(2 \le X \le 3.5)$ (d) $P(X = 4)$

Solution The histogram is shown in Figure 3.

Figure 3

(a) We can calculate $P(0 \le X \le 4)$ from the table by adding the corresponding probabilities:

$$P(0 \le X \le 4) = .20 + .28 + .20 + .15 = .83$$

This corresponds to the shaded region of the histogram shown in Figure 4.

Figure 4

Notice that because each rectangle has width equal to 1 unit and height equal to the associated probability, its *area* is equal to the probability that X is in the associated range. Thus, $P(0 \le X \le 4)$ is also equal to the area of the shaded region.

(b) Similarly, $P(X \ge 4)$ is given by the area of the *unshaded* portion of Figure 4, so

$$P(X \ge 4) = .10 + .05 + .02 = .17.$$

(Notice that $P(0 \le X \le 4) + P(X \ge 4) = 1$. Why?)

(c) To calculate $P(2 \le X \le 3.5)$, we need to make an educated guess, because neither the table nor the histogram has subdivisions of width .5. Referring to the graph, we can approximate the probability by the shaded area shown in Figure 5.

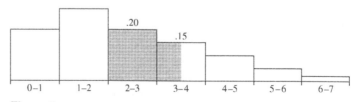

Figure 5

Thus,

$$P(2 \leq X \leq 3.5) \approx .20 + \frac{1}{2}(.15) = .275.$$

(d) To calculate $P(X = 4)$, we would need to calculate $P(4 \leq X \leq 4)$. But this would correspond to a region of the histogram with zero area (Figure 6), so we conclude that $P(X = 4) = 0$.

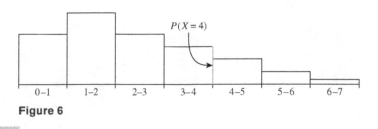

Figure 6

Q: *In Example 2, $P(X = 4)$ was zero. Is it true that $P(X = a)$ is zero for every number a in the interval associated with X?*

A: As a general rule, yes. If X is a *continuous* random variable, then X can assume infinitely many values, and so it is reasonable that the probability of its assuming any specific value we choose beforehand is zero.

Caution

If you wish to use a histogram to calculate probability as *area*, make sure that the subdivisions for X have width 1—for instance, $1 \leq X \leq 2, 2 \leq X \leq 3$, and so on.

The histogram in Example 1 (Figure 1) had bars corresponding to larger ranges for X. The first bar has a width of 5 units, so its area is 5×0.22, which is 5 times the probability that $15 \leq X \leq 20$. If you wish to use a histogram to give probability as area, divide the area by the width of the intervals.

There is another way around this problem that we shall not use, but which is used by working statisticians: Draw your histograms so that the heights are not necessarily the probabilities but are chosen so that the *area* of each bar gives the corresponding probability. This is necessary if, for example, the bars do not all have the same width.

P.1 EXERCISES

▼ more advanced

In Exercises 1–10, identify the random variable (for example, "X is the price of rutabagas") and say whether it is continuous or discrete, and if continuous, give its interval of possible values.

1. A die is cast and the number that appears facing up is recorded.

2. A die is cast and the time it takes for the die to become still is recorded.

3. A dial is spun, and the angle the pointer makes with the vertical is noted. (See the figure.)

4. A dial is spun, and the quadrant in which the pointer comes to rest is noted.

5. The temperature is recorded at midday.

6. The U.S. Balance of Payments is recorded (fractions of a dollar permitted).

7. The U.S. Balance of Payments is recorded, rounded to the nearest billion dollars.

8. The time it takes a new company to become profitable is recorded.

9. In each batch of 100 computer chips manufactured, the number that fail to work is recorded.

10. The time it takes a TV set to break down after sale is recorded.

In Exercises 11–14, sketch the probability distribution histogram of the given continuous random variable.

11.

X = Height of a jet fighter (ft.)	0–20,000	20,000–30,000	30,000–40,000	40,000–50,000	50,000–60,000
Probability	.1	.2	.3	.3	.1

12.

X = Time to next eruption of a volcano (yrs.)	0–2,000	2,000–3,000	3,000–4,000	4,000–5,000	5,000–6,000
Probability	.1	.3	.3	.2	.1

13.

X = Average temperature (°F)	0–50	50–60	60–70	70–80	80–90
Number of cities	4	7	2	5	2

14.

X = Cost of a used car ($)	0–2,000	2,000–4,000	4,000–6,000	6,000–8,000	8,000–10,000
Number of cars	200	500	800	500	500

APPLICATIONS

15. ▼ *U.S. Population, Female* The following table shows the number of females in the United States in 2000, broken down by age.[4] Numbers are in millions.

Age	0–18	18–25	25–35	35–45	45–55	55–65	65–75	75 and over
Number	35.2	13.3	19.8	22.7	19.2	12.6	10.1	10.5

Construct the associated probability distribution (with probabilities rounded to four decimal places) and use the distribution to compute the following.

(a) $P(18 \leq X \leq 55)$ **(b)** $P(X \leq 45)$ **(c)** $P(X \leq 45)$

16. ▼ *U.S. Population, Male* The following table shows the number of males in the United States in 2000, broken down by age.[5] Numbers are in millions.

Age	0–18	18–25	25–35	35–45	45–55	55–65	65–75	75 and over
Number	37.1	13.9	20.1	22.4	18.5	11.6	8.3	6.1

Construct the associated probability distribution (with probabilities rounded to four decimal places) and use the distribution to compute the following.

(a) $P(25 \leq X \leq 65)$ **(b)** $P(X \leq 18)$ **(c)** $P(X \geq 15)$

17. ▼ *Meteors* The following histogram shows part of the probability distribution of the size (in megatons of released energy) of large meteors that hit the Earth's atmosphere. (A large meteor is one that releases at least one megaton of energy, equivalent to the energy released by a small nuclear bomb.)[6]

[4]Source: U.S. Census Bureau, Census 2000 Summary File 1, obtained from http://factfinder.census.gov/.

[5]*Ibid.*

[6]The authors' model, based on data released by NASA International Near-Earth-Object Direction Workshop/*The New York Times*, January 25, 1994, p. C1.

Calculate or estimate the following probabilities.

(a) That a large meteor hitting the Earth's atmosphere will release between 1 and 4 megatons of energy.

(b) That a large meteor hitting the Earth's atmosphere will release between 3 and 4.5 megatons of energy.

(c) That a large meteor will release at least 5 megatons of energy.

18. ▼ *Meteors* Repeat the preceding exercise using the following histogram for meteor impacts on the planet Zor in the Cygnus III system in Andromeda.

19. ▼ *Quality Control* An automobile parts manufacturer makes heavy-duty axles with a cross-section radius of 2.3 cm. In order for one of its axles to meet the accuracy standard demanded by the customer, the radius of the cross section cannot be off by more than 0.02 cm. Construct a histogram with X = the measured radius of an axle, using categories of width 0.01 cm, so that all of the following conditions are met.

(a) X lies in the interval [2.26, 2.34].

(b) 80% of the axles have a cross-sectional radius between 2.29 and 2.31.

(c) 10% of the axles are rejected.

20. ▼ *Damage Control* As a campaign manager for a presidential candidate who always seems to be getting himself into embarrassing situations, you have decided to conduct a statistical analysis of the number of times per week he makes a blunder. Construct a histogram with X = the number of times he blunders in a week, using categories of width 1 unit, so that all of the following conditions are met.

(a) X lies in the interval [0, 10].

(b) During a given week, there is an 80% chance that he will make 3 to 5 blunders.

(c) Never a week goes by that he doesn't make at least one blunder.

(d) On occasion, he has made 10 blunders in one week.

COMMUNICATION AND REASONING EXERCISES

21. ▼ How is a random variable related to the outcomes in an experiment?

22. ▼ Give an example of an experiment and two associated continuous random variables.

23. ▼ You are given a probability distribution histogram with the bars having a width of 2 units. How is the probability $P(a \leq X \leq b)$ related to the area of the corresponding portion of the histogram?

24. ▼ You are given a probability distribution histogram with the bars having a width of 1 unit, and you wish to convert it into one with bars of width 2 units. How would you go about this?

 P.2 **Probability Density Functions: Uniform, Exponential, Normal, and Beta**

We have seen that a histogram is a convenient way to picture the probability distribution associated with a continuous random variable X and that if we use subdivisions of 1 unit, the probability $P(c \leq X \leq d)$ is given by the area under the histogram between $X = c$ and $X = d$. But we have also seen that it is difficult to calculate probabilities for ranges of X that are not a whole number of units. The following example—based on an example in the previous section—introduces the solution to this problem.

EXAMPLE 1 Car Rentals

A survey finds the following probability distribution for the age of a rented car.

X = Age (Years)	0-1	1–2	2–3	3-4	4–5	5-6	6-7
Probability	.20	.28	.20	.15	.10	.05	.02

The histogram of this distribution is shown in Figure 7a, and it suggests a curve something like the one given in Figure 7b.[7]

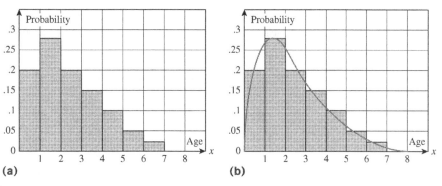

(a)   **(b)**

Figure 7

This curve is the graph of some function f, which we call a **probability density function**. We take the domain of f to be $[0, +\infty)$, because this is the possible range of values X can take (in principle). Also, we use x to refer to specific values of X, so it is no coincidence that these values are shown on the x-axis. In general, a probability distribution function will have some (possibly unbounded) interval as its domain.

Suppose now that as in Section P.1, we wanted to calculate the probability that a rented car is between 0 and 4 years old. Referring to the table, we find

$$P(0 \leq X \leq 4) = .20 + .28 + .20 + .15 = .83.$$

Referring to Figure 8, we can obtain the same result by adding the areas of the corresponding bars, because each bar has a width of 1 unit. Ideally, our probability density curve should have the property that the area under it for $0 \leq X \leq 4$ is the same, that is,

$$P(0 \leq X \leq 4) = \int_0^4 f(x)\,dx = .83.$$

(This area is shown in Figure 8 as well.)

---

[7]There are many similarly shaped curves suggested by the bar graph. The question of finding the most appropriate curve is one we shall be considering below.

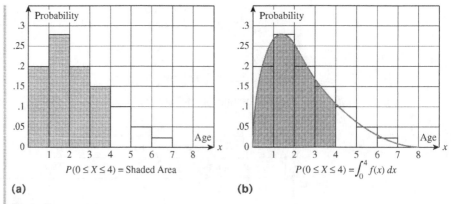

(a) $P(0 \le X \le 4) = $ Shaded Area

(b) $P(0 \le X \le 4) = \int_0^4 f(x)\,dx$

Figure 8

Now, what happens if we want to find $P(2 \le X \le 3.5)$? In the previous section we estimated this by taking half of the rectangle between 3 and 4 (see Figure 9).

(a) $P(2 \le X \le 3.5) = $ Shaded Area

(b) $P(2 \le X \le 3.5) = \int_2^{3.5} f(x)\,dx$

Figure 9

Instead, we could use the definite integral

$$P(2 \le X \le 3.5) = \int_2^{3.5} f(x)\,dx.$$

➡ **Before we go on...** Although we haven't given you a formula for $f(x)$, we would *like* $f(x)$ to behave as described above. Here is something else we would like: Because a car has probability 1 of having an age between 0 and $+\infty$, we want

$$P(0 \le X < +\infty) = \int_0^{+\infty} f(x)\,dx = 1. \quad \blacksquare$$

The discussion in Example 1 motivates the following.

Probability Density Function

A **probability density function** is a function f defined on an interval (a, b) and having the following properties.

(a) $f(x) \geq 0$ for every x

(b) $\int_a^b f(x)\,dx = 1$

We allow a, b, or both to be infinite, as in the above example; this would make the integral in (b) an improper one.

Using a Probability Density Function to Compute Probability

A continuous random variable X **admits a probability density function** f if, for every c and d,

$$P(c \leq X \leq d) = \int_c^d f(x)\,dx.$$

Quick Example

Let $f(x) = \dfrac{2}{x^2}$ on the interval $[a, b] = [1, 2]$. Then property (a) holds, because $\dfrac{2}{x^2}$ is positive on the interval $[1, 2]$. For property (b),

$$\int_a^b f(x)\,dx = \int_1^2 \frac{2}{x^2}\,dx = \left[-\frac{2}{x}\right]_1^2 = -1 + 2 = 1.$$

If X admits this probability density function, then

$$P(1.5 \leq x \leq 2) = \int_{1.5}^2 \frac{2}{x^2}\,dx = \frac{1}{3}.$$

Note If X is specified by a probability density function f, then

$$P(X = c) = P(c \leq X \leq c) = \int_c^c f(x)\,dx = 0,$$

showing once again that there is a zero probability that X will assume any specified value. ■

Uniform Density Function

A **uniform density function** f is a density function that is constant, making it the simplest kind of density function. Because we require $f(x) = k$ for some constant k, requirement (b) in the definition of a probability density function tells us that

$$1 = \int_a^b f(x)\,dx = \int_a^b k\,dx = k(b - a).$$

Thus, we must have

$$k = \frac{1}{b - a}.$$

In other words, a uniform density function must have the following form.

Uniform Density Function

The **uniform density function on the interval $[a, b]$** is given by

$$f(x) = \frac{1}{b-a}.$$

Its graph is a horizontal line.

Calculating Probability with a Uniform Density Function

Because probability is given by area, it is not hard to compute probabilities based on a uniform distribution.

$$P(c \leq X \leq d) = \text{Area of shaded rectangle} = \frac{d-c}{b-a}.$$

Quick Example

Let X be a random real number between 0 and 5. Then X has a uniform distribution given by

$$f(x) = \frac{1}{5-0} = \frac{1}{5},$$

and $P(2 \leq X \leq 4.5) = \dfrac{4.5 - 2}{5 - 0} = .5.$

Figure 10

EXAMPLE 2 Spinning a Dial

Suppose that you spin the dial shown in Figure 10 so that it comes to rest at a random position. Model this with a suitable probability density function, and use it to find the probability that the dial will land somewhere between 5° and 300°.

Solution We take X to be the angle at which the pointer comes to rest, so we use the interval $[0, 360]$. Because all angles are equally likely, the probability density function should not depend on x and therefore should be constant. That is, we take f to be uniform.

$$f(x) = \frac{1}{b-a}$$

$$= \frac{1}{360 - 0} = \frac{1}{360}.$$

Thus,

$$P(5 \leq X \leq 300) = \frac{300 - 5}{360 - 0} = \frac{295}{360} \approx .8194.$$

➡ **Before we go on...** Notice that, in Example 2, we could have used the integral formula and obtained the same answer:

$$\int_5^{300} \frac{1}{360} dx = \frac{1}{360}(300 - 5) = \frac{295}{360}.$$

You can also check the following probabilities. Why are these the answers you expect?

$P(0 \leq X \leq 90) = 1/4.$

$P(90 \leq X \leq 180) = 1/4.$

$P(0 \leq X \leq 180) = 1/2.$

$P(0 \leq X \leq 270) = 3/4.$

$P(0 \leq X \leq 120) = 1/3.$ ∎

Exponential Density Functions

Suppose that troubled saving and loan (S&L) institutions are failing continuously at a fractional rate of 5% per year. What is the probability that a troubled S&L will fail sometime within the next T years?

To answer the question, suppose that you started with 100 troubled S&Ls. Because they are failing continuously at a fractional rate of 5% per year, the number left after T years is given by the decay equation

Number left $= 100e^{-0.05T}$,

so

Number that fail $=$ Total number $-$ Number left

$= 100 - 100e^{-0.05T}$

$= 100(1 - e^{-0.05T}).$

Thus, the percentage that will have failed by that time—and hence the probability that we are asking for—is given by

$$P = \frac{100(1 - e^{-0.05T})}{100} = 1 - e^{-0.05T}.$$

Now let X be the number of years a randomly chosen troubled S&L will take to fail. We have just calculated the probability that X is between 0 and T. In other words,

$$P(0 \leq X \leq T) = 1 - e^{-0.05T}.$$

Notice that this result can also be obtained by calculating a certain integral:

$$\int_0^T 0.05e^{-0.05x} dx = [e^{-0.05x}]_0^T = 1 - e^{-0.05T}.$$

Thus,

$$P(0 \leq X \leq T) = \int_0^T 0.05e^{-0.05x} dx,$$

and so we use $f(x) = 0.05e^{-0.05x}$ as a probability density function to model this situation.

Q: *Does this function satisfy the mathematical conditions necessary for it to be a probability density function?*

A: First, the domain of *f* is [0, +∞), since *x* refers to the number of years from now. Checking requirements (a) and (b) for a probability density function,

(a) $0.05e^{-0.05x} \geq 0$,

(b) $\displaystyle\int_{0}^{+\infty} 0.05e^{-0.05x}\,dx = \lim_{M \to +\infty} \int_{0}^{M} 0.05e^{-0.05x}\,dx$

$$= \lim_{M \to +\infty} [-e^{-0.05x}]_{0}^{M}$$

$$= \lim_{M \to +\infty} (e^{0} - e^{-0.05M}) = 1 - 0 = 1.$$

There is nothing special about the number 0.05. Any function of the form

$$f(x) = ae^{-ax} \qquad\qquad a > 0 \quad \text{constant}$$

is a probability density function. A density function of this form is referred to as an **exponential density function**.

Exponential Density Function

An **exponential density function** is a function of the form

$$f(x) = ae^{-ax} \text{ (}a \text{ a positive constant)}$$

with domain $[0 + \infty)$. Its graph is shown in Figure 11.

Figure 11

Quick Example

Continuing the example in the text, we find that the probability that a given troubled S&L will fail between 2 and 4 years from now is

$$P(2 \leq X \leq 4) = \int_{2}^{4} 0.05e^{-0.05x}\,dx = [-e^{-0.05x}]_{2}^{4}$$

$$= -e^{-0.2} + e^{-0.1} \approx .086.$$

The probability that it will last 5 or more years is

$$P(X \geq 5) = \int_{0}^{+\infty} 0.05e^{-0.05x}\,dx$$

$$= \lim_{M \to +\infty} \int_{5}^{M} 0.05e^{-0.05x}\,dx$$

$$= \lim_{M \to +\infty} \left[-e^{-0.05x} \right]_5^M = \lim_{M \to +\infty} (e^{-0.25} - e^{-0.05M})$$

$$= e^{-0.25} \approx .779.$$

So there is an 8.6% chance that a given S&L will fail between 2 and 4 years from now, and a 77.9% chance that it will last 5 or more years.

EXAMPLE 3   Radioactive Decay

Plutonium 239 decays continuously at a rate of 0.00284% per year. If X is the time a randomly chosen plutonium atom will decay, write down the associated probability density function, and use it to compute the probability that a plutonium atom will decay between 100 and 500 years from now.

Solution Using the discussion on failing S&Ls as our guide, we see that $a = 0.0000284$, so the probability density function is

$$f(x) = 0.0000284e^{-0.0000284x}.$$

For the second part of the question,

$$P(100 \le X \le 500) = \int_{100}^{500} (0.0000284e^{-0.0000284x}) dx$$

$$\approx .011.$$

Thus, there is a 1.1% chance that a plutonium atom will decay sometime during the given 400- year period.

Normal Density Functions

Perhaps the most interesting class of probability density functions are the **normal density functions**, defined as follows.[8]

Normal Density Function

A **normal density function** is a function of the form

$$f(x) = \frac{1}{\sigma \sqrt{2\pi}} e^{-\frac{(x-\mu)^2}{2\sigma^2}},$$

with domain $(-\infty, +\infty)$. The quantity μ is called the **mean** and can be any real number, while σ is called the **standard deviation** and can be any positive real number. The graph of a normal density function is shown in Figure 12.

---

[8]You may recall encountering exercises using the normal density function in the chapter on integration.

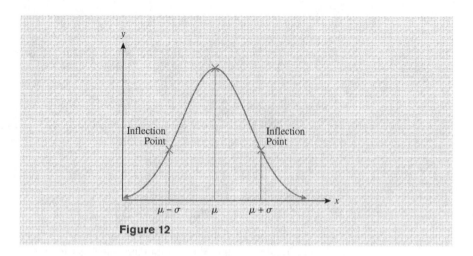

Figure 12

The following properties can be checked using calculus and a little algebra.

Properties of a Normal Density Curve

(a) It is "bell-shaped" with the peak occurring at $x = \mu$.

(b) It is symmetric about the vertical line $x = \mu$.

(c) It is concave down in the range $\mu - \sigma \leq x \leq \mu + \sigma$.

(d) It is concave up outside that range, with inflection points at $x = \mu - \sigma$ and $x = \mu + \sigma$.

The normal density function applies in many situations that involve measurement and testing. For instance, repeated imprecise measurements of the length of a single object, a measurement made on many items from an assembly line, and collections of SAT scores tend to be distributed normally. It is partly for this reason that the normal density curve is so important in quality control and in assessing the results of standardized tests.

In order to use the normal density function to compute probabilities, we need to calculate integrals of the form $\int_a^b f(x)\,dx$. However, the antiderivative of the normal density function cannot be expressed in terms of any commonly used functions. Traditionally, statisticians and others have used tables coupled with transformation techniques to evaluate such integrals. This approach is rapidly becoming obsolete as the technology of spreadsheets, handheld computers, and programmable calculators puts the ability to do numerical integration quickly and accurately in everybody's hands (literally). In keeping with this trend, in the Technology Guides at the end of this chapter we show how to use technology to do the calculations in the following example.

⛶ Using Technology

See the Technology Guides at the end of the chapter to find out how to compute the definite integral of a normal distribution using a TI-83/84 Plus or Excel.

⛶ EXAMPLE 4 Quality Control

Pressure gauges manufactured by Precision Corp. must be checked for accuracy before being placed on the market. To test a pressure gauge, a worker uses it to measure the pressure of a sample of compressed air known to be at a pressure of exactly 50 pounds per square inch. If the gauge reading is off by more than 1% (0.5 pounds/square inch), the gauge is rejected. Assuming that the reading of a pressure gauge under these circumstances is a normal random variable with mean 50 and standard deviation 0.5, find the percentage of gauges rejected.

Solution For a gauge to be accepted, its reading X must be 50 to within 1%, in other words, $49.5 \leq X \leq 50.5$. Thus, the probability that a gauge will be accepted is $P(49.5 \leq X \leq 50.5)$. X is a normal random variable with $\mu = 50$ and $\sigma = 0.5$. The formula tells us that

$$P(49.5 \leq X \leq 50.5) = \int_{49.5}^{50.5} f(x)\,dx,$$

where f is the normal distribution with mean $\mu = 50$ and standard deviation $\sigma = 0.5$;

$$f(x) = \frac{1}{\sigma\sqrt{2\pi}}\, e^{-\frac{(x-\mu)^2}{2\sigma^2}}$$

$$= \frac{1}{0.5\sqrt{2\pi}}\, e^{-\frac{(x-50)^2}{0.5}}.$$

Using technology, we can calculate that

$$P(49.5 \leq X \leq 50.5) = \int_{49.5}^{50.5} f(x)\,dx \approx .6827.$$

In other words, 68.27% of the gauges will be accepted. Thus, the remaining 31.73% of the gauges will be rejected.

➡ **Before we go on...** As we mentioned above, the traditional and still common way of calculating normal probabilities is to use tables. The tables most commonly published are for the **standard normal distribution**, the one with mean 0 and standard deviation 1. If X is a normal variable with mean μ and standard deviation σ, the variable $Z = (X - \mu)/\sigma$ is a standard normal variable (see the exercises). Thus, to use a table we first write

$$P(a \leq X \leq b) = P\left(\frac{a - \mu}{\sigma} \leq Z \leq \frac{b - \mu}{\sigma}\right)$$

and then use the table to calculate the latter probability. ■

Q: *Why can we assume in Example 4 that the reading of a pressure gauge is given by a normal distribution? Why is the normal distribution so common in this kind of situation?*

A: The reason for this is rather deep. There is a theorem in probability theory called the Central Limit Theorem, which says that a large class of probability density functions, given, for example, by repeated measurement of the same random variable, may be approximated by normal density functions.

Beta Density Functions

There are many random variables whose values are percentages or fractions. These variables have density functions defined on [0,1]. A large class of random variables, such as the percentage of new businesses that turn a profit in their first year, the percentage of banks that default in a given year, and the percentage of time a plant's machinery is inactive, can be modeled by a **beta density function**.

Beta Density Function

A **beta density function** is a function of the form

$$f(x) = (\beta + 1)(\beta + 2)x^\beta(1 - x),$$

with domain [0, 1]. The number β can be any constant ≥ 0. Figure 13 shows the graph of $f(x)$ for several values of β.

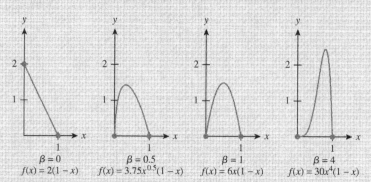

$\beta = 0$
$f(x) = 2(1 - x)$

$\beta = 0.5$
$f(x) = 3.75x^{0.5}(1 - x)$

$\beta = 1$
$f(x) = 6x(1 - x)$

$\beta = 4$
$f(x) = 30x^4(1 - x)$

Figure 13

EXAMPLE 5 Downsizing in the Utilities Industry

A utilities industry consultant predicts a cutback in the Canadian utilities industry during 2000–2005 by a percentage specified by a beta distribution with $\beta = 0.25$. Calculate the probability that Ontario Hydro will downsize by between 10% and 30% during the given five-year period.[9]

Solution The beta density function with $\beta = 0.25$ is

$$\begin{aligned}
f(x) &= (\beta + 1)(\beta + 2)x^\beta(1 - x) \\
&= 2.8125x^{0.25}(1 - x) \\
&= 2.8125(x^{0.25} - x^{1.25}).
\end{aligned}$$

Thus,

$$\begin{aligned}
P(0.10 \leq X \leq 0.30) &= \int_{0.10}^{0.30} 2.8125(x^{0.25} - x^{1.25})dx \\
&= 2.8125 \int_{0.10}^{0.30} (x^{0.25} - x^{1.25})dx \\
&= 2.8125\left[\frac{x^{1.25}}{1.25} - \frac{x^{2.25}}{2.25}\right]_{0.10}^{0.30} \\
&\approx .2968.
\end{aligned}$$

So there is approximately a 30% chance that Ontario Hydro will downsize by between 10% and 30%.

➡ **Before we go on...** Figure 14 shows the density function. Notice that its shape is "in between" those for $\beta = 0$ and $\beta = 0.5$ in Figure 13. ■

$\beta = 0.25$

Figure 14

[9]This model is fictitious. Ontario Hydro did announce plans to downsize by 8.4% in 1995, however [*Report on Business* (Canada), Feb. 15, 1994, p. B1].

P.2 EXERCISES

▼ more advanced ◆ challenging

🔢 indicates exercises that should be solved using technology

In Exercises 1–12, check whether the given function is a probability density function. If a function fails to be a probability density function, say why.

1. $f(x) = 1$ on $[0, 1]$

2. $f(x) = x$ on $[0, 2]$

3. $f(x) = \dfrac{x}{2}$ on $[0, 1]$

4. $f(x) = 2$ on $[0, \dfrac{1}{2}]$

5. ▼ $f(x) = \dfrac{3}{2}(x^2 - 1)$ on $[0, 2]$

6. ▼ $f(x) = \dfrac{1}{3}(1 - x^2)$ on $[0, 1]$

7. ▼ $f(x) = \dfrac{1}{x}$ on $[1, e]$

8. ▼ $f(x) = e^x$ on $[0, \ln 2]$

9. ▼ $f(x) = 2xe^{-x^2}$ on $[0, +\infty)$

10. ▼ $f(x) = -2xe^{-x^2}$ on $(-\infty, 0]$

11. ▼ $f(x) = xe^{-x^2}$ on $(-\infty, +\infty)$

12. ▼ $f(x) = |x|e^{-x^2}$ on $(-\infty, +\infty)$

In Exercises 13–16, find the values of k for which the given functions are probability density functions.

13. ▼ $f(x) = 2k$ on $[-1, 1]$

14. ▼ $f(x) = k$ on $[-2, 0]$

15. ▼ $f(x) = ke^{kx}$ on $[0, 1]$

16. ▼ $f(x) = kxe^{x^2}$ on $[0, 1]$

In Exercises 17–26, say which kind of probability density function is most appropriate for the given random variable: uniform, exponential, normal, beta, or none of these.

17. ▼ The time it takes a Carbon-14 atom to decay.

18. ▼ The time it takes you to drive home.

19. ▼ The SAT score of a randomly selected student.

20. ▼ The value of a random number between 0 and 1.

21. ▼ The time of day at a randomly chosen moment.

22. ▼ The time it takes a careless driver to be involved in an accident.

23. ▼ The fraction of fast-food restaurants that are profitable in their first year.

24. ▼ The time it will take for the sun to die.

25. ▼ The time it takes before a gambler loses on a bet.

26. ▼ The length of a 2000 Ford Mustang®

APPLICATIONS

Unless otherwise stated, round answers to all applications to four decimal places.

27. Salaries Assuming that workers' salaries in your company are uniformly distributed between \$10,000 and \$40,000 per year, find the probability that a randomly chosen worker earns an annual salary between \$14,000 and \$20,000.

28. Grades The grade point averages of members of the Gourmet Society are uniformly distributed between 2.5 and 3.5. Find the probability that a randomly chosen member of the society has a grade point average between 3 and 3.2.

29. ▼ **Boring Television Series** Your company's new series "Avocado Comedy Hour" has been a complete flop, with viewership continuously declining at a rate of 30% per month. Use a suitable density function to calculate the probability that a randomly chosen viewer will be lost sometime in the next three months.

30. ▼ **Bad Investments** Investments in junk bonds are declining continuously at a rate of 5% per year. Use a suitable density function to calculate the probability that a dollar invested in junk bonds will be pulled out of the junk bond market within the next two years.

31. ▼ **Radioactive Decay** The half-life of Carbon-14 is 5,730 years. What is the probability that a randomly selected Carbon-14 atom will not yet have decayed in 4,000 years' time?

32. ▼ **Radioactive Decay** The half-life of Plutonium-239 is 24,400 years. What is the probability that a randomly selected Plutonium-239 atom will not yet have decayed in 40,000 years' time?

33. ▼ **The Doomsday Meteor** The probability that a "doomsday meteor" will hit the Earth in any given year and release a billion megatons or more of energy is on the order of 0.000 000 01.[10]

  (a) What is the probability that the Earth will be hit by a doomsday meteor at least once during the next 100 years? (Use an exponential distribution with $a = 0.000\ 000\ 01$. Give the answer correct to 2 significant digits.)

  (b) What is the probability that the Earth has been hit by a doomsday meteor at least once since the appearance of life (about 4 billion years ago)?

34. ▼ **Galactic Cataclysm** The probability that the galaxy MX-47 will explode within the next million years is estimated to be 0.0003.

  (a) What is the probability that MX-47 will explode within the next 5 million years? (Use an exponential distribution with $a = 0.0003$.)

  (b) What is the probability that MX-47 will still be around 10 million years hence?

---

[10]Source: NASA International Near-Earth-Object Detection Workshop/*The New York Times*, January 25, 1994, p. C1.

Exercises 35–42 use the normal probability density function and require the use of either technology or a table of values of the standard normal distribution.

35. ▦ ▼ *Physical Measurements* Repeated measurements of a metal rod yield a mean of 5.3 inches, with a standard deviation of 0.1. What is the probability that the rod is between 5.25 and 5.35 inches long?

36. ▦ ▼ *IQ Testing* Repeated measurements of a student's IQ yield a mean of 135, with a standard deviation of 5. What is the probability that the student has an IQ between 132 and 138?

37. ▦ ▼ *Psychology Tests* It is known that subjects score an average of 100 points on a new personality test. If the standard deviation is 10 points, what percentage of all subjects will score between 75 and 80?

38. ▦ ▼ *Examination Scores* Professor Easy's students earned an average grade of 3.5, with a standard deviation of 0.2. What percentage of his students earned between 3.5 and 3.9?

39. ▦ ▼ *Operating Expenses* The cash operating expenses of the regional *Bell* companies during the first half of 1994 were distributed about a mean of $29.87 per access line per month, with a standard deviation of $2.65. *Ameritech Corporation's* operating expenses were $28.00 per access line per month.[11] Assuming a normal distribution of operating expenses, estimate the percentage of regional Bell companies whose operating expenses were closer to the mean than those of Ameritech.

40. ▦ ▼ *Operating Expenses Nynex Corporation's* operating expenses were $35.80 per access line per month in the first half of 1994.[12] Referring to the distribution in the previous exercise, estimate the percentage of regional Bell companies whose operating expenses were higher than those of Nynex.

41. ▦ ▼ *Operating Expenses SBC Corporation* (formerly Southwestern Bell) had operating expenses of $27.70 per access line per month in the first half of 1994.[13] Could SBC justifiably claim that its operating expenses were among the lowest 25% of all the regional Bell companies? Explain. (Use the normal distribution of the above exercises.)

42. ▦ ▼ *Operating Expense U.S. West Corporation* had operating expenses of $29.10 per access line per month in the first half of 1994.[14] Were U.S. West's operating expenses closer to the mean than those of most other regional Bells? Explain. (Use the normal distribution of the above exercises.)

Cumulative Distribution *If f is a probability density function defined on the interval (a, b), then the **cumulative distribution function** F is given by*

$$F(x) = \int_a^x f(t)\,dt.$$

Exercises 43–52 deal with the cumulative distribution function.

43. ◆ Why is $F'(x) = f(x)$?

44. ◆ Use the result of the previous exercise to show that

$$P(c \le X \le d) = F(d) - F(c)$$

for $a \le c \le d \le b$.

45. ◆ Show that $F(a) = 0$ and $F(b) = 1$.

46. ◆ Can $F(x)$ can have any local extrema? (Give a reason for your answer.)

47. ▼ Find the cumulative distribution functions for the situation described in Exercise 27.

48. ▼ Find the cumulative distribution functions for the situation described in Exercise 28.

49. ▼ Find the cumulative distribution functions for the situation described in Exercise 29.

50. ▼ Find the cumulative distribution functions for the situation described in Exercise 30.

51. ▼ Find the cumulative distribution functions for the situation described in Exercise 31.

52. ▼ Find the cumulative distribution functions for the situation described in Exercise 32.

COMMUNICATION AND REASONING EXERCISES

53. ▼ Why is a probability density function often more convenient than a histogram?

54. ▼ Give an example of a probability density function that is increasing everywhere on its domain.

55. ▼ Give an example of a probability density function that is concave up everywhere on its domain.

56. ▼ Suppose that X is a normal random variable with mean μ and standard deviation σ, and that Z is a standard normal variable. Using the substitution $z = (x - \mu)/\sigma$ in the integral, show that

$$P(a \le X \le b) = P\left(\frac{a - \mu}{\sigma} \le Z \le \frac{b - \mu}{\sigma}\right).$$

57. ▼ Your friend thinks that if *f* is a probability density function for the continuous random variable X, then $f(a)$ is the probability that $X = a$. Explain to your friend why this is wrong.

58. ◆ Not satisfied with your explanation in the previous exercise, your friend then challenges you by asking, "If $f(a)$ is not the probability that $X = a$, then just what does $f(a)$ signify?" How would you respond?

59. ◆ Your friend now thinks that if F is a *cumulative* probability density function for the continuous random variable X, then $F(a)$ is the probability that $X = a$. Explain why your friend is *still* wrong.

60. ◆ Once again not satisfied with your explanation in the previous exercise, your friend challenges you by asking, "If $F(a)$ is not the probability that $X = a$, then just what does $F(a)$ signify?" How would you respond?

---

[11] Source: NatWest Securities/Company Reports/*The New York Times,* November 22, 1994, p. D1.
[12]*Ibid.*
[13]*Ibid.*
[14]*Ibid.*

P.3 Mean, Median, Variance, and Standard Deviation

Mean

In the last section we saw that if savings and loan institutions are continuously failing at a rate of 5% per year, then the associated probability density function is

$$f(x) = 0.05e^{-0.05x}$$

with domain $[0, +\infty)$. An interesting and important question to ask is: What is the average length of time such an institution will last before failing? To answer this question, we use the following:

Mean or Expected Value

If X is a continuous random variable with probability density function f defined on an interval with (possibly infinite) endpoints a and b, then the **mean** or **expected value** of X is

$$E(X) = \int_a^b x f(x) \, dx.$$

$E(X)$ is also called the **average value** of X. It is what we expect to get if we take the average of many values of X obtained in experiments.

Quick Example

Let X have probability density function given by $f(x) = 3x^2$, with domain $[0, 1]$. Then

$$E(X) = \int_a^b x f(x) \, dx = \int_0^1 (x \cdot 3x^2) \, dx = \int_0^1 3x^3 \, dx = \left[\frac{3x^4}{4}\right]_0^1 = \frac{3}{4}.$$

We shall explain shortly why $E(X)$ is given by the integral formula.

EXAMPLE 1 Failing S&Ls

Given that troubled S&Ls are failing continuously at a rate of 5% per year, how long will the average troubled S&L last?

Solution If X is the number of years that a given S&L will last, we know that its probability density function is $f(x) = 0.05e^{-0.05x}$. To answer the question we compute $E(X)$.

$$E(X) = \int_a^b xf(x)\,dx$$

$$= \int_0^{+\infty} (0.05xe^{-0.05x})\,dx$$

$$= \lim_{M \to +\infty} \int_0^M (0.05xe^{-0.05x})\,dx$$

Using integration by parts, we get

$$E(x) = \lim_{M \to +\infty} -0.05 \left[e^{-0.05x}(20x + 400) \right]_0^M = (0.05)(400) = 20.$$

Thus, the expected lifespan of a troubled S&L is 20 years.

➡ **Before we go on...** Notice that in Example 1, the answer, 20, is the reciprocal of the failure rate 0.05. This is true in general: if $f(x) = ae^{-ax}$, then $E(X) = 1/a$. ∎

Q : *Why is E(X) given by that integral formula?*

A : Suppose for simplicity that the domain of f is a finite interval $[a, b]$. Break up the interval into n subintervals $[x_{k-1}, x_k]$, each of length Δx, as we did for Riemann sums. Now, the probability of seeing a value of X in $[x_{k-1}, x_k]$ is approximately $f(x_k)\Delta x$ (the approximate area under the graph of f over $[x_{k-1}, x_k]$). Think of this as the fraction of times we expect to see values of X in this range. These values, all close to x_k, then contribute approximately $x_k f(x_k)\Delta x$ to the average, if we average together many observations of X. Adding together all of these contributions, we get

$$E(X) \approx \sum_{k=1}^{n} x_k f(x_k)\,\Delta x.$$

Now, these approximations get better as $n \longrightarrow \infty$, and the sum above is a Riemann sum converging to

$$E(X) = \int_a^b xf(x)\,dx,$$

which is the formula we have been using.

We can compute, one by one, the expected values of the distributions we discussed in the preceding section.

Mean of a Uniform Distribution

If X is uniformly distributed on $[a, b]$, then

$$E(X) = \frac{a+b}{2}.$$

Quick Example

Suppose that you spin the dial shown so that it comes to rest at a random position X.

Then $E(X) = \dfrac{0 + 360}{2} = 180°$.

Mean of an Exponential Distribution

If X has the exponential distribution function $f(x) = ae^{-ax}$, then

$$E(X) = \frac{1}{a}.$$

Quick Example

If Internet startup companies are failing at a rate of 10% per year, then the expected lifetime of an Internet startup company is

$$E(X) = \frac{1}{0.1} = 10 \text{ years.}$$

We saw why this formula works in Example 1.

Mean of a Normal Distribution

If X is normally distributed with parameters μ and σ, then

$$E(X) = \mu.$$

Quick Example

If the final exam scores in your class are normally distributed with mean 72.6 and standard deviation 8.3, then the expected value for a test score is

$$E(X) = \mu = 72.6.$$

That is why we called μ the mean, but we ought to do the calculation. Here we go.

$$E(X) = \int_{-\infty}^{+\infty} x \cdot \frac{1}{\sigma\sqrt{2\pi}} e^{-(x-\mu)^2/2\sigma^2}dx$$

$$= \int_{-\infty}^{+\infty} (\sigma w + \mu)\frac{1}{\sqrt{2\pi}}e^{-w^2/2}dw \qquad \text{after substituting } w = (x - \mu)/\sigma$$

$$= \frac{\sigma}{\sqrt{2\pi}} \int_{-\infty}^{+\infty} we^{-w^2/2}dw + \mu \int_{-\infty}^{+\infty} \frac{1}{\sqrt{2\pi}} e^{-w^2/2} \, dw.$$

Now, the first integral can be done easily (substitute $v = -w^2/2$) and converges to 0. The second integral we recognize as the area under another normal distribution curve (the one with $\mu = 0$ and $\sigma = 1$), so it is equal to 1. Therefore, the whole thing simplifies to

$$E(X) = \mu$$

as claimed.

Mean of a Beta Distribution

If X has the beta distribution function $f(x) = (\beta + 1)(\beta + 2)x^\beta(1 - x)$, then

$$E(X) = \frac{\beta + 1}{\beta + 3}.$$

Again, we shall leave this as an exercise.

EXAMPLE 2 Downsizing in the Utilities Industry

A utilities industry consultant predicts a cutback in the Canadian Utilities industry during 2000–2005 by a percentage specified by a beta distribution with $\beta = 0.25$. What is the expected size of the cutback by Ontario Hydro?[15]

Solution Because $\beta = 0.25$,

$$E(X) = \frac{\beta + 1}{\beta + 3} = \frac{1.25}{3.25} \approx 0.38.$$

Therefore, we can expect about a 38% cutback by Ontario Hydro.

➡ **Before we go on...** What $E(X)$ really tells us is that the *average* downsizing of many utilities will be 38%. Some will cut back more, and some will cut back less. ■

---

[15]This model is fictitious. Ontario Hydro did announce plans to downsize by 8.4% in 1995, however (*Report on Business* (Canada), Feb. 15, 1994, p. B1).

There is a generalization of the mean that we shall use below. If X is a random variable on the interval (a, b) with probability density function f, and if g is any function defined on that interval, then we can define the **expected value of g** to be

$$E(g(X)) = \int_a^b g(x) f(x) \, dx.$$

Thus, in particular, the mean is just the expected value of the function $g(x) = x$. We can interpret this as the average we expect if we compute $g(X)$ for many experimental values of X.

Variance and Standard Deviation

Statisticians use the variance and standard deviation of a continuous random variable X as a way of measuring its dispersion, or the degree to which is it "scattered." The definitions are as follows:

Variance and Standard Deviation

Let X be a continuous random variable with density function f defined on the interval (a, b), and let $\mu = E(X)$ be the mean of X. Then the **variance** of X is given by

$$Var(X) = E((X - \mu)^2) = \int_a^b (x - \mu)^2 f(x) \, dx.$$

The **standard deviation** of X is the square root of the variance,

$$\sigma(X) = \sqrt{Var(X)}.$$

Notes

1. In order to calculate the variance and standard deviation, we first need to calculate the mean.

2. $Var(X)$ is the expected value of the function $(x - \mu)^2$, which measures the square of the distance of X from its mean. It is for this reason that $Var(X)$ is sometimes called the *mean square deviation*, and $\sigma(X)$ is called the *root mean square deviation*. $Var(X)$ will be larger if X tends to wander far away from its mean, and smaller if the values of X tend to cluster near its mean.

3. The reason we take the square root in the definition of $\sigma(X)$ is that $Var(X)$ is the expected value of the *square* of the deviation from the mean, and thus is measured in square units. Its square root $\sigma(X)$, therefore, gives us a measure in ordinary units. ∎

We now state the variances and standard deviations of the distributions we discussed in the previous section. We'll leave the actual computations (or special cases) for the exercises.

Variance and Standard Deviation of Some Distributions

Uniform Distribution
If X is uniformly distributed on $[a, b]$, then

$$Var(X) = \frac{(b-a)^2}{12}$$

and

$$\sigma(X) = \frac{b-a}{\sqrt{12}}.$$

Exponential Distribution

If X has the exponential distribution function $f(x) = ae^{-ax}$, then

$$Var(X) = \frac{1}{a^2}$$

and

$$\sigma(X) = \frac{1}{a}.$$

Normal Distribution

If X is normally distributed with parameters μ and σ, then

$$Var(X) = \sigma^2$$

and

$$\sigma(X) = \sigma. \qquad \text{This is what you might have expected.}$$

Beta Distribution

If X has the beta distribution function $f(x) = (\beta + 1)(\beta + 2)x^\beta(1 - x)$, then

$$Var(X) = \frac{2(\beta + 1)}{(\beta + 4)(\beta + 3)^2}$$

and

$$\sigma(X) = \sqrt{\frac{2(\beta + 1)}{(\beta + 4)(\beta + 3)^2}}.$$

You can see the significance of the standard deviation quite clearly in the normal distribution. As we mentioned in the previous section, σ is the distance from the maximum at μ to the points of inflection at $\mu - \sigma$ and $\mu + \sigma$. The larger σ is, the wider the bell. Figure 15 shows three normal distributions with three different standard deviations (all with $\mu = 0.5$).

Again, a small standard deviation means that the values of X will be close to the mean with high probability, while a large standard deviation means that the values may wander far away with high probability.

Median

The *median income* in the United States is the income M such that half the population earns incomes $\leq M$ (so the other half earns incomes $\geq M$). In terms of probability, we can think of income as a random variable X. Then the probability that $X \leq M$ is $1/2$, and the probability that $X \geq M$ is also $1/2$.

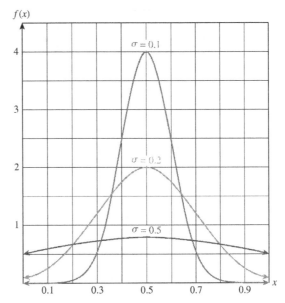

Figure 15

Median

Let X be a continuous random variable. The **median** of X is the number M such that

$$P(X \leq M) = \frac{1}{2}.$$

Then, $P(M \leq X) = \frac{1}{2}$ also.

If f is the probability density function for X and f is defined on (a, b), then we can calculate M by solving the equation

$$P(a \leq X \leq M) = \int_{a}^{M} f(x)\,dx = \frac{1}{2}$$

for M. Graphically, the vertical line $x = M$ divides the total area under the graph of f into two equal parts (Figure 16).

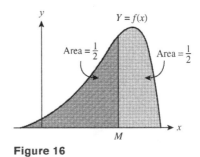

Figure 16

Q: *What is the difference between the median and the mean?*

A: Roughly speaking, the median divides the area under the distribution curve into two equal parts, while the mean is the value of *X* at which the graph would *balance*. If a probability curve has as much area to the left of the mean as to the right, then the mean is equal to the median. This is true of uniform and normal distributions, which are *symmetric* about their means. On the other hand, the medians and means are different for the exponential distributions and most of the beta distributions, because their areas are not distributed symmetrically.

EXAMPLE 3 Lines at the Post Office

The time in minutes between individuals joining the line at an Ottawa Post Office is a random variable with the exponential distribution

$$f(x) = 2e^{-2x}, \ (x \geq 0).$$

Find the mean and median time between individuals joining the line and interpret the answers.

Solution The expected value for an exponential distribution $f(x) = ae^{-ax}$ is $1/a$. Here, $a = 2$, so $E(X) = 1/2$. We interpret this to mean that, on average, a new person will join the line every half a minute, or 30 seconds. For the median, we must solve

$$\int_a^M f(x)\,dx = \frac{1}{2}.$$

That is,

$$\int_0^M (2e^{-2x})\,dx = \frac{1}{2}.$$

Evaluating the integral gives

$$-\left[e^{-2x}\right]_0^M = \frac{1}{2},$$

or

$$1 - e^{-2M} = \frac{1}{2}$$

so

$$e^{-2M} = \frac{1}{2},$$

or

$$-2M = \ln\left(\frac{1}{2}\right) = -\ln 2.$$

Thus,

$$M = \frac{\ln 2}{2} \approx 0.3466 \text{ minutes.}$$

This means that half the people get in line less than 0.3466 minutes (about 21 seconds) after the previous person, while half arrive more than 0.3466 minutes later. The mean time for a new person to arrive in line is larger than this because there are some occasional long waits between people, and these pull the average up.

Sometimes we cannot solve the equation $\int_a^M f(x)\,dx = 1/2$ for M analytically, as the next example shows.

EXAMPLE 4 **Median**

Find the median of the random variable with beta density function for $\beta = 4$.

Solution Here,

$$f(x) = (\beta + 1)(\beta + 2)x^\beta(1 - x)$$
$$= 30x^4(1 - x).$$

Thus we must solve

$$\int_0^M (30x^4(1 - x))\,dx = \frac{1}{2}.$$

That is,

$$30 \int_0^M (x^4 - x^5)\,dx = \frac{1}{2}.$$

So

$$30\left[\frac{M^5}{5} - \frac{M^6}{6}\right] = \frac{1}{2},$$

or, multiplying through and clearing denominators,

$$12M^5 - 10M^6 - 1 = 0.$$

This is a degree six polynomial equation that has no easy factorization. Because there is no general analytical method for obtaining the solution, the only method we can use is numerical. Figure 17 shows three successive views of a TI-83/84 Plus plot of $Y = 12X^5 - 10X^6 - 1$, obtained by zooming in toward one of the zeros.

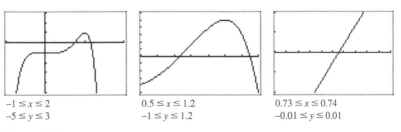

| $-1 \le x \le 2$ | $0.5 \le x \le 1.2$ | $0.73 \le x \le 0.74$ |
| $-5 \le y \le 3$ | $-1 \le y \le 1.2$ | $-0.01 \le y \le 0.01$ |

Figure 17

In the first two plots we can see two zeros, one between 0.7 and 0.8 and the other between 1.1 and 1.2. We are interested only in the zero that occurs between 0 and 1. (Why?) In the third plot, each tick on the horizontal axis represents 0.001, and we see that $M \approx 0.736$ to three decimal places.

➡ **Before we go on...** This method required us first to calculate $\int_a^M f(x)\,dx$ analytically. What if even this is impossible to do? We could solve the equation $\int_a^M f(x)\,dx = 1/2$ graphically by having the calculator compute and graph this function of M by numerical integration. For example, to redo the above example on the TI-83/84 Plus, enter

```
Y₁ = fnInt(30T^4(1-T),T,0,X)-0.5
```

which corresponds to

$$y = \int_0^x 30t^4(1-t)\,dt - \frac{1}{2},$$

a function of x. Because the median of M is the solution obtained by setting $y = 0$, we can obtain the answer by plotting Y_1 and finding its x-intercept. The plot should be identical to the one we obtained above, except half as high. (Why?) ∎

P.3 EXERCISES

▼ more advanced   ◆ challenging
🔢 indicates exercises that should be solved using technology

Find the expected value $E(X)$, the variance $Var(X)$ and the standard deviation $\sigma(X)$ for each of the density functions in Exercises 1–20.

1. $f(x) = \dfrac{1}{3}$ on $[0, 3]$

2. $f(x) = 3$ on $[0, \dfrac{1}{3}]$

3. ▼ $f(x) = \dfrac{x}{50}$ on $[0, 10]$

4. ▼ $f(x) = 5x$ on $[0, \sqrt{2/5}]$

5. ▼ $f(x) = \dfrac{3}{2}(1 - x^2)$ on $[0, 1]$

6. ▼ $f(x) = \dfrac{3}{4}(1 - x^2)$ on $[-1, 1]$

7. ▼ $f(x) = e^x$ on $[0, \ln 2]$

8. ▼ $f(x) = \dfrac{1}{x}$ on $[1, e]$

9. ▼ $f(x) = 0.1e^{-0.1x}$ on $[0, +\infty)$

10. ▼ $f(x) = 4e^{4x}$ on $(-\infty, 0]$

11. ▼ $f(x) = 0.03e^{0.03x}$ on $(-\infty, 0]$

12. ▼ $f(x) = 0.02e^{-0.02x}$ on $[0, +\infty)$

13. ▼ $f(x) = \dfrac{2}{x^3}$ on $[1, +\infty)$

14. ▼ $f(x) = \dfrac{1}{2\sqrt{x}}$ on $(0, 1]$

15. Normal density function with $\mu = 1$ and $\sigma = 1$ on $(-\infty, +\infty)$

16. Normal density function with $\mu = -1$ and $\sigma = 1$ on $(-\infty, +\infty)$

17. Beta density function with $\beta = 0.5$

18. Beta density function with $\beta = 1.5$

19. Beta density function with $\beta = 3.2$

20. Beta density function with $\beta = 4.6$

🔢 *Use technology to find $E(X)$, $Var(X)$ and $\sigma(X)$ for each of the density functions in Exercises 21–24. (Round all answers to four significant digits.)*

21. 🔢 ▼ $f(x) = \dfrac{4}{\pi(1 + x^2)}$ on $[0, 1]$

22. 🔢 ▼ $f(x) = \dfrac{3}{\pi\sqrt{1 - x^2}}$ on $[\dfrac{1}{2}, 1]$

23. 🔢 ▼ $f(x) = 2xe^{-x^2}$ on $[0, +\infty)$

24. 🔢 ▼ $f(x) = -2xe^{-x^2}$ on $(-\infty, 0]$

Find the medians of the random variables with the probability density functions given in Exercises 25–34.

25. $f(x) = 0.25$ on $[0, 4]$

26. $f(x) = 4$ on $[0, 0.25]$

27. ▼ $f(x) = 3e^{-3x}$ on $[0, +\infty)$

28. ▼ $f(x) = 0.5e^{-0.5x}$ on $[0, +\infty)$

29. ▼ $f(x) = 0.03e^{0.03x}$ on $(-\infty, 0]$

30. ▼ $f(x) = 0.02e^{-0.02x}$ on $[0, +\infty)$

31. ▼ $f(x) = 2(1 - x)$ on $[0, 1]$

32. ▼ $f(x) = \dfrac{1}{x^2}$ on $[1, +\infty)$

33. ▼ $f(x) = \dfrac{1}{2\sqrt{x}}$ on $(0, 1]$

34. ▼ $f(x) = \dfrac{1}{x}$ on $[1, e]$

35. ▼ *Mean of a Uniform Distribution* Verify the formula for the mean of a uniform distribution by computing the integral.

36. ▼ *Mean of a Beta Distribution* Verify the formula for the mean of a beta distribution by computing the integral.

37. ▼ *Variance of a Uniform Distribution* Verify the formula for the variance of a uniform distribution by computing the integral.

38. ▼ *Variance of an Exponential Distribution* Verify the formula for the variance of an exponential distribution by computing the integral.

39. ▼ *Median of an Exponential Random Variable* Show that if X is a random variable with density function $f(x) = ae^{-ax}$ on $[0, +\infty)$, then X has median $\ln 2/a$.

40. ▼ *Median of a Uniform Random Variable* Show that if X is a uniform random variable taking values in the interval $[a, b]$, then X has median $(a + b)/2$.

Use technology to find the medians of the random variables with the probability density functions given in Exercises 41–50. (Round all answers to two decimal places.)

41. ▦ ▼ $f(x) = \dfrac{3}{2}(1 - x^2)$ on $[0, 1]$

42. ▦ ▼ $f(x) = \dfrac{3}{4}(1 - x^2)$ on $[-1, 1]$

43. ▦ ▼ beta density function with $\beta = 2$

44. ▦ ▼ beta density function with $\beta = 3$

45. ▦ ▼ beta density function with $\beta = 2.5$

46. ▦ ▼ beta density function with $\beta = 0.5$

47. ▦ ▼ $f(x) = \dfrac{4}{\pi(1 + x^2)}$ on $[0, 1]$

48. ▦ ▼ $f(x) = \dfrac{3}{\pi\sqrt{1 - x^2}}$ on $\left[\dfrac{1}{2}, 1\right]$

49. ▦ ▼ $f(x) = 2xe^{-x^2}$ on $[0, +\infty)$

50. ▦ ▼ $f(x) = -2xe^{-x^2}$ on $(-\infty, 0]$

*The **mean square** of a random variable X with density function f is given by the formula*

$$E(X^2) = \int_a^b x^2 f(x)\,dx.$$

51–60. ▼ In Exercises 1–10, compute $E(X^2)$. In each case, compute also $E(X^2) - E(X)^2$.

61. ▼ Compare the answers in 51–60 to those in 1–10, and hence suggest a formula expressing $E(X^2)$ in terms of $E(X)$ and $Var(X)$.

62. ◆ Calculate $E(e^{tX}) = \displaystyle\int_a^b e^{tx} f(x)\,dx$ with $f(x) = 0.1e^{-0.1x}$ on $[0, +\infty)$. Then evaluate $\left.\dfrac{d}{dt}E(e^{tX})\right|_{t=0}$ and $\left.\dfrac{d^2}{dt^2}E(e^{tX})\right|_{t=0}$, comparing these answers with the answer to Exercise 59. What do you notice?

APPLICATIONS

63. *Salaries* Assuming that workers' salaries in your company are uniformly distributed between \$10,000 and \$40,000 per year, calculate the average salary in your company.

64. *Grades* The grade point averages (GPAs) of members of the Gourmet Society are uniformly distributed between 2.5 and 3.5. Find the average GPA in the Gourmet Society.

65. ▼ *Boring Television Series* Your company's new series "Avocado Comedy Hour" has been a complete flop, with viewership continuously declining at a rate of 30% per month. How long will the average viewer continue to watch the show?

66. ▼ *Bad Investments* Investments in junk bonds are declining continuously at a rate of 5% per year. How long will an average dollar remain invested in junk bonds?

67. ▼ *Radioactive Decay* The half-life of Carbon-14 is 5,730 years. How long, to the nearest year, do you expect it to take for a randomly selected Carbon-14 atom to decay?

68. ▼ *Radioactive Decay* The half-life of plutonium-239 is 24,400 years. How long, to the nearest year, do you expect it to take for a randomly selected plutonium-239 atom to decay?

69. ▼ *The Doomsday Meteor* The probability that a "doomsday meteor" will hit the Earth in any given year and release a billion megatons or more of energy is on the order of 0.00000001.[16] When do you expect the Earth to be hit by a doomsday meteor? (Use an exponential distribution with $a = 0.00000001$.)

70. ▼ *Galactic Cataclysm* The probability that the galaxy MX-47 will explode within the next million years is estimated to be 0.0003. When do you expect MX-47 to explode? (Use an exponential distribution with $a = 0.0003$.)

[16]Source: NASA International Near-Earth-Object Detection Workshop (*New York Times*, January 25, 1994, p. C1.)

Exercises 71–74 use the normal probability density function and require the use of technology for numerical integration. (Alternatively, see Exercise 61.) Find the root mean square value for X (i.e., $\sqrt{E(X^2)}$) in each exercise.

71. ▼ *Physical Measurements* Repeated measurements of a metal rod yield a mean of 5.3 inches, with a standard deviation of 0.1.

72. ▼ *IQ Testing* Repeated measurements of a student's IQ yield a mean of 135, with a standard deviation of 5.

73. ▼ *Psychology Tests* It is known that subjects score an average of 100 points on a new personality test, with a standard deviation of 10 points.

74. ▼ *Examination Scores* Professor May's students earned an average grade of 3.5 with a standard deviation of 0.2.

75. ◆ *Learning* A graduate psychology student finds that 64% of all first-semester calculus students in Prof. Mean's class have a working knowledge of the derivative by the end of the semester.

(a) Take X = percentage of students who have a working knowledge of calculus after 1 semester, and find a beta density function that models X, assuming that the performance of students in Prof. Mean's is average.

(b) Find the median of X (rounded to two decimal places) and comment on any difference between the median and the mean.

76. ◆ *Plant Shutdowns* An automobile plant is open an average of 78% of the year.

(a) Take X = fraction of the year for which the plant is open, and find a beta density function that models X.

(b) Find the median of X (rounded to two decimal places) and comment on any difference between the median and the mean.

COMMUNICATION AND REASONING EXERCISES

77. ▼ Sketch the graph of a probability distribution function with the property that its median is larger than its mean.

78. ▼ Sketch the graph of a probability distribution function with a large standard deviation and a small mean.

79. Complete the following sentence. The ___ measures the degree to which the values of X are distributed, while the ___ is the value of X such that half the measurements of X are below and half are above (for a large number of measurements).

80. Complete the following sentence. (See Exercise 61.) Given two of the quantities ___, ___ and ___, we can calculate the third using the formula ___.

81. ▼ A value of X for which the probability distribution function f has a local maximum is called a **mode** of the distribution. (If there is more than one mode, the distribution is called bimodal (2 modes), trimodal (3 modes), etc. as the case may be.) If a distribution has a single mode, what does it tell you?

82. ▼ Referring to Exercise 81, sketch a bimodal distribution whose mean coincides with neither of the modes.

CHAPTER P REVIEW

KEY CONCEPTS

P.1 Continuous Random Variables and Histograms

Random variables, continuous and discrete *p. 2*

Probability *p. 2*

Probability distribution histogram *p. 3*

P.2 Probability Density Functions: Uniform, Exponential, Normal, and Beta

Probability density function *p. 11*

Calculation of probability from a probability density function *p. 11*

Uniform density function on $[a, b]$: $f(x) = 1/(b - a)$ *p. 12*

Exponential density function on $[0, +\infty)$: $f(x) = ae^{-ax}$ *p. 14*

Normal density function on $(-\infty, +\infty)$:
$$f(x) = \frac{1}{\sigma\sqrt{2\pi}} e^{-\frac{(x-\mu)^2}{2\sigma^2}}$$ *p. 15*

Beta density function on $[0, 1]$: $f(x) = (\beta + 1)(\beta + 2)x^\beta(1 - x)$ *p. 18*

P.3 Mean, Median, Variance, and Standard Deviation

Mean, expected, or average value of a random variable *p. 21*

Mean of a uniform distribution: $(a + b)/2$ *p. 22*

Mean of an exponential distribution: $1/a$ *p. 23*

Mean of a normal distribution: μ *p. 23*

Mean of a beta distribution: $(\beta + 1)/(\beta + 3)$ *p. 24*

Expected value of a function of a random variable *p. 25*

Variance and standard deviation of a random variable *p. 25*

Variance and standard deviation of a uniform distribution: $Var(X) = (b - a)^2/12$, $\sigma(X) = (b - a)/\sqrt{12}$ *p. 25*

Variance and standard deviation of an exponential distribution: $Var(X) = 1/a^2$, $\sigma(X) = 1/a$ *p. 26*

Variance and standard deviation of a normal distribution: $Var(X) = \sigma^2$, $\sigma(X) = \sigma$ *p. 26*

Variance and standard deviation of a beta distribution: $Var(X) = 2(\beta + 1)/[(\beta + 4)(\beta + 3)^2]$, $\sigma(X) = \sqrt{2(\beta + 1)/[(\beta + 4)(\beta + 3)^2]}$ *p. 26*

Median of a random variable *p. 27*

REVIEW EXERCISES

In each of Exercises 1–10, (a) determine the value of k that makes the function a probability density function, (b) find the expected value of the corresponding random variable, and (c) find the variance and standard deviation of the random variable.

1. $f(x) = k$ on $[-2, 2]$

2. $f(x) = k$ on $[1, 10]$

3. $f(x) = kx$ on $[0, 4]$

4. $f(x) = kx$ on $[0, 10]$

5. $f(x) = kx^2$ on $[-1, 1]$

6. $f(x) = kx^2$ on $[0, 1]$

7. $f(x) = k(1 - x^2)$ on $[-1, 1]$

8. $f(x) = k(1 - x^2)$ on $[0, 1]$

9. $f(x) = ke^x$ on $(-\infty, 0]$

10. $f(x) = ke^{-x}$ on $[0, +\infty)$

11. If X is the random variable with the distribution from Exercise 1, find $P(-1 \le X \le 1)$.

12. If X is the random variable with the distribution from Exercise 2, find $P(1 \le X \le 4)$.

13. If X is the random variable with the distribution from Exercise 3, find $P(0 \le X \le 2)$.

14. If X is the random variable with the distribution from Exercise 4, find $P(4 \le X \le 6)$.

15. If X is the random variable with the distribution from Exercise 5, find $P(1/2 \le X \le 1)$.

16. If X is the random variable with the distribution from Exercise 6, find $P(1/2 \le X \le 1)$.

17. If X is the random variable with the distribution from Exercise 7, find $P(0 \le X \le 1/2)$.

18. If X is the random variable with the distribution from Exercise 8, find $P(0 \le X \le 1/2)$.

19. If X is the random variable with the distribution from Exercise 9, find $P(X \le -1)$.

20. If X is the random variable with the distribution from Exercise 10, find $P(2 \le X)$.

21–30. Find the medians of the distributions given in Exercises 1–10.

APPLICATIONS

31. *Farm Population, Female* OHagansBooks.com is considering a new advertising campaign aimed at women living on farms. The following table shows the number of females residing on U.S. farms in 1990, broken down by age.[17] Numbers are in thousands.

Age	0–15	15–25	25–35	35–45	45–55	55–65	65–75	75–95
Number	459	265	247	319	291	291	212	126

OHaganBooks.com is interested in the probability of reaching various age groups with random mailings to farms. Construct the associated probability distribution for the ages of women

[17]Source: Economic Research Service, U.S. Department of Agriculture and Bureau of the Census, U.S. Department of Commerce, 1990.

living on farms (with probabilities rounded to four decimal places) and use the distribution to compute the following:

(a) $P(15 \leq X \leq 55)$ (b) $P(X \leq 45)$ (c) $P(X \geq 45)$

32. Farm Population, Male OHagansBooks.com is considering a new advertising campaign aimed at men living on farms. The following table shows the number of males residing on U.S. farms in 1990, broken down by age.[18] Numbers are in thousands.

Age	0–15	15–25	25–35	35–45	45–55	55–65	65–75	75–95
Number	480	324	285	314	302	314	247	118

OHaganBooks.com is interested in the probability of reaching various age groups with random mailings to farms. Construct the associated probability distribution for the ages of men living on farms (with probabilities rounded to four decimal places) and use the distribution to compute the following:

(a) $P(25 \leq X \leq 65)$ (b) $P(X \leq 15)$ (c) $P(X \geq 15)$

33. Quality Control OHaganBooks.com is worried about quality control of the boxes they use to ship their books. The widths of the boxes are normally distributed with a mean of 6 inches and a standard deviation of 0.1 inches. Any box with a width smaller than 5.8 inches must be rejected. Find the probability that a randomly chosen box will be rejected. (Give your answer to three significant digits.)

34. Book Weight OHaganBooks.com stocks books of many sizes. The weights of the books are normally distributed with a mean of 10 ounces and a standard deviation of 2 ounces. If a customer chooses a book at random, what is the probability that it will weigh at least 11 ounces? (Give your answer to three significant digits.)

35. Book Sales Few books sell well. For each new book published, OHaganBooks.com orders a certain number of copies and tracks how many they can sell in the first year. It has found that the fraction, X, of copies they sell of the number they ordered, is a random variable with a beta distribution with parameter $\beta = 0.6$. Find the probability that a given book will sell, in its first year, between 0.5 and 0.7 of the number of copies ordered. (Give your answer to three significant digits.)

36. Book Sales Given the information in Exercise 35, what is the expected fraction of new books sold in the first year, and what is the standard deviation?

Case Study   Creating a Family Trust

Your position as financial consultant to the clients of Family Bank, Inc., often entails your having to give financial advice to clients with complex questions about savings. One of your newer clients, 22-year old Malcolm Adams, recently graduated from college, presents you with a perplexing question. "I would like to set up my own insurance policy by opening a trust account into which I can make monthly payments starting now, so that upon my death or my ninety-fifth birthday—whichever comes sooner—the trust can be expected to be worth $500,000. How much should I invest each month?"

This is not one of those questions that you can answer by consulting a table, so you promise Malcolm an answer by the next day and begin to work on the problem. After a little thought, you realize that the question is one about *expected value*—the expected future value of an annuity into which monthly payments are made. Because the annuity would terminate upon his death (or his ninety-fifth birthday), you decide that you need a model for the probability distribution of the life span of a male in the United States. To obtain this information, you consult mortality tables and come up with the histogram in Figure 18. (You work with the actual numbers, but they are not important for the discussion to follow).[19]

From the data, you calculate that the mean is $\mu = 70.778$ and the standard deviation is $\sigma = 16.5119$.

---

[18]*Ibid.*

[19]Probabilities are normalized (scaled) so that the total area of the histogram is one square unit. Thus the area (not the height) of each bar is the probability of mortality in a two-year period. The data on which the histogram is based were obtained from the 1980 Standard Ordinary Mortality Table, Male Lives (Source: Black/Skipper, *Life Insurance*, Eleventh Edition, Englewood Cliffs, NJ: Prentice-Hall, Inc., 1987, p. 314).

Figure 18

Next, you decide to model these data with a suitable probability density function. You rule out the uniform and exponential density functions, because they have the wrong shape, and you first try the normal distribution. The normal distribution is

$$f(x) = \frac{1}{\sigma\sqrt{2\pi}}\, e^{-\frac{(x-\mu)^2}{2\sigma^2}}$$

$$= \frac{1}{16.5119\sqrt{2\pi}}\, e^{-\frac{(x-70.778)^2}{2(16.5119)^2}}.$$

Figure 19 shows the graph of the normal density function superimposed on the actual data.

Normal density function
($\mu = 70.778$, $\sigma = 16.5119$)

Figure 19

This does not seem like a very good fit at all! Because the actual histogram looks as though it is "pushed over" to the right, you think of the beta distribution, which has that general shape. The beta distribution is given by

$$f(x) = (\beta + 1)(\beta + 2)x^{\beta}(1 - x),$$

where β can be obtained from the mean μ using the equation

$$\mu = \frac{\beta + 1}{\beta + 3}.$$

There is one catch: The beta distribution assumes that X is between 0 and 1, whereas your distribution is between 0 and 100. This doesn't deter you: all you need to do is scale the X-values to $1/100$ of their original value. Thus you substitute $\mu = 1/100(70.778) = 0.70778$ in the above equation and solve for β, you obtain $\beta = 3.8442$. You then plot the associated beta function (after scaling it to fit the range $0 \le X \le 100$ and again discover that, although better, the fit still leaves something to be desired (Figure 20).

Beta density function
($\beta = 3.8442$)

Figure 20

Now you just want some function that fits the data. You turn to your statistical software and ask it to find the cubic equation that best fits the data using the least squares method. It promptly tells you that the cubic function that best fits the data is

$$f(x) = ax^3 + bx^2 + cx + d,$$

where

$$a = -3.815484 \times 10^{-7}$$
$$b = 5.7399145 \times 10^{-5}$$
$$c = -0.0020856085$$
$$d = 0.0190315095.$$

Its graph is shown in Figure 21. Note that the curve, although erratic for small values of X, fits the large peak on the right more closely than the others.

Encouraged, you use the same software to obtain a quartic (degree 4) approximation and you find:

$$f(x) = ax^4 + bx^3 + cx^2 + dx + e,$$

where

$$a = -9.583507 \times 10^{-9}$$
$$b = 1.650155 \times 10^{-6}$$
$$c = -8.523081 \times 10^{-5}$$
$$d = 0.0016190575$$
$$e = -0.007865381.$$

Figure 21

Figure 22 shows the result.

Figure 22

This seems like the best fit of them all—especially for the range of X you are interested in: $22 \le X \le 95$. (Malcolm is 22 years old and the trust will mature at 95.)

Now that you have the density function you wish to use, you use it to find the expected future value of an annuity into which monthly payments are made. The simplest formula for the future value V of an annuity is

$$V = 12P \left(\frac{\left(1 + \frac{i}{12}\right)^{12n} - 1}{i} \right).$$

(This is a standard formula from finance. This formula assumes that interest is paid at the end of each month.) Here, P is the monthly payment—the quantity that Malcolm wants to know—i is the interest rate, and n is the number of years for which payments are made. Because Malcolm will be making investments starting at age 22, this means that $n = x - 22$, so the future value of his annuity at age x is

$$V(x) = 12P\left(\frac{\left(1 + \frac{i}{12}\right)^{12(x-22)} - 1}{i}\right).$$

As for the interest rate i, you decide to use a conservative estimate of 5%.

Now the expected value of $V(X)$ is given by

$$E(V) = \int_{22}^{95} V(x)f(x)dx,$$

where $f(x)$ is the quartic approximation to the distribution function. Because Malcolm wants this to be $500,000, you set

$$500,000 = \int_{22}^{95} V(x)f(x)dx$$

$$= \int_{22}^{95} 12P\left(\frac{\left(1 + \frac{i}{12}\right)^{12(x-22)} - 1}{i}\right)f(x)dx$$

$$= P\int_{22}^{95} 12\left(\frac{\left(1 + \frac{0.05}{12}\right)^{12(x-22)} - 1}{0.05}\right)f(x)dx$$

Solving for P,

$$P = \frac{500,000}{\int_{22}^{95} 12\left(\frac{\left(1 + \frac{0.005}{12}\right)^{12(x-22)} - 1}{0.05}\right)f(x)dx}$$

You now calculate the integral numerically (using the quartic approximation to $f(x)$), obtaining

$$P \approx \frac{500,000}{3,409.8019} \approx \$146.64 \text{ per month}$$

The next day, you can tell Malcolm that at a 5% interest rate, his family can expect the trust to be worth $500,000 upon maturity if he deposits $146.64 each month.

EXERCISES

1. How much smaller will the payments be if the interest rate is 6%?

2. How much larger would the payments be if Malcolm began payments at the age of 30?

3. Repeat the original calculation using the normal distribution described above. Give reasons for the discrepancy between the answers, explaining why your answer is smaller or larger than the one calculated above.

4. Repeat Exercise 3 using the cubic distribution.

5. If Malcolm wanted to terminate the trust at age 65, which model would you use for the probability density? Give reasons for your choice.

6. Suppose you were told by your superior that, because the expected male life span is 71, you could have saved yourself a lot of trouble by using the formula for the future value of an annuity maturing at age 71. Based on that, the payment comes out to about $198 per month. Why is it higher? Why is it the wrong amount?

7. Explain how an insurance company might use the above calculations to compute life insurance premiums.

TI-83/84 Plus Technology Guide

Section P.2

Example 4 Pressure gauges manufactured by Precision Corp. must be checked for accuracy before being placed on the market. To test a pressure gauge, a worker uses it to measure the pressure of a sample of compressed air known to be at a pressure of exactly 50 pounds per square inch. If the gauge reading is off by more than 1% (0.5 pounds), the gauge is rejected. Assuming that the reading of a pressure gauge under these circumstances is a normal random variable with mean 50 and standard deviation 0.5, find the percentage of gauges rejected.

Solution with Technology

As in the text, the solution of this example comes down to the calculation

$$P(49.5 \leq X \leq 50.5) = \int_{49.5}^{50.5} f(x)\,dx,$$

where f is the normal distribution with mean $\mu = 50$ and standard deviation $\sigma = 0.5$:

$$f(x) = \frac{1}{\sigma\sqrt{2\pi}} e^{-\frac{(x-\mu)^2}{2\sigma^2}}$$

$$= \frac{1}{0.5\sqrt{2\pi}} e^{-\frac{(x-50)^2}{0.5}}.$$

There are two methods to calculate this integral on a TI-83/84 Plus.

Method 1: *Calculate the integral directly.*

1. Enter

Y₁ = (1/(0.5(2π)^0.5))e^(-(X - 50)^2/0.5)

in the Y = screen.

2. Enter

fnInt(Y₁,X,49.5,50.5)

in the home screen.

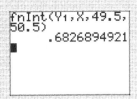

Method 2: *Use the built-in normal distribution function.*

The TI-83/84 Plus has a built-in normal distribution function.

1. Press [2nd] VARS to obtain the selection of distribution functions. The second function, normalcdf, gives $P(a \leq X \leq b)$ directly.

2. To compute $P(49.5 \leq X \leq 50.5)$, enter

normalcdf(49.5,50.5,50,.5)

Format: normalcdf (Lower bound, Upper bound, μ, σ)

in the home screen.

Both methods yield an answer of approximately 0.6827. In other words, 68.27% of the gauges will be accepted. Thus, the remaining 31.73% of the gauges will be rejected.

EXCEL Technology Guide
Section P.2

Example 4 Pressure gauges manufactured by Precision Corp. must be checked for accuracy before being placed on the market. To test a pressure gauge, a worker uses it to measure the pressure of a sample of compressed air known to be at a pressure of exactly 50 pounds per square inch. If the gauge reading is off by more than 1% (0.5 pounds), the gauge is rejected. Assuming that the reading of a pressure gauge under these circumstances is a normal random variable with mean 50 and standard deviation 0.5, find the percentage of gauges rejected.

Solution with Technology

As in the text, the solution of this example comes down to the calculation

$$P(49.5 \leq X \leq 50.5) = \int_{49.5}^{50.5} f(x)\,dx,$$

where f is the normal distribution with mean $\mu = 50$ and standard deviation $\sigma = 0.5$:

$$f(x) = \frac{1}{\sigma\sqrt{2\pi}}\,e^{-\frac{(x-\mu)^2}{2\sigma^2}}$$

$$= \frac{1}{0.5\sqrt{2\pi}}\,e^{-\frac{(x-50)^2}{0.5}}.$$

Excel has built-in statistical software that allows you to compute $P(a \leq X \leq b)$. The function NORMDIST $(a, \mu, \sigma, 1)$ computes $P(X \leq a)$ for the normal distribution with mean μ and standard deviation σ. (The last argument, 1, tells Excel that we want the cumulative distribution, i.e., the integral, rather than the value of the density function at a.) To compute $P(49.5 \leq X \leq 50.5)$ in Excel, enter

```
=NORMDIST(50.5,50,0.5,1)
-NORMDIST(49.5,50,0.5,1)
```

in any vacant cell.

Excel yields an answer of approximately 0.6827. In other words, 68.27% of the gauges will be accepted. Thus, the remaining 31.73% of the gauges will be rejected.

◇	A	B	C	D
1	=NORMDIST(50.5,50,0.5,1)-NORMDIST(49.5,50,0.5,1)			
2				

◇	A	B	C	D
1	0.68268948			
2				

Extreme Values: Boundaries and the Extreme Value Theorem

In our discussion of maxima and minima of functions of a single variable in Section 12.1, we saw that extrema frequently occurred at endpoints of the domain. To generalize this idea to functions of more than one variable, we should think of the endpoints of the domain of a function of a single variable as *boundary points* of the domain; for instance, the boundary of the closed interval [1, 3] consists of the two endpoints 1 and 3, whereas the open interval (1, 3) has no boundary points. (The boundary points 1 and 3 are outside the interval.)

As we have seen, the domains of functions of two variables are subsets of the plane; for instance, the natural domain of the function $f(x, y) = \sqrt{x^2 + y^2 - 1}$ consists of all points (x, y) in the plane with $x^2 + y^2 - 1 \geq 0$, or $x^2 + y^2 \geq 1$, and its boundary is the unit circle (Figure 1).

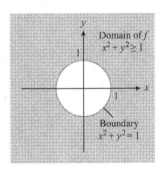

Figure 1

Even if the function is mathematically defined for all x and y, we may need to restrict the domain in real life applications: For example, if $C(x, y) = 10{,}000 + 20x + 40y$ is the monthly cost of producing x Ultra Mini speakers and y Big Stack speakers (see Example 1 of Section 15.1), then the function makes sense only if $x \geq 0$ and $y \geq 0$, and would be restricted further by the maximum number of Ultra Minis and Big Stacks the company can produce in a month—for instance, $x \leq 100$ and $y \leq 75$. The domain of the cost function would then be the region of the plane described by $0 \leq x \leq 100$ and $0 \leq y \leq 75$ (Figure 2), and its boundary is a rectangle.

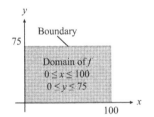

Figure 2

We can now state the counterpart of the method we used in Chapter 12 to locate maxima and minima:

Locating Candidates for Extrema for a Function f of Two Variables

Step 1: *Locate critical points in the interior of the domain.*
To locate interior points, we use the method discussed in Section 15.3: Set $f_x = 0$ and $f_y = 0$ simultaneously, and solve for x and y.

Step 2: *Locate extrema on the boundary of the domain.*
To locate critical extrema on the boundary of the domain, we examine the behavior of the function along each segment of the boundary.

Quick Example

Consider the function f with domain $0 \le x \le 4$, $0 \le y \le 4$, whose graph is shown here:

$$f(x, y) = (x - 2)^2 + 2(y - 2)^2 - (x - 2)(y - 2)$$
$$0 \le x \le 4, \, 0 \le y \le 4$$

We observe the following:

- There is an absolute minimum at the critical point $T(2, 2, 0)$. Note that $(2, 2)$ is an interior point of the domain.
- There are absolute maxima at $P(4, 0, 16)$ and $Q(0, 4, 16)$. These are not critical points but correspond to points on the boundary of the domain (endpoints of its edges).
- There are relative maxima at $R(0, 0, 8)$ and $S(4, 4, 8)$, again corresponding to points on the boundary of the domain.
- The points U, V, W, X are critical points on boundary segments, but neither maxima nor minima. (Can you see why?)

The domains illustrated in the above examples are all **closed** sets: sets that include all their boundary points. The rectangular domain in the quick example above is also **bounded**—that is, the entire domain can be enclosed in a (large enough) disc. The domain shown in Figure 1 is **unbounded**, as it cannot be enclosed in any disc, no matter how large. The following result states that, when the domain of a continuous function is both closed and bounded, we can always expect to find an absolute maximum and an absolute minimum, as in the quick example above.

Extreme Value Theorem for Functions of Two Variables

If f is a continuous function of two variables whose domain D is both closed and bounded, then there are points (x_1, y_1) and (x_2, y_2) in D such that f has an absolute minimum at (x_1, y_1) and an absolute maximum at (x_2, y_2).

Quick Examples

1. In the quick example above, we saw from its graph that the function
$$f(x, y) = (x - 2)^2 + 2(y - 2)^2 - (x - 2)(y - 2),$$
with closed and bounded domain $0 \le x \le 4$ and $0 \le y \le 4$, has an absolute minimum at $(2, 2)$ and absolute maxima at both $(4, 0)$ and $(0, 4)$.

2. If the domain is not closed and bounded, the function need not have an absolute maximum or minimum: The function
$$f(x, y) = x^2 + y^2$$
with domain all of the xy-plane has an absolute minimum at $(0, 0)$ but no absolute maximum. (Its graph is the paraboloid shown in Example 5 of Section 15.1.)

EXAMPLE 1 Absolute Maximum: Rectangular Domain

You own a company that makes two models of stereo speakers, the Ultra Mini and the Big Stack. Your monthly profit is estimated to be
$$f(x, y) = 10x + 20y - 0.5xy.$$
Here, x is the number of Ultra Minis, y is the number of Big Stacks, and f is your profit in dollars. You can produce up to 100 Ultra Minis and 75 Big Stacks in a month. Find the number of each model you should make each week in order to maximize your profit.

Solution We are asked to find the absolute maximum value of the function f. The domain of f is specified by the production limits: $0 \le x \le 100$ and $0 \le y \le 75$, and is the one shown in Figures 2 and 3. Because the domain is closed and bounded, we know from the Extreme Value Theorem that there is a point somewhere in the domain at which f is a maximum. To identify that point, we locate all candidates for extrema in the interior of the domain and on its boundary by using the procedure outlined earlier:

Step 1: Locate critical points in the interior of the domain.
The partial derivatives are
$$f_x = 10 - 0.5y \qquad\qquad f_y = 20 - 0.5x$$

Setting these equal to zero and solving for x and y gives the only critical point as $(40, 20)$. This point is in the interior of the domain, so it is one of our candidates for extrema.

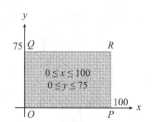

Figure 3

Step 2: Locate extrema on the boundary of the domain.

The boundary of the domain consists of four line segments OP, OQ, QR, and PR (Figure 3), which we consider one at a time.

Segment OP: $y = 0, 0 \le x \le 100$:
The behavior of the function f along this segment is seen by substituting $y = 0$ into the expression for f:

$$f(x, 0) = 10x + 20(0) - 0.5x(0) = 10x, \ 0 \le x \le 100$$

This means that, *along the line segment OP*, the value of f is determined by the function $f(x, 0) = 10x$ of a single variable, with domain $0 \le x \le 100$. We now find the relative extrema of this function of one variable by the methods we used in the chapter on applications of the derivative. The endpoints are 0 and 100, while there are no critical points because

$$f'(x, 0) = 10$$ We are taking the derivative of this function of x.

and so is never zero. The endpoints $x = 0$ and $x = 100$ give, with $y = 0$ for this segment, the points $O(0, 0)$ and $P(100, 0)$ as two candidates for extrema.

Segment OQ: $x = 0, 0 \le y \le 75$:
Substitute $x = 0$ into the function f to obtain

$$f(0, y) = 10(0) + 20y - 0.5(0)y = 20y, \ 0 \le y \le 75,$$

a function of the single variable y that determines the value of f along the segment OQ. Again, there are no critical points, only the endpoints $y = 0$ and $y = 75$. These give us $O(0, 0)$ again and $Q(0, 75)$ as candidates for extrema.

Segment QR: $y = 75, 0 \le x \le 100$:
Substitute $y = 75$ into the function f to obtain

$$f(x, 75) = 10x + 20(75) - 0.5x(75) = -27.5x + 1{,}500, \ 0 \le x \le 100.$$

Since the derivative of this function is $-27.5 \ne 0$, we find again that there are no critical points; only the endpoints $x = 0$ and 100. Since here $y = 75$, these give us $Q(0, 75)$ again and one new point $R(100, 75)$ as candidates for extrema.

Segment PR: $x = 100, 0 \le y \le 75$:
Substitute $x = 100$ into the function f to obtain

$$f(100, y) = 10(100) + 20y - 0.5(100)y = 1{,}000 - 30y, \ 0 \le y \le 75.$$

Again, there are no critical points, only the endpoints $y = 0$ and $y = 75$. These give us $P(100, 0)$ and $R(100, 75)$ again as candidates for extrema.

Our analysis has yielded the following five candidate points, shown here along with the values of f:

Point	Value of f	
(40, 20)	400	
(0, 0)	0	
(100, 0)	1,000	
(0, 75)	1,500	Absolute maximum
(100, 75)	−1,250	Absolute minimum

Since the absolute maximum *has* to be at one of these points, it must be at the point (0, 75), which yields a maximum monthly profit of $1,500.

➡ **Before we go on...** In Example 1 we did not classify the three points (40, 20), (0, 0), and (100, 0) as relative maxima, minima, or neither. While we could analyze the function further to obtain this information, it is easier to simply graph the function. Figure 4 shows the graph of $f(x, y) = 10x + 20y - 0.5xy$ as plotted on the Surface Grapher at the Website.

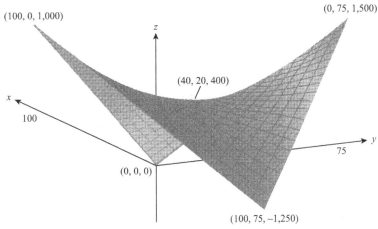

Technology format: $10*x+20*y-0.5*x*y$

Figure 4

From the figure, we see that f has a saddle point at the interior critical point (40, 20), a relative minimum at (0, 0), and a relative maximum at (100, 0).

We can restate the problem in Example 1 as a *constrained optimization problem* as follows:

$$\text{Maximize } f = 10x + 20y - 0.5xy \qquad \text{Objective function}$$
$$\text{subject to } 0 \le x \le 100 \qquad \text{Inequality constraint}$$
$$\text{and } 0 \le y \le 75 \qquad \text{Inequality constraint}$$

If you have studied linear programming, this example should remind you of the problems you solved by that technique. However, the techniques of linear programming cannot, in general, be used to solve problems with nonlinear objective functions. ∎

EXAMPLE 2 Absolute Extrema: Triangular Domain

Find the maximum and minimum value of $f(x, y) = 8 + xy - x - 2y$ on the triangular region R with vertices (0, 0), (2, 0), and (0, 4).

Solution The domain of f is the region R shown in Figure 5.

Step 1: Locate critical points in the interior of the domain.
We take the partial derivatives as usual.

$$f_x = y - 1 \qquad\qquad f_y = x - 2$$

Setting these partial derivatives equal to zero, we find that the only critical point is (2, 1). Since this lies outside the domain (the region R), we ignore it. Thus, there are no critical points in the interior of the domain of f.

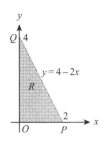

Figure 5

Step 2: Locate extrema on the boundary of the domain.
The boundary of the domain consists of three line segments, OP, OQ, and PQ.

Segment OP: $y = 0, 0 \le x \le 2$. The behavior of the function f along this segment is seen by substituting $y = 0$ into the expression for f:

$$f(x, 0) = 8 + x(0) - x - 2(0) = 8 - x$$

There are no critical points (the derivative of this function is never zero) and there are two endpoints, $x = 0$ and $x = 2$. Since $y = 0$, these endpoints give us the following two candidates for relative extrema: $O(0, 0)$ and $P(2, 0)$.

Segment OQ: $x = 0, 0 \le y \le 4$. Along this segment we see

$$f(0, y) = 8 + (0)y - 0 - 2y = 8 - 2y.$$

Once again, there are no critical points, and only the endpoints $y = 0$ and $y = 4$. Since $x = 0$, this again gives us two candidates, $O(0, 0)$ and $Q(0, 4)$.

Segment PQ: This line segment has equation $y = 4 - 2x$ with $0 \le x \le 2$. Along this segment we see

$$f(x, 4 - 2x) = 8 + x(4 - 2x) - x - 2(4 - 2x) \qquad \text{Substitute } y = 4 - 2x.$$
$$= -2x^2 + 7x.$$

This function of x (whose graph is an upside-down parabola) has a maximum when its derivative, $-4x + 7$, is 0, which occurs when $x = 7/4$. When $x = 7/4$, $y = 4 - 2(7/4) = 1/2$. Thus, we have a critical point at $(7/4, 1/2) = (1.75, 0.5)$. The endpoints are $x = 0$ and $x = 2$, giving us $P(2, 0)$ and $Q(0, 4)$ once again.

If we compute the value of f at each candidate point, we obtain:

Point	Value of f	
(0, 0)	8	Absolute maximum
(2, 0)	6	
(0, 4)	0	Absolute minimum
(1.75, 0.5)	6.125	

We see that f has an absolute maximum of 8 at the point $(0, 0)$ and an absolute minimum of 0 at the point $(0, 4)$.

➡ **Before we go on...** Figure 6 shows the graph[1] of $f(x, y) = 8 + xy - x - 2y$ from Example 2, and tells us that f has a relative minimum at $P(2, 0)$. It also shows that f has neither a relative maximum nor a minimum at $(1.75, 0.5)$—it has a maximum at

---

[1] We sketched it on the Surface Grapher at the Website. To show the restriction to the triangular domain, we used the parametric surface feature with

```
x = u,  y = (4 − 2*u) * (1 − v),  z = 8 + u* (4 − 2*u) * (1 − v)
 − u − 2* (4 − 2*u) * (1 − v) (0 ≤ u ≤ 2,  0 ≤ v ≤ 1)
```

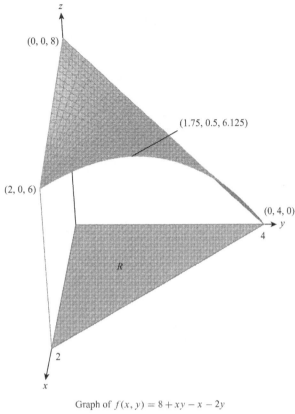

Graph of $f(x, y) = 8 + xy - x - 2y$
$0 \leq x \leq 2, 0 \leq y \leq 4 - 2x$

Figure 6

$(1.75, 0.5)$ *along the edge PQ*, but the value $f(1.75, 0.75) = 6.125$ is smaller than the values of f at interior points immediately behind it. ∎

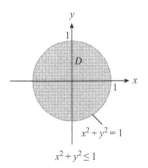

Figure 7

EXAMPLE 3 **Absolute Extrema: Circular Domain**

Find the maximum and minimum value of $f(x, y) = x^2 + y^2 + y + 1$ subject to $x^2 + y^2 \leq 1$.

Solution The domain D of the function f is the unit disc $\{(x, y) | x^2 + y^2 \leq 1\}$ shown in Figure 7.

Step 1: Locate critical points in the interior of the domain.
We take the partial derivatives:

$$f_x = 2x \qquad\qquad\qquad f_y = 2y + 1$$

Setting these partial derivatives equal to zero, we find that the only critical point is $(0, -1/2)$, which is in the interior of D.

Step 2: Locate extrema on the boundary of the domain.
The boundary of D consists of all points (x, y) with $x^2 + y^2 = 1$. We can substitute this equation in the formula for f to obtain a function of a single variable:

$$f = (x^2 + y^2) + y + 1 = 2 + y$$

Notice that y cannot take an arbitrary value—since (x, y) is a point on the circle, we must have $-1 \le y \le 1$. This function of y has no critical points but does have two end points: 1 and -1. When $y = \pm 1$, the equation $x^2 + y^2 = 1$ tells us that $x = 0$. So, our candidate boundary points are $(0, -1)$ and $(0, 1)$.

The values of f at these candidate points are shown in the following table:

Point	Value of f	
$(0, -1/2)$	3/4	Absolute minimum
$(0, -1)$	1	
$(0, 1)$	3	Absolute maximum

Thus, f has an absolute maximum of 3 at $(0, 1)$ and an absolute minimum of 3/4 at $(0, -1/2)$.

➡ **Before we go on...** Figure 8 shows the graph of $f(x, y) = x^2 + y^2 + y + 1$ from Example 3, and tells us that the point $(0, -1, 1)$ is not a relative extremum. (It is a

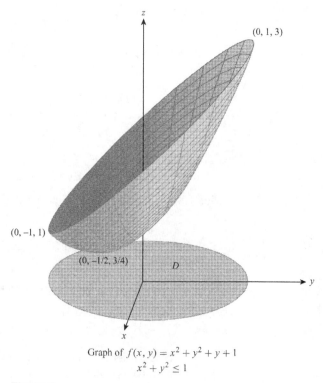

Graph of $f(x, y) = x^2 + y^2 + y + 1$
$x^2 + y^2 \le 1$

Figure 8

minimum along the boundary, but the value of f there is higher than its value at interior points immediately to its right.)

Notice also, that in locating extreme points on the boundary, we were actually solving the following constrained optimization problem:

Find the optimum values of $f(x, y) = x^2 + y^2 + y + 1$ subject to $x^2 + y^2 = 1$.

Here, the constraint takes the form of an equation rather than an inequality. Similarly, in the preceding examples, restricting to each of the various line segments amounted to solving an optimization problem with an equation constraint; for instance, in Example 2, on the segment PQ, we were finding the optimum values of $f(x, y) = 8 + xy - x - 2y$ subject to $y = 4 - 2x$. Solving optimization problems with equality constraints is discussed further in Section 15.4. ∎

Some software packages, such as Excel, have built-in algorithms that seek absolute extrema with or without constraints. In the next example, we use the "Solver" add-in[2] in Excel to solve an optimization problem whose objective function has a more complicated domain.

EXAMPLE 4 ▪ Solving an Optimization Problem Using Excel's Solver

Use Excel's Solver to solve the following problem:

Maximize $P = 10x + 60y + 0.5xy$		Objective function
subject to	$x + 5y \le 100$	Constraint 1
	$3x + 9y \le 270$	Constraint 2
	$x \ge 0$ and $y \ge 0$	Constraints 3 and 4

Solution First, we set up the problem in spreadsheet form as follows:

◇	A	B	C	D	E	F
1	x	y	Objective	Constraints		
2	0	0	=10*A2+60*B2+0.5*A2*B2	=A2+5*B2	100	Constraint 1
3	Initial value of x	Initial value of y		=3*A2+9*B2	270	Constraint 2
4				=A2	0	Constraint 3
5				=B2	0	Constraint 4

A2 will be the cell that contains the value of x and B2 the cell that contains the value of y. Solver requires us to give them initial values, so we've set them both equal to 0; Solver will adjust them to find the optimal solution. Next, we select "Solver" in the "Tools" menu to bring up the Solver dialog box. Here is the dialog box with all the necessary fields completed to solve the problem:

---

[2] If "Solver" does not appear in the "Tools" menu, you should first install it using your Excel installation software. (Solver is one of the "Excel Add-Ins.")

Notes

- The Target Cell refers to the cell that contains the objective function.
- "Max" is selected because we are maximizing the objective function.
- "Changing Cells" are obtained by selecting the cells that contain the current values of x and y.
- Constraints are added one at a time by pressing the "Add" button and selecting the cells that contain the left- and right-hand sides of each inequality, as well as the type of inequality. (Equality constraints are also permitted.)

Once we've entered the parameters, we click on "Solve" and the (approximate) optimal solution appears in A2 and B2, with the maximum value of P appearing in cell C2. The optimal solution is therefore $x = 40$, $y = 12$, $P = 1,360$.

◇	A	B	C	D	E
1	x	y	Objective	Constraints	
2	40	12	1360	100	100
3	Final value of x	Final value of y		228	270
4				40	0
5				12	0

➡ **Before we go on...**

Q: *Can a software package such as Excel Solver be used interchangeably with the analytic method?*

A: Some optimization problems lead to equations that cannot be solved analytically, and so some form of numerical approach (such as that used in Solver) is essential in those cases. However, with all numerical approaches there is always a chance of running into one or more of these problems:

- The solution given will be a relative extremum rather than an absolute extremum.
- The solution is not exact.
- Roundoff errors lead to an incorrect solution or prevent finding a solution.
- Only one solution is given even if there is more than one absolute extremum.

So, use Solver with caution.

EXERCISES

▼ more advanced

ℹ In all of the exercises for this section, a software package such as Excel Solver can be used as a check on your analytic work. (Bear in mind, however, the cautions at the end of Example 4.)

In Exercises 1–16, find the maximum and minimum values of the given function and the points at which they occur.

1. $f(x, y) = x^2 + y^2$; $0 \le x \le 2, 0 \le y \le 2$

2. $g(x, y) = \sqrt{x^2 + y^2}$; $1 \le x \le 2, 1 \le y \le 2$

3. $h(x, y) = (x - 1)^2 + y^2$; $x^2 + y^2 \le 4$

4. $k(x, y) = x^2 + (y - 1)^2$; $x^2 + y^2 \le 9$

5. $f(x, y) = e^{x^2 + y^2}$; $4x^2 + y^2 \le 4$

6. $g(x, y) = e^{-(x^2 + y^2)}$; $x^2 + 4y^2 \le 4$

7. $h(x, y) = e^{4x^2 + y^2}$; $x^2 + y^2 \le 1$

8. $k(x, y) = e^{-(x^2 + 4y^2)}$; $x^2 + y^2 \le 4$

9. $f(x, y) = x + y + 1/(xy)$; $x \ge 1/2, y \ge 1/2, x + y \le 3$

10. $g(x, y) = x + y + 8/(xy)$; $x \ge 1, y \ge 1, x + y \le 6$

11. $h(x, y) = xy + 8/x + 8/y$; $x \ge 1, y \ge 1, xy \le 9$

12. $k(x, y) = xy + 1/x + 4/y$; $x \ge 1, y \ge 1, xy \le 10$

13. ▼ $f(x, y) = x^2 + 2x + y^2$; on the region in the figure

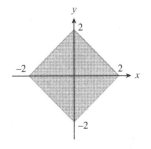

14. ▼ $g(x, y) = x^2 + y^2$; on the region in the figure

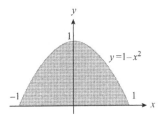

15. ▼ $h(x, y) = x^3 + y^3$; on the region in the figure

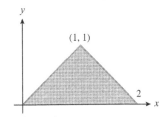

16. ▼ $k(x, y) = x^3 + 2y^3$; on the region in the figure

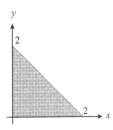

APPLICATIONS

17. *Cost* Your bicycle factory makes two models, five-speeds and ten-speeds. Each week, your total cost (in dollars) to make x five-speeds and y ten-speeds is

$$C(x, y) = 10,000 + 50x + 70y - 0.5xy$$

You want to make between 100 and 150 five-speeds and between 80 and 120 ten-speeds. What combination will cost you the least? What combination will cost you the most?

18. *Cost* Your bicycle factory makes two models, five-speeds and ten-speeds. Each week, your total cost (in dollars) to make x five-speeds and y ten-speeds is

$$C(x, y) = \ 10,000 \ + 50x + 70y - 0.46xy$$

You want to make between 100 and 150 five-speeds, and between 80 and 120 ten-speeds. What combination will cost you the least? What combination will cost you the most?

19. ▼ *Profit* Your software company sells two operating systems, Walls and Doors. Your profit (in dollars) from selling x copies of Walls and y copies of Doors is given by

$$P(x, y) = 20x + 40y - 0.1(x^2 + y^2).$$

If you can sell a maximum of 200 copies of the two operating systems together, what combination will bring you the greatest profit?

20. ▼ *Profit* Your software company sells two operating systems, Walls and Doors. Your profit (in dollars) from selling x copies of Walls and y copies of Doors is given by

$$P(x, y) = 20x + 40y - 0.1(x^2 + y^2).$$

If you can sell a maximum of 400 copies of the two operating systems together, what combination will bring you the largest profit?

21. *Temperature* The temperature at the point (x, y) on the square with vertices $(0, 0)$, $(0, 1)$, $(1, 0)$, and $(1, 1)$ is given by $T(x, y) = x^2 + 2y^2$. Find the hottest and coldest points on the square.

22. *Temperature* The temperature at the point (x, y) on the square with vertices $(0, 0)$, $(0, 1)$, $(1, 0)$, and $(1, 1)$ is given by $T(x, y) = x^2 + 2y^2 - x$. Find the hottest and coldest points on the square.

23. ▼ *Temperature* The temperature at the point (x, y) on the disc $\{(x, y)|x^2 + y^2 \le 1\}$ is given by $T(x, y) = x^2 + 2y^2 - x$. Find the hottest and coldest points on the disc.

24. ▼ *Temperature* The temperature at the point (x, y) on the disc $\{(x, y)|x^2 + y^2 \le 1\}$ is given by $T(x, y) = 2x^2 + y^2$. Find the hottest and coldest points on the disc.

Extreme Values: Answers to Odd-Numbered Exercises

1. Maximum value of 8 at $(2, 2)$, minimum value of 0 at $(0, 0)$

3. Maximum value of 9 at $(-2, 0)$, minimum value of 0 at $(1, 0)$

5. Maximum value of e^4 at $(0, \pm2)$, minimum value of 1 at $(0, 0)$

7. Maximum value of e^4 at $(\pm1, 0)$, minimum value of 1 at $(0, 0)$

9. Maximum value of 5 at $(1/2, 1/2)$, minimum value of 3 at $(1, 1)$

11. Maximum value of $161/9$ at $(1, 9)$ and $(9, 1)$, minimum value of 12 at $(2, 2)$

13. Maximum value of 8 at $(2, 0)$, minimum value of -1 at $(-1, 0)$

15. Maximum value of 8 at $(2, 0)$, minimum value of 0 at $(0, 0)$

17. For minimum cost of $16,600, make 100 5-speeds and 80 10-speeds. For maximum cost of $17,400, make 100 5-speeds and 120 10-speeds.

19. For a maximum profit of $4,500, sell 50 copies of Walls and 150 copies of Doors.

21. Hottest point: $(1, 1)$, coldest point: $(0, 0)$

23. Hottest points: $(-1/2, \pm\sqrt{3}/2)$, coldest point: $(1/2, 0)$

Logic

Introduction

Logic is the underpinning of all reasoned argument. The ancient Greeks recognized its role in mathematics and philosophy, and studied it extensively. Aristotle, in his *Organon*, wrote the first systematic treatise on logic. His work had a heavy influence on philosophy, science and religion through the Middle Ages.

But Aristotle's logic was expressed in ordinary language, so was subject to the ambiguities of ordinary language. Philosophers came to want to express logic more formally and symbolically, more like the way that mathematics is written (Leibniz, in the 17th century, was probably the first to envision and call for such a formalism). It was with the publication in 1847 of G. Boole's *The Mathematical Analysis of Logic* and A. DeMorgan's *Formal Logic* that **symbolic logic** came into being, and logic became recognized as part of mathematics. Since Boole and DeMorgan, logic and mathematics have been inextricably intertwined. Logic is part of mathematics, but at the same time it is the language of mathematics.

The study of symbolic logic is usually broken into several parts. The first and most fundamental is the **propositional logic**. Built on top of this is the **predicate logic**, which is the language of mathematics. In this appendix we give an introduction to propositional logic.

A.1 Statements and Logical Operators

Propositional logic is the study of *propositions*. A **statement**, or **proposition**, is any declarative sentence which is either true (T) or false (F). We refer to T or F as the **truth value** of the statement.

For a much more extensive interactive treatment of logic, including discussion of proofs, rules of inference, and an introduction to the predicate calculus, go online and follow:

Online Text

→ Online Topics in Finite Mathematics

→ Introduction to Logic

EXAMPLE 1 Statements

a. "$2 + 2 = 4$" is a statement because it can be either true or false.* Because it happens to be a true statement, its truth value is T.

b. "$1 = 0$" is also a statement, but its truth value is F.

c. "It will rain tomorrow" is a statement. To determine its truth value, we shall have to wait for tomorrow.

d. "Solve the following equation for x" is not a statement, because it cannot be assigned any truth value whatsoever. It is an imperative, or command, rather than a declarative sentence.

e. "The number 5" is not a statement, because it is not even a complete sentence.

---

* Is "$2 + 2 = 4$" a sentence? Read it aloud: "Two plus two equals four," is a perfectly respectable English sentence.

A1

f. "This statement is false" gets us into a bind: If it were true, then, because it is declaring itself to be false, it must be false. On the other hand, if it were false, then its declaring itself false is a lie, so it is true! In other words, if it is true, then it is false, and if it is false, then it is true, and we go around in circles. We get out of this bind by saying that because the sentence cannot be either true or false, we refuse to call it a statement. An equivalent pseudo-statement is: "I am lying," so this sentence is known as **the liar's paradox**.

Note Sentences that refer to themselves, or *self-referential sentences*, as illustrated in Example 1(f), are not permitted to be statements. This eliminates the liar's paradox and several similar problems. ∎

We shall use letters like p, q, r and so on to stand for statements. Thus, for example, we might decide that p should stand for the statement "the moon is round." We write

p: "the moon is round"   *p is the statement that the moon is round*

to express this.

We can form new statements from old ones in several different ways. For example, starting with p: "I am an Anchovian," we can form the **negation** of p: "It is not the case that I am an Anchovian" or simply "I am not an Anchovian."

Negation of a Statement

If p is a statement, then its **negation** is the statement "not p" and is denoted by $\sim p$. We mean by this that, if p is true, then $\sim p$ is false, and vice versa.

Quick Examples

1. If p: "$2 + 2 = 4$," then $\sim p$: "It is not the case that $2 + 2 = 4$," or, more simply, $\sim p$: "$2 + 2 \neq 4$."
2. If q: "$1 = 0$," then $\sim q$: "$1 \neq 0$."
3. If r: "Diamonds are a pearl's best friend," then $\sim r$: "Diamonds are not a pearl's best friend."
4. If s: "All politicians are crooks," then $\sim s$: "Not all politicians are crooks."
5. **Double Negation:** If p is any statement, then the negation of $\sim p$ is $\sim(\sim p)$: "not (not p)," or, in other words, p. Thus $\sim(\sim p)$ has the same meaning as p.

Notes

1. Notice in Quick Example 1 above that $\sim p$ is false, because p is true. However, in Quick Example 2, $\sim q$ is true, because q is false. A statement of the form $\sim q$ can very well be true; it is a common mistake to think it must be false.

2. Saying that not all politicians are crooks is not the same as saying that no politicians are crooks, but is the same as saying that some (meaning one or more) politicians are not crooks.

3. The symbol $\sim$ is our first example of a **logical operator**.

4. When we say in Quick Example 5 above that $\sim(\sim p)$ has the same meaning as p, we mean that they are *logically equivalent*—a notion we will make precise below. ∎

Here is another way we can form a new statement from old ones. Starting with p: "I am wise," and q: "I am strong," we can form the statement "I am wise and I am strong." We denote this new statement by $p \wedge q$, read "p and q." In order for $p \wedge q$ to be true, *both p and q* must be true. Thus, for example, if I am wise but not strong, then $p \wedge q$ is false. The symbol $\wedge$ is another logical operator. The statement $p \wedge q$ is called the **conjunction** of p and q.

Conjunction

The **conjunction** of p and q is the statement $p \wedge q$, which we read "p and q." It can also be said in a number of different ways, such as "p even though q." The statement $p \wedge q$ is true when both p and q are true and false otherwise.

Quick Examples

1. If p: "This galaxy will ultimately disappear into a black hole" and q: "$2 + 2 = 4$," then $p \wedge q$ is the statement "Not only will this galaxy ultimately disappear into a black hole, but $2 + 2 = 4$!"
2. If p: "$2 + 2 = 4$" and q: "$1 = 0$," then $p \wedge q$: "$2 + 2 = 4$ and $1 = 0$." Its truth value is F because q is F.
3. With p and q as in Quick Example 1, the statement $p \wedge (\sim q)$ says: "This galaxy will ultimately disappear into a black hole and $2 + 2 \neq 4$," or, more colorfully, as "Contrary to your hopes, this galaxy is doomed to disappear into a black hole; moreover, two plus two is decidedly *not* equal to four!"

Notes

1. We sometimes use the word "but" as an emphatic form of "and." For instance, if p: "It is hot," and q: "It is not humid," then we can read $p \wedge q$ as "It is hot but not humid." There are always many ways of saying essentially the same thing in a natural language; one of the purposes of symbolic logic is to strip away the verbiage and record the underlying logical structure of a statement.
2. A **compound statement** is a statement formed from simpler statements via the use of logical operators. Examples are $\sim p$, $(\sim p) \wedge (q \wedge r)$ and $p \wedge (\sim p)$. A statement that cannot be expressed as a compound statement is called an **atomic statement**.[1] For example, "I am clever" is an atomic statement. In a compound statement such as $(\sim p) \wedge (q \wedge r)$, we refer to p, q and r as the **variables** of the statement. Thus, for example, $\sim p$ is a compound statement in the single variable p. ∎

Before discussing other logical operators, we pause for a moment to talk about **truth tables**, which give a convenient way to analyze compound statements.

Truth Table

The **truth table** for a compound statement shows, for each combination of possible truth values of its variables, the corresponding truth value of the statement.

---

[1] "Atomic" comes from the Greek for "not divisible." Atoms were originally thought to be the indivisible components of matter, but the march of science proved that wrong. The name stuck, though.

Quick Examples

1. The truth table for negation, that is, for $\sim p$, is:

p	$\sim p$
T	F
F	T

Each row shows a possible truth value for p and the corresponding value of $\sim p$.

2. The truth table for conjunction, that is, for $p \wedge q$, is:

p	q	$p \wedge q$
T	T	T
T	F	F
F	T	F
F	F	F

Each row shows a possible combination of truth values of p and q and the corresponding value of $p \wedge q$.

EXAMPLE 2 Construction of Truth Tables

Construct truth tables for the following compound statements.

a. $\sim(p \wedge q)$ **b.** $(\sim p) \wedge q$

Solution

a. Whenever we encounter a complex statement, we work from the inside out, just as we might do if we had to evaluate an algebraic expression like $-(a + b)$. Thus, we start with the p and q columns, then construct the $p \wedge q$ column, and finally, the $\sim(p \wedge q)$ column.

p	q	$p \wedge q$	$\sim(p \wedge q)$
T	T	T	F
T	F	F	T
F	T	F	T
F	F	F	T

Notice how we get the $\sim(p \wedge q)$ column from the $p \wedge q$ column: we reverse all the truth values.

b. Because there are two variables, p and q, we again start with the p and q columns. We then evaluate $\sim p$, and finally take the conjunction of the result with q.

p	q	$\sim p$	$(\sim p) \wedge q$
T	T	F	F
T	F	F	F
F	T	T	T
F	F	T	F

Because we are "and-ing" $\sim p$ with q, we look at the values in the $\sim p$ and q columns and combine these according to the instructions for "and." Thus, for example, in the first row we have $F \wedge T = F$ and in the third row we have $T \wedge T = T$.

Here is a third logical operator. Starting with p: "You are over 18" and q: "You are accompanied by an adult," we can form the statement "You are over 18 or are accompanied by an adult," which we write symbolically as $p \vee q$, read "p or q." Now in English the word "or" has several possible meanings, so we have to agree on which one we want here. Mathematicians have settled on the **inclusive or:** $p \vee q$ means p is true or q is true *or both are true.*[2] With p and q as above, $p \vee q$ stands for "You are over 18 or are accompanied by an adult, or both." We shall sometimes include the phrase "or both" for emphasis, but even if we leave it off we still interpret "or" as inclusive.

Disjunction

The **disjunction** of p and q is the statement $p \vee q$, which we read "p or q." Its truth value is defined by the following truth table.

p	q	$p \vee q$
T	T	T
T	F	T
F	T	T
F	F	F

This is the **inclusive** or, so $p \vee q$ is true when p is true or q is true *or both* are true.

Quick Examples

1. Let p: "The butler did it" and let q: "The cook did it." Then $p \vee q$: "Either the butler or the cook did it."

2. Let p: "The butler did it," and let q: "The cook did it," and let r: "The lawyer did it." Then $(p \vee q) \wedge (\sim r)$: "Either the butler or the cook did it, but not the lawyer."

Note The only way for $p \vee q$ to be false is for *both* p and q to be false. For this reason, we can say that $p \vee q$ also means "p and q are not both false." ■

To introduce our next logical operator, we ask you to consider the following statement: "If you earn an A in logic, then I'll buy you a new car." It seems to be made up out of two simpler statements,

p: "You earn an A in logic," and
q: "I will buy you a new car."

---

[2] There is also the **exclusive or:** "p or q but not both." This can be expressed as $(p \vee q) \wedge \sim (p \wedge q)$. Do you see why?

The original statement says: *if p is true, then q is true*, or, more simply, **if** *p*, **then** *q*. We can also phrase this as *p* **implies** *q*, and we write the statement symbolically as $p \rightarrow q$.

Now let us suppose for the sake of argument that the original statement: "If you earn an A in logic, then I'll buy you a new car," is true. This does *not* mean that you *will* earn an A in logic. All it says is that *if* you do so, then I will buy you that car. Thinking of this as a promise, the only way that it can be broken is if you *do* earn an A and I do *not* buy you a new car. With this in mind, we define the logical statement $p \rightarrow q$ as follows.

Conditional

The **conditional** $p \rightarrow q$, which we read "if *p*, then *q*" or "*p* implies *q*," is defined by the following truth table:

p	*q*	$p \rightarrow q$
T	T	T
T	F	F
F	T	T
F	F	T

The arrow "$\rightarrow$" is the **conditional** operator, and in $p \rightarrow q$ the statement *p* is called the **antecedent,** or **hypothesis,** and *q* is called the **consequent,** or **conclusion.** A statement of the form $p \rightarrow q$ is also called an **implication.**

Quick Examples

1. "If $1 + 1 = 2$ then the sun rises in the east" has the form $p \rightarrow q$ where *p*: "$1 + 1 = 2$" is true and *q*: "the sun rises in the east." is also true. Therefore the statement is true.

2. "If the moon is made of green cheese, then I am Arnold Schwartzenegger" has the form $p \rightarrow q$ where *p* is false. From the truth table, we see that $p \rightarrow q$ is therefore true, regardless of whether or not I am Arnold Schwartzenegger.

3. "If $1 + 1 = 2$ then $0 = 1$" has the form $p \rightarrow q$ where this time *p* is true but *q* is false. Therefore, by the truth table, the given statement is false.

Notes

1. The only way that $p \rightarrow q$ can be false is if *p* is true and *q* is false—this is the case of the "broken promise" in the car example above.

2. If you look at the last two rows of the truth table, you see that we say that "$p \rightarrow q$" is true when *p* is false, *no matter what the truth value of q*. Think again about the promise—if you don't get that A, then whether or not I buy you a new car, I have not broken my promise. It may seem strange at first to say that $F \rightarrow T$ is T and $F \rightarrow F$ is also T, but, as they did in choosing to say that "or" is always inclusive, mathematicians agreed that the truth table above gives the most useful definition of the conditional. ∎

It is usually misleading to think of "if *p* then *q*" as meaning that *p causes q*. For instance, tropical weather conditions cause hurricanes, but one cannot claim that if there are tropical weather conditions, then there are (always) hurricanes. Here is a list of some English phrases that *do* have the same meaning as $p \rightarrow q$.

Some Phrasings of the Conditional

We interpret each of the following as equivalent to the conditional $p \to q$.

If p then q.	p implies q.
q follows from p.	Not p unless q.
q if p.	p only if q.
Whenever p, q.	q whenever p.
p is sufficient for q.	q is necessary for p.
p is a sufficient condition for q.	q is a necessary condition for p.

Quick Example

"If it's Tuesday, this must be Belgium" can be rephrased in several ways as follows:

"Its being Tuesday implies that this is Belgium."
"This is Belgium if it's Tuesday."
"It's Tuesday only if this is Belgium."
"It can't be Tuesday unless this is Belgium."
"Its being Tuesday is sufficient for this to be Belgium."
"That this is Belgium is a necessary condition for its being Tuesday."

Notice the difference between "if" and "only if." We say that "p only if q" means $p \to q$ because, assuming that $p \to q$ is true, p can be true only if q is also. In other words, the only line of the truth table that has $p \to q$ true and p true also has q true. The phrasing "p is a sufficient condition for q" says that it suffices to know that p is true to be able to conclude that q is true. For example, it is sufficient that you get an A in logic for me to buy you a new car. Other things might induce me to buy you the car, but an A in logic would suffice. The phrasing "q is necessary for p" says that for p to be true, q must be true (just as we said for "p only if q").

Q: *Does the commutative law hold for the conditional? In other words, is $p \to q$ the same as $q \to p$?*

A: No, as we can see in the following truth table:

p	q	$p \to q$	$q \to p$
T	T	T	T
T	F	F	T
F	T	T	F
F	F	T	T

not the same

Converse and Contrapositive

The statement $q \to p$ is called the **converse** of the statement $p \to q$. A conditional and its converse are *not* the same.

The statement $\sim q \to \sim p$ is the **contrapositive** of the statement $p \to q$. A conditional and its contrapositive are logically equivalent in the sense we define below: they have the same truth value for all possible values of p and q.

EXAMPLE 3 **Converse and Contrapositive**

Give the converse and contrapositive of the statement "If you earn an A in logic, then I'll buy you a new car."

Solution This statement has the form $p \to q$ where p: "you earn an A" and q: "I'll buy you a new car." The converse is $q \to p$. In words, this is "If I buy you a new car then you earned an A in logic."

   The contrapositive is $(\sim q) \to (\sim p)$. In words, this is "If I don't buy you a new car, then you didn't earn an A in logic."

   Assuming that the original statement is true, notice that the converse is not necessarily true. There is nothing in the original promise that prevents me from buying you a new car if you do not earn the A. On the other hand, the contrapositive is true. If I don't buy you a new car, it must be that you didn't earn an A; otherwise I would be breaking my promise.

It sometimes happens that we do want both a conditional and its converse to be true. The conjunction of a conditional and its converse is called a **biconditional**.

Biconditional

The **biconditional**, written $p \leftrightarrow q$, is defined to be the statement $(p \to q) \wedge (q \to p)$. Its truth table is the following:

p	q	$p \leftrightarrow q$
T	T	T
T	F	F
F	T	F
F	F	T

Phrasings of the Biconditional

We interpret each of the following as equivalent to $p \leftrightarrow q$.

   p if and only if q.
   p is necessary and sufficient for q.
   p is equivalent to q.

Quick Example

"I teach math if and only if I am paid a large sum of money." can be rephrased in several ways as follows:

   "I am paid a large sum of money if and only if I teach math."
   "My teaching math is necessary and sufficient for me to be paid a large sum of money."
   "For me to teach math, it is necessary and sufficient that I be paid a large sum of money."

A.2 Logical Equivalence

We mentioned above that we say that two statements are **logically equivalent** if for all possible truth values of the variables involved the two statements always have the same truth values. If s and t are equivalent, we write $s \equiv t$. This is *not* another logical statement. It is simply the claim that the two statements s and t are logically equivalent. Here are some examples.

EXAMPLE 4 Logical Equivalence

Use truth tables to show the following:

a. $p \equiv \sim(\sim p)$. This is called **double negation**.

b. $\sim(p \wedge q) \equiv (\sim p) \vee (\sim q)$. This is one of **DeMorgan's Laws**.

Solution

a. To demonstrate the logical equivalence of these two statements, we construct a truth table with columns for both p and $\sim(\sim p)$.

same

p	$\sim p$	$\sim(\sim p)$
T	F	T
F	T	F

Because the p and $\sim(\sim p)$ columns contain the same truth values in all rows, the two statements are logically equivalent.

b. We construct a truth table showing both $\sim(p \wedge q)$ and $(\sim p) \vee (\sim q)$.

same

p	q	$p \wedge q$	$\sim(p \wedge q)$	$\sim p$	$\sim q$	$(\sim p) \vee (\sim q)$
T	T	T	F	F	F	F
T	F	F	T	F	T	T
F	T	F	T	T	F	T
F	F	F	T	T	T	T

Because the $\sim(p \wedge q)$ column and $(\sim p) \vee (\sim q)$ column agree, the two statements are equivalent.

➡ **Before we go on...** The statement $\sim(p \wedge q)$ can be read as "It is not the case that both p and q are true" or "p and q are not both true." We have just shown that this is equivalent to "Either p is false or q is false." ■

Here are the two equivalences known as DeMorgan's Laws.

DeMorgan's Laws

If p and q are statements, then
$$\sim(p \wedge q) \equiv (\sim p) \vee (\sim q)$$
$$\sim(p \vee q) \equiv (\sim p) \wedge (\sim q)$$

Quick Example

Let p: "the President is a Democrat," and q: "the President is a Republican." Then the following two statements say the same thing:

$\sim(p \wedge q)$: "the President is not both a Democrat and a Republican."

$(\sim p) \vee (\sim q)$: "either the President is not a Democrat, or he is not a Republican (or he is neither)."

Here is a list of some important logical equivalences, some of which we have already encountered. All of them can be verified using truth tables as in Example 4. (The verifications of some of these are in the exercise set.)

Important Logical Equivalences

$\sim(\sim p) \equiv p$	the Double Negative Law
$p \wedge q \equiv q \wedge p$	the Commutative Law for Conjunction.
$p \vee q \equiv q \vee p$	the Commutative Law for Disjunction.
$(p \wedge q) \wedge r \equiv p \wedge (q \wedge r)$	the Associative Law for Conjunction.
$(p \vee q) \vee r \equiv p \vee (q \vee r)$	the Associative Law for Disjunction.
$\sim(p \vee q) \equiv (\sim p) \wedge (\sim q)$	DeMorgan's Laws
$\sim(p \wedge q) \equiv (\sim p) \vee (\sim q)$	
$p \wedge (q \vee r) \equiv (p \wedge q) \vee (p \wedge r)$	the Distributive Laws
$p \vee (q \wedge r) \equiv (p \vee q) \wedge (p \vee r)$	
$p \wedge p \equiv p$	Absorption Laws
$p \vee p \equiv p$	
$p \rightarrow q \equiv (\sim q) \rightarrow (\sim p)$	Contrapositive Law

Note that these logical equivalences apply to *any* statement. The ps, qs and rs can stand for atomic statements or compound statements, as we see in the next example.

EXAMPLE 5 Applying Logical Equivalences

a. Apply DeMorgan's law (once) to the statement $\sim([p \wedge (\sim q)] \wedge r)$.

b. Apply the distributive law to the statement $(\sim p) \wedge [q \vee (\sim r)]$.

c. Consider: "You will get an A if either you are clever and the sun shines, or you are clever and it rains." Rephrase the condition more simply using the distributive law.

Solution

a. We can analyze the given statement from the outside in. It is first of all a negation, but further, it is the negation $\sim(A \wedge B)$, where A is the compound statement $[p \wedge (\sim q)]$ and B is r:

$$\sim(\ \overset{A}{} \wedge \ B)$$

$$\sim(\ \overbrace{[p \wedge (\sim q)]} \wedge \ \ r)$$

Now one of DeMorgan's laws is

$$\sim(A \wedge B) \equiv (\sim A) \vee (\sim B)$$

Applying this equivalence gives

$$\sim([p \wedge (\sim q)] \wedge r) \equiv (\sim[p \wedge (\sim q)]) \vee (\sim r)$$

b. The given statement has the form $A \wedge [B \vee C]$, where $A = (\sim p)$, $B = q$, and $C = (\sim r)$. So, we apply the distributive law $A \wedge [B \vee C]$, $\equiv [A \wedge B] \vee [A \wedge C]$:

$$(\sim p) \wedge [q \vee (\sim r)] \equiv [(\sim p) \wedge q] \vee [(\sim p) \wedge (\sim r)]$$

(We need not stop here: The second expression on the right is just begging for an application of DeMorgan's law. . .)

c. The condition is "either you are clever and the sun shines, or you are clever and it rains." Let's analyze this symbolically: Let p: "You are clever," q: "The sun shines," and r: "It rains." The condition is then $(p \wedge q) \vee (p \wedge r)$. We can "factor out" the p using one of the distributive laws in reverse, getting

$$(p \wedge q) \vee (p \wedge r) \equiv p \wedge (q \vee r)$$

We are taking advantage of the fact that the logical equivalences we listed can be read from right to left as well as from left to right. Putting $p \wedge (q \vee r)$ back into English, we can rephrase the sentence as "You will get an A if you are clever and either the sun shines or it rains."

➡ **Before we go on...** In part (a) of Example 5 we could, if we wanted, apply DeMorgan's law again, this time to the statement $\sim[p \wedge (\sim q)]$ that is part of the answer. Doing so gives

$$\sim[p \wedge (\sim q)] \equiv (\sim p) \vee \sim(\sim q) \equiv (\sim p) \vee q$$

Notice that we've also used the double negative law. Therefore, the original expression can be simplified as follows:

$$\sim([p \wedge (\sim q)] \wedge r) \equiv (\sim[p \wedge (\sim q)]) \vee (\sim r) \equiv ((\sim p) \vee q) \vee (\sim r)$$

which we can write as

$$(\sim p) \vee q \vee (\sim r)$$

because the associative law tells us that it does not matter which two expressions we "or" first. ∎

A.3 Tautologies, Contradictions, and Arguments

Tautologies and Contradictions

A compound statement is a **tautology** if its truth value is always T, regardless of the truth values of its variables. It is a **contradiction** if its truth value is always F, regardless of the truth values of its variables.

Quick Examples

1. $p \vee (\sim p)$ has truth table

p	$\sim p$	$p \vee (\sim p)$
T	F	T
F	T	T

— all T's

and is therefore a tautology.

2. $p \wedge (\sim p)$ has truth table

p	$\sim p$	$p \wedge (\sim p)$
T	F	F
F	T	F

and is therefore a contradiction.

When a statement is a tautology, we also say that the statement is **tautological**. In common usage this sometimes means simply that the statement is self-evident. In logic it means something stronger: that the statement is always true, under all circumstances. In contrast, a contradiction, or **contradictory** statement, is *never* true, under any circumstances.

Some of the most important tautologies are the **tautological implications**, tautologies that have the form of implications. We look at two of them: Direct Reasoning, and Indirect Reasoning:

Modus Ponens or Direct Reasoning

The following tautology is called *modus ponens* or **direct reasoning**:

$$[(p \to q) \wedge p] \to q$$

In Words

If an implication and its antecedent (p) are both true, then so is its consequent (q).

Quick Example

If my loving math implies that I will pass this course, and if I do love math, then I will pass this course.

Note You can check that the statement $[(p \to q) \wedge p] \to q$ is a tautology by drawing its truth table. ∎

Tautological implications are useful mainly because they allow us to check the validity of **arguments**.

Argument

An **argument** is a list of statements called **premises** followed by a statement called the **conclusion.** If the premises are $P_1, P_2, \ldots, P_n$ and the conclusion is C, then we say that the argument is **valid** if the statement $(P_1 \wedge P_2 \wedge \ldots \wedge P_n) \rightarrow C$ is a tautology. In other words, an argument is valid if the truth of all its premises logically implies the truth of its conclusion.

Quick Examples

1. The following is a valid argument:

$$p \rightarrow q$$
$$\underline{p}$$
$$\therefore \quad q$$

(This is the traditional way of writing an argument: We list the premises above a line and then put the conclusion below; the symbol "$\therefore$" stands for the word "therefore.") This argument is valid because the statement $[(p \rightarrow q) \wedge p] \rightarrow q$ is a tautology, namely *modus ponens*.

2. The following is an invalid argument:

$$p \rightarrow q$$
$$\underline{q}$$
$$\therefore \quad p$$

The argument is invalid because the statement $[(p \rightarrow q) \wedge q] \rightarrow p$ is not a tautology. In fact, if p is F and q is T, then the whole statement is F.

The argument in Quick Example 2 above is known as the *fallacy of affirming the consequent*. It is a common invalid argument and not always obviously flawed at first sight, so is often exploited by advertisers. For example, consider the following claim: All Olympic athletes drink Boors, so you should too. The suggestion is that, if you drink Boors, you will be an Olympic athlete:

If you are an Olympic Athlete you drink Boors.	Premise (Let's pretend this is True)
You drink Boors.	Premise (True)
$\therefore$ You are an Olympic Athlete.	Conclusion (May be false!)

This is an error that Boors hopes you will make!

There is, however, a correct argument in which we *deny* the consequent:

Modus Tollens or **Indirect Reasoning**

The following tautology is called *modus tollens* or **indirect reasoning:**

$$[(p \rightarrow q) \wedge (\sim q)] \rightarrow (\sim p)$$

In Words
If an implication is true but its consequent (q) is false, then its antecedent (p) is false.

In Argument Form

$$p \to q$$
$$\frac{\sim q}{\therefore \quad \sim q}$$

Quick Example

If my loving math implies that I will pass this course, and if I do not pass the course, then it must be the case that I do not love math.
In argument form:

If I love math, then I will pass this course.

I will not pass the course.

Therefore, I do not love math.

Note This argument is not as direct as *modus ponens;* it contains a little twist: "If I loved math I would pass this course. However, I will not pass this course. Therefore, it must be that I don't love math (else I *would* pass this course)." Hence the name "indirect reasoning."

Note that, again, there is a similar, but fallacious argument to avoid, for instance: "If I were an Olympic athlete then I would drink Boors ($p \to q$). However, I am not an Olympic athlete ($\sim p$). Therefore, I won't drink Boors. ($\sim q$)." This is a mistake Boors certainly hopes you do *not* make! ∎

There are other interesting tautologies that we can use to justify arguments. We mention one more and refer the interested reader to the website for more examples and further study.

For an extensive list of tautologies go online and follow:

Chapter L Logic
→ List of Tautologies and Tautological Implications

Disjunctive Syllogism or "One or the Other"

The following tautologies are both known as the **disjunctive syllogism** or **one-or-the-other:**

$$[(p \vee q) \wedge (\sim p)] \to q \qquad [(p \vee q) \wedge (\sim q)] \to p$$

In Words
If one or the other of two statements is true, but one is known to be false, then the other must be true.

In Argument Form

$$p \vee q \qquad\qquad p \vee q$$
$$\frac{\sim p}{\therefore \quad q} \qquad\qquad \frac{\sim q}{\therefore \quad p}$$

Quick Example

The butler or the cook did it. The butler didn't do it. Therefore, the cook did it.
In argument form:

The butler or the cook did it.

The butler did not do it.

Therefore, the cook did it.

A EXERCISES

Which of Exercises 1–10 are statements? Comment on the truth values of all the statements you encounter. If a sentence fails to be a statement, explain why. HINT [See Example 1.]

1. All swans are white.   **2.** The fat cat sat on the mat.

3. Look in thy glass and tell whose face thou viewest.[3]

4. My glass shall not persuade me I am old.[4]

5. There is no largest number.

6. 1,000,000,000 is the largest number.

7. Intelligent life abounds in the universe.

8. There may or may not be a largest number.

9. This is exercise number 9.   **10.** This sentence no verb.[5]

Let p: "Our mayor is trustworthy," q: "Our mayor is a good speller," and r = "Our mayor is a patriot." Express each of the statements in Exercises 11–16 in logical form: HINT [See Quick Examples on pp. A2, A3, A5.]

11. Although our mayor is not trustworthy, he is a good speller.

12. Either our mayor is trustworthy, or he is a good speller.

13. Our mayor is a trustworthy patriot who spells well.

14. While our mayor is both trustworthy and patriotic, he is not a good speller.

15. It may or may not be the case that our mayor is trustworthy.

16. Our mayor is either not trustworthy or not a patriot, yet he is an excellent speller.

Let p: "Willis is a good teacher," q: "Carla is a good teacher," r: "Willis' students hate math," s: "Carla's students hate math." Express the statements in Exercises 17–24 in words.

17. $p \wedge (\sim r)$ **18.** $(\sim p) \wedge (\sim q)$

19. $q \vee (\sim q)$ **20.** $((\sim p) \wedge (\sim s)) \vee q$

21. $r \wedge (\sim r)$ **22.** $(\sim s) \vee (\sim r)$

23. $\sim(q \vee s)$ **24.** $\sim(p \wedge r)$

Assume that it is true that "Polly sings well," it is false that "Quentin writes well," and it is true that "Rita is good at math." Determine the truth of each of the statements in Exercises 25–32.

25. Polly sings well and Quentin writes well.

26. Polly sings well or Quentin writes well.

27. Polly sings poorly and Quentin writes well.

28. Polly sings poorly or Quentin writes poorly.

29. Either Polly sings well and Quentin writes poorly, or Rita is good at math.

30. Either Polly sings well and Quentin writes poorly, or Rita is not good at math.

31. Either Polly sings well or Quentin writes well, or Rita is good at math.

32. Either Polly sings well and Quentin writes well, or Rita is bad at math.

Find the truth value of each of the statements in Exercises 33–48. HINT [See Quick Examples on p. A6.]

33. "If $1 = 1$, then $2 = 2$."   **34.** "If $1 = 1$, then $2 = 3$."

35. "If $1 \neq 0$, then $2 \neq 2$."   **36.** "If $1 = 0$, then $1 = 1$."

37. "A sufficient condition for 1 to equal 2 is $1 = 3$."

38. "$1 = 1$ is a sufficient condition for 1 to equal 0."

39. "$1 = 0$ is a necessary condition for 1 to equal 1."

40. "$1 = 1$ is a necessary condition for 1 to equal 2."

41. "If I pay homage to the great Den, then the sun will rise in the east."

42. "If I fail to pay homage to the great Den, then the sun will still rise in the east."

43. "In order for the sun to rise in the east, it is necessary that it sets in the west."

44. "In order for the sun to rise in the east, it is sufficient that it sets in the west."

45. "The sun rises in the west only if it sets in the west."

46. "The sun rises in the east only if it sets in the east."

47. "In order for the sun to rise in the east, it is necessary and sufficient that it sets in the west."

48. "In order for the sun to rise in the west, it is necessary and sufficient that it sets in the east."

Construct the truth tables for the statements in Exercises 49–62. HINT [See Example 2.]

49. $p \wedge (\sim q)$ **50.** $p \vee (\sim q)$

51. $\sim(\sim p) \vee p$ **52.** $p \wedge (\sim p)$

53. $(\sim p) \wedge (\sim q)$ **54.** $(\sim p) \vee (\sim q)$

55. $(p \wedge q) \wedge r$ **56.** $p \wedge (q \wedge r)$

57. $p \wedge (q \vee r)$ **58.** $(p \wedge q) \vee (p \wedge r)$

59. $p \to (q \vee p)$ **60.** $(p \vee q) \to \sim p$

61. $p \leftrightarrow (p \vee q)$ **62.** $(p \wedge q) \leftrightarrow \sim p$

Use truth tables to verify the logical equivalences given in Exercises 63–72.

63. $p \wedge p \equiv p$ **64.** $p \vee p \equiv p$

65. $p \vee q \equiv q \vee p$ **66.** $p \wedge q \equiv q \wedge p$
(Commutative law for disjunction)   (Commutative law for conjunction)

---

[3] William Shakespeare Sonnet 3

[4] Ibid., Sonnet 22.

[5] From *Metamagical Themas: Questing for the Essence of Mind and Pattern* by Douglas R. Hofstadter (Bantam Books, New York 1986)

67. $\sim(p \vee q) \equiv (\sim p) \wedge (\sim q)$ **68.** $\sim(p \wedge (\sim q)) \equiv (\sim p) \vee q$

69. $(p \wedge q) \wedge r \equiv p \wedge (q \wedge r)$ **70.** $(p \vee q) \vee r \equiv p \vee (q \vee r)$
(Associative law for conjunction)   (Associative law for disjunction)

71. $p \rightarrow q \equiv (\sim q) \rightarrow (\sim p)$ **72.** $\sim(p \rightarrow q) \equiv p \wedge (\sim q)$

In Exercises 73–78, use truth tables to check whether the given statement is a tautology, a contradiction, or neither. HINT [See Quick Examples on p. A11.]

73. $p \wedge (\sim p)$ **74.** $p \wedge p$

75. $p \wedge \sim(p \vee q)$ **76.** $p \vee \sim(p \vee q)$

77. $p \vee \sim(p \wedge q)$ **78.** $q \vee \sim(p \wedge (\sim p))$

Apply the stated logical equivalence to the given statement in Exercises 79–84. HINT [See Example 5a, b.]

79. $p \vee (\sim p)$; the commutative law

80. $p \wedge (\sim q)$; the commutative law

81. $\sim(p \wedge (\sim q))$; DeMorgan's law

82. $\sim(q \vee (\sim q))$; DeMorgan's law

83. $p \vee ((\sim p) \wedge q)$; the distributive law

84. $(\sim q) \wedge ((\sim p) \vee q)$; the distributive law.

In Exercises 85–88, use the given logical equivalence to rewrite the given sentence. HINT [See Example 5c.]

85. It is not true that both I am Julius Caesar and you are a fool. DeMorgan's law.

86. It is not true that either I am Julius Caesar or you are a fool. DeMorgan's law.

87. Either it is raining and I have forgotten my umbrella, or it is raining and I have forgotten my hat. The distributive law.

88. I forgot my hat or my umbrella, and I forgot my hat or my glasses. The distributive law.

Give the contrapositive and converse of each of the statements in Exercises 89 and 90, phrasing your answers in words.

89. "If I think, then I am."

90. "If these birds are of a feather, then they flock together."

Exercises 91 and 92 are multiple choice. Indicate which statement is equivalent to the given statement, and say why that statement is equivalent to the given one.

91. "In order for you to worship Den, it is necessary for you to sacrifice beasts of burden."
  (A) "If you are not sacrificing beasts of burden, then you are not worshiping Den."
  (B) "If you are sacrificing beasts of burden, then you are worshiping Den."
  (C) "If you are not worshiping Den, then you are not sacrificing beasts of burden."

92. "In order to read the Tarot, it is necessary for you to consult the Oracle."
  (A) "In order to consult the Oracle, it is necessary to read the Tarot."
  (B) "In order not to consult the Oracle, it is necessary not to read the Tarot."
  (C) "In order not to read the Tarot, it is necessary not to read the Oracle."

In Exercises 93–102, write the given argument in symbolic form (use the underlined letters to represent the statements containing them), then decide whether it is valid or not, If it is valid, name the validating tautology. HINT [See Quick Examples on pp. A12, A13, A14.]

93. If I am <u>h</u>ungry I am also <u>t</u>hirsty. I am hungry. Therefore, I am thirsty.

94. If I am not <u>h</u>ungry, then I certainly am not <u>t</u>hirsty either. I am not thirsty, and so I cannot be hungry.

95. For me to bring my <u>u</u>mbrella, it's sufficient that it <u>r</u>ain. It is not raining. Therefore, I will not bring my umbrella.

96. For me to bring my <u>u</u>mbrella, it's necessary that it <u>r</u>ain. But it is not raining. Therefore, I will not bring my umbrella.

97. For me to pass <u>m</u>ath, it is sufficient that I have a good <u>t</u>eacher. I will not pass math. Therefore, I have a bad teacher.

98. For me to pass <u>m</u>ath, it is necessary that I have a good <u>t</u>eacher. I will pass math. Therefore, I have a good teacher.

99. I will either pass <u>m</u>ath or I have a <u>b</u>ad teacher. I have a good teacher. Therefore, I will pass math.

100. Either <u>r</u>oses are not red or <u>v</u>iolets are not blue. But roses are red. Therefore, violets are not blue.

101. I am either <u>s</u>mart or <u>a</u>thletic, and I am athletic. So I must not be smart.

102. The president is either <u>w</u>ise or <u>s</u>trong. She is strong. Therefore, she is not wise.

In Exercises 103–108, use the stated tautology to complete the argument.

103. If John is a swan, it is necessary that he is green. John is indeed a swan. Therefore, ____. (*Modus ponens.*)

104. If Jill had been born in Texas, then she would be able to ride horses. But Jill cannot ride horses. Therefore, ___. (*Modus tollens.*)

105. If John is a swan, it is necessary that he is green. But John is not green. Therefore, ____. (*Modus tollens.*)

106. If Jill had been born in Texas, then she would be able to ride horses. Jill was born in Texas. Therefore, ___ (*Modus ponens.*)

107. Peter is either a scholar or a gentleman. He is not, however, a scholar. Therefore, ___. (*Disjunctive syllogism.*)

108. Pam is either a plumber or an electrician. She is not, however, an electrician. Therefore, ___ (*Disjunctive syllogism.*)

COMMUNICATION AND REASONING EXERCISES

109. If two statements are logically equivalent, what can be said about their truth tables?

110. If a proposition is neither a tautology nor a contradiction, what can be said about its truth table?

111. If A and B are two compound statements such that $A \vee B$ is a contradiction, what can you say about A and B?

112. If A and B are two compound statements such that $A \wedge B$ is a tautology, what can you say about A and B?

113. Give an example of an instance where $p \to q$ means that q causes p.

114. Complete the following. If $p \to q$, then its converse, ___ , is the statement that ___ and (is/is not) logically equivalent to $p \to q$.

115. Give an instance of a biconditional $p \leftrightarrow q$ where neither one of p or q causes the other. Answers may vary.

Appendix B   **Area Under a Normal Curve**

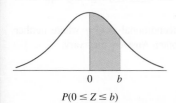

$P(0 \leq Z \leq b)$

The table below gives the probabilities $P(0 \leq Z \leq b)$ where Z is a standard normal variable. For example, to find $P(0 \leq Z \leq 2.43)$, write 2.43 as $2.4 + 0.03$, and read the entry in the row labeled 2.4 and the column labeled 0.03. From the portion of the table shown at left, you will see that $P(0 \leq Z \leq 2.43) = .4925$.

Z	0.00	0.01	0.02	0.03
2.3	.4893	.4896	.4898	.4901
2.4	.4918	.4920	.4922	.4925
2.5	.4938	.4940	.4941	.4943

Z	0.00	0.01	0.02	0.03	0.04	0.05	0.06	0.07	0.08	0.09
0.0	.0000	.0040	.0080	.0120	.0160	.0199	.0239	.0279	.0319	.0359
0.1	.0398	.0438	.0478	.0517	.0557	.0596	.0636	.0675	.0714	.0753
0.2	.0793	.0832	.0871	.0910	.0948	.0987	.1026	.1064	.1103	.1141
0.3	.1179	.1217	.1255	.1293	.1331	.1368	.1406	.1443	.1480	.1517
0.4	.1554	.1591	.1628	.1664	.1700	.1736	.1772	.1808	.1844	.1879
0.5	.1915	.1950	.1985	.2019	.2054	.2088	.2123	.2157	.2190	.2224
0.6	.2257	.2291	.2324	.2357	.2389	.2422	.2454	.2486	.2517	.2549
0.7	.2580	.2611	.2642	.2673	.2704	.2734	.2764	.2794	.2823	.2852
0.8	.2881	.2910	.2939	.2967	.2995	.3023	.3051	.3078	.3106	.3133
0.9	.3159	.3186	.3212	.3238	.3264	.3289	.3315	.3340	.3365	.3389
1.0	.3413	.3438	.3461	.3485	.3508	.3531	.3554	.3577	.3599	.3621
1.1	.3643	.3665	.3686	.3708	.3729	.3749	.3770	.3790	.3810	.3830
1.2	.3849	.3869	.3888	.3907	.3925	.3944	.3962	.3980	.3997	.4015
1.3	.4032	.4049	.4066	.4082	.4099	.4115	.4131	.4147	.4162	.4177
1.4	.4192	.4207	.4222	.4236	.4251	.4265	.4279	.4292	.4306	.4319
1.5	.4332	.4345	.4357	.4370	.4382	.4394	.4406	.4418	.4429	.4441
1.6	.4452	.4463	.4474	.4484	.4495	.4505	.4515	.4525	.4535	.4545
1.7	.4554	.4564	.4573	.4582	.4591	.4599	.4608	.4616	.4625	.4633
1.8	.4641	.4649	.4656	.4664	.4671	.4678	.4686	.4693	.4699	.4706
1.9	.4713	.4719	.4726	.4732	.4738	.4744	.4750	.4756	.4761	.4767
2.0	.4772	.4778	.4783	.4788	.4793	.4798	.4803	.4808	.4812	.4817
2.1	.4821	.4826	.4830	.4834	.4838	.4842	.4846	.4850	.4854	.4857
2.2	.4861	.4864	.4868	.4871	.4875	.4878	.4881	.4884	.4887	.4890
2.3	.4893	.4896	.4898	.4901	.4904	.4906	.4909	.4911	.4913	.4916
2.4	.4918	.4920	.4922	.4925	.4927	.4929	.4931	.4932	.4934	.4936
2.5	.4938	.4940	.4941	.4943	.4945	.4946	.4948	.4949	.4951	.4952
2.6	.4953	.4955	.4956	.4957	.4959	.4960	.4961	.4962	.4963	.4964
2.7	.4965	.4966	.4967	.4968	.4969	.4970	.4971	.4972	.4973	.4974
2.8	.4974	.4975	.4976	.4977	.4977	.4978	.4979	.4979	.4980	.4981
2.9	.4981	.4982	.4982	.4983	.4984	.4984	.4985	.4985	.4986	.4986
3.0	.4987	.4987	.4987	.4988	.4988	.4989	.4989	.4989	.4990	.4990

Answers to Selected Exercises

Chapter 0

Section 0.1
1. -48 **3.** $2/3$ **5.** -1 **7.** 9 **9.** 1 **11.** 33 **13.** 14
15. $5/18$ **17.** 13.31 **19.** 6 **21.** $43/16$ **23.** 0
25. `3*(2-5)`   **27.** `3/(2-5)`   **29.** `(3-1)/(8+6)`
31. `3-(4+7)/8`   **33.** `2/(3+x)-x*y^2`
35. `3.1x^3-4x^(-2)-60/(x^2-1)`   **37.** `(2/3)/5`
39. `3^(4-5)*6`   **41.** `3*(1+4/100)^(-3)`
43. `3^(2*x-1)+4^x-1`   **45.** `2^(2x^2-x+1)`
47. `4*e^(-2*x)/(2-3e^(-2*x))` or `4(*e^(-2*x))/`
`(2-3e^(-2*x))`   **49.** `3(1-(-1/2)^2)^2+1`

Section 0.2
1. 27 **3.** -36 **5.** $4/9$ **7.** $-1/8$ **9.** 16 **11.** 2 **13.** 32
15. 2 **17.** x^5 **19.** $-\dfrac{y}{x}$ **21.** $\dfrac{1}{x}$ **23.** $x^3 y$ **25.** $\dfrac{z^4}{y^3}$ **27.** $\dfrac{x^6}{y^6}$
29. $\dfrac{x^4 y^6}{z^4}$ **31.** $\dfrac{3}{x^4}$ **33.** $\dfrac{3}{4x^{2/3}}$ **35.** $1 - 0.3x^2 - \dfrac{6}{5x}$ **37.** 2
39. $1/2$ **41.** $4/3$ **43.** $2/5$ **45.** 7 **47.** 5 **49.** -2.668
51. $3/2$ **53.** 2 **55.** 2 **57.** ab **59.** $x + 9$ **61.** $x\sqrt[3]{a^3 + b^3}$
63. $\dfrac{2y}{\sqrt{x}}$ **65.** $3^{1/2}$ **67.** $x^{3/2}$ **69.** $(xy^2)^{1/3}$ **71.** $x^{3/2}$
73. $\dfrac{3}{5} x^{-2}$ **75.** $\dfrac{3}{2} x^{-1.2} - \dfrac{1}{3} x^{-2.1}$ **77.** $\dfrac{2}{3} x - \dfrac{1}{2} x^{0.1} + \dfrac{4}{3} x^{-1.1}$
79. $\dfrac{3}{4} x^{1/2} - \dfrac{5}{3} x^{-1/2} + \dfrac{4}{3} x^{-3/2}$ **81.** $\dfrac{3}{4} x^{2/5} - \dfrac{7}{2} x^{-3/2}$
83. $(x^2 + 1)^{-3} - \dfrac{3}{4}(x^2 + 1)^{-1/3}$ **85.** $\sqrt[3]{2^2}$ **87.** $\sqrt[3]{x^4}$
89. $\sqrt[5]{\sqrt{x}\sqrt[3]{y}}$ **91.** $-\dfrac{3}{2\sqrt[4]{x}}$ **93.** $\dfrac{0.2}{\sqrt[3]{x^2}} + \dfrac{3\sqrt{x}}{7}$
95. $\dfrac{3}{4\sqrt{(1-x)^5}}$ **97.** 64 **99.** $\sqrt{3}$ **101.** $1/x$ **103.** xy
105. $\left(\dfrac{y}{x}\right)^{1/3}$ **107.** ± 4 **109.** $\pm 2/3$ **111.** $-1, -1/3$
113. -2 **115.** 16 **117.** ± 1 **119.** $33/8$

Section 0.3
1. $4x^2 + 6x$ **3.** $2xy - y^2$ **5.** $x^2 - 2x - 3$
7. $2y^2 + 13y + 15$ **9.** $4x^2 - 12x + 9$ **11.** $x^2 + 2 + 1/x^2$
13. $4x^2 - 9$ **15.** $y^2 - 1/y^2$ **17.** $2x^3 + 6x^2 + 2x - 4$
19. $x^4 - 4x^3 + 6x^2 - 4x + 1$ **21.** $y^5 + 4y^4 + 4y^3 - y$
23. $(x + 1)(2x + 5)$ **25.** $(x^2 + 1)^5 (x + 3)^3 (x^2 + x + 4)$
27. $-x^3 (x^3 + 1)\sqrt{x + 1}$ **29.** $(x + 2)\sqrt{(x + 1)^3}$
31. a. $x(2 + 3x)$ **b.** $x = 0, -2/3$ **33. a.** $2x^2 (3x - 1)$
b. $x = 0, 1/3$ **35. a.** $(x - 1)(x - 7)$ **b.** $x = 1, 7$
37. a. $(x - 3)(x + 4)$ **b.** $x = 3, -4$ **39. a.** $(2x + 1)(x - 2)$
b. $x = -1/2, 2$ **41. a.** $(2x + 3)(3x + 2)$
b. $x = -3/2, -2/3$ **43. a.** $(3x - 2)(4x + 3)$

b. $x = 2/3, -3/4$ **45. a.** $(x + 2y)^2$ **b.** $x = -2y$
47. a. $(x^2 - 1)(x^2 - 4)$ **b.** $x = \pm 1, \pm 2$

Section 0.4
1. $\dfrac{2x^2 - 7x - 4}{x^2 - 1}$ **3.** $\dfrac{3x^2 - 2x + 5}{x^2 - 1}$ **5.** $\dfrac{x^2 - x + 1}{x + 1}$
7. $\dfrac{x^2 - 1}{x}$ **9.** $\dfrac{2x - 3}{x^2 y}$ **11.** $\dfrac{(x + 1)^2}{(x + 2)^4}$ **13.** $\dfrac{-1}{\sqrt{(x^2 + 1)^3}}$
15. $\dfrac{-(2x + y)}{x^2 (x + y)^2}$

Section 0.5
1. -1 **3.** 5 **5.** $13/4$ **7.** $43/7$ **9.** -1 **11.** $(c - b)/a$
13. $x = -4, 1/2$ **15.** No solutions   **17.** $\pm\sqrt{\dfrac{5}{2}}$ **19.** -1
21. $-1, 3$ **23.** $\dfrac{1 \pm \sqrt{5}}{2}$ **25.** 1 **27.** $\pm 1, \pm 3$
29. $\pm\sqrt{\dfrac{-1 \pm \sqrt{5}}{2}}$ **31.** $-1, -2, -3$ **33.** -3 **35.** 1
37. -2 **39.** $1, \pm\sqrt{5}$ **41.** $\pm 1, \pm\dfrac{1}{\sqrt{2}}$ **43.** $-2, -1, 2, 3$

Section 0.6
1. $0, 3$ **3.** $\pm\sqrt{2}$ **5.** $-1, -5/2$ **7.** -3 **9.** $0, -1, 1$
11. $x = -1$ ($x = -2$ is not a solution.)   **13.** $-2, -3/2, -1$
15. -1 **17.** $\pm\sqrt[4]{2}$ **19.** ± 1 **21.** ± 3 **23.** $2/3$ **25.** $-4, -1/4$

Section 0.7
1. $P(0, 2)$, $Q(4, -2)$, $R(-2, 3)$, $S(-3.5, -1.5)$,
$T(-2.5, 0)$, $U(2, 2.5)$.

3.

5.

7.

9.

A19

11.

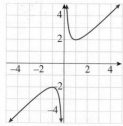

29. `(x^2-1)/(x^2+1)`

x	0.5	1.5	2.5	3.5
$h(x)$	−0.6000	0.3846	0.7241	0.8491
x	4.5	5.5	6.5	7.5
$h(x)$	0.9059	0.9360	0.9538	0.9651
x	8.5	9.5	10.5	
$h(x)$	0.9727	0.9781	0.9820	

13. $\sqrt{2}$

15. $\sqrt{a^2 + b^2}$

17. 1/2

19. Circle with center (0, 0) and radius 3

Chapter 1

Section 1.1

1. a. 2 **b.** 0.5   **3. a.** −1.5 **b.** 8 **c.** −8   **5. a.** 20 **b.** 30
c. 30 **d.** 20 **e.** 0   **7. a.** −1 **b.** 1.25 **c.** 0 **d.** 1 **e.** 0
9. a. Yes; $f(4) = 63/16$ **b.** Not defined **c.** Not defined
11. a. Not defined **b.** Not defined **c.** Yes, $f(−10) = 0$
13. a. −7 **b.** −3 **c.** 1 **d.** $4y − 3$ **e.** $4(a + b) − 3$ **15. a.** 3
b. 6 **c.** 2 **d.** 6 **e.** $a^2 + 2a + 3$ **f.** $(x + h)^2 + 2(x + h) + 3$
17. a. 2 **b.** 0 **c.** 65/4 **d.** $x^2 + 1/x$ **e.** $(s + h)^2 + 1/(s + h)$
f. $(s + h)^2 + 1/(s + h) − (s^2 + 1/s)$

19.   **21.**

`-(x^3)`

`x^4`

23.

`1/x^2`

25. a. (I) **b.** (IV) **c.** (V) **d.** (VI) **e.** (III) **f.** (II)
27. `0.1*x^2-4*x+5`

x	0	1	2	3
$f(x)$	5	1.1	−2.6	−6.1
x	4	5	6	7
$f(x)$	−9.4	−12.5	−15.4	−18.1
x	8	9	10	
$f(x)$	−20.6	−22.9	−25	

31. a. −1 **b.** 2 **c.** 2

`x* (x<0) +2* (x>=0)`

33. a. 1 **b.** 0 **c.** 1

`(x^2) * (x<=0) + (1 / x) *
(0<x)`

35. a. 0 **b.** 2 **c.** 3 **d.** 3

`x* (x<=0) + (x+1) *
(0<x) * (x<=2) + x*
(2<x)`

37. a. $h(2x + h)$ **b.** $2x + h$ **39. a.** $−h(2x + h)$
b. $−(2x + h)$ **41. a.** $I(3) = 1.55$. In 2003 the United States
imported 1.55 million gallons/day. $I(5) = 1.5$. In 2005 the
United States imported 1.5 million gallons/day. $I(6) = 1.5$.
In 2006 the United States imported 1.5 million gallons/day.
b. [1, 6] **c.** Graph:

$I(4.5) \approx 1.55$. Thus the United States imported 1.55 million
gallons/day in the year ending June 30, 2005 (or the year
starting July 1, 2004).   **43.** $f(4) \approx 1,600, f(5) \approx 1,700,$
$f(6.5) \approx 1,300.$ There were 1.6 million housing starts in 2004,
1.7 million housing starts in 2005, and 1.3 million housing
starts in the year beginning July 2006.   **45.** $f(7) − f(5)$
The change in the number of housing starts from 2005 to 2007
was larger in magnitude than the change from 2000 to 2005.

47. a. [0, 10]. $t \geq 0$ is not an appropriate domain because it would predict U.S. trade with China into the indefinite future with no basis. **b.** $280 billion; U.S. trade with China in 2004 was valued at approximately $280 billion.   **49. a.** [1, 6] **b.** $L(2) \approx 400$; $L(5) \approx 900$, $L(6) \approx 1,100$. Sirius lost around $400 million in 2002, $900 million in 2005, and $1,100 million (or $1.1 billion) in 2006. **c.** $t \approx 4.5$; Sirius' losses were increasing fastest approximately midway through 2004.
51. a. $P(0) = 200$: At the start of 1995 the processor speed was 200 megahertz. $P(4) = 500$: At the start of 1999 the processor speed was 500 megahertz. $P(5) = 1,100$: At the start of 2000 the processor speed was 1,100 megahertz.
b. Graph:

Midway through 2001 **c.**:

t	0	1	2	3	4	5	6	7	8	9
$P(t)$	200	275	350	425	500	1,100	1,700	2,300	2,900	3,500

53. $T(26,000) = \$3,508.75$; $T(65,000) = \$12,673.75$
55. a. `100*(1-12200/t^4.48)`
b. Graph:

c.

t	9	10	11	12	13	14
$p(t)$	35.2	59.6	73.6	82.2	87.5	91.1
t	15	16	17	18	19	20
$p(t)$	93.4	95.1	96.3	97.1	97.7	98.2

d. 82.2% **e.** 14 months **57.** t; m **59.** $y(x) = 4x^2 - 2$ (or $f(x) = 4x^2 - 2$) **61.** True. We can construct a table of values from any graph by reading off a set of values. **63.** False. In a numerically specified function, only certain values of the function are specified so we cannot know its value on every real number in [0, 10], whereas an algebraically specified function would give values for every real number in [0, 10]. **65.** False: Functions with infinitely many points in their domain (such as $f(x) = x^2$) cannot be specified numerically. **67.** As the text reminds us: to evaluate f of a quantity (such as $x + h$) replace x everywhere by the *whole quantity* $x + h$, getting $f(x + h) = (x + h)^2 - 1$.
69. They are different portions of the graph of the associated equation $y = f(x)$. **71.** The graph of $g(x)$ is the same as the graph of $f(x)$, but shifted 5 units to the right.

Section 1.2
1. $N(t) = 200 + 10t$ (N = number of sound files, t = time in days) **3.** $A(x) = x^2/2$ **5.** $C(x) = 12x$

7. $C(x) = 1,500x + 1,200$ per day **a.** $5,700 **b.** $1,500
c. $1,500 **d.** Variable cost $= \$1,500x$; Fixed cost $= \$1,200$; Marginal cost $= \$1,500$ per piano
e. Graph:

9. a. $C(x) = 0.4x + 70$, $R(x) = 0.5x$, $P(x) = 0.1x - 70$
b. $P(500) = -20$; a loss of $20 **c.** 700 copies
11. $R(x) = 100x$, $P(x) = -2,000 + 90x - 0.2x^2$; at least 24 jerseys. **13.** $P(x) = -1.7 - 0.02x + 0.0001x^2$; approximately 264 thousand square feet
15. $P(x) = 100x - 5,132$, with domain [0, 405]. For profit, $x \geq 52$ **17.** 5,000 units **19.** $FC/(SP - VC)$
21. $P(x) = 579.7x - 20,000$, with domain $x \geq 0$; $x = 34.50$ g per day for break even
23. a. Graph:

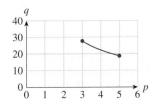

b. Ridership drops by about 3,070 rides per day.
25. a. 358,600 **b.** 361,200 **c.** $6.00 **27.** $240 per skateboard. **29. a.** $110 per phone. **b.** Shortage of 25 million phones **31. a.** $3.50 per ride.
Graph:

b. A surplus of around 9,170 rides.
33. a. $12,000 **b.** $N(q) = 2,000 + 100q^2 - 500q$; $N(20) = \$32,000$ **35. a. (B) b.** $36.8 billion
37. a. Models **(A)** and **(B)** **b.** Model **(A)**, which predicts about 3,757 tons of Freon. **39. a. (C) b.** $20.80 per shirt if the team buys 70 shirts
Graph:

41. A quadratic model (B) is the best choice; the other models either predict perpetually increasing value of the euro or perpetually decreasing value of the euro.   **43.** $A(t) = 5,000$ $(1 + 0.0494/12)^{12t}$; $7,061   **45.** At the beginning of 2016   **47.** 31.0 grams, 9.25 grams, 2.76 grams   **49.** 20,000 years   **51. a.** 1,000 years: 65%, 2,000 years: 42%, 3,000 years: 27%   **b.** 1,600 years   **53.** 30   **55.** Curve-fitting. The model is based on fitting a curve to a given set of observed data.   **57.** The cost of downloading a movie was $4 in January and is decreasing by 20¢ per month.   **59.** Variable; marginal.   **61.** Yes, as long as the supply is going up at a faster rate, as illustrated by the following graph:

63. Extrapolate both models and choose the one that gives the most reasonable predictions.

Section 1.3

1. $m = 3$ **3.** $m = -1$ **5.** $m = 3/2$ **7.** $f(x) = -x/2 - 2$ **9.** $f(0) = -5$, $f(x) = -x - 5$ **11.** f is linear: $f(x) = 4x + 6$ **13.** g is linear: $g(x) = 2x - 1$ **15.** $-3/2$ **17.** $1/6$ **19.** Undefined   **21.** 0   **23.** $-4/3$

25.

27.

29.

31.

33.

35.

37.

39. 2   **41.** 2   **43.** -2 **45.** Undefined   **47.** 1.5   **49.** -0.09 **51.** $1/2$ **53.** $(d - b)/(c - a)$ **55. a.** 1   **b.** 1/2   **c.** 0   **d.** 3   **e.** $-1/3$ **f.** -1 **g.** Undefined   **h.** $-1/4$ **i.** -2 **57.** $y = 3x$ **59.** $y = \frac{1}{4}x - 1$ **61.** $y = 10x - 203.5$ **63.** $y = -5x + 6$ **65.** $y = -3x + 2.25$ **67.** $y = -x + 12$ **69.** $y = 2x + 4$ **71.** $y = \frac{q}{p}x$ **73.** $y = q$ **75.** Fixed cost $= \$8,000$, marginal cost $= \$25$ per bicycle   **77.** $C = 145x + 75$; $145 per iPod; $14,575   **79.** $q = -40p + 2000$ **81. a.** $q = -p + 156.4$; 53.4 million phones; **b.** $1, 1 million   **83. a.** $q = -4,500p + 41,500$ **b.** Rides/day per $1 increase in the fare; ridership decreases by 4,500 rides per day for every $1 increase in the fare.   **c.** 14,500 rides/day   **85. a.** Demand: $q = -60p + 150$; supply: $q = 80p - 60$ **b.** $1.50 each   **87. a.** $q = 40t + 290$ **b.** $q(15) = 890$ million pounds   **89. a.** $N = 1.45t - 4.05$ **b.** Million subscribers per year; the number of Sirius Satellite Radio subscribers grew at a rate of 1.45 million subscribers per year.   **c.** 4.65 million subscribers, considerably less than the actual number.   **91. a.** 2.5 ft/s   **b.** 20 feet along the track   **c.** after 6 seconds   **93. a.** 130 miles per hour   **b.** $s = 130t - 1,300$ **95.** $F = 1.8C + 32$; 86°F; 72°F; 14°F; 7°F   **97.** $I(N) = 0.05N + 50,000$; $N = \$1,000,000$; marginal income is $m = 5¢$ per dollar of net profit   **99.** $T(r) = (1/4)r + 45$; $T(100) = 70°$F   **101.** Increasing by $130,000 per year.   **103. a.** $y = -30t + 200$ **b.** $y = 60t - 250$

c. $y = \begin{cases} -30t + 200 & \text{if } 0 \le t \le 5 \\ 60t - 250 & \text{if } 5 < t \le 12 \end{cases}$ **d.** 170

105. $N = \begin{cases} 0.22t + 3 & \text{if } 0 \le t \le 5 \\ -0.15t + 4.85 & \text{if } 5 < t \le 9 \end{cases}$

3.8 million jobs

107. Compute the corresponding successive changes Δx in x and Δy in y, and compute the ratios $\Delta y/\Delta x$. If the answer is always the same number, then the values in the table come from a linear function.   **109.** $f(x) = -\frac{a}{b}x + \frac{c}{b}$. If $b = 0$, then $\frac{a}{b}$ is undefined, and y cannot be specified as a function of x. (The graph of the resulting equation would be a vertical line.)   **111.** slope, 3.   **113.** If m is positive, then y will increase as x increases; if m is negative then y will decrease as x increases; if m is zero then y will not change as x changes.   **115.** The slope increases, because an increase in the y-coordinate of the second point increases Δy while leaving Δx fixed.   **117.** The units of the slope m are units of y (bootlags) per unit of x (zonars). The intercept b is on the y-axis, and is thus measured in units of y (bootlags). Thus, m is measured in bootlags per zonar and b is measured in bootlags.   **119.** It must increase by 10 units each day, including the third.   **121.** (B)   **123.** Increasing the number of items from the break even results in a profit: Because the slope of the revenue graph is larger than the slope of the cost graph, it is higher than the cost graph to the right of the point of intersection, and hence corresponds to a profit.

Section 1.4

1. 6   **3.** 86   **5. a.** 0.5 (better fit) **b.** 0.75
7. a. 27.42 **b.** 27.16 (better fit)
9. $y = 1.5x - 0.6667$ **11.** $y = 0.4118x + 0.9706$

13. a. $r = 0.9959$ (best, not perfect) **b.** $r = 0.9538$
c. $r = 0.3273$ (worst)

15.

x	y	xy	x^2
3	500	1,500	9
5	600	3,000	25
7	800	5,600	49
Totals 15	1,900	10,100	83

$y = 75x + 258.33$; 858.33 million

17. $y = 3.65t + 4.62$; \$26.52 billion   **19.** $y = 0.135x + 0.15$; 6.9 million jobs   **21. a.** $y = 1.62x - 23.87$.
Graph:

b. Each acre of cultivated land produces about 1.62 tons of soybeans.   **23. a.** Regression line: $y = 0.032x + 0.042$
Graph:

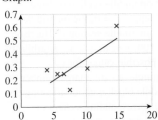

b. There are about 32 motorcycles per 1,000 automobiles.
c. $r \approx 0.7739$; not a strong correlation.

25. a. $p = 0.13t + 0.22$
Graph:

b. Yes; the first and last points lie above the regression line, while the central points lie below it, suggesting a curve.
c.

	A	B	C	D
1	t	p (Observed)	p (predicted)	Residual
2	0	0.38	0.22	0.16
3	2	0.4	0.48	-0.08
4	4	0.6	0.74	-0.14
5	6	0.95	1	-0.05
6	8	1.2	1.26	-0.06
7	10	1.6	1.52	0.08
8				

Notice that the residuals are positive at first, become negative, and then become positive, confirming the impression from the graph.   **27.** The line that passes through (a, b) and (c, d) gives a sum-of-squares error SSE $= 0$, which is the smallest value possible.   **29.** The regression line is the line passing through the given points.   **31.** 0   **33.** No. The regression line through $(-1, 1)$, $(0, 0)$, and $(1, 1)$ passes through none of these points.

Chapter 1 Review

1. a. 1 **b.** -2 **c.** 0 **d.** -1 **3. a.** 1 **b.** 0 **c.** 0 **d.** -1
5.   **7.**

9. Absolute value   **11.** Linear   **13.** Quadratic
15. $y = -3x + 11$ **17.** $y = (1/2)x + 3/2$ **19.** The second line, $y = -x/4 + 1$, is a better fit.   **21.** $y = -0.214x + 1.14$, $r \approx -0.33$ **23. a.** Exponential.
Graph:

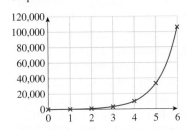

b. The ratios (rounded to 1 decimal place) are:

$V(1)/V(0)$	$V(2)/V(1)$	$V(3)/V(2)$	$V(4)/V(3)$	$V(5)/V(4)$	$V(6)/V(5)$
3	3.3	3.3	3.2	3.2	3.2

They are close to 3.2.

c. About 343,700 visits/day   **25. a.** (A) **b.** (A) Leveling off (B) Rising (C) Rising; they begin to fall after 7 months (D) Rising   **27. a.** 2,080 hits per day **b.** Probably not. This model predicts that Web site traffic will start to decrease as advertising increases beyond \$8,500 per month, and then drop toward zero.   **29. a.** $q = -60p + 950$ **b.** 50 novels per month **c.** \$10, for a profit of \$1,200.

Chapter 2

Section 2.1

1. $(2, 2)$ **3.** $(3, 1)$ **5.** $(6, 6)$ **7.** $(5/3, -4/3)$ **9.** $(0, -2)$ **11.** $(x, (1 - 2x)/3)$ or $\left(\frac{1}{2}(1 - 3y), y\right)$ **13.** No solution   **15.** $(5, 0)$ **17.** $(0.3, -1.1)$ **19.** $(116.6, -69.7)$ **21.** $(3.3, 1.8)$ **23.** $(3.4, 1.9)$ **25.** 200 quarts of vanilla and 100 quarts of mocha   **27.** Two servings of Mixed Cereal and one serving of Mango Tropical Fruit   **29. a.** Four servings of beans and five slices of bread **b.** No. One of the variables in the solution of the system has a negative value.   **31.** Mix 12 servings of Designer Whey and 2 servings of Muscle Milk for a cost of \$9.20.   **33.** 65 g   **35.** 30 AAPL, 20 MSFT   **37.** 200 BAC, 400 JPM   **39.** 242 in favor and 193 against   **41.** 5 soccer games and 7 football games   **43.** 7   **45.** \$1.50 each   **47.** 55 widgets   **49.** Demand: $q = -4p + 47$; supply: $q = 4p - 29$; equilibrium price: \$9.50   **51.** 33 pairs of dirty socks and 11 T-shirts   **53.** \$1,200   **55.** A system of three equations in two unknowns will have a unique solution if either (1) the three corresponding lines intersect in a single point, or (2) two of the equations correspond to the same line, and the third line intersects it in a single point.   **57.** Yes. Even if two lines have negative slope, they will still intersect if the slopes differ.   **59.** You cannot round both of them up; there will not be sufficient eggs and cream. Rounding both answers down will ensure that you will not run out of ingredients. It may be possible to round one answer down and the other up, and this should be tried.   **61.** (B) **63.** (B)   **65.** Answers will vary.   **67.** It is very likely. Two randomly chosen straight lines are unlikely to be parallel.

Section 2.2

1. $(3, 1)$ **3.** $(6, 6)$ **5.** $\left(\frac{1}{3}(1 - 3y), y\right)$; y arbitrary   **7.** No solution   **9.** $(1/4, 3/4)$ **11.** No solution   **13.** $(10/3, 1/3)$ **15.** $(4, 4, 4)$ **17.** $\left(-1, -3, \frac{1}{2}\right)$ **19.** (z, z, z), z arbitrary   **21.** No solution   **23.** $(-1, 1, 1)$ **25.** $(1, z - 2, z)$, z arbitrary   **27.** $(4 + y, y, -1)$, y arbitrary   **29.** $(4 - y/3 + z/3, y, z)$, y arbitrary, z arbitrary   **31.** $(-17, 20, -2)$ **33.** $\left(-\frac{3}{2}, 0, \frac{1}{2}, 0\right)$ **35.** $(-3z, 1 - 2z, z, 0)$, z arbitrary   **37.** $\left(\frac{1}{5}(7 - 17z + 8w), \frac{1}{5}(1 - 6z - 6w), z, w\right)$, z, w arbitrary   **39.** $(1, 2, 3, 4, 5)$ **41.** $(-2, -2 + z - u, z, u, 0)$ z, u arbitrary   **43.** $(16, 12/7, -162/7, -88/7)$ **45.** $(-8/15, 7/15, 7/15, 7/15, 7/15)$ **47.** $(1.0, 1.4, 0.2)$ **49.** $(-5.5, -0.9, -7.4, -6.6)$ **51.** A pivot is an entry in a matrix that is selected to "clear a column"; that is, use the row operations of a certain type to obtain zeros everywhere above and below it. "Pivoting" is the procedure of clearing a column using a designated pivot.   **53.** $2R_1 + 5R_4$, or $6R_1 + 15R_4$ (which is less desirable).   **55.** It will include a row of zeros.   **57.** The claim is wrong. If there are more equations than unknowns, there can be a unique solution as well as row(s) of zeros in the reduced matrix, as in Example 6.   **59.** Two   **61.** The number of pivots must equal the number of variables, because no variable will be used as a parameter.   **63.** A simple example is: $x = 1$; $y - z = 1$; $x + y - z = 2$.

Section 2.3

1. 100 batches of vanilla, 50 batches of mocha, and 100 batches of strawberry   **3.** Three sections of Finite Math, two sections of Applied Calculus and one section of Computer Methods   **5.** \$3.4 billion for rock music, \$0.4 billion for religious music, and \$0.2 billion for classical music   **7.** Four Airbus A330-300s, four Boeing 767-200ERs and eight Dreamliners   **9.** 22 tons from Cheesy Cream, 56 tons from Super Smooth & Sons, and 22 tons from Bagel's Best Friend   **11.** 10 evil sorcerers, 50 trolls and 500 orcs   **13.** It donated \$600 to each of the MPBF and the SCN, and \$1,200 to the Jets   **15.** United: 120; American: 40; Southwest: 50   **17.** \$5,000 in FCTFX, \$2,000 in FSAZX, \$2,000 in FUSFX   **19.** 100 shares of GE, 50 shares of WMT, 50 shares of XOM   **21.** Microsoft: 88 million, Time Warner: 79 million, Yahoo: 75 million, Google: 42 million   **23.** The third equation is $x + y + z + w = 100$. General Solution: $x = 50.5 - 0.5w$, $y = 33.5 - 0.3w$, $z = 16 - 0.2w$, w arbitrary. State Farm is most impacted by other companies.   **25. a.** Brooklyn to Manhattan: 500 books; Brooklyn to Long Island: 500 books; Queens to Manhattan: 1,000 books; Queens to Long Island: 1,000 books. **b.** Brooklyn to Manhattan: 1,000 books; Brooklyn to Long Island: none; Queens to Manhattan: 500 books; Queens to Long Island: 1,500 books, giving a total cost of \$8,000.   **27. a.** The associated system of equations has infinitely many solutions. **b.** No; the associated system of equations still has infinitely many solutions. **c.** Yes; North America to Australia: 440,000, North America to South Africa: 190,000, Europe to Australia: 950,000, Europe to South Africa: 950,000.   **29. a.** $x + y = 14,000$; $z + w = 95,000$; $x + z = 63,550$; $y + w = 45,450$. The system does not have a unique solution, indicating that the given data are insufficient to obtain the missing data. **b.** $(x, y, z, w) = (5,600, 8,400, 57,950, 37,050)$ **31. a.** No; the general solution is: Eastward Blvd.: $S + 200$; Northwest La.: $S + 50$; Southwest La.: S, where S is arbitrary. Thus it would suffice to know the traffic along Southwest La. **b.** Yes, as it leads to the solution Eastward Blvd.: 260; Northwest La.: 110; Southwest La.: 60. **c.** 50 vehicles per day   **33. a.** With $x = $ traffic on middle section of Bree, $y = $ traffic on middle section of Jeppe, $z = $ traffic on middle section of Simmons, $w = $ traffic on middle section of Harrison, the general solution is $x = w - 100$, $y = w$, $z = w$, w arbitrary. **b.** No; there are infinitely many possible values for y. **c.** 500 cars/minute **d.** 100 cars/minute **e.** No; a large number of cars can circulate around the middle block without affecting the numbers shown.   **35. a.** No; the corresponding system of equations is underdetermined. The net flow of traffic along any of the three stretches of Broadway would suffice. **b.** West   **37.** \$10 billion   **39.** $x = $ Water, $y = $ Gray matter, $z = $ Tumor   **41.** $x = $ Water, $y = $ Bone, $z = $ Tumor, $u = $ Air   **43.** Tumor   **45.** 200 Democrats, 20 Republicans, 13 of other parties

47. Yes; $20m in Company X; $5m in Company Y, $10m in Company Z, and $30m in Company W   49. It is not realistic to expect to use exactly all of the ingredients. Solutions of the associated system may involve negative numbers or not exist. Only solutions with non-negative values for all the unknowns correspond to being able to use up all of the ingredients.
51. Yes; $x = 100$ 53. Yes; $0.3x - 0.7y + 0.3z = 0$ is one form of the equation.   55. No; represented by an inequality rather than an equation.   57. Answers will vary.

Chapter 2 Review

1. One solution   3. Infinitely many solutions

5. One solution

7. $(6/5, 7/5)$ 9. $(3y/2, y)$; y arbitrary   11. $(-0.7, 1.7)$
13. $(-1, -1, -1)$ 15. $(z - 2, 4(z - 1), z)$; z arbitrary
17. No solution   19. $-40°$ 21. It is impossible; setting $F = 1.8C$ leads to an inconsistent system of equations.
23. $x + y + z + w = 10$; linear   25. $w = 0$; linear
27. $-1.3y + z = 0$ or $1.3y - z = 0$; linear   29. 550 packages from Duffin House, 350 from Higgins Press   31. 1,200 packages from Duffin House, 200 from Higgins Press   33. $40
35. Seven of each   37. 5,000 hits per day at OHaganBooks.com, 1,250 at JungleBooks.com, 3,750 at FarmerBooks.com
39. 100 shares of HAL, 20 shares of POM, and 80 shares of WELL   41. Billy-Sean is forced to take exactly the following combination: Liberal Arts: 52 credits, Sciences: 12 credits, Fine Arts: 12 credits, Mathematics: 48 credits.   43. a. $x = 100$, $y = 100 + w$, $z = 300 - w$, w arbitrary   b. 100 book orders per day   c. 300 book orders per day   d. $x = 100$, $y = 400$, $z = 0$, $w = 300$ e. 100 book orders per day   45. New York to OHaganBooks.com: 450 packages, New York to FantasyBooks.com: 50 packages, Illinois to OHaganBooks.com: 150 packages, Illinois to FantasyBooks.com: 150 packages

Chapter 3

Section 3.1

1. 1×4; 0   3. 4×1; 5/2   5. $p \times q$; e_{22} 7. 2×2; 3
9. $1 \times n$; d_r 11. $x = 1, y = 2, z = 3, w = 4$

13. $\begin{bmatrix} 0.25 & -2 \\ 1 & 0.5 \\ -2 & 5 \end{bmatrix}$ 15. $\begin{bmatrix} -0.75 & -1 \\ 0 & -0.5 \\ -1 & 6 \end{bmatrix}$

17. $\begin{bmatrix} -1 & -1 \\ 1 & -1 \\ -1 & 5 \end{bmatrix}$ 19. $\begin{bmatrix} 0 & 2 & -2 \\ -2 & 0 & 4 \end{bmatrix}$

21. $\begin{bmatrix} 4 & -1 & -1 \\ 5 & 1 & 0 \end{bmatrix}$ 23. $\begin{bmatrix} -2+x & 0 & 1+w \\ -5+z & 3+r & 2 \end{bmatrix}$

25. $\begin{bmatrix} -1 & -2 & 1 \\ -5 & 5 & -3 \end{bmatrix}$ 27. $\begin{bmatrix} 9 & 15 \\ 0 & -3 \\ -3 & 3 \end{bmatrix}$

29. $\begin{bmatrix} -8.5 & -22.35 & -24.4 \\ 54.2 & 20 & 42.2 \end{bmatrix}$

31. $\begin{bmatrix} 1.54 & 8.58 \\ 5.94 & 0 \\ 6.16 & 7.26 \end{bmatrix}$ 33. $\begin{bmatrix} 7.38 & 76.96 \\ 20.33 & 0 \\ 29.12 & 39.92 \end{bmatrix}$

35. $\begin{bmatrix} -19.85 & 115.82 \\ -50.935 & 46 \\ -57.24 & 94.62 \end{bmatrix}$

37. $[2.2 \ \ 10.3 \ \ 1.1]$, $[2.6 \ \ 11.2 \ \ 6.9]$

39. Sales $= \begin{bmatrix} 700 & 1{,}300 & 2{,}000 \\ 400 & 300 & 500 \end{bmatrix}$

Inventory $-$ Sales $= \begin{bmatrix} 300 & 700 & 3{,}000 \\ 600 & 4{,}700 & 1{,}500 \end{bmatrix}$

41. Profit = Revenue − Cost;

	2004	*2005*	*2006*
Full Boots	$8,000	$7,200	$8,800
Half Boots	$5,600	$5,760	$7,040
Sandals	$2,800	$3,500	$4,000

43. 1980 distribution $= A = [49.1 \ \ 58.9 \ \ 75.4 \ \ 43.2]$. 1990 distribution $= B = [50.8 \ \ 59.7 \ \ 85.4 \ \ 52.8]$. Net change 1980 to 1990 $= B - A = [1.7 \ \ 0.8 \ \ 10 \ \ 9.6]$ (all net increases).
45. Total Foreclosures = Foreclosures in California + Foreclosures in Florida + Foreclosures in Texas = $[7{,}100 \ \ 3{,}300 \ \ 5{,}700 \ \ 5{,}000 \ \ 4{,}300]$ + $[3{,}500 \ \ 900 \ \ 2{,}400 \ \ 2{,}800 \ \ 2{,}300]$ + $[1{,}900 \ \ 1{,}000 \ \ 1{,}900 \ \ 2{,}100 \ \ 2{,}100]$ = $[12{,}500 \ \ 5{,}200 \ \ 10{,}000 \ \ 9{,}900 \ \ 8{,}700]$
47. Foreclosures in California − Foreclosures in Florida $= [7{,}100 \ \ 3{,}300 \ \ 5{,}700 \ \ 5{,}000 \ \ 4{,}300]$ − $[3{,}500 \ \ 900 \ \ 2{,}400 \ \ 2{,}800 \ \ 2{,}300]$ = $[3{,}600 \ \ 2{,}400 \ \ 3{,}300 \ \ 2{,}200 \ \ 2{,}000]$; the difference was greatest in August 2008.

49. a. Use $= \begin{matrix} \text{Pom II} \\ \text{Pom Classic} \end{matrix} \begin{matrix} \text{Proc} & \text{Mem} & \text{Tubes} \end{matrix} \begin{bmatrix} 2 & 16 & 20 \\ 1 & 4 & 40 \end{bmatrix}$

Inventory $= \begin{bmatrix} 500 & 5{,}000 & 10{,}000 \\ 200 & 2{,}000 & 20{,}000 \end{bmatrix}$

Inventory $- 100 \times$ Use $= \begin{bmatrix} 300 & 3{,}400 & 8{,}000 \\ 100 & 1{,}600 & 16{,}000 \end{bmatrix}$

b. After 4 months

51. a. $A = \begin{bmatrix} 440 & 190 \\ 950 & 950 \\ 1{,}790 & 200 \end{bmatrix}$ $D = \begin{bmatrix} -20 & 40 \\ 50 & 50 \\ 0 & 100 \end{bmatrix}$

2008 Tourism $= A + D = \begin{bmatrix} 420 & 230 \\ 1{,}000 & 1{,}000 \\ 1{,}790 & 300 \end{bmatrix}$

b. $\frac{1}{2}(A + B)$; $\begin{bmatrix} 430 & 210 \\ 975 & 975 \\ 1{,}790 & 250 \end{bmatrix}$

53. No; for two matrices to be equal, they must have the same dimension. **55.** The ijth entry of the sum $A + B$ is obtained by adding the ijth entries of A and B. **57.** It would have zeros down the main diagonal:

$A = \begin{bmatrix} 0 & \# & \# & \# & \# \\ \# & 0 & \# & \# & \# \\ \# & \# & 0 & \# & \# \\ \# & \# & \# & 0 & \# \\ \# & \# & \# & \# & 0 \end{bmatrix}$ The symbols # indicate arbitrary

numbers. **59.** $(A^T)_{ij} = A_{ji}$ **61.** Answers will vary.

a. $\begin{bmatrix} 0 & -4 \\ 4 & 0 \end{bmatrix}$ **b.** $\begin{bmatrix} 0 & -4 & 5 \\ 4 & 0 & 1 \\ -5 & -1 & 0 \end{bmatrix}$ **63.** The associativity of

matrix addition is a consequence of the associativity of addition of numbers because we add matrices by adding the corresponding entries (which are real numbers).

Section 3.2

1. $[13]$ **3.** $[5/6]$ **5.** $[-2y + z]$ **7.** Undefined
9. $[3 \quad 0 \quad -6 \quad -2]$ **11.** $[-6 \quad 37 \quad 7]$

13. $\begin{bmatrix} -4 & -7 & -1 \\ 9 & 17 & 0 \end{bmatrix}$ **15.** $\begin{bmatrix} 0 & 1 \\ 0 & 0 \end{bmatrix}$ **17.** $\begin{bmatrix} 1 & -1 \\ 1 & -1 \end{bmatrix}$ **19.** $\begin{bmatrix} 0 & 0 \\ 0 & 0 \end{bmatrix}$

21. Undefined **23.** $\begin{bmatrix} 1 & -5 & 3 \\ 0 & 0 & 9 \\ 0 & 4 & 1 \end{bmatrix}$ **25.** $\begin{bmatrix} 3 \\ -4 \\ 0 \\ 3 \end{bmatrix}$

27. $\begin{bmatrix} 0.23 & 5.36 & -21.65 \\ -13.18 & -5.82 & -16.62 \\ -11.21 & -9.9 & 0.99 \\ -2.1 & 2.34 & 2.46 \end{bmatrix}$

29. $A^2 = \begin{bmatrix} 0 & 0 & 1 & 2 \\ 0 & 0 & 0 & 1 \\ 0 & 0 & 0 & 0 \\ 0 & 0 & 0 & 0 \end{bmatrix}$ $A^3 = \begin{bmatrix} 0 & 0 & 0 & 1 \\ 0 & 0 & 0 & 0 \\ 0 & 0 & 0 & 0 \\ 0 & 0 & 0 & 0 \end{bmatrix}$

$A^4 = \begin{bmatrix} 0 & 0 & 0 & 0 \\ 0 & 0 & 0 & 0 \\ 0 & 0 & 0 & 0 \\ 0 & 0 & 0 & 0 \end{bmatrix}$ $A^{100} = \begin{bmatrix} 0 & 0 & 0 & 0 \\ 0 & 0 & 0 & 0 \\ 0 & 0 & 0 & 0 \\ 0 & 0 & 0 & 0 \end{bmatrix}$

31. $\begin{bmatrix} 4 & -1 \\ -1 & -7 \end{bmatrix}$ **33.** $\begin{bmatrix} 4 & -1 \\ -12 & 2 \end{bmatrix}$ **35.** $\begin{bmatrix} -2 & 1 & -2 \\ 10 & -2 & 2 \\ -10 & 2 & -2 \end{bmatrix}$

37. $\begin{bmatrix} -2 + x - z & 2 - r & -6 + w \\ 10 + 2z & -2 + 2r & 10 \\ -10 - 2z & 2 - 2r & -10 \end{bmatrix}$

39. a.–d. $P^2 = P^4 = P^8 = P^{1{,}000} = \begin{bmatrix} 0.2 & 0.8 \\ 0.2 & 0.8 \end{bmatrix}$

41. a. $P^2 = \begin{bmatrix} 0.01 & 0.99 \\ 0 & 1 \end{bmatrix}$ **b.** $P^4 = \begin{bmatrix} 0.0001 & 0.9999 \\ 0 & 1 \end{bmatrix}$

c and d. $P^8 \approx P^{1{,}000} \approx \begin{bmatrix} 0 & 1 \\ 0 & 1 \end{bmatrix}$

43. a.–d. $P^2 = P^4 = P^8 = P^{1{,}000} = \begin{bmatrix} 0.25 & 0.25 & 0.50 \\ 0.25 & 0.25 & 0.50 \\ 0.25 & 0.25 & 0.50 \end{bmatrix}$

45. $2x - y + 4z = 3$; $-4x + 3y/4 + z/3 = -1$; $-3x = 0$
47. $x - y + w = -1$; $x + y + 2z + 4w = 2$

49. $\begin{bmatrix} 1 & -1 \\ 2 & -1 \end{bmatrix} \begin{bmatrix} x \\ y \end{bmatrix} = \begin{bmatrix} 4 \\ 0 \end{bmatrix}$

51. $\begin{bmatrix} 1 & 1 & -1 \\ 2 & 1 & 1 \\ \frac{3}{4} & 0 & \frac{1}{2} \end{bmatrix} \begin{bmatrix} x \\ y \\ z \end{bmatrix} = \begin{bmatrix} 8 \\ 4 \\ 1 \end{bmatrix}$

53. Revenue = Price × Quantity =

$[15 \quad 10 \quad 12] \begin{bmatrix} 50 \\ 40 \\ 30 \end{bmatrix} = [1{,}510]$

55. Price: $\begin{matrix} \text{Hard} \\ \text{Soft} \\ \text{Plastic} \end{matrix} \begin{bmatrix} 30 \\ 10 \\ 15 \end{bmatrix}$;

$\begin{bmatrix} 700 & 1{,}300 & 2{,}000 \\ 400 & 300 & 500 \end{bmatrix} \begin{bmatrix} 30 \\ 10 \\ 15 \end{bmatrix} = \begin{bmatrix} \$64{,}000 \\ \$22{,}500 \end{bmatrix}$

57. $264,000 **59.** $5,100 billion (or $5.1 trillion)
61. $D = N(F - M)$ where N is the income per person, and F and M are, respectively, the female and male populations in 2020; $400 billion **63.** $[1.2 \quad 1.0]$, which represents the amount, in billions of pounds, by which cheese production in north central states exceeded that in western states. **65.** Number of foreclosures handled by firm = Percentage handled by firm × Total number =

$[0.10 \quad 0.05 \quad 0.20] \begin{bmatrix} 5{,}700 & 5{,}000 & 4{,}300 \\ 2{,}400 & 2{,}800 & 2{,}300 \\ 1{,}900 & 2{,}100 & 2{,}100 \end{bmatrix} =$

$[1{,}070 \quad 1{,}060 \quad 965]$
67. The number of foreclosures in California and Florida combined in each of the months shown.

69. $[1 \quad -1 \quad 1] \begin{bmatrix} 5{,}700 & 5{,}000 & 4{,}300 \\ 2{,}400 & 2{,}800 & 2{,}300 \\ 1{,}900 & 2{,}100 & 2{,}100 \end{bmatrix} \begin{bmatrix} 1 \\ 1 \\ 1 \end{bmatrix} = [13{,}600]$

71. $\begin{bmatrix} 2 & 16 & 20 \\ 1 & 4 & 40 \end{bmatrix} \begin{bmatrix} 100 & 150 \\ 50 & 40 \\ 10 & 15 \end{bmatrix} = \begin{bmatrix} \$1{,}200 & \$1{,}240 \\ \$700 & \$910 \end{bmatrix}$

73. $AB = \begin{bmatrix} 29.6 \\ 85.5 \\ 97.5 \end{bmatrix}$ $AC = \begin{bmatrix} 22 & 7.6 \\ 47.5 & 38 \\ 89.5 & 8 \end{bmatrix}$ The entries of AB give the number of people from each of the three regions who settle in Australia or South Africa, while the entries in AC break those figures down further into settlers in South Africa and settlers in Australia.   **75.** Distribution in 2006 = A = [55.1 66.2 110.0 70.0]; distribution in 2007 = $A \cdot P \approx$ [54.8 66.3 110.3 69.9]   **77.** Answers will vary. One example: $A = [1 \quad 2]$, $B = \begin{bmatrix} 1 & 2 & 3 \\ 4 & 5 & 6 \end{bmatrix}$. Another example: $A = [1]$, $B = [1 \quad 2]$.   **79.** Multiplication of 1×1 matrices is just ordinary multiplication of the single entries: $[a][b] = [ab]$.   **81.** The claim is correct. Every matrix equation represents the equality of two matrices. Equating the corresponding entries gives a system of equations.   **83.** Answers will vary. Here is a possible scenario: costs of items A, B, and C in 1995 = [10 20 30], percentage increases in these costs in 1996 = [0.5 0.1 0.20], actual increases in costs = [10 × 0.5 20 × 0.1 30 × 0.20]   **85.** It produces a matrix whose ij entry is the product of the ij entries of the two matrices.

Section 3.3

1. Yes   **3.** Yes   **5.** No   **7.** $\begin{bmatrix} -1 & 1 \\ 2 & -1 \end{bmatrix}$ **9.** $\begin{bmatrix} 0 & 1 \\ 1 & 0 \end{bmatrix}$

11. $\begin{bmatrix} 1 & -1 \\ -1 & 2 \end{bmatrix}$ **13.** Singular   **15.** $\begin{bmatrix} 1 & -1 & 0 \\ 0 & 1 & -1 \\ 0 & 0 & 1 \end{bmatrix}$

17. $\begin{bmatrix} 1 & -1 & 1 \\ \frac{1}{2} & 0 & -\frac{1}{2} \\ -\frac{1}{2} & 1 & -\frac{1}{2} \end{bmatrix}$ **19.** $\begin{bmatrix} 1 & \frac{1}{3} & -\frac{1}{3} \\ 1 & -\frac{2}{3} & -\frac{1}{3} \\ -1 & \frac{1}{3} & \frac{2}{3} \end{bmatrix}$

21. Singular   **23.** $\begin{bmatrix} 0 & 1 & -2 & 1 \\ 0 & 1 & -1 & 0 \\ 1 & -1 & 2 & -1 \\ 0 & 1 & -1 & 1 \end{bmatrix}$

25. $\begin{bmatrix} 1 & -2 & 1 & 0 \\ 0 & 1 & -2 & 1 \\ 0 & 0 & 1 & -2 \\ 0 & 0 & 0 & 1 \end{bmatrix}$ **27.** $-2; \begin{bmatrix} \frac{1}{2} & \frac{1}{2} \\ \frac{1}{2} & -\frac{1}{2} \end{bmatrix}$

29. $-2; \begin{bmatrix} -2 & 1 \\ \frac{3}{2} & -\frac{1}{2} \end{bmatrix}$ **31.** $1/36; \begin{bmatrix} 6 & 6 \\ 0 & 6 \end{bmatrix}$ **33.** 0; Singular

35. $\begin{bmatrix} 0.38 & 0.45 \\ 0.49 & -0.41 \end{bmatrix}$ **37.** $\begin{bmatrix} 0.00 & -0.99 \\ 0.81 & 2.87 \end{bmatrix}$ **39.** Singular

41. $\begin{bmatrix} 91.35 & -8.65 & 0 & -71.30 \\ -0.07 & -0.07 & 0 & 2.49 \\ 2.60 & 2.60 & -4.35 & 1.37 \\ 2.69 & 2.69 & 0 & -2.10 \end{bmatrix}$ **43.** (5/2, 3/2)

45. (6, −4)   **47.** (6, 6, 6)   **49. a.** (10, −5, −3)   **b.** (6, 1, 5)   **c.** (0, 0, 0)   **51. a.** 10/3 servings of beans, and 5/6 slices of bread

b. $\begin{bmatrix} -1/2 & 1/6 \\ 7/8 & -5/24 \end{bmatrix} \begin{bmatrix} A \\ B \end{bmatrix} = \begin{bmatrix} -A/2 + B/6 \\ 7A/8 - 5B/24 \end{bmatrix}$; that is, $-A/2 + B/6$ servings of beans and $7A/8 - 5B/24$ slices of bread   **53. a.** 100 batches of vanilla, 50 batches of mocha, 100 batches of strawberry   **b.** 100 batches of vanilla, no mocha, 200 batches of strawberry   **c.** $\begin{bmatrix} 1 & -1/3 & -1/3 \\ -1 & 0 & 1 \\ 0 & 2/3 & -1/3 \end{bmatrix} \begin{bmatrix} A \\ B \\ C \end{bmatrix}$, or

$A - B/3 - C/3$ batches of vanilla, $-A + C$ batches of mocha, and $2B/3 - C/3$ batches of strawberry   **55.** $5,000 in FCTFX, $2,000 in FSAZX, $2,000 in FUSFX   **57.** 100 shares of GE, 50 shares of WMT, 50 shares of XOM   **59.** Distribution in 2006 = A = [55.1 66.2 110.0 70.0]; distribution in 2005 = $A \cdot P^{-1} \approx$ [55.4 66.1 109.7 70.1]   **61. a.** (−0.7071, 3.5355)   **b.** R^2, R^3 **c.** R^{-1} **63.** [37 81 40 80 15 45 40 96 29 59 4 8]   **65.** CORRECT ANSWER   **67.** (A)   **69.** The inverse does not exist—the matrix is singular. (If two rows of a matrix are the same, then row reducing it will lead to a row of zeros, and so it cannot be reduced to the identity.)   **73.** When one or more of the d_i are zero. If that is the case, then the matrix $[D \mid I]$ easily reduces to a matrix that has a row of zeros on the left-hand portion, so that D is singular. Conversely, if none of the d_i are zero, then $[D \mid I]$ easily reduces to a matrix of the form $[I \mid E]$, showing that D is invertible.   **75.** $(AB)(B^{-1}A^{-1}) = A(BB^{-1})A^{-1} = AIA^{-1} = AA^{-1} = I$ **77.** If A has an inverse, then every system of equations $AX = B$ has a unique solution, namely $X = A^{-1}B$. But if A reduces to a matrix with a row of zeros, then such a system has either infinitely many solutions or no solution at all.

Section 3.4

1. -1 **3.** -0.25 **5.** [0 0 1 0]; $e = 2.25$ **7.** $[1 \quad 0 \quad 0]^T$ or $[0 \quad 1 \quad 0]^T$; $e = 1/4$

9. $\begin{array}{c} \\ A \end{array}\begin{array}{cc} & B \\ & \begin{array}{cc} p & r \end{array} \\ \begin{array}{c} a \\ b \end{array} \begin{bmatrix} 1 & 10 \\ 2 & -4 \end{bmatrix} \end{array}$ **11.** $\begin{array}{c} \\ A \end{array}\begin{array}{c} B \\ c \\ 3 \ [-1] \end{array}$ **13.** $\begin{array}{c} \\ A \end{array}\begin{array}{c} B \\ b \\ q \ [0] \end{array}$

15. Strictly determined. A's optimal strategy is a; B's optimal strategy is q; value: 1   **17.** Not strictly determined   **19.** Not strictly determined   **21.** $R = [1/4 \quad 3/4]$, $C = [3/4 \quad 1/4]^T$, $e = -1/4$ **23.** $R = [3/4 \quad 1/4]$, $C = [3/4 \quad 1/4]^T$, $e = -5/4$

25.
$$\begin{array}{c} \\ \text{You} \end{array}\begin{array}{cc} & \text{Friend} \\ & \begin{array}{cc} H & T \end{array} \\ \begin{array}{c} H \\ T \end{array} \begin{bmatrix} -1 & 1 \\ 1 & -1 \end{bmatrix} \end{array}$$

27. F = France; S = Sweden; N = Norway;

Your Opponent Defends

$$\begin{array}{c} \\ \text{You Invade} \end{array} \begin{array}{c} \\ F \\ S \\ N \end{array} \begin{array}{ccc} F & S & N \\ \begin{bmatrix} -1 & 1 & 1 \\ 1 & -1 & 1 \\ 1 & 1 & -1 \end{bmatrix} \end{array}$$

29. B = Brakpan; N = Nigel; S = Springs;

Your Opponent

$$\begin{array}{c} \\ \text{You} \end{array} \begin{array}{c} \\ B \\ N \\ S \end{array} \begin{array}{ccc} B & N & S \\ \begin{bmatrix} 0 & 0 & 1,000 \\ 0 & 0 & 1,000 \\ -1,000 & -1,000 & 0 \end{bmatrix} \end{array}$$

31. P = PleasantTap; T = Thunder Rumble; S = Strike the Gold, N = None;

Winner

$$\begin{array}{c} \\ \text{You Bet} \end{array} \begin{array}{c} \\ P \\ T \\ S \end{array} \begin{array}{cccc} P & T & S & N \\ \begin{bmatrix} 25 & -10 & -10 & -10 \\ -10 & 35 & -10 & -10 \\ -10 & -10 & 40 & -10 \end{bmatrix} \end{array}$$

33. You can expect to lose 39 customers.   **35.** Option 2: Move to the suburbs.   **37. a.** About 66% **b.** Yes; spend the whole night studying game theory; 75% **c.** Game theory; 57.5%   **39. a.** Lay off 10 workers; cost: $40,000 **b.** 60 inches of snow, costing $350,000 **c.** Lay off 15 workers   **41. a.** CE should charge $1,000 and GCS should charge $900; 15% gain in market share for CE **b.** CE should charge $1,200 (the more CE can charge for the same market, the better!)   **43.** Pablo vs. Noto; evenly matched   **45.** Both commanders should use the northern route; 1 day   **47.** Confess

49. a.

$$\begin{array}{c} \\ \text{McCain} \end{array} \begin{array}{c} \\ F \\ O \end{array} \begin{array}{cc} F & O \\ \begin{bmatrix} 24 & 21 \\ 25 & 24 \end{bmatrix} \end{array}$$

Obama

b. Both candidates should visit Ohio, leaving Bush with a 21% chance of winning the election.
51. Allocate 1/7 of the budget to WISH and the rest (6/7) to WASH. Softex will lose approximately $2,860.   **53.** Like a saddle point in a payoff matrix, the center of a saddle is a low point (minimum height) in one direction and a high point (maximum) in a perpendicular direction.   **55.** Although there is a saddle point in the 2,4 position, you would be wrong to use saddle points (based on the minimax criterion) to reach the conclusion that row strategy 2 is best. One reason is that the entries in the matrix do not represent payoffs because high numbers of employees in an area do not necessarily represent benefit to the row player. Another reason for this is that there is no opponent deciding what your job will be in such a way as to force you into the least populated job.   **57.** If you strictly alternate the two strategies the column player will know which pure strategy you will play on each move, and can choose a pure strategy accordingly. For example, consider the game $A \begin{array}{c} a \quad b \\ \begin{bmatrix} 1 & 0 \\ 0 & 1 \end{bmatrix} \end{array}$ with rows labeled A, B. By the analysis of Example 3 (or the symmetry of the game), the best strategy for the row player is [0.5 0.5] and the best strategy for the column player is $[0.5 \ 0.5]^T$. This gives an expected

value of 0.5 for the game. However, suppose that the row player alternates A and B strictly and that the column player catches on to this. Then, whenever the row player plays A the column player will play b and whenever the row player plays B the column player will play a. This gives a payoff of 0 each time, worse for the row player than the expected value of 0.5.

Section 3.5

1. a. 0.8 **b.** 0.2 **c.** 0.05   **3.** $\begin{bmatrix} 0.2 & 0.1 \\ 0.5 & 0 \end{bmatrix}$

5. $[52,000 \quad 40,000]^T$ **7.** $[50,000 \quad 50,000]^T$
9. $[2,560 \quad 2,800 \quad 4,000]^T$
11. $[27,000 \quad 28,000 \quad 17,000]^T$ **13.** Increase of 100 units in each sector.   **15.** Increase of $[1.5 \quad 0.2 \quad 0.1]^T$; the ith column of $(I - A)^{-1}$ gives the change in production necessary to meet an increase in external demand of one unit for the product of Sector i.

17. $A = \begin{bmatrix} 0.2 & 0.4 & 0.5 \\ 0 & 0.8 & 0 \\ 0 & 0.2 & 0.5 \end{bmatrix}$ **19.** Main DR: $80,000, Bits &

Bytes: $38,000   **21.** Equipment Sector production approximately $86,000 million, Components Sector production approximately $140,000 million   **23. a.** 0.006 **b.** textiles; clothing and footwear

25. Columns of $\begin{bmatrix} 1,140.99 & 2.05 & 13.17 & 20.87 \\ 332.10 & 1,047.34 & 26.05 & 111.18 \\ 0.12 & 0.13 & 1,031.19 & 1.35 \\ 93.88 & 95.69 & 215.50 & 1,016.15 \end{bmatrix}$

(in millions of dollars)   **27. a.** $0.78 **b.** Other food products
29. It would mean that all of the sectors require neither their own product or the product of any other sector.   **31.** It would mean that all of the output of that sector was used internally in the economy; none of the output was available for export and no importing was necessary.   **33.** It means that an increase in demand for one sector (the column sector) has no effect on the production of another sector (the row sector).   **35.** Usually, to produce one unit of one sector requires less than one unit of input from another. We would expect then that an increase in demand of one unit for one sector would require a smaller increase in production in another sector.

Chapter 3 Review

1. Undefined   **3.** $\begin{bmatrix} 1 & 8 \\ 5 & 11 \\ 6 & 13 \end{bmatrix}$ **5.** $\begin{bmatrix} 1 & 3 \\ 2 & 3 \\ 3 & 3 \end{bmatrix}$ **7.** $\begin{bmatrix} 1 & -2 \\ 0 & 1 \end{bmatrix}$

9. $\begin{bmatrix} 2 & 4 \\ 1 & 12 \end{bmatrix}$ **11.** $\begin{bmatrix} 1 & 1 \\ 0 & 1 \end{bmatrix}$ **13.** $\begin{bmatrix} 1 & -1/2 & -5/2 \\ 0 & 1/4 & -1/4 \\ 0 & 0 & 1 \end{bmatrix}$

15. Singular   **17.** $\begin{bmatrix} 1 & 2 \\ 3 & 4 \end{bmatrix}\begin{bmatrix} x \\ y \end{bmatrix} = \begin{bmatrix} 0 \\ 2 \end{bmatrix}$; $\begin{bmatrix} x \\ y \end{bmatrix} = \begin{bmatrix} 2 \\ -1 \end{bmatrix}$

19. $\begin{bmatrix} 1 & 1 & 1 \\ 1 & 2 & 1 \\ 1 & 1 & 2 \end{bmatrix}\begin{bmatrix} x \\ y \\ z \end{bmatrix} = \begin{bmatrix} 2 \\ 3 \\ 1 \end{bmatrix}$; $\begin{bmatrix} x \\ y \\ z \end{bmatrix} = \begin{bmatrix} 2 \\ 1 \\ -1 \end{bmatrix}$

21. $R = \begin{bmatrix} 1 & 0 & 0 \end{bmatrix}, C = \begin{bmatrix} 0 & 1 & 0 & 0 \end{bmatrix}^T, e = 1$

23. $R = \begin{bmatrix} 0 & 0.8 & 0.2 \end{bmatrix}, C = \begin{bmatrix} 0.2 & 0 & 0.8 \end{bmatrix}, e = -0.2$

25. $\begin{bmatrix} 1,100 \\ 700 \end{bmatrix}$ **27.** $\begin{bmatrix} 48,125 \\ 22,500 \\ 10,000 \end{bmatrix}$

29. Inventory − Sales + Purchases =

$\begin{bmatrix} 2,500 & 4,000 & 3,000 \\ 1,500 & 3,000 & 1,000 \end{bmatrix} - \begin{bmatrix} 300 & 500 & 100 \\ 100 & 600 & 200 \end{bmatrix} +$

$\begin{bmatrix} 400 & 400 & 300 \\ 200 & 400 & 300 \end{bmatrix} = \begin{bmatrix} 2,600 & 3,900 & 3,200 \\ 1,600 & 2,800 & 1,100 \end{bmatrix}$

31. $N = \begin{bmatrix} 2,600 & 3,900 & 3,200 \\ 1,600 & 2,800 & 1,100 \end{bmatrix} - x\begin{bmatrix} 280 & 550 & 100 \\ 50 & 500 & 120 \end{bmatrix} +$

$x\begin{bmatrix} 400 & 400 & 300 \\ 200 & 400 & 300 \end{bmatrix} = \begin{bmatrix} 2,600 & 3,900 & 3,200 \\ 1,600 & 2,800 & 1,100 \end{bmatrix} +$

$x\begin{bmatrix} 120 & -150 & 200 \\ 150 & -100 & 180 \end{bmatrix}$; 28 months from now (July 1)

December 1 of next year.

33. Revenue = Quantity × Price =

$\begin{bmatrix} 280 & 550 & 100 \\ 50 & 500 & 120 \end{bmatrix}\begin{bmatrix} 5 \\ 6 \\ 5.5 \end{bmatrix} = \begin{bmatrix} 5,250 \\ 3,910 \end{bmatrix}$ Texas Nevada

35. July 1: 1,000 shares, August 1: 2,000 shares, September 1: 2,000 shares   **37.** Loss = Number of shares × (Purchase price − Dividends − Selling price) =

$\begin{bmatrix} 1,000 & 2,000 & 2,000 \end{bmatrix}\left(\begin{bmatrix} 20 \\ 10 \\ 5 \end{bmatrix} - \begin{bmatrix} 0.10 \\ 0.10 \\ 0 \end{bmatrix} - \begin{bmatrix} 3 \\ 1 \\ 1 \end{bmatrix}\right) =$

$[42,700]$

39. $\begin{bmatrix} 2,000 & 4,000 & 4,000 \end{bmatrix}\begin{bmatrix} 0.8 & 0.1 & 0.1 \\ 0.4 & 0.6 & 0 \\ 0.2 & 0 & 0.8 \end{bmatrix} =$

$[4,000 \quad 2,600 \quad 3,400]$ **41.** The matrix shows that no JungleBooks customers switched directly to FarmerBooks, so the only way to get to FarmerBooks is via OHaganBooks. **43.** Go with the "3 for 1" promotion and gain 20,000 customers from JungleBooks.   **45.** JungleBooks will go with "3 for 2" and OHaganBooks will go with Finite Math, resulting in a gain of 15,000 customers to OHaganBooks.   **47.** Choose between the "3 for 1" and Finite Math promotions with probabilities 60% and 40%, respectively. You would expect to gain 12,000 customers from JungleBooks (if you played this game many times).

49. $A = \begin{bmatrix} 0.1 & 0.5 \\ 0.01 & 0.05 \end{bmatrix}$ **51.** $1,190 worth of paper, $1,802 worth of books

Chapter 4

Section 4.1

1.

Unbounded

3.

Unbounded

5.

Unbounded

7.

Unbounded

9.

Unbounded

11.

Unbounded

13.
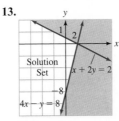
Unbounded;
corner point: (2, 0)

15.

Unbounded;
corner points: (2, 0), (0, 3)

17.

Bounded; corner points:
(5, 0), (10, 0), (10, 8),
(0, 8), (0, 5)

19.

Bounded; corner points:
(0, 0), (5, 0), (0, 5),
(2, 4), (4, 2)

21.

Unbounded; corner points:
(0, 10), (10, 0), (2, 6), (6, 2)

23.

Unbounded;
corner points:
(0, 0), (0, 5/2), (3, 3/2)

25.

Unbounded; corner point: (0, 0)

27.

29.

Corner point: (−7.74, 2.50)

31.

Corner points:
(0.36, −0.68), (1.12, 0.61)

33. $x = $ # quarts of Creamy Vanilla,
$y = $ # quarts of Continental Mocha

Corner points: (0, 0), (250, 0), (0, 300), (200, 100)

35. $x = $ # ounces of chicken, $y = $ # ounces of grain

Corner points: (30, 0), (10, 50), (0, 100)

37. $x = $ # servings of Mixed Cereal for Baby, $y = $ # servings of Mango Tropical Fruit Dessert

Corner points:
(0, 7/4), (1, 1), (32/11, 0)

39. $x = $ # dollars in PNF, $y = $ # dollars in FDMMX

Corner points:
(70,000, 0), (80,000, 0), (20,000, 60,000)

41. $x = $ # shares of ED, $y = $ # shares of GE

Corner points:
(0, 625), (0, 500), (250, 0)

43. $x = $ # full-page ads in Sports Illustrated,
$y = $ # full-page ads in GQ

Corner points: (3, 7), (4, 3) (Rounded)

45. An example is $x \geq 0$, $y \geq 0$, $x + y \geq 1$.   **47.** The given triangle can be described as the solution set of the system $x \geq 0$, $y \geq 0$, $x + 2y \leq 2$.   **49.** Answers may vary. One limitation is that the method is only suitable for situations with two unknown quantities. Accuracy is also limited when graphing.   **51. (C) 53. (B)   55.** There are no feasible solutions; that is, it is impossible to satisfy all the constraints.   **57.** Answers will vary.

Section 4.2

1. $p = 6$, $x = 3$, $y = 3$ **3.** $c = 4$, $x = 2$, $y = 2$ **5.** $p = 24$, $x = 7$, $y = 3$ **7.** $p = 16$, $x = 4$, $y = 2$ **9.** $c = 1.8$, $x = 6$, $y = 2$ **11.** Max: $p = 16$, $x = 4$, $y = 6$. Min: $p = 2$, $x = 2$, $y = 0$ **13.** No optimal solution; objective function unbounded   **15.** $c = 28$; $(x, y) = (14, 0)$ and $(6, 4)$ and the line connecting them   **17.** $c = 3$, $x = 3$, $y = 2$ **19.** No solution; feasible region empty   **21.** You should make 200 quarts of vanilla and 100 quarts of mocha.   **23.** Ruff, Inc., should use 100 oz of grain and no chicken.   **25.** Feed your child 1 serving of cereal and 1 serving of dessert.   **27.** Purchase 60 compact fluorescent light bulbs and 960 square feet of insulation for a saving of $312 per year in energy costs.   **29.** Mix 5 servings of Cell-Tech and 6 servings of RiboForce HP for a cost of $20.60.   **31.** Make 200 Dracula Salamis and 400 Frankenstein Sausages, for a profit of $1,400.   **33.** 30 spots on "American Idol" and 30 spots on "Back to You"   **35.** Buy no shares of ATRI and 500 shares of BBY for maximum company earnings of $1,600.   **37.** Purchase 250 shares of ED and no shares of GE for a total risk index of 500.   **39.** He should instruct in diplomacy for 10 hours per week and in battle for 40 hours per week, giving a weekly profit of 2,400 ducats.   **41.** Gillian could expend a minimum of 360,000 pico-shirleys of energy by using 480 sleep spells and 160 shock spells. (There is actually a whole line of solutions joining the one above with $x = 2,880/7$, $y = 1,440/7$.)   **43.** 100 hours per week for new customers and 60 hours per week for old customers.   **45. (A)   47.** Every point along the line connecting them is also an optimal solution.   **53.** A simple example is the following: Maximize profit $p = 2x + y$ subject to $x \geq 0$, $y \geq 0$. Then p can be made as large as we like by choosing large values of x and/or y. Thus there is no optimal solution to the problem.   **55.** Mathematically, this means that there are infinitely many possible solutions: one for each point along the line joining the two corner points in question. In practice, select those points with integer solutions (since x and y must be whole numbers in this problem) that are in the feasible region and close to this line, and choose the one that gives the largest profit.

Section 4.3

1. $p = 8$; $x = 4$, $y = 0$ **3.** $p = 4$; $x = 4$, $y = 0$ **5.** $p = 80$; $x = 10$, $y = 0$, $z = 10$ **7.** $p = 53$; $x = 5$, $y = 0$, $z = 3$ **9.** $z = 14,500$; $x_1 = 0$, $x_2 = 500/3$, $x_3 = 5,000/3$ **11.** $p = 6$; $x = 2$, $y = 1$, $z = 0$, $w = 3$ **13.** $p = 7$; $x = 1$, $y = 0$, $z = 2$, $w = 0$, $v = 4$ (or: $x = 1$, $y = 0$, $z = 2$, $w = 1$, $v = 3$.)   **15.** $p = 21$; $x = 0$, $y = 2.27$, $z = 5.73$

17. $p = 4.52$; $x = 1$, $y = 0$, $z = .67$, $w = 1.52$ **19.** $p = 7.7$; $x = 1.1$, $y = 0$, $z = 2.2$, $w = 0$, $v = 4$ **21.** You should purchase 500 calculus texts, no history texts, and no marketing texts. The maximum profit is $5,000 per semester.   **23.** The company can make a maximum profit of $650 by making 100 gallons of PineOrange, 200 gallons of PineKiwi, and 150 gallons of OrangeKiwi.   **25.** The department should offer no Ancient History, 30 sections of Medieval History, and 15 sections of Modern History, for a profit of $1,050,000. There will be 500 students without classes, but all sections and professors are used.   **27.** Plant 80 acres of tomatoes and leave the other 20 acres unplanted. This will give you a profit of $160,000.   **29.** It can make a profit of $10,000 by selling 1,000 servings of Granola, 500 servings of Nutty Granola and no Nuttiest Granola. It is left with 2,000 oz almonds.   **31.** Allocate 5 million gals to process A and 45 million gals to process C. Another solution: Allocate 10 million gals to process B and 40 million gals to process C.   **33.** Use 15 servings of RiboForce HP and none of the others for a maximum of 75g creatine.   **35.** She is wrong; you should buy 500 shares of SNE and no others.   **37.** Allocate $2,250,000 to automobile loans, $500,000 to signature loans, and $2,250,000 to any combination of furniture loans and other secured loans.   **39.** Invest $75,000 in Universal, none in the rest. Another optimal solution is: Invest $18,750 in Universal, and $75,000 in EMI.   **41.** Tucson to Honolulu: 290 boards; Tucson to Venice Beach: 330 boards; Toronto to Honolulu: 0 boards; Toronto to Venice Beach: 200 boards, giving 820 boards shipped.   **43.** Fly 10 people from Chicago to Los Angeles, 5 people from Chicago to New York, and 10 people from Denver to New York.   **45.** Yes; the given problem can be stated as: Maximize $p = 3x - 2y$ subject to $-x + y - z \leq 0$, $x - y - z \leq 6$, $x \geq 0$, $y \geq 0$, $z \geq 0$.   **47.** The graphical method applies only to LP problems in two unknowns, whereas the simplex method can be used to solve LP problems with any number of unknowns.   **49.** She is correct. There are only two constraints, so there can be only two active variables, giving two or fewer nonzero values for the unknowns at each stage.   **51.** A basic solution to a system of linear equations is a solution in which all the non-pivotal variables are taken to be zero; that is, all variables whose values are arbitrary are assigned the value zero. To obtain a basic solution for a given system of linear equations, one can row reduce the associated augmented matrix, write down the general solution, and then set all the parameters (variables with "arbitrary" values) equal to zero.   **53.** No. Let us assume for the sake of simplicity that all the pivots are 1's. (They may certainly be changed to 1's without affecting the value of any of the variables.) Because the entry at the bottom of the pivot column is negative, the bottom row gets replaced by itself plus a positive multiple of the pivot row. The value of the objective function (bottom-right entry) is thus replaced by itself plus a positive multiple of the non-negative rightmost entry of the pivot row. Therefore, it cannot decrease.

Section 4.4

1. $p = 20/3$; $x = 4/3$, $y = 16/3$ **3.** $p = 850/3$; $x = 50/3$, $y = 25/3$ **5.** $p = 750$; $x = 0$, $y = 150$, $z = 0$ **7.** $p = 135$; $x = 0$, $y = 25$, $z = 0$, $w = 15$ **9.** $c = 80$; $x = 20/3$, $y = 20/3$ **11.** $c = 100$; $x = 0$, $y = 100$, $z = 0$ **13.** $c = 111$; $x = 1$, $y = 1$, $z = 1$ **15.** $c = 200$; $x = 200$, $y = 0$, $z = 0$, $w = 0$ **17.** $p = 136.75$; $x = 0$, $y = 25.25$, $z = 0$, $w = 15.25$ **19.** $c = 66.67$; $x = 0$, $y = 66.67$, $z = 0$ **21.** $c = -250$; $x = 0$, $y = 500$, $z = 500$; $w = 1,500$ **23.** Plant 100 acres of tomatoes and no other crops. This will give you a profit of $200,000. (You will be using all 100 acres of your farm.) **25.** 10 mailings to the East Coast, none to the Midwest, 10 to the West Coast. Cost: $900. Another solution resulting in the same cost is no mailings to the East Coast, 15 to the Midwest, none to the West Coast. **27.** 10,000 quarts of orange juice and 2,000 quarts of orange concentrate **29.** Stock 10,000 rock CDs, 5,000 rap CDs, and 5,000 classical CDs for a maximum retail value of $255,000. **31.** One serving of cereal, one serving of juice, and no dessert! **33.** 15 bundles from Nadir, 5 from Sonny, and none from Blunt. Cost: $70,000. Another solution resulting in the same cost is 10 bundles from Nadir, none from Sonny, and 10 from Blunt. **35.** Mix 6 servings of Riboforce HP and 10 servings of Creatine Transport for a cost of $15.60. **37. a.** Build 1 convention-style hotel, 4 vacation-style hotels, and 2 small motels. The total cost will amount to $188 million. **b.** Because 20% of this is $37.6 million, you will still be covered by the subsidy. **39.** Tucson to Honolulu: 500 boards/week; Tucson to Venice Beach: 120 boards/week; Toronto to Honolulu: 0 boards/week; Toronto to Venice Beach: 410 boards/week. Minimum weekly cost is $9,700. **41.** $2,500 from Congressional Integrity Bank, $0 from Citizens' Trust, $7,500 from Checks R Us. **43.** Fly 10 people from Chicago to LA, 5 from Chicago to New York, none from Denver to LA, 10 from Denver to NY at a total cost of $4,520. **45.** Hire no more cardiologists, 12 rehabilitation specialists, and 5 infectious disease specialists. **47.** The solution $x = 0$, $y = 0$, ..., represented by the initial tableau may not be feasible. In phase I we use pivoting to arrive at a basic solution that is feasible. **49.** The basic solution corresponding to the initial tableau has all the unknowns equal to zero, and this is not a feasible solution because it does not satisfy the given inequality. **51. (C)** **53.** Answers may vary. Examples are Exercises 1 and 2. **55.** Answers may vary. A simple example is: Maximize $p = x + y$ subject to $x + y \le 10$, $x + y \ge 20$, $x \ge 0$, $y \ge 0$.

Section 4.5

1. Minimize $c = 6s + 2t$ subject to $s - t \ge 2$, $2s + t \ge 1$, $s \ge 0$, $t \ge 0$ **3.** Maximize $p = 100x + 50y$ subject to $x + 2y \le 2$, $x + y \le 1$, $x \le 3$, $x \ge 0$, $y \ge 0$. **5.** Minimize $c = 3s + 4t + 5u + 6v$ subject to $s + u + v \ge 1$, $s + t + v \ge 1$, $s + t + u \ge 1$, $t + u + v \ge 1$, $s \ge 0$, $t \ge 0$, $u \ge 0$, $v \ge 0$. **7.** Maximize $p = 1,000x + 2,000y + 500z$ subject to $5x + z \le 1$, $-x + z \le 3$, $y \le 1$, $x - y \le 0$, $x \ge 0$, $y \ge 0$, $z \ge 0$. **9.** $c = 4$; $s = 2$, $t = 2$ **11.** $c = 80$; $s = 20/3$, $t = 20/3$ **13.** $c = 1.8$; $s = 6$, $t = 2$ **15.** $c = 25$; $s = 5$, $t = 15$ **17.** $c = 30$; $s = 30$, $t = 0$, $u = 0$ **19.** $c = 100$;

$s = 0$, $t = 100$, $u = 0$ **21.** $c = 30$; $s = 10$, $t = 10$, $u = 10$ **23.** $R = [3/5 \quad 2/5]$, $C = [2/5 \quad 3/5 \quad 0]^T$, $e = 1/5$ **25.** $R = [1/4 \quad 0 \quad 3/4]$, $C = [1/2 \quad 0 \quad 1/2]^T$, $e = 1/2$ **27.** $R = [0 \quad 3/11 \quad 3/11 \quad 5/11]$, $C = [8/11 \quad 0 \quad 2/11 \quad 1/11]^T$, $e = 9/11$ **29.** 4 ounces each of fish and cornmeal, for a total cost of 40¢ per can; 5/12¢ per gram of protein, 5/12¢ per gram of fat. **31.** 100 oz of grain and no chicken, for a total cost of $1; 1/2¢ per gram of protein, 0¢ per gram of fat. **33.** One serving of cereal, one serving of juice, and no dessert! for a total cost of 37¢; 1/6¢ per calorie and 17/120¢ per % U.S. RDA of vitamin C. **35.** 10 mailings to the East coast, none to the Midwest, 10 to the West Coast. Cost: $900; 20¢ per Democrat and 40¢ per Republican. OR 15 mailings to the Midwest and no mailing to the coasts. Cost: $900; 20¢ per Democrat and 40¢ per Republican. **37.** Gillian should use 480 sleep spells and 160 shock spells, costing 360,000 pico-shirleys of energy OR 2,880/7 sleep spells and 1,440/7 shock spells. **39.** T. N. Spend should spend about 73% of the days in Littleville, 27% in Metropolis, and skip Urbantown. T. L. Down should spend about 91% of the days in Littleville, 9% in Metropolis, and skip Urbantown. The expected outcome is that T. L. Down will lose about 227 votes per day of campaigning. **41.** Each player should show one finger with probability 1/2, two fingers with probability 1/3, and three fingers with probability 1/6. The expected outcome is that player A will win 2/3 point per round, on average. **43.** Write moves as (x, y) where x represents the number of regiments sent to the first location and y represents the number sent to the second location. Colonel Blotto should play $(0, 4)$ with probability 4/9, $(2, 2)$ with probability 1/9, and $(4, 0)$ with probability 4/9. Captain Kije has several optimal strategies, one of which is to play $(0, 3)$ with probability 1/30, $(1, 2)$ with probability 8/15, $(2, 1)$ with probability 16/45, and $(3, 0)$ with probability 7/90. The expected outcome is that Colonel Blotto will win 14/9 points on average. **45.** The dual of a standard minimization problem satisfying the non-negative objective condition is a standard maximization problem, which can be solved using the standard simplex algorithm, thus avoiding the need to do Phase I. **47.** Answers will vary. An example is: Minimize $c = x - y$ subject to $x - y \ge 100$, $x + y \ge 200$, $x \ge 0$, $y \ge 0$. This problem can be solved using the techniques in Section 4.4. **49.** Build 1 convention-style hotel, 4 vacation-style hotels, and 2 small motels. **51.** Answers will vary.

Chapter 4 Review

1.

Unbounded

3.

Bounded; corner points: (0, 0), (0, 10), (5, 15/2), (10, 0)

5. $p = 21$; $x = 9$, $y = 3$ **7.** $c = 22$; $x = 8$, $y = 6$
9. $p = 45$; $x = 0$, $y = 15$, $z = 15$
11. $p = 220$; $x = 20$, $y = 20$, $z = 60$
13. $c = 30$; $x = 30$, $y = 0$, $z = 0$
15. $c = 50$; $x = 20$, $y = 10$, $z = 0$, $w = 20$
17. $c = 60$; $x = 24$, $y = 12$ **19.** $c = 20$; $x = 0$, $y = 20$
21. $R = [1/2 \quad 1/2 \quad 0]$, $C = [0 \quad 1/3 \quad 2/3]^T$, $e = 0$
23. $R = [1/27 \quad 7/9 \quad 5/27]$, $C = [8/27 \quad 5/27 \quad 14/27]^T$,
$e = 8/27$ **25. (A)** **27.** 35 **29.** 400 packages from each for a
minimum cost of \$52,000 **31. a.** (B), (D) **b.** 450 packages
from Duffin House, 375 from Higgins Press for a minimum cost
of \$52,500 **33.** 220 shares of EEE and 20 shares of RRR. The
minimum total risk index is 500. **35.** 240 Sprinkles, 120
Storms, and no Hurricanes **37.** Order 600 packages from
Higgins and none from the others, for a total cost of \$90,000.
39. a. Let $x = $ # science credits, $y = $ # fine arts credits, $z = $
liberal arts credits, and $w = $ # math credits. Minimize $C = $
$300x + 300y + 200z + 200w$ subject to: $x + y + z + w \geq 120$;
$x - y \geq 0$; $-2x + w \leq 0$; $-y + 3z - 3w \leq 0$; $x \geq 0$, $y \geq 0$,
$z \geq 0$, $w \geq 0$. **b.** Billy-Sean should take the following
combination: Sciences—24 credits, Fine Arts—no credits,
Liberal Arts—48 credits, Mathematics—48 credits, for a
total cost of \$26,400. **41.** Smallest cost is \$20,000;
New York to OHaganBooks.com: 600 packages, New York to
FantasyBooks.com: 0 packages, Illinois to OHaganbooks.com:
0 packages, Illinois to FantasyBooks.com: 200 packages.
43. FantasyBooks.com should choose between "2 for 1" and
"3 for 2" with probabilities 20% and 80%, respectively.
OHaganBooks.com should choose between "3 for 1" and
"Finite Math" with probabilities 60% and 40%, respectively.
OHaganBooks.com expects to gain 12,000 customers from
FantasyBooks.com.

Chapter 5

Section 5.1

1. $INT = \$120$, $FV = \$2,120$ **3.** $INT = \$505$, $FV = \$20,705$
5. $INT = \$250$, $FV = \$10,250$ **7.** $PV = \$9,090.91$
9. $PV = \$966.18$ **11.** $PV = \$14,457.83$ **13.** \$5,200
15. \$787.40 **17.** 5% **19.** About 0.2503% **21.** In 2 years
23. 3.775% **25.** 65% **27.** 10% **29.** 98.73% **31.** 7.45% if
you had sold in June 2008 **33.** No. Simple interest increase is
linear. The graph is visibly not linear in that time period. Further,
the slopes of the lines through the successive pairs of marked
points are quite different. **35.** 9.2% **37.** 3,260,000
39. $P = 500 + 46t$ ($t = $ time in years since 1950) Graph:

41. Graph (A) is the only possible choice, because the equation
$FV = PV(1 + rt) = PV + PVrt$ gives the future value as a
linear function of time. **43.** Wrong. In simple interest growth,
the change each year is a fixed percentage of the *starting* value,
and not the preceding year's value. (Also see Exercise 44.)
45. Simple interest is always calculated on a constant amount,
PV. If interest is paid into your account, then the amount on
which interest is calculated does not remain constant.

Section 5.2

1. \$13,439.16 **3.** \$11,327.08 **5.** \$19,154.30 **7.** \$12,709.44
9. \$613.91 **11.** \$810.65 **13.** \$1,227.74 **15.** 5.09%
17. 10.47% **19.** 10.52% **21.** \$268.99 **23.** \$728.91
25. \$2,927.15 **27.** \$21,161.79 **29.** \$163,414.56
31. \$55,526.45 per year **33.** \$174,110 **35.** \$750.00
37. \$27,171.92 **39.** \$111,678.96 **41.** \$1,039.21 **43.** The one
earning 11.9% compounded monthly **45.** Yes. The investment
will have grown to about \$150,281 million **47.** 136 reals
49. 245 bolivianos **51.** 223 bolivars **53.** The Nicaragua
investment is better: it is worth about 1.006 units of currency (in
constant units) per unit invested as opposed to about 1.003 units
for Mexico. **55.** 74.36% **57.** 7.61% if you had sold in June
2008 **59.** No. Compound interest increase is exponential, and
exponential curves either increase continually (in the case of
appreciation) or decrease continually (in the case of deprecia-
tion). The graph of the stock price first decreases and then
increases during the given period, so the curve cannot be
compound interest change. **61.** 31 years; about \$26,100
63. 2.3 years **65. a.** \$1,510.31 **b.** \$54,701.29 **c.** 23.51%
67. The function $y = P(1 + r/m)^{mx}$ is not a linear function
of x, but an exponential function. Thus, its graph is not a
straight line. **69.** Wrong. Its growth is exponential and can be
modeled by $0.01(1.10)^t$. **71.** The graphs are the same because
the formulas give the same function of x; a compound-interest
investment behaves as though it were being compounded once a
year at the effective rate. **73.** The effective rate exceeds the
nominal rate when the interest is compounded more than once a
year because then interest is being paid on interest accumulated
during each year, resulting in a larger effective rate. Conversely, if
the interest is compounded less frequently than once a year, the
effective rate is less than the nominal rate. **75.** Compare their
future values in constant dollars. The investment with the larger
future value is the better investment. **77.** The graphs are
approaching a particular curve as m gets larger, approximately the
curve given by the largest two values of m.

Section 5.3

1. \$15,528.23 **3.** \$171,793.82 **5.** \$23,763.28 **7.** \$147.05
9. \$491.12 **11.** \$105.38 **13.** \$90,155.46 **15.** \$69,610.99
17. \$95,647.68 **19.** \$554.60 **21.** \$1,366.41 **23.** \$524.14
25. \$248.85 **27.** \$1,984.65 **29.** \$999.61 **31.** \$998.47
33. 3.617% **35.** 3.059% **37.** \$973.54 **39.** \$7,451.49
41. You should take the loan from Solid Savings & Loan:
It will have payments of \$248.85 per month. The payments
on the other loan would be more than \$300 per month.

43. Answers using correctly rounded intermediate results:

Year	Interest	Payment on Principal
1	$3,934.98	$1,798.98
2	$3,785.69	$1,948.27
3	$3,623.97	$2,109.99
4	$3,448.84	$2,285.12
5	$3,259.19	$2,474.77
6	$3,053.77	$2,680.19
7	$2,831.32	$2,902.64
8	$2,590.39	$3,143.57
9	$2,329.48	$3,404.48
10	$2,046.91	$3,687.05
11	$1,740.88	$3,993.08
12	$1,409.47	$4,324.49
13	$1,050.54	$4,683.42
14	$661.81	$5,072.15
15	$240.84	$5,491.80

45. First five years: $402.62/month; last 25 years: $601.73
47. Original monthly payments were $824.79. The new monthly payments will be $613.46. You will save $36,481.77 in interest.
49. 10.81%   **51.** 13 years   **53.** 4.5 years   **55.** 24 years
57. He is wrong because his estimate ignores the interest that will be earned by your annuity—both while it is increasing and while it is decreasing. Your payments will be considerably smaller (depending on the interest earned).   **59.** He is not correct. For instance, the payments on a $100,000 10-year mortgage at 12% are $1,434.71, while for a 20-year mortgage at the same rate, they are $1,101.09, which is a lot more than half the 10-year mortgage payment.   **61.** $PV = FV(1 + i)^{-n} =$
$$PMT\frac{(1 + i)^n - 1}{i}(1 + i)^{-n} = PMT\frac{1 - (1 + i)^{-n}}{i}$$

Chapter 5 Review
1. $7,425.00   **3.** $7,604.88   **5.** $6,757.41   **7.** $4,848.48
9. $4,733.80   **11.** $5,331.37   **13.** $177.58   **15.** $112.54
17. $187.57   **19.** $9,584.17   **21.** 5.346%   **23.** 14.0 years
25. 10.8 years   **27.** 7.0 years   **29.** 168.85%   **31.** 85.28% if she sold in February 2010.   **33.** No. Simple interest increase is linear. We can compare slopes between successive points to see if the slope remained roughly constant: From December 2002 to August 2004 the slope was $(16.31 - 3.28)/(20/12) = 7.818$, while from August 2004 to March 2005 the slope was $(33.95 - 16.31)/(7/12) = 30.24$. These slopes are quite different.   **35.** 2003

Year	2000	2001	2002	2003	2004
Revenue	$180,000	$216,000	$259,200	$311,040	$373,248

37. At least 52,515 shares   **39.** $3,234.94   **41.** $231,844
43. 7.75%   **45.** $420,275   **47.** $140,778   **49.** $1,453.06
51. $2,239.90 per month   **53.** $53,055.66   **55.** 5.99%

Chapter 6

Section 6.1
1. $F = \{\text{spring, summer, fall, winter}\}$ **3.** $I = \{1, 2, 3, 4, 5, 6\}$
5. $A = \{1, 2, 3\}$ **7.** $B = \{2, 4, 6, 8\}$ **9. a.** $S = \{(H, H), (H, T), (T, H), (T, T)\}$ **b.** $S = \{(H, H), (H, T), (T, T)\}$
11. $S = \{(1, 5), (2, 4), (3, 3), (4, 2), (5, 1)\}$
13. $S = \{(1, 5), (2, 4), (3, 3)\}$ **15.** $S = \emptyset$
17.

19.

21. A **23.** A **25.** {June, Janet, Jill, Justin, Jeffrey, Jello, Sally, Solly, Molly, Jolly}   **27.** {Jello}   **29.** $\emptyset$ **31.** {Jello}
33. {Janet, Justin, Jello, Sally, Solly, Molly, Jolly}
35. {(small, triangle), (small, square), (medium, triangle), (medium, square), (large, triangle), (large, square)}
37. {(small, blue), (small, green), (medium, blue), (medium, green), (large, blue), (large, green)}
39.

	A	B	C
1		Triangle	Square
2	Blue	Blue Triangle	Blue Square
3	Green	Green Triangle	Green Square

41.

	A	B	C
1		Blue	Green
2	Small	Small Blue	Small Green
3	Medium	Medium Blue	Medium Green
4	Large	Large Blue	Large Green

43. $B \times A = \{$1H, 1T, 2H, 2T, 3H, 3T, 4H, 4T, 5H, 5T, 6H, 6T$\}$
45. $A \times A \times A = \{$HHH, HHT, HTH, HTT, THH, THT, TTH, TTT$\}$
47. {(1,1), (1,3), (1,5), (3,1), (3,3), (3,5), (5,1), (5,3), (5,5)}
49. $\emptyset$ **51.** {(1,1), (1,3), (1,5), (3,1), (3,3), (3,5), (5,1), (5,3), (5,5), (2,2), (2,4), (2,6), (4,2), (4,4), (4,6), (6,2), (6,4), (6,6)}
61. $A \cap B = \{$Acme, Crafts$\}$ **63.** $B \cup C = \{$Acme, Brothers, Crafts, Dion, Effigy, Global, Hilbert$\}$ **65.** $A' \cap C = \{$Dion, Hilbert$\}$ **67.** $A \cap B' \cap C' = \emptyset$

69. $\{2003, 2004, 2005, 2006\} \times \{\text{Sail Boats, Motor Boats, Yachts}\}$

	A	B	C	D
1		**Sail Boats**	**Motor Boats**	**Yachts**
2	**2003**	(2003 Sail Boats)	(2003 Motor Boats)	(2003 Yachts)
3	**2004**	(2004 Sail Boats)	(2004 Motor Boats)	(2004 Yachts)
4	**2005**	(2005 Sail Boats)	(2005 Motor Boats)	(2005 Yachts)
5	**2006**	(2006 Sail Boats)	(2006 Motor Boats)	(2006 Yachts)

71. $I \cup J$ **73.** (B) **75.** Answers may vary. Let $A = \{1\}$, $B = \{2\}$, and $C = \{1, 2\}$. Then $(A \cap B) \cup C = \{1, 2\}$ but $A \cap (B \cup C) = \{1\}$. In general, $A \cap (B \cup C)$ must be a subset of A, but $(A \cap B) \cup C$ need not be; also, $(A \cap B) \cup C$ must contain C as a subset, but $A \cap (B \cup C)$ need not.
77. A universal set is a set containing all "things" currently under consideration. When discussing sets of positive integers, the universe might be the set of all positive integers, or the set of all integers (positive, negative, and 0), or any other set containing the set of all positive integers. **79.** A is the set of suppliers who deliver components on time, B is the set of suppliers whose components are known to be of high quality, and C is the set of suppliers who do not promptly replace defective components. **81.** Let $A = \{\text{movies that are violent}\}$, $B = \{\text{movies that are shorter than two hours}\}$, $C = \{\text{movies that have a tragic ending}\}$, and $D = \{\text{movies that have an unexpected ending}\}$. The given sentence can be rewritten as "She prefers movies in $A' \cap B \cap (C \cup D)'$." It can also be rewritten as "She prefers movies in $A' \cap B \cap C' \cap D'$."

Section 6.2
1. 9 **3.** 7 **5.** 4 **7.** $n(A \cup B) = 7, n(A) + n(B) - n(A \cap B) = 4 + 5 - 2 = 7$ **9.** 4 **11.** 18 **13.** 72 **15.** 60 **17.** 20
19. 6 **21.** 9 **23.** 4 **25.** $n((A \cap B)') = 9$,
$n(A') + n(B') - n((A \cup B)') = 6 + 7 - 4 = 9$
27.   **29.**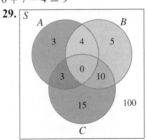

31. 496,000 **33.** 2 **35.** $C \cap N$ is the set of authors who are both successful and new. $C \cup N$ is the set of authors who are either successful or new (or both). $n(C) = 30$; $n(N) = 20$; $n(C \cap N) = 5$; $n(C \cup N) = 45$; $45 = 30 + 20 - 5$
37. $C \cap N'$ is the set of authors who are successful but not new. $n(C \cap N') = 25$ **39.** 31.25%; 83.33%
41. $M \cap C$; $n(M \cap C) = 1.1$ million
43. $B \cap T'$; $n(B \cap T') = 3.4$ million
45. $B \cap (W \cup M)$; $n(B \cap (W \cup M)) = 2.4$ million
47. $V \cap I'$; $n(V \cap I') = 15$ **49.** 80; The number of stocks that were either not pharmaceutical stocks, or were unchanged in value after a year (or both). **51.** 3/8; the fraction of Internet stocks that increased in value **53. a.** 931 **b.** 382

55. a.

[Venn diagram: S. Three overlapping circles labeled Science Fiction, Adventure, and Horror. Values: Science Fiction only 5; Science Fiction ∩ Adventure 20; Adventure only 30; Science Fiction ∩ Horror 10; center 5; Adventure ∩ Horror 0; Horror only 20; outside 10.]

b. 37.5% **57.** 17 **59.** $n(A) < n(B)$ **61.** The number of elements in the Cartesian product of two finite sets is the product of the number of elements in the two sets.
65. When $A \cap B \neq \emptyset$ **67.** When $B \subseteq A$ **69.** $n(A \cup B \cup C) = n(A) + n(B) + n(C) - n(A \cap B) - n(B \cap C) - n(A \cap C) + n(A \cap B \cap C)$

Section 6.3
1. 10 **3.** 30 **5.** 6 outcomes **7.** 15 outcomes **9.** 13 outcomes **11.** 25 outcomes **13.** 4 **15.** 93 **17.** 16 **19.** 30 **21.** 13 **23.** 18 **25.** 25,600 **27.** 3,381 **29. a.** 288 **b.** 288 **31.** 256 **33.** 10 **35.** 286 **37.** 4 **39. a.** 8,000,000 **b.** 30,000 **c.** 4,251,528 **41. a.** $4^3 = 64$ **b.** 4^n **c.** $4^{2.1 \times 10^{10}}$
43. a. $16^6 = 16,777,216$ **b.** $16^3 = 4,096$ **c.** $16^2 = 256$ **d.** 766
45. $(10 \times 9 \times 8 \times 7 \times 6 \times 5 \times 4) \times (8 \times 7 \times 6 \times 5)$ $= 1,016,064,000$ possible casts **47. a.** $26^3 \times 10^3 = 17,576,000$
b. $26^2 \times 23 \times 10^3 = 15,548,000$ **c.** $15,548,000 - 3 \times 10^3 = 15,545,000$ **49. a.** 4 **b.** 4 **c.** There would be an infinite number of routes. **51. a.** 72 **b.** 36 **53.** 96 **55. a.** 36
b. 37 **57.** Step 1: Choose a day of the week on which Jan. 1 will fall: 7 choices. Step 2: Decide whether or not it is a leap year; 2 choices. Total: $7 \times 2 = 14$ possible calendars. **59.** 1,900
61. Step 1: choose a position in the left-right direction; m choices. Step 2: Choose a position in the front-back direction; n choices. Step 3: Choose a position in the up-down direction; r choices. Hence, there are $m \cdot n \cdot r$ possible outcomes. **63.** 4 **65.** Cartesian product **67.** The decision algorithm produces every pair of shirts twice, first in one order and then in the other. **69.** Think of placing the five squares in a row of five empty slots. Step 1: Choose a slot for the blue square; Five choices. Step 2: Choose a slot for the green square; four choices. Step 3: Choose the remaining three slots for the yellow squares; one choice. Hence, there are 20 possible five-square sequences.

Section 6.4
1. 720 **3.** 56 **5.** 360 **7.** 15 **9.** 3 **11.** 45 **13.** 20
15. 4,950 **17.** 360 **19.** 35 **21.** 120 **23.** 120 **25.** 20
27. 60 **29.** 210 **31.** 7 **33.** 35 **35.** 24 **37.** 126
39. 196 **41.** 105 **43.** $\dfrac{C(30, 5) \times 5^{25}}{6^{30}} \approx 0.192$
45. $\dfrac{C(30, 15) \times 3^{15} \times 3^{15}}{6^{30}} \approx 0.144$ **47.** 24
49. $C(13, 2)C(4, 2)C(4, 2) \times 44 = 123,552$

51. $13 \times C(4, 2)C(12, 3) \times 4 \times 4 \times 4 = 1{,}098{,}240$
53. 10,200   **55. a.** 252 **b.** 20 **c.** 26   **57. a.** 300 **b.** 3
c. 1 in 100 or .01   **59. a.** 210 **b.** 91 **c.** No   **61. a.** 23! **b.** 18!
c. $19 \times 18!$ **63.** $C(11, 1)C(10, 4)C(6, 4)C(2, 2)$
65. $C(11, 2)C(9, 1)C(8, 1)C(7, 3)C(4, 1)C(3, 1)C(2, 1)C(1, 1)$
67. $C(10, 2)C(8, 4)C(4, 1)C(3, 1)C(2, 1)C(1, 1)$ **69.** (A)
71. (D)   **73. a.** 9,880 **b.** 1,560 **c.** 11,480   **75. a.** $C(20, 2) = 190$
b. $C(n, 2)$ **77.** The multiplication principle; it can be used to
solve all problems that use the formulas for permutations.
79. (A), (D)   **81.** A permutation. Changing the order in a list of
driving instructions can result in a different outcome; for
instance, "1. Turn left. 2. Drive one mile." and "1. Drive one
mile. 2. Turn left." will take you to different locations.
83. Urge your friend not to focus on formulas, but instead learn to
formulate decision algorithms and use the principles of counting.
85. It is ambiguous on the following point: Are the three students
to play different characters, or are they to play a group of three,
such as "three guards." This should be made clear in the exercise.

Chapter 6 Review
1. $N = \{-3, -2, -1\}$ **3.** $S = \{(1, 2), (1, 3), (1, 4), (1, 5),$
$(1, 6), (2, 1), (2, 3), (2, 4), (2, 5), (2, 6), (3, 1), (3, 2), (3, 4),$
$(3, 5), (3, 6), (4, 1), (4, 2), (4, 3), (4, 5), (4, 6), (5, 1), (5, 2),$
$(5, 3), (5, 4), (5, 6), (6, 1), (6, 2), (6, 3), (6, 4), (6, 5)\}$
5. $A \cup B' = \{a, b, d\}, A \times B' = \{(a, a), (a, d), (b, a), (b, d)\}$
7. $A \times B$ **9.** $(P \cap E' \cap Q)'$ or $P' \cup E \cup Q'$ **11.** $n(A \cup B) =$
$n(A) + n(B) - n(A \cap B), n(C') = n(S) - n(C); 100$
13. $n(A \times B) = n(A)n(B), n(A \cup B) = n(A) + n(B) -$
$n(A \cap B), n(A') = n(S) - n(A), 21$
15. $C(12, 1)C(4, 2)C(11, 3)C(4, 1)C(4, 1)C(4, 1)$
17. $C(4, 1)C(10, 1)$ **19.** $C(4, 4)C(8, 1) = 8$
21. $C(3, 2)C(9, 3) + C(3, 3)C(9, 2) = 288$ **23.** The set
of books that are either sci-fi or stored in Texas (or both);
$n(S \cup T) = 112{,}000$ **25.** The set of books that are either
stored in California or not sci-fi; $n(C \cup S') = 175{,}000$
27. The romance books that are also horror books or
stored in Texas; $n(R \cap (T \cup H)) = 20{,}000$ **29.** 1,000
31. FarmerBooks.com; 1,800   **33.** FarmerBooks.com; 5,400
35. $26 \times 26 \times 26 = 17{,}576$ **37.** $26 \times 25 \times 9 \times 10 = 58{,}500$
39. 60,000   **41.** 19,600

Chapter 7

Section 7.1
1. $S = \{\text{HH, HT, TH, TT}\}; E = \{\text{HH, HT, TH}\}$ **3.** $S = \{\text{HHH,}$
HHT, HTH, HTT, THH, THT, TTH, TTT$\}; E = \{\text{HTT, THT,}$
TTH, TTT$\}$

5. $S = \left\{ \begin{array}{l} (1, 1)\,(1, 2)\,(1, 3)\,(1, 4)\,(1, 5)\,(1, 6) \\ (2, 1)\,(2, 2)\,(2, 3)\,(2, 4)\,(2, 5)\,(2, 6) \\ (3, 1)\,(3, 2)\,(3, 3)\,(3, 4)\,(3, 5)\,(3, 6) \\ (4, 1)\,(4, 2)\,(4, 3)\,(4, 4)\,(4, 5)\,(4, 6) \\ (5, 1)\,(5, 2)\,(5, 3)\,(5, 4)\,(5, 5)\,(5, 6) \\ (6, 1)\,(6, 2)\,(6, 3)\,(6, 4)\,(6, 5)\,(6, 6) \end{array} \right\}$;

$E = \{(1, 4), (2, 3), (3, 2), (4, 1)\}$

7. $S = \left\{ \begin{array}{l} (1, 1)\,(1, 2)\,(1, 3)\,(1, 4)\,(1, 5)\,(1, 6) \\ (2, 2)\,(2, 3)\,(2, 4)\,(2, 5)\,(2, 6) \\ (3, 3)\,(3, 4)\,(3, 5)\,(3, 6) \\ (4, 4)\,(4, 5)\,(4, 6) \\ (5, 5)\,(5, 6) \\ (6, 6) \end{array} \right\}$;

$E = \{(1, 3), (2, 2)\}$
9. S as in Exercise 7; $E = \{(2, 2), (2, 3), (2, 5), (3, 3),$
$(3, 5), (5, 5)\}$ **11.** $S = \{\text{m, o, z, a, r, t}\}; E = \{\text{o, a}\}$
13. $S = \{(\text{s, o}), (\text{s, r}), (\text{s, e}), (\text{o, s}), (\text{o, r}), (\text{o, e}), (\text{r, s}), (\text{r, o}),$
$(\text{r, e}), (\text{e, s}), (\text{e, o}), (\text{e, r})\}; E = \{(\text{o, s}), (\text{o, r}), (\text{o, e}), (\text{e, s}),$
$(\text{e, o}), (\text{e, r})\}$ **15.** $S = \{01, 02, 03, 04, 10, 12, 13, 14, 20, 21,$
$23, 24, 30, 31, 32, 34, 40, 41, 42, 43\}; E = \{10, 20, 21, 30, 31,$
$32, 40, 41, 42, 43\}$ **17.** $S = \{\text{domestic car, imported car, van,}$
antique car, antique truck$\}; E = \{\text{van, antique truck}\}$
19. a. All sets of 4 gummy candies chosen from the packet of 12
b. All sets of four gummy candies in which two are strawberry
and two are black currant   **21. a.** All lists of 15 people chosen
from 20 **b.** All lists of 15 people chosen from 20, in which
Hillary Clinton occupies the eleventh position
23. $A \cap B; n(A \cap B) = 1$ **25.** $B'; n(B') = 33$
27. $B' \cap D'; n(B' \cap D') = 2$ **29.** $C \cup B; n(C \cup B) = 12$
31. $W \cap I$ **33.** $E \cup I'$ **35.** $I \cup (W \cap E')$
37. $(I \cup W) \cap E'$ **39.** $E = \{\text{Pacific, Mountain, South Atlantic}\}$
41. $E \cup F$ is the event that you choose a region that saw a
decrease in housing prices of 4% or more or is on the east coast.
$E \cup F = \{\text{Pacific, Mountain, New England, Middle Atlantic,}$
South Atlantic$\}$. $E \cap F$ is the event that you choose a region that
saw a decrease in housing prices of 4% or more and is on the east
coast. $E \cap F = \{\text{South Atlantic}\}$.   **43. a.** Mutually exclusive
b. Not mutually exclusive   **45.** $S \cap N$ is the event that an author
is successful and new. $S \cup N$ is the event that an author is either
successful or new; $n(S \cap N) = 5; n(S \cup N) = 45$ **47.** N and E
49. $S \cap N'$ is the event that an author is successful but not a
new author. $n(S \cap N') = 25$ **51.** 31.25%; 83.33%
53. $V \cap I'; n(V \cap I') = 15$ **55.** 80; the number of stocks that
were either not pharmaceutical stocks, or were unchanged in
value after a year (or both)   **57.** P and E, P and I, E and I, N
and E, V and N, V and D, N and D **59.** 3/8; the fraction of
Internet stocks that increased in value   **61. a.** $E' \cap H$
b. $E \cup H$ **c.** $(E \cup G)' = E' \cap G'$ **63. a.** $\{9\}$ **b.** $\{6\}$
65. a. The dog's "fight" drive is weakest. **b.** The dog's "fight"
and "flight" drives are either both strongest or both weakest.
c. Either the dog's "fight" drive is strongest, or its "flight" drive
is strongest.   **67.** $C(6, 4) = 15; C(1, 1)C(5, 3) = 10$
69. a. $n(S) = P(7, 3) = 210$ **b.** $E \cap F$ is the event that Celera
wins and Electoral College is in second or third place. In other
words, it is the set of all lists of three horses in which Celera is
first and Electoral College is second or third. $n(E \cap F) = 10$
71. $C(8, 3) = 56$ **73.** $C(4, 1) C(2, 1) C(2, 1) = 16$
75. Subset of the sample space   **77.** E and F do not both occur
79. (B)   **81.** True; consider the following experiment: Select an
element of the set S at random.   **83.** Answers may vary. Cast a
die and record the remainder when the number facing up is

divided by 2.   **85.** Yes. For instance, $E = \{(2, 5), (5, 1)\}$ and $F = \{(4, 3)\}$ are two such events.

Section 7.2

1. .4   **3.** .8   **5.** .6

7.

Outcome	HH	HT	TH	TT
Rel. Frequency	.275	.2375	.3	.1875

9. .575   **11.** The second coin *seems* slightly biased in favor of heads, as heads comes up approximately 58% of the time. On the other hand, it is conceivable that the coin is fair and that heads came up 58% of the time purely by chance. Deciding which conclusion is more reasonable requires some knowledge of inferential statistics.   **13.** Yes   **15.** No; relative frequencies cannot be negative.   **17.** Yes   **19.** Missing value: .3 **a.** .6 **b.** .4   **21.** Answers will vary.   **23.** Answers will vary.   **25. a.** .32 **b.** .15 **c.** .68
27. a.

Mortgage Status	Current	Past Due	In Foreclosure	Repossessed
Rel. Frequency	.67	.26	.045	.025

b. .33
29. a.

Age	18–25	26–35	36–45	46–55	>55
Rel. Frequency	.29	.47	.20	.03	.01

b. .33
31. a.

Test Rating	3	2	1	0
Rel. Frequency	.1	.4	.4	.1

b. .5   **33.** Dial-up: 1256, Cable Modem: 412, DSL: 302, Other: 30
35.

Outcome	Surge	Plunge	Steady
Rel. Frequency	.2	.3	.5

37. .25   **39.** .2   **41.** .7   **43.** 5/6   **45.** 5/16
47.

Outcome	U	C	R
Rel. Frequency	.2	.64	.16

49.

Conventional	No pesticide	Single pesticide	Multiple pesticide
Probability	.27	.13	.60
Organic	No pesticide	Single pesticide	Multiple pesticide
Probability	.77	.13	.10

51. $P(\text{false negative}) = 10/400 = .025$, $P(\text{false positive}) = 10/200 = .05$ **53.** Answers will vary.   **55.** The fraction of times E occurs   **57.** 101; $fr(E)$ can be any number between 0 and 100 inclusive, so the possible answers are $0/100 = 0$, $1/100 = .01, 2/100 = .02, \ldots, 99/100 = .99, 100/100 = 1$.
59. Wrong. For a pair of fair dice, the probability of a pair of matching numbers is 1/6, as Ruth says. However, it is quite

possible, although not very likely, that if you cast a pair of fair dice 20 times, you will never obtain a matching pair (in fact, there is approximately a 2.6% chance that this will happen). In general, a nontrivial claim about probability can never be absolutely validated or refuted experimentally. All we can say is that the evidence suggests that the dice are not fair.   **61.** For a (large) number of days, record the temperature prediction for the next day and then check the actual high temperature the next day. Record whether the prediction was accurate (within, say, 2°F of the actual temperature). The fraction of times the prediction was accurate is the relative frequency.

Section 7.3

1. $P(e) = .2$ **a.** 0.9 **b.** 0.95 **c.** 0.1 **d.** 0.8   **3.** $P(E) = 1/4$
5. $P(E) = 1$ **7.** $P(E) = 3/4$ **9.** $P(E) = 3/4$
11. $P(E) = 1/2$ **13.** $P(E) = 1/9$ **15.** $P(E) = 0$
17. $P(E) = 1/4$ **19.** $1/12$; $\{(4, 4), (2, 3), (3, 2)\}$
21.

Outcome	1	2	3	4	5	6
Probability	1/9	2/9	1/9	2/9	1/9	2/9

$P(\{1, 2, 3\}) = 4/9$

23.

Outcome	1	2	3	4
Probability	8/15	4/15	2/15	1/15

25. .65   **27.** .1   **29.** .7   **31.** .4   **33.** .25   **35.** 1.0   **37.** .3
39. 1.0   **41.** No; $P(A \cup B)$ should be $\leq P(A) + P(B)$.
43. Yes   **45.** No; $P(A \cup B)$ should be $\geq P(B)$.
47. a. .93 **b.** .33
49.

Outcome	Hispanic or Latino	White (not Hispanic)	African American	Asian	Other
Probability	0.48	0.29	0.08	0.08	0.07

$P(\text{Neither White nor Asian}) = .63$
51. a. $S = \{\text{Stock market success, Sold to other concern, Fail}\}$
b.

Outcome	Stock Market Success	Sold to Other Concern	Fail
Probability	.2	.3	.5

c. .5
53.

Outcome	SUV	Pickup	Passenger Car	Minivan
Probability	.25	.15	.50	.10

55. $P(1) = 0$, $P(6) = 0$; $P(2) = P(3) = P(4) = P(5) = 1/4 = .25$ **57.** $P(1) = P(6) = 1/10$; $P(2) = P(3) = P(4) = P(5) = 1/5$, $P(\text{odd}) = 1/2$ **59.** $P(1, 1) = P(2, 2) = \ldots = P(6, 6) = 1/66$; $P(1, 2) = \ldots = P(6, 5) = 1/33$, $P(\text{odd sum}) = 6/11$ **61.** $P(2) = 15/38$; $P(4) = 3/38$, $P(1) = P(3) = P(5) = P(6) = 5/38$, $P(\text{odd}) = 15/38$
63. 5/6   **65.** .39   **67.** .61   **69.** .24   **71.** .00   **73.** .76
75. .46   **77.** .54   **79.** .04   **81.** .51   **83.** .45   **85.** 22%; 100%
87. All of them   **89.** 88.4%   **91.** Here is one possible experiment: Roll a die and observe which of the following outcomes occurs. Outcome A: 1 or 2 facing up; $P(A) = 1/3$,

Outcome B: 3 or 4 facing up; $P(B) = 1/3$, Outcome C: 5 or 6 facing up; $P(C) = 1/3$. **93.** He is wrong. It is possible to have a run of losses of any length. Tony may have grounds to *suspect* that the game is rigged, but no proof. **95.** They are mutually exclusive. **97.** Wrong. For example, the modeled probability of winning a state lotto is small but nonzero. However, the vast majority of people who play lotto every day of their lives never win no matter how frequently they play, so the relative frequency is zero for these people. **99.** When $A \cap B = \emptyset$ we have $P(A \cap B) = P(\emptyset) = 0$, so $P(A \cup B) = P(A) + P(B) - P(A \cap B) = P(A) + P(B) - 0 = P(A) + P(B)$. **101.** Zero. According to the assumption, no matter how many thunderstorms occur, lightning cannot strike a given spot more than once, and so, after n trials the relative frequency will never exceed $1/n$, and so will approach zero as the number of trials gets large. Since the modeled probability models the limit of relative frequencies as the number of trials gets large, it must therefore be zero. **103.** $P(A \cup B \cup C) = P(A) + P(B) + P(C) - P(A \cap B) - P(A \cap C) - P(B \cap C) + P(A \cap B \cap C)$

Section 7.4
1. $1/42$ **3.** $7/9$ **5.** $1/7$ **7.** $1/2$ **9.** $41/42$ **11.** $1/15$
13. $4/15$ **15.** $1/5$ **17.** $1/(2^8 \times 5^5 \times 5!)$ **19.** $.4226$
21. $.0475$ **23.** $.0020$ **25.** $1/27^{39}$ **27.** $1/7$ **29.** Probability of being a big winner $= 1/2{,}118{,}760 \approx .000000472$. Probability of being a small-fry winner $= 225/2{,}118{,}760 \approx .000106194$. Probability of being either a winner or a small-fry winner $= 226/2{,}118{,}760 \approx .000106666$. **31. a.** $C(600,300)/C(700,400)$ **b.** $C(699,399)/C(700,400)$ or $400/700$ **33.** $P(10, 3)/10^3 = 18/25 = .72$ **35.** $8!/8^8$ **37.** $1/8$ **39.** $1/8$ **41.** $37/10{,}000$ **43. a.** $90{,}720$ **b.** $25{,}200$ **c.** $25{,}200/90{,}720 = 25/90 \approx .28$ **45.** The four outcomes listed are not equally likely; for example, (red, blue) can occur in four ways. The methods of this section yield a probability for (red, blue) of $C(2, 2)/C(4, 2) = 1/6$ **47.** No. If we do not pay attention to order, the probability is $C(5, 2)/C(9, 2) = 10/36 = 5/18$. If we do pay attention to order, the probability is $P(5, 2)/P(9, 2) = 20/72 = 5/18$ again. The difference between permutations and combinations cancels when we compute the probability.

Section 7.5
1. $.4$ **3.** $.08$ **5.** $.75$ **7.** $.2$ **9.** $.5$
11.

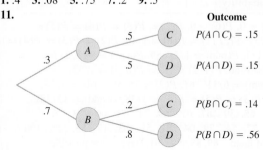

	Outcome
	$P(A \cap C) = .15$
	$P(A \cap D) = .15$
	$P(B \cap C) = .14$
	$P(B \cap D) = .56$

13.

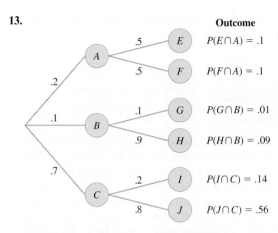

	Outcome
	$P(E \cap A) = .1$
	$P(F \cap A) = .1$
	$P(G \cap B) = .01$
	$P(H \cap B) = .09$
	$P(I \cap C) = .14$
	$P(J \cap C) = .56$

15. $1/10$ **17.** $1/5$ **19.** $2/9$ **21.** $1/84$ **23.** $5/21$ **25.** $24/175$
27. Mutually exclusive **29.** Neither **31.** $\dfrac{1}{2} \cdot \dfrac{1}{2} = \dfrac{1}{4}$ Independent
33. $\dfrac{5}{18} \cdot \dfrac{1}{2} \ne \dfrac{1}{9}$ Dependent **35.** $\dfrac{25}{36} \cdot \dfrac{5}{18} \ne \dfrac{2}{9}$ Dependent
37. $(1/2)^{11} = 1/2{,}048$ **39.** $P(D) = .10$; $P(D|M) = .30$
41. $P(A|L) = .30$; $P(L|A) = .10$ **43.** $P(E|M) = .55$;
$P(E|M') = .05$ **45.** $.8$ **47. a.** $.38$ **b.** $.24$ **49.** $.34$
51. Not independent; $P(\text{giving up} \mid \text{used Brand X}) = .1$ is larger than $P(\text{giving up}) = .05$. **53.** $.00015$ **55.** $5/6$ **57.** $3/4$
59. $11/16$ **61.** $11/14$
63.

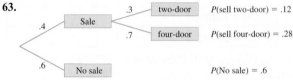

			Probability
		two-door	$P(\text{sell two-door}) = .12$
		four-door	$P(\text{sell four-door}) = .28$
			$P(\text{No sale}) = .6$

65.

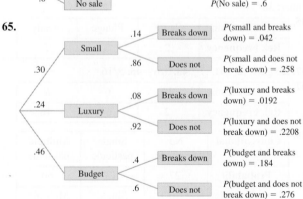

		Probability
	Breaks down	$P(\text{small and breaks down}) = .042$
	Does not	$P(\text{small and does not break down}) = .258$
	Breaks down	$P(\text{luxury and breaks down}) = .0192$
	Does not	$P(\text{luxury and does not break down}) = .2208$
	Breaks down	$P(\text{budget and breaks down}) = .184$
	Does not	$P(\text{budget and does not break down}) = .276$

67.

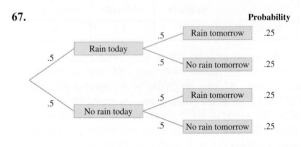

	Probability
Rain tomorrow	$.25$
No rain tomorrow	$.25$
Rain tomorrow	$.25$
No rain tomorrow	$.25$

69. .77 **71.** .35 **73.** .37 **75.** .98 **77.** The claim is correct. The probability that an unemployed person has a high school diploma only is .31, while the corresponding figure for an employed person is .29. **79.** $P(K \mid D) = 1.31P(K \mid D')$ **81. a.** $P(I \mid T) > P(I)$ **b.** It was ineffective. **83. a.** .59 **b.** \$35,000 or more: $P(\text{Internet user} \mid < \$35,000) \approx .27 <$ $P(\text{Internet user} \mid \geq \$35,000) \approx .59$. **85.** $P(R \mid J)$ **87.** (D) **89. a.** .000057 **b.** .015043 **91.** 11% **93.** 106 **95.** .631 **97.** Answers will vary. Here is a simple one: E: the first toss is a head; F: the second toss is a head; G: the third toss is a head. **99.** The probability you seek is $P(E \mid F)$, or should be. If, for example, you were going to place a wager on whether E occurs or not, it is crucial to know that the sample space has been reduced to F (you know that F did occur). If you base your wager on $P(E)$ rather than $P(E \mid F)$ you will misjudge your likelihood of winning. **101.** You might explain that the conditional probability of E is not the *a priori* probability of E, but it is the probability of E in a hypothetical world in which the outcomes are restricted to be what is given. In the example she is citing, yes, the probability of throwing a double-six is $1/36$, in the absence of any other knowledge. However by the "conditional probability" of throwing a double-six given that the sum is larger than 7, we might mean the probability of a double-six in a situation in which the dice have already been thrown, but all we know is that the sum is greater than 7. Because there are only 15 ways in which that can happen, the conditional probability is $1/15$. For a more extreme case, consider the conditional probability of throwing a double-six given that the sum is 12. **103.** If $A \subseteq B$ then $A \cap B = A$, so $P(A \cap B) = P(A)$ and $P(A \mid B) = P(A \cap B)/P(B) = P(A)/P(B)$. **105.** Your friend is correct. If A and B are mutually exclusive, then $P(A \cap B) = 0$. On the other hand, if A and B are independent, then $P(A \cap B) = P(A)P(B)$. Thus, $P(A)P(B) = 0$. If a product is 0, then one of the factors must be 0, so either $P(A) = 0$ or $P(B) = 0$. Thus, it cannot be true that A and B are mutually exclusive, have nonzero probabilities, and are independent all at the same time. **107.** $P(A' \cap B') =$ $1 - P(A \cup B) = 1 - [P(A) + P(B) - P(A \cap B)] =$ $1 - [P(A) + P(B) - P(A)P(B)] = (1 - P(A))(1 - P(B)) =$ $P(A')P(B')$

Section 7.6

1. .4 **3.** .7887 **5.** .7442 **7.** .1163 **9.** 26.8% **11.** .1724 **13.** .73 **15.** .71 **17.** .1653 **19.** 82% **21.** 12% **23. a.** 14.43%; **b.** 19.81% of single homeowners have pools. Thus they should go after the single homeowners. **25.** 9 **27.** .9310 **29.** 1.76% **31.** .20 **33.** K: child killed; D: Airbag deployed; $P(K \mid D) = 1.31P(K \mid D')$; $P(D \mid K) =$ $1.31(.25)/[1.31(.25) + .75] = .30$ **35.** Show him an example like Example 1 of this section, where $P(T \mid A) = .95$ but $P(A \mid T) \approx .64$. **37.** Suppose that the steroid test gives 10% false negatives and that only 0.1% of the tested population uses steroids. Then the probability that an athlete uses steroids, given that he or she has tested positive, is

$$\frac{(.9)(.001)}{(.9)(.001) + (.01)(.999)} \approx .083.$$ **39.** Draw a tree in which the

first branching shows which of R_1, R_2, or R_3 occurred, and the second branching shows which of T or T' then occurred. There are three final outcomes in which T occurs:
$P(R_1 \cap T) = P(T \mid R_1) \, P(R_1)$, $P(R_2 \cap T) = P(T \mid R_2)P(R_2)$, and $P(R_3 \cap T) = P(T \mid R_3)P(R_3)$. In only one of these, the first, does R_1 occur. Thus,

$$P(R_1 \mid T) = \frac{P(R_1 \cap T)}{P(T)}$$
$$= \frac{P(T \mid R_1)P(R_1)}{P(T \mid R_1)P(R_1) + P(T \mid R_2)P(R_2) + P(T \mid R_3)P(R_3)}$$

41. The reasoning is flawed. Let A be the event that a Democrat agrees with Safire's column, and let F and M be the events that a Democrat reader is female and male respectively. Then A. D. makes the following argument:

$$P(M \mid A) = 0.9, \ P(F \mid A') = 0.9. \ \text{Therefore,} \ P(A \mid M) = 0.9.$$

According to Bayes' Theorem we cannot conclude anything about $P(A \mid M)$ unless we know $P(A)$, the percentage of all Democrats who agreed with Safire's column. This was not given.

Section 7.7

1. $\begin{bmatrix} 1/4 & 3/4 \\ 1/2 & 1/2 \end{bmatrix}$ **3.** $\begin{bmatrix} 0 & 1 \\ 1/6 & 5/6 \end{bmatrix}$ **5.** $\begin{bmatrix} 0 & .8 & .2 \\ .9 & 0 & .1 \\ 0 & 0 & 1 \end{bmatrix}$

7. $\begin{bmatrix} 1 & 0 & 0 \\ 0 & 1 & 0 \\ 0 & 0 & 1 \end{bmatrix}$ **9.** $\begin{bmatrix} 1 & 0 & 0 & 0 & 0 & 0 \\ 2/3 & 0 & 1/3 & 0 & 0 & 0 \\ 0 & 2/3 & 0 & 1/3 & 0 & 0 \\ 0 & 0 & 2/3 & 0 & 1/3 & 0 \\ 0 & 0 & 0 & 2/3 & 0 & 1/3 \\ 0 & 0 & 0 & 0 & 1 & 0 \end{bmatrix}$

11. a. $\begin{bmatrix} .25 & .75 \\ 0 & 1 \end{bmatrix}$ **b.** distribution after one step: [.5 .5]; after two steps: [.25 .75]; after three steps: [.125 .875]

13. a. $\begin{bmatrix} .36 & .64 \\ .32 & .68 \end{bmatrix}$ **b.** distribution after one step: [.3 .7]; after two steps: [.34 .66]; after three steps: [.332 .668]

15. a. $\begin{bmatrix} 3/4 & 1/4 \\ 1/2 & 1/2 \end{bmatrix}$ **b.** distribution after one step: [2/3 1/3]; after two steps: [2/3 1/3]; after three steps: [2/3 1/3]

17. a. $\begin{bmatrix} 3/4 & 1/4 \\ 3/4 & 1/4 \end{bmatrix}$ **b.** distribution after one step: [3/4 1/4]; after two steps: [3/4 1/4]; after three steps: [3/4 1/4]

19. a. $\begin{bmatrix} .25 & .75 & 0 \\ 0 & 1 & 0 \\ 0 & .75 & .25 \end{bmatrix}$ **b.** distribution after one step: [.5 .5 0]; after two steps: [.25 .75 0]; after three steps: [.125 .875 0] **21. a.** $\begin{bmatrix} 1/3 & 1/3 & 1/3 \\ 4/9 & 4/9 & 1/9 \\ 0 & 1 & 0 \end{bmatrix}$ **b.** distribution after one step: [1/2 1/2 0]; after two steps: [1/6 2/3 1/6]; after three steps: [7/18 7/18 2/9]

23. a. $\begin{bmatrix} .01 & .99 & 0 \\ 0 & 1 & 0 \\ 0 & .36 & .64 \end{bmatrix}$ **b.** distribution after one step:

[.05 .55 .4]; after two steps: [.005 .675 .32]; after three steps: [.0005 .7435 .256] **25.** [2/3 1/3] **27.** [3/7 4/7]
29. [2/5 3/5] **31.** [2/5 1/5 2/5] **33.** [1/3 1/2 1/6]

35. [0 1 0] **37.** 1 = Sorey state, 2 = C&T; $P = \begin{bmatrix} \frac{1}{2} & \frac{1}{2} \\ \frac{1}{4} & \frac{3}{4} \end{bmatrix}$;

$3/8 = .375$ **39. a.** 1 = not checked in; 2 = checked in
$P = \begin{bmatrix} .4 & .6 \\ 0 & 1 \end{bmatrix}$, $P^2 = \begin{bmatrix} .16 & .84 \\ 0 & 1 \end{bmatrix}$,

$P^3 = \begin{bmatrix} .064 & .936 \\ 0 & 1 \end{bmatrix}$ **b.** 1 hour: .6; 2 hours: .84; 3 hours: .936

c. Eventually, all the roaches will have checked in. **41.** 16.67% fall into the high-risk category and 83.33% into the low-risk category. **43. a.** $47/300 \approx .156667$ **b.** 3/13 **45.** 41.67% of the customers will be in the Paid up category, 41.67% in the 0–90 days category, and 16.67% in the bad debt category.

47. a. $P = \begin{bmatrix} .729 & .271 & 0 \\ .075 & .84 & .085 \\ 0 & .304 & .696 \end{bmatrix}$ **b.** 2.3%

c. Affluent: 17.8%; middle class: 64.3%; poor: 18.0%
49. Long-term income distribution (top to bottom):
[8.43%, 41.57%, 41.57%, 8.43%]

51. a. $P = \begin{bmatrix} .981 & .005 & .005 & .009 \\ .01 & .972 & .006 & .012 \\ .01 & .006 & .973 & .011 \\ .008 & .006 & .005 & .981 \end{bmatrix}$

b. Verizon: 29.6%, Cingular: 19.3%, AT&T: 18.1%, Other: 32.8%
c. Verizon: 30.3%, Cingular: 18.6%, AT&T: 17.6%,
Other: 33.5%. The biggest gainers are Verizon and Other, each gaining 0.6%. **53.** [1/5 1/5 1/5 1/5 1/5]
55. Answers will vary. **57.** There are two assumptions made by Markov systems that may not be true about the stock market: the assumption that the transition probabilities do not change over time, and the assumption that the transition probability depends only on the current state. **59.** If q is a row of Q, then by assumption $qP = q$. Thus, when we multiply the rows of Q by P, nothing changes, and $QP = Q$. **61.** At each step, only 0.4 of the population in state 1 remains there, and nothing enters from any other state. Thus, when the first entry in the steady-state distribution vector is multiplied by 0.4 it must remain unchanged. The only number for which this true is 0.
63. An example is

65. If $vP = v$ and $wP = w$, then $\frac{1}{2}(v + w)P = \frac{1}{2}vP + \frac{1}{2}wP = \frac{1}{2}v + \frac{1}{2}w = \frac{1}{2}(v + w)$. Further, if the entries of v and w add up to 1, then so do the entries of $(v + w)/2$.

Chapter 7 Review

1. $n(S) = 8$, $E = \{HHT, HTH, HTT, THH, THT, TTH, TTT\}$,
$P(E) = 7/8$ **3.** $n(S) = 36$; $E = \{(1, 6), (2, 5), (3, 4), (4, 3),$
$(5, 2), (6, 1)\}$; $P(E) = 1/6$ **5.** $n(S) = 6$; $E = \{2\}$;
$P(E) = 1/8$ **7.** .76 **9.** .25 **11.** .5 **13.** 7/15 **15.** 8/792
17. 48/792 **19.** 288/792 **21.** $C(8, 5)/C(52, 5)$
23. $C(4, 3)C(1, 1)C(3, 1)/C(52, 5)$
25. $C(9, 1)C(8, 1)C(4, 3)C(4, 2)/C(52, 5)$ **27.** 1/5;
dependent **29.** 1/6; independent **31.** 1; dependent
33. $P = \begin{bmatrix} 1/2 & 1/2 \\ 1/4 & 3/4 \end{bmatrix}$

35. Brand A: $65/192 \approx .339$, Brand B: $127/192 \approx .661$
37. 14/25 **39.** 15/94 **41.** 79/167 **43.** 98%
45. 6.9% **47.** .931 **49.** $P(H \cap C)$, since $P(H|C) > P(H)$
gives $P(H \cap C) > P(H)P(C)$ **51.** 16 **53.** .2462

55. $[.2 \quad .4 \quad .4] \begin{bmatrix} 0.8 & 0.1 & 0.1 \\ 0.4 & 0.6 & 0 \\ 0.2 & 0 & 0.8 \end{bmatrix} = [.4 \quad .26 \quad .34]$, so 40% for

OHaganBooks.com, 26% for JungleBooks.com, and 34% for FarmerBooks.com **57.** Here are three: (1) it is possible for someone to be a customer at two different enterprises; (2) some customers may stop using all three of the companies; and (3) new customers can enter the field.

Chapter 8

Section 8.1

1. Finite; $\{2, 3, \ldots, 12\}$ **3.** Discrete infinite; $\{0, 1, -1,$
$2, -2, \ldots\}$ (negative profits indicate loss) **5.** Continuous; X
can assume any value between 0 and 60. **7.** Finite; $\{0, 1,$
$2, \ldots, 10\}$ **9.** Discrete infinite $\{k/1, k/4, k/9, k/16, \ldots\}$
11. a. $S = \{HH, HT, TH, TT\}$
b. X is the rule that assigns to each outcome the number of tails.
c.

Outcome	HH	HT	TH	TT
Value of X	0	1	1	2

13. a. $S = \{(1, 1), (1, 2), \ldots, (1, 6), (2, 1), (2, 2), \ldots, (6, 6)\}$
b. X is the rule that assigns to each outcome the sum of the two numbers.
c.

Outcome	(1, 1)	(1, 2)	(1, 3)	...	(6, 6)
Value of X	2	3	4	...	12

15. a. $S = \{(4, 0), (3, 1), (2, 2)\}$ (listed in order (red, green))
b. X is the rule that assigns to each outcome the number of red marbles.
c.

Outcome	(4, 0)	(3, 1)	(2, 2)
Value of X	4	3	2

17. a. S = the set of students in the study group.
b. X is the rule that assigns to each student his or her final exam score. **c.** The values of X, in the order given, are 89%, 85%, 95%, 63%, 92%, 80%.   **19. a.** $P(X = 8) = P(X = 6) = .3$ **b.** .7

21.

x	1	2	3	4	5	6
$P(X = x)$	$\frac{1}{6}$	$\frac{1}{6}$	$\frac{1}{6}$	$\frac{1}{6}$	$\frac{1}{6}$	$\frac{1}{6}$

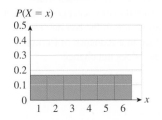

23.

x	0	1	4	9
$P(X = x)$	$\frac{1}{8}$	$\frac{3}{8}$	$\frac{3}{8}$	$\frac{1}{8}$

25.

x	2	3	4	5	6	7	8	9	10	11	12
$P(X = x)$	$\frac{1}{36}$	$\frac{2}{36}$	$\frac{3}{36}$	$\frac{4}{36}$	$\frac{5}{36}$	$\frac{6}{36}$	$\frac{5}{36}$	$\frac{4}{36}$	$\frac{3}{36}$	$\frac{2}{36}$	$\frac{1}{36}$

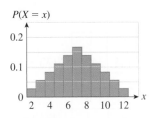

27.

x	1	2	3	4	5	6
$P(X = x)$	$\frac{1}{36}$	$\frac{3}{36}$	$\frac{5}{36}$	$\frac{7}{36}$	$\frac{9}{36}$	$\frac{11}{36}$

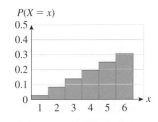

29. a.

x	10,000	30,000	50,000	70,000	90,000
$P(X = x)$	.24	.27	.22	.16	.11

b. .27 Histogram:

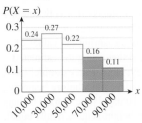

31. The random variable is X = age of a working adult in Mexico.

x	20	30	40	50	60
$P(X = x)$	.288	.472	.200	.032	.008

33. a. 2,000, 3,000, 4,000, 5,000, 6,000, 7,000, 8,000 (7,000 is optional)
b.

x	2,000	3,000	4,000	5,000	6,000	7,000	8,000
Freq.	2	1	1	1	2	0	3
$P(X = x)$	.2	.1	.1	.1	.2	0	.3

c. $P(X \le 5,000) = .5$ **35. a.** $-700, -600, -500, -400,$ $-300, -200, -100, 0, 100, 200, 300, 400, 500, 600, 700, 800,$ 900 ($-600, 0, 100, 300, 500, 600, 700,$ and 800 are optional.)
b.

x	−700	−600	−500	−400	−300	−200	−100	0
Freq.	2	0	2	1	1	4	4	0
$P(X = x)$	.1	0	.1	.05	.05	.2	.2	0

x	100	200	300	400	500	600	700	800	900
Freq.	0	2	0	2	0	0	0	0	2
$P(X = x)$	0	.1	0	.1	0	0	0	0	.1

c. .3

37.

Class	1.1 − 2.0	2.1 − 3.0	3.1 − 4.0
Freq.	4	7	9

x	1.5	2.5	3.5
$P(X = x)$	.20	.35	.45

39. 95.5%

41.

x	3	2	1	0
$P(X = x)$	.0625	.6875	.125	.125

43. .75 The probability that a randomly selected small car is rated Good or Acceptable is .75.   **45.** $P(Y \ge 2) = .50$, $P(Z \ge 2) \approx .53$, suggesting that medium SUVs are safer than small SUVs in frontal crashes   **47.** Small cars   **49.** .375

51.

x	1	2	3	4
$P(X = x)$	$\dfrac{4}{35}$	$\dfrac{18}{35}$	$\dfrac{12}{35}$	$\dfrac{1}{35}$

$P(X \geq 2) = 31/35 \approx .886$
53. Answers will vary. **55.** No; for instance, if X is the number of times you must toss a coin until heads comes up, then X is infinite but not continuous. **57.** By measuring the values of X for a large number of outcomes, and then using the estimated probability (relative frequency) **59.** Here is an example: Let X be the number of days a diligent student waits before beginning to study for an exam scheduled in 10 days' time. **61.** The bars should be 1 unit wide, so that their height is numerically equal to their area. **63.** Answers may vary. If we are interested in exact page counts, then the number of possible values is very large and the values are (relatively speaking) close together, so using a continuous random variable might be advantageous. In general, the finer and more numerous the measurement classes, the more likely it becomes that a continuous random variable could be advantageous.

Section 8.2
1. .0729 **3.** .59049 **5.** .00001 **7.** .99144 **9.** .00856
11. .27648 **13.** .54432 **15.** .04096 **17.** .77414
19. $P(X = x)$

21. $P(X = x)$

$P(X \leq 2) = .8889$
23. .2637 **25.** .8926 **27.** .875 **29. a.** .0081 **b.** .08146
31. .41 **33. a.** .0509 **b.** Probability distribution (entries rounded to four decimal places):

x	0	1	2	3	4
$P(X = x)$	.0643	.2030	.2885	.2429	.1343
5	6	7	8	9	10
.0509	.0134	.0024	.0003	.0000	.0000

c. 2 **35.** .000298 **37.** .8321 **39. a.** 21 **b.** 20 **c.** The graph for $n = 50$ trials is more widely distributed than the graph for $n = 20$. **41.** 69 trials **43.** $.562 \times 10^{-5}$ **45.** .0266; because there is only a 2.66% chance of detecting the disease in a given year, the government's claim seems dubious. **47.** No; in a

sequence of Bernoulli trials, the occurrence of one success does not affect the probability of success on the next attempt. **49.** No; if life is a sequence of Bernoulli trials, then the occurrence of one misfortune ("success") does not affect the probability of a misfortune on the next trial. Hence, misfortunes may very well not "occur in threes." **51.** Think of performing the experiment as a Bernoulli trial with "success" being the occurrence of E. Performing the experiment n times independently in succession would then be a sequence of n Bernoulli trials. **53.** The probability of selecting a red marble changes after each selection, as the number of marbles left in the bag decreases. This violates the requirement that, in a sequence of Bernoulli trials, the probability of "success" does not change.

Section 8.3
1. $\bar{x} = 6$, median $= 5$, mode $= 5$
3. $\bar{x} = 3$, median $= 3.5$, mode $= -1$
5. $\bar{x} = -0.1875$, median $= 0.875$, every value is a mode
7. $\bar{x} = 0.2$, median $= -0.1$, mode $= -0.1$ **9.** Answers may vary. Two examples are: 0, 0, 0, 0, 0, 6 and 0, 0, 0, 1, 2, 3
11. 0.9 **13.** 21 **15.** -0.1 **17.** 3.5 **19.** 1 **21.** 4.472
23. 2.667 **25.** 2 **27.** 0.385 **29.** $\bar{x} = -150$, $m = -150$; -150
31. $\bar{x} = \$918.30$, median $= \$915.50$, mode $= \$905$. Over the 10-business day period sampled, the price of gold averaged $\$915.30$ per ounce. It was above $\$915.50$ as many times as it was below that, and stood at $\$905$ more often than any other price.
33. a. 6.5; there was an average of 6.5 checkout lanes in each supermarket that was surveyed. **b.** $P(X < \mu) = .42$; $P(X > \mu) = .58$, and is thus larger. Most supermarkets have more than the average number of checkout lanes.
35.

X	5	10	15	20	25	35
$P(X)$	.17	.33	.21	.19	.03	.07

$E(X) = 14.3$;

the average age of a school goer in 1998 was 14.3. **37.** 30
39. $\$41,000$
41.

x	3	2	1	0
$P(X = x)$	.0625	.6875	.125	.125

$E(X) = 1.6875$

y	3	2	1	0
$P(Y = y)$	.1	.4	.4	.1

$E(Y) = 1.5$;

small cars
43. Large cars **45.** Expect to lose 5.3¢. **47.** 25.2 students
49. a. Two defective airbags **b.** 120 airbags
51.

x	1	2	3	4
$P(X = x)$	$\dfrac{4}{35}$	$\dfrac{18}{35}$	$\dfrac{12}{35}$	$\dfrac{1}{35}$

$E(X) = 16/7 \approx 2.2857$ tents

53. FastForward: 3.97%; SolidState: 5.51%; SolidState gives the higher expected return. **55.** A loss of $\$29,390$ **57.** (A) **59.** He is wrong; for example, the collection 0, 0, 300 has mean 100 and median 0.   **61.** No. The expected number of times you will hit the dart-board is the average number of times you will hit the bull's eye per 50 shots; the average of a set of whole numbers need not be a whole number.   **63.** Wrong. It might be the case that only a small fraction of people in the class scored better than you but received exceptionally high scores that raised the class average. Suppose, for instance, that there are 10 people in the class. Four received 100%, you received 80%, and the rest received 70%. Then the class average is 83%, 5 people have lower scores than you, but only 4 have higher scores.   **65.** No; the mean of a very large sample is only an *estimate* of the population mean. The means of larger and larger samples *approach* the population mean as the sample size increases.   **67.** Wrong. The statement attributed to President Bush asserts that the mean tax refund would be $1,000, whereas the statements referred to as "The Truth" suggest that the *median* tax refund would be close to $100 [and that the 31st percentile would be zero].   **69.** Select a U.S. household at random, and let X be the income of that household. The expected value of X is then the population mean of all U.S. household incomes.

Section 8.4

1. $s^2 = 29$; $s = 5.39$ **3.** $s^2 = 12.4$; $s = 3.52$
5. $s^2 = 6.64$; $s = 2.58$ **7.** $s^2 = 13.01$; $s = 3.61$ **9.** 1.04
11. 9.43   **13.** 3.27   **15.** Expected value = 3.5, variance = 2.918, standard deviation = 1.71   **17.** Expected value = 1, variance = 0.5, standard deviation = 0.71
19. Expected value = 4.47, variance = 1.97, standard deviation = 1.40   **21.** Expected value = 2.67, variance = 0.36, standard deviation = 0.60
23. Expected value = 2, variance = 1.8, standard deviation = 1.34   **25. a.** $\bar{x} = 3$, $s = 3.54$ **b.** [0, 6.54] We must assume that the population distribution is bell-shaped and symmetric.   **27. a.** $\bar{x} = 5.0$, $s = 0.6$ **b.** 3.8, 6.2
29. a. $\bar{x} = -150$, $s \approx 495$ **b.** 645, 20%   **31. a.** 2.18
b. [11.22, 24.28]   **c.** 100%; Empirical rule   **33.** $\mu = 1.5$, $\sigma = 1.43$; 100%   **35.** $\mu = 40.6$, $\sigma \approx 26$; $52,000
37. a. $\mu \approx 30.2$ yrs. old, $\sigma = 11.78$ years   **b.** 18–42   **39.** At most 6.25%   **41.** At most; 12.5%   **43. a.** $\mu = 25.2$, $\sigma = 3.05$ **b.** 31
45. a. $\mu = 780$, $\sigma \approx 13.1$ **b.** 754, 806   **47. a.** $\mu = 6.5$, $\sigma^2 = 4.0$, $\sigma = 2.0$ **b.** [2.5, 10.5]; three checkout lanes
49. $10,700 or less   **51.** $65,300 or more   **53.** U.S.   **55.** U.S.
57. 16%   **59.** 0–$76,000   **61.** $\mu = 12.56\%$, $\sigma \approx 1.8885\%$
63. 78%; the empirical rule predicts 68%. The associated probability distribution is roughly bell-shaped but not symmetric.
65. 96%. Chebyshev's rule is valid, since it predicts that *at least* 75% of the scores are in this range.   **67.** (B), (D)   **69.** The sample standard deviation is bigger; the formula for sample standard deviation involves division by the smaller term $n - 1$ instead of n, which makes the resulting number larger.   **71.** The grades in the first class were clustered fairly close to 75. By Chebyshev's inequality, at least 88% of the class had grades in the range 60–90. On the other hand, the grades in the second class were widely dispersed. The second class had a much wider spread of ability than did the first class.   **73.** The variable must take on only the value 10, with probability 1.   **75.** $(y - x)/2$

Section 8.5

1. .1915   **3.** .5222   **5.** .6710   **7.** .2417   **9.** .8664
11. .8621   **13.** .2286   **15.** .3830   **17.** .5028   **19.** .35
21. .05   **23.** .3830   **25.** .6687   **27.** 26%   **29.** 29,600,000
31. 0   **33.** About 6,680   **35.** 28%   **37.** 5%   **39.** The U.S.
41. Wechsler. As this test has a smaller standard deviation, a greater percentage of scores fall within 20 points of the mean.
43. This is surprising, because the time between failures was more than five standard deviations away from the mean, which happens with an extremely small probability.   **45.** .6103
47. .6103 × .5832 ≈ .3559   **49.** .6255   **51.** .7257   **53.** .8708
55. .0029   **57.** Probability that a person will say Goode = .54. Probability that Goode polls more than 52% ≈ .8925.
59. 23.4   **61.** When the distribution is normal   **63.** Neither. They are equal.   **65.** $1/(b - a)$ **67.** A normal distribution with standard deviation 0.5, because it is narrower near the mean, but must enclose the same amount of area as the standard curve, and so it must be higher.

Chapter 8 Review

1.

x	0	1	2
$P(X = x)$	1/4	1/2	1/4

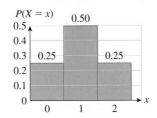

3.

x	2	3	4	5	6	7	8
$P(X = x)$	1/16	2/16	3/16	4/16	3/16	2/16	1/16

5.

x	0	1	2	3
$P(X = x)$	.2071	.4439	.2908	.0582

7. $\bar{x} = 2, m = 2, s \approx 2.7386$ **9.** Two examples are: 0, 0, 0, 4 and $-1, -1, 1, 5$ **11.** An example is $-1, -1, -1, 1, 1, 1$
13. .4165   **15.** .9267   **17.** .0067   **19.** .7330   **21.** $\mu = 1.5$, $\sigma = 0.8660$; 2
23.

x	-3	-2	-1	0	1	2	3
$P(X = x)$	1/16	2/16	3/16	4/16	3/16	2/16	1/16

$\mu = 0, \sigma = 1.5811$; within 1.3 standard deviations of the mean
25. [49.4, 150.6]   **27.** 260   **29.** .4332   **31.** .0358   **33.** .3085
35. $12.15   **37.** $27,210   **39.** False; let $X =$ price and $Y =$ weekly sales. Then weekly Revenue $= XY$. However, $27,210 \neq 12.15 \times 2,620$. In other words, $E(XY) \neq E(X)E(Y)$.
41. a.

x	2	4	6	8	10
$P(X = x)$	.25	.35	.15	.15	.1

$\mu = 5, \sigma = 2.5690$ **b.** Between 2.431 and 7.569 orders per million residents; the empirical rule does not apply because the distribution is not symmetric. **c.** (A)   **43.** .190   **45.** .060
47. 0.5   **49.** .284   **51.** .108   **53.** Using normal distribution table: 364,000 people. More accurate answer: 378,000 people.
55. 148

Chapter 9

Section 9.1
1. Vertex: $(-3/2, -1/4)$,
y-intercept: 2,
x-intercepts: $-2, -1$

3. Vertex: $(2,0)$,
y-intercept: -4,
x-intercept: 2

5. Vertex: $(-20, 900)$,
y-intercept: 500,
x-intercepts: $-50, 10$

7. Vertex: $(-1/2, -5/4)$,
y-intercept: -1,
x-intercepts: $-1/2 \pm \sqrt{5}/2$

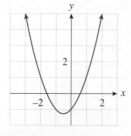

9. Vertex: $(0, 1)$,
y-intercept: 1,
no x-intercepts

11. $R = -4p^2 + 100p$;
Maximum revenue
when $p = \$12.50$

13. $R = -2p^2 + 400p$; Maximum revenue when $p = \$100$

15. $y = -0.7955x^2 + 4.4591x - 1.6000$
17. $y = -1.1667x^2 - 6.1667x - 3.0000$
19. a. Positive because the data suggest a curve that is concave up. **b.** (C) **c.** 1998. Extrapolating in the positive direction leads one to predict more and more steeply rising military expenditure, which may or may not occur; extrapolating in the negative direction predicts continually more an more steeply rising military expenditure as we go back in time, contradicting history.
21. 2003; about 1.6 million barrels/day   **23.** 5,000 pounds. The model is not trustworthy for vehicle weights larger than 5,000 pounds, as it predicts increasing fuel economy with increasing weight, and 5,000 is close to the upper limit of the domain of the function.   **25.** Maximum revenue when $p = \$140$, $R = \$9,800$ **27.** Maximum revenue with 70 houses, $R = \$9,800,000$ **29. a.** $q = -4,500p + 41,500$
b. $4.61 for a daily revenue of $95,680.55 **c.** No
31. a. $q = -560x + 1,400$; $R = -560x^2 + 1,400x$
b. $P = -560x^2 + 1,400x - 30$; $x = \$1.25$;
$P = \$845$ per month   **33.** $C = -200x + 620$;
$P = -400x^2 + 1,400x - 620$; $x = \$1.75$ per log-on;
$P = \$605$ per month   **35. a.** $q = -10p + 400$
b. $R = -10p^2 + 400p$ **c.** $C = -30p + 4,200$
d. $P = -10p^2 + 430p - 4,200$; $p = \$21.50$
37. $f(t) = 6.25t^2 - 100t + 1,200$; $1,425 billion, which is $25 billion lower than the actual value.
39. a. $S(t) = -391t^2 + 3,278t - 4,844$;
Graph:

b. −1,057 thousand units. This makes no sense, and shows the danger of extrapolating mathematical models beyond their domains. Actual sales in the third quarter of 2008 were 5.9 million.   **41.** The graph is a straight line.   **43.** (C)
45. Positive; the x coordinate of the vertex is negative, so $−b/(2a)$ must be negative. Because a is positive (the parabola is concave up), this means that b must also be positive to make $−b/(2a)$ negative.   **47.** The x coordinate of the vertex represents the unit price that leads to the maximum revenue, the y coordinate of the vertex gives the maximum possible revenue, the x-intercepts give the unit prices that result in zero revenue, and the y-intercept gives the revenue resulting from zero unit price (which is obviously zero).   **49.** Graph the data to see whether the points suggest a curve rather than a straight line. If the curve suggested by the graph is concave up or concave down, then a quadratic model would be a likely candidate.
51. No; the graph of a quadratic function is a parabola. In the case of a concave-up parabola, the curve would unrealistically predict sales increasing without bound in the future. In the case of a concave-down parabola, the curve would predict "negative" sales from some point on.   **53.** If $q = mp + b$ (with $m < 0$), then the revenue is given by $R = pq = mp^2 + bp$. This is the equation of a parabola with $a = m < 0$, and so is concave down. Thus, the vertex is the highest point on the parabola, showing that there is a single highest value for R, namely, the y coordinate of the vertex.   **55.** Since $R = pq$, the demand must be given by

$$q = \frac{R}{p} = \frac{-50p^2 + 60p}{p} = -50p + 60.$$

Section 9.2

1. $4\char94 x$

x	−3	−2	−1	0	1	2	3
$f(x)$	$\frac{1}{64}$	$\frac{1}{16}$	$\frac{1}{4}$	1	4	16	64

3. $3\char94(-x)$

x	−3	−2	−1	0	1	2	3
$f(x)$	27	9	3	1	$\frac{1}{3}$	$\frac{1}{9}$	$\frac{1}{27}$

5. $2*2\char94 x$ or $2*(2\char94 x)$

x	−3	−2	−1	0	1	2	3
$f(x)$	$\frac{1}{4}$	$\frac{1}{2}$	1	2	4	8	16

7. $-3*2\char94(-x)$

x	−3	−2	−1	0	1	2	3
$f(x)$	−24	−12	−6	−3	$-\frac{3}{2}$	$-\frac{3}{4}$	$-\frac{3}{8}$

9. $2\char94 x-1$

x	−3	−2	−1	0	1	2	3
$f(x)$	$-\frac{7}{8}$	$-\frac{3}{4}$	$-\frac{1}{2}$	0	1	3	7

11. $2\char94(x-1)$

x	−3	−2	−1	0	1	2	3
$f(x)$	$\frac{1}{16}$	$\frac{1}{8}$	$\frac{1}{4}$	$\frac{1}{2}$	1	2	4

13.   **15.**   **17.**

$y = 3^{-x}$

$y = 2(2^x)$ $y = -3(2^{-x})$

19. Both; $f(x) = 4.5(3^x)$. $g(x) = 2(1/2)^x$, or $2(2^{-x})$
21. Neither   **23.** g; $g(x) = 4(0.2)^x$
25. $\text{e}\char94(-2*x)$ or $\text{EXP}(-2*x)$

x	−3	−2	−1	0	1	2	3
$f(x)$	403.4	54.60	7.389	1	0.1353	0.01832	0.002479

27. $1.01*2.02\char94(-4*x)$

x	−3	−2	−1	0	1	2	3
$f(x)$	4662	280.0	16.82	1.01	0.06066	0.003643	0.0002188

29. $50*(1+1/3.2)\char94(2*x)$

x	−3	−2	−1	0	1	2	3
$f(x)$	9.781	16.85	29.02	50	86.13	148.4	255.6

31. $2\char94(x-1)$ *not* $2\char94 x-1$ **33.** $2/(1-2\char94(-4*x))$
not $2/1-2\char94-4*x$ *and not* $2/1-2\char94(-4*x)$
35. $(3+x)\char94(3*x)/(x+1)$ or $((3+x)\char94(3*x))/(x+1)$
not $(3+x)\char94(3*x)/x+1$ *and not* $(3+x\char94(3*x))/(x+1)$
37. $2*\text{e}\char94((1+x)/x)$ or $2*\text{EXP}((1+x)/x)$ *not*
$2*\text{e}\char941+x/x$ *and not* $2*\text{e}\char94(1+x)/x$ *and not*
$2*\text{EXP}(1+x)/x$
39.   **41.**

$y1 = 1.6\char94 x$ $y2 = 1.8\char94 x$

$y1 = 300*1.1\char94 x$
$y2 = 300*1.1\char94(2*x)$

43.   **45.**

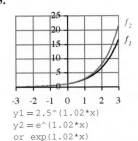
$y1 = 2.5\char94(1.02*x)$
$y2 = \text{e}\char94(1.02*x)$
or $\exp(1.02*x)$

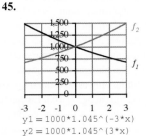
$y1 = 1000*1.045\char94(-3*x)$
$y2 = 1000*1.045\char94(3*x)$

47. $f(x) = 500(0.5)^x$ **49.** $f(x) = 10(3)^x$
51. $f(x) = 500(0.45)^x$ **53.** $f(x) = -100(1.1)^x$
55. $y = 4(3^x)$ **57.** $y = -1(0.2^x)$ **59.** $y = 2.1213(1.4142^x)$
61. $y = 3.6742(0.9036^x)$ **63.** $f(t) = 5,000e^{0.10t}$
65. $f(t) = 1,000e^{-0.063t}$ **67.** $y = 1.0442(1.7564)^x$
69. $y = 15.1735(1.4822)^x$ **71.** $f(t) = 300(0.5)^t$; 9.375 mg
73. a. Linear model: $F = 65t - 60$. Exponential model:
$F = 97.2(1.20)^t$. The exponential model is more appropriate.
b. 418 tons, not too far off the projected figure
75. a. $P = 180(1.01091)^t$ million **b.** 5 significant digits
c. 345 million   **77. a.** $y = 50,000(1.5^{t/2})$, t = time in years
since two years ago **b.** 91,856 tags   **79.** $y = 1,000(2^{t/3})$;
65,536,000 bacteria after 2 days   **81.** $A(t) = 167(1.18)^t$;
1,695 cases   **83.** $A(t) = 5,000(1 + 0.0494/12)^{12t}$; $7,061
85. At the beginning of 2016   **87.** 491.82   **89.** $A(t) = 1.3e^{-0.3t}$;
2008: 0.53 million; 2009: 0.39 million
91. a.

Year	1950	2000	2050	2100
$C(t)$ parts per million	561	669	799	953

b. 2010 ($t = 260$)
93. a. $P(t) = 0.339(1.169)^t$.
Graph:

b. $1.9 million
95. a. $n = 1.127(3.544)^t$
Graph:

b. 3.544 **c.** 178 million   **97.** (B)   **99.** Exponential functions of
the form $f(x) = Ab^x$ ($b > 0$) increase rapidly for large values
of x. In real-life situations, such as population growth, this
model is reliable only for relatively short periods of growth.
Eventually, population growth tapers off because of pressures
such as limited resources and overcrowding.   **101.** The article
was published about a year before the "housing bubble" burst in
2006, whereupon house prices started to fall, contrary to the
prediction of the graph, as documented in Exercise 90. This
shows the danger of using any mathematical model to extrapolate. The blogger was, however, cautious in the choice of words,
claiming only to be estimating what the future U.S. median house
price "might be."   **103.** Linear functions better: cost models
where there is a fixed cost and a variable cost; simple interest,
where interest is paid on the original amount invested.
Exponential models better: compound interest, population
growth. (In both of these, the rate of growth depends on the

present number of items, rather than on some fixed quantity.)
105. Take the ratios y_2/y_1 and y_3/y_2. If they are the same, the
points fit on an exponential curve.   **107.** This reasoning is
suspect—the bank need not use its computer resources to
update all the accounts every minute, but can instead use the
continuous compounding formula to calculate the balance in
any account at any time.

Section 9.3

1.

Logarithmic Form	$\log_{10}10,000 = 4$	$\log_4 16 = 2$	$\log_3 27 = 3$	$\log_5 5 = 1$	$\log_7 1 = 0$	$\log_4 \frac{1}{16} = -2$

3.

Exponential Form	$(0.5)^2 = 0.25$	$5^0 = 1$	$10^{-1} = 0.1$	$4^3 = 64$	$2^8 = 256$	$2^{-2} = \frac{1}{4}$

5. 1.4650   **7.** −1.1460   **9.** −0.7324   **11.** 6.2657
13.   **15.**

17.

19. $Q = 1000e^{-t \ln 2}$ **21.** $Q = 1000e^{t(\ln 2)/2}$
23. Doubling time = 2 ln 2   **25.** Half-life = (ln 2)/4
27. $f(x) = 4(7.389)^x$ **29.** $f(t) = 2.1e^{0.000\,9995t}$
31. $f(t) = 10e^{-0.01309t}$.   **33.** 3.36 years   **35.** 11 years
37. 23.1%   **39.** 63,000 years old   **41.** 11 years
43. 207 months   **45.** 12 years   **47.** 17.77 years
49. 1,600 years   **51. a.** $b = 3^{1/6} \approx 1.20$ **b.** 3.8 months
53. a. $Q(t) = Q_0e^{-0.139t}$ **b.** 3 years   **55.** 2,360 million years
57. 3.2 hours   **59.** 3.89 days
61. a. $P(t) = 6.591 \ln(t) - 17.69$ **b.** 1 digit **c.** (A)
63. $57.51 \ln t + 30.96$
Graph:

Extrapolating in the positive direction results in a prediction of
ever-increasing R&D expenditures by industry. This is reasonable
to a point, as expenditures cannot reasonably be expected to
increase without bound. Extrapolating in the negative direction
eventually leads to negative values, which does not model
reality.   **65. a.** About 1.259×10^{24} ergs **b.** about 2.24%
c. $E = 10^{1.5R+11.8}$ **d.** Proof **e.** 1,000   **67. a.** 75 dB, 69 dB,

61 dB **b.** $D = 95 - 20 \log r$ **c.** 57,000 feet
69. Graph:

The green curve is $y = \ln x$. The blue curve is $y = 2 \ln x$, and the red curve is $y = 2 \ln x + 0.5$. Multiplying by A stretches the graph in the y-direction by a factor of A. Adding C moves the graph C units vertically up. **71.** The logarithm of a negative number, were it defined, would be the power to which a base must be raised to give that negative number. But raising a base to a power never results in a negative number, so there can be no such number as the logarithm of a negative number. **73.** Any logarithmic curve $y = \log_b t + C$ will eventually surpass 100%, and hence not be suitable as a long-term predictor of market share. **75.** $\log_4 y$ **77.** 8 **79.** x **81.** Time is increasing logarithmically with population; solving $P = Ab^t$ for t gives $t = \log_b(P/A) = \log_b P - \log_b A$, which is of the form $t = \log_b P + C$. **83.** (Proof)

Section 9.4

1. $N = 7$, $A = 6$, $b = 2$;
  7/(1+6*2^-x)

3. $N = 10$, $A = 4$, $b = 0.3$;
  10/(1+4*0.3^-x)

5. $N = 4$, $A = 7$, $b = 1.5$;
  4/(1+7*1.5^-x)

7. $f(x) = \dfrac{200}{1 + 19(2^{-x})}$ **9.** $f(x) = \dfrac{6}{1 + 2^{-x}}$

11. (B) **13.** (B) **15.** (C)

17. $y = \dfrac{7.2}{1 + 2.4(1.05)^{-x}}$ **19.** $y = \dfrac{97}{1 + 2.2(0.942)^{-x}}$

21. a. (A) **b.** 2003 **23. a.** (A) **b.** 20% per year
25. a. 91% **b.** $P(x) \approx 14.33(1.05)^x$ **c.** \$38,000

27. $N(t) = \dfrac{10,000}{1 + 9(1.25)^{-t}}$; $N(7) \approx 3,463$ cases

29. $N(t) = \dfrac{3,000}{1 + 29(2^{1/5})^{-t}}$; $t = 16$ days

31. a. $A(t) = \dfrac{6.3}{1 + 4.8(1.2)^{-t}}$; 6,300 articles

b. 5,200 articles **33. a.** $B(t) = \dfrac{1,070}{1 + 0.391(1.10)^{-t}}$;

Leveling off value $\approx 1,070$

b. $t \approx -9.85$. According to the model, the number of teams was rising fastest about 9.85 years *prior* to 1990; that is, some time during 1980. **c.** The number of men's basketball teams was growing by about 10% per year around 1990.

35. $y = \dfrac{4,500}{1 + 1.1466(1.0357)^{-t}}$; 2013

37. Just as diseases are communicated via the spread of a pathogen (such as a virus), new technology is communicated via the spread of information (such as advertising and publicity). Further, just as the spread of a disease is ultimately limited by the number of susceptible individuals, so the spread of a new technology is ultimately limited by the size of the potential market. **39.** It can be used to predict where the sales of a new commodity might level off. **41.** The curve is still a logistic curve, but decreases when $b > 1$ and increases when $b < 1$. **43.** (Proof)

Chapter 9 Review
1.

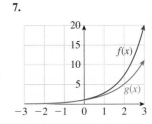

3. $f: f(x) = 5(1/2)^x$, or $5(2^{-x})$

5. **7.**

9. \$3,484.85 **11.** \$3,705.48 **13.** \$3,485.50

15. $f(x) = 4.5(9^x)$ **17.** $f(x) = \dfrac{2}{3}3^x$ **19.** $-\dfrac{1}{2} \log_3 4$

21. $\dfrac{1}{3} \log 1.05$

23.

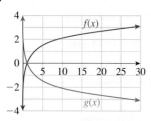

25. $Q = 5e^{-0.00693t}$ **27.** $Q = 2.5e^{0.347t}$ **29.** 10.2 years

31. 10.8 years   **33.** $f(x) = \dfrac{900}{1 + 8(1.5)^{-x}}$

35. $f(x) = \dfrac{20}{1 + 3(0.8)^{-x}}$ **37. a.** \$8,500 per month;

an average of approximately 2,100 hits per day
b. \$29,049 per month **c.** The fact that -0.000005,
the coefficient of c^2, is negative.   **39. a.** $R = -60p^2 + 950p$;
$p = \$7.92$ per novel, Monthly revenue $= \$3,760.42$
b. $P = -60p^2 + 1{,}190p - 4{,}700$; $p = \$9.92$ per novel,
Monthly profit $= \$1{,}200.42$ **41. a.** 10, 34
b. About 360,000 pounds   **43.** 2008   **45.** 299,000 pounds
47. $n(t) = 10(0.66^t)$ million pounds of lobster   **49.** (C)

Chapter 10

Section 10.1

1. 0   **3.** 4   **5.** Does not exist   **7.** 1.5   **9.** 0.5   **11.** Diverges to
$+\infty$ **13.** 0   **15.** 1   **17.** 0   **19. a.** -2 **b.** -1 **21. a.** 2 **b.** 1
c. 0 **d.** $+\infty$ **23. a.** 0 **b.** 2 **c.** -1 **d.** Does not exist **e.** 2
f. $+\infty$ **25. a.** 1 **b.** 1 **c.** 2 **d.** Does not exist **e.** 1 **f.** 2
27. a. 1 **b.** $+\infty$ **c.** $+\infty$ **d.** $+\infty$ **e.** not defined **f.** -1
29. a. -1 **b.** $+\infty$ **c.** $-\infty$ **d.** Does not exist **e.** 2 **f.** 1   **31.** 210
trillion pesos per year. In the long term, the model predicts that the
value of sold goods in Mexico will approach 210 trillion pesos per
year.   **33.** 7.0; in the long term, the number of research articles in
Physical Review written by researchers in Europe approaches 7,000
per year.   **35.** 470. This suggests that students whose parents earn
an exceptionally large income score an average of 470 on the SAT
verbal test.   **37.** $\lim_{t \to +\infty} p(t) = 15$; the home price index will
approach a value 15% above the 2003 level in the long term.
39. $\lim_{t \to 1^-} C(t) = 0.06$, $\lim_{t \to 1^+} C(t) = 0.08$, so
$\lim_{t \to 1} C(t)$ does not exist.   **41.** $\lim_{t \to +\infty} I(t) = +\infty$,
$\lim_{t \to +\infty}(I(t)/E(t)) \approx 2.5$. In the long term, U.S. imports from
China will rise without bound and be 2.5 times U.S. exports to
China. In the real world, imports and exports cannot rise without
bound. Thus, the given models should not be extrapolated far into
the future.   **43.** To approximate $\lim_{x \to a} f(x)$ numerically, choose
values of x closer and closer to, and on either side of $x = a$, and
evaluate $f(x)$ for each of them. The limit (if it exists) is then the
number that these values of $f(x)$ approach. A disadvantage of this
method is that it may never give the exact value of the limit, but
only an approximation. (However, we can make this as accurate as
we like.)   **45.** Any situation in which there is a sudden change can
be modeled by a function in which $\lim_{t \to a^+} f(t)$ is not the same

as $\lim_{t \to a^-} f(t)$. One example is the value of a stock market
index before and after a crash: $\lim_{t \to a^-} f(t)$ is the value immediately before the crash at time $t = a$, while $\lim_{t \to a^+} f(t)$ is the
value immediately after the crash. Another example might be the
price of a commodity that is suddenly increased from one level to
another.   **47.** It is possible for $\lim_{x \to a} f(x)$ to exist even though
$f(a)$ is not defined. An example is $\lim_{x \to 1} \dfrac{x^2 - 3x + 2}{x - 1}$.
49. The limit may not be defined and, even if it is, may not equal
$f(a)$. See, for example, Exercises 23 and 24.   **51.** An example is
$f(x) = (x - 1)(x - 2)$.

Section 10.2

1. Continuous on its domain   **3.** Continuous on its domain
5. Discontinuous at $x = 0$ **7.** Discontinuous at $x = -1$
9. Continuous on its domain   **11.** Discontinuous at $x = -1$
and 0   **13.** (A), (B), (D), (E)   **15.** 0   **17.** -1 **19.** No
value possible   **21.** -1 **23.** Continuous on its domain
25. Continuous on its domain   **27.** Discontinuity at $x = 0$
29. Discontinuity at $x = 0$ **31.** Continuous on its domain
33. Not unless the domain of the function consists of all real
numbers. (It is impossible for a function to be continuous at
points not in its domain.) For example, $f(x) = 1/x$ is continuous on its domain—the set of nonzero real numbers—but not
at $x = 0$.   **35.** True. If the graph of a function has a break in its
graph at any point a, then it cannot be continuous at the point a.
37. Answers may vary. $f(x) = 1/[(x - 1)(x - 2)(x - 3)]$ is
such a function; it is undefined at $x = 1, 2, 3$ and so its graph consists of three distinct curves.   **39.** Answers may vary.

41. Answers may vary. The price of OHaganBooks.com stocks
suddenly drops by \$10 as news spreads of a government
investigation. Let $f(x)$ = Price of OHaganBooks.com stocks.

Section 10.3

1. $x = 1$ **3.** 2   **5.** Determinate; diverges to $+\infty$
7. Determinate; does not exist   **9.** Determinate; diverges to
$-\infty$ **11.** Determinate; 0   **13.** Indeterminate; $-1/3$
15. Indeterminate; 0   **17.** Determinate; 0   **19.** Determinate;
-60 **21.** 1   **23.** 2   **25.** 0   **27.** 6   **29.** 4   **31.** 2   **33.** 0   **35.** 0
37. 12   **39.** $+\infty$ **41.** Does not exist; left and right (infinite)
limits differ.   **43.** $-\infty$ **45.** Does not exist   **47.** $+\infty$ **49.** 3/2
51. 1/2   **53.** $+\infty$ **55.** 0   **57.** 3/2   **59.** 1/2   **61.** $-\infty$ **63.** 0
65. 12   **67.** 0   **69.** $+\infty$ **71.** 0   **73.** Discontinuity at $x = 0$
75. Continuous everywhere   **77.** Discontinuity at $x = 0$
79. Discontinuity at $x = 0$ **81. a.** $\lim_{t \to 5^-} N(t) = \lim_{t \to 5^+}$
$N(t) = 4.1$; shortly before and after 2000 $(t = 5)$ the number
of workers employed in manufacturing jobs in Mexico was

close to 4.1 million. **b.** N is continuous at $t = 5$; no abrupt changes **83. a.** 0.49, 1.16. Shortly before 1999 annual advertising expenditures were close to $0.49 billion. Shortly after 1999 annual advertising expenditures were close to $1.16 billion. **b.** Not continuous; movie advertising expenditures jumped suddenly in 1999. **85.** 1.59; if the trend continued indefinitely, the annual spending on police would be 1.59 times the annual spending on courts in the long run. **87.** 825; in the long term, annual revenues will approach $825 million. **89.** $\lim_{t \to +\infty} I(t) = +\infty$, $\lim_{t \to +\infty}(I(t)/E(t)) = 2.5$. In the long term, U.S. imports from China will rise without bound and be 2.5 times U.S. exports to China. In the real world, imports and exports cannot rise without bound. Thus, the given models should not be extrapolated far into the future. **91.** $\lim_{t \to +\infty} p(t) = 100$. The percentage of children who learn to speak approaches 100% as their age increases. **93.** To evaluate $\lim_{x \to a} f(x)$ algebraically, first check whether $f(x)$ is a closed-form function. Then check whether $x = a$ is in its domain. If so, the limit is just $f(a)$; that is, it is obtained by substituting $x = a$. If not, then try to first simplify $f(x)$ in such a way as to transform it into a new function such that $x = a$ is in its domain, and then substitute. A disadvantage of this method is that it is sometimes extremely difficult to evaluate limits algebraically, and rather sophisticated methods are often needed. **95.** She is wrong. Closed-form functions are continuous only at points in their domains, and $x = 2$ is not in the domain of the closed-form function $f(x) = 1/(x-2)^2$. **97.** Answers may vary. (1) See Example 2: $\lim_{x \to 2} \dfrac{x^3 - 8}{x - 2}$, which leads to the indeterminate form $0/0$ but the limit is 12. (2) $\lim_{x \to +\infty} \dfrac{60x}{2x}$, which leads to the indeterminate form ∞/∞, but where the limit exists and equals 30. **99.** The statement may not be true, for instance, if $f(x) = \begin{cases} x + 2 & \text{if } x < 0 \\ 2x - 1 & \text{if } x \geq 0 \end{cases}$, then $f(0)$ is defined and equals -1, and yet $\lim_{x \to 0} f(x)$ does not exist. The statement can be corrected by requiring that f be a closed-form function: "If f is a closed form function, and $f(a)$ is defined, then $\lim_{x \to a} f(x)$ exists and equals $f(a)$." **101.** Answers may vary, for example $f(x) = \begin{cases} 0 & \text{if } x \text{ is any number other than 1 or 2} \\ 1 & \text{if } x = 1 \text{ or } 2 \end{cases}$

103. Answers may vary.

(1) $\lim_{x \to +\infty} [(x + 5) - x] = \lim_{x \to +\infty} 5 = 5$

(2) $\lim_{x \to +\infty} [x^2 - x] = \lim_{x \to +\infty} x(x - 1) = +\infty$

(3) $\lim_{x \to +\infty} [(x - 5) - x] = \lim_{x \to +\infty} -5 = -5$

Section 10.4

1. -3 **3.** 0.3 **5.** $-\$25,000$ per month **7.** -200 items per dollar **9.** 1.33 per month **11.** 0.75 percentage point increase in unemployment per 1 percentage point increase in the deficit **13.** 4 **15.** 2 **17.** 7/3

19.

h	Ave. Rate of Change
1	2
0.1	0.2
0.01	0.02
0.001	0.002
0.0001	0.0002

21.

h	Ave. Rate of Change
1	-0.1667
0.1	-0.2381
0.01	-0.2488
0.001	-0.2499
0.0001	-0.24999

23.

h	Ave. Rate of Change
1	9
0.1	8.1
0.01	8.01
0.001	8.001
0.0001	8.0001

25. a. $25 billion per year; world military expenditure increased at an average rate of $25 billion per year during 1994–2006. **b.** $50 billion per year; world military expenditure increased at an average rate of $50 billion per year during 1998–2006. **27. a.** $-20,000$ barrels/year; during 2002–2007, daily oil production by **Pemex** was decreasing at an average rate of 20,000 barrels of oil per year. **b.** (C) **29. a.** 1.7; the percentage of mortgages classified as subprime was increasing at an average rate of around 1.7 percentage points per year between 2000 and 2006. **b.** 2004–2006 **31. a.** The second and third quarter of 2007. During the second and third quarter of 2007 iPhone sales were increasing at an average rate of 1,022,500 phones per quarter. **b.** Fourth quarter of 2007 and first quarter of 2008. During the fourth quarter of 2007 and first quarter of 2008 iPhone sales were decreasing at an average rate of 797,500 phones per quarter. **33. a.** [3, 5]; -0.25 thousand articles per year. During the period 1993–1995, the number of articles authored by U.S. researchers decreased at an average rate of 250 articles per year. **b.** Percentage rate ≈ -0.1765, Average rate $= -0.09$ thousand articles/year. Over the period 1993–2003, the number of articles authored by U.S. researchers decreased at an average rate of 90 per year, representing a 17.65% decrease over that period. **35. a.** 12 teams per year **b.** Decreased **37. a.** (C) **b.** (A) **c.** (B) **d.** Approximately -0.0063 (to two significant digits) billion dollars per year ($-\$6,300,000$ per year). This is much less than the (positive) slope of the regression line, $0.0125 \approx 0.013$ billion dollars per year ($13,000,000$ per year). **39.** Answers may vary. Graph:

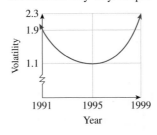

41. The index was increasing at an average rate of 300 points per day.   **43. a.** $0.15 per year **b.** No; according to the model, during that 25-year period the price of oil went down from around $93 to a low of around $25 in 1993 before climbing back up.   **45. a.** 47.3 new cases per day; the number of SARS cases was growing at an average rate of 47.3 new cases per day over the period March 17 to March 23. **b.** (A)
47. a. 8.85 manatee deaths per 100,000 boats; 23.05 manatee deaths per 100,000 boats **b.** More boats result in more manatee deaths per additional boat.   **49. a.** $-0.88, -0.79, -0.69, -0.60, -0.51, -0.42$ **b.** For household incomes between $40,000 and $40,500, the poverty rate decreases at an average rate of 0.69 percentage points per $1,000 increase in the median household income. **c.** (B) **d.** (B)   **51.** The average rate of change of f over an interval $[a, b]$ can be determined numerically, using a table of values, graphically, by measuring the slope of the corresponding line segment through two points on the graph, or algebraically, using an algebraic formula for the function. Of these, the least precise is the graphical method, because it relies on reading coordinates of points on a graph.   **53.** No, the formula for the average rate of a function f over $[a, b]$ depends only on $f(a)$ and $f(b)$, and not on any values of f between a and b.   **55.** Answers will vary. Graph:

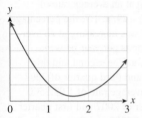

57. 6 units of quantity A per unit of quantity C   **59.** (A)
61. Yes. Here is an example:

Year	2000	2001	2002	2003
Revenue ($ billion)	$10	$20	$30	$5

63. (A)

Section 10.5
1. 6   **3.** -5.5

5.

h	1	0.1	0.01
Ave. rate	39	39.9	39.99

Instant. Rate = $40 per day

7.

h	1	0.1	0.01
Ave. Rate	140	66.2	60.602

Instant. Rate = $60 per day

9.

h	10	1
C_{ave}	4.799	4.7999

11.

h	10	1
C_{ave}	99.91	99.90

$C'(1,000) = \$4.8$ per item $C'(100) = \$99.9$ per item

13. $1/2$ **15.** 0   **17. a.** R **b.** P **19. a.** P **b.** R **21. a.** Q **b.** P
23. a. Q **b.** R **c.** P **25. a.** R **b.** Q **c.** P **27. a.** $(1, 0)$
b. None **c.** $(-2, 1)$ **29. a.** $(-2, 0.3)$, $(0, 0)$, $(2, -0.3)$
b. None **c.** None   **31.** $(a, f(a))$; $f'(a)$ **33.** (B)
35. a. (A) **b.** (C) **c.** (B) **d.** (B) **e.** (C)   **37.** -2 **39.** -1.5
41. -5 **43.** 16   **45.** 0   **47.** -0.0025

49. a. 3 **b.** $y = 3x + 2$ **51. a.** $\dfrac{3}{4}$ **b.** $y = \dfrac{3}{4}x + 1$

53. a. $\dfrac{1}{4}$ **b.** $y = \dfrac{1}{4}x + 1$

55. 1.000   **57.** 1.000   **59.** (C)   **61.** (A)   **63.** (F)
65. Increasing for $x < 0$; decreasing for $x > 0$.   **67.** Increasing for $x < -1$ and $x > 1$; decreasing for $-1 < x < 1$
69. Increasing for $x > 1$; decreasing for $x < 1$.   **71.** Increasing for $x < 0$; decreasing for $x > 0$.   **73.** $x = -1.5, x = 0$
Graph:

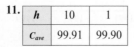

75. Note: Answers depend on the form of technology used. Excel ($h = 0.1$):

Graphs:

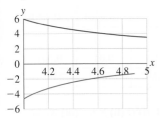

77. $q(100) = 50,000$, $q'(100) = -500$. A total of 50,000 pairs of sneakers can be sold at a price of \$100, but the demand is decreasing at a rate of 500 pairs per \$1 increase in the price. **79. a.** -0.05; daily oil imports from Mexico in 2005 were 1.6 million barrels and declining at a rate of 0.05 million barrels (or 50,000 barrels) per year. **b.** Decreasing **81. a.** (B) **b.** (B) **c.** (A) **d.** 1992 **e.** 0.05; in 1996, the total number of state prisoners was increasing at a rate of approximately 50,000 prisoners per year. **83. a.** -96 ft/s **b.** -128 ft/s **85. a.** \$0.60 per year; the price per barrel of crude oil in constant 2008 dollars was growing at an average rate of about 60¢ per year over the 28-year period beginning at the start of 1980. **b.** $-$\$12 per year; the price per barrel of crude oil in constant 2008 dollars was dropping at an instantaneous rate of about \$12 per year at the start of 1980. **c.** The price of oil was decreasing in January 1980, but eventually began to increase (making the average rate of change in part (a) positive). **87. a.** 144.7 new cases per day; the number of SARS cases was growing at a rate of about 144.7 new cases per day on March 27. **b.** (A) **89.** $S(5) \approx 109$, $\dfrac{dS}{dt}\Big|_{t=5} \approx 9.1$. After 5 weeks, sales are 109 pairs of sneakers per week, and sales are increasing at a rate of 9.1 pairs per week each week. **91.** $A(0) = 4.5$ million; $A'(0) = 60,000$ subscribers/week **93. a.** 60% of children can speak at the age of 10 months. At the age of 10 months, this percentage is increasing by 18.2 percentage points per month. **b.** As t increases, p approaches 100 percentage points (all children eventually learn to speak), and dp/dt approaches zero because the percentage stops increasing. **95. a.** $A(6) \approx 12.0$; $A'(6) \approx 1.4$; at the start of 2006, about 12% of U.S. mortgages were subprime, and this percentage was increasing at a rate of about 1.4 percentage points per year **b.** Graphs:

Graph of A:

Graph of A':

From the graphs, $A(t)$ approaches 15 as t becomes large (in terms of limits, $\lim_{x \to +\infty} A(t) = 15$) and $A'(t)$ approaches 0 as t becomes large (in terms of limits, $\lim_{x \to +\infty} A'(t) = 0$).

Interpretation: If the trend modeled by the function A had continued indefinitely, in the long term 15% of U.S. mortgages would have been subprime, and this percentage would not be changing. **97. a.** (D) **b.** 33 days after the egg was laid **c.** 50 days after the egg was laid. Graph:

99. $L(.95) = 31.2$ meters and $L'(.95) = -304.2$ meters/warp. Thus, at a speed of warp 0.95, the spaceship has an observed length of 31.2 meters and its length is decreasing at a rate of 304.2 meters per unit warp, or 3.042 meters per increase in speed of 0.01 warp. **101.** The difference quotient is not defined when $h = 0$ because there is no such number as $0/0$. **103.** (D) **105.** The derivative is positive and decreasing toward zero. **107.** Company B. Although the company is currently losing money, the derivative is positive, showing that the profit is increasing. Company A, on the other hand, has profits that are declining. **109.** (C) is the only graph in which the instantaneous rate of change on January 1 is greater than the one-month average rate of change. **111.** The tangent to the graph is horizontal at that point, and so the graph is almost horizontal near that point. **113.** Answers may vary.

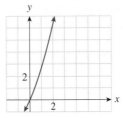

115. If $f(x) = mx + b$, then its average rate of change over any interval $[x, x + h]$ is $\dfrac{m(x + h) + b - (mx + b)}{h} = m$. Because this does not depend on h, the instantaneous rate is also equal to m. **117.** Increasing because the average rate of change appears to be rising as we get closer to 5 from the left. (See the bottom row.)

119. Answers may vary.

121. Answers may vary.

123. (B)   **125.** Answers will vary.

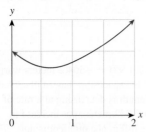

Section 10.6

1. 4   **3.** 3   **5.** 7   **7.** 4   **9.** 14   **11.** 1   **13.** m **15.** $2x$
17. 3   **19.** $6x + 1$ **21.** $2 - 2x$ **23.** $3x^2 + 2$ **25.** $1/x^2$
27. m **29.** -1.2 **31.** 30.6   **33.** -7.1 **35.** 4.25   **37.** -0.6
39. $y = 4x - 7$ **41.** $y = -2x - 4$ **43.** $y = -3x - 1$
45. $s'(t) = -32t$; $s'(4) = -128$ ft/s

47. $\dfrac{dI}{dt} = -0.030t + 0.1$, daily oil imports were decreasing at a
rate of 0.11 million barrels per year.   **49.** $R'(t) = 24t + 500$;
annual U.S. sales of bottled water were increasing by
620 million gallons per year in 2005.   **51.** $f'(8) = 26.6$
manatee deaths per 100,000 boats. At a level of 800,000 boats,
the number of manatee deaths is increasing at a rate of
26.6 manatees per 100,000 additional boats.   **53. a.** Yes;
$\lim_{t\to 8^-} C(t) = \lim_{t\to 8^+} C(t) = 1.24 = C(8)$. **b.** No;
$\lim_{t\to 8^-} C'(t) = 0.08$ while $\lim_{t\to 8^+} C'(t) = 0.13$. Until 1998,
the cost of a Super Bowl ad was increasing at a rate of $80,000
per year. Immediately thereafter, it was increasing at a rate of
$130,000 per year.   **55.** The algebraic method because it gives
the exact value of the derivative. The other two approaches give
only approximate values (except in some special cases).
57. The error is in the second line: $f(x + h)$ is *not* equal to
$f(x) + h$. For instance, if $f(x) = x^2$, then
$f(x + h) = (x + h)^2$, whereas $f(x) + h = x^2 + h$.   **59.** The
error is in the second line: One could only cancel the h if it
were a *factor* of both the numerator and denominator; it is not a
factor of the numerator.   **61.** Because the algebraic computation of $f'(a)$ is exact and not an approximation, it makes no
difference whether one uses the balanced difference quotient or
the ordinary difference quotient in the algebraic computation.
63. The computation results in a limit that cannot be evaluated.

Chapter 10 Review

1. 5   **3.** Does not exist   **5. a.** -1 **b.** 3 **c.** Does not exist
7. $-4/5$ **9.** -1 **11.** Does not exist   **13.** Does not exist
15. $+\infty$ **17.** Diverges to $-\infty$ **19.** 0   **21.** 2/5   **23.** 1

25.

h	1	0.01	0.001
Ave. Rate of Change	-0.5	-0.9901	-0.9990

Slope ≈ -1

27.

h	1	0.01	0.001
Avg. Rate of Change	6.3891	2.0201	2.0020

Slope ≈ 2

29. (i) P **(ii)** Q **(iii)** R **(iv)** S **31. (i)** Q **(ii)** None **(iii)** None
(iv) None   **33. a.** (B) **b.** (B) **c.** (B) **d.** (A) **e.** (C)
35. $2x + 1$ **37.** $2/x^2$
39.

41.

43. a. $P(3) = 25$: O'Hagan purchased the stock at $25.
$\lim_{t\to 3^-} P(t) = 25$: The value of the stock had been approaching $25 up the time he bought it. $\lim_{t\to 3^+} P(t) = 10$: The value
of the stock dropped to $10 immediately after he bought it.
b. Continuous but not differentiable. Interpretation: the stock
price changed continuously but suddenly reversed direction
(and started to go up) the instant O'Hagan sold it.
45. a. $\lim_{t\to 3} p(t) \approx 40$; $\lim_{t\to +\infty} p(t) = +\infty$. Close to 2007
$(t = 3)$, the home price index was about 40. In the long term,
the home price index will rise without bound. **b.** 10
(The slope of the linear portion of the curve is 10.) In the long
term, the home price index will rise about 10 points per year.
47. a. 500 books per week **b.** [3, 4], [4, 5] **c.** [3, 5]; 650 books
per week   **49. a.** 3 percentage points per year **b.** 0 percentage
points per year **c.** (D)   **51. a.** $72t + 250$ **b.** 322 books per
week **c.** 754 books per week.

Chapter 11

Section 11.1

1. $5x^4$ **3.** $-4x^{-3}$ **5.** $-0.25x^{-0.75}$ **7.** $8x^3 + 9x^2$

9. $-1 - 1/x^2$ **11.** $\dfrac{dy}{dx} = 10(0) = 0$ (constant multiple and

power rule)   **13.** $\dfrac{dy}{dx} = \dfrac{d}{dx}(x^2) + \dfrac{d}{dx}(x)$ (sum rule) $= 2x + 1$

(power rule)   **15.** $\dfrac{dy}{dx} = \dfrac{d}{dx}(4x^3) + \dfrac{d}{dx}(2x) - \dfrac{d}{dx}$ (1) (sum
and difference)

17. $f'(x) = 2x - 3$ **19.** $f'(x) = 1 + 0.5x^{-0.5}$

21. $g'(x) = -2x^{-3} + 3x^{-2}$ **23.** $g'(x) = -\dfrac{1}{x^2} + \dfrac{2}{x^3}$

25. $h'(x) = -\dfrac{0.8}{x^{1.4}}$ **27.** $h'(x) = -\dfrac{2}{x^3} - \dfrac{6}{x^4}$

29. $r'(x) = -\dfrac{2}{3x^2} + \dfrac{0.1}{2x^{1.1}}$ **31.** $r'(x) = \dfrac{2}{3} - \dfrac{0.1}{2x^{0.9}} - \dfrac{4.4}{3x^{2.1}}$

33. $t'(x) = |x|/x - 1/x^2$ **35.** $s'(x) = \dfrac{1}{2\sqrt{x}} - \dfrac{1}{2x\sqrt{x}}$

37. $s'(x) = 3x^2$ **39.** $t'(x) = 1 - 4x$ **41.** $2.6x^{0.3} + 1.2x^{-2.2}$
43. $1.2(1 - |x|/x)$ **45.** $3at^2 - 4a$ **47.** $5.15x^{9.3} - 99x^{-2}$

49. $-\dfrac{2.31}{t^{2.1}} - \dfrac{0.3}{t^{0.4}}$ **51.** $4\pi r^2$ **53.** 3   **55.** -2 **57.** -5

59. $y = 3x + 2$ **61.** $y = \dfrac{3}{4}x + 1$

63. $y = \dfrac{1}{4}x + 1$ **65.** $x = -3/4$

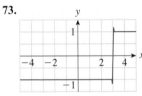

67. No such values

69. $x = 1, -1$

73.

(a) $x = 3$ **(b)** None

75.

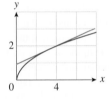

(a) $x = 1$ **(b)** $x = 4.2$

77. a. $f'(1) = 1/3$ **b.** Not differentiable at 0
79. a. Not differentiable at 1   **b.** Not differentiable at 0
81. Yes; 0   **83.** Yes; 12   **85.** No; 3   **87.** Yes; 3/2
89. Yes; diverges to $-\infty$ **91.** Yes; diverges to $-\infty$
93. $P'(t) = 0.9t - 12$; $P'(20) = 6$; the price of a barrel of crude oil was increasing at a rate of \$6 per year in 2000.

95. a. $n'(t) = -1.12t + 14$ **b.** 7 teams/year   **c.** Decreases; $n'(t)$ is a linear function with negative slope, so it decreases with increasing t.   **97.** 0.55   **99. a.** $s'(t) = -32t$; $0, -32, -64, -96, -128$ ft/s   **b.** 5 seconds; downward at 160 ft/s
101. a. $S'(t) = -780t + 3{,}300$; dropping at a rate of 600,000 iPhones per quarter.   **b.** (B); geometrically: The graph is rising but less steeply, over [2, 4]. Algebraically: The slope is the derivative: $-780t + 3{,}300$, which is positive but decreasing over [2, 4].   **103. a.** $f'(x) = 7.1x - 30.2$ manatees per 100,000 boats.   **b.** Increasing; the number of manatees killed per additional 100,000 boats increases as the number of boats increases.   **c.** $f'(8) = 26.6$ manatees per 100,000 additional boats. At a level of 800,000 boats, the number of manatee deaths is increasing at a rate of 26.6 manatees per 100,000 additional boats.   **105. a.** $c(t) - m(t)$ measures the combined market share of the other three providers (Comcast, Earthlink, and AOL); $c'(t) - m'(t)$ measures the rate of change of the combined market share of the other three providers.   **b.** (A)   **c.** (A)
d. 3.72% per year. In 1992, the combined market share of the other three providers was increasing at a rate of about 3.72 percentage points per year.   **107.** After graphing the curve $y = 3x^2$, draw the line passing through $(-1, 3)$ with slope -6.
109. The slope of the tangent line of g is twice the slope of the tangent line of f.   **111.** $g'(x) = -f'(x)$ **113.** The left-hand side is not equal to the right-hand side. The *derivative* of the left-hand side is equal to the right-hand side, so your friend should have written $\dfrac{d}{dx}(3x^4 + 11x^5) = 12x^3 + 55x^4$.

115. The derivative of a constant times a function is the constant times the derivative of the function, so that $f'(x) = (2)(2x) = 4x$. Your enemy mistakenly computed the *derivative* of the constant times the derivative of the function. (The derivative of a product of two functions is not the product of the derivative of the two functions. The rule for taking the derivative of a product is discussed later in the chapter.).
117. For a general function f, the derivative of f is defined to be $f'(x) = \lim\limits_{h \to 0} \dfrac{f(x + h) - f(x)}{h}$. One then finds by calculation that the derivative of the specific function x^n is nx^{n-1}. In short, nx^{n-1} is the derivative of a specific function: $f(x) = x^n$, it is not the *definition* of the derivative of a general function or even the definition of the derivative of the function $f(x) = x^n$.
119. Answers may vary.

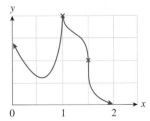

Section 11.2

1. $C'(1,000) = \$4.80$ per item   **3.** $C'(100) = \$99.90$ per item
5. $C'(x) = 4$; $R'(x) = 8 - x/500$; $P'(x) = 4 - x/500$;
$P'(x) = 0$ when $x = 2,000$. Thus, at a production level of 2,000, the profit is stationary (neither increasing nor decreasing) with respect to the production level. This may indicate a maximum profit at a production level of 2,000.   **7. a.** (B) **b.** (C) **c.** (C)
9. a. $C'(x) = 2,250 - 0.04x$. The cost is going up at a rate of $2,249,840 per television commercial. The exact cost of airing the fifth television commercial is $C(5) - C(4) = \$2,249,820$.
b. $\bar{C}(x) = 150/x + 2,250 - 0.02x$; $\bar{C}(4) = \$2,287,420$ per television commercial. The average cost of airing the first four television commercials is $2,287,420.   **11. a.** $R'(x) = 0.90$, $P'(x) = 0.80 - 0.002x$ **b.** Revenue: $450, Profit: $80, Marginal revenue: $0.90, Marginal profit: $-\$0.20$. The total revenue from the sale of 500 copies is $450. The profit from the production and sale of 500 copies is $80. Approximate revenue from the sale of the 501st copy is 90¢. Approximate loss from the sale of the 501st copy is 20¢. **c.** $x = 400$. The profit is a maximum when you produce and sell 400 copies.   **13.** The profit on the sale of 1,000 DVDs is $3,000, and is decreasing at a rate of $3 per additional DVD sold.   **15.** $P \approx \$257.07$ and $dP/dx \approx 5.07$. Your current profit is $257.07 per month, and this would increase at a rate of $5.07 per additional magazine in sales.   **17. a.** $2.50 per pound **b.** $R(q) = 20,000/q^{0.5}$
c. $R(400) = \$1,000$. This is the monthly revenue that will result from setting the price at $2.50 per pound. $R'(400) = -\$1.25$ per pound of tuna. Thus, at a demand level of 400 pounds per month, the revenue is decreasing at a rate of $1.25 per pound. **d.** The fishery should raise the price (to reduce the demand).   **19.** $P'(50) = \$350$. This means that, at an employment level of 50 workers, the firm's daily profit will increase at a rate of $350 per additional worker it hires.
21. a. (B) **b.** (B) **c.** (C)
23. a. $C(x) = 500,000 + 1,600,000x - 100,000\sqrt{x}$;

$$C'(x) = 1,600,000 - \frac{50,000}{\sqrt{x}};$$

$$\bar{C}(x) = \frac{500,000}{x} + 1,600,000 - \frac{100,000}{\sqrt{x}}$$

b. $C'(3) \approx \$1,570,000$ per spot, $\bar{C}(3) \approx \$1,710,000$ per spot. The average cost will decrease as x increases.
25. a. $C'(q) = 200q$; $C'(10) = \$2,000$ per one-pound reduction in emissions. **b.** $S'(q) = 500$. Thus $S'(q) = C'(q)$ when $500 = 200q$, or $q = 2.5$ pounds per day reduction.
c. $N(q) = C(q) - S(q) = 100q^2 - 500q + 4,000$. This is a parabola with lowest point (vertex) given by $q = 2.5$. The net cost at this production level is $N(2.5) = \$3,375$ per day. The

value of q is the same as that for part (b). The net cost to the firm is minimized at the reduction level for which the cost of controlling emissions begins to increase faster than the subsidy. This is why we get the answer by setting these two rates of increase equal to each other.   **27.** $M'(10) \approx 0.0002557$ mpg/mph. This means that, at a speed of 10 mph, the fuel economy is increasing at a rate of 0.0002557 miles per gallon per 1-mph increase in speed. $M'(60) = 0$ mpg/mph. This means that, at a speed of 60 mph, the fuel economy is neither increasing nor decreasing with increasing speed. $M'(70) \approx -0.00001799$. This means that, at 70 mph, the fuel economy is decreasing at a rate of 0.00001799 miles per gallon per 1-mph increase in speed. Thus 60 mph is the most fuel-efficient speed for the car.
29. (C)   **31.** (D)   **33.** (B)   **35.** Cost is often measured as a function of the number of items x. Thus, $C(x)$ is the cost of producing (or purchasing, as the case may be) x items.
a. The average cost function $\bar{C}(x)$ is given by $\bar{C}(x) = C(x)/x$. The marginal cost function is the derivative, $C'(x)$, of the cost function. **b.** The average cost $\bar{C}(r)$ is the slope of the line through the origin and the point on the graph where $x = r$. The marginal cost of the rth unit is the slope of the tangent to the graph of the cost function at the point where $x = r$.
c. The average cost function $\bar{C}(x)$ gives the average cost of producing the first x items. The marginal cost function $C'(x)$ is the rate at which cost is changing with respect to the number of items x, or the incremental cost per item, and approximates the cost of producing the $(x + 1)$st item.   **37.** The marginal cost
39. Not necessarily. For example, it may be the case that the marginal cost of the 101st item is larger than the average cost of the first 100 items (even though the marginal cost is decreasing). Thus, adding this additional item will *raise* the average cost.   **41.** The circumstances described suggest that the average cost function is at a relatively low point at the current production level, and so it would be appropriate to advise the company to maintain current production levels; raising or lowering the production level will result in increasing average costs.

Section 11.3

1. 3   **3.** $3x^2$ **5.** $2x + 3$ **7.** $210x^{1.1}$ **9.** $-2/x^2$
11. $2x/3$ **13.** $3(4x^2 - 1) + 3x(8x) = 36x^2 - 3$
15. $3x^2(1 - x^2) + x^3(-2x) = 3x^2 - 5x^4$
17. $2(2x + 3) + (2x + 3)(2) = 8x + 12$ **19.** $3\sqrt{x}/2$
21. $(x^2 - 1) + 2x(x + 1) = (x + 1)(3x - 1)$
23. $(x^{-0.5} + 4)(x - x^{-1}) + (2x^{0.5} + 4x - 5)(1 + x^{-2})$
25. $8(2x^2 - 4x + 1)(x - 1)$
27. $(1/3.2 - 3.2/x^2)(x^2 + 1) + 2x(x/3.2 + 3.2/x)$
29. $2x(2x + 3)(7x + 2) + 2x^2(7x + 2) + 7x^2(2x + 3)$

31. $5.3(1 - x^{2.1})(x^{-2.3} - 3.4) - 2.1x^{1.1}(5.3x - 1)(x^{-2.3} - 3.4) - 2.3x - 3.3(5.3x - 1)(1 - x^{2.1})$

33. $\dfrac{1}{2\sqrt{x}}\left(\sqrt{x} + \dfrac{1}{x^2}\right) + (\sqrt{x} + 1)\left(\dfrac{1}{2\sqrt{x}} - \dfrac{2}{x^3}\right)$ **35.** $\dfrac{2(3x - 1) - 3(2x + 4)}{(3x - 1)^2} = -14/(3x - 1)^2$

37. $\dfrac{(4x + 4)(3x - 1) - 3(2x^2 + 4x + 1)}{(3x - 1)^2} = (6x^2 - 4x - 7)/(3x - 1)^2$

39. $\dfrac{(2x - 4)(x^2 + x + 1) - (x^2 - 4x + 1)(2x + 1)}{(x^2 + x + 1)^2} = (5x^2 - 5)/(x^2 + x + 1)^2$

41. $\dfrac{(0.23x^{-0.77} - 5.7)(1 - x^{-2.9}) - 2.9x^{-3.9}(x^{0.23} - 5.7x)}{(1 - x^{-2.9})^2}$ **43.** $\dfrac{\dfrac{1}{2}x^{-1/2}(x^{1/2} - 1) - \dfrac{1}{2}x^{-1/2}(x^{1/2} + 1)}{(x^{1/2} - 1)^2} = \dfrac{-1}{\sqrt{x}\left(\sqrt{x} - 1\right)^2}$

45. $-3/x^4$ **47.** $\dfrac{[(x + 1) + (x + 3)](3x - 1) - 3(x + 3)(x + 1)}{(3x - 1)^2} = (3x^2 - 2x - 13)/(3x - 1)^2$

49. $\dfrac{[(x + 1)(x + 2) + (x + 3)(x + 2) + (x + 3)(x + 1)](3x - 1) - 3(x + 3)(x + 1)(x + 2)}{(3x - 1)^2}$

51. $4x^3 - 2x$ **53.** 64 **55.** 3
57. Difference; $4x^3 - 12x^2 + 2x - 480$
59. Sum; $1 + 2/(x + 1)^2$

61. Product; $\left[\dfrac{x}{x + 1}\right] + (x + 2)\dfrac{1}{(x + 1)^2}$

63. Difference; $2x - 1 - 2/(x + 1)^2$ **65.** $y = 12x - 8$
67. $y = x/4 + 1/2$ **69.** $y = -2$ **71.** $q'(5) = 1{,}000$ units/
month (sales are increasing at a rate of 1,000 units per month);
$p'(5) = -\$10$/month (the price of a sound system is dropping
at a rate of $10 per month); $R'(5) = 900{,}000$ (revenue is
increasing at a rate of $900,000 per month).   **73.** $242 million;
increasing at a rate of $39 million per year.   **75.** Decreasing at
a rate of $1 per day   **77.** Decreasing at a rate of approximately
$0.10 per month

79. $M'(x) = \dfrac{3{,}000(3{,}600x^{-2} - 1)}{(x + 3{,}600x^{-1})^2}$; $M'(10) \approx 0.7670$ mpg/mph.

This means that, at a speed of 10 mph, the fuel economy is
increasing at a rate of 0.7670 miles per gallon per one mph
increase in speed. $M'(60) = 0$ mpg/mph. This means that, at a
speed of 60 mph, the fuel economy is neither increasing nor
decreasing with increasing speed. $M'(70) \approx -0.0540$. This
means that, at 70 mph, the fuel economy is decreasing at a rate
of 0.0540 miles per gallon per one mph increase in speed.
60 mph is the most fuel-efficient speed for the car. (In the next
chapter we shall discuss how to locate largest values in general.)
81. a. $P(t) - I(t)$ represents the daily production of oil in
Mexico that was not exported to the United States. $I(t)/P(t)$
represents U.S. imports of oil from Mexico as a fraction of the
total produced there. **b.** -0.023 per year; at the start of 2008,
the fraction of oil produced in Mexico that was imported by the
United States was decreasing at a rate of 0.023 (or 2.3 percentage points) per year.   **83.** Increasing at a rate of about
$3,420 million per year.

85. $R'(p) = -\dfrac{5.625}{(1 + 0.125p)^2}$; $R'(4) = -2.5$ thousand
organisms per hour, per 1,000 organisms. This means that the
reproduction rate of organisms in a culture containing 4,000
organisms is declining at a rate of 2,500 organisms per hour, per
1,000 additional organisms.   **87.** Oxygen consumption is
decreasing at a rate of 1,600 milliliters per day. This is due to
the fact that the number of eggs is decreasing, because $C'(25)$ is
positive.   **89.** 20; 33   **91.** 5/4; $-17/16$ **93.** The analysis is
suspect, as it seems to be asserting that the annual increase in
revenue, which we can think of as dR/dt, is the product of the
annual increases, dp/dt in price, and dq/dt in sales. However,
because $R = pq$, the product rule implies that dR/dt is not
the product of dp/dt and dq/dt, but is instead

$$\dfrac{dR}{dt} = \dfrac{dp}{dt} \cdot q + p \cdot \dfrac{dq}{dt}.$$ **95.** Answers will vary.

$q = -p + 1{,}000$ is one example.   **97.** Mine; it is increasing
twice as fast as yours. The rate of change of revenue is given by
$R'(t) = p'(t)q(t)$ because $q'(t) = 0$. Thus, $R'(t)$ does not depend
on the selling price $p(t)$.   **99.** (A)

Section 11.4
1. $4(2x + 1)$ **3.** $-(x - 1)^{-2}$ **5.** $2(2 - x)^{-3}$
7. $(2x + 1)^{-0.5}$ **9.** $-4(4x - 1)^{-2}$ **11.** $-3/(3x - 1)^2$
13. $4(x^2 + 2x)^3(2x + 2)$ **15.** $-4x(2x^2 - 2)^{-2}$
17. $-5(2x - 3)(x^2 - 3x - 1)^{-6}$ **19.** $-6x/(x^2 + 1)^4$
21. $1.5(0.2x - 4.2)(0.1x^2 - 4.2x + 9.5)^{0.5}$
23. $4(2s - 0.5s^{-0.5})(s^2 - s^{0.5})^3$ **25.** $-x/\sqrt{1 - x^2}$
27. $-[(x + 1)(x^2 - 1)]^{-3/2}(3x - 1)(x + 1)$
29. $6.2(3.1x - 2) + 6.2/(3.1x - 2)^3$
31. $2[(6.4x - 1)^2 + (5.4x - 2)^3][12.8(6.4x - 1) +$
$16.2(5.4x - 2)^2]$ **33.** $-2(x^2 - 3x)^{-3}(2x - 3)(1 - x^2)^{0.5}$
$-x(x^2 - 3x)^{-2}(1 - x^2)^{-0.5}$

35. $-56(x + 2)/(3x - 1)^3$ **37.** $3z^2(1 - z^2)/(1 + z^2)^4$

39. $3[(1 + 2x)^4 - (1 - x)^2]^2[8(1 + 2x)^3 + 2(1 - x)]$

41. $-0.43(x + 1)^{-1.1}[2 + (x + 1)^{-0.1}]^{3.3}$

43. $-\dfrac{\left(\dfrac{1}{\sqrt{2x + 1}} - 2x\right)}{\left(\sqrt{2x + 1} - x^2\right)^2}$

45. $54(1 + 2x)^2 \left(1 + (1 + 2x)^3\right)^2 \left(1 + \left(1 + (1 + 2x)^3\right)^3\right)^2$

47. $(100x^{99} - 99x^{-2})dx/dt$ **49.** $(-3r^{-4} + 0.5r^{-0.5})dr/dt$

51. $4\pi r^2 dr/dt$ **53.** $-47/4$ **55.** $1/3$ **57.** $-5/3$ **59.** $1/4$

61. $\left.\dfrac{dP}{dn}\right|_{n=10} = 146,454.9$. At an employment level of

10 engineers, Paramount will increase its profit at a rate of $146,454.90 per additional engineer hired.

63. $y = 35(7 + 0.2t)^{-0.25}$; -0.11 percentage points per month.

65. $-$\$30 per additional ruby sold. The revenue is decreasing at a rate of $30 per additional ruby sold.

67. $\dfrac{dy}{dt} = \dfrac{dy}{dx}\dfrac{dx}{dt} = (1.5)(-2) = -3$ murders per 100,000

residents/yr each year.   **69.** $5/6 \approx 0.833$; relative to the 2003 levels, home sales were changing at a rate of 0.833 percentage points per percentage point change in price. (Equivalently, home sales in 2008 were dropping at a rate of 0.833 percentage points per percentage point drop in price.)   **71.** 12π mi²/h

73. $\$200,000\pi$/week $\approx \$628,000$/week   **75. a.** $q'(4) \approx 333$ units per month   **b.** $dR/dq = \$800$/unit   **c.** $dR/dt \approx \$267,000$ per month   **77.** 3% per year   **79.** 8% per year   **81.** The glob squared, times the derivative of the glob.   **83.** The derivative of a quantity cubed is three times the *original quantity* squared, times the derivative of the quantity, not three times the derivative of the quantity squared. Thus, the correct answer is $3(3x^3 - x)^2(9x^2 - 1)$.   **85.** First, the derivative of a quantity cubed is three times the *original quantity* squared times the derivative of the quantity, not three times the derivative of the quantity squared. Second, the derivative of a quotient is not the quotient of the derivatives; the quotient rule needs to be used in calculating the derivative of $\dfrac{3x^2 - 1}{2x - 2}$.

Thus, the correct result (before simplifying) is

$$3\left(\frac{3x^2 - 1}{2x - 2}\right)^2 \left(\frac{6x(2x - 2) - (3x^2 - 1)(2)}{(2x - 2)^2}\right).$$

87. Following the calculation thought experiment, pretend that you were evaluating the function at a specific value of x. If the last operation you would perform is addition or subtraction, look at each summand separately. If the last operation is multiplication, use the product rule first; if it is division, use the quotient rule first; if it is any other operation (such as raising a quantity to a power or taking a radical of a quantity) then use the chain rule first.   **89.** An example is

$$f(x) = \sqrt{x + \sqrt{x + \sqrt{x + \sqrt{x + \sqrt{x + 1}}}}}.$$

Section 11.5

1. $1/(x - 1)$ **3.** $1/(x \ln 2)$ **5.** $2x/(x^2 + 3)$ **7.** e^{x+3}

9. $-e^{-x}$ **11.** $4^x \ln 4$ **13.** $2^{x^2-1}2x \ln 2$ **15.** $1 + \ln x$

17. $2x\ln x + (x^2 + 1)/x$ **19.** $10x(x^2 + 1)^4\ln x + (x^2 + 1)^5/x$

21. $3/(3x - 1)$ **23.** $4x/(2x^2 + 1)$

25. $(2x - 0.63x^{-0.7})/(x^2 - 2.1x^{0.3})$

27. $-2/(-2x + 1) + 1/(x + 1)$ **29.** $3/(3x + 1) - 4/(4x - 2)$

31. $1/(x + 1) + 1/(x - 3) - 2/(2x + 9)$ **33.** $5.2/(4x - 2)$

35. $2/(x + 1) - 9/(3x - 4) - 1/(x - 9)$

37. $\dfrac{1}{(x + 1)\ln 2}$ **39.** $\dfrac{1 - 1/t^2}{(t + 1/t)\ln 3}$ **41.** $\dfrac{2\ln|x|}{x}$

43. $\dfrac{2}{x} - \dfrac{2\ln(x - 1)}{x - 1}$ **45.** $e^x(1 + x)$

47. $1/(x + 1) + 3e^x(x^3 + 3x^2)$ **49.** $e^x(\ln|x| + 1/x)$

51. $2e^{2x+1}$ **53.** $(2x - 1)e^{x^2-x+1}$ **55.** $2xe^{2x-1}(1 + x)$

57. $4(e^{2x-1})^2$ **59.** $2 \cdot 3^{2x-4}\ln 3$ **61.** $2 \cdot 3^{2x+1}\ln 3 + 3e^{3x+1}$

63. $\dfrac{2x3^{x^2}[(x^2 + 1)\ln 3 - 1]}{(x^2 + 1)^2}$ **65.** $-4/(e^x - e^{-x})^2$

67. $5e^{5x-3}$ **69.** $-\dfrac{\ln x + 1}{(x \ln x)^2}$ **71.** $2(x - 1)$ **73.** $\dfrac{1}{x \ln x}$

75. $\dfrac{1}{2x\ln x}$ **77.** $y = (e/\ln 2)(x - 1) \approx 3.92(x - 1)$

79. $y = x$ **81.** $y = -[1/(2e)](x - 1) + e$ **83.** $163 billion and increasing at a rate of $5.75 billion per year   **85.** $163 billion and increasing at a rate of $5.75 billion per year.

87. $-1,653$ years per gram; the age of the specimen is decreasing at a rate of about 1,653 years per additional one gram of carbon 14 present in the sample. (Equivalently, the age of the specimen is increasing at a rate of about 1,653 years per additional one gram less of carbon 14 in the sample.)   **89.** Average price: $1.4 million; increasing at a rate of about $220,000 per year.   **91. a.** $N(15) \approx 1,762 \approx 1,800$ (rounded to 2 significant digits) wiretap orders; $N'(15) \approx 89.87 \approx 90$ wiretap orders per year (rounded to 2 significant digits). The constants in the model are specified to 2 significant digits, so we cannot expect the answer to be accurate to more than 2 digits.   **b.** In 2005, the number of people whose communications were intercepted was about 180,000 and increasing at a rate of about 9,000 people per year.   **c.** (C)   **93.** $451.00 per year   **95.** $446.02 per year   **97.** $A(t) = 167(1.18)^t$; 280 new cases per day   **99. a.** (A)   **b.** The verbal SAT increases by approximately 1 point.   **c.** $S'(x)$ decreases with increasing x, so that as parental income increases, the effect on SAT scores decreases.   **101. a.** -6.25 years/child; when the fertility rate is 2 children per woman, the average age of a population is dropping at a rate of 6.25 years per one-child increase in the fertility rate.   **b.** 0.160

103. 3,300,000 cases/week; 11,000,000 cases/week; 640,000 cases/week   **105.** 2.1 percentage points per year; the rate of change is the slope of the tangent at $t = 3$. This is also approximately the average rate of change over [2, 4], which is about $4/2 = 2$, in approximate agreement with the answer.

107. 2.1 percentage points per year   **109.** 277,000 people per year   **111.** 0.000283 g/yr

113. a.

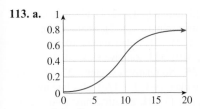

$p'(10) \approx 0.09$, so the percentage of firms using numeric control is increasing at a rate of 9 percentage points per year after 10 years. **b.** 0.80. Thus, in the long run, 80% of all firms will be using numeric control.

c. $p'(t) = 0.3816e^{4.46-0.477t}/(1 + e^{4.46-0.477t})^2$. $p'(10) = 0.0931$.
Graph:

115. $R(t) = 350e^{-0.1t}(39t + 68)$ million dollars; $R(2) \approx$ $42 billion; $R'(2) \approx 7 billion per year **117.** e raised to the glob, times the derivative of the glob. **119.** 2 raised to the glob, times the derivative of the glob, times the natural logarithm of 2. **121.** The derivative of $\ln |u|$ is not $\dfrac{1}{|u|}\dfrac{du}{dx}$; it is $\dfrac{1}{u}\dfrac{du}{dx}$.

Thus, the correct derivative is $\dfrac{3}{3x+1}$. **123.** The power rule does not apply when the exponent is not constant. The derivative of 3 raised to a quantity is 3 raised to the quantity, times the derivative of the quantity, times $\ln 3$. Thus, the correct answer is $3^{2x} \, 2 \ln 3$. **125.** No. If $N(t)$ is exponential, so is its derivative. **127.** If $f(x) = e^{kx}$, then the fractional rate of change is $\dfrac{f'(x)}{f(x)} = \dfrac{ke^{kx}}{e^{kx}} = k$, the fractional growth rate.

129. If $A(t)$ is growing exponentially, then $A(t) = A_0e^{kt}$ for constants A_0 and k. Its percentage rate of change is then

$\dfrac{A'(t)}{A(t)} = \dfrac{kA_0e^{kt}}{A_0e^{kt}} = k$, a constant.

Section 11.6

1. $-2/3$ **3.** x **5.** $(y-2)/(3-x)$ **7.** $-y$

9. $-\dfrac{y}{x(1 + \ln x)}$ **11.** $-x/y$ **13.** $-2xy/(x^2 - 2y)$

15. $-(6 + 9x^2y)/(9x^3 - x^2)$ **17.** $3y/x$
19. $(p + 10p^2q)/(2p - q - 10pq^2)$
21. $(ye^x - e^y)/(xe^y - e^x)$ **23.** $se^{st}/(2s - te^{st})$
25. $ye^x/(2e^x + y^3e^y)$ **27.** $(y - y^2)/(-1 + 3y - y^2)$
29. $-y/(x + 2y - xye^y - y^2e^y)$ **31. a.** 1 **b.** $y = x - 3$
33. a. -2 **b.** $y = -2x$ **35. a.** -1 **b.** $y = -x + 1$
37. a. $-2,000$ **b.** $y = -2,000x + 6,000$ **39. a.** 0
b. $y = 1$ **41. a.** -0.1898 **b.** $y = -0.1898x + 1.4721$

43. $\dfrac{2x+1}{4x-2}\left[\dfrac{2}{2x+1} - \dfrac{4}{4x-2}\right]$

45. $\dfrac{(3x+1)^2}{4x(2x-1)^3}\left[\dfrac{6}{3x+1} - \dfrac{1}{x} - \dfrac{6}{2x-1}\right]$

47. $(8x-1)^{1/3}(x-1)\left[\dfrac{8}{3(8x-1)} + \dfrac{1}{x-1}\right]$

49. $(x^3+x)\sqrt{x^3+2}\left[\dfrac{3x^2+1}{x^3+x} + \dfrac{1}{2}\dfrac{3x^2}{x^3+2}\right]$

51. $x^x(1 + \ln x)$ **53.** $-\$3,000$ per worker. The monthly budget to maintain production at the fixed level P is decreasing by approximately $3,000 per additional worker at an employment level of 100 workers and a monthly operating budget of $200,000. **55.** -125 T-shirts per dollar; when the price is set at $5, the demand is dropping by 125 T-shirts per $1 increase in price. **57.** $\dfrac{dk}{de}\Big|_{e=15} = -0.307$ carpenters per electrician. This means that, for a $200,000 house whose construction employs 15 electricians, adding one more electrician would cost as much as approximately 0.307 additional carpenters. In other words, one electrician is worth approximately 0.307 carpenters.

59. a. 22.93 hours. (The other root is rejected because it is larger than 30.) **b.** $\dfrac{dt}{dx} = \dfrac{4t - 20x}{0.4t - 4x}$; $\dfrac{dt}{dx}\Big|_{x=3.0} \approx -11.2$ hours per grade point. This means that, for a 3.0 student who scores 80 on the examination, 1 grade point is worth approximately 11.2 hours.

61. $\dfrac{dr}{dy} = 2\dfrac{r}{y}$, so $\dfrac{dr}{dt} = 2\dfrac{r}{y}\dfrac{dy}{dt}$ by the chain rule.

63. x, y, y, x **65.** Let $y = f(x)g(x)$.
Then $\ln y = \ln f(x) + \ln g(x)$, and

$\dfrac{1}{y}\dfrac{dy}{dx} = \dfrac{f'(x)}{f(x)} + \dfrac{g'(x)}{g(x)}$, so $\dfrac{dy}{dx} = y\left(\dfrac{f'(x)}{f(x)} + \dfrac{g'(x)}{g(x)}\right) =$

$f(x)g(x)\left(\dfrac{f'(x)}{f(x)} + \dfrac{g'(x)}{g(x)}\right) = f'(x)g(x) + f(x)g'(x)$.

67. Writing $y = f(x)$ specifies y as an explicit function of x. This can be regarded as an equation giving y as an *implicit* function of x. The procedure of finding dy/dx by implicit differentiation is then the same as finding the derivative of y as an explicit function of x: We take d/dx of both sides. **69.** Differentiate both sides of the equation $y = f(x)$ with respect to y to get $1 = f'(x) \cdot \dfrac{dx}{dy}$, giving $\dfrac{dx}{dy} = \dfrac{1}{f'(x)} = \dfrac{1}{dy/dx}$.

Chapter 11 Review

1. $50x^4 + 2x^3 - 1$ **3.** $9x^2 + x^{-2/3}$ **5.** $1 - 2/x^3$
7. $-\dfrac{4}{3x^2} + \dfrac{0.2}{x^{1.1}} + \dfrac{1.1x^{0.1}}{3.2}$ **9.** $e^x(x^2 + 2x - 1)$
11. $20x(x^2 - 1)^9$ **13.** $e^x(x^2 + 1)^9(x^2 + 20x + 1)$
15. $3^x[(x-1)\ln 3 - 1]/(x-1)^2$ **17.** $2xe^{x^2-1}$
19. $2x/(x^2 - 1)$ **21.** $x = 7/6$ **23.** $x = \pm 2$
25. $x = (1 - \ln 2)/2$ **27.** None **29.** $\dfrac{2x-1}{2y}$ **31.** $-y/x$

33. $\dfrac{(2x-1)^4(3x+4)}{(x+1)(3x-1)^3}\left[\dfrac{8}{2x-1}+\dfrac{3}{3x+4}-\dfrac{1}{x+1}-\dfrac{9}{3x-1}\right]$

35. $y=-x/4+1/2$ **37.** $y=-3ex-2e$ **39.** $y=x+2$
41. a. 274 books per week **b.** 636 books per week **c.** The function w begins to decrease more and more rapidly after $t=14$ Graph:

d. Because the data suggest an upward curving parabola, the long-term prediction of sales for a quadratic model would be that sales will increase without bound, in sharp contrast to (c)
43. a. $2.88 per book **b.** $3.715 per book **c.** Approximately $-$0.000104 per book, per additional book sold. **d.** At a sales level of 8,000 books per week, the cost is increasing at a rate of $2.88 per book (so that the 8,001st book costs approximately $2.88 to sell), and it costs an average of $3.715 per book to sell the first 8,000 books. Moreover, the average cost is decreasing at a rate of $0.000104 per book, per additional book sold.
45. a. $3,000 per week (rising) **b.** 300 books per week

47. $R=pq$ gives $R'=p'q+pq'$. Thus, $R'/R=R'/(pq)=(p'q+pq')/pq=p'/p+q'/q$ **49.** $110 per year

51. a. $s'(t)=\dfrac{2{,}475e^{-0.55(t-4.8)}}{(1+e^{-0.55(t-4.8)})^2}$; 556 books per week

b. 0; In the long term, the rate of increase of weekly sales slows to zero. **53.** 616.8 hits per day per week.
55. a. $-$17.24 copies per $1. The demand for the gift edition of *The Complete Harry Potter* is dropping at a rate of about 17.24 copies per $1 increase in the price. **b.** $138 per dollar is positive, so the price should be raised.

Chapter 12

Section 12.1

1. Absolute min: $(-3,-1)$, relative max: $(-1,1)$, relative min: $(1,0)$, absolute max: $(3,2)$ **3.** Absolute min: $(3,-1)$ and $(-3,-1)$, absolute max: $(1,2)$ **5.** Absolute min: $(-3,0)$ and $(1,0)$, absolute max: $(-1,2)$ and $(3,2)$ **7.** Relative min: $(-1,1)$ **9.** Absolute min: $(-3,-1)$, relative max: $(-2,2)$, relative min: $(1,0)$, absolute max: $(3,3)$ **11.** Relative max: $(-3,0)$, absolute min: $(-2,-1)$, stationary non-extreme point: $(1,1)$ **13.** Absolute max: $(0,1)$, absolute min: $(2,-3)$, relative max: $(3,-2)$ **15.** Absolute min: $(-4,-16)$, absolute max: $(-2,16)$, absolute min: $(2,-16)$, absolute max: $(4,16)$
17. Absolute min: $(-2,-10)$, absolute max: $(2,10)$
19. Absolute min: $(-2,-4)$, relative max: $(-1,1)$, relative min: $(0,0)$ **21.** Relative max: $(-1,5)$, absolute min: $(3,-27)$
23. Absolute min: $(0,0)$ **25.** Absolute maxima at $(0,1)$ and $(2,1)$, absolute min at $(1,0)$ **27.** Relative maximum at

$(-2,-1/3)$, relative minimum at $(-1,-2/3)$, absolute maximum at $(0,1)$ **29.** Relative min: $(-2,5/3)$, relative max: $(0,-1)$, relative min: $(2,5/3)$ **31.** Relative max: $(0,0)$; absolute min: $(1/3,-2\sqrt3/9)$ **33.** Relative max: $(0,0)$, absolute min: $(1,-3)$ **35.** No relative extrema **37.** Absolute min: $(1,1)$ **39.** Relative max: $(-1,1+1/e)$, absolute min: $(0,1)$, absolute max: $(1,e-1)$ **41.** Relative max: $(-6,-24)$, relative min: $(-2,-8)$ **43.** Absolute max $(1/\sqrt2,\sqrt{e/2})$, absolute min: $(-1/\sqrt2,-\sqrt{e/2})$ **45.** Relative min at $(0.15,-0.52)$ and $(2.45,8.22)$, relative max at $(1.40,0.29)$
47. Absolute max at $(-5,700)$, relative max at $(3.10,28.19)$ and $(6,40)$, absolute min at $(-2.10,-392.69)$ and relative min at $(5,0)$. **49.** Stationary minimum at $x=-1$ **51.** Stationary minima at $x=-2$ and $x=2$, stationary maximum at $x=0$
53. Singular minimum at $x=0$, stationary non-extreme point at $x=1$ **55.** Stationary minimum at $x=-2$, singular non-extreme points at $x=-1$ and $x=1$, stationary maximum at $x=2$
57. Answers will vary.   **59.** Answers will vary.

61. Not necessarily; it could be neither a relative maximum nor a relative minimum, as in the graph of $y=x^3$ at the origin.
63. Answers will vary.

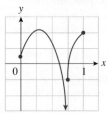

65. The graph oscillates faster and faster above and below zero as it approaches the end-point at 0, so 0 cannot be either a relative minimum or maximum.

Section 12.2

1. $x=y=5$; $P=25$ **3.** $x=y=3$; $S=6$ **5.** $x=2$, $y=4$; $F=20$ **7.** $x=20$, $y=10$, $z=20$; $P=4{,}000$
9. 5×5 **11.** 1,500 per day for an average cost of $130 per iPod **13.** $\sqrt{40}\approx6.32$ pounds of pollutant per day, for an average cost of about $1,265 per pound **15.** 2.5 lb
17. 5×10 **19.** 50×10 for an area of 250 sq. ft.
21. 11×22 **23.** $10 **25.** $78 for a quarterly revenue of $6,084 million, or $6.084 billion **27.** $4.61 for a daily revenue of $95,680.55 **29. a.** $1.41 per pound **b.** 5,000 pounds
c. $7,071.07 per month **31.** 34.5¢ per pound, for an annual (per capita) revenue of $5.95 **33.** $98 for an annual profit of $3,364 million, or $3.364 billion **35. a.** 656 headsets, for a

profit of $28,120 **b.** $143 per headset   **37.** Height = Radius of base ≈ 20.48 cm.   **39.** Height ≈ 10.84 cm; Radius ≈ 2.71 cm; Height/Radius = 4   **41.** $13\frac{1}{3}$ in $\times$ $3\frac{1}{3}$ in $\times$ $1\frac{1}{3}$ in for a volume of $1,600/27 \approx 59$ cubic inches   **43.** $5 \times 5 \times 5$ cm   **45.** $l = w = h \approx 20.67$ in, volume $\approx 8,827$ in^3 **47.** $l = 30$ in, $w = 15$ in, $h = 30$ in   **49.** $l = 36$ in, $w = h = 18$ in, $V = 11,664$ in^3 **51. a.** 1.6 years, or year 2001.6; **b.** $R_{max} = \$28,241$ million   **53.** $t = 2.5$ or midway through 1972; $D(2.5)/S(2.5) \approx 4.09$. The number of new (approved) drugs per $1 billion of spending on research and development reached a high of around four approved drugs per $1 billion midway through 1972.   **55.** 30 years from now   **57.** 55 days   **59.** 1,600 copies. At this value of x, average profit equals marginal profit; beyond this the marginal profit is smaller than the average.   **61.** 40 laborers and 250 robots   **63.** 71 employees   **65.** Increasing most rapidly in 1990; increasing least rapidly in 2007   **67.** Maximum when $t = 17$ days. This means that the embryo's oxygen consumption is increasing most rapidly 17 days after the egg is laid.   **69.** Graph of derivative:

The absolute maximum occurs at approximately (3.7, 2.2) during the year 2003. The percentage of mortgages that were subprime was increasing most rapidly during 2003, when it increased at a rate of around 2.2 percentage points per year.   **71.** You should sell them in 17 years' time, when they will be worth approximately $3,960.   **73.** 25 additional trees   **75.** (D)   **77.** (A); (B)   **79.** The problem is uninteresting because the company can accomplish the objective by cutting away the entire sheet of cardboard, resulting in a box with surface area zero.   **81.** Not all absolute extrema occur at stationary points; some may occur at an endpoint or singular point of the domain, as in Exercises 29, 30, 65, and 66.   **83.** The minimum of dq/dp is the fastest that the demand is dropping in response to increasing price.

Section 12.3

1. 6   **3.** $4/x^3$ **5.** $-0.96x^{-1.6}$ **7.** $e^{-(x-1)}$ **9.** $2/x^3 + 1/x^2$ **11. a.** $a = -32$ ft/s^2 **b.** $a = -32$ ft/s^2 **13. a.** $a = 2/t^3 + 6/t^4$ ft/s ^{2} **b.** $a = 8$ ft/s^2 **15. a.** $a = -1/(4t^{3/2}) + 2$ ft/s^2 **b.** $a = 63/32$ ft/s^2 **17.** (1, 0)   **19.** (1, 0)   **21.** None   **23.** $(-1, 0), (1, 1)$ **25.** Points of inflection at $x = -1$ and $x = 1$ **27.** One point of inflection, at $x = -2$ **29.** Points of inflection at $x = -2, x = 0, x = 2$ **31.** Points of inflection at $x = -2$ and $x = 2$ **33.** $x = 2$; minimum   **35.** Maximum at $x = -2$, minimum at $x = 2$ **37.** Maximum at $t = -1/\sqrt{3}$, minimum at $t = 1/\sqrt{3}$ **39.** Non-extreme stationary point at $x = 0$ minimum at $x = 3$ **41.** Maximum at $x = 0$ **43.** Minimum at

$x = -1/\sqrt{2}$; maximum at $x = 1/\sqrt{2}$ **45.** $f'(x) = 8x - 1$; $f''(x) = 8$; $f'''(x) = f^{(4)}(x) = \ldots = f^{(n)}(x) = 0$ **47.** $f'(x) = -4x^3 + 6x$; $f''(x) = -12x^2 + 6$; $f'''(x) = -24x$; $f^{(4)}(x) = -24$; $f^{(5)}(x) = f^{(6)}(x) = \ldots = f^{(n)}(x) = 0$ **49.** $f'(x) = 8(2x + 1)^3$; $f''(x) = 48(2x + 1)^2$; $f'''(x) = 192(2x + 1)$; $f^{(4)}(x) = 384$; $f^{(5)}(x) = f^{(6)}(x) = \ldots$ $= f^{(n)}(x) = 0$ **51.** $f'(x) = -e^{-x}$; $f''(x) = e^{-x}$; $f'''(x) = -e^{-x}$; $f^{(4)}(x) = e^{-x}$; $f^{(n)}(x) = (-1)^n e^{-x}$ **53.** $f'(x) = 3e^{3x-1}$; $f''(x) = 9e^{3x-1}$; $f'''(x) = 27e^{3x-1}$; $f^{(4)}(x) = 81e^{3x-1}$; $f^{(n)}(x) = 3^n e^{3x-1}$ **55.** -3.8 m/s^2 **57.** $6t - 2$ ft/s^2; increasing   **59.** Accelerating by 24 million gals/yr^2 **61. a.** 400 ml **b.** 36 ml/day **c.** -1 ml/day^2 **63. a.** 0.6% **b.** Speeding up **c.** Speeding up for $t < 3.33$ (prior to 1/3 of the way through March) and slowing for $t > 3.33$ (after that time)   **65. a.** December 2005: -0.202% (deflation rate of 0.202%) February 2006: 0.363% **b.** Speeding up **c.** Decreasing for $t < 4.44$ (prior to mid-November) and increasing for $t > 4.44$ (after that time).   **67.** Concave up for $8 < t < 20$, concave down for $0 < t < 8$, point of inflection around $t = 8$. The percentage of articles written by researchers in the United States was decreasing most rapidly at around $t = 8$ (1991).   **69. a.** (B) **b.** (B) **c.** (A)   **71.** Graphs:

$A(t)$:

$A'(t)$:

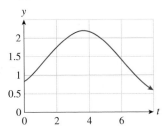

$A''(t)$:

Concave up when $t < 4$; concave down when $t > 4$; point of inflection when $t \approx 4$. The percentage of U.S. mortgages that were subprime was increasing fastest at the beginning of 2004. **73. a.** 2 years into the epidemic **b.** 2 years into the epidemic **75. a.** 2024 **b.** 2026 **c.** 2022; (A) **77. a.** There are no points of inflection in the graph of S. **b.** Because the graph is concave up, the derivative of S is increasing, and so the rate of *decrease* of SAT scores with increasing numbers of prisoners is diminishing. In other words, the apparent effect of more prisoners is

diminishing. **79. a.** $\left.\dfrac{d^2n}{ds^2}\right|_{s=3} = -21.494$. Thus, for a firm

with annual sales of \$3 million, the rate at which new patents are produced decreases with increasing firm size. This means that the returns (as measured in the number of new patents per increase of \$1 million in sales) are diminishing as the firm size

increases. **b.** $\left.\dfrac{d^2n}{ds^2}\right|_{s=7} = 13.474$. Thus, for a firm with annual

sales of \$7 million, the rate at which new patents are produced increases with increasing firm size by 13.474 new patents per \$1 million increase in annual sales. **c.** There is a point of inflection when $s \approx 5.4587$, so that in a firm with sales of \$5,458,700 per year, the number of new patents produced per additional \$1 million in sales is a minimum.
81. Graphs:

$I(t)/P(t)$:

$[I(t)/P(t)]'$:

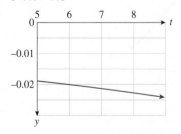

Concave down; (D)   **83.** (Proof)   **85.** $t \approx 4$; the population of Puerto Rico was increasing fastest in 1954.   **87.** About \$570 per year, after about 12 years   **89.** Increasing most rapidly in 17.64 years, decreasing most rapidly now (at $t = 0$)
91. Non-negative   **93.** Daily sales were decreasing most rapidly in June 2002.

95.

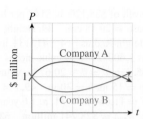

97. At a point of inflection, the graph of a function changes either from concave up to concave down, or vice versa. If it changes from concave up to concave down, then the derivative changes from increasing to decreasing, and hence has a relative maximum. Similarly, if it changes from concave down to concave up, the derivative has a relative minimum.

Section 11.4
1. a. x-intercept: -1; y-intercept: 1 **b.** Absolute min at $(-1, 0)$
c. None **d.** None **e.** $y \to +\infty$ as $x \to \pm\infty$
Graph:

3. a. x-intercepts: $-\sqrt{12}, 0, \sqrt{12}$; y-intercept: 0 **b.** Absolute min at $(-4, -16)$ and $(2, -16)$, absolute max at $(-2, 16)$ and $(4, 16)$ **c.** $(0, 0)$ **d.** None **e.** None
Graph:

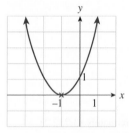

5. a. x-intercepts: $-3.6, 0, 5.1$; y-intercept: 0 **b.** Relative max at $(-2, 44)$, relative min at $(3, -81)$ **c.** $(0.5, -18.5)$
d. None **e.** $y \to -\infty$ as $x \to -\infty$; $y \to +\infty$ as $x \to +\infty$
Graph:

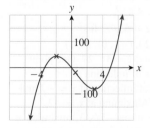

7. a. x-intercepts: 0.1, 1.8; y-intercept: 1 **b.** Relative max at $(-2, 21)$, relative min at $(1, -6)$ **c.** $(-1/2, 15/2)$ **d.** None
e. $y \to -\infty$ as $x \to -\infty$; $y \to +\infty$ as $x \to +\infty$
Graph:

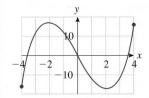

9. a. x-intercepts: -2.9, 4.2; y-intercept: 10 **b.** Relative max at $(-2, 74)$, relative min at $(0, 10)$, absolute max at $(3, 199)$
c. $(-1.12, 44.8)$, $(1.79, 117.3)$ **d.** None
e. $y \to -\infty$ as $x \to -\infty$; $y \to -\infty$ as $x \to +\infty$
Graph:

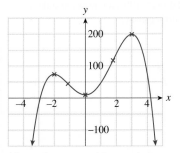

11. a. x-intercepts: None; y-intercept: 0 **b.** Absolute min at $(0, 0)$ **c.** $(1/3, 11/324)$ and $(1, 1/12)$ **d.** None
e. $y \to +\infty$ as $x \to -\infty$; $y \to +\infty$ as $x \to +\infty$
Graph:

13. a. x-intercepts: None; y-intercept: None **b.** Relative min at $(1, 2)$, relative max at $(-1, -2)$ **c.** None **d.** $y \to -\infty$ as $x \to 0^-$; $y \to +\infty$ as $x \to 0^+$, so there is a vertical asymptote at $x = 0$. **e.** $y \to -\infty$ as $x \to -\infty$; $y \to +\infty$ as $x \to +\infty$
Graph:

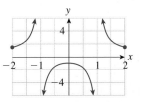

15. a. x-intercept: 0; y-intercept: 0 **b.** None **c.** $(0, 0)$, $(-3, -9/4)$, and $(3, 9/4)$ **d.** None **e.** $y \to -\infty$ as $x \to -\infty$; $y \to +\infty$ as $x \to +\infty$

Graph:

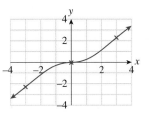

17. a. t-intercepts: None; y-intercept: -1 **b.** Relative min at $(-2, 5/3)$ and $(2, 5/3)$, relative max at $(0, -1)$ **c.** None
d. $y \to +\infty$ as $t \to -1^-$; $y \to -\infty$ as $t \to -1^+$; $y \to -\infty$ as $t \to 1^-$; $y \to +\infty$ as $t \to 1^+$; so there are vertical asymptotes at $t = \pm 1$. **e.** None
Graph:

19. a. x-intercepts: -0.6; y-intercept: 1 **b.** Relative maximum at $(-2, -1/3)$, relative minimum at $(-1, -2/3)$ **c.** None
d. None. **e.** $y \to -\infty$ as $x \to -\infty$; $y \to +\infty$ as $x \to +\infty$
Graph:

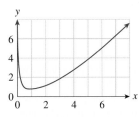

21. a. x-intercepts: None; y-intercept: None **b.** Absolute min at $(1, 1)$ **c.** None **d.** Vertical asymptote at $x = 0$
e. $y \to +\infty$ as $x \to +\infty$
Graph:

23. a. x-intercepts: ± 0.8; x-intercept: None **b.** None **c.** $(1,1)$ and $(-1, 1)$ **d.** $y \to -\infty$ as $x \to 0$; vertical asymptote at $x = 0$
e. $y \to +\infty$ as $x \to \pm\infty$

Graph:

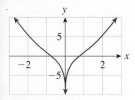

25. a. *t*-intercepts: None; *y*-intercept: 1 **b.** Absolute min at (0, 1). Absolute max at $(1, e - 1)$, relative max at $(-1, e^{-1} + 1)$. **c.** None **e.** None
Graph:

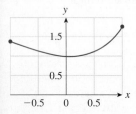

27. Absolute min at $(1.40, -1.49)$; points of inflection: $(0.21, 0.61)$, $(0.79, -0.55)$
Graph:

29. $f(x) = e^x - x^3$. Relative min at $(-0.46, 0.73)$, relative max at $(0.91, 1.73)$, absolute min at $(3.73, -10.22)$; points of inflection at $(0.20, 1.22)$ and $(2.83, -5.74)$
Graph:

31. *y*-intercept: 10; *t*-intercepts: None; the home price index was 10 percentage points at the start of 2004; absolute minimum at (0, 10); absolute maximum at (2, 40); the home price index was lowest in 2004 when it stood at 10 percentage points. The index was at its highest in 2006 at 40 points. Point of inflection at (3.5, 30); the home price index was decreasing most rapidly midway through 2007 when it stood at 30 percentage points. As $t \to +\infty$, $y \to 15$; assuming the trend shown in the graph continues indefinitely, the home price index will approach a value of 15 percentage points in the long term.   **33. a.** Intercepts: No *t*-intercept; *y*-intercept at $I(0) = 195$. The CPI was never zero

during the given period; in July 2005 the CPI was 195. Absolute min at (0, 195), absolute max at (8, 199.3), relative max at (2.9, 198.7), relative min at (6.0, 197.8). The CPI was at a low of 195 in July 2005, rose to 198.7 around October 2005, dipped to 197.8 around January 2006, and then rose to a high of 199.3 in March 2006. There is a point of inflection at (4.4, 198.2). The rate of change of the CPI (inflation) reached a minimum around mid-November 2005 when the CPI was 198.2.
b. The inflation rate was zero at around October 2005 and January 2006.   **35.** Extrema: Relative max at (0, 100), absolute min at (1, 99); point of inflection (0.5, 99.5); $s \to +\infty$ as $t \to +\infty$. At time $t = 0$ seconds, the UFO is stationary, 100 feet away from the observer, and begins to move closer. At time $t = 0.5$ seconds, when the UFO is 99.5 feet away, its distance is decreasing most rapidly (it is moving toward the observer most rapidly). It then slows down to a stop at $t = 1$ second when it is at its closest point (99 feet away) and then begins to move further and further away.
Graph:

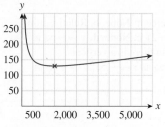

37. Intercepts: None; Absolute minimum at (1,500, 130); No points of inflection; vertical asymptote at $x = 0$. As $x \to +\infty$, $y \to +\infty$. The average cost is never zero, nor is it defined for zero iPods. The average cost is a minimum ($130) when 1,500 iPods are manufactured per day. The average cost becomes extremely large for very small or very large numbers of iPods.
Graph:

39. Graph of derivative:

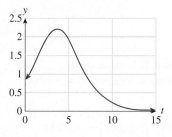

The absolute maximum occurs at approximately (3.7, 2.2); during the year 2003. The percentage of mortgages that were subprime was increasing most rapidly during 2003, when it increased at a rate of around 2.2 percentage points per year. As $t \to +\infty$, $A'(t) \to 0$; In the long term, assuming the trend shown in the model continues, the rate of change of the percentage of mortgages that were subprime approaches zero; that is, the percentage of mortgages that were subprime approaches a constant value. **41.** No; yes. Near a vertical asymptote the value of y increases without bound, and so the graph could not be included between two horizontal lines; hence, no vertical asymptotes are possible. Horizontal asymptotes are possible, as for instance in the graph in Exercise 31. **43.** It too has a vertical asymptote at $x = a$; the magnitude of the derivative increases without bound as $x \to a$. **45.** No. If the leftmost critical point is a relative maximum, the function will decrease from there until it reaches the rightmost critical point, so can't have a relative maximum there. **47.** Between every pair of zeros of $f(x)$ there must be a local extremum, which must be a stationary point of $f(x)$, hence a zero of $f'(x)$.

Section 12.5

1. $P = 10,000$; $\dfrac{dP}{dt} = 1,000$ **3.** Let R be the annual revenue of my company, and let q be annual sales. $R = 7,000$ and $\dfrac{dR}{dt} = -700$. Find $\dfrac{dq}{dt}$. **5.** Let p be the price of a pair of shoes, and let q be the demand for shoes. $\dfrac{dp}{dt} = 5$. Find $\dfrac{dq}{dt}$.

7. Let T be the average global temperature, and let q be the number of Bermuda shorts sold per year. $T = 60$ and $\dfrac{dT}{dt} = 0.1$. Find $\dfrac{dq}{dt}$. **9. a.** $6/(100\pi) \approx 0.019$ km/sec

b. $6/(8\sqrt{\pi}) \approx 0.4231$ km/sec **11.** $3/(4\pi) \approx 0.24$ ft/min **13.** 7.5 ft/s **15.** Decreasing at a rate of $1.66 per player per week **17.** Monthly sales will drop at a rate of 26 T-shirts per month. **19.** Raise the price by 3¢ per week. **21.** Increasing at a rate of $233.68 million per year **23.** 1 laborer per month **25.** The daily operating budget is dropping at a rate of $2.40 per year. **27.** The price is decreasing at a rate of approximately 31¢ per pound per month. **29.** $2,300/\sqrt{4,100} \approx 36$ miles/hour. **31.** 10.7 ft/s **33.** The y coordinate is decreasing at a rate of 16 units per second. **35.** $1,814 per year **37.** Their prior experience must increase at a rate of approximately 0.97 years every year. **39.** $\dfrac{2,500}{9\pi}\left(\dfrac{3}{5,000}\right)^{2/3} \approx 0.63$ m/sec

41. $\dfrac{\sqrt{1 + 128\pi}}{4\pi} \approx 1.6$ cm/sec **43.** 0.5137 computers per household, and increasing at a rate of 0.0230 computers per household per year. **45.** The average SAT score was 904.71 and decreasing at a rate of 0.11 per year. **47.** Decreasing by 2 percentage points per year **49.** The section is called "related rates" because the goal is to compute the rate of change of a quantity based on a knowledge of the rate of change of a related quantity. **51.** Answers may vary: A rectangular solid has

dimensions 2 cm $\times$ 5 cm $\times$ 10 cm, and each side is expanding at a rate of 3 cm/second. How fast is the volume increasing? **53.** (Proof) **55.** Linear **57.** Let $x =$ my grades and $y =$ your grades. If $dx/dt = 2\,dy/dt$, then $dy/dt = (1/2)\,dx/dt$.

Section 12.6

1. $E = 1.5$; the demand is going down 1.5% per 1% increase in price at that price level; revenue is maximized when $p = \$25$; weekly revenue at that price is $12,500. **3. a.** $E = 6/7$; the demand is going down 6% per 7% increase in price at that price level; thus, a price increase is in order. **b.** Revenue is maximized when $p = 100/3 \approx \$33.33$ **c.** Demand would be $(100 - 100/3)^2 = (200/3)^2 \approx 4,444$ cases per week. **5. a.** $E = (4p - 33)/(-2p + 33)$ **b.** 0.54; the demand for $E = mc^2$ T-shirts is going down by about 0.54% per 1% increase in the price. **c.** $11 per shirt for a daily revenue of $1,331 **7. a.** $E = 1.81$. Thus, the demand is elastic at the given tuition level, showing that a decrease in tuition will result in an increase in revenue. **b.** They should charge an average of $2,250 per student, and this will result in an enrollment of about 4,950 students, giving a revenue of about $11,137,500. **9. a.** $E = 51$; the demand is going down 51% per 1% increase in price at that price level; thus, a large price decrease is advised. **b.** Revenue is maximized when $p = ¥0.50$. **c.** Demand would be $100e^{-3/4+1/2} \approx 78$ paint-by-number sets per month. **11. a.** $E = -\dfrac{mp}{mp + b}$ **b.** $p = -\dfrac{b}{2m}$ **13. a.** $E = r$ **b.** E is independent of p. **c.** If $r = 1$, then the revenue is not affected by the price. If $r > 1$, then the revenue is always elastic, while if $r < 1$, the revenue is always inelastic. This is an unrealistic model because there should always be a price at which the revenue is a maximum. **15. a.** $q = -1,500p + 6,000$. **b.** $2 per hamburger, giving a total weekly revenue of $6,000. **17.** $E \approx 0.77$. At a family income level of $20,000, the fraction of children attending a live theatrical performance is increasing by 0.77% per 1% increase in household income. **19. a.** $E \approx 0.46$. The demand for computers is increasing by 0.46% per one percent increase in household income. **b.** E decreases as income increases. **c.** Unreliable; it predicts a likelihood greater than 1 at incomes of $123,000 and above. In a more appropriate model, one would expect the curve to level off at or below 1. **d.** $E \approx 0$ **21.** $\dfrac{Y}{Q} \cdot \dfrac{dQ}{dY} = \beta$. An increase in income of x% will result in an increase in demand of βx%. (Note that we do *not* take the negative here, because we expect an increase in income to produce an *increase* in demand.) **23. a.** $q = 1,000e^{-0.30p}$ **b.** At $p = \$3$, $E = 0.9$; at $p = \$4$, $E = 1.2$; at $p = \$5$, $E = 1.5$ **c.** $p = \$3.33$ **d.** $p = \$5.36$. Selling at a lower price would increase demand, but you cannot sell more than 200 pounds anyway. You should charge as much as you can and still be able to sell all 200 pounds. **25.** The price is lowered. **27.** Start with $R = pq$, and differentiate with respect to p to obtain $\dfrac{dR}{dp} = q + p\dfrac{dq}{dp}$. For a stationary point, $dR/dp = 0$, and so $q + p\dfrac{dq}{dp} = 0$.

Rearranging this result gives $p\dfrac{dq}{dp} = -q$, and hence

$-\dfrac{dq}{dp} \cdot \dfrac{p}{q} = 1$, or $E = 1$, showing that stationary points of R correspond to points of unit elasticity.   **29.** The distinction is best illustrated by an example. Suppose that q is measured in weekly sales and p is the unit price in dollars. Then the quantity $-dq/dp$ measures the drop in weekly sales per \$1 increase in price. The elasticity of demand E, on the other hand, measures the *percentage* drop in sales per *one percent* increase in price. Thus, $-dq/dp$ measures absolute change, while E measures fractional, or percentage, change.

Chapter 12 Review

1. Relative max: $(-1, 5)$, absolute min: $(-2, -3)$ and $(1, -3)$
3. Absolute max: $(-1, 5)$, absolute min: $(1, -3)$
5. Absolute min: $(1, 0)$ **7.** Absolute min: $(-2, -1/4)$
9. Relative max at $x = 1$, point of inflection at $x = -1$
11. Relative max at $x = -2$, relative min at $x = 1$, point of inflection at $x = -1$ **13.** One point of inflection, at $x = 0$
15. a. $a = 4/t^4 - 2/t^3$ m/sec² **b.** 2 m/sec²   **17.** Relative max: $(-2, 16)$; absolute min: $(2, -16)$; point of inflection: $(0, 0)$; no horizontal or vertical asymptotes

19. Relative min: $(-3, -2/9)$; relative max: $(3, 2/9)$; inflection: $(-3\sqrt{2}, -5\sqrt{2}/36)$, $(3\sqrt{2}, 5\sqrt{2}/36)$; vertical asymptote: $x = 0$; horizontal asymptote: $y = 0$

21. Relative max at $(0, 0)$, absolute min at $(1, -2)$, no asymptotes

23. \$22.14 per book   **25. a.** Profit $= -p^3 + 42p^2 - 288p - 181$
b. \$24 per copy; \$3,275 **c.** For maximum revenue, the company should charge \$22.14 per copy. At this price, the cost per book is decreasing with increasing price, while the revenue is not

decreasing (its derivative is zero). Thus, the profit is increasing with increasing price, suggesting that the maximum profit will occur at a higher price.   **27.** 12 in × 12 in × 6 in, for a volume of 864 in³   **29. a.** $E = \dfrac{2p^2 - 33p}{-p^2 + 33p + 9}$ **b.** 0.52, 2.03; when the price is \$20, demand is dropping at a rate of 0.52% per 1% increase in the price; when the price is \$25, demand is dropping at a rate of 2.03% per 1% increase in the price.
c. \$22.14 per book   **31. a.** $E = 2p^2 - p$ **b.** 6; the demand is dropping at a rate of 6% per 1% increase in the price. **c.** \$1.00, for a monthly revenue of \$1,000   **33. a.** week 5 **b.** Point of inflection on the graph of s; maximum on the graph of s', t-intercept in the graph of s''. **c.** 10,500; if weekly sales continue as predicted by the model, they will level off at around 10,500 books per week in the long term. **d.** 0; if weekly sales continue as predicted by the model, the rate of change of sales approaches zero in the long term.   **35. a.–d.** $10/\sqrt{2}$ ft/s

Chapter 13

Section 13.1

1. $x^6/6 + C$ **3.** $6x + C$ **5.** $x^2/2 + C$
7. $x^3/3 - x^2/2 + C$ **9.** $x + x^2/2 + C$ **11.** $-x^{-4}/4 + C$
13. $x^{3.3}/3.3 - x^{-0.3}/0.3 + C$ **15.** $u^3/3 - \ln|u| + C$
17. $\dfrac{4x^{5/4}}{5} + C$ **19.** $3x^5/5 + 2x^{-1} - x^{-4}/4 + 4x + C$
21. $2\ln|u| + u^2/8 + C$ **23.** $\ln|x| - \dfrac{2}{x} + \dfrac{1}{2x^2} + C$
25. $3x^{1.1}/1.1 - x^{5.3}/5.3 - 4.1x + C$ **27.** $\dfrac{x^{0.9}}{0.3} + \dfrac{40}{x^{0.1}} + C$
29. $2.55t^2 - 1.2\ln|t| - \dfrac{15}{t^{0.2}} + C$
31. $2e^x + 5\ln|x| + x/4 + C$
33. $12.2x^{0.5} + x^{1.5}/9 - e^x + C$ **35.** $\dfrac{2^x}{\ln 2} - \dfrac{3^x}{\ln 3} + C$
37. $\dfrac{100(1.1^x)}{\ln(1.1)} + C$ **39.** $1/x - 1/x^2 + C$ **41.** $f(x) = x^2/2 + 1$
43. $f(x) = e^x - x - 1$ **45.** $\dfrac{3x|x| - x^2}{2} + C$
47. $C(x) = 5x - x^2/20,000 + 20,000$
49. $C(x) = 5x + x^2 + \ln x + 994$
51. a. $M(t) = 4t^3 - 10t^2 + 10t + 1$ **b.** 85 million
53. $I(t) = 42,000 + 1200t$; \$48,000
55. $S(t) = 4t^3 + 250t^2 + 4700t$; 38,064 million gallons
57. a. $H'(t) = 3.5t + 65$ billion dollars per year
b. $H(t) = 1.75t^2 + 65t + 700$ billion dollars
59. a. $-0.4t + 1$ percentage points per year
b. $-0.2t^2 + t + 13$; 13.8   **61. a.** $s = t^3/3 + t + C$
b. $C = 1$; $s = t^3/3 + t + 1$ **63.** 320 ft/s downward
65. a. $v(t) = -32t + 16$ **b.** $s(t) = -16t^2 + 16t + 185$; zenith at $t = 0.5$ sec $s = 189$ feet, 4 feet above the top of the tower.
67. a. $s = 525t + 25t^2$ **b.** 3 hours **c.** The negative solution indicates that, at time $t = -24$, the tail wind would have been large

and negative, causing the plane to be moving backward through that position 24 hours prior to departure and arrive at the starting point of the flight at time 0!   **69.** (Proof)
71. $(1,280)^{1/2} \approx 35.78$ ft/s   **73. a.** 80 ft/s **b.** 60 ft/s
c. 1.25 seconds   **75.** $\sqrt{2} \approx 1.414$ times as fast   **77.** The term *indefinite* refers to the arbitrary constant term in the indefinite integral; we do not obtain a definite value for C and hence the integral is "not definite."   **79.** Constant; because the derivative of a linear function is constant, linear functions are antiderivatives of constant functions.   **81.** No; there are infinitely many antiderivatives of a given function, each pair of them differing by a constant. Knowing the value of the function at a specific point suffices.   **83.** They differ by a constant, $G(x) - F(x) =$ Constant   **85.** Antiderivative, marginal   **87.** $\int f(x)\,dx$ represents the total cost of manufacturing x items. The units of $\int f(x)\,dx$ are the product of the units of $f(x)$ and the units of x.
89. $\int (f(x) + g(x))\,dx$ is, by definition, an antiderivative of $f(x) + g(x)$. Let $F(x)$ be an antiderivative of $f(x)$ and let $G(x)$ be an antiderivative of $g(x)$. Then, because the derivative of $F(x) + G(x)$ is $f(x) + g(x)$ (by the rule for sums of derivatives), this means that $F(x) + G(x)$ is an antiderivative of $f(x) + g(x)$. In symbols, $\int (f(x) + g(x))\,dx = F(x) + G(x) + C = \int f(x)\,dx + \int g(x)\,dx$, the sum of the indefinite integrals.   **91.** Answers will vary. $\int x \cdot 1\,dx = \int x\,dx = x^2/2 + C$, whereas $\int x\,dx \cdot \int 1\,dx = (x^2/2 + D) \cdot (x + E)$, which is not the same as $x^2/2 + C$, no matter what values we choose for the constants C, D, and E.
93. Derivative; indefinite integral; indefinite integral; derivative

Section 13.2
1. $(3x - 5)^4/12 + C$ **3.** $(3x - 5)^4/12 + C$ **5.** $-e^{-x} + C$
7. $-e^{-x} + C$ **9.** $\frac{1}{2}e^{(x+1)^2} + C$ **11.** $(3x + 1)^6/18 + C$
13. $(-2x + 2)^{-1}/2 + C$ **15.** $1.6(3x - 4)^{3/2} + C$
17. $2e^{(0.6x+2)} + C$ **19.** $(3x^2 + 3)^4/24 + C$
21. $(x^2 + 1)^{2.3}/4.6 + C$ **23.** $x + 3e^{3.1x-2} + C$
25. $2(3x^2 - 1)^{3/2}/9 + C$ **27.** $-(1/2)e^{-x^2+1} + C$
29. $-(1/2)e^{-(x^2+2x)} + C$ **31.** $(x^2 + x + 1)^{-2}/2 + C$
33. $(2x^3 + x^6 - 5)^{1/2}/3 + C$ **35.** $(x - 2)^7/7 + (x - 2)^6/3 + C$
37. $4[(x + 1)^{5/2}/5 - (x + 1)^{3/2}/3] + C$
39. $20 \ln |1 - e^{-0.05x}| + C$ **41.** $3e^{-1/x} + C$
43. $(e^x - e^{-x})/2 + C$ **45.** $\ln(e^x + e^{-x}) + C$
47. $(e^{2x^2-2x} + e^{x^2})/2 + C$ **53.** $-e^{-x} + C$
55. $(1/2)e^{2x-1} + C$ **57.** $(2x + 4)^3/6 + C$
59. $(1/5) \ln |5x - 1| + C$ **61.** $(1.5x)^4/6 + C$
63. $\dfrac{1.5^{3x}}{3 \ln(1.5)} + C$ **65.** $\dfrac{1}{4}(2x + 4)|2x + 4| + C$
67. $\dfrac{2^{3x+4} - 2^{-3x+4}}{3 \ln 2} + C$ **69.** $f(x) = (x^2 + 1)^4/8 - 1/8$
71. $f(x) = (1/2)e^{x^2-1}$ **73.** $210t + 1,240e^{-0.05t} - 1,240$
75. $825t + 600e^{-0.4t} - 600$; $7,660$ million
77. $C(x) = 5x - 1/(x + 1) + 995.5$
79. a. $N(t) = 35 \ln(5 + e^{0.2t}) - 63$ **b.** 80,000 articles
81. $S(t) = 3,600[\ln(3 + e^{0.25t}) - \ln 4]$; 6,310 sets
83. a. $s = (t^2 + 1)^5/10 + t^2/2 + C$ **b.** $C = 9/10$;

$s = (t^2 + 1)^5/10 + t^2/2 + 9/10$ **85.** $S(t) = 4(t - 2,000)^3 + 250(t - 2,000)^2 + 4,700(t - 2,000) - 16,458$; 39,190 million gallons   **87.** None; the substitution $u = x$ simply replaces the letter x throughout by the letter u, and thus does not change the integral at all. For instance, the integral $\int x(3x^2 + 1)\,dx$ becomes $\int u(3u^2 + 1)\,du$ if we substitute $u = x$.
89. (D); to compute the integral, first break it up into a sum of two integrals: $\displaystyle \int \frac{x}{x^2 - 1}\,dx + \int \frac{3x}{x^2 + 1}\,dx$, and then compute the first using $u = x^2 - 1$ and the second using $u = x^2 + 1$.
91. The purpose of substitution is to introduce a new variable that is defined in terms of the variable of integration. One cannot say $u = u^2 + 1$, since u is not a new variable. Instead, define $w = u^2 + 1$ (or any other letter different from u).
93. The integral $\int x(x^2 + 1)\,dx$ can be solved by the substitution $u = x^2 + 1$, because it leads to
$$\frac{1}{2}\int u\,du = \frac{1}{4}u^2 + C = \frac{(x^2 + 1)^2}{4} + C.$$

Section 13.3
1. 30   **3.** 22   **5.** -2 **7.** 0   **9.** 4   **11.** 6   **13.** 0.7456
15. 2.3129   **17.** 2.5048   **19.** 1   **21.** 1/2   **23.** 1/4   **25.** 2
27. 0   **29.** 6   **31.** 0   **33.** 0.5   **35.** 3.3045, 3.1604, 3.1436
37. 0.0275, 0.0258, 0.0256   **39.** $99.95
41. 29 billion gallon   **43.** 4,900 million items   **45. a.** Left sum: about 46,000 articles, right sum: about 55,000 articles
b. 50.5; a total of about 50,500 articles in *Physical Review* were written by researchers in Europe in the 16-year period beginning 1983.   **47.** 118,750 degrees   **49.** Left sum: 20.5; right sum: 21   **51.** 54,000 students   **53.** -84.8; after 4 seconds, the stone is about 84.8 ft below where it started.   **55.** 91.2 ft
57. 9,450; a total of about 9,450 million barrels of oil was produced by **Pemex** from the start of 2001 to the start of 2009.
59. 18,400; a total of 18,400 wiretaps were authorized by U.S. state and federal courts during the 15-year period starting January 1990.   **61.** Yes. The Riemann sum gives an estimated area of 420 square feet.
63. a. Graph:

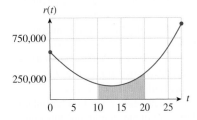

Total expenditure on oil in the United States from 1990 to 2000.
b. 2,010,000; a total of $2,010,000 million, or $2.01 trillion, was spent on oil in the U.S. from 1990 to 2000.   **65. a.** 99.4%
b. 0 (to at least 15 decimal places)   **67.** Stays the same
69. Increases   **71.** The area under the curve and above the x axis equals the area above the curve and below the x axis.
73. Answers will vary. One example: Let $r(t)$ be the rate of

change of net income at time t. If $r(t)$ is negative, then the net income is decreasing, so the change in net income, represented by the definite integral of $r(t)$, is negative.

75. Answers may vary.

77. The total cost is $c(1) + c(2) + \cdots + c(60)$, which is represented by the Riemann sum approximation of $\int_1^{61} c(t)\, dt$ with $n = 60$.   **79.** $[f(x_1) + f(x_2) + \cdots + f(x_n)]\Delta x = \sum_{k=1}^{n} f(x_k)\Delta x$

Section 13.4

1. 14/3   **3.** 5   **5.** 0   **7.** 40/3   **9.** −0.9045   **11.** $2(e − 1)$
13. 2/3   **15.** $1/\ln 2$ **17.** $4^6 − 1 = 4{,}095$ **19.** $(e^1 − e^{-3})/2$
21. $3/(2\ln 2)$ **23.** $50(e^{-1} − e^{-2})$ **25.** 40/3   **27.** $e^{2.1} − e^{-0.1}$
29. 0   **31.** $(5/2)(e^3 − e^2)$ **33.** $(1/3)[\ln 26 − \ln 7]$

35. $\dfrac{0.1}{2.2\ln(1.1)}$ **37.** $e − e^{1/2}$ **39.** $2 − \ln 3$ **41.** −4/21

43. $3^{5/2}/10 − 3^{3/2}/6 + 1/15$ **45.** 1/2   **47.** 16/3   **49.** 9/2
51. 56/3   **53.** 1/2   **55.** \$783   **57.** 296 miles   **59.** 260 ft
61. 30 billion gallons   **63.** 9,451 million barrels   **65.** 18,470; a total of 18,470 wiretaps were authorized by U.S. state and federal courts during the 15-year period starting January 1990.
67. $210t + 1{,}240e^{-0.05t} − 1{,}240$ **69.** 9 gallons
71. 907 T-shirts   **73.** 68 milliliters   **75.** 4,200; a total of around 4,200 million items were listed on **eBay** during 2005 and 2006.
77. Change in cost $= \int_0^x m(t)\, dt = C(x) − C(0)$ by the FTC, so $C(x) = C(0) + \int_0^x m(t)\, dt$. $C(0)$ is the *fixed cost*.   **79.** 80,000 articles   **81. a., b.** (Proofs) **c.** 2,401 thousand students
85. They are related by the Fundamental Theorem of Calculus, which (briefly) states that the definite integral of a suitable function can be calculated by evaluating the indefinite integral at the two end-points and subtracting.   **87.** Computing its definite integral from a to b.   **89.** Calculate definite integrals by using antiderivatives.   **91.** An example is $v(t) = t − 5$.
93. An example is $f(x) = e^{-x}$.   **95.** By the FTC, $\int_a^x f(t)\, dt = G(x) − G(a)$ where G is an antiderivative of f. Hence, $F(x) = G(x) − G(a)$. Taking derivatives of both sides, $F'(x) = G'(x) + 0 = f(x)$, as required. The result gives us a formula, in terms of area, for an antiderivative of any continuous function.

Chapter 13 Review

1. $x^3/3 − 5x^2 + 2x + C$ **3.** $4x^3/15 + 4/(5x) + C$

5. $-e^{-2x+11}/2 + C$ **7.** $\dfrac{1}{22}(x^2 + 4)^{11} + C$ **9.** $-\dfrac{5}{2}e^{-2x} + C$

11. $(x + 2) − \ln|x + 2| + C$ or $x − \ln|x + 2| + C$
13. 1   **15.** 2.75   **17.** −0.24   **19.** 0.7778, 0.7500, 0.7471

21. 0   **23.** 1/4   **25.** $2 + e − e^{-1}$ **27.** 52/9
29. $[\ln 5 − \ln 2]/8 = \ln(2.5)/8$ **31.** 32/3   **33.** $(1 − e^{-25})/2$
35. a. $N(t) = 196t + t^2/2 − 0.16t^6/6$ **b.** 4 books   **37. a.** At a height of $-16t^2 + 100t$ ft **b.** 156.25 ft **c.** After 6.25 seconds
39. 5,000 copies.   **41.** 0 books   **43.** 39,200 hits   **45.** \$8,200
47. About 86,000 books   **49.** About 35,800 books

Chapter 14

Section 14.1

1. $2e^x(x − 1) + C$ **3.** $-e^{-x}(2 + 3x) + C$

5. $e^{2x}(2x^2 − 2x − 1)/4 + C$

7. $-e^{-2x+4}(2x^2 + 2x + 3)/4 + C$

9. $2^x[(2 − x)/\ln 2 + 1/(\ln 2)^2] + C$

11. $-3^{-x}[(x^2 − 1)/\ln 3 + 2x/(\ln 3)^2 + 2/(\ln 3)^3] + C$

13. $-e^{-x}(x^2 + x + 1) + C$ **15.** $\dfrac{1}{7}x(x + 2)^7 − \dfrac{1}{56}(x + 2)^8 + C$

17. $-\dfrac{x}{2(x − 2)^2} − \dfrac{1}{2(x − 2)} + C$ **19.** $(x^4 \ln x)/4 − x^4/16 + C$

21. $(t^3/3 + t)\ln(2t) − t^3/9 − t + C$

23. $(3/4)t^{4/3}(\ln t − 3/4) + C$ **25.** $x \log_3 x − x/\ln 3 + C$

27. $e^{2x}(x/2 − 1/4) − 4e^{3x}/3 + C$

29. $e^x(x^2 − 2x + 2) − e^{x^2}/2 + C$ **31.** e **33.** 38,229/286

35. $\dfrac{1}{3}(3x − 4)(2x − 1)^{3/2} − \dfrac{1}{5}(2x − 1)^{5/2} + C$

37. $(7/2)\ln 2 − 3/4$ **39.** 1/4   **41.** $1 − 11e^{-10}$ **43.** $4\ln 2 − 7/4$

45. $\dfrac{1}{2}x(x − 3)|x − 3| − \dfrac{1}{6}(x − 3)^2|x − 3| + C$

47. $2x|x − 3| − (x − 3)|x − 3| + C$

49. $-x^2(-x + 4)|-x + 4| − \dfrac{2}{3}x(-x + 4)^2|-x + 4| − \dfrac{1}{6}(-x + 4)^3|-x + 4| + C$

51. $\dfrac{1}{2}(x^2 − 2x + 3)(x − 4)|x − 4| − \dfrac{1}{3}(x − 1)(x − 4)^2|x − 4| + \dfrac{1}{12}(x − 4)^3|x − 4| + C$ **53.** $28{,}800{,}000(1 − 2e^{-1})$ ft

55. $5{,}001 + 10x − 1/(x + 1) − [\ln(x + 1)]/(x + 1)$

57. \$4,252 billion   **59.** 11,919 million gallons

61. 19 billion square feet   **63.** $e^{0.1x}(250[-8x^2 + 70x + 1{,}000] − 2{,}500[-16x + 70] − 400{,}000) + 325{,}000$ **65.** 33,598

67. a. $r(t) = -0.075t + 2.75 + [0.025t − 0.25]\dfrac{|t − 10|}{t − 10}$

b. 42.5 million people   **69.** Answers will vary. Examples are xe^{x^2} and $e^{x^2} = 1 \cdot e^{x^2}$.   **71.** Answers will vary. Examples are Exercises 35 and 36, or more simply, integrals like $\int x(x + 1)^5\, dx$.   **73.** Substitution   **75.** Parts   **77.** Substitution
79. Parts   **81.** $n + 1$ times

Section 14.2

1. 16/3   **3.** 9.75   **5.** 2   **7.** 31/3   **9.** 8/3   **11.** 4   **13.** 1/3
15. 1   **17.** 2   **19.** 39   **21.** $e − 3/2$ **23.** 2/3   **25.** 3/10

27. $1/20$ **29.** $4/15$ **31.** $1/3$ **33.** 32 **35.** $2\ln 2 - 1$
37. $8\ln 4 + 2e - 16$ **39.** 0.9138 **41.** 0.3222 **43.** 112.5. This represents your total profit for the week, $\$112.50$. **45.** 608; there were approximately 608,000 housing starts from the start of 2002 to the start of 2006 not for sale purposes.
47. a. Graph: (The upper curve is **MySpace**.)

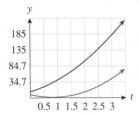

MySpace; about 93 million members **b.** The area between the curves $y = f(t)$ and $y = m(t)$ over $[0.5, 2]$
49. $16{,}078(e^{0.051t} - 1) - 7{,}333.3(e^{0.06t} - 1)$; the total number of wiretaps authorized by federal courts from the start of 1990 up to time t was about $16{,}078(e^{0.051t} - 1) - 7{,}333.3(e^{0.06t} - 1)$.
51. Wrong: It could mean that the graphs of f and g cross, as shown in the caution at the start of this topic in the textbook.
53. The area between the export and import curves represents the United States's accumulated trade deficit (that is, the total excess of imports over exports) from 1960 to 2007. **55.** (A)
57. The claim is wrong because the area under a curve can only represent income if the curve is a graph of income *per unit time*. The value of a stock price is not income per unit time— the income can be realized only when the stock is sold, and it amounts to the current market price. The total net income (per share) from the given investment would be the stock price on the date of sale minus the purchase price of $\$50$.

Section 14.3

1. Average $= 2$

3. Average $= 1$

5. Average $= (1 - e^{-2})/2$

7. Average $= 17/8$

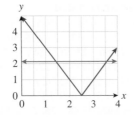

9.

x	0	1	2	3	4	5	6	7
r(x)	3	5	10	3	2	5	6	7
$\bar{r}(x)$			6	6	5	10/3	13/3	6

11.

x	0	1	2	3	4	5	6	7
r(x)	1	2	6	7	11	15	10	2
$\bar{r}(x)$			3	5	8	11	12	9

13. Moving average:
$$\bar{f}(x) = x^3 - (15/2)x^2 + 25x - 125/4$$

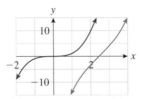

15. Moving average:
$$\bar{f}(x) = (3/25)[x^{5/3} - (x - 5)^{5/3}]$$

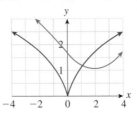

17. $\bar{f}(x) = \dfrac{2}{5}(e^{0.5x} - e^{0.5(x-5)})$

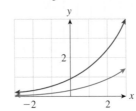

19. $\bar{f}(x) = \dfrac{2}{15}(x^{3/2} - (x - 5)^{3/2})$

21. $\bar{f}(x) = \dfrac{1}{5}\left[5 - \dfrac{1}{2}|2x - 1| + \dfrac{1}{2}|2x - 11|\right]$

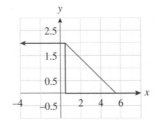

ANSWERS TO SELECTED EXERCISES

23. $\bar{f}(x) = \dfrac{1}{5}\left[2x - \dfrac{1}{2}(x+1)|x+1| + \dfrac{1}{2}x|x| - 2(x-5)\right.$

$\left. + \dfrac{1}{2}(x-4)|x-4| - \dfrac{1}{2}(x-5)|x-5|\right]$

25.

27.

29.

31.

33.

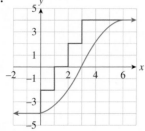

35. $6,718.8 million   **37.** $1.955 million   **39.** 16 million members per year   **41.** 277 tons   **43.** $10,410.88   **45.** $1,500   **47.** 537 million items per quarter

49.

Year t	1999	2000	2001	2002	2003	2004	2005	2006	2007	2008
Stock Price	36	44	41	36	38	49	56	71	92	62
Moving Average (rounded)				39	40	41	45	54	67	70

The moving average continued up at a lower rate.

51. a. To obtain the moving averages from January to June, use the fact that the data repeats every 12 months. Graph:

b. The 12-month moving average is constant and equal to the year-long average of approximately 79°.
53. a. Graph:

— Sales — Moving average

b. Approximately 0.3 million iPods per quarter
55. a. 7,000 million gallons per year

b. $\dfrac{1}{2}[4[t^3 - (t-2)^3] + 250[t^2 - (t-2)^2] + 9,400]$

c. Quadratic   **57. a.** $s = 14.4t + 240$ **b.** $\bar{s}(t) = 14.4t + 211.2$
c. The slope of the moving average is the same as the slope of

the original function.   **59.** $\bar{f}(x) = mx + b - \dfrac{ma}{2}$ **61.** The

moving average "blurs" the effects of short-term oscillations in the price, and shows the longer-term trend of the stock price.
63. They repeat every six months.   **65.** The area above the x-axis equals the area below the x-axis. Example: $y = x$ on $[-1,1]$
67. This need not be the case; for instance, the function $f(x) = x^2$ on $[0, 1]$ has average value $1/3$, whereas the value midway between the maximum and minimum is $1/2$.   **69.** (C) A shorter term moving average most closely approximates the original function because it averages the function over a shorter period, and continuous functions change by only a small amount over a small period.

Section 14.4
1. $6.25   **3.** $512   **5.** $119.53   **7.** $900   **9.** $416.67
11. $326.27   **13.** $25   **15.** $0.50   **17.** $386.29   **19.** $225
21. $25.50   **23.** $12,684.63   **25.** $TV = 300,000$,
$FV = 434,465.45$ **27.** $TV = 350,000$, $FV = 498,496.61$
29. $TV = 389,232.76$, $FV = 547,547.16$
31. $TV = 100,000$, $PV = 82,419.99$ **33.** $TV = 112,500$,
$PV = 92,037.48$ **35.** $TV = 107,889.50$, $PV = 88,479.69$
37. $\bar{p} = 5,000$, $\bar{q} = 10,000$, $CS = 25$ million,
$PS = 100$ million. The total social gain is $125 million.

39. $CS = \dfrac{1}{2m}(b - m\bar{p})^2$ **41.** €220 billion   **43.** $1,380 billion

45. €250 billion **47.** $1,210 billion **49.** $1,943,162.44
51. $3,086,245.73 **53.** $58,961.74 **55.** $1,792,723.35
57. Total **59.** She is correct, provided there is a positive
rate of return, in which case the future value (which includes
interest) is greater than the total value (which does not).
61. $PV < TV < FV$

Section 14.5

1. Diverges **3.** Converges to $2e$ **5.** Converges to e^2
7. Converges to ½ **9.** Converges to $1/108$ **11.** Converges to
$3 \times 5^{2/3}$ **13.** Diverges **15.** Diverges **17.** Converges to
$\frac{5}{4}(3^{4/5} - 1)$ **19.** Diverges **21.** Converges to 0 **23.** Diverges

25. Diverges **27.** 0.9, 0.99, 0.999, ... ; converges to 1.
29. 7.602, 95.38, 993.1, ... ; diverges. **31.** 1.368, 1.800,
1.937, 1.980, 1.994, 1.998, 1.999, 2.000, ... ; converges to 2.
33. 9.000, 99.00, 999.0, ... ; diverges to $+\infty$. **35.** 2.79 million homes **37.** 13,600 billion cigarettes **39.** No; you will not
sell more than 2,000 of them. **41.** The integral diverges, and so
the number of graduates each year will rise without bound.
43. a. $R(t) = 350e^{-0.1t}(39t + 68)$ million dollars/yr;
b. $1,603,000 million **45.** $20,700 billion **47.** $\int_0^{+\infty} N(t)\,dt$
diverges, indicating that there is no bound to the expected
future total online sales of mousse. $\int_{-\infty}^0 N(t)\,dt$ converges to
approximately 2.006, indicating that total online sales of
mousse prior to the current year amounted to approximately
2 million gallons. **49.** 1 **51.** 0.1587 **53.** $70,833
55. a. 2.468 meteors on average **b.** The integral diverges.
We can interpret this as saying that the number of impacts
by meteors smaller than 1 megaton is very large. (This makes
sense because, for example, this number includes meteors
no larger than a grain of dust.) **57. a.** $\Gamma(1) = 1; \Gamma(2) = 1$
59. The integral does not converge, so the number given
by the FTC is meaningless. **61.** Yes; the integrals converge
to 0, and the FTC also gives 0. **63. a.** Not improper.
$|x|/x$ is not defined at zero, but $\lim_{x \to 0^-} |x|/x = -1$ and
$\lim_{x \to 0^+} |x|/x = 1$. Because these limits are finite, the integral
is not improper. **b.** Improper, because $x^{-1/3}$ has infinite left and
right limits at 0. **c.** Improper, since $(x - 2)/(x^2 - 4x + 4) =$
$1/(x - 2)$, which has an infinite left limit at 2. **65.** In all cases,
you need to rewrite the improper integral as a limit and use
technology to evaluate the integral of which you are taking the
limit. Evaluate for several values of the endpoint approaching
the limit. In the case of an integral in which one of the limits of
integration is infinite, you may have to instruct the calculator or
computer to use more subdivisions as you approach $+\infty$.

Section 14.6

1. $y = \dfrac{x^3}{3} + \dfrac{2x^{3/2}}{3} + C$ **3.** $\dfrac{y^2}{2} = \dfrac{x^2}{2} + C$ **5.** $y = Ae^{x^2/2}$

7. $y = -\dfrac{2}{(x + 1)^2 + C}$ **9.** $y = \pm\sqrt{(\ln x)^2 + C}$

11. $y = \dfrac{x^4}{4} - x^2 + 1$ **13.** $y = (x^3 + 8)^{1/3}$ **15.** $y = 2x$

17. $y = e^{x^2/2} - 1$ **19.** $y = -\dfrac{2}{\ln(x^2 + 1) + 2}$ **21.** With $s(t) =$

monthly sales after t months, $\dfrac{ds}{dt} = -0.05s; s = 1,000$ when

$t = 0$. Solution: $s = 1,000e^{-0.05t}$ quarts per month.
23. a. $75 + 125e^{-0.05t}$ **b.** 64.4 minutes **25.** $k \approx 0.04274$;
$H(t) = 75 + 115e^{-0.04274t}$ degrees Fahrenheit after t minutes.
27. With $S(t)$ = total sales after t months,

$\dfrac{ds}{dt} = 0.1(100,000 - S); S(0) = 0.$

Solution: $S = 100,000(1 - e^{-0.1t})$ monitors after t months.
29. $q = 0.6078e^{-0.05p}p^{1.5}$ **31.** $y = e^{-t}(t + 1)$

33. $y = e^{t/2}\left[-2te^{-t/2} - 4e^{-t/2} + 5\right]$

35. $i = 5e^{-t}(e^t - e)\left[1 + \dfrac{|t - 1|}{t - 1}\right]$

Graph:

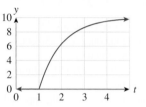

37. a. $\dfrac{dp}{dt} = k(D(p) - S(p)) = k(20,000 - 1,000p)$

b. $p = 20 - Ae^{-kt}$ **c.** $p = 20 - 10e^{-0.2231t}$ dollars after t months.

41. $S = \dfrac{2/1,999}{e^{-0.5t} + 1/1,999}$

Graph:

It will take about 27 months to saturate the market.

43. a. $y = be^{Ae^{-at}}$, A = constant **b.** $y = 10e^{-0.69315e^{-t}}$
Graph:

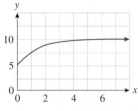

45. A general solution gives all possible solutions to the equation, using at least one arbitrary constant. A particular solution
is one specific function that satisfies the equation. We obtain a

particular solution by substituting specific values for any arbitrary constants in the general solution. **47.** Example: $y'' = x$ has general solution $y = \frac{1}{6}x^3 + Cx + D$ (integrate twice).
49. $y' = -4e^{-x} + 3$

Chapter 14 Review

1. $(x^2 - 2x + 4)e^x + C$ **3.** $(1/3)x^3 \ln 2x - x^3/9 + C$
5. $\frac{1}{2}x(2x + 1)|2x + 1| - \frac{1}{12}(2x + 1)^2|2x + 1| + C$
7. $-5x|-x + 3| - \frac{5}{2}(-x + 3)|-x + 3| + C$
9. $-e^2 - 39/e^2$ **11.** $\frac{3}{2 \cdot 2^{1/3}} - \frac{1}{2}$ **13.** $\frac{2\sqrt{2}}{3}$ **15.** -1
17. $e - 2$ **19.** $3x - 2$ **21.** $\frac{3}{14}[x^{7/3} - (x - 2)^{7/3}]$
23. \$1,600 **25.** \$2,500 **27.** $1/4$ **29.** Diverges **31.** 1
33. $y = -\frac{3}{x^3 + C}$ **35.** $y = \sqrt{2\ln|x| + 1}$ **37.** \$18,200
39. a. \$2,260 **b.** $50{,}000e^{0.01t}(1 - e^{-0.04}) \approx 1{,}960.53e^{0.01t}$
41. a. $\bar{p} = 20$, $\bar{q} = 40{,}000$ **b.** $CS = \$240{,}000$, $PS = \$30{,}000$
43. Approximately \$910,000 **45. a.** \$5,549,000
b. Principal: \$5,280,000, interest: \$269,000 **47.** \$51 million
49. The amount in the account would be given by
$y = 10{,}000/(1 - t)$ where t is time in years, so would approach infinity 1 year after the deposit.

Chapter 15

Section 15.1

1. a. 1 **b.** 1 **c.** 2 **d.** $a^2 - a + 5$ **e.** $y^2 + x^2 - y + 1$
f. $(x + h)^2 + (y + k)^2 - (x + h) + 1$ **3. a.** 0 **b.** 0.2
c. -0.1 **d.** $0.18a + 0.2$ **e.** $0.1x + 0.2y - 0.01xy$
f. $0.2(x + h) + 0.1(y + k) - 0.01(x + h)(y + k)$ **5. a.** 1
b. e **c.** e **d.** e^{x+y+z} **e.** $e^{x+h+y+k+z+l}$ **7. a.** Does not exist
b. 0 **c.** 0 **d.** $xyz/(x^2 + y^2 + z^2)$ **e.** $(x + h)(y + k)(z + l)/$
$[(x + h)^2 + (y + k)^2 + (z + l)^2]$ **9. a.** Increases; 2.3
b. Decreases; 1.4 **c.** Decreases; 1 unit increase in z
11. Neither **13.** Linear **15.** Linear **17.** Interaction
19. a. 107 **b.** -14 **c.** -113

21.

$x \rightarrow$	10	20	30	40
10	52	107	162	217
20	94	194	294	394
30	136	281	426	571
40	178	368	558	748

(left column header: y $\downarrow$)

25. 18, 4, 0.0965, 47,040 **27.** 6.9078, 1.5193, 5.4366, 0
29. Let $z = $ annual sales of Z (in millions of dollars),
$x = $ annual sales of X, and $y = $ annual sales of Y. The model is
$z = -2.1x + 0.4y + 16.2$.

31.

33.

35.

37.

39.

41. (H) **43.** (B) **45.** (F) **47.** (C)

49.

51.

53.

55.

57.

59.

61.

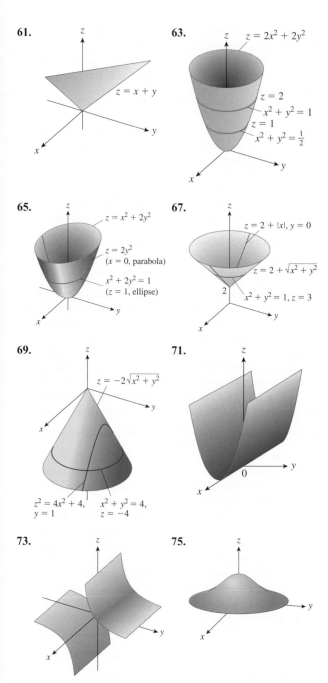

$z = x + y$

63.

$z = 2x^2 + 2y^2$

$z = 2$

$x^2 + y^2 = 1$

$z = 1$

$x^2 + y^2 = \frac{1}{2}$

65.

$z = x^2 + 2y^2$

$z = 2y^2$
$(x = 0,\ \text{parabola})$

$x^2 + 2y^2 = 1$
$(z = 1,\ \text{ellipse})$

67.

$z = 2 + |x|,\ y = 0$

$z = 2 + \sqrt{x^2 + y^2}$

$x^2 + y^2 = 1,\ z = 3$

69.

$z = -2\sqrt{x^2 + y^2}$

$z^2 = 4x^2 + 4,$
$y = 1$

$x^2 + y^2 = 4,$
$z = -4$

71.

0

73.

75.

77. a. The marginal cost of cars is $6,000 per car. The marginal cost of trucks is $4,000 per truck. **b.** The graph is a plane with x-intercept -40, y-intercept -60, and z-intercept $240,000$. **c.** The slice $x = 10$ is the straight line with equation $z = 300,000 + 4,000y$. It describes the cost function for the manufacture of trucks if car production is held fixed at 10 cars per week. **d.** The level curve $z = 480,000$ is the straight line $6,000x + 4,000y = 240,000$. It describes the number of cars and trucks you can manufacture to maintain weekly costs at $480,000. **79.** $C(x, y) = 10 + 0.03x + 0.04y$ where C is the

cost in dollars, $x = $ # video clips sold per month, $y = $ # audio clips sold per month   **81. a.** 28% **b.** 21% **c.** Percentage points per year   **83.** The graph is a plane with x_1-intercept 0.3, x_2-intercept 33, and x_3-intercept 0.66. The slices by $x_1 = $ constant are straight lines that are parallel to each other. Thus, the rate of change of **General Motors**' share as a function of **Ford**'s share does not depend on **Chrysler**'s share. Specifically, GM's share decreases by 0.02 percentage points per one percentage-point increase in **Ford**'s market share, regardless of **Chrysler**'s share.   **85. a.** 189 thousand prisoners **b.** $y = 300$: $N = -0.02x + 51$; $y = 500$: $N = 0.02x + 67$; when there are 300,000 prisoners in local jails, the number in federal prisons decreases by 20 per 1,000 additional prisoners in state prisons. When there are 500,000 prisoners in local jails, the number in federal prisons increases by 20 per 1,000 additional prisoners in state prisons.   **87. a.** The slices $x = $ constant and $y = $ constant are straight lines. **b.** No. Even though the slices $x = $ constant and $y = $ constant are straight lines, the level curves are not, and so the surface is not a plane. **c.** The slice $x = 10$ has a slope of 3,800. The slice $x = 20$ has a slope of 3,600. Manufacturing more cars lowers the marginal cost of manufacturing trucks. **89. a.** $9,980 **b.** $R(z) = 9,850 + 0.04z$ **91.** $f(x, t) = 6x - 2$; $313 billion   **93.** $U(11, 10) - U(10, 10) \approx 5.75$. This means that, if your company now has 10 copies of Macro Publish and 10 copies of Turbo Publish, then the purchase of one additional copy of Macro Publish will result in a productivity increase of approximately 5.75 pages per day.   **95.** Answers will vary. $(a, b, c) = (3, 1/4, 1/\pi)$; $(a, b, c) = (1/\pi, 3, 1/4)$. **97.** 7,000,000   **99. a.** $100 = K(1,000)^a(1,000,000)^{1-a}$; $10 = K(1,000)^a(10,000)^{1-a}$ **b.** $\log K - 3a = -4$; $\log K - a = -3$ **c.** $P = 71$ pianos (to the nearest piano) **101. a.** 4×10^{-3} gram per square meter **b.** The total weight of sulfates in the earth's atmosphere   **103. a.** The value of N would be doubled. **b.** $N(R, f_p, n_e, f_l, f_i, L) = R\,f_p\,n_e\,f_l\,f_i\,L$, where here L is the average lifetime of an intelligent civilization. **c.** Take the logarithm of both sides, since this would yield the linear function $\ln(N) = \ln(R) + \ln(f_p) + \ln(n_e) + \ln(f_l) + \ln(f_i) + \ln(f_c) + \ln(L)$.   **105.** They are reciprocals of each other. **107.** For example, $f(x, y) = x^2 + y^2$.   **109.** For example, $f(x, y, z) = xyz$ **111.** For example, take $f(x, y) = x + y$. Then setting $y = 3$ gives $f(x, 3) = x + 3$. This can be viewed as a function of the single variable x. Choosing other values for y gives other functions of x.   **113.** The slope is independent of the choice of $y = k$.   **115.** That CDs cost more than cassettes **117.** Plane   **119. (B)** Traveling in the direction B results in the shortest trip to nearby isotherms, and hence the fastest rate of increase in temperature.   **121.** Agree: Any slice through a plane is a straight line.   **123.** The graph of a function of three or more variables lives in four-dimensional (or higher) space, which makes it difficult to draw and visualize.

Section 15.2

1. $f_x(x, y) = -40$; $f_y(x, y) = 20$; $f_x(1, -1) = -40$; $f_y(1, -1) = 20$ **3.** $f_x(x, y) = 6x + 1$; $f_y(x, y) = -3y^2$; $f_x(1, -1) = 7$; $f_y(1, -1) = -3$ **5.** $f_x(x, y) = -40 + 10y$; $f_y(x, y) = 20 + 10x$; $f_x(1, -1) = -50$; $f_y(1, -1) = 30$

7. $f_x(x, y) = 6xy$; $f_y(x, y) = 3x^2$; $f_x(1, -1) = -6$; $f_y(1, -1) = 3$ **9.** $f_x(x, y) = 2xy^3 - 3x^2y^2 - y$; $f_y(x, y) = 3x^2y^2 - 2x^3y - x$; $f_x(1, -1) = -4$; $f_y(1, -1) = 4$ **11.** $f_x(x, y) = 6y(2xy + 1)^2$; $f_y(x, y) = 6x(2xy + 1)^2$; $f_x(1, -1) = -6$; $f_y(1, -1) = 6$ **13.** $f_x(x, y) = e^{x+y}$; $f_y(x, y) = e^{x+y}$; $f_x(1, -1) = 1$; $f_y(1, -1) = 1$ **15.** $f_x(x, y) = 3x^{-0.4}y^{0.4}$; $f_y(x, y) = 2x^{0.6}y^{-0.6}$; $f_x(1, -1)$ undefined; $f_y(1, -1)$ undefined   **17.** $f_x(x, y) = 0.2ye^{0.2xy}$; $f_y(x, y) = 0.2xe^{0.2xy}$; $f_x(1, -1) = -0.2e^{-0.2}$; $f_y(1, -1) = 0.2e^{-0.2}$ **19.** $f_{xx}(x, y) = 0$; $f_{yy}(x, y) = 0$; $f_{xy}(x, y) = f_{yx}(x, y) = 0$; $f_{xx}(1, -1) = 0$; $f_{yy}(1, -1) = 0$; $f_{xy}(1, -1) = f_{yx}(1, -1) = 0$ **21.** $f_{xx}(x, y) = 0$; $f_{yy}(x, y) = 0$; $f_{xy}(x, y) = f_{yx}(x, y) = 10$; $f_{xx}(1, -1) = 0$; $f_{yy}(1, -1) = 0$; $f_{xy}(1, -1) = f_{yx}(1, -1) = 10$ **23.** $f_{xx}(x, y) = 6y$; $f_{yy}(x, y) = 0$; $f_{xy}(x, y) = f_{yx}(x, y) = 6x$; $f_{xx}(1, -1) = -6$; $f_{yy}(1, -1) = 0$; $f_{xy}(1, -1) = f_{yx}(1, -1) = 6$ **25.** $f_{xx}(x, y) = e^{x+y}$; $f_{yy}(x, y) = e^{x+y}$; $f_{xy}(x, y) = f_{yx}(x, y) = e^{x+y}$; $f_{xx}(1, -1) = 1$; $f_{yy}(1, -1) = 1$; $f_{xy}(1, -1) = f_{yx}(1, -1) = 1$ **27.** $f_{xx}(x, y) = -1.2x^{-1.4}y^{0.4}$; $f_{yy}(x, y) = -1.2x^{0.6}y^{-1.6}$; $f_{xy}(x, y) = f_{yx}(x, y) = 1.2x^{-0.4}y^{-0.6}$; $f_{xx}(1, -1)$ undefined; $f_{yy}(1, -1)$ undefined; $f_{xy}(1, -1)$ & $f_{yx}(1, -1)$ undefined   **29.** $f_x(x, y, z) = yz$; $f_y(x, y, z) = xz$; $f_z(x, y, z) = xy$; $f_x(0, -1, 1) = -1$; $f_y(0, -1, 1) = 0$; $f_z(0, -1, 1) = 0$ **31.** $f_x(x, y, z) = 4/(x + y + z^2)^2$; $f_y(x, y, z) = 4/(x + y + z^2)^2$; $f_z(x, y, z) = 8z/(x + y + z^2)^2$; $f_x(0, -1, 1)$ undefined; $f_y(0, -1, 1)$ undefined; $f_z(0, -1, 1)$ undefined   **33.** $f_x(x, y, z) = e^{yz} + yze^{xz}$; $f_y(x, y, z) = xze^{yz} + e^{xz}$; $f_z(x, y, z) = xy(e^{yz} + e^{xz})$; $f_x(0, -1, 1) = e^{-1} - 1$; $f_y(0, -1, 1) = 1$; $f_z(0, -1, 1) = 0$ **35.** $f_x(x, y, z) = 0.1x^{-0.9}y^{0.4}z^{0.5}$; $f_y(x, y, z) = 0.4x^{0.1}y^{-0.6}z^{0.5}$; $f_z(x, y, z) = 0.5x^{0.1}y^{0.4}z^{-0.5}$; $f_x(0, -1, 1)$ undefined; $f_y(0, -1, 1)$ undefined; $f_z(0, -1, 1)$ undefined   **37.** $f_x(x, y, z) = yze^{xyz}$, $f_y(x, y, z) = xze^{xyz}$, $f_z(x, y, z) = xye^{xyz}$; $f_x(0, -1, 1) = -1$; $f_y(0, -1, 1) = f_z(0, -1, 1) = 0$ **39.** $f_x(x, y, z) = 0$; $f_y(x, y, z) = -\dfrac{600z}{y^{0.7}(1 + y^{0.3})^2}$; $f_z(x, y, z) = \dfrac{2,000}{1 + y^{0.3}}$; $f_x(0, -1, 1)$ undefined; $f_y(0, -1, 1)$ undefined; $f_z(0, -1, 1)$ undefined   **41.** $\partial C/\partial x = 6,000$, the marginal cost to manufacture each car is $6,000. $\partial C/\partial y = 4,000$, the marginal cost to manufacture each truck is $4,000.   **43.** $\partial y/\partial t = -0.78$. The number of articles written by researchers in the United States was decreasing at a rate of 0.78 percentage points per year. $\partial y/\partial x = -1.02$. The number of articles written by researchers in the United States was decreasing at a rate of 1.02 percentage points per one percentage point increase in articles written in Europe.   **45.** $5,600 per car   **47. a.** $\partial M/\partial c = -3.8$, $\partial M/\partial f = 2.2$. For every 1 point increase in the percentage of **Chrysler** owners who remain loyal, the percentage of **Mazda** owners who remain loyal decreases by 3.8 points. For every 1 point increase in the percentage of **Ford** owners who remain loyal, the percentage of **Mazda** owners who remain loyal increases by 2.2 points. **b.** 16%   **49. a.** $36,600; $52,900

b. $270 per year; $410 per year **c.** Widening **d.** The rate at which the income gap is widening   **51.** The marginal cost of cars is $6,000 + 1,000e^{-0.01(x+y)}$ per car. The marginal cost of trucks is $4,000 + 1,000e^{-0.01(x+y)}$ per truck. Both marginal costs decrease as production rises.   **53.** $\bar{C}(x, y) = \dfrac{200,000 + 6,000x + 4,000y - 100,000e^{-0.01(x+y)}}{x + y}$; $\bar{C}_x(50, 50) = -\$2.64$ per car. This means that at a production level of 50 cars and 50 trucks per week, the average cost per vehicle is decreasing by $2.64 for each additional car manufactured. $\bar{C}_y(50, 50) = -\$22.64$ per truck. This means that at a production level of 50 cars and 50 trucks per week, the average cost per vehicle is decreasing by $22.64 for each additional truck manufactured.   **55.** No; your marginal revenue from the sale of cars is $\$15,000 - \dfrac{2,500}{\sqrt{x + y}}$ per car and $\$10,000 - \dfrac{2,500}{\sqrt{x + y}}$ per truck from the sale of trucks. These increase with increasing x and y. In other words, you will earn more revenue per vehicle with increasing sales, and so the rental company will pay more for each additional vehicle it buys.   **57.** $P_z(10, 100,000, 1,000,000) \approx 0.0001010$ papers/$ **59. a.** $U_x(10, 5) = 5.18$, $U_y(10, 5) = 2.09$. This means that if 10 copies of Macro Publish and 5 copies of Turbo Publish are purchased, the company's daily productivity is increasing at a rate of 5.18 pages per day for each additional copy of Macro purchased and by 2.09 pages per day for each additional copy of Turbo purchased. **b.** $\dfrac{U_x(10, 5)}{U_y(10, 5)} \approx 2.48$ is the ratio of the usefulness of one additional copy of Macro to one of Turbo. Thus, with 10 copies of Macro and 5 copies of Turbo, the company can expect approximately 2.48 times the productivity per additional copy of Macro compared to Turbo.   **61.** 6×10^9 N/sec   **63. a.** $A_P(100, 0.1, 10) = 2.59$; $A_r(100, 0.1, 10) = 2,357.95$; $A_t(100, 0.1, 10) = 24.72$. Thus, for a $100 investment at 10% interest, after 10 years the accumulated amount is increasing at a rate of $2.59 per $1 of principal, at a rate of $2,357.95 per increase of 1 in r (note that this would correspond to an increase in the interest rate of 100%), and at a rate of $24.72 per year. **b.** $A_P(100, 0.1, t)$ tells you the rate at which the accumulated amount in an account bearing 10% interest with a principal of $100 is growing per $1 increase in the principal, t years after the investment.   **65. a.** $P_x = Ka\left(\dfrac{y}{x}\right)^b$ and $P_y = Kb\left(\dfrac{x}{y}\right)^a$. They are equal precisely when

$$\frac{a}{b} = \left(\frac{x}{y}\right)^b\left(\frac{x}{y}\right)^a.$$ Substituting $b = 1 - a$ now gives $\dfrac{a}{b} = \dfrac{x}{y}$.

b. The given information implies that $P_x(100, 200) = P_y(100, 200)$. By part (a), this occurs precisely when $a/b = x/y = 100/200 = 1/2$. But $b = 1 - a$, so $a/(1 - a) = 1/2$, giving $a = 1/3$ and $b = 2/3$.   **67.** Decreasing at 0.0075 parts of nutrient per part of water/sec   **69.** _f_ is increasing at a rate of _s_ units per unit of x, _f_ is increasing at a rate of _t_ units per unit of y, and the value of

f is $\underline{r}$ when $x = \underline{a}$ and $y = \underline{b}$ **71.** The marginal cost of building an additional orbicus; zonars per unit. **73.** Answers will vary. One example is $f(x, y) = -2x + 3y$. Others are $f(x, y) = -2x + 3y + 9$ and $f(x, y) = xy - 3x + 2y + 10$. **75. a.** b is the z-intercept of the plane. m is the slope of the intersection of the plane with the xz-plane. n is the slope of the intersection of the plane with the yz-plane. **b.** Write $z = b + rx + sy$. We are told that $\partial z/\partial x = m$, so $r = m$. Similarly, $s = n$. Thus, $z = b + mx + ny$. We are also told that the plane passes through (h, k, l). Substituting gives $l = b + mh + nk$. This gives b as $l - mh - nk$. Substituting in the equation for z therefore gives $z = l - mh - nk + mx + ny = l + m(x - h) + n(y - k)$, as required.

Section 15.3

1. P: relative minimum; Q: none of the above; R: relative maximum **3.** P: saddle point; Q: relative maximum; R: none of the above **5.** Relative minimum **7.** Neither **9.** Saddle point **11.** Relative minimum at $(0, 0, 1)$ **13.** Relative maximum at $(-1/2, 1/2, 3/2)$ **15.** Saddle point at $(0, 0, 0)$ **17.** Minimum at $(4, -3, -10)$ **19.** Maximum at $(-7/4, 1/4, 19/8)$ **21.** Relative maximum at $(0, 0, 0)$, saddle points at $(\pm 4 , 2, -16)$ **23.** Relative minimum at $(0, 0, 0)$, saddle points at $(-1, \pm 1, 1)$ **25.** Relative minimum at $(0, 0, 1)$ **27.** Relative minimum at $(-2, \pm 2, -16)$, $(0, 0)$ a critical point that is not a relative extremum **29.** Saddle point at $(0, 0, -1)$ **31.** Relative maximum at $(-1, 0, e)$ **33.** Relative minimum at $(2^{1/3}, 2^{1/3}, 3(2^{2/3}))$ **35.** Relative minimum at $(1, 1, 4)$ and $(-1, -1, 4)$ **37.** Absolute minimum at $(0, 0, 1)$ **39.** None; the relative maximum at $(0, 0, 0)$ is not absolute. (Look at, say, $(10, 10)$.) **41.** Minimum of $1/3$ at $(c, f) = (2/3, 2/3)$. Thus, at least $1/3$ of all **Mazda** owners would choose another new **Mazda**, and this lowest loyalty occurs when $2/3$ of **Chrysler** and **Ford** owners remain loyal to their brands. **43.** It should remove 2.5 pounds of sulfur and 1 pound of lead per day. **45.** You should charge $580.81 for the Ultra Mini and $808.08 for the Big Stack **47.** $l = w = h \approx 20.67$ in, volume $\approx 8,827$ cubic inches **49.** 18 in $\times$ 18 in $\times$ 36 in, volume $= 11,664$ cubic inches

51.

53. Continues up indefinitely

Continues down indefinitely
Function not defined on circle

55. H must be positive. **57.** No. In order for there to be a relative maximum at (a, b), *all* vertical planes through (a, b) should yield a curve with a relative maximum at (a, b). It could happen that a slice by another vertical plane through (a, b) (such as

$x - a = y - b$) does not yield a curve with a relative maximum at (a, b). [An example is $f(x, y) = x^2 + y^2 - \sqrt{xy}$, at the point $(0, 0)$. Look at the slices through $x = 0$, $y = 0$ and $y = x$.]

59. $\bar{C}_x = \dfrac{\partial}{\partial x}\left(\dfrac{C}{x + y}\right) = \dfrac{(x + y)C_x - C}{(x + y)^2}$. If this is zero, then

$(x + y)C_x = C$, or $C_x = \dfrac{C}{x + y} = \bar{C}$. Similarly, if $\bar{C}_y = 0$ then

$C_y = \bar{C}$. This is reasonable because if the average cost is decreasing with increasing x, then the average cost is greater than the marginal cost C_x. Similarly, if the average cost is increasing with increasing x, then the average cost is less than the marginal cost C_x. Thus, if the average cost is stationary with increasing x, then the average cost equals the marginal cost C_x. (The situation is similar for the case of increasing y.) **61.** The equation of the tangent plane at the point (a, b) is $z = f(a, b) + f_x(a, b)(x - a) + f_y(a, b)(y - b)$. If f has a relative extremum at (a, b), then $f_x(a, b) = 0 = f_y(a, b)$. Substituting these into the equation of the tangent plane gives $z = f(a, b)$, a constant. But the graph of $z = constant$ is a plane parallel to the xy-plane.

Section 15.4

1. 1; $(0, 0, 0)$ **3.** 1.35; $(1/10, 3/10, 1/2)$ **5.** Minimum value $= 6$ at $(1, 2, 1/2)$ **7.** 200; $(20, 10)$ **9.** 16; $(2, 2)$ and $(-2, -2)$ **11.** 20; $(2, 4)$ **13.** 1; $(0, 0, 0)$ **15.** 1.35; $(1/10, 3/10, 1/2)$ **17.** Minimum value $= 6$ at $(1, 2, 1/2)$ **19.** $5 \times 10 = 50$ sq. ft. **21.** $10 **23.** $(1/\sqrt{3}, 1/\sqrt{3}, 1/\sqrt{3})$, $(-1/\sqrt{3}, -1/\sqrt{3}, 1/\sqrt{3})$, $(1/\sqrt{3}, -1/\sqrt{3}, -1/\sqrt{3})$, $(-1/\sqrt{3}, 1/\sqrt{3}, -1/\sqrt{3})$ **25.** $(0, 1/2, -1/2)$ **27.** $(-5/9, 5/9, 25/9)$ **29.** $l \times w \times h = 1 \times 1 \times 2$ **31.** 18 in $\times$ 18 in $\times$ 36 in, volume $= 11,664$ cubic inches **33.** $(2l/h)^{1/3} \times (2l/h)^{1/3} \times 2^{1/3}(h/l)^{2/3}$, where $l = $ cost of lightweight cardboard and $h = $ cost of heavy-duty cardboard per square foot **35.** $1 \times 1 \times 1/2$ **37.** 6 laborers, 10 robots for a productivity of 368 pairs of socks per day **39.** Method 1: Solve $g(x, y, z) = 0$ for one of the variables and substitute in $f(x, y, z)$. Then find the maximum value of the resulting function of 2 variables. Advantage (answers may vary): We can use the second derivative test to check whether the resulting critical points are maxima, minima, saddle points, or none of these. Disadvantage (answers may vary): We may not be able to solve $g(x, y, z) = 0$ for one of the variables. Method 2: Use the method of Lagrange multipliers. Advantage (answers may vary): We do not need to solve the constraint equation for one of the variables. Disadvantage (answers may vary): The method does not tell us whether the critical points obtained are maxima, minima, points of inflection, or none of these. **41.** If the only constraint is an equality constraint, and if it is impossible to eliminate one of the variables in the objective function by substitution (solving the constraint equation for a variable or some other method). **43.** Answers may vary: Maximize $f(x, y) = 1 - x^2 - y^2$ subject to $x = y$. **45.** Yes. There may be relative extrema at points on the boundary of the domain of the function. The partial derivatives of the function need not be 0 at such points. **47.** If the solution were located in the interior of one of the line segments making up the boundary of the domain of f, then the derivative of a certain function would be 0. This function is obtained by substituting the linear equation $C(x, y) = 0$ in the linear objective function. But since the result would again be a linear function, it is either constant, or its derivative is a non-zero constant. In either event, extrema lie on the boundary of that line segment; that is, at one of the corners of the domain.

Section 15.5

1. $-1/2$　**3.** $e^2/2 - 7/2$　**5.** $(e^3 - 1)(e^2 - 1)$　**7.** $7/6$　**9.** $[e^3 - e - e^{-1} + e^{-3}]/2$　**11.** $1/2$　**13.** $(e - 1)/2$　**15.** $45/2$　**17.** $8/3$　**19.** $4/3$　**21.** 0　**23.** $2/3$　**25.** $2/3$　**27.** $2(e - 2)$　**29.** $2/3$

31. $\displaystyle\int_0^1 \int_0^{1-x} f(x, y)\, dy\, dx$　**33.** $\displaystyle\int_0^1 \int_0^{1-x} f(x, y)\, dy\, dx$

35. $\displaystyle\int_1^4 \int_1^{2/\sqrt{y}} f(x, y)\, dx\, dy$

37. $4/3$　**39.** $1/6$　**41.** 162,000 gadgets　**43.** $312,750
45. $17,500　**47.** 8,216　**49.** 1 degree　**51.** The area between the curves $y = r(x)$ and $y = s(x)$ and the vertical lines $x = a$ and $x = b$ is given by $\int_a^b \int_{r(x)}^{s(x)} dy\, dx$ assuming that $r(x) \le s(x)$ for $a \le x \le b$.　**53.** The first step in calculating an integral of the form $\int_a^b \int_{r(x)}^{s(x)} f(x, y)\, dy\, dx$ is to evaluate the integral $\int_{r(x)}^{s(x)} f(x, y)\, dy$, obtained by holding x constant and integrating with respect to y.　**55.** Paintings per picasso per dali　**57.** Left-hand side is $\int_a^b \int_c^d f(x) g(y)\, dx\, dy = \int_a^b \left(g(y) \int_c^d f(x)\, dx \right)\, dy$ (because $g(y)$ is treated as a constant in the inner integral) $= \left(\int_c^d f(x)\, dx \right) \int_a^b g(y)\, dy$ (because $\int_c^d f(x)\, dx$ is a constant and can therefore be taken outside the integral).

$\displaystyle\int_0^1 \int_1^2 y e^x\, dx\, dy = \frac{1}{2}(e^2 - e)$ no matter how we compute it.

Chapter 15 Review

1. 0; $14/3$; $1/2$; $\dfrac{1}{1+z} + z^3$; $\dfrac{x+h}{y+k+(x+h)(z+l)} +$
$(x+h)^2(y+k)$　**3.** Decreases by 0.32 units; increases by 12.5 units　**5.** Reading left to right, starting at the top: 4, 0, 0, 3,

$0, 1, 2, 0, 2$　**7.** Answers may vary; two examples are $f(x, y) = 3(x - y)/2$ and $f(x, y) = 3(x - y)^3/8$.　**9.** $f_x = 2x + y$, $f_y = x$, $f_{yy} = 0$　**11.** 0　**13.** $\dfrac{\partial f}{\partial x} = \dfrac{-x^2 + y^2 + z^2}{(x^2 + y^2 + z^2)^2}$, $\dfrac{\partial f}{\partial y} = \dfrac{2xy}{(x^2 + y^2 + z^2)^2}$, $\dfrac{\partial f}{\partial z} = -\dfrac{2xz}{(x^2 + y^2 + z^2)^2}$, $\dfrac{\partial f}{\partial x}\Big|_{(0,1,0)} = 1$
15. Absolute minimum at $(1, 3/2)$　**17.** Saddle point at $(0, 0)$　**19.** Absolute maximum at each point on the circle $x^2 + y^2 = 1$　**21.** $1/27$ at $(1/3, 1/3, 1/3)$　**23.** $(0, 2, \sqrt{2})$　**25.** 4; $(\sqrt{2}, \sqrt{2})$ and $(-\sqrt{2}, -\sqrt{2})$　**27.** Minimum value $= 5$ at $(2, 1, 1/2)$
29. 2　**31.** $\ln 5$　**33.** 1　**35. a.** $h(x, y) = 5,000 - 0.8x - 0.6y$ hits per day ($x =$ number of new customers at JungleBooks.com, $y =$ number of new customers at FarmerBooks.com)　**b.** 250　**c.** $h(x, y, z) = 5,000 - 0.8x - 0.6y + 0.0001z$ ($z =$ number of new Internet shoppers)　**d.** 1.4 million　**37. a.** 2,320 hits per day　**b.** $0.08 + 0.00003x$ hits (daily) per dollar spent on television advertising per month; increases with increasing x　**c.** $4,000 per month　**39.** (A)　**41. a.** About 15,800 additional orders per day
b. 11　**43.** $23,050

Chapter 16

Section 16.1

1.

3.

5.

7.

9.

11.

13. $f(x) = \sin(2\pi x) + 1$　**15.** $f(x) = 1.5 \sin(4\pi(x - 0.25))$
17. $f(x) = 50 \sin(\pi(x - 5)/10) - 50$　**19.** $f(x) = \cos(2\pi x)$
21. $f(x) = 1.5 \cos(4\pi(x - 0.375))$
23. $f(x) = 40 \cos(\pi(x - 10)/10) + 40$
25. $f(t) = 4.2 \sin(\pi/2 - 2\pi t) + 3$
27. $g(x) = 4 - 1.3 \sin[\pi/2 - 2.3(x - 4)]$　**31.** $\sqrt{3}/2$
37. $\tan(x + \pi) = \tan(x)$　**39. a.** $2\pi/0.602 \approx 10.4$ years.
b. Maximum: $58.8 + 57.7 = 116.5 \approx 117$;
minimum: $58.8 - 57.7 = 1.1 \approx 1$　**c.** $1.43 + P/4 + P =$
$1.43 + 13.05 \approx 14.5$ years, or midway through 2011

41. a. Maximum sales occurred when $t \approx 4.5$ (during the first quarter of 1996). Minimum sales occurred when $t \approx 2.2$ (during the third quarter of 1995) and $t \approx 6.8$ (during the third quarter of 1996). **b.** Maximum quarterly revenues were $0.561 billion; minimum quarterly revenues were $0.349 billion. **c.** Maximum: $0.455 + 0.106 = 0.561$; minimum: $0.455 - 0.106 = 0.349$ **43.** Amplitude $= 0.106$, vertical offset $= 0.455$, phase shift $= -1.61/1.39 \approx -1.16$, angular frequency $= 1.39$, period $= 4.52$. In 1995 and 1996, quarterly revenue from the sale of computers at **Computer City** fluctuated in cycles of 4.52 quarters about a baseline of $0.455 billion. Every cycle, quarterly revenue peaked at $0.561 billion ($0.106 billion above the baseline) and dipped to a low of $0.349 billion. Revenue peaked early in the middle of the first quarter of 1996 (at $t = -1.16 + (5/4) \times 4.52 = 4.49$).

45. $P(t) = 7.5 \sin[\pi(t - 13)/26] + 12.5$

47. $T(t) = 3.5 \cos[\pi(t - 7)/6] + 78.5$

49. $n(t) = 1.25 \sin[\pi(t - 1)/2] + 5.75$

51. $n(t) = 1.25 \cos[\pi(t - 2)/2] + 5.75$

53. $d(t) = 5 \sin(2\pi(t - 1.625)/13.5) + 10$

55. a. $u(t) = 2.5 \sin(2\pi(t - 0.75)) + 7.5$

b. $c(t) = 1.04^t[2.5 \sin(2\pi(t - 0.75)) + 7.5]$

57. a. $C \approx 50$, $A \approx 8$, $P \approx 12$, $\beta \approx 6$

b. $f(t) = 5.882 \cos[2\pi(t - 5.696)/12.263] + 49.238$

c. 12; 43; 55

59. a.

b. $y_{11} = \dfrac{2}{\pi} \cos x + \dfrac{2}{3\pi} \cos 3x$
$+ \dfrac{2}{5\pi} \cos 5x + \dfrac{2}{7\pi} \cos 7x$
$+ \dfrac{2}{9\pi} \cos 9x + \dfrac{2}{11\pi} \cos 11x$

61. The period is approximately 12.6 units

63. Lows: $B - A$; highs: $B + A$.   **65.** He is correct. The other trig functions can be obtained from the sine function by first using the formula $\cos x = \sin(x + \pi/2)$ to obtain cosine, and then using the formulas $\tan x = \dfrac{\sin x}{\cos x}$, $\cot x = \dfrac{\cos x}{\sin x}$, $\sec x = \dfrac{1}{\cos x}$, $\csc x = \dfrac{1}{\sin x}$ to obtain the rest   **67.** The largest B can be is A. Otherwise, if B is larger than A, the low figure for sales would have the negative value of $A - B$.

Section 16.2

1. $\cos x + \sin x$ **3.** $(\cos x)(\tan x) + (\sin x)(\sec^2 x)$

5. $-2 \csc x \cot x - \sec x \tan x + 3$ **7.** $\cos x - x \sin x + 2x$

9. $(2x - 1) \tan x + (x^2 - x + 1) \sec^2 x$

11. $-[\csc^2 x(1 + \sec x) + \cot x \sec x \tan x]/(1 + \sec x)^2$

13. $-2 \cos x \sin x$ **15.** $2 \sec^2 x \tan x$ **17.** $3 \cos(3x - 5)$

19. $2 \sin(-2x + 5)$ **21.** $\pi \cos\left[\dfrac{\pi}{5}(x - 4)\right]$

23. $-(2x - 1) \sin(x^2 - x)$

25. $(2.2x^{1.2} + 1.2) \sec(x^{2.2} + 1.2x - 1) \tan(x^{2.2} + 1.2x - 1)$

27. $\sec x \tan x \tan(x^2 - 1) + 2x \sec x \sec^2(x^2 - 1)$

29. $e^x[-\sin(e^x) + \cos x - \sin x]$ **31.** $\sec x$

37. $e^{-2x}[-2 \sin(3\pi x) + 3\pi \cos(3\pi x)]$

39. $1.5[\sin(3x)]^{-0.5} \cos(3x)$

41. $\dfrac{x^4 - 3x^2}{(x^2 - 1)^2} \sec\left(\dfrac{x^3}{x^2 - 1}\right) \tan\left(\dfrac{x^3}{x^2 - 1}\right)$

43. $\dfrac{\cot(2x - 1)}{x} - 2 \ln|x| \csc^2(2x - 1)$

45. a. Not differentiable at 0   **b.** $f'(1) \approx 0.5403$ **47.** 0

49. 2   **51.** Does not exist   **53.** $1/\sec^2 y$

55. $-[1 + y \cos(xy)]/[1 + x \cos(xy)]$

57. $c'(t) = 7\pi \cos[2\pi(t - 0.75)]$; $c'(0.75) \approx \$21.99$ per *year* $\approx \$0.42$ per week   **59.** $N'(6) \approx -32.12$ On January 1, 2003, the number of sunspots was decreasing at a rate of 32.12 sunspots per year.   **61.** $c'(t) = 1.035^t \times [\ln(1.035)(0.8 \sin(2\pi t) + 10.2) + 1.6\pi \cos(2\pi t)]$; $c'(1) = 1.035[10.2 \ln|1.035| + 1.6\pi] \approx \$5.57$ per year, or $0.11 per week.   **63. a.** $d(t) = 5 \cos(2\pi t/13.5) + 10$

b. $d'(t) = -(10\pi/13.5) \sin(2\pi t/13.5)$; $d'(7) \approx 0.270$. At noon, the tide was rising at a rate of 0.270 feet per hour.

65. $\dfrac{dV}{dt} = 11{,}000\pi \dfrac{|\sin(100\pi t)|}{\sin(100\pi t)} \cos(100\pi t)$

Graph:

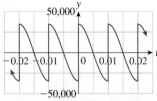

The sudden jumps in the graph are due to the non-differentiability of V at the times $0, \pm 0.01, \pm 0.02, \ldots$. The derivative is negative immediately to the left and positive immediately to the right of these points. **67. a.** 1.2 cm above the rest position **b.** 0 cm/sec; not moving; moving downward at 18.85 cm/sec **c.** 2.5 cycles per second **69. a.** Moving downward at 0.12 cm/sec; moving downward at 18.66 cm/sec **b.** 0.1 sec Graphs: of p:

Graphs of p':

71. a. (III) b. Increasing at a rate of 0.157 degrees per thousand years **73.** $-6; 6$ **75.** Answers will vary. Examples: $f(x) = \sin x; f(x) = \cos x$ **77.** Answers will vary. Examples: $f(x) = e^{-x}; f(x) = -2e^{-x}$ **79.** The graph of $\cos x$ slopes down over the interval $(0, \pi)$, so that its derivative is negative over that interval. The function $-\sin x$, and not $\sin x$, has this property. **81.** The velocity is $p'(t) = A\omega \cos(\omega t + d)$, which is a maximum when its derivative, $p''(t) = -A\omega^2 \sin(\omega t + d)$, is zero. But this occurs when $\sin(\omega t + d) = 0$, so that $p(t)$ is zero as well, meaning that the stock is at yesterday's close. **83.** The derivative of $\sin x$ is $\cos x$. When $x = 0$, this is $\cos(0) = 1$. Thus, the tangent to the graph of $\sin x$ at the point $(0, 0)$ has slope 1, which means it slopes upward at $45°$.

Section 16.3

1. $-\cos x - 2 \sin x + C$ **3.** $2 \sin x + 4.3 \cos x - 9.33x + C$
5. $3.4 \tan x + (\sin x)/1.3 - 3.2e^x + C$
7. $(7.6/3) \sin(3x - 4) + C$ **9.** $-(1/6) \cos(3x^2 - 4) + C$
11. $-2 \cos(x^2 + x) + C$ **13.** $(1/6) \tan(3x^2 + 2x^3) + C$
15. $-(1/6) \ln|\cos(2x^3)| + C$
17. $3 \ln|\sec(2x - 4) + \tan(2x - 4)| + C$
19. $(1/2) \sin(e^{2x} + 1) + C$ **21.** -2 **23.** $\ln(2)$ **25.** 0 **27.** 1
33. $-\dfrac{1}{4} \cos(4x) + C$ **35.** $-\sin(-x + 1) + C$

37. $[\cos(-1.1x - 1)]/1.1 + C$ **39.** $-\dfrac{1}{4} \ln|\sin(-4x)| + C$
41. 0 **43.** 2π **45.** $-x \cos x + \sin x + C$
47. $\left[\dfrac{x^2}{2} - \dfrac{1}{4}\right] \sin(2x) + \dfrac{x}{2} \cos(2x) + C$
49. $-\dfrac{1}{2}e^{-x} \cos x - \dfrac{1}{2}e^{-x} \sin x + C$ **51.** $\pi^2 - 4$
53. Average $= 2/\pi$

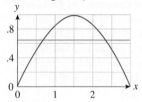

55. Diverges **57.** Converges to $1/2$
59. $C(t) = 0.04t + \dfrac{2.6}{\pi} \cos\left[\dfrac{\pi}{26}(t - 25)\right] + 1.02$

61. 12 feet **63.** 79 sunspots
65. $P(t) = 7.5 \sin[(\pi/26(t - 13)] + 12.5; 7.7\%$
67. a. Average voltage over $[0, 1/6]$ is zero; 60 cycles per second.
b.

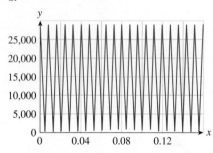

c. 116.673 volts **69.** \$50,000 **71.** It is always zero. **73.** 1
75. $s = -\dfrac{K}{\omega^2} \sin(\omega t - \alpha) + Lt + M$ for constants L and M

Chapter 16 Review

1. $f(x) = 1 + 2 \sin x$
3. $f(x) = 2 + 2 \sin[\pi(x - 1)] = 2 + 2 \sin[\pi(x + 1)]$
5. $f(x) = 1 + 2 \cos(x - \pi/2)$
7. $f(x) = 2 + 2 \cos[\pi(x + 1/2)] = 2 + 2 \cos[\pi(x - 3/2)]$
9. $-2x \sin(x^2 - 1)$ **11.** $2e^x \sec^2(2e^x - 1)$
13. $4x \sin(x^2) \cos(x^2)$ **15.** $2 \sin(2x - 1) + C$
17. $\tan(2x^2 - 1) + C$ **19.** $-\dfrac{1}{2} \ln|(\cos(x^2 + 1)| + C$
21. 1 **23.** $-x^2 \cos x + 2x \sin x + 2 \cos x + C$
25. $s(t) = 10,500 + 1,500 \sin[(2\pi/52)t - \pi] = 10,500 + 1,500 \sin(0.12083t - 3.14159)$ **27.** Decreasing at a rate of \$3,852 per month **29.** \$2,029,700
31. $150t - \dfrac{100}{\pi} \cos\left[\dfrac{\pi}{2}(t - 1)\right]$ grams

Index

General Interest

Index of Companies, Products, and Agencies